SOCIAL PSYCHOLOGY AND MENTAL HEALTH

SOCIAL PSYCHOLOGY AND MENTAL HEALTH

Edited by

HENRY WECHSLER
The Medical Foundation, Inc.
Boston, Massachusetts

LEONARD SOLOMON
Boston University

BERNARD M. KRAMER
Tufts University

Published for
The Society for the Psychological Study of Social Issues

HOLT, RINEHART AND WINSTON, INC.

New York   Chicago   San Francisco   Atlanta
Dallas   Montreal   Toronto   London   Sydney

Dedicated to the Memory of
GORDON W. ALLPORT
Teacher, Scholar, Humanist

Foreword

Since its formation in the mid-thirties, the Society for the Psychological Study of Social Issues has consistently aimed to make the theories, methods, and empirical research findings of social psychology relevant to the multitude of social issues we face daily in our local, national, and international affairs. A major way in which the Society has tried to implement this aim is through the many publications it has sponsored—in social psychology, race relations, international behavior, the field of education, public opinion and propaganda, industrial conflict, civilian morale, problems of war and peace, and research methods in social psychology. The Society is very proud to add the present volume on *Social Psychology and Mental Health* to this ever-growing list of socially salient topics.

A few words are in order about how this volume came into existence. In 1963, members of the Council of the Society for the Psychological Study of Social Issues agreed, following extensive discussions, that one of the major social issues that would confront Americans in the next few decades was the problem of mental health. The sheer magnitude of the problem led the Council members to see it as a major social issue; in addition, recent studies had suggested that to understand more fully the determinants and frequency of mental illness in different segments of our society would require a marked shift of emphasis from individual to social causation.

Early in 1964, SPSSI Council appointed a standing committee composed of the three editors of this volume and asked them to explore the possibility of a major publication, to be sponsored by SPSSI, that would emphasize a social psychological rather than individual approach to the understanding of mental health and illness. This committee met several times in 1964 and the decision was made to develop a book of readings that would bring together under one cover the best exemplifications of what social psychology had to contribute to the field of mental health and illness, particularly in strategies of research and in new techniques and methods of behavior analysis. As was the case with other SPSSI-sponsored publications, the editors worked closely with members of an Editorial Advisory Committee.

This volume is the culmination of several years of hard work by the Editors, Henry Wechsler, Leonard Solomon, and Bernard Kramer. The Society owes them a great debt of gratitude for their devotion and for the tremendous amount of time and energy they have expended in the preparation of this volume. The Society also wishes to express its appreciation to the members of the Editorial Advisory Committee for the unstinting advice, guidance, and wise counsel they gave the Editors in the course of preparing this volume for publication. Finally, the Society is greatly indebted to the authors who gave permission for their various papers to be included in this volume.

Conceptions of mental health and illness have changed markedly over the past two or three decades. Those of us who were undergraduate and graduate students long ago will readily recall that the courses we took in clinical and abnormal psychology were overwhelmingly individualistic in emphasis. Traditionally, these were areas considered to be primarily within the province of the psychiatrist, the psychoanalyst, and the clinical psychologist. The role played by the social system in producing maladjustment and mental illness was but dimly perceived, and barely mentioned. Mental problems were seen to be mainly personal, intrapsychic affairs, arising from disorders of character, defects of personality, and/or dysfunctions of the nervous system. Treatment followed the medical model and concentrated on the alleviation or removal of the problem confronting the patient by a form of individual therapy, or by physical, chemical, or electrical means. Such concepts as "milieu therapy," "the therapeutic community," and "community mental health" had not yet been formulated. Over the past few decades, the emphasis has clearly shifted from a trait, personalistic approach to a situational, field-theoretical approach.

We believe that this volume is unique in that it stresses a social psychological approach to the field of mental health and illness. It is our hope that professional workers in this and related fields will find it a useful and refreshing reference work to add to their libraries. It is also our hope that with the availability of this volume many psychology departments throughout the country will be stimulated to consider the possibility of adding *Social Psychology and Mental Health* to their curriculum of undergraduate and graduate course offerings.

Milton Rokeach
President (1966–67)
Society for the Psychological Study of Social Issues

Acknowledgments

The impetus for this book originated from a meeting of the Subcommittee on Social Psychological Aspects of Mental Health of the Society for the Psychological Study of Social Issues (SPSSI) in 1964. Members of the committee included Jack French, Harold Proshansky, Milton Rokeach, and Leonard Solomon. To the members of this committee, we owe a debt of gratitude for not only initiating the project but also for their help throughout this endeavor. The committee selected the three editors for this volume along with an advisory committee of twelve experts. The advisory committee provided much encouragement and support as well as valuable suggestions. The original outlines were revised several times in order to incorporate specific suggestions from the committee. The list from which the final readings were chosen represented an editorial consensus. Though we consulted with members of the committee frequently, they provided us with a large margin of freedom of choice, especially during the final phase. The authors wish to express their gratitude to this group for demonstrating an interest and volunteering their time above and beyond the call of duty.

The preparation of the volume was greatly aided by a number of individuals and institutions. Particular thanks are due to Joanne Dwinnell for her monumental effort in the compilation of materials for the volume. In addition to the support provided to each of the editors by their home institutions, The Medical Foundation, Inc., Boston University, and Tufts University, a Special Rehabilitation Research Fellowship was awarded to Leonard Solomon by the Social and Rehabilitation Service of the Department of Health, Education and Welfare.

We also wish to thank all the various experts in the areas of social science and mental health and illness whom we contacted in the search for contents to this volume. Lastly, we wish to thank our wives, Joan Wechsler, Francine Solomon, and Barbara Kramer, for their patience and forbearance during the preparation of this monograph.

H. W.
L. S.
B. M. K.

Contents

SOCIAL PSYCHOLOGY AND MENTAL HEALTH

INTRODUCTION

Why Social Psychologists Study
Mental Health and Mental Illness

Mental health and illness now comprise one of the major fields of research for social psychologists and other social scientists. Why is this so? What is there about mental health and illness that attracts increasing numbers of social scientists? The following properties provide a partial answer.

The Definition of Mental Illness and Health

Mental illness can be viewed as an interpersonal deviation from socially accepted standards of behavior, or as a breakdown in the performance of social roles. Conversely, mental health is definable as interpersonal behavior which seems to fulfill social norm and role requirements. Under prevailing social conditions of normlessness, anomie, and family disruption, criteria for mental illness tend to be vague and ill-defined; indeed, "pathological" interpersonal behavior may have transient adaptive functions. Solely medical or psychophysiological conceptions of mental illness are no longer tenable; interpersonal space always frames the picture. Mental health or illness does not inhere in the individual but in his interaction with a social matrix. The person is an ongoing decision maker,

1

rehearsing plans in the light of social expectancies. His interpersonal behavior is organized by social setting and contextual circumstances. As Raush (1965) aptly states: "Children are, for example, no more taught not to be dependent than they are taught not to urinate. What they are taught are right and wrong times and places. For some parents and for some cultures, as compared to others, there are more wrong places, and in that sense one might speak of quantitatively greater or lesser amounts of expression or inhibition. But this is a rather different matter than presumed quantities of traits" (p. 498).

Psychiatric disorders such as paranoia and passive-aggressive personality, despite their medical origin, still are diagnosed on the basis of specific patterns of interpersonal behavior.

The Origins of Mental Illness and Health

Mental illness is social, not only in definition, but also in origin. "Proximal" variables, such as child-rearing practices, family interaction, parental loss, peer groups, race, socioeconomic status, migration, social crises, war, and unemployment, are all believed in some degree to cause mental illness. The likelihood of social factors playing a role in the etiology of mental illness and health gains support from recurring evidence that different population groups differ in frequency and type of mental illness. Social scientists have been intrigued by the challenge of discovering the ways in which different population groups produce varying rates of healthy or unhealthy individuals.

Therapeutic Strategies for Mental Illness

Methods of therapy and health promotion are frequently social in nature, ranging from two-person psychotherapy through changes in the hospital milieu to organizational restructuring in industry. Strategies for therapeutic change seek to transform social conditions viewed as causative and/or supportive of maladaptive behavior.

Societal Reactions to Mental Illness

Because mental illness is viewed as intimately related to value commitments regarding social deviance, it has become subject to strong and persistent reactions in the form of social movements. The mental health effort in this country is now a significant social movement, and has generated a countermovement exemplified by test-burning as well as authentic civil libertarian opposition. Public attitudes stigmatizing the mentally ill add social psychological dimensions to the problem. Attitudes of the family as well as other social audiences influence the status of the prepatient. Factors affecting the development and change of such attitudes, as well as their effect on "patienthood," fall within a traditional domain of social psychology.

Interdisciplinary Dimensions of Mental Health

The mental health effort is multifaceted and draws upon many disciplines to fulfill treatment, research, and educational needs. Status conflicts and cooperation among professional groups, value conflicts, and differential roles in patient treatment have significant implications for therapy and rehabilitation. As these disciplines evolve in their interrelationships, they become significant objects of social psychological analysis.

Availability of Funds for Mental Health Research

A major reason for growth of interest in mental health has been the large-scale availability of federal funds for research and training in this area. Obviously, this alone has not been enough to generate the volume of work we have seen emerge in the past decade or so. The importance of mental health as a social issue also reinforces the development of research interest and productiv-

The facts compelling society and social scientists toward concern over mental health looms large as a social issue.

Mental Illness as a Social Issue

The facts compelling society and social scientists toward concern over mental health as a social issue may be summarized as follows:

1. The sheer size of the problem—the number of persons presently afflicted with some form of mental disorder may be as high as one in three. Many of these will be severely impaired over a long term.
2. The cost of mental illness is very high in human terms (personal anguish, family disruption) and social economic terms. Lost productivity and waste of human resources, along with direct expenditures of capital and operational funds, contribute to the total cost.
3. Present means are inadequate to cope fully with the problem. The supply of facilities and personnel is insufficient. Moreover, methods of treatment proven effective are pitifully rare.
4. Mental illness is unevenly distributed through the sectors of society and is inversely related to availability of treatment. This fact has important implications for the social and political structure of American society.
5. The incidence and nature of mental symptoms are likely to be affected by such social forces as automation, population growth, the culture of poverty, racial conflict, and international tensions. An understanding of the manner in which such distal social forces affect family and personal life may help shape planned change.
6. The magnitude of mental disorder and the relative shortage of coping resources may be symptoms of pathology in our social system and, as such, are fit subjects for social psychological study. The social psychologist rejects the assumption that personal maladjustment is almost exclusively a function of personality defects. Neither does he accept the idea that such defects necessarily require clinical help in order to adjust the individual to meet the demands of society. Instead, he tends to ask how the social order can be adapted to meet fundamental human social needs. Thus, for example, social psychology seeks to discover the psychological "tolerance limits" for population density, social deprivation (especially in childhood), and interpersonal conflict.

The Social Psychological Point of View

Social psychology brings to bear upon the field of mental health a special point of view implicit in its definition as a discipline. Like other social sciences, social psychology inquires into the social nature of man and his interrelationship with his environment. It concentrates, however, on "an attempt to understand and explain how the thought, feeling, and behavior of individuals are influenced by the actual, imagined, or implied presence of other human beings" (Allport, 1954, p. 5). Also of major interest to most social psychologists is the question of how man in turn influences his social environment.

Social psychologists seek to examine the mutual interaction between social system and personality. For example, they want to know how the social system (or the family or hospital) collides with or challenges personality predispositions. How does the individual adapt to new social systems? What is the process by which "identity transformation" occurs? What are the demands and opportunities generated by a particular social system? How are its norms, social influences, and reward structures experienced by the individual? What consequences do these have for his thinking, feeling, and acting as he engages the social order? How do his self-concepts, inner wishes, and defenses shape his personal construction of social reality? How do they affect his decisions and modes of adaptation?

The Contribution of Social Psychology

Social psychology's contributions to the field of mental health include the following:

1. Social psychology stresses the social medium in which behavior occurs, and seeks to evolve concepts and measures which will capture the relational and interactive quality of interpersonal behavior. It attempts to characterize patterns of social interaction in terms of both intrapsychic constructs and extrinsic social concepts. Thus, one deals not only with disturbed behavior or symptoms but also with disturbed relationships among family members. Such disturbed relationships may serve to preserve the microsocial system of the total family. This approach would view the interview or testing situation as a two-person social system in which the tester's role, power relationship, and values all interact with the subject's identity, values, and orientation toward authority.
2. Social psychology highlights the role played by values in defining well-being and disorder. It distinguishes among "personal maladjustment," "social deviance," and "productive nonconformity." Therapeutic goals such as adjustment, self-realization, and maturity are viewed in relation to the values of the society in which they are to occur.
3. Social psychology offers a balanced conception of the field by deemphasizing pathological aspects and urging equal consideration of the ingredients of positive mental health. It examines the individual's executive and adaptive functions as well as maladaptive reactions under varying social conditions.
4. Social psychology has served a bridging function between social environment and personality. Through the study of measurable dimensions of the social

environment, it illuminates the relationship between the social context and psychic processes. It asks: How does the social system influence and interact with, for example, the career of the mental patient? How do social system variables contribute to etiology, maintenance, and efforts to change the process? In addition, certain commonly used variables, such as social class and sibling order, have been studied in terms of their underlying psychological meanings. Social class, to the social psychologist, can become an interlacing of such variables as value system, social deprivation, living conditions, and child-rearing practices.

5. On the individual level, social psychology has contributed to the development of new categories of analysis, particularly interpersonal ones. New approaches to nomenclature may assist in breaking the constraints imposed on theory and practice by traditional medical models. Particularly helpful has been the codification of family interaction.

6. Recognition of mental illness as cognate to deviant behavior has permitted the social psychologist to draw upon findings from work in such areas as addiction and delinquency. Moreover, attention to cross-cultural variations in symptomatic patterns can clarify the relationship between social environment and mental illness.

7. A potential but largely untapped contribution lies in the view that action research enhances social theory. In this view, championed by Lewin, a close link with practice can be a blessing for the development of theory. In action research, direct involvement with the system under study may be vital to both understanding and effecting change. Although there is far from unanimous agreement on this view, it still constitutes an important stream in social psychology.

General Aims of This Volume

This volume attempts to bring together major exemplifications of social psychological contributions to mental health and, in so doing, offer a social psychological perspective for the field. By presenting theoretical orientations, research strategies, techniques for analysis of interpersonal behavior, models of social change, and evaluation of change efforts, it illustrates diversity as well as distinctiveness in the social psychological approach. The problem-centered focus of the Society for the Psychological Study of Social Issues (SPSSI) draws attention to environmental conditions which may bear upon the psychological well-being of our citizenry.

The reader's primary aims are to help define the field and to provide a point of view for individuals concerned with the social psychology of mental health. Many of the articles present models for theory and research strategy which can generate fruitful hypotheses and experiments.

Many clinical psychologists are questioning the traditional emphasis upon strictly "intrapsychic" factors. They look for additional anchorage in social theory, and express readiness to join hands in partnership with social psychologists. An understanding of group processes, social system functions, and role and status relationships, as well as psychodynamic factors, has helped to generate such approaches as "milieu therapy," "group therapy," and "full-time" therapeutic social relationships as alternatives to individual psychotherapy.

Thus, there is reason to believe that this collection of readings will be useful to the various helping professions as well.

American psychology is split between those whose primary concern is with the "helping process" and those whose central interest is in accumulating new knowledge. For many clinicians, the helping enterprise is essential and rests largely on the qualities of the artist and the creative theoretician. Researchers, on the other hand, tend to value precision, experimental elegance, and statistical design. Several selections pursue the possibility of fruitful partnerships between the two frameworks. They reveal that knowledge generated by research has implications for social engineering, and that clinically generated observations can yield a rich foundation for the "context of discovery." Behavioral science can make progress toward its goals of prediction, control, and understanding of mental health by capitalizing upon the multiple sources of knowledge.

Criteria for the Selection of Articles

It is not possible to collect a set of readings in the social psychology of mental health under a single theoretical umbrella without sacrificing the scope of significant research contributions or stretching segmented and "middle range" theories. Any attempt to do so would be premature—it would require including more abstract and untested levels of theory than would be feasible. Such an approach might be more likely to close off rather than stimulate vitality and variety. For this reason, we have chosen a number of problem areas and present some of the significant contributions in these areas.

We have sought to include papers which go beyond the presentation of a single study and suggest a range of research within a broader spectrum. We have favored works reflecting key ideas for future research strategies. Since social research in mental health does not occur in a prescribed sequence, we have included some papers based on advances in research technology, particularly when their relevance to theory or social issue has been clarified.

In selecting articles, we have used one or more of the following criteria. The article must offer:

a. A substantive contribution by way of advancing understanding, prediction, and control of a significant problem.

b. A strategy of research or set of methods in relation to some theoretical orientation which provides a model for future research.

c. A theoretical contribution which exemplifies an important orientation to mental health among social psychologists, or suggests new departures, new sets of variables, and modes of analysis.

d. A discovery of some neglected but valuable factors which serve to reintegrate current efforts.

e. A confrontation of significant social problems and issues with available conceptual and methodological tools holding promise for social improvement.

Audience

The audience for this volume is broad, since the field of mental health has become the crossroads for a number of professional and academic fields—psychiatry, social planning, social work, nursing, sociology, anthropology, religion, and philosophy. The volume addresses itself to members of all these fields and more. It offers, we hope, a perspective and point of view characteristic of social psychology which will assist them in their appointed tasks.

Responsibility of the Editors

Although all three editors are responsible for the total volume, specialization was introduced in the following manner: For Parts I and II—The Nature of Mental Health and Illness and Assessment of Causal Factors—Henry Wechsler; for Parts III and V—The Social Context of Treatment and Mental Health Aspects of Social Problems—Leonard Solomon; and for Part IV—Mental Health Attitudes—Bernard M. Kramer.

In retrospect, the editors are impelled to make certain confessions: Although we are dissatisfied with the application of the medical model to behavioral and interpersonal phenomena, we have found it impossible to avoid such "loaded" terms as patient, treatment, illness, and health. We have not found a sufficiently broad substitute system.

In assessing the contribution of social psychology and the social sciences to the study of mental health and mental illness, we have made certain deliberate omissions in the design of the book. We have required that contributions have empirical or research components, and thus have not included material wholly theoretical or programmatic in nature. For this reason, community mental health literature is underrepresented in the volume.

But we do have an abiding commitment to the increasing sophistication of our research methodology, which has not only limited the excesses of clinical speculation but has also served to transform the language of denotation and observation. We hope the volume will highlight some basic issues and stimulate young psychologists to do better.

Part I

THE NATURE OF MENTAL HEALTH AND ILLNESS

A search of the social science literature concerning the nature and meaning of mental health and illness reveals several basic themes.

1. There is no consensus regarding a definition of mental health and mental illness.
2. There is general agreement that the two terms—mental health and mental illness—refer to behavior which is interpersonal in nature and, with respect to mental illness, is judged to be dysfunctional according to the norms of an observer. This judgment is often made without any somatic or physiological evidence.
3. Many social scientists oppose the application of a "medical model" to the area of disturbances in interpersonal behavior.
4. Many others question the medical model on pragmatic grounds. They assert that treatment under this model has not been effective.
5. Use of the medical model has led to a preoccupation with pathology and a relative absence of work in the area of positive health.

The current status of research and theory in the field has resulted in separate listings of the attributes of mental illness and health. Most of the literature has concerned itself with pathological conditions, although some of the more recent studies have focused more on mental health. In the selection of articles for this part, we have started with an exposition of the many approaches researchers have taken toward the problem of definition of mental illness and health. The article by Scott lists the numerous criteria used and discusses problems incurred with each. Although it was first published in 1958, it is still representative of the major approaches in the field up to this time. Jahoda's contribution concentrates on the multiple criteria used to evaluate positive mental health. A result of a special study conducted for the Joint Commission on Mental Illness and Health, Jahoda's article represents the most systematic approach to date concerning multiple definitions of mental health.

A series of articles have been included which question whether there is such a thing as mental illness. Szasz, Adams, and Sarbin argue against the existence of mental illness, and oppose the application of a medical model to describe interpersonal behavior from an evaluative perspective. Inappropriate and dysfunctional responses to the problems of living are not to be considered as symptoms of illness in the same sense as are physical symptoms. Szasz presents the classic statement of this position. Adams calls for the scrapping of the designation, "mental illness," and the substitution of systematic classification and study of interpersonal behavior. Sarbin provides a historical perspective by tracing the term mental illness to the metaphor "as if mentally ill," which was first derived when demonological conceptions of causes of conduct disturbances were abandoned.

The paper by Ausubel has been included to present the other side of the issue. He states that not only is it possible to consider behaviors as symptoms of an illness, but also that abandonment of the concept of mental illness would involve a return to sin, blame, and punitive treatment. An interesting aspect of this debate is the "all or none" postulation of positions. Perhaps both sides are correct. Certain behaviors may very well be symptoms of illness which may have physiological or biochemical roots. Other behaviors may be expressions of problems of living or inability to relate to the interpersonal environment. The condition of autism in children or reactive schizophrenia in adolescence may differ both in severity and quality from conditions labeled psychoneurotic reactions or character disturbances.

Regardless of whether or not the medical model is the most appropriate for conceptualizing all of these behaviors, treatment and hospitalization will continue to be provided under this general framework for years to come. Goffman and Levinson and Gallagher discuss some implications of the adaptation of the medical model. Goffman illustrates numerous ways in which environmental conditions influence the behavior of the person designated as patient. He shows vividly the stigma of hospitalization, the loss of privacy, and the invasion of all of the patient's personal areas by the psychiatrist. Levinson and Gallagher concentrate more on the definition of the situation by the patient in the light of his personality predispositions and past experience. They view the patient as more of an active agent in the treatment process than does Goffman. The different approaches of the two papers reflect differences in focus of sociology and psychology.

Analogous to the weather, many individuals have decried the lack of psychological research into mental health, but very few have done anything about it. Bradburn is one of these few; his contribution reports the outcome of research he has conducted with Kaplovitz. Abandoning a global conception of mental health, he has examined psychological well-being and has concluded that it is a resultant of two independent dimensions—positive and negative affect. Each of these varies independently of the other, but in combination they are able to predict the overall state of well-being.

The concluding contribution is that of Smith, who argues against adoption of a definitive list of criteria of mental health. Mental health should be regarded not as a theoretical concept, but rather as a rubric on chapter headings under which fall a variety of evaluative concerns. Smith would free the psychologist from previous exclusion of values from his work, so long as values are not introduced surreptitiously under the guise of scientific concepts. He feels that psychologists are as qualified as anyone, perhaps better than most, to make judgments concerning human values.

The contents of this part are not intended to provide a definitive conception of the nature of mental illness. They should, however, provide a framework from which certain widely held assumptions can be questioned. Is there such a thing as mental illness? Is it possible to define it as well as its antonym, mental health? If it is so difficult to pinpoint and define, how can it be studied?

1 / Research Definitions of Mental Health and Mental Illness

William A. Scott

A serious obstacle to research in the area of mental illness lies in the lack of a clear definition of the phenomenon to be studied. The term "mental ill health" has been used by different researchers to refer to such diverse manifestations as schizophrenia, suicide, unhappiness, juvenile delinquency, and passive acceptance of an intolerable environment. Whether some or all of these various reactions should be included in a single category of "mental illness" is not clear from a survey of the current literature. Theories describing the nature and antecedents of one sort of disturbance rarely relate it to another, and there is a paucity of research evidence indicating the extent to which such manifestations are empirically intercorrelated.

In the face of such ambiguity it would appear useful to attempt an organized review of the various definitions of mental illness which are explicit or implicit in recent research, with a view toward highlighting their commonalities and discrepancies on both a theoretical and an empirical level. Such a presentation might help students concerned with causative factors to assess the comparability of previous research findings on correlates of "mental illness," and also point toward some next steps in research to discover the degree to which these diverse phenomena represent either unitary, or multifold, psychological processes.

The research criteria for mental illness to be reviewed here are subsumed under the following categories: (*a*) exposure to psychiatric treatment; (*b*) social maladjustment; (*c*) psychiatric diagnosis; (*d*) subjective unhappiness; (*e*) objective psychological symptoms; and (*f*) failure of positive adaptation. For each category we shall review studies which appear to have employed the definition, either explicitly or implicitly. This will be accompanied by a critical discussion of the adequacy of each definition, together with an assessment, based on empirical data where possible, of the relation between this and other definitions. Finally, we shall attempt to summarize the differences among the definitions, by indicating their divergent approaches to certain basic problems in the conceptualization of mental illness and health.

Mental Illness as Exposure to Psychiatric Treatment

The most frequently used operational definition of mental illness, at least in terms of the number of studies employing it, is simply the fact of a person's

From the *Psychological Bulletin*, 1958, **55**, 29–45. Copyright © 1958. Reprinted by permission of the author and the American Psychological Association.

being under psychiatric treatment. And this definition is usually restricted to hospital treatment, rather than outpatient service. Nearly all the ecological studies (e.g., Belknap and Jaco, 1953; Faris and Dunham, 1939; Gruenberg, 1954; Jaco, 1954; Lemert, 1948; Schroeder, 1942) and most of the studies correlating mental illness with demographic characteristics (e.g., Clark, 1949; Frumkin, 1955; Hyde and Kingsley, 1944; Malzberg, 1940; Rose and Stub, 1955) use this as a criterion. They obtain their information from hospital records or, in unusual instances (Hollingshead and Redlich, 1953), from psychiatrists in the area who furnish information about persons treated on an outpatient basis.

Such a definition of mental illness is operational rather than conceptual, but its implicit meaning for the interpretation of research results is that anyone who is regarded by someone (hospital authorities, relatives, neighbors, or himself) as disturbed enough to require hospitalization or outpatient treatment is mentally ill, and people who do not fit into such diagnoses are mentally healthy. Use of hospital records, moreover, requires that the criterion of the nature of the mental illness be the diagnosis which appears on the record.

Shortcomings of such an operational definition are recognized by no one better than its users. The reliability of psychiatric diagnosis is of course open to question, and any attempt to determine correlates of particular kinds of mental disturbance must take into account the large error inherent in the measuring process. (One study of the association between diagnosis at Boston Psychopathic Hospital and previous diagnoses of the patients at other hospitals showed only 51 per cent above-chance agreement between the two [cf. Milbank Memorial Fund, 1950, pp. 42–43].)

If "under the care of a psychiatrist" is to be regarded as the criterion of mental illness, one must realize the automatic limitation on the size of the mentally ill population that such a definition imposes. Kramer (1953, p. 124) has estimated that the maximum possible number of mentally ill, under such a definition, would be less than 7,000,000, given the present number of available psychiatrists.

It has been suggested by both sociologists (Clausen and Kohn, 1954; Dunham, 1947) and physicians (Felix and Bowers, 1948) that different rates of hospital admissions for different geographical areas may indicate more than anything else about the areas the relative degree to which the communities tolerate or reject persons with deviant behavior (Dunham, 1953). Or as the Chief of the National Institute of Mental Health puts it: Researchers using hospital records are dependent on the public's rather uneven willingness to give up its mentally ill members and to support them in institutions (Felix and Bowers, 1948); this in addition to the admittedly unstandardized and often substandard methods of record-keeping used by the various hospitals is likely to render incomparable prevalence and incidence data from various geographical areas.

The effects of such differential thresholds for admission in various communities are difficult to estimate, since they cannot be uniform from study to study. In 1938 a house-to-house survey in Williamson County, Tennessee, yielded nearly one person diagnosed as psychotic, but never having been in a mental hospital, for every hospitalized psychotic from the county (Roth and Luton,

1943). By contrast, Eaton found in his study of the Hutterites (Eaton and Weil, 1955a) that more intensive canvassing by psychiatrists did not yield a larger number of persons deemed psychotic than did a more superficial count based on community reports.

Eaton's study *did* yield higher proportions of neurotic diagnoses the more intensive the case-finding procedure became, and this observation relates to the finding in New Haven that neurotics under outpatient treatment came disproportionately from the upper socioeconomic strata (Hollingshead and Redlich, 1953). At first consideration, such differential rates seem readily attributable to the cost of psychiatric treatment, but Hollingshead and Redlich prefer to seek an explanation in the greater social distance between lower-class neurotics and the psychiatrists than in the case of middle- and upper-class neurotics. Whatever the sources of rate differences, it is clear that such correlations as have been reported make one wary of the hospital admissions or outpatient figures as indicative of the "true" incidence of psychiatric disorders. Thus the criterion of exposure to psychiatric treatment is at best a rough indicator of any underlying conceptual definition of mental illness.

Maladjustment as Mental Illness

Adjustment is necessarily determined with reference to norms of the total society or of some more restricted community within the society. Accordingly, one may conceptually define adjustment as adherence to social norms. Such a definition of mental health has an advantage over the preceding in encompassing a range of more-or-less healthy, more-or-less ill behavior, rather than posing a forced dichotomy. The operation for assessing mental health by this criterion might ideally be a community (or other relevant group) consensus concerning a given subject's degree of adjustment. This has been approximated by at least one set of studies (Beilin, 1957, 1958).

Rather than assess consensus by pooling many divergent individual opinions, it is possible to assume that a law or other visible sign of social norms constitutes the criterion against which adjustment is determined. Such reference is employed in studies of suicide (Durkheim, 1951; Henry and Short, 1954) or juvenile delinquency (Hathaway and Monachesi, 1955) or divorce (Locke, 1951; Terman and Wallin, 1949) as indicants of maladjustment. While the operational criterion may become dichotomous in such cases (whether or not the person comes in contact with the law), this is not necessarily so. Gordon (1950) has suggested considering the "biologic gradient" of suicide, extending from contemplation of the act to its actual accomplishment.

Finally, it would be possible to assess degree of adjustment with reference to some externally defined set of requirements for a given social system. Thus a work situation might be seen as demanding a high level of productivity from all its members, and the degree of adherence to this standard becomes the criterion of adjustment, without reference to the individual opinions of the group members or to the manifest norms of the group. This criterion of conformity to the requirements of a given social structure has not been explicitly employed by any of the researchers covered in the present review, but it has been hinted at (Lindemann *et al.*, 1950) and remains a possibility, provided that the structural requirements of a social system can be determined independently of the members' behaviors.

Theory of social structure suggests that these three criteria of adjustment would tend toward congruence: The demands of a particular social system lead to the development of social norms, which are expressed in laws or customs and also in the individual participants' notions of what is acceptable behavior. Lack of congruence may be taken as evidence of cultural lag, of poor correspondence between manifest and latent function within the social structure, or of defensive psychological processes within the participating individuals. Since all of these factors supporting discrepancy do occur within most social systems, the criteria may be expected to yield somewhat different results.

When maladjustment is assessed by community consensus, one finds considerable divergence of opinion among various segments of the public regarding what constitutes good and poor adjustment. The Minnesota Child Welfare Studies (Beilin, 1958) showed differences in criteria for assessing adjustment among different occupational groups in the community. Teachers tended to emphasize standards different from those emphasized by ministers, who in turn displayed some differences from a more heterogeneous group of community adults. Beilin concludes that it is meaningless to discuss "adjustment" in the abstract or to contemplate the prediction of "adjustment" in general. One must specify *adjustment to what, adjustment to whose standards* (Beilin, 1957). Lindemann reflects this relativistic conception of mental health when he states: "We find it preferable not to talk about a 'case' in psychiatry—rather we try to assess functional impairment in specific situations as viewed by different professional groups in the community. So a 'case' is really a relationship of possibly pathogenic situation and appropriate or inappropriate behavior to that situation. It is often a matter of arbitrary choice whether such a person becomes an object of psychiatric care" (Lindemann, 1953, p. 130).

Thus, though adjustment appears a more conceptually adequate criterion of mental health than does exposure to treatment, the necessity for considering different personal frames of reference and the demands of different social structures poses seemingly insurmountable obstacles to the establishment of mutually consistent operational definitions. All such difficulties which lie "hidden," as it were, under the psychiatric treatment criterion, come to the fore to plague the researcher trying to establish a criterion for adjustment which applies to the treated and nontreated alike.

Psychiatric Diagnosis as Criterion for Mental Illness

There have been a few studies in which entire communities or samples of them have been systematically screened, either by direct examination (Rennie, 1953; Roth and Luton, 1943) or by evidence from community records or hearsay (Eaton and Weil, 1955a; Tietze *et al.*, 1942). Here the criterion for mental illness or health need not be dichotomous, but can be divided into several gra-

dations. Such intensive case-finding can be expected to increase the yield of persons classified as neurotic (Kramer, 1953, p. 124) over that provided by the criterion of exposure to treatment, but whether the psychotic group is thereby increased will depend on the community (Kramer, 1953, p. 124; Roth and Luton, 1943) and, of course, on the standards for diagnosis employed by the particular investigator.

The lack of standardization of diagnostic procedures and criteria contributes to the incomparability of mental illness rates derived from such studies (Kramer, 1953, p. 139; Tietze *et al.*, 1943). So long as the criterion of assessment is largely dependent on the psychiatrist's subjective integration of a different set of facts for each subject, nonuniform results can be anticipated. Expensive and unreliable though the method may be, it at least places the judgment regarding mental illness or health in the hands of professionals, which is not the case when adjustment is the criterion. And though hospitalization is in part determined by the judgment of professionals, *who* is sent to the hospitals for psychiatric diagnosis is, for the most part, out of the hands of the psychiatrists. As Felix and Bowers (1948) have observed, it is the community rather than the clinician that operates the case-finding process today, and this will continue to be so until diagnostic examinations are given regularly to all people.

Mental Illness Defined Subjectively

It has been maintained by some that a major indication of need for psychotherapy is the person's own feeling of unhappiness or inadequacy. Conversely the degree of mental health may be assessed by manifestations of subjective happiness, self-confidence, and morale. Lewis (1951a) quotes Ernest Jones the effect that the main criterion for effect of therapy is the patient's subjective sense of strength, confidence, and well-being. Terman (1938, 1949) has used "marriage happiness" test, composed largely of subjective items, and Pol (1948) has suggested that old-age adjustment be assessed in terms of the son's degree of happiness or well-being in various areas of his life.

That such criteria of mental health correlate somewhat with indeper diagnoses by physicians has been indicated in two sorts of studies. In the timore Eastern Health District (Downes and Simon, 1954), cases diag psychoneurotic were found to express complaints about their own p health; it is suggested that persons who report chronic nervousness classified as suffering from a psychiatric condition. Rogers has maintain a marked discrepancy between one's "perceived self" and "ideal self" tutes evidence of psychiatric disturbance (Rogers, 1951), and some studies lend support to this position. When Q sorts of subjects' self are compared with Q sorts of their ideal selves, it is possible to psychiatric groups from nonpsychiatric groups on the basis of the discrepancy between these two measures (Chase, 1956). Furthermor in therapy (as judged by the therapist) tends to be associated with similarity between the patient's self-concept and ideal self (Roge mond, 1954).

Though subjective well-being is an appealing criterion for mer

ordinary daily living, it might be presumed that under some circumstances psychological defense mechanisms could operate to prevent the person's reporting, or becoming aware of, his own underlying unhappiness and disturbance. Jahoda (1953a) has rejected happiness as a criterion for mental health on somewhat different grounds: Happiness, she says, is a function not only of the person's behavior patterns, but of the environment in which he moves. If one wants to relate mental health to characteristics of the environment, then one must not take as a criterion of mental health something that already presupposes a benign environment. "There are certain circumstances in which to be happy would make it necessary first to be completely sick" (Jahoda, 1953a, p. 105).

Such objections to this criterion imply that it is possible to find persons who are mentally ill by some other criterion, yet who nevertheless report themselves as happy or self-satisfied. Empirical demonstration of this implication is not available at present. In fact, while one study predicted defensively high Q sorts for the self-concept of paranoid psychotics, they were found to have a greater discrepancy between self- and ideal-sorts than normals, and no less discrepancy between these measures than psychoneurotics (Chase, 1956).

Mental Illness Defined by
Objective Psychological Symptoms

It is generally accepted almost by definition that mental illness entails both a disordering of psychological processes and a deviation of behavior from social norms (Clausen, 1956). The latter aspect of disturbance may be assessed as maladjustment to one's social environment (discussed above); the former aspect can presumably be assessed by psychological inventories aimed at the assumedly critical processes. The distinction between the psychological inventory approach and the subjective assessment procedure discussed above is not really a clear one. Subjective well-being may be regarded as one of the psychological processes which becomes disordered. Yet more "objective" measures of psychological process, which do not require the subject's verbal report of his degree of happiness, are frequently preferred, both to guard against purposeful distortion and to tap areas of disorder which may not be accompanied by subjective counterparts.

Such "objective" psychological inventories may represent various degrees of manifest purpose. For some, the objective of assessment is transparent, and the only reason they are not classed as devices for subjective report is that they stop just short of requiring the subject to report his overall level of well-being. Such a manifest-level inventory is Halmos' questionnaire concerning the respondent's difficulties in social relations (Halmos, 1952).

At a somewhat less obvious level are such inventories as the MMPI, the War Department Neuropsychiatric Screening Battery, and the Cornell Medical Index, which require subjects to check the presence of various subjective and objective symptoms (e.g., "I smoke too much"). Once validated against an accepted criterion, such as psychiatric diagnosis, these are frequently used as criteria themselves. Rennie constructed a composite instrument of this type to assess his respondents' levels of mental health in the Yorkville study (Rennie,

1953); at the same time, a validity analysis of the index was undertaken, by correlating each item with independent psychiatric diagnosis on a subsample of the respondents. On the basis of their experience with such a composite instrument, one of Rennie's colleagues (Langner, personal communication, August 1956) suggests caution in abstracting parts of previously validated batteries, since the item validities are sometimes not maintained when they are used out of context of the total instrument.

An adaptation of the psychiatric screening battery approach for use with children is suggested in the work of the St. Louis County Public Health Department (Glidewell et al., 1957). It involves obtaining information about symptoms from the children's mothers rather than from the children themselves. Naturally, the symptoms covered must be of the "objective" type ("Does Johnny wet the bed?") rather than of the "subjective" type ("Does Johnny worry a lot?"). As validated by an outside criterion (teachers' and psychiatric social workers' ratings of the child's level of adjustment), the number of symptoms reported by the mothers appears to be a promising index of the child's mental health.

A general characteristic of the types of psychological inventories reviewed so far is that each item in the battery is assumed, a priori, to involve a "directional" quality, such that one type of answer (e.g., "yes" to "Are you troubled with nightmares?") may be taken as indicative of psychological disorder, and the opposite answer as indicative of normal functioning. Thus the index of disturbance is computed by adding all the positive indicators, weighted equally. That alternative methods of test construction may yield equally, or more, valid indices of mental illness is indicated by the extensive investigations of McQuitty (1954).

McQuitty proposes several different methods of diagnostic test scoring, each based on explicit assumptions about the diagnostic procedure which the test is supposed to represent. One of the simplest assumptions, for example, is that an individual is mentally ill to the extent that his psychological processes deviate from the culturally modal processes. Thus, any type of multiple-alternative test may be administered to a group of subjects representing a "normal" population. Each alternative of each item is then scored for its "popularity." The score for a subject is then computed by adding the popularity scores of the items he checks (McQuitty calls this the T method of scoring); a high popularity score is taken as evidence of mental health (by this "typicality" criterion).

An alternative assumption proposed by McQuitty as underlying the diagnostic procedure might be that mental health is manifest to the degree that the subject's responses conform to *any* pattern of answers represented by a significant number of community people, regardless of whether that pattern is the most popular one. Such an assumption leads to a scoring procedure (H method) whereby a subject's index of "cultural harmony" is based on the degree to which his responses to different questions "go together" in the same manner as do the responses of all people in the sample who check the same alternatives he does.

Elaborations on these basic procedures provide for differential weighting of responses depending on their degree of deviance (WH method), and correction for "linkage" between successive pairs of items (WHc method).

The Bernreuter Personality Test and the Strong Vocational Interest Inventory were administered by McQuitty to a group of mental patients and to a group of university students; they were scored by different methods, the scores for the two tests were correlated, and the mean scores of the two groups compared. Results of the comparisons indicate that: (a) when appropriately scored, the Strong can discriminate mental patients from normals, though not so well as the Bernreuter; (b) better results are obtained if, instead of treating each answer as a separate, independent measure, it is evaluated in terms of the pattern of other answers with which it occurs (WHc scoring method); (c) within the Bernreuter, those items which correlated best with the total score (McQuitty's WHc method of scoring) and provided the best discrimination between patients and normals tended to be of the "subjective" type (i.e., they depended on the subject's introspection, as in "Do you often have disturbing thoughts?") rather than the "objective" (items which an observer could report, such as "Do you talk very much?"); (d) different scoring procedures appeared differentially appropriate for the "subjective" and "objective" items; (e) when the "subjective" items were scored by the method most appropriate to them (i.e., the method which best discriminated patients from normals), and the "objective" items by their most appropriate method, the correlation between the two scores on the same group of subjects was about zero, indicating that two independent dimensions of mental health were being tapped by these two sets of items.

A separate study reported by McQuitty (1954) indicated that the simple T method of scoring (based on the popularity of the subject's responses) both subjective and objective items significantly discriminated groups of school children classified on the basis of independent criteria of mental health. There is considerable evidence from these studies that, especially with respect to those traits measured by the "objective" items, the person may be regarded as mentally ill to the extent that he deviates from the dominant community pattern.

The foregoing studies provide a certain amount of evidence that measures of mental illness according to psychometric criteria relate to two of the criteria discussed earlier—maladjustment and psychiatric diagnosis. That such concurrent validation may yield somewhat different results from studies of predictive validity is indicated in Beilin's report of the Nobles County study (1957). Two indices of student adjustment predictors were constructed, one (the "pupil index") based on students' responses to five different instruments, and the other (the "teacher index") based on teacher ratings. Both were concurrently validated against juvenile court judges' nominations of delinquent youngsters and against teachers' descriptions of the youngsters. Four years later the mental health of the youth was assessed by a number of different criteria—community reputation, interviewers' ratings, self-assessment, and an adaptation of the Rundquist-Sletto morale scale. The predictors correlated significantly with only some of the subsequent criteria, and all of the correlations were at best moderate. The "pupil index" correlated better with the interviewer's rating than with the community reputation criterion; while the "teacher index" correlated better with the subject's subsequent community reputation than with the interviewer's rating. Or, stated more generally, the psychologist's predictor predicted better to a psychologist's criterion, and a community predictor predicted better to a community criterion. Though the time span (four years) between the predictor and criterion measures may have been such as to allow for considerable change in the subjects, one is nevertheless reminded by these results that various criteria for mental health are not necessarily highly correlated.

In summarizing the various studies of mental health and illness defined by psychological testing batteries, we may note that many of them lack an underlying conception of the nature of mental illness from which to derive items and scoring procedures (a notable exception being McQuitty's measures), that some of them challenge the notion of the unidimensional nature of mental health, and that their degree of correlation with other criteria, such as adjustment or psychiatric diagnosis, depends on the nature of the criterion.

Mental Health as Positive Striving

A radically different approach to the assessment of mental health is indicated in the definitions proposed by some writers with a mental hygiene orientation. Gruenberg suggests that, though failure to live up to the expectations of those around him may constitute mental illness, one should also consider the person's failure to live up to his own potentialities (Gruenberg, 1953, p. 131). Frank speaks of the "positive" aspect of mental health—healthy personalities are those who "continue to grow, develop, and mature through life, accepting responsibilities, finding fulfillments, without paying too high a cost personally or socially, as they participate in maintaining the social order and carrying on our culture" (Frank, 1953). In a less exhortative tone, Henry (1953) discusses successful adaptation of the person in the "normal stressful situation." He sees many normal situations as situations of inherent stress. Some individuals in them develop mental disease, while others may develop out of them a more complex, but more successful, personality. It is this successful coping with the "normal stressful situation" that Henry regards as indicative of mental health.

Jahoda has translated this kind of emphasis on the positive, striving, aspects of behavior into a set of criteria amenable to empirical research. She proposes three basic features of mental health (Jahoda, 1955): (a) The person displays active adjustment, or attempts at mastery of his environment, in contrast to lack of adjustment or indiscriminate adjustment through passive acceptance of social conditions. (b) The person manifests unity of personality—the maintenance of a stable integration which remains intact in spite of the flexibility of behavior which derives from active adjustment. (c) The person perceives the world and himself correctly, independent of his personal needs.

Active mastery of the environment, according to Jahoda, presupposes a deliberate choice of what one does and does not conform to, and consists of the deliberate modification of environmental conditions. "In a society in which regimentation prevails, active adjustment will hardly be possible; in a society where overt regimentation is replaced by the invisible compulsiveness of conformity pressures, active adjustment will be equally rare. Only where there exists social recognition of alternative forms of behavior is there a chance for the individual to master his surroundings and attain mental health" (Jahoda, 1955, p. 563).

Such an approach is quite at odds with the subjective criterion of personal happiness, and with the conformity criterion referred to above as "adjustment."

Attempted adjustment does not necessarily result in success, for success is dependent on the environment. The best mode of adjustment only maximizes the chances of success. It is mentally healthy behavior even if the environment does not permit a solution of the problem (Jahoda, 1953a). Jahoda proposes that the criterion of happiness be replaced with some more "objective" definition of mental health, based on an explicit set of values.

In an unpublished community study, Jahoda apparently attempted to assess only two of the aspects of mental health incorporated in her definition. Veridicality of perception (actually, of judgment) was determined by asking respondents to estimate certain characteristics of their communities concerning which objective data were available (e.g., proportion of people with only grade-school education), and at the same time inferring needs to distort reality from the respondent's evaluative statements about the problem (e.g., how important R believed education to be). This method of assessing need-free perception was regarded as something less than satisfactory (Jahoda, personal communication, August 1956), since the need was so difficult to determine, and it was difficult to establish unambiguously that distortion of judgment was due to the operation of a need rather than simply to lack of valid information.

The degree of attempted active adjustment was assessed by first asking a respondent to mention a particular problem in the community, then determining what he had done, or tried to do, about it, and how he felt about the problem at the time of interview (Jahoda, 1953a). Three aspects of respondents' reactions were coded from their replies (Jahoda, 1953): (a) the stage of problem solution—mere consideration of the problem, consideration of solutions, or actual implementation; (b) the feeling tone associated with the problem— continued worry or improvement in feeling (either through partial solution or through passive acceptance); (c) the directness or indirectness of the approach —i.e., whether R went to the heart of the problem in his attempted solution or merely dealt temporarily with recurrent nuisances.

In her analysis Jahoda relates her measures of problem-solving and need-free perception to various characteristics of the respondents and of the communities in which they live. The relationships are interesting (e.g., in one of the communities the level of problem-solving was related to the degree of community participation of the respondent), but they appear to leave unanswered a basic question about the appropriateness of the criteria. If one accepts Jahoda's definition of mental health as involving the two components assessed in the study, then the results can be interpreted as showing what patterns of social interaction are associated with mental health. But if one is skeptical about the meaningfulness of the definition, then he is impelled to search for correlations between her two measures and other, more commonly accepted, criteria of mental health. These are not reported, although it would appear to be a fair question to ask about the relation of her concepts to those employed by other researchers.

If one is wedded to the happiness criterion of mental health, for example, one may speculate about the possibility of a negative relation between it and those provided by Jahoda. Unhappiness could conceivably lead to excessive coping behavior (attempted adjustment), or excessive coping behavior might elicit negative reactions from others which, in turn, would increase one's unhappiness. In like fashion, it could be that need-free perception would lead to increased unhappiness, since psychological defenses are not available to bolster one's self image. Though Jahoda might reject the suggestion that happiness is even relevant to her criteria, it would appear useful to explore, both conceptually and empirically, the interrelations among other measures of mental health and the novel one proposed by her.

Clausen (1956) has maintained that researchers must ultimately face the task of relating mental health defined in positive terms to the individual's ability to resist mental illness under stress. At present it is not known whether they represent a common factor or are independent characteristics. Jahoda (personal communication, August 1956) suspects that positive mental health, as she defines it, may indeed represent a dimension orthogonal to that represented by the conventional psychological symptoms of mental illness. Thus, from a different approach than that employed by McQuitty comes the suggestion that mental health and illness may be a multidimensional phenomenon.

In employing these particular criteria, especially that of active adaptation, Jahoda seems willing to defend the evaluative standards implicit in it. And it may well be that values relating to attempted mastery of problems are every bit as defensible as the values of conformity implied in the adjustment criteria discussed above. Nevertheless, the former appear to exemplify the application of the Protestant ethic to the mental health movement in a manner which might introduce culture and class biases into one's conclusions. Miller and Swanson (1953) have hypothesized that lower-class children will show more defeatism than middle-class children, as a result of different interpersonal and environmental experiences. Would they thereby be less mentally healthy by any standards besides those of the middle class? Truly, the problems posed in setting up absolute values from which to judge mental health and illness are perplexing.

Basic Problems in the Definition of Mental Health and Illness

Underlying the diversities in definition of mental illness one can discern certain basic differences of viewpoint concerning how the phenomena should be conceptualized. We may abstract certain foci of disagreement by posing the following four points of contention: (a) Does mental illness refer to a unitary concept or to an artificial grouping of basically different specific disorders? (b) Is mental illness an acute or chronic state of the organism? (c) Is maladjustment (or deviance from social norms) an essential concomitant of mental illness? (d) Should mental illness be explicitly defined according to values other than social conformity?

Each of the proposed definitions takes a stand, either explicitly or implicitly, on one or more of these issues. It is likely that resolution of disagreements will depend in part on the outcome of future empirical research. But at least some of the divergence inheres in the theoretical formulation of the problem, and is more a matter of conceptual predilection than of empirical fact. In either case, if one is to arrive at consistent theoretical and operational definitions of mental illness, it would be well to make explicit one's bias concerning each of these issues, and attempt to rationalize it in terms of his conception of the causes of disturbance.

The Unitary or Specific Nature of Mental Illness

The position that mental illness is manifest in some rather general form, regardless of the specific diagnostic category in which the patient is placed, would appear to be implicit in the subjective definition of the phenomenon. If the person's feeling of happiness or adequacy is regarded as the crucial indicator of his mental state, this would appear to imply that overall health or illness can be assessed for a particular person, regardless of the area of functioning referred to. Likewise, the definition of mental health in terms of purposeful striving or active adjustment tends to ignore differences in the underlying bases for such striving or lack thereof. Such a position has been stated explicitly by Stieglitz: "The mensuration of health . . . closely parallels the measurement of biological age as contrasted to chronological age. . . . We are no longer seeking to discover specific disease entities, or even clinical syndromes, but attempting to measure biological effectiveness in adaptation" (Stieglitz, 1949, p. 79). And such a unitary view of the phenomenon is implied in Schneider's comment: "The major 'cause' of mental disease is seen as some form of disorientation between the personality and society" (Schneider, 1953, p. 31).

By contrast, the specific view of mental illness is taken by Gordon: "What we choose to call mental disease is an artificial grouping of many morbid processes. The first essential, in my opinion, is to separate the various entities, and in the approach to an epidemiology of mental diseases, to center attention on some one condition, or a few selected conditions, which have functions in common with other mass diseases well understood in their group relationships" (Milbank Memorial Fund, 1950, p. 107). McQuitty offers empirical evidence in favor of a specific view, in his isolation of two quite independent measures of mental illness (by psychological testing), both of which correlate with external diagnostic criteria. And he further speculates that the number of areas in which the degree of personality integration varies rather independently is probably greater than the two which he has isolated. "One might expect that mental illness might develop within any one or more patterns. In order to understand the mental illness of a particular subject, we must isolate the pattern, or patterns, of characteristics to which his mental illness pertains" (McQuitty, 1954, p. 22).

While the weight of opinion and evidence appears to favor the multidimensional view, this may simply be a function of the operational definitions employed (e.g., mental health defined by responses to a battery of tests is bound to turn out multidimensional to the extent that intercorrelations among the test items are low). But there are yet insufficient empirical data collected from the unitary point of view to test whether its assumption is correct. Indeed, it seems quite plausible that both happiness and active adaptation may be partially a function of the situation, hence the concept of mental health implied by them must become multidimensional to the extent that they allow for intersituational variability.

The Acute or Chronic Nature of Mental Illness

The psychologist's testing approach to assessing mental illness inclines him toward a view of the condition as chronic. That is, the predisposing conditions within the organism are generally presumed to be relatively enduring, though perhaps triggered off into an actual psychotic break by excessively stressful situations. The epidemiological approach, on the other hand, is usually concerned with the counting of actual hospitalized cases, and this may incline one toward a view of mental illness as predominantly acute. Felix has espoused this position explicitly: "Unless the kinds of mental illness are specified, I can't conceive that mental illness is a chronic disease. More mental illnesses by far are acute and even short term than there are mental illnesses which are chronic and long term" (Milbank Memorial Fund, 1950, p. 163). Of course, the epidemiological approach traditionally considers characteristics of the host, as well as characteristics of the agent and the environment. But the predisposing factors within the organism seem to be regarded, like "low resistance," not as a subliminal state of the disease, but rather as a general susceptibility to any acute attack precipitated by external factors.

It is easier to regard a psychosis as acute than it is similarly to regard a neurosis, since in the former disorder the break with normal behavior appears more precipitate. However, such a judgment, based on easily observable external behaviors, may be unduly superficial. Even in the case of such a discrete disturbance as suicide, at least one writer (Gordon *et al.*, 1950) recommends considering the biologic gradient of the disorder. He distinguishes varying degrees of suicide, with successful accomplishment as merely a possible end product. Where such continuity between morbid and nonmorbid states can be discerned, the possibility of chronic disturbance might well be considered.

The Problem of Mental
Health as Conformity to Social Norms

The criterion of mental health based on adjustment clearly implies that conformity to the social situation in which the individual is permanently imbedded is a healthy response. And such an assumption would appear to be lurking, in various shapes, behind nearly all of the other definitions considered (with the possible exception of some of the "positive striving" criteria, which stress conformity to a set of standards independent of the person's immediate social group). In fact, McQuitty's methods of scoring psychological inventories are all explicitly based on the assumption that conformity (either to the total community or to a significant subgroup) is healthy.

If the stability of the larger social system be regarded as the final good, or if human development be seen as demanding harmony in relation to that social system, then such an assumption would appear basic and defensible. But one is still impelled to consider the possibility that the social system, or even an entire society, may be sick, and conformity to its norms would constitute mental illness, in some more absolute sense. If any particular behavior pattern is considered both from the standpoint of its adaptability within the social structure to which the individual maintains primary allegiance and from the standpoint of its relation to certain external ideal standards imposed by the observer, perhaps a comparison of the two discrepancy measures would yield information about the degree to which the social system approaches the ideal. On the other hand, such a comparison might be interpreted as merely indicating the degree to which the researcher who sets the external standards is himself adapted to the social system which he is studying. The dilemma appears insoluble.

The Problem of Values in Criteria for Mental Health

The mental hygiene movement has traditionally been identified with one or another set of values—ideal standards from which behavior could be assessed as appropriate or inappropriate. The particular set of values adopted probably depends to a considerable degree on who is doing the judging. Such a diversity of evaluative judgments leads to chaos in the popular literature and to considerable confusion in the usage of the term "mental health" in scientific research. Kingsley Davis (1938) presented a rather strong case for the proposition that mental hygiene, being a social movement and source of advice concerning personal conduct, has inevitably been influenced by the Protestant ethic inherent in our culture. The main features of this Protestant ethic, as seen by him, are its democratic, worldly, ascetic, individualistic, rationalistic, and utilitarian orientations.

To the extent that research on mental health is based on criteria devolved from such an ideology, it is middle-class-Protestant biased. To the extent that it is based on some other set of "absolute" norms for behavior, it is probably biased toward some other cultural configuration. At least one researcher, Jahoda (1953a), has clearly taken the position that mental health criteria must be based on an explicit set of values. There is some advantage in allowing the assumptions to come into full view, but in this case the resulting criteria appear to be rather specialized and not comparable with those used by other researchers. Perhaps the difficulty lies not so much in the existence of explicit assumptions as in their level of generality. If a more basic set of assumptions could be found, from which the diverse criteria for mental health and illness can be derived, then comparability among researches might better be achieved. One would be in a better position to state when mental illness, as defined by psychological tests or by absence of active adjustment, is likely to be displayed in mental illness defined by psychiatric diagnosis or deviance from community standards.

Summary

The various categories of definitions of mental illness discussed here have been distinguished primarily on the basis of their differing operational definitions: the dependent variables employed in empirical research on the phenomena are clearly different. Moreover, the conceptualizations of mental illness explicit or implicit in the empirical criteria are often quite divergent—viz., the radically different viewpoints underlying the "maladjustment," "subjective unhappiness," and "lack of positive striving" definitions.

Certain conceptual and methodological difficulties in each of these types of definition have been noted: "Exposure to treatment" is deficient in that only a limited proportion of those diagnosable as mentally ill ever reach psychiatric treatment. "Social maladjustment" is open to question because of the varying requirements of different social systems and the diversity of criteria for adjustment employed by community members. "Psychiatric diagnosis" provides an expensive, and often unreliable, method of assessing the state of mental health. "Subjective unhappiness" can be criticized as a criterion since it may be a function of intolerable environmental conditions as well as the psychological state of the person, and is subject to distortion by defense mechanisms. The validity of "objective testing procedures" appears to depend considerably on the method by which they are scored, and there is strong evidence that a major component of their score may simply be the degree of conformity of the person to the community average. Finally, criteria included under the heading of "positive striving" are subject to question in that they are inevitably based on disputable value systems of their proponents.

While many of these difficulties would not be considered damaging from the point of view of certain of the definitions of mental illness, they run into conflict with others. Also they suggest certain basic incompatibilities among the various approaches to conceptualization of mental illness. Whether these incompatibilities should be reconciled by further theoretical and empirical exploration, or whether they should be regarded as valid indicators that mental health and illness constitute multidimensional phenomena is still a moot question. We can only note that various studies employing two or more of these different categories of criteria have tended to yield moderate, but not impressive, interrelations.

The criterion of "exposure to psychiatric treatment" has been related to "maladjustment," "psychiatric diagnosis," "subjective unhappiness," and "objective psychometrics." Also "maladjustment" has been related to "psychiatric diagnosis" and to certain "objective" measures; and "psychiatric diagnosis" has been related to both "subjective" and "objective" measures of mental illness. The areas of interrelationship for which no empirical studies have been found are between "subjective" measures and both "maladjustment" and "objective" assessment; also between the "positive striving" criteria and all of the other types of measures.

Two directions for future theory and research are indicated by these results. First, more investigations are needed of the extent of relationship among the various criteria, and of the conditions under which the magnitudes of the intercorrelations vary. Second, assuming absence of high intercorrelations under many conditions, it would be worthwhile to explore the implications of poor congruence between one measure and another—implications both for the person and for the social system in which he lives.

2 / The Psychological Meaning of Various Criteria for Positive Mental Health

Marie Jahoda

So far, three efforts to give psychological meaning to the notion of positive mental health have been examined and found more or less wanting. To regard the absence of mental disease as a criterion has proved to be an insufficient indication in view of the difficulty of defining disease. Normality, in one connotation, is but a synonym for mental health; in another sense it was found to be unspecific and bare of psychological content. Various states of well-being proved unsuitable because they reflect not only individual functioning but also external circumstances.

A survey of the relevant literature reveals a host of other approaches to the subject which seem more promising; at least, at first sight, it appears that the objections raised in the preceding pages do not apply to them. Although no claim can be made that this survey discovered every contribution to the topic, the search was extensive. It is hoped that no major idea in the area has escaped our attention.

Six Approaches to a Concept

From an inspection of the diverse approaches uncovered, six major categories of concepts emerge.

1. There are several proposals suggesting that indicators of positive mental health should be sought in the *attitudes of an individual toward his own self.* Various distinctions in the manner of perceiving oneself are regarded as demonstrating higher or lower degrees of health.
2. Another group of criteria designates the individual's style and degree of *growth, development, or self-actualization* as expressions of mental health. This group of criteria, in contrast to the first, is concerned not with self-perception but with what a person does with his self over a period of time.
3. Various proposals place the emphasis on a central synthesizing psychological function, incorporating some of the suggested criteria defined in (1) and (2) above. This function will here be called *integration.*

The following three groups of criteria concentrate more exclusively than the preceding ones on the individual's relation to reality.

4. *Autonomy* singles out the individual's degree of independence from social influences as most revealing of the state of his mental health.
5. A number of proposals suggest that mental health is manifested in the adequacy of an individual's *perception of reality*.
6. Finally, there are suggestions that *environmental mastery* be regarded as a criterion for mental health.

All ideas on positive mental health examined can be assigned to one of these six categories with relative ease, even though there is a certain amount of overlap. As will become apparent, many authors have made contributions to several of the categories. And it could be argued that there exists an empirical or theoretical relationship between these groups. But the purpose of this review is to present current thoughts on criteria of positive mental health; not—at least, not yet—to inquire into the relationship of these criteria to each other, to an author's other contributions, or to theories.

One consequence of this emphasis on criteria is that similarities may appear where theoretical differences have not led one to expect them. Another is that it will be possible to examine these criteria from the point of view of mental health, rather than of the fruitfulness of the general approach of which they form a part.

Attitudes toward the Self as Criteria for Mental Health

A recurring theme in many efforts to give meaning to the concept of mental health is the emphasis on certain qualities of a person's self. The mentally healthy attitude toward the self is described by terms such as self-acceptance, self-confidence, or self-reliance, each with slightly different connotations. Self-acceptance implies that a person has learned to live with himself, accepting both the limitations and possibilities he may find in himself. Self-confidence, self-esteem, and self-respect have a more positive slant; they express the judgment that in balance the self is "good," capable, and strong. Self-reliance carries the connotation of self-confidence and, in addition, of independence from others and of initiative from within. However, the terms have become entrenched in everyday language in a manner leading to a large overlap in their connotation.

There exists also an overlap in meaning with other terms that indicate qualities of an attitude toward the self. Such terms are, for example, self-assertion, self-centeredness or egotism, and self-consciousness. These latter terms, however, have not been proposed as criteria for mental health.

A number of different dimensions or components appear to run through the various proposals. Those aspects of the self-concept that stand out most clearly are: (1) accessibility to consciousness, (2) correctness, (3) feeling about the self, and (4) sense of identity. Although not all of these components are made explicit by the writers who use attributes of the self as criteria for mental health, they are implicit in many of their contributions. Inevitably, there is a certain amount of overlap between these aspects.

Growth, Development, and
Self-Actualization as Criteria for Mental Health

A number of authors see the essence of mental health in an ongoing process variously called self-actualization, self-realization, growth, or becoming. The idea that the organism strives permanently to realize its own potentialities is old. Fromm (1947) credits Spinoza with having seen the process of development as one of becoming what one potentially is. "A horse would be as much destroyed if it were changed into a man as if it were changed into an insect," Spinoza said. Fromm continues: "We might add that, according to Spinoza, a man would be as much destroyed if he became an angel as if he became a horse. Virtue is the unfolding of the specific potentialities of every organism; for man it is the state in which he is most human."

The term self-actualization probably originated with Goldstein (1940). He spoke about the process of self-actualization as occurring in every organism and not only in the healthy one: "There is only one motive by which human activity is set going: the tendency to actualize oneself." The idea is echoed in Sullivan's dictum, "the basic direction of the organism is forward," and it also dominates the thinking of authors such as Carl Rogers, Fromm, Maslow, and Gordon Allport. Sometimes the term is used as implying a general principle of life, holding for every organism; at other times it is applied specifically to mentally healthy functioning.

It is not always easy to distinguish these two meanings in the mental health literature. This lack of clarity probably has something to do with the controversial philosophical concept of Aristotelian teleology, to which the notion of realizing one's potentialities is related. The need for making the distinction in a discussion of mental health becomes urgent if one realizes that not only the development of civilization but also self-destruction and crime, from petty thievery to genocide, are among the unique potentialities of the human species.

Mayman (1955) is of the opinion that some of the proponents of self-actualization as a criterion of health have not succeeded in making the distinction. In a critical discussion of Rogers' use of the term, he says: "This position is insufficient in several respects: it presumes that this growth force is equally potent in all people; that if given the right of way, this force will inevitably assert itself for good; but most important of all it treats this force with almost religious awe rather than scientific curiosity. This urge to grow and be healthy is treated as an irreducible essence of life."

To make this life force an aspect of positive mental health requires that certain qualifications be introduced to distinguish its manifestations in healthy persons.

The process of self-actualization, as a rule, is described in rather global terms that make it difficult to identify constituent parts. Nonetheless, the various authors who regard it as a criterion of positive mental health seem to emphasize one or more of the following aspects: (1) self-concept (which has already been discussed and is mentioned here only to indicate the breadth of the term self-actualization); (2) motivational processes; and (3) the investment in living, referring to the achievements of the self-actualizing person as demonstrated in a high degree of differentiation, or maximum of development, of his basic equipment.

Integration as a Criterion for Mental Health

In the proposals suggesting certain qualities of the self-concept or self-actualization, or both, as criteria for mental health, there is as a rule, implicit or explicit, another criterion: this is generally called integration of the personality. Indeed, some writers clearly treat this additional criterion as part of either the self-concept or of self-actualization. Others single it out for special treatment. In view of its great importance to some, it will be treated here as a major category in its own right.

Integration refers to the relatedness of all processes and attributes in an individual. The coherence of personality, often referred to as the unity or continuity of personality, is an axiomatic assumption in much psychological thought. Indeed, psychological treatment of mental patients as a rule is predicated on the search for a unifying principle in terms of which the apparently most bizarrely inconsistent manifestations of personality can be understood to hang together. When integration is proposed as a criterion for positive mental health, something additional or different is implied. Some authors suggest that integration as a criterion for mental health refers to the interrelation of certain areas of the psyche; others, that it lies in the individual's awareness of the unifying principle. Still others imply that there are distinctions in the degree or strength of the integrating factor. And some are silent on this point.

Integration as a criterion for mental health is treated, as a rule, with emphasis on one of the following aspects: (1) a balance of psychic forces in the individual, (2) a unifying outlook on life, emphasizing cognitive aspects of integration, and (3) resistance to stress.

A Note on Reality-Orientation

Three criteria—autonomy, perception of reality, and environmental mastery—share an explicit emphasis on reality-orientation. To be sure, this also has played a role in the criteria for positive mental health already presented. But as reality becomes the focus of attention, discussion in the mental health literature leads not infrequently into philosophical problems about its nature. This eternal question we wish to avoid. This is made easier by the fact that some relevant central and tangential aspects of this question actually are no longer controversial. The central aspect concerns the shift brought about by the development of modern science from a concept of *static* to a concept of *changing* reality. Says Wendell Johnson (1946): "No other fact so unrelenting shapes and reshapes our lives as this: that reality, in the broadest sense, continually changes; once we grasp clearly what has been 'known' for centuries and what is, in fact, the central theme of modern science, that no two things are identical and that no one thing is ever twice the same, that everywhere is change, flux, process, we understand that we must live in a world of differences. . . ."

The tangential aspect of the philosophic question directly bearing on mental health—the dispute over whether there exists an essential hostility or a compatibility between man and the reality he is born into—no longer splits various schools of psychological thought into opposed camps. With the development of psychoanalytic ego-psychology and its conception of ego-forces and conflict-free ego functions as part of the native equipment (Hartmann, 1951), the psychoanalytic school has clearly indicated that it does not subscribe to the unqualified view of reality as hostile to man. Academic psychology, which long has accused psychoanalysis of just this sin, always has had room for aspects of reality both supporting and thwarting the individual's needs.

The positive aspect of reality as a pleasurable challenge and stimulation to the individual has recently been restated by Charlotte Bühler (1954). Taking note of psychoanalytic ego-psychology, Bühler says: "This concept of a positive reality would also imply the postulation of pleasurable activity ('function pleasure,' K. Bühler); that is, a pleasure in the stimulating process as such, not only in its elimination. Coping or mastery is from this point of view not identical with abolishment of stimulation, which is only one of two possible resolutions. Only harmful stimuli are mastered by way of elimination. The mastery of 'positive stimuli' lies in the integrative utilization of the organism's building process by means of which the living being becomes active in structuralizing material and imposing its own law on it."

The thought that the enjoyment of reality is good in itself is already embodied in the wisdom of the Talmud; it states that everyone will have to justify himself in the life hereafter for every failure to enjoy a legitimately offered pleasure in this world.

The emphasis on the positive aspects of reality is called for because, although the controversy has virtually been resolved on the theoretical level, it still lingers in discussions of mental health. Here the tacit assumption frequently still is that the world is fundamentally hostile to the individual. This may be the result of the fact that, historically, concern with health grew out of concern with disease.

The point has been raised here to avoid repetitive interpretation in the following sections. Unless there are good reasons to the contrary, we will assume that the authors quoted do not take an either-or position with regard to the relation of man to reality and that they are aware of the complexity of human experience in which positive and negative aspects of reality are not neatly separated.

Autonomy as a Criterion for Mental Health

Many persons regard an individual's relation to the world as mentally healthy if it shows what is referred to variously as autonomy, self-determination, or independence. Most often, these terms connote a relation between individual and environment with regard to decision-making. In this sense, autonomy means a conscious discrimination by the individual of environmental factors he wishes to accept or reject. But occasionally autonomy is interpreted as a withdrawal from reality, as less need for the stimulation offered by the world, or as a small degree of involvement in external matters.

Expositions of the criterion of autonomy deal with one or both of two aspects: (1) The nature of the decision-making process, emphasizing the regulation of behavior from within, in accordance with internalized standards; (2) The outcome of the decision-making process in terms of independent actions.

Perception of Reality as a Criterion for Mental Health

Pervading many efforts to conceptualize mental health is the idea that the way an individual perceives the world around him supplies an important criterion for his mental health. As a rule, the perception of reality is called mentally healthy when what the individual sees corresponds to what is actually there. In the mental health literature, perception is discussed invariably as social perception, meaning that the conditions under which perception occurs or the object of perception, or both, involve other human beings. This has an implication for terminology. Even if it makes sense under different conditions to speak of perception as distinguishable from other cognitive processes such as attention, judgment, and thinking, social perception cannot be so isolated. The term perception will here be used as implying various modes of cognition.

Two aspects of reality perception are suggested as criteria for mental health: perception free from need-distortion, and empathy or social sensitivity.

Perception Free from Need-distortion

At first glance the stipulation that reality perception be correct in a mentally healthy person appears so self-evident—perhaps as contrasted with the psychotic's loss of contact with reality—that many authors present the criterion in an almost axiomatic fashion. Indeed, it is often treated as the *sine qua non* for reality adaptation. John Porterfield defines mental health as "that state of mind in which the perception of the environment, if not objectively accurate, is approximate enough to permit efficient interaction between the person and his milieu; . . ." (Ewalt, 1956).

Jahoda (1950) introduces correct perception as a criterion also in close conjunction with adaptation to reality: ". . . correct perception of reality (including, of course, the self) may serve as another useful criterion of mental health. Unless active adjustment involving the modification of the environment is to rely on hit-or-miss methods, it must be based on correct perception of the environment." Maslow (1954) accepts the same position: "Recently Money-Kyrle, an English psychoanalyst, has indicated that he believes it possible to call a neurotic person not only *relatively* inefficient but *absolutely* inefficient, simply because he does not perceive the real world as accurately or as efficiently as does the healthy person. The neurotic is not only emotionally sick—he is cognitively *wrong!*"

Barron (1955), too, speaks of correct perception of reality as one of his criteria for mental health.

Yet there is a major difficulty inherent in this apparently self-evident criterion of mental health: it lies in the word "correct." Particularly when the object of perception is social in nature—but even when it is physical stimuli—who is to say what is "correct"? If one perceives a landscape in terms of form, another perceives it in terms of color, and a third in terms of both these or of other facets, who is most "correct"? Or, with regard to a social object, if a teacher sees in a child his limitations while another sees his potentialities, which one is "correct"? Correctness as a criterion seems to carry the implication that reality is static and limited and that there is only one way of looking at it. Yet seeing new hitherto unnoticed things in the world around us which, while they remain new, may appear incorrect to others, is certainly not mentally unhealthy in the opinion of the writers on the subject.

The point at issue here is that "correctness" of perception cannot mean that there is one and only one right way of looking at the world around us. But whatever the individual, and perhaps peculiar, way of perceiving the world, there must be some objective cues to fit the resulting percept. This is what accuracy or correctness mean when one speaks of mentally healthy perception.

To avoid the connotation that there is one correct way of seeing the world, the effort has been made to eliminate the word "correct" altogether from the mental health criterion and replace it by "relative freedom from need-distortion." The author uses this phrase in suggesting that mentally healthy perception means a process of viewing the world so that one is able to take in matters one wishes were different, without distorting them to fit these wishes—that is, without inventing cues not actually existing (Jahoda, 1953). To perceive with relative freedom from need-distortion does not mean, of course, that needs and motives are eliminated; nor that they have no function in perception. The requirement is of a different nature: the mentally healthy person will *test* reality for its degree of correspondence to his wishes or fears. One lacking in mental health will assume such correspondence without testing.

Parents, for example, ordinarily wish that their children will do well in school or fear that they may fail. A mentally healthy parent will seek objective evidence and accept it, even if it goes against his wishes. One lacking in mental health will not seek evidence, or will reject it if it is presented to him and it does not suit him.

As a mental health criterion, perception free from need-distortion reveals itself in a person's concern for evidence to support what he sees and anticipates.

Empathy or Social Sensitivity

Perception free from need-distortion is, perhaps, most difficult when the object of perception is a person—the self or others. The former has already been discussed as the correctness aspect of the self-concept. The latter, the perception of the feelings and attitudes of others, has been suggested as a separate criterion for positive mental health.

The major requirement of the healthy person in this area is that he treat the inner life of other people as a matter worthy of his concern and attention. Implicitly, he is also expected to arrive at conclusions about others that are free from distortion. Foote and Cottrell (1955) make this one of the ingredients of interpersonal competence, a term they use synonymously with mental health. They say: "People appear to differ in their ability correctly to interpret the attitudes and intentions of others, in the accuracy with which they can perceive situations from others' standpoint, and thus anticipate and predict their behavior. This type of social sensitivity rests on what we call the empathic responses."

It is perhaps worth noting that this criterion, although appearing quite rarely in the mental health literature, has received a good deal of attention from research psychologists. They have demonstrated by their errors and successes the enormous difficulties in discovering its presence or absence. This is a point one suspects to be true for most of these criteria, but there is evidence for this instance.

Environmental Mastery as a Criterion for Mental Health

Perhaps no other area of human functioning has more frequently been selected as a criterion for mental health than the individual's reality orientation and his efforts at mastering the environment.

There are two central themes pervading the relevant literature: the theme of success and the theme of adaptation. As a rule, the former is specified as achievement in some significant areas of living; the latter is a toned-down version of the former, implying appropriate functioning with the emphasis more often on the process than on its result.

In the mental health literature adaptation and environmental mastery are treated on different levels of specificity. Ordering these emphases roughly from most to least specific forms of human functioning, these aspects can be distinguished: (1) the ability to love; (2) adequacy in love, work, and play; (3) adequacy in interpersonal relations; (4) efficiency in meeting situational requirements; (5) capacity for adaptation and adjustment; (6) efficiency in problem-solving.

3 / The Myth of Mental Illness

Thomas S. Szasz

My aim in this essay is to raise the question "Is there such a thing as mental illness?" and to argue that there is not. Since the notion of mental illness is extremely widely used nowadays, inquiry into the ways in which this term is employed would seem to be especially indicated. Mental illness, of course, is not literally a "thing"—or physical object—and hence it can "exist" only in the same sort of way in which other theoretical concepts exist. Yet, familiar theories

From the *American Psychologist*, 1960, **15**, 113–118. Copyright © 1960. Reprinted by permission of the author and the American Psychological Association.

are in the habit of posing, sooner or later—at least to those who come to believe in them—as "objective truths" (or "facts"). During certain historical periods, explanatory conceptions such as deities, witches, and microorganisms appeared not only as theories but as self-evident *causes* of a vast number of events. I submit that today mental illness is widely regarded in a somewhat similar fashion, that is, as the cause of innumerable diverse happenings. As an antidote to the complacent use of the notion of mental illness—whether as a self-evident phenomenon, theory, or cause—let us ask this question: What is meant when it is asserted that someone is mentally ill?

In what follows I shall describe briefly the main uses to which the concept of mental illness has been put. I shall argue that this notion has outlived whatever usefulness it might have had and that it now functions merely as a convenient myth.

Mental Illness as a Sign of Brain Disease

The notion of mental illness derives its main support from such phenomena as syphilis of the brain or delirious conditions—intoxications, for instance—in which persons are known to manifest various peculiarities or disorders of thinking and behavior. Correctly speaking, however, these are diseases of the brain, not of the mind. According to one school of thought, *all* so-called mental illness is of this type. The assumption is made that some neurological defect, perhaps a very subtle one, will ultimately be found for all the disorders of thinking and behavior. Many contemporary psychiatrists, physicians, and other scientists hold this view. This position implies that people *cannot* have troubles—expressed in what are *now called* "mental illnesses"—because of differences in personal needs, opinions, social aspirations, values, and so on. *All problems in living* are attributed to physicochemical processes which in due time will be discovered by medical research.

"Mental illnesses" are thus regarded as basically no different than all other diseases (that is, of the body). The only difference, in this view, between mental and bodily diseases is that the former, affecting the brain, manifest themselves by means of mental symptoms; whereas the latter, affecting other organ systems (for example, the skin, liver, etc.), manifest themselves by means of symptoms referable to those parts of the body. This view rests on and expresses what are, in my opinion, two fundamental errors.

In the first place, what central nervous system symptoms would correspond to a skin eruption or a fracture? It would *not* be some emotion or complex bit of behavior. Rather, it would be blindness or a paralysis of some part of the body. The crux of the matter is that a disease of the brain, analogous to a disease of the skin or bone, is a neurological defect, and not a problem in living. For example, a *defect* in a person's visual field may be satisfactorily explained by correlating it with certain definite lesions in the nervous system. On the other hand, a person's *belief*—whether this be a belief in Christianity, in Communism, or in the idea that his internal organs are "rotting" and that his body is, in fact, already "dead"—cannot be explained by a defect or disease of the nervous system. Explanations of this sort of occurrence—assuming that one is interested in the belief itself and does not regard it simply as a "symptom" or expression of something else that is *more interesting*—must be sought along different lines.

The second error in regarding complex psychosocial behavior, consisting of communications about ourselves and the world about us, as mere symptoms of neurological functioning is *epistemological*. In other words, it is an error pertaining not to any mistakes in observation or reasoning, as such, but rather to the way in which we organize and express our knowledge. In the present case, the error lies in making a symmetrical dualism between mental and physical (or bodily) symptoms, a dualism which is merely a habit of speech and to which no known observations can be found to correspond. Let us see if this is so. In medical practice, when we speak of physical disturbances, we mean either signs (for example, a fever) or symptoms (for example, pain). We speak of mental symptoms, on the other hand, when we refer to a patient's *communications about himself, others, and the world about him.* He might state that he is Napoleon or that he is being persecuted by the Communists. These would be considered mental symptoms *only* if the observer believed that the patient was *not* Napoleon or that he was *not* being persecuted by the Communists. This makes it apparent that the statement that "X is a mental symptom" involves rendering a judgment. The judgment entails, moreover, a covert comparison or matching of the patient's ideas, concepts, or beliefs with those of the observer and the society in which they live. The notion of mental symptom is therefore inextricably tied to the *social* (including *ethical*) *context* in which it is made in much the same way as the notion of bodily symptom is tied to an *anatomical* and *genetic context* (Szasz, 1957a, 1957b).

To sum up what has been said thus far: I have tried to show that for those who regard mental symptoms as signs of brain disease, the concept of mental illness is unnecessary and misleading. For what they mean is that people so labeled suffer from diseases of the brain; and, if that is what they mean, it would seem better for the sake of clarity to say that and not something else.

Mental Illness as a Name for Problems in Living

The term "mental illness" is widely used to describe something which is very different than a disease of the brain. Many people today take it for granted that living is an arduous process. Its hardship for modern man, moreover, derives not so much from a struggle for biological survival as from the stresses and strains inherent in the social intercourse of complex human personalities. In this context, the notion of mental illness is used to identify or describe some feature of an individual's so-called personality. Mental illness—as a deformity of the personality, so to speak—is then regarded as the *cause* of the human disharmony. It is implicit in this view that social intercourse between people is regarded as something *inherently harmonious*, its disturbance being due solely to the presence of "mental illness" in many people. This is obviously fallacious reasoning, for it makes the abstraction "mental illness" into a *cause*, even though this abstraction was created in the first place to serve only as a shorthand expression for certain types of human behavior. It now becomes necessary to ask: "What kinds of behavior are regarded as indicative of mental illness, and by whom?"

The concept of illness, whether bodily or mental, implies *deviation from some clearly defined norm*. In the case of physical illness, the norm is the structural and functional integrity of the human body. Thus, although the desirability of physical health, as such, is an ethical value, what health *is* can be stated in anatomical and physiological terms. What is the norm deviation from which is regarded as mental illness? This question cannot be easily answered. But whatever this norm might be, we can be certain of only one thing: namely, that it is a norm that must be stated in terms of *psychosocial, ethical,* and *legal* concepts. For example, notions such as "excessive repression" or "acting out an unconscious impulse" illustrate the use of psychological concepts for judging (so-called) mental health and illness. The idea that chronic hostility, vengefulness, or divorce are indicative of mental illness would be illustrations of the use of ethical norms (that is, the desirability of love, kindness, and a stable marriage relationship). Finally, the widespread psychiatric opinion that only a mentally ill person would commit homicide illustrates the use of a legal concept as a norm of mental health. The norm from which deviation is measured whenever one speaks of a mental illness is a *psychosocial and ethical one*. Yet, the remedy is sought in terms of *medical* measures which—it is hoped and assumed—are free from wide differences of ethical value. The definition of the disorder and the terms in which its remedy are sought are therefore at serious odds with one another. The practical significance of this covert conflict between the alleged nature of the defect and the remedy can hardly be exaggerated.

Having identified the norms used to measure deviations in cases of mental illness, we will now turn to the question: "Who defines the norms and hence the deviation?" Two basic answers may be offered: (*a*) It may be the person himself (that is, the patient) who decides that he deviates from a norm. For example, an artist may believe that he suffers from a work inhibition; and he may implement this conclusion by seeking help *for* himself from a psychotherapist. (*b*) It may be someone other than the patient who decides that the latter is deviant (for example, relatives, physicians, legal authorities, society generally, etc.). In such a case a psychiatrist may be hired by others to do something *to* the patient in order to correct the deviation.

These considerations underscore the importance of asking the question "Whose agent is the psychiatrist?" and of giving a candid answer to it (Szasz, 1956, 1958a). The psychiatrist (psychologist or nonmedical psychotherapist), it now develops, may be the agent of the patient, of the relatives, of the school, of the military services, of a business organization, of a court of law, and so forth. In speaking of the psychiatrist as the agent of these persons or organizations, it is not implied that his values concerning norms, or his ideas and aims concerning the proper nature of remedial action, need to coincide exactly with those of his employer. For example, a patient in individual psychotherapy may believe that his salvation lies in a new marriage; his psychotherapist need not share this hypothesis. As the patient's agent, however, he must abstain from bringing social or legal force to bear on the patient which would prevent him from putting his beliefs into action. If his *contract* is with the patient, the psychiatrist (psychotherapist) may disagree with him or stop his treatment;

but he cannot engage others to obstruct the patient's aspirations. Similarly, if a psychiatrist is engaged by a court to determine the sanity of a criminal, he need not fully share the legal authorities' values and intentions in regard to the criminal and the means available for dealing with him. But the psychiatrist is expressly barred from stating, for example, that it is not the criminal who is "insane" but the men who wrote the law on the basis of which the very actions that are being judged are regarded as "criminal." Such an opinion could be voiced, of course, but not in a courtroom, and not by a psychiatrist who makes it his practice to assist the court in performing its daily work.

To recapitulate: In actual contemporary social usage, the finding of a mental illness is made by establishing a deviance in behavior from certain psychosocial, ethical, or legal norms. The judgment may be made, as in medicine, by the patient, the physician (psychiatrist), or others. Remedial action, finally, tends to be sought in a therapeutic—or covertly medical—framework, thus creating a situation in which *psychosocial, ethical,* and/or *legal deviations* are claimed to be correctable by (so-called) *medical action.* Since medical action is designed to correct only medical deviations, it seems logically absurd to expect that it will help solve problems whose very existence has been defined and established on nonmedical grounds. I think that these considerations may be fruitfully applied to the present use of tranquilizers and, more generally, to what might be expected of drugs of whatever type in regard to the amelioration or solution of problems in human living.

The Role of Ethics in Psychiatry

Anything that people *do*—in contrast to things that *happen* to them (Peters, 1958)—takes place in a context of value. In this broad sense, no human activity is devoid of ethical implications. When the values underlying certain activities are widely shared, those who participate in their pursuit may lose sight of them altogether. The discipline of medicine, both as a pure science (for example, research) and as a technology (for example, therapy), contains many ethical considerations and judgments. Unfortunately, these are often denied, minimized, or merely kept out of focus; for the ideal of the medical profession as well as of the people whom it serves seems to be having a system of medicine (allegedly) free of ethical value. This sentimental notion is expressed by such things as the doctor's willingness to treat and help patients irrespective of their religious or political beliefs, whether they are rich or poor, etc. While there may be some grounds for this belief—albeit it is a view that is not impressively true even in these regards—the fact remains that ethical considerations encompass a vast range of human affairs. By making the practice of medicine neutral in regard to some specific issues of value need not, and cannot, mean that it can be kept free from all such values. The practice of medicine is intimately tied to ethics; and the first thing that we must do, it seems to me, is to try to make this clear and explicit. I shall let this matter rest here, for it does not concern us specifically in this essay. Lest there be any vagueness, however, about how or where ethics and medicine meet, let me remind the reader of such issues as birth control, abortion, suicide, and euthanasia as only a few of the major areas of current ethicomedical controversy.

Psychiatry, I submit, is very much more intimately tied to problems of ethics than is medicine. I use the word "psychiatry" here to refer to that contemporary discipline which is concerned with *problems in living* (and not with diseases of the brain, which are problems for neurology). Problems in human relations can be analyzed, interpreted, and given meaning only within given social and ethical contexts. Accordingly, it *does* make a difference—arguments to the contrary notwithstanding—what the psychiatrist's socioethical orientations happen to be; for these will influence his ideas on what is wrong with the patient, what deserves comment or interpretation, in what possible directions change might be desirable, and so forth. Even in medicine proper, these factors play a role, as for instance, in the divergent orientations which physicians, depending on their religious affiliations, have toward such things as birth control and therapeutic abortion. Can anyone really believe that a psychotherapist's ideas concerning religious belief, slavery, or other similar issues play no role in his practical work? If they do make a difference, what are we to infer from it? Does it not seem reasonable that we ought to have different psychiatric therapies—each expressly recognized for the ethical positions which they embody—for, say, Catholics and Jews, religious persons and agnostics, Democrats and Communists, white supremacists and Negroes, and so on? Indeed, if we look at how psychiatry is actually practiced today (especially in the United States), we find that people do seek psychiatric help in accordance with their social status and ethical beliefs (Hollingshead and Redlich, 1958). This should really not surprise us more than being told that practicing Catholics rarely frequent birth control clinics.

The foregoing position which holds that contemporary psychotherapists deal with problems in living, rather than with mental illnesses and their cures, stands in opposition to a currently prevalent claim, according to which mental illness is just as "real" and "objective" as bodily illness. This is a confusing claim since it is never known exactly what is meant by such words as "real" and "objective." I suspect, however, that what is intended by the proponents of this view is to create the idea in the popular mind that mental illness is some sort of disease entity, like an infection or a malignancy. If this were true, one could *catch* or *get* a "mental illness," one might *have* or *harbor* it, one might *transmit* it to others, and finally one could get *rid* of it. In my opinion, there is not a shred of evidence to support this idea. To the contrary, all the evidence is the other way and supports the view that what people now call mental illnesses are for the most part *communications* expressing unacceptable ideas, often framed, moreover, in an unusual idiom. The scope of this essay allows me to do no more than mention this alternative theoretical approach to this problem (Szasz, 1957).

This is not the place to consider in detail the similarities and differences between bodily and mental illnesses. It shall suffice for us here to emphasize only one important difference between them: namely, that whereas bodily disease refers to public, physicochemical occurrences, the notion of mental illness is used to codify relatively more private, sociopsychological happenings of which the observer (diagnostician) forms a part. In other words, the psychiatrist does not stand *apart* from what he observes, but is, in Harry Stack Sullivan's apt words, a "participant observer." This means that he is *committed* to some picture of what he considers reality—and to what he thinks society considers reality—and he observes and judges the patient's behavior in the light of these considerations. This touches on our earlier observation that the notion of mental symptom itself implies a comparison between observer and observed, psychiatrist and patient. This is so obvious that I may be charged with belaboring trivialities. Let me therefore say once more that my aim in presenting this argument was expressly to criticize and counter a prevailing contemporary tendency to deny the moral aspects of psychiatry (and psychotherapy) and to substitute for them allegedly value-free medical considerations. Psychotherapy, for example, is being widely practiced as though it entailed nothing other than restoring the patient from a state of mental sickness to one of mental health. While it is generally accepted that mental illness has something to do with' man's social (or interpersonal) relations, it is paradoxically maintained that problems of values (that is, of ethics) do not arise in this process.[1] Yet, in one sense, much of psychotherapy may revolve around nothing other than the elucidation and weighing of goals and values—many of which may be mutually contradictory—and the means whereby they might best be harmonized, realized, or relinquished.

The diversity of human values and the methods by means of which they may be realized is so vast, and many of them remain so unacknowledged, that they cannot fail but lead to conflicts in human relations. Indeed, to say that human relations at all levels—from mother to child, through husband and wife, to nation and nation—are fraught with stress, strain, and disharmony is, once again, making the obvious explicit. Yet, what may be obvious may be also poorly understood. This I think is the case here. For it seems to me that—at least in our scientific theories of behavior—we have failed to *accept* the simple fact that human relations are inherently fraught with difficulties and that to make them even relatively harmonious requires much patience and hard work. I submit that the idea of mental illness is now being put to work to obscure certain difficulties which at present may be inherent—not that they need be unmodifiable—in the social intercourse of persons. If this is true, the concept functions as a disguise; for instead of calling attention to conflicting human needs, aspirations, and values, the notion of mental illness provides an amoral and impersonal "thing" (an "illness") as an explanation for *problems in living* (Szasz, 1959). We may recall in this connection that not so long ago it was devils and witches who were held responsible for men's problems in social living. The belief in mental illness, as something other than man's trouble in getting along with his fellow man, is the proper heir to the belief in demonology and witchcraft. Mental illness exists or is "real" in exactly the same sense in which witches existed or were "real."

---

[1] Freud went so far as to say that: "I consider ethics to be taken for granted. Actually I have never done a mean thing" (Jones, 1957, p. 247). This surely is a strange thing to say for someone who has studied man as a social being as closely as did Freud. I mention it here to show how the notion of "illness" (in the case of psychoanalysis, "psychopathology," or "mental illness") was used by Freud—and by most of his followers—as a means for classifying certain forms of human behavior as falling within the scope of medicine, and hence (by *fiat*) outside that of ethics!

Choice, Responsibility, and Psychiatry

While I have argued that mental illnesses do not exist, I obviously did not imply that the social and psychological occurences to which this label is currently being attached also do not exist. Like the personal and social troubles which people had in the Middle Ages, they are real enough. It is the labels we give them that concerns us and, having labeled them, what we do about them. While I cannot go into the ramified implications of this problem here, it is worth noting that a demonologic conception of problems in living gave rise to therapy along theological lines. Today, a belief in mental illness implies —nay, requires—therapy along medical or psychotherapeutic lines.

What is implied in the line of thought set forth here is something quite different. I do not intend to offer a new conception of "psychiatric illness" nor a new form of "therapy." My aim is more modest and yet also more ambitious. It is to suggest that the phenomena now called mental illnesses be looked at afresh and more simply, that they be removed from the category of illnesses, and that they be regarded as the expressions of man's struggle with the problem of *how* he should live. The last mentioned problem is obviously a vast one, its enormity reflecting not only man's inability to cope with his environment, but even more his increasing self-reflectiveness.

By problems in living, then, I refer to that truly explosive chain reaction which began with man's fall from divine grace by partaking of the fruit of the tree of knowledge. Man's awareness of himself and of the world about him seems to be a steadily expanding one, bringing in its wake an ever larger *burden of understanding* (an expression borrowed from Susanne Langer, 1953). *This burden, then, is to be expected and must not be misinterpreted.* Our only *rational* means for lightening it is *more understanding*, and appropriate *action* based on such understanding. The main alternative lies in acting as though the burden were not what in fact we perceive it to be and taking refuge in an outmoded theological view of man. In the latter view, man does not fashion his life and much of his world about him, but merely lives out his fate in a world created by superior beings. This may logically lead to pleading nonresponsibility in the face of seemingly unfathomable problems and difficulties. Yet, if man fails to take increasing responsibility for his actions, individually as well as collectively, it seems unlikely that some higher power or being would assume this task and carry this burden for him. Moreover, this seems hardly the proper time in human history for obscuring the issue of man's responsibility for his actions by hiding it behind the skirt of an all-explaining conception of mental illness.

Conclusions

I have tried to show that the notion of mental illness has outlived whatever usefulness it might have had and that it now functions merely as a convenient myth. As such, it is a true heir to religious myths in general, and to the belief in witchcraft in particular; the role of all these belief-systems was to act as *social tranquilizers,* thus encouraging the hope that mastery of certain specific problems may be achieved by means of substitutive (symbolic-magical) operations. The notion of mental illness thus serves mainly to obscure the everyday fact that life for most people is a continuous struggle, not for biological survival, but for a "place in the sun," "peace of mind," or some other human value. For man aware of himself and of the world about him, once the needs for preserving the body (and perhaps the race) are more or less satisfied, the problem arises as to what he should do with himself. Sustained adherence to the myth of mental illness allows people to avoid facing this problem, believing that mental health, conceived as the absence of mental illness, automatically insures the making of right and safe choices in one's conduct of life. But the facts are all the other way. It is the making of good choices in life that others regard, retrospectively, as good mental health!

The myth of mental illness encourages us, moreover, to believe in its logical corollary: that social intercourse would be harmonious, satisfying, and the secure basis of a "good life" were it not for the disrupting influences of mental illness or "psychopathology." The potentiality for universal human happiness, in this form at least, seems to me but another example of the I-wish-it-were-true type of fantasy. I do believe that human happiness or well-being on a hitherto unimaginably large scale, and not just for a select few, is possible. This goal could be achieved, however, only at the cost of many men, and not just a few being willing and able to tackle their personal, social, and ethical conflicts. This means having the courage and integrity to forego waging battles on false fronts, finding solutions for substitute problems—for instance, fighting the battle of stomach acid and chronic fatigue instead of facing up to a marital conflict.

Our adversaries are not demons, witches, fate, or mental illness. We have no enemy whom we can fight, exorcise, or dispel by "cure." What we do have are *problems in living*—whether these be biologic, economic, political, or socio-psychological. In this essay I was concerned only with problems belonging in the last mentioned category, and within this group mainly with those pertaining to moral values. The field to which modern psychiatry addresses itself is vast, and I made no effort to encompass it all. My argument was limited to the proposition that mental illness is a myth, whose function it is to disguise and thus render more palatable the bitter pill of moral conflicts in human relations.

4 / "Mental Illness" or Interpersonal Behavior?

Henry B. Adams

There is no such thing as a "mental illness" in any significantly meaningful sense. In medicine the term "illness" is used in a literal, nonfigurative way to denote an undesirable alteration or change away from optimal levels of organic bodily functioning. But the term "mental illness" is applied to various patterns of behavior considered maladaptive or inappropriate by implicit psychological and social standards (Szasz, 1960, 1961).

The concept of a functional mental illness is a *verbal analogy*. While it is appropriate to speak of neurological disorders as true organic illnesses of the nervous system, comparable to organic illnesses involving the circulatory or digestive system, it seems questionable to apply the term "illness" to arbitrarily defined patterns of behavior, particularly when there may be no evidence of any physiological malfunctioning. The plain fact is that the term "mental illness" is applied in an indiscriminate way to a motley collection of interpersonal behavior patterns. Often there is no positive evidence whatever of any physiological or organic malfunctioning, as in the so-called "functional disorders." Actually, organic physical illnesses and the functional types of mental illnesses are defined by *different kinds of criteria,* and they are modified or ameliorated ("treated" or "cured") by *fundamentally different procedures*.

Failure to clarify these distinctions has had unfortunate consequences. Efforts toward understanding and effective alleviation have long been hampered by the semantic confusion which results when the word "illness" is used to denote both physical disease entities and maladaptive patterns of interpersonal behavior. This ambiguous usage has perpetuated the glib fallacy that mental and physical illnesses are the same thing. It has interfered with the understanding of fundamental psychological phenomena and made for an ineffectual and often harmful approach to some of the most serious recurring problems in human relationships.

The semantic confusion is an important fact in the history of psychiatry since 1800. A number of studies have been published in recent years on the "moral therapy" of the early nineteenth century (Bockoven, 1956, 1957; Brown, 1960; Joint Commission on Mental Illness and Health, 1961; Rees, 1957). These studies all agree that the results of moral therapy (at a time when physical medicine was in a relatively primitive stage of development) compare favorably with the very best mental hospital programs of today. "Moral therapy" was essentially a program of planned psychological retraining within a positive, sympathetic social milieu.

Moral therapy had its inception near the end of the eighteenth century under

Abridged from the *Amercian Psychologist*, 1964, **19**, 191–197. Copyright © 1964. Reprinted by permission of the author and the American Psychological Association.

the leadership of Pinel, Tuke, Chiarugi, and others. The word "moral" was used at that time in a sense comparable to the contemporary usage of the words "psychological" or "interpersonal." During that era more attention began to be given to

> social and environmental factors in the causation of mental illness, and it was found that organic changes in the brain were rather rare at post mortem examinations. The insane came to be regarded as normal people who had lost their reason as a result of having been exposed to severe psychological and social stresses. These stresses were called the moral causes of insanity, and moral treatment aimed at relieving the patient by friendly association, discussion of his difficulties, and the daily pursuit of purposeful activity; in other words, social therapy, individual therapy, and occupational therapy. Moral treatment reached its zenith in the years between 1820 and 1860. The results of treatment during that period were outstandingly good and bear comparison with some of the figures obtainable today. For example, in all patients admitted to the York Retreat [in England] within three months of the onset of illness— between the years 1796 and 1861 the discharge rate was 71% . . . . These are truly remarkable figures, especially when one takes into consideration that a substantial portion of the patients must have been general paralytics, for which there was at that time no effective treatment (Rees, 1957, pp. 306–307).

Cope and Packard (1841) reported on the results of moral treatment in state institutions in the United States. They mentioned institutions in nine states and observed that with moral treatment "90 per cent of the recent cases can be restored so as to be able to maintain themselves and family." Bockoven (1956) found comparable figures from private institutions utilizing moral treatment. Beginning in the 1820s, the Hartford Retreat reported recoveries in over 90 per cent of all patients admitted with mental illnesses of less than a year's duration. Bockoven also supplied statistics extending from 1833 to 1950 on discharges from the Worcester State Hospital in Massachusetts. During the 1833–1852 period, when moral therapy was being practiced, 71 per cent of all patients ill less than 1 year when admitted were discharged as recovered or improved. Patients discharged during the years 1833–1846 were later followed up until 1893, and it was found that half suffered no recurrences.

Despite ample evidence of its effectiveness, moral therapy was quietly abandoned in American and British mental institutions after 1860 and later almost completely forgotten. The consequences are illustrated by Bockoven's (1956) data from the Worcester State Hospital, showing that recovery rates declined over 90 per cent after 1860, reaching their lowest point between 1923 and 1950 (pp. 292–293). Certainly, one may raise legitimate questions about these old statistics and the validity of conclusions drawn from them. Nevertheless, every recent study on the subject of moral therapy agreed that the results have not been surpassed during the contemporary period, despite all the advances made by physical medicine since 1860.

One important reason for its abandonment was that moral therapy was supposed to be a form of treatment for mental illnesses. But as physical medicine developed during the late nineteenth century, it was thought that the types of procedures found effective with physical illnesses could be carried over unaltered into the treatment of mental illnesses. Since both kinds of phenomena were defined as illnesses this notion sounded reasonable, so long as no one inquired seriously into the possibility that there might be an error in semantics.

An additional factor in the abandonment of moral therapy was that it was regarded as "unscientific" according to the scientific and medical doctrines which developed in the intellectual climate of the last half of the nineteenth century. These doctrines held that true science is impersonal and concerned solely with material things, that feeling, beauty, and moral values are mere illusions in a world of fact, that the human will is powerless against the laws of nature and society, and that every observable phenomenon is reducible to the motions of material particles.[1] Since psychiatric patients were regarded as suffering from a medical condition defined as mental illness, it was held that treatment procedures had to rest on a scientific physical basis, as conceptualized by a mechanistic, materialistic view which held that things rather than persons were the only reality. In keeping with this tough-minded impersonal dogma, the psychological sensitivity and insight which were major factors in the success of moral therapy were dismissed from serious consideration as mystical, sentimental, and unscientific. The treatment of hospitalized psychiatric patients became cold, distant, and unfeeling, consistent with a *Zeitgeist* of impersonal scientism. Discharge and recovery rates, which had been high wherever moral therapy programs were in effect, declined steadily after 1860. In time, falling discharge rates led to the piling up of chronic patients in hospitals, attitudes of hopelessness, and a growing belief in the "incurability" of insanity. This pessimistic belief had become widespread by 1900, despite the fact that 70 per cent to 90 per cent recovery rates had been commonplace in 1840 during the moral therapy era.

As recovery rates fell and the treatment of hospitalized patients became more detached and impersonal, leaders in psychiatry turned to the laboratory hoping to find a scientific cure for mental illness. They were persuaded that the answers lay in the discovery and identification of physical disease entities. Physicalistic and mechanistic concepts of mental illness were adopted by analogy with physical medicine, while efforts to understand psychiatric patients as individual persons were largely discontinued (Zilboorg, 1941). Patients were no longer thought of as human beings with problems in human relationships, but as "cases." This impersonal approach led one of the leading American psychiatrists of the 1880s to state in all sincerity that the insane do not suffer unhappiness, and that depressed patients go through the motions of acting sad in a machine-like fashion without feeling genuine sadness (Bockoven, 1956). As Brown's (1960) data indicate, changing attitudes of the medical profession at different historical periods have played a great part in changing rates of discharge and chronicity among hospitalized patients.

The great irony is that after 100 years these laboratory-centered physically oriented research efforts have failed to produce techniques for the "treatment"

---

[1] The doctrines of nineteenth century impersonal scientism have been more fully described elsewhere by Barzun (1958). He analyzes the modes of thought inherited from that era and shows how strongly they still influence contemporary thinking. Bockoven (1956) notes that the widespread acceptance of these doctrines in both popular and scientific circles contributed to the abandonment of moral therapy after 1860.

and "cure" of functional personality disorders significantly more effective than the best techniques of 1840. Actually, the most progressive contemporary mental hospital programs are those which have revived practices much like those generally prevalent during the moral therapy era (Greenblatt, York, and Brown, 1955; Rees, 1957).

The Impersonal Approach to Personality

The theoretical concepts most widely used in the mental health professions today consist largely of misleading analogies, metaphors, and figures of speech. These sonorous but inappropriate terms have made for confusion, trained incapacities, and intellectual stagnation. The Joint Commission on Mental Illness and Health (1961) has commented on this stagnation with the observation that "twentieth-century psychiatry can add little" to Pinel's principles for the moral treatment of psychotics, which were first published in 1801,

> except to convert them into modern terminological dress, contribute more systematic thought to the significance of various symptoms, intensify the doctor-patient relationship through scientific knowledge of psychological mechanisms, treat the patient as a member of a social group which expects him to behave in accepted ways, and specify that moral treatment has been subject to an incredible amount of distortion and misinterpretation . . . (pp. 29–30).

Similarly, psychotherapy in essentially its present-day form was described by Reil in a book published in the year 1803 (Harms, 1957b). Almost every important issue in contemporary clinical psychology was discussed at length by leaders of the moral therapy movement between 1790 and 1860 (Harms, 1957, 1957a, 1957b; Roback, 1961).

Much of the terminology now used in contemporary psychology developed in an intellectual climate of impersonal scientism quite different in its basic outlook from the humanitarianism of the moral therapy era. Psychology first arose as a separate independent science during the 1870s and 1880s. Reflecting the predominant spirit of their times, the early founders of experimental psychology were not concerned with the systematic understanding of human problems and personal relationships. Instead, they imitated the outward appearances and procedures of the physical and biological sciences, hoping that they too might thus be regarded as true scientists. They felt that in order to be scientifically respectable they had to study man impersonally, using techniques, assumptions, and conceptual approaches much like those of the physical and biological sciences. For example, the doctrine of determinism was carried over from the physical sciences without any empirical evidence to show that it was appropriate in explaining human conduct.

The impersonal approach adopted in the late nineteenth century is reflected in the conceptual language of psychology today. These concepts center around words borrowed from nonpsychological fields such as medicine, physics, mechanical engineering, biology, and electronics. This point is best illustrated by listing some verbal analogies commonly used in psychology. All the examples listed below appeared in psychological or psychiatric journals, or in books written for professional readers:

1. *Pseudomedical analogies:* mental illness, mental health, mental hygiene, prophylaxis, diagnosis, pathology, prognosis, etiology, therapy, treatment, cure, trauma, nosology, catharsis, syndrome, neurosis, psychosis, psychopathy, sick
2. *Pseudophysical and pseudoengineering analogies:* motor apparatus, dynamics, reaction potential, valences, field forces, psychic energy, power system, energy transformation, tension, stress, drive, mechanism, dynamogenesis, adjustment, reinforcing machine
3. *Pseudobiological analogies:* organism, homeostasis, phenotypic, genotypic, polymorphous, ontogenetic
4. *Pseudoelectronic analogies:* input, output, amplitude, radar, circuit, feedback, scanning, encoding, signals, charge, discharge, servomechanism
5. *Pseudogenitourinary and pseudogastrointestinal (i.e., psychoanalytic) analogies:* urethral character, phallic character, castration, oral optimism, anal submission, vaginal libido organization, anal-expulsive expression

Such analogies implicitly suggest that human behavior is *just like* the events observed in the nonpsychological sciences from which these words were borrowed. In using such terminology a false assumption is unwittingly made (but rarely recognized) that the *psychological phenomena* to which these terms are applied are therefore just like the *nonpsychological phenomena* where the terms originated. It is taken as *having already been decided* that these words are suitable for labeling and describing human behavior. The actions of living persons are thus conceptualized in the language of impersonal things and processes. Having accepted this glib semantic juggling, it is then quite easy to coin confusing, misleading slogans such as "mental illness is just like any other illness."

What Is "Mental Illness"?

What is the phenomenon to which the label "mental illness" is applied? It is applied to arbitrarily designated types of maladaptive interpersonal behavior, often accompanied by reports of subjective discomfort, unsatisfying human relationships, and social rejection.

Explicit distinctions must be made between these behavioral phenomena and illnesses of the body. Physical illnesses (including neurological disorders) are not in themselves patterns of interaction with other persons. They are disturbances in the organic functions of the body. So far as immediate experience is concerned, a bodily illness such as a cold, fever, or pneumonia is an abnormal, usually unpleasant, subjective condition which *happens to* the individual person. It is not a direct overt manifestation of his characteristic patterns of interacting with others.

But, in cases where the term "mental illness" is used and no organic pathology is in evidence, the term refers to some arbitrarily defined pattern of conduct, with "symptoms" of a psychosocial rather than a medical nature. Any effective program directed toward "cure" must consequently provide opportunities for learning new, more adaptive patterns. It should be remembered that the learning process is a normal function of the nervous system, regardless of the nature of the material being learned, be it the subject of medicine, playing a musical instrument, or new social skills.

A Comprehensive Approach to Interpersonal Behavior

Mental illness is a phenomenon involving interpersonal behavior, not a health or medical problem. Programs of alleviation and prevention must therefore rest upon a systematic understanding of interpersonal conduct. A considerable body of recent research in this area suggests that the basic dimensions are surprisingly simple. The supposed complexity of personality and interaction between persons has been shown to be a purely semantic, verbal complexity, rather than a real complexity in actual fact.

These empirical studies have three distinguishing features: (a) The basic observations involve interpersonal actions. To be more explicit, the observations are focused on the acts of *persons* interacting with other *persons*, rather than organisms, psychobiological units, dynamic systems, or other impersonal abstractions. (b) The observers are concerned not with superficial stylistic features, but with the *content* of the interpersonal acts themselves. Content variables are to be contrasted with formalistic or stylistic variables, such as percentage of adjectives, manner of speaking, speed of tapping, etc. "Content" refers to *what* the individual person is doing or communicating to others by word and deed. (c) The investigators aim for *comprehensiveness*, classifying every act systematically in relation to every other.

Most of these studies have dispensed with terminology not meaningfully related to observable conduct. If behavior can be systematically described in *behavioral* terms, there is no need for the confusing nonpsychological analogies and metaphors which have long plagued the mental health professions. It becomes unnecessary to borrow words from medicine, engineering, or electronics to describe human relationships. This approach makes it possible to clarify fundamental principles which have long been concealed by inappropriate, misleading jargon.

The results of these studies indicate that all interpersonal behavior, both adaptive ("healthy" or "normal") and maladaptive ("sick" or "abnormal"), can be meaningfully categorized within one systematic frame of reference. In a review of these studies, Foa (1961) was impressed by the "strong convergence" of thinking and results obtained in research on interpersonal interaction, since the investigators "proceeded from different research traditions, studied different types of groups . . . and, apparently, followed independent lines of design and analysis. The convergence is toward a simple ordered structure for the organization of interpersonal behavior." Foa suggested that the observations can be ordered into a simple comprehensive framework "that accounts for the empirical interrelations in a parsimonious and meaningful manner." The findings "suggest a circumplex structure around the two orthogonal axes of Dominance-Submission and Affection-Hostility."

Let us examine these two axes or dimensions in more detail. One pole of the Dominance-Submission axis is defined by acts of self-confident, assertive leadership and achievement in the face of obstacles. At the opposite pole are acts of passivity, submissiveness, and acquiescence. This dimension is of course a continuum, with most acts falling midway between extremes. The Affection-Hostility dimension reflects variations in the degree of positive or negative affect manifested toward others. The positive extreme describes warm, friendly, kind, affiliative acts, while the negative extreme describes hostile, critical, angry, disaffiliative acts.

Foa suggests that "an interpersonal act is an attempt to establish the emotional relationship of the actor toward himself and toward the other person," and that "the same act states the position of the actor toward the self and toward the other. . . ." Each type of behavior is thus meaningful toward the self and the other person. The Dominance-Submission axis defines the degree of acceptance or rejection of self, while the Affection-Hostility axis defines the degree of acceptance or rejection of the other. An interpersonal act may be regarded as the Cartesian product of these two sets of values.

The basic framework systematized by this two-dimensional structure has been described repeatedly ever since the time of Hippocrates. If there are only two dimensions of variation in the content of interpersonal acts, and the individual's personality is identified by the relative frequency, intensity, and nature of his acts, we have a simple but comprehensive basis for categorizing all personality types. Classification above and below the mean of these two axes would give four categories which correspond roughly to the traditional four temperaments, as they have been delineated by Hippocrates, Galen, Kant, Wundt, Höffding, Herbart, Külpe, Ebbinghaus, Klages, and Pavlov (Allport, 1961). Thus, persons with the "sanguine" temperament would show behavior which falls above the mean on both dimensions. Such persons typically show active leadership, optimism, and assertiveness, coupled with friendly acceptance of others. Likewise, the other three groups correspond to the traditional choleric, melancholic, and phlegmatic temperaments.

Freud has alluded to these dimensions in his writings (Leary, 1957, pp. 71–72). He has delineated a love-hate, sex-aggression, libido-mortido, or Eros-Thanatos polarity, which is comparable to the Affection-Hostility dimension. He also refers to power or domination in social interaction, analogous to Foa's Dominance-Submission dimension. . . .

A factor analysis of rating scales and questionnaires by Goldman-Eisler (1956) tested certain hypotheses drawn from psychoanalytic theory. Two orthogonal factors emerged, the first being a factor of "oral" optimism versus "oral" pessimism. Oral optimists show the same traits of active, friendly, assertiveness as the sanguine temperament, while oral pessimists show the contrasting patterns of the melancholic temperament. The second factor was interpreted as Impatience-Aggression-Autonomy versus Deliberation-Conservatism-Dependence. The traits of impatience, aggression, and autonomy are analogous to the hostile dominance of the choleric temperament, while deliberation, conservatism, and dependence describe the affectionate submissiveness ascribed to the phlegmatic temperament. The factor loadings emerging from this analysis were interrelated in a circular order, much like the circumplex structure of interpersonal behavior described by Foa. . . . Although Goldman-Eisler considered her findings as a confirmation of psychoanalytic theory, her results are much like those of other investigators whose theoretical orientation was quite different. The convergences between her results and other studies imply that the elaborate verbal complexities of psychoanalytic theory are needlessly involved. The empirical data can be much more parsimoniously explained.

It is clear that the same fundamental patterns have been repeatedly observed by many contemporary and historical writers, even though the words used may seem very different. These similarities and convergences would not have been so consistently noted unless there were certain universal features in all human conduct. Apparently these universal features were perceived, understood, and implicitly acted upon during the moral therapy era, overlooked by later generations enamored of impersonal scientism, and spelled out once again in recent empirical investigations. It seems obvious that a sound understanding of human behavior must begin with these universal features rather than the vague jargon that has dominated psychological and psychiatric theorizing to date.

How do these universal features relate to mental health and mental illness? Within the two-dimensional circular structure outlined above an elaborate system has been developed for classifying the interpersonal behavior of both psychiatric patients and "normals" (Leary, 1956, 1957). The major differences between mental illness and mental health are to be found in the characteristic frequency, intensity, and nature of interpersonal acts.

For example, schizophrenics manifest intense degrees of passivity and hostility by unconventional, bizarre, negativistic, and distrustful acts. In contrast, hysterics prefer bland, pleasant, friendly, conventional types of interaction. Hostile, rebellious, and distrustful acts are infrequent and extremely mild in intensity among hysterics. These two contrasting types of interpersonal behavior have long been considered mental illnesses. Both are differentiated from normality, adjustment, or mental health, i.e., versatile, appropriate, effective, adaptive behavior patterns. In this semantic usage the words "illness" and "health" are applied to observable patterns of conduct, not to states of the mind or body. The most effective programs of "therapy," "treatment," or "cure" for these illnesses are those which succeed best in altering the characteristic nature, frequency, and intensity of maladaptive acts in the direction of greater moderation, versatility, appropriateness, and effectiveness.

The more we question the terminology of the mental health professions today, the more obvious its inadequacies become. It is doubtful that any major advances can be expected so long as understanding is obscured by unsuitable, misleading terms. Every concept in our professional vocabulary needs to be carefully and critically reassessed by asking the question: *"Is it appropriate?"* Many fundamental problems need to be completely restated in words that communicate rather than obfuscate. Suitable *psychological* terminology is badly needed to clarify numerous vaguely worded, inappropriately phrased, and poorly understood questions in psychology today. Only in this way can psychologists create a basis for genuine understanding of human behavior.

5 / On the Futility of the Proposition that Some People Be Labeled "Mentally Ill"

Theodore R. Sarbin

The writing of a dispassionate account of the current utility of the mental illness concept reflects a noble purpose. Ellis (1967), by juxtaposing pro et contra arguments, tries to implement this purpose. On the one hand, he recognizes the massive negative utilities that result from the use of the mental-illness label; on the other hand, he points to occasions where the employment of the label appears to have positive utility. His studied conclusion is that the label, when used by professional diagnosticians in an operational way, identifies a limited number of people who are "really mentally ill." He adds the caution that the person who uses the label must subtract from it the pejorative components that have become part and parcel of the concept. Of several definitions, the following is representative of Ellis's viewpoint:

> This is what we really mean when we say that an individual is "mentally ill"—that he has *symptoms* of *mental malfunctioning* or *illness*. More operationally stated, he thinks, emotes, and acts *irrationally* and he can usually uncondemningly acknowledge and change his acts. If this, *without any moralistic overtones*, is the definition of "mental illness," then it can distinctly help the *afflicted* individual to accept himself while he is *ill* . . . (p. 440; italics added).

The general conclusions drawn by Ellis must be rejected on logical grounds. They represent not so much a lack of attention to the rules of evidence (to be mentioned later) as the acceptance of an entrenched and unwarranted belief that operates as a major premise. When operative, the premise may be stated: The label "mental illness" reliably denotes certain forms of conduct that are discriminable from forms of conduct that may be reliably denoted as "not mentally ill."

Since Ellis does not establish the ontological argument for "mental illness," his conclusions are illicit. That is to say, he assumes the truth of the proposition he sets out to demonstrate. (Note the italicized phrases in the quotation above.) The fundamental question is by-passed; to wit, is there a set of observations for which the dual metaphor "mental illness" is appropriate?

Most of Ellis's (and others', for example Ausubel, 1961) arguments aimed at retaining the mental-illness label flow from concealed, tacit, and disguised implications now contained within the label itself. Further, such arguments do not take into account the fact that the choice of label not only constrains further descriptive elaborations of the conduct under observation, but also indirectly restricts alternatives to action. The sentence, "a child . . . is known to have tendencies toward severe (mental) illness . . ." contains implications different from "a child has tendencies to hit other children."

To anticipate a criticism of the semiotic approach as a legitimate entrée into the argument, let me assert that the choice of a metaphor to designate an object or event is not inconsequential. Every metaphor contains a wealth of connotations, each connotation has the potential for manifold implications, and each implication is a directive to action. While metaphors are ordinarily used by people to facilitate communication, the peril is always at hand that people may be used by metaphors (Turbayne, 1962). Such a peril is activated when the user of a metaphor ignores, forgets, or purposely drops syntactical modifiers (e.g., *as if*) that denote the metaphor and, instead, employs the word in a literal fashion. To say "Jones is a saint" carries one set of implications if we supply the tacit modifier ("It is *as if* Jones is a saint"); the sentence carries a radically different set of implications if the predicate is treated as literal. The effects of permanently ignoring the metaphoric properties of a word, that is, of dropping the expressed or tacit modifiers, is to hypostatize an entity. Such hypostatization sets the stage for myth making.

Most of Ellis's arguments topple of their own structural defects, defects related to the uncritical acceptance of "illness of the mind" as the proper concept for describing the conduct of people who violate propriety norms (the mores of Sumner, 1906). Much of the undiagnosed confusion currently noted in the helping professions and in relevant juridical decisions is reflected in Ellis's paper. Such confusion might be reduced if we looked at the metaphorical background of our constraining vocabularies. First, let us look at "illness."

The basic referent for illness and for synonyms such as sickness and disease is a stable one, extending over centuries. The referent is discomfort of some kind, such as aches, pains, cramps, chills, paralyses, and so on. The discomfort is a self-appraisal through attention to unusual proximal stimuli, that is, stimuli located "inside" the organism. These proximal stimuli, when they occur simultaneously with dysfunction of bodily organs, are the so-called symptoms of illness. A diagnosis of illness or disease meant not only that a person reported discomforts, but that the associated somatic dysfunction interfered with the performance of some of his customary roles. This general paradigm of sickness or illness is widespread and may be found in ancient writings and in ethnographic reports.

A compelling question arises: How did the concept "illness" come to include gross behavior, that is, misconduct, rather than complaints and somatic symptoms which were the defining criteria of pre-Renaissance diagnosis? What additional criteria were employed to increase the breadth of the concept "illness"?

The inclusion of behavior disorders in the concept "illness" did not come about suddenly or accidentally. Rather, the label "illness" was at first used as a metaphor and later transformed into a myth.

The beginning of this metaphor-to-myth transformation may be located in the 16th Century. The demoniacal model of conduct disorders, codified in the 15th Century *Malleus Mallificarum*, had embraced all conduct that departed from the existing norms and was policed by zealous church and secular authorities. The most outstanding result of this thought model was the Inquisition, a social movement that among other things influenced the diagnosis and treatment of unusual imaginings, esoteric beliefs, and extraordinary conduct. The diagnosis of witchcraft and the prescription of treatment (burning) was the province of ecclesiastical specialists.

The 16th Century witnessed the beginnings of a reaction against the excesses of the Inquisition. The beginnings of humanistic philosophy, the discovery and serious study of Galen and other classical writers, the renunciation of scholasticism—the whole thrust of the Renaissance was opposite that of the Inquisition. In this atmosphere, Teresa of Avila, an outstanding figure of the Counter-Reformation, contributed to the shift from demons to "illness" as the cause of conduct disturbances. A group of nuns was exhibiting conduct which at a later date would have been called hysteria. By declaring these women to be infirm or ill, Teresa was able to fend off the Inquisition. However, the appeal that a diagnosis should be changed from witchcraft to illness required some cognitive elaboration. She invoked the notion of natural causes. Among the natural causes were (a) melancholy (Galenic humoral pathology), (b) weak imagination, and (c) drowsiness. If a person's conduct could be accounted for by such natural causes, it was to be regarded not as evil, but comas enfermas, *as if sick*. By employing the metaphor "as if sick," she implied that practitioners of physic rather than clergymen should be the responsible social specialists (Sarbin and Juhasz, 1967).

When employing metaphorical expressions there is a common human tendency to drop the qualifying "as if" (Turbayne, 1962). That is to say, the metaphor is used without a qualifier to designate it as figurative rather than literal. In the case of illness as a metaphor for conditions not meeting the usual criteria of illness, the dropping of the "as if" was facilitated by the practitioners of physic. It was awkward for them to talk about two kinds of illness, "real" illness and "as if" illness. When Galenic classifications were reintroduced, the "as if" was dropped. Thus, post-Renaissance physicians could concern themselves with illness as traditionally understood and also with norm violations as illness. A review of the 16th and 17th Century treatises on "physic" reveals clearly that Galen's humoral theory was the standard for diagnosis and treatment. The diagnostic problem was how to construct inferences about the balance of humors inside the organism.

The decline of the power of church authorities in diagnosing extraordinary imaginings and perplexing conduct was parallel to the rise of science. The prestige of the scientist helped in establishing the model of Galen for both kinds of "illness"—those with somatic complaints and observable somatic symptoms and those without somatic complaints but with unusual behavior standing for somatic symptoms.

Whereas the concept illness had been satisfied by the exclusive use of conjunctive criteria (complaints and observable somatic symptoms), it was now satisfied by the use of disjunctive criteria (complaints and somatic symptoms or complaints by others of perplexing, embarrassing, mystifying conduct). As a result of the uncritical acceptance of the humoral pathology of Galen as the overriding explanation for both somatic and behavior disorders, the latter became assimilated to the former. That is to say, to meet the requirements of the basic Galenic model, symptoms of disease had to be observed, so the observed behavior sequences were regarded as if they were the symptoms. Thus, the verbal report of strange imaginings on the one hand and fever on the other, were treated as belonging to the same class, that is, symptoms. As a result of shifting from a metaphoric to a literal interpretation of gross behavior as symptom, Galenic medicine embraced not only everything somatic but also all conduct. Now, any bit of behavior—laughing, crying, threatening, spitting, silence, imagining, lying, and believing—could be called symptoms of underlying internal pathology.

The basic Galenic model was not rejected by psychiatry or clinical psychology. Microbes, toxins, and growths, which were material and operated according to mechanical principles, were appropriate "causes" of diseases of the body. They were inside. The appropriate causes for abnormal behavior had to be sought on different dimensions. Since the mind-body conception was taken as truth, the hypothesis could be entertained that the causes of abnormal conduct were in the mind. If this were so, then the most appropriate label for such nonsomatic diseases would be "mental illness."

Before considering the meaning of "mental" in the phrase "mental illness," let me recapitulate. "Illness," as in mental illness, is an illicit transformation of a metaphorical concept to a literal one. To save unfortunate people from being labeled witches, it was humane to treat persons who exhibited misconduct of certain kinds as if they were ill. The Galenic model facilitated the eliding of the hypothetical phrase, the "as if," and the concept of illness was thus deformed to include events that did not meet the original conjunctive criteria for illness. A second transformation assured the validity of the Galenic model. The mystifying behaviors could be treated as if they were symptoms equivalent to somatic symptoms. By dropping the "as if" modifier, observed behavior could be interpreted as symptomatic of underlying internal pathology.

How did the notion of "illness of the mind" become so widely accepted that it served as the groundwork for several professions? A searching historical analysis makes clear that mind was originally employed as a metaphor to denote such events as remembering and thinking. (Colloquial English has retained this formulation, as in "mind your manners.") The shift of meaning to that of a substantive or agency can best be understood as another instance of metaphor-to-myth transformation (Ryle, 1948).

The modern practitioner of Galenic psychiatry and psychology operates from the principle that the "illness" about which he is concerned is in the mind (or psyche, or psychic apparatus). But the mind, even for Galenic practitioners, was too abstract and undifferentiated a concept.

Since the mind was invisible and immaterial, it could not have the same properties as the body—properties that could be denoted by physicalistic terms. Visual palpable organs being the components of the material body, what differentiating components of the invisible impalpable mental entity could one discover or invent? A new metaphor was required—the metaphor of states of mind. States of love, fear, anxiety, apathy, etc. were invented to account for differences in observed conduct. The practitioner now had the job of discovering through chains of inferences which mental states were responsible for normal and abnormal conduct.

Mind as an Organ of Illness

Three developments contributed to the construction of mind as the repository of special states and as an organ that was subject to "illness": (1) the ready availability of dispositional terms, (2) the introduction of new terms of faith and religion that located religious experience "inside" the person, and (3) the development of a scientific lexicon.

1. Dispositional terms are shorthand expressions for combinations or orderings of distal and/or proximal events—in principle, a dispositional term can be reduced to a series of observable occurrences. For example, "bravery" implies a set of concrete behaviors under certain conditions. No implication is carried that the referent is an internal mental state. The development of dispositional terms, however, appears to be a necessary (though not sufficient) prerequisite for the postulation of mental states. In time, dispositional terms become elided and remote from the original metaphorical beginnings.

2. Dispositional terms were conveniently borrowed to denote religious conceptions which followed the shift from an emphasis on ritual and ceremony to inward, personal aspects of faith. Theologians and preachers gave a new set of referents to these dispositional terms, referents that changed dispositional terms from brief notations of observable conduct to states of the soul. The context in which mental states are employed is best expressed by the polarity inside-outside. The problem for the medieval thinker was to find a paradigm for locating events on the inside. Such a model could have been constructed from the following observations: two classes of proximal inputs may be identified. The first occurs in a context of distal events: for example, pain in the ankle occurs in a context of tripping over a curb; a burning irritation in the fingers occurs in the context of leaning on a hot radiator. The second class of proximal inputs occurs in the absense of associated distal events, such as toothache, headache, gastritis, neuritis, etc. Since the antecedents of the latter inputs could not be located in the outside world, the locus of the somatic perception inside the body was taken as the causal locus. Medieval man had little reliable knowledge of anatomy save that there were bones, sinews, tubes, and fluids and there were also empty spaces. Under the authority of the priests, he acquired the belief that an immaterial and invisible soul resided in these otherwise empty spaces. On this belief system, events for which there were no observed distal contexts could be attributed to the workings of this inner entity or soul. Such an analysis probably prepared the way for locating dispositions inside the person and calling them states of mind. If the cause of an event had no obvious external locus, then it must have an internal locus. Dispositions, when they are codified as substantives, tend to be treated in the same way as other nouns, as possessing "thingness." Thus bravery, lust, conscience, purity, devotion—all dispositional terms originally tied to ordering of behavior—are framed as nouns. If nouns are names of things, and things have location, the problem emerged: where to locate the referents for these nouns? The answer is similar to the process of locating inside the person the cause of pain and discomfort in the absence of external occurrences. Thus, anger, joy, courage, happiness, etc. came to be located in the soul.

3. The replacement of theologians by scientists in the 16th and 17th Centuries in matters pertaining to strange and mysterious conduct made necessary a shift from such theological terms as "soul" to scientific metaphors. However, the scientists could not break completely with the entrenched dualistic philosophy. They took as their point of departure the facts of thinking and knowing and, as a substitute for the soul, employed *mind* as the organ for such activities. With the development of classical scholarship, Greek terms were substituted for the ver-

nacular, the most popular being "psyche" (Boring, 1966). The efforts of the post-Renaissance Galenic practitioners, then, were directed toward analyzing states of mind or psychic events. Those sequences of perplexing conduct that could not be related to external occurrences were declared to be outcomes of internal mental or psychic processes.

Thus mental states—the objects of interest and study for the diagnostician of "mental illness"— were postulated to fill gaps in early knowledge. Through historical and linguistic processes, the construct was reified. Contemporary users of the mental-illness concept are guilty of illicitly shifting from metaphor to myth. Instead of maintaining the metaphorical rhetoric "it is as if there were states of mind," and "it is as if some 'states of mind' could be characterized as sickness," the contemporary mentalist conducts much of his work as if he believes that minds are "real" entities and that, like bodies, they can be sick or healthy.

The most potent implication of the metaphor is that persons labeled mentally ill are categorized as significantly discontinuous from persons labeled with the un-modified term "ill." Of course, referring to persons simply as ill or sick suggests that they belong to a class different from the mutually exclusive class "not ill" or "healthy." Assigning persons to the class "ill" carries the meaning of objective symptoms of a recognized or named disease, in addition to subjectively experienced discomfort. In most societies, persons so classified are temporarily excused from the performance of selected role obligations. The label carries no hint of negative valuation. Sickness, in general, is something for which one is not responsible.

However, when the adjective "mental" is prefixed, a whole new set of implications follows. Contrary to the humane intent of those who resisted the Inquisitors by employing the nonpejorative diagnostic label of illness, present usage is transparently pejorative.

In adding the word "mental" to "illness," the whole meaning structure changes. In the first place, the necessity for adding a prefix to "illness" imposes a special constraint on the interpreter: He asks, "What about this person or his behavior calls for such a special designation?" Since it is a special kind of illness, does the same expectation hold that he (the patient) is to be temporarily excused from the enactment of his roles?

The answers to these questions may be found in a number of studies (Cumming and Cumming, 1962; Goffman, 1961; Nunnally, 1961; Phillips, 1963). Persons who are labeled mentally ill are not regarded as merely sick; they are regarded as a special class of beings, to be feared or scorned, sometimes to be pitied, but nearly always to be degraded. Coincident with such negative valuations are the beliefs that such "mentally ill" persons discharge obligations only of the most simple kinds. The author has elsewhere argued that the process whereby a person is converted into a mental patient carries with it the potential for self-devaluation. The stigmatization, then, may work in the nature of a self-fulfilling prophecy (Sarbin, 1968).

Further, because of the inherent vagueness in the concept of mind, its assumed independence from the body, and its purported timelessness (derived from the immortal soul), there is a readiness to regard this special kind of sickness as permanent. Thus, a person with a fractured wrist or a patient suffering from influenza, that is, a sick person, may take up his customary roles upon being restored to health. A person diagnosed as mentally ill, however, is stigmatized. Although "cured" of the behavior that initiated the sequence of social and political acts that resulted in his being classified as mentally ill, his public will not usually accept such "cures" as permanent. It is as if the mental states were capable of disguising the person as healthy, although the underlying mental illness remains in a dormant or latent state.

The pejorative connotation is an integral part of the concept. Ellis's advice to subtract the "moralistic overtones" is gratuitous. One can no more delete by fiat the valuational component from "mental illness" than eliminate the "pleasantness" from the act of eating a preferred food.

Another implication of the mental-illness concept stemming from the demonstrated utility of germ theory for nonmental illness is the internal causal locus of mental illness. But the shadowy interior of the mind is not easily entered. The experts must depend on chains of inference forged out of the verbal and nonverbal communications of patients and informants. From such communications, today's experts draw conclusions about the mental structures, their dynamic properties, and their relation to observed behavior in the same manner as Galenic practitioners drew conclusions about the distribution of the humors. One outcome of the exclusive verbal preoccupation with psychic states is the neglect and avoidance of events in the social systems that might be antecedent to instances of misconduct illicitly and arbitrarily called symptoms.

The heuristic implications of the mental-illness metaphor are no less important than the practical implications. Scientists of many kinds have discovered the causes for many (nonmental) illnesses by looking inside the body. By adding a postulate that all mental states are caused by organic conditions (the somatopsychic hypothesis) and also accepting disordered conduct as symptomatic of underlying disease entities, the corollary follows that the ultimate causal agents will be discovered through searching for biochemical, toxicological, and bacteriological substrates. Again, such search methods deploy attention and effort away from the social ecology as a possible source of antecedent conditions of misconduct.

Rejection of the Mental-Illness Concept

The analysis offered so far supports the argument that the label "mental illness" should be eliminated from our vocabulary. Following from the implications contained in the label, the logical arguments by themselves would predict the social discrimination and self-denigration consequent to the establishment of social institutions to segregate, house, treat, manage, and reform norm violators. The tacit semantic relation between sin (or evil) and mental illness (Crumpton, Weinstein, Acker, and Annis, 1967), as well as the juridically endorsed relation of mental illness to danger (Platt and Diamond, 1965; Sarbin, 1967), also grows out of the label's implications.

It is one thing to demonstrate that "mental illness" has achieved mythic status and that its continued employment stands in the way of developing policies and practices for meeting some important social problems; it is another thing to recognize that some people, sometimes, somewhere, engage in conduct that violates propriety norms, including norms controlling ingroup aggression. Ellis is justifiably concerned with the problem of what disposition to make of these norm violators. His solution to the problem is to label them mentally ill (sans "moral overtones"). Such labeling provides a warrant for segregating norm violators in mental hospitals or referring them to psychotherapists. The warrant contains (sometimes explicitly) the notion "for the patient's own good." The history of the mental hospital system and of the mental health movement in America witnesses that "the patient's good" is little more than a cliché uttered to offset the degradation and desocialization outcomes.

If my previous arguments are not footless, then Ellis's recommendation that we continue the practice of labeling people mentally ill should be forcefully rejected. If his advice is rejected on the grounds of logic and of humanitarian values, then we are left with a gap in the social fabric. What should citizens and officials of an open society do about the problem of norm violation? What, if anything, should we do about people who are sometimes described as silly, unpredictably eccentric, perturbed, deviant, mute, shameless, rude, impertinent, immodest, dishonest, childish, dangerous, hostile, aggressive, and so on? Current practice is, under some conditions, to regard the behavior described by such terms as symptoms of, or caused by, mental illness. Ellis (1967) illustrates this point nicely. With impressive documentation, he says:

> In the last analysis, almost all neurosis and psychosis consists of some self-dishonesty. . . . When, therefore, one fully faces the fact that one is "mentally ill," that this is not a pleasant way to be, and that one is partially responsible for being so, one becomes at that very point, more honest with oneself and begins to get a little better (p. 440).

What function is served other than the imputation of a discredited mental-state causality? More continuous with observation would be the substitution of the word "dishonest" for "mentally ill."

In exposing mental illness as a myth that has outlived its usefulness, the label becomes improper and futile. Thus we are left with a far-reaching problem in jurisprudence, law enforcement, social engineering, and community psychology. The problem may be formulated as a question: What criteria should be employed to deprive a man of his liberty, his civil rights, his capacity for self-determinism, and so on? It would be foolhardy for me to try even to suggest answers in this brief paper. However, I can point to some partially charted areas that require further exploration.

All of us must put our heads together and decide how free and open a society we want. This decision is prerequisite for establishing criteria to identify those persons who should not be free. It is my belief that with increasing application of democratic principles the use of "mental illness" will be dropped as an intervening category between overt conduct and juridically established status as free or restrained. The arguments of Szasz (1963); the observations of Goffman (1961); the historico-legal studies of Platt and Diamond (1965); the persisting dissatisfaction with such legal precedents as McNaughten, Durham, and others (Diamond, 1964; Dreher, 1967); the disillusionment of psychiatric and psychological practitioners with mentalistic and scholastic theories (Sarbin, 1964); and the development of community psychology (The Conference Committee, 1966)

—these and other forces are converging toward finding a fair and more efficient process for arresting, detaining, and incarcerating individuals whose public conduct violates current propriety norms.

In this connection, we must confront the implications of a currently common practice of regarding deviant conduct (e.g., homosexuality) as equivalent to sickness. The refusal of an individual to accept the pejorative classification of mental illness and, correlatively, his refusal to enter psychotherapy, are taken as signs that he, according to Ellis, does not want "to improve his lot." The careful work of Hooker (1957, 1958) suggests that in the culture of male homosexuals the distributions of conventionally used indicators of psychopathology (e.g., Rorschach variables) are not substantially different from the distributions of heterosexuals. Deviance from cultural norms is a societal problem. It is doubtful whether the use of the mental-illness label or any other epithet of degradation will contribute to the solution of the problem. I know of no evidence that supports the contrary notion that societal problems associated with cultural deviance are ameliorated by diagnosing deviant individuals as "ill."

We turn our attention briefly to the problems in jurisprudence generated by the facts of norm violation and by the continued use of the mental-illness doctrine. A cursory review of legal treatises makes clear that the law, its writers, and interpreters, although deeply involved in the problems of equity and justice, have not been concerned with questioning the ontological status of mental illness. Such verdicts as "not guilty by reason of insanity" reflect the dualism upon which much of our jurisprudence rests, not to mention our theology and metaphysics. This verdict is not unlike many constructions to be found in legal treatises. The hidden metaphor is this: It is as if there is a body and a mind normally functioning in harmony. The body performs actions under the governance of the immaterial invisible mind. Where the acts of the body and the intent of the mind are not in harmony in meeting normative standards of conduct, explanations in terms of rule-following models are inadequate. Under these conditions a causal explanation is required: The mind is not properly controlling the body. Therefore the body is declared "not guilty" and the mind becomes the object of punishment or retribution. The aim of such actions is to exorcise the evil influences or mental states that guided the body to perform improper or sinful acts.

While I may be charged with unrestrained hyperbole, the historical facts are undeniable. The same cultural thought model that generated the medieval demoniacal model also produced the modern mental-illness model to explain conduct that does not meet rule-following prescriptions.

The rejection of such an entrenched thought model by the relevant professionals is in the nature of a scientific revolution. As in all scientific revolutions, a new metaphor is needed to replace an exploded myth. The most likely candidate for such replacement is a metaphor that denotes recent and current observations not convincingly assimilated into the older labels. Elsewhere, I have presented arguments in support of a new metaphor—the transformation of social identity—a metaphor that captures the antecedent and concurrent process of becoming a norm violator (Sarbin, 1967, 1968, in press; Sarbin, Scheibe, and Kroger, 1965). Because of space limitations, I can say only that the metaphor arises from a comprehensive social theory—a theory that rejects mentalistic metaphors as being feebly inappropriate to the enormity of the theoretical and societal problems that confront us.

In these few pages I have tried to make the case that it is futile to try to support the proposition that some people be labeled "mentally ill." The case stands or falls on the coherence of the ontological argument. My argument declares that the label is vacuous, save as an epithet of pejoration. Further, its scientific utility is suspect because of its reliance on an outworn mentalistic concept—the ghost in the machine, to use Ryle's (1948) apt metaphor.

6 / Personality Disorder *Is* Disease

David P. Ausubel

In two recent articles in the *American Psychologist*, Szasz (1960) and Mowrer (1960) have argued the case for discarding the concept of mental illness. The essence of Mowrer's position is that since medical science lacks "demonstrated competence . . . in psychiatry," psychology would be wise to "get out" from "under the penumbra of medicine," and to regard the behavior disorders as manifestations of sin rather than of disease (p. 302). Szasz' position, as we shall see shortly, is somewhat more complex than Mowrer's, but agrees with the latter in emphasizing the moral as opposed to the psychopathological basis of abnormal behavior.

For a long time now, clinical psychology has both repudiated the relevance of moral judgment and accountability for assessing behavioral acts and choices, and has chafed under medical (psychiatric) control and authority in diagnosing and treating the personality disorders. One can readily appreciate, therefore, Mowrer's eagerness to sever the historical and professional ties that bind clinical psychology to medicine, even if this means denying that psychological disturbances constitute a form of illness, and even if psychology's close working relationship with psychiatry must be replaced by a new rapprochement with sin and theology, as "the lesser of two evils" (pp. 302–303). One can also sympathize with Mowrer's and Szasz' dissatisfaction with prevailing amoral and nonjudgmental trends in clinical psychology and with their entirely commendable efforts to restore moral judgment and accountability to a respectable place among the criteria used in evaluating human behavior, both normal and abnormal.

Opposition to these two trends in the handling of the behavior disorders (i.e., to medical control and to nonjudgmental therapeutic attitudes), however, does not necessarily imply abandonment of the concept of mental illness. There is no inconsistency whatsoever in maintaining, on the one hand, that most pur-

From the *American Psychologist*, 1961, **16**, 69–74. Copyright © 1961. Reprinted by permission of the author and the American Psychological Association.

poseful human activity has a moral aspect the reality of which psychologists cannot afford to ignore (Ausubel, 1952, p. 462), that man is morally accountable for the majority of his misdeeds (Ausubel, 1952, p. 469), and that psychological rather than medical training and sophistication are basic to competence in the personality disorders (Ausubel, 1956, p. 101), and affirming, on the other hand, that the latter disorders are genuine manifestations of illness. In recent years psychology has been steadily moving away from the formerly fashionable stance of ethical neutrality in the behavioral sciences; and in spite of strident medical claims regarding superior professional qualifications and preclusive legal responsibility for treating psychiatric patients, and notwithstanding the nominally restrictive provisions of medical practice acts, clinical psychologists have been assuming an increasingly more important, independent, and responsible role in treating the mentally ill population of the United States.

It would be instructive at this point to examine the tactics of certain other medically allied professions in freeing themselves from medical control and in acquiring independent, legally recognized professional status. In no instance have they resorted to the devious stratagem of denying that they were treating diseases, in the hope of mollifying medical opposition and legitimizing their own professional activities. They took the position instead that simply because a given condition is defined as a disease, its treatment need not necessarily be turned over to doctors of medicine if other equally competent professional specialists were available. That this position is legally and politically tenable is demonstrated by the fact that an impressively large number of recognized diseases are legally treated today by both medical *and* nonmedical specialists (e.g., diseases of the mouth, face, jaws, teeth, eyes, and feet). And there are few convincing reasons for believing that psychiatrists wield that much more political power than physicians, maxillofacial surgeons, ophthalmologists, and orthopedic surgeons, that they could be successful where these latter specialists have failed, in legally restricting practice in their particular area of competence to holders of the medical degree. Hence, even if psychologists were not currently managing to hold their own vis-à-vis psychiatrists, it would be far less dangerous and much more forthright to press for the necessary ameliorative legislation than to seek cover behind an outmoded and thoroughly discredited conception of the behavior disorders.

The Szasz-Mowrer Position

Szasz' (1960) contention that the concept of mental illness "now functions merely as a convenient myth" (p. 118) is grounded on four unsubstantiated and logically untenable propositions, which can be fairly summarized as follows:

1. Only symptoms resulting from demonstrable physical lesions qualify as legitimate manifestations of disease. Brain pathology is a type of physical lesion, but its symptoms, properly speaking, are neurological rather than psychological in nature. Under no circumstances, therefore, can mental symptoms be considered a form of illness.

2. A basic dichotomy exists between *mental* symptoms, on the one hand, which are subjective in nature, dependent on subjective judgment and personal

involvement of the observer, and referable to cultural-ethical norms, and *physical* symptoms, on the other hand, which are allegedly objective in nature, ascertainable without personal involvement of the observer, and independent of cultural norms and ethical standards. Only symptoms possessing the latter set of characteristics are genuinely reflective of illness and amenable to medical treatment.

3. Mental symptoms are merely expressions of problems of living and, hence, cannot be regarded as manifestations of a pathological condition. The concept of mental illness is misleading and demonological because it seeks to explain psychological disturbance in particular and human disharmony in general in terms of a metaphorical but nonexistent disease entity, instead of attributing them to inherent difficulties in coming to grips with elusive problems of choice and responsibility.

4. Personality disorders, therefore, can be most fruitfully conceptualized as products of moral conflict, confusion, and aberration. Mowrer (1960) extends this latter proposition to include the dictum that psychiatric symptoms are primarily reflective of unacknowledged sin, and that individuals manifesting these symptoms are responsible for and deserve their suffering, both because of their original transgressions and because they refuse to avow and expiate their guilt (pp. 301, 304).

Widespread adoption of the Szasz-Mowrer view of the personality disorders would, in my opinion, turn back the psychiatric clock 2500 years. The most significant and perhaps the only real advance registered by mankind in evolving a rational and humane method of handling behavioral aberrations has been in substituting a concept of disease for the demonological and retributional doctrines regarding their nature and etiology that flourished until comparatively recent times. Conceptualized as illness, the symptoms of personality disorders can be interpreted in the light of underlying stresses and resistances, both genic and environmental, and can be evaluated in relation to *specifiable* quantitative and qualitative norms of appropriately adaptive behavior, both cross-culturally and within a particular cultural context. It would behoove us, therefore, before we abandon the concept of mental illness and return to the medieval doctrine of unexpiated sin or adopt Szasz' ambiguous criterion of difficulty in ethical choice and responsibility, to subject the foregoing propositions to careful and detailed study.

Mental Symptoms and Brain Pathology

Although I agree with Szasz in rejecting the doctrine that ultimately some neuroanatomic or neurophysiologic defect will be discovered in *all* cases of personality disorder, I disagree with his reasons for not accepting this proposition. Notwithstanding Szasz' straw man presentation of their position, the proponents of the extreme somatic view do not really assert that the *particular nature* of a patient's disordered beliefs can be correlated with "certain definite lesions in the nervous system" (Szasz, 1960, p. 113). They hold rather that normal cognitive and behavioral functioning depends on the anatomic and physiologic integrity of certain key areas of the brain, and that impairment of this substrate integrity, therefore, provides a physical basis for disturbed ideation and behavior, but does not explain, except in a very gross way, the particular kinds of symptoms involved. In fact, they are generally inclined to attribute the *specific* character of the patient's symptoms to the nature of his pre-illness personality structure, the substrate integrity of which is impaired by the lesion or metabolic defect in question.

Nevertheless, even though this type of reasoning plausibly accounts for the psychological symptoms found in general paresis, various toxic deleria, and other comparable conditions, it is an extremely improbable explanation of *all* instances of personality disorder. Unlike the tissues of any other organ, brain tissue possesses the unique property of making possible awareness of and adjustment to the world of sensory, social, and symbolic stimulation. Hence by virtue of this unique relationship of the nervous system to the environment, diseases of behavior and personality may reflect abnormalities in personal and social adjustment, quite apart from any structural or metabolic disturbance in the underlying neural substrate. I would conclude, therefore, that although brain pathology is probably not the most important cause of behavior disorder, it is undoubtedly responsible for the incidence of *some* psychological abnormalities *as well as* for various neurological signs and symptoms.

But even if we completely accepted Szasz' view that brain pathology does not account for any symptoms of personality disorder, it would still be unnecessary to accept his assertion that to qualify as a genuine manifestation of disease a given symptom must be caused by a physical lesion. Adoption of such a criterion would be arbitrary and inconsistent both with medical and lay connotations of the term "disease," which in current usage is generally regarded as including any marked deviation, physical, mental, or behavioral, from normally desirable standards of structural and functional integrity.

Mental versus Physical Symptoms

Szasz contends that since the analogy between physical and mental symptoms is patently fallacious, the postulated parallelism between physical and mental disease is logically untenable. This line of reasoning is based on the assumption that the two categories of symptoms can be sharply dichotomized with respect to such basic dimensions as objectivity-subjectivity, the relevance of cultural norms, and the need for personal involvement of the observer. In my opinion, the existence of such a dichotomy cannot be empirically demonstrated in convincing fashion.

Practically all symptoms of bodily disease involve some elements of subjective judgment—both on the part of the patient and of the physician. Pain is perhaps the most important and commonly used criterion of physical illness. Yet, any evaluation of its reported locus, intensity, character, and duration is dependent upon the patient's subjective appraisal of his own sensations and on the physician's assessment of the latter's pain threshold, intelligence, and personality structure. It is also a medical commonplace that the severity of pain in most instances of bodily illness may be mitigated by the administration of a placebo. Furthermore, in taking a meaningful history the physician must not only serve as a participant observer but also as a skilled interpreter of human behavior. It is the rare patient who does not react psychologically to the signs of physical illness; and hence physicians are constantly called upon to decide, for example, to what extent precordial pain and reported tightness in the chest are manifestations of coronary insufficiency, of fear of cardiac disease and impending death, or of combinations of both conditions. Even such allegedly objective signs as pulse rate, BMR, blood pressure, and blood cholesterol have their subjective and relativistic aspects. Pulse rate and blood pressure are notoriously susceptible to emotional influences, and BMR and blood cholesterol fluctuate widely from one cultural environment to another (Dreyfuss and Czaczkes, 1959). And anyone who believes that ethical norms have no relevance for physical illness has obviously failed to consider the problems confronting Catholic patients and/or physicians when issues of contraception, abortion, and preferential saving of the mother's as against the fetus' life must be faced in the context of various obstetrical emergencies and medical contraindications to pregnancy.

It should now be clear, therefore, that symptoms not only do not need a physical basis to qualify as manifestations of illness, but also that the evaluation of *all* symptoms, physical as well as mental, is dependent in large measure on subjective judgment, emotional factors, cultural-ethical norms, and personal involvement on the part of the observer. These considerations alone render no longer tenable Szasz' contention (1960, p. 114) that there is an inherent contradiction between using cultural and ethical norms as criteria of mental disease, on the one hand, and of employing medical measures of treatment on the other. But even if the postulated dichotomy between mental and physical symptoms were valid, the use of physical measures in treating subjective and relativistic psychological symptoms would still be warranted. Once we accept the proposition that impairment of the neutral substrate of personality can result in behavior disorder, it is logically consistent to accept the corollary proposition that other kinds of manipulation of the same neutral substrate can conceivably have therapeutic effects, irrespective of whether the underlying cause of the mental symptoms is physical or psychological.

Mental Illness and Problems of Living

"The phenomena now called mental illness," argues Szasz (1960), can be regarded more forthrightly and simply as "expressions of man's struggle with the problem of how he should live" (p. 117). This statement undoubtedly oversimplifies the nature of personality disorders; but even if it were adequately inclusive it would not be inconsistent with the position that these disorders are a manifestation of illness. There is no valid reason why a particular symptom cannot both reflect a problem in living *and* constitute a manifestation of disease. The notion of mental illness, conceived in this way, would not "obscure the everyday fact that life for most people is a continuous struggle . . . for a 'place in the sun,' 'peace of mind,' or some other human value" (p. 118). It is quite true, as Szasz points out, that "human relations are inherently fraught with difficulties" (p. 117), and that most people manage to cope with such difficulties without becoming mentally ill. But conceding this fact hardly precludes the possibility that some individuals, either because of the magnitude of the stress involved, or because of genically or environmentally induced susceptibility to ordinary degrees of stress, respond to the problems of living with behavior that is either seriously distorted or sufficiently unadaptive to prevent normal interpersonal relations and vocational functioning. The latter outcome—gross deviation from a designated range of desirable behavioral variability—conforms to the generally understood meaning of mental illness.

The plausibility of subsuming abnormal behavioral reactions to stress under the general rubric of disease is further enhanced by the fact that these reactions include the same three principal categories of symptoms found in physical illness. Depression and catastrophic impairment of self-esteem, for example, are manifestations of personality disorder which are symptomologically comparable to edema in cardiac failure or to heart murmurs in valvular disease. They are indicative of underlying pathology but are neither adaptive nor adjustive. Symptoms such as hypomanic overactivity and compulsive striving toward unrealistically high achievement goals, on the other hand, are both adaptive and adjustive, and constitute a type of compensatory response to basic feelings of inadequacy, which is not unlike cardiac hypertrophy in hypertensive heart disease or elevated white blood cell count in acute infections. And finally, distortive psychological defenses that have some adjustive value but are generally maladaptive (e.g., phobias, delusions, autistic fantasies) are analogous to the pathological situation found in conditions like pneumonia, in which the excessive outpouring of serum and phagocytes in defensive response to pathogenic bacteria literally causes the patient to drown in his own fluids.

Within the context of this same general proposition, Szasz repudiates the concept of mental illness as demonological in nature, i.e., as the "true heir to religious myths in general and to the belief in witchcraft in particular" (p. 118) because it allegedly employs a reified abstraction ("a deformity of personality") to account in causal terms both for "human disharmony" and for symptoms of behavior disorder (p. 114). But again he appears to be demolishing a straw man. Modern students of personality disorder do not regard mental illness as a cause of human disharmony, but as a comanifestation with it of inherent difficulties in personal adjustment and interpersonal relations; and in so far as I can accurately interpret the literature, psychopathologists do not conceive of mental illness as a cause of particular behavioral symptoms but as a generic term under which these symptoms can be subsumed.

Mental Illness and Moral Responsibility

Szasz' final reason for regarding mental illness as a myth is really a corollary of his previously considered more general proposition that mental symptoms are essentially reflective of problems of living and hence do not legitimately qualify as manifestations of disease. It focuses on difficulties of ethical choice and responsibility as the particular life problems most likely to be productive of personality disorder. Mowrer (1960) further extends this corollary by asserting that neurotic and psychotic individuals are responsible for their suffering (p. 301), and that unacknowledged and unexpiated sin, in turn, is the basic cause of this suffering (p. 304). As previously suggested, however, one can plausibly accept the proposition that psychiatrists and clinical psychologists have erred in trying to divorce behavioral evaluation from ethical considerations, in conducting psychotherapy in an amoral setting, and in confusing the psychological explanation of unethical behavior with absolution from accountability for same, *without* necessarily endorsing the view that personality disorders are basically a reflection of sin, and that victims of these disorders are less ill than responsible for their symptoms (Ausubel, 1952, pp. 392–397, 465–471).

In the first place, it is possible in most instances (although admittedly difficult in some) to distinguish quite unambiguously between mental illness and ordinary cases of immorality. The vast majority of persons who are guilty of moral lapses knowingly violate their own ethical precepts for expediential reasons—despite being volitionally capable at the time, both of choosing the more moral alternative and of exercising the necessary inhibitory control (Ausubel, 1952, pp. 465–471). Such persons, also, usually do not exhibit any signs of behavior disorder. At crucial choice points in facing the problems of living they simply choose the opportunistic instead of the moral alternative. They are not mentally ill, but they are clearly accountable for their misconduct. Hence, since personality disorder and immorality are neither coextensive nor mutually exclusive conditions, the concept of mental illness need not necessarily obscure the issue of moral accountability.

Second, guilt may be a contributory factor in behavior disorder, but is by no means the only or principal cause thereof. Feelings of guilt may give rise to anxiety and depression; but in the absence of catastrophic impairment of self-esteem induced by *other* factors, these symptoms tend to be transitory and peripheral in nature (Ausubel, 1952, pp. 362–363). Repression of guilt is more a consequence than a cause of anxiety. Guilt is repressed in order to avoid the anxiety producing trauma to self-esteem that would otherwise result if it were acknowledged. Repression per se enters the causal picture in anxiety only secondarily—by obviating "the possibility of punishment, confession, expiation, and other guilt reduction mechanisms" (Ausubel, 1952, p. 456). Furthermore, in most types of personality disorder other than anxiety, depression, and various complications of anxiety such as phobias, obsessions, and compulsion, guilt feelings are either not particularly prominent (schizophrenic reactions), or are conspicuously absent (e.g., classical cases of inadequate or aggressive, antisocial psychopathy).

Third, it is just as unreasonable to hold an individual responsible for symptoms of behavior disorder as to deem him accountable for symptoms of physical illness. He is no more culpable for his inability to cope with sociopsychological stress than he would be for his inability to resist the spread of infectious organisms. In those instances where warranted guilt feelings *do* contribute to personality disorder, the patient is accountable for the misdeeds underlying his guilt, but is hardly responsible for the symptoms brought on by the guilt feelings or for unlawful acts committed during his illness. Acknowledgment of guilt may be therapeutically beneficial under these circumstances, but punishment for the original misconduct should obviously be deferred until after recovery.

Lastly, even if it were true that all personality disorder is a reflection of sin and that people are accountable for their behavioral symptoms, it would still be unnecessary to deny that these symptoms are manifestations of disease. Illness is no less real because the victim happens to be culpable for his illness. A glutton with hypertensive heart disease undoubtedly aggravates his condition by overeating, and is culpable in part for the often fatal symptoms of his disease, but what reasonable person would claim that for this reason he is not really ill?

Conclusions

Four propositions in support of the argument for discarding the concept of mental illness were carefully examined, and the following conclusions were reached:

First, although brain pathology is probably not the major cause of personality disorder, it does account for *some* psychological symptoms by impairing the neural substrate of personality. In any case, however, a symptom need not reflect a physical lesion in order to qualify as a genuine manifestation of disease.

Second, Szasz' postulated dichotomy between mental and physical symptoms is untenable because the assessment of *all* symptoms is dependent to some extent on subjective judgment, emotional factors, cultural-ethical norms, and personal involvement of the observer. Furthermore, the use of medical measures in treating behavior disorders—irrespective of whether the underlying causes are neural or psychological—is defensible on the grounds that if inadvertent impairment of the neural substrate of personality can have distortive effects on behavior, directed manipulation of the same substrate may have therapeutic effects.

Third, there is no inherent contradiction in regarding mental symptoms both as expressions of problems in living *and* as manifestations of illness. The latter situation results when individuals are for various reasons unable to cope with such problems, and react with seriously distorted or maladaptive behavior. The three principal categories of behavioral symptoms—manifestations of impaired functioning, adaptive compensation, and defensive overreaction—are also found in bodily disease. The concept of mental illness has never been advanced as a demonological cause of human disharmony, but only as a comanifestation with it of certain inescapable difficulties and hazards in personal and social adjustment. The same concept is also generally accepted as a generic term for all behavioral symptoms rather than as a reified cause of these symptoms.

Fourth, the view that personality disorder is less a manifestation of illness than of sin, i.e., of culpable inadequacy in meeting problems of ethical choice and responsibility, and that victims of behavior disorder are therefore morally accountable for their symptoms, is neither logically nor empirically tenable. In most instances immoral behavior and mental illness are clearly distinguishable conditions. Guilt is only a secondary etiological factor in anxiety and depression, and in other personality disorders is either not prominent or conspicuously absent. The issue of culpability for symptoms is largely irrelevant in handling the behavior disorders, and in any case does not detract from the reality of the illness.

In general, it is both unnecessary and potentially dangerous to discard the concept of mental illness on the grounds that only in this way can clinical psychology escape from the professional domination of medicine. Dentists, podiatrists, optometrists, and osteopaths have managed to acquire an independent professional status without rejecting the concept of disease. It is equally unnecessary and dangerous to substitute the doctrine of sin for illness in order to counteract prevailing amoral and nonjudgmental trends in psychotherapy. The hypothesis of repressed guilt does not adequately explain most kinds and instances of personality disorder, and the concept of mental illness does not preclude judgments of moral accountability where warranted. Definition of behavior disorder in terms of sin or of difficulties associated with ethical choice and responsibility would substitute theological disputation and philosophical wrangling about values for specifiable quantitative and qualitative criteria of disease.

7 / The Medical Model and Mental Hospitalization: Some Notes on the Vicissitudes of the Tinkering Trades

Erving Goffman

The Western history of the interpretation of persons who seem to act oddly is a dramatic one: willful or involuntary consort with the devil, seizure by the tendencies of wild animals, etc. (Deutsch, 1949, pp. 12–23). In Britain, in the latter part of the eighteenth century, the medical mandate over these offenders began in earnest. Inmates were called patients, nurses were trained, and medically styled case records were kept (Jones, 1955, pp. 55–58). Mad-houses, which had been retitled asylums for the insane, were retitled again, this time as mental hospitals. A similar movement was led in America by the Pennsylvania Hospital, beginning in 1756 (Deutsch, 1949, p. 58ff). Today in the West there are differences in stress between practitioners with an "organic" approach and those with a "functional" one, but the assumptions underlying both approaches similarly support the legitimacy of applying the medical version of the service model to asylum inmates. For example, in many communities certification by a physician is a legal requirement for involuntary mental hospitalization.

When a patient-to-be comes to his first admissions interview, the admitting physicians immediately apply the medical-service model. Whatever the patient's social circumstances, whatever the particular character of his "disorder," he can in this setting be treated as someone whose problem can be approached, if not dealt with, by applying a single technical-psychiatric view. That one patient differs from another in sex, age, race grouping, marital status, religion, or social class is merely an item to be taken into consideration, to be corrected for, as it were, so that general psychiatric theory can be applied and universal themes detected behind the superficialities of outward differences in social life. Just as anyone in the social system can have an inflamed appendix, so anyone can manifest one of the basic psychiatric syndromes. A uniform professional courtesy shown to patients is matched with a uniform applicability of psychiatric doctrine.

There are certainly cases of mental disorder (associated with brain tumors, paresis, arteriosclerosis, meningitis, etc.) that appear beautifully to fulfill all the requirements of the service model: a randomly distributed rare event injures the client's mental functioning without anyone intending it and without his being personally to blame. After a while he and/or others sense that "something is wrong." Through a route of referrals he is brought, voluntarily or involuntarily, to the attention of psychiatrists. They gather information, make observations, provide a diagnosis, a prescription, and suggest a course of treatment. The patient then recovers, or the progress of his pathology is checked, or (a likelihood with "organic reactions") the disease follows its known and inevitable course, ending in the patient's death or his reduction to an incurable state of mere vegetative functioning. In the more benign cases, where the patient can benefit markedly from treatment, he is likely to re-evaluate his past experience so as to recognize that the psychiatric service was performed in his own interests and that he would have sought it out voluntarily had he realized what was wrong and what could be done for him. Everything ends happily ever after,[1] and if not happily then at least tidily. One can find framed case records in the hallways of the medical-surgical buildings of some mental hospitals that provide, in regard to an actual case, an outline of early ("prodromal") social signs and symptoms, documentation of the lay failure to assess these correctly, description of the behavior of the patient while he was sick, and drawings of the autopsy findings confirming the correctness of the diagnosis and appropriateness of the treatment. Social misconduct and visible organic pathology are brought together in a perfect confirmation of the applicability of the medical model.

While some psychiatric cases may be neatly handled within the framework established by the medical model there are very evident sources of difficulty, especially in regard to the largest category of mental patients, those with so-called "functional" psychoses. Many of these difficulties have been described in the literature and are well known in psychiatry. I would like to review them briefly here, starting with the more incidental kinds and working up to ones that are more fundamental.

One issue in the applicability of the service model to institutional psychiatry arises from the fact that part of the official mandate of the public mental hospital is to protect the community from the danger and nuisance of certain kinds of misconduct. In terms of the law and of the public pressures to which the mental hospital is sensitive, this custodial function is of major importance. Within the institution surprisingly little explicit reference is made to it, however, the focus being on the medical-like therapeutic services the hospital sup-

---

[1] A good illustration of this is provided in Berton Roueché's *New Yorker* article "Ten Feet Tall," detailing an incident of manic-depressive side effects caused by cortisone treatment. This article is available in Roueché's collection, *The Incurable Wound* (New York: Berkeley Publishing Corp., n.d.), pp. 114–43.

plies patients. If we view the mentally ill as persons that others have had a special kind of trouble with, then the custodial role of the hospital (much like the custodial role of the prison) is understandable and, many would feel, justifiable; the point here, however, is that a service to the patient's kin, neighborhood, or employer is not necessarily a service to the community at large (whatever that may be) and a service to any of these is not necessarily a service, especially not a medical service, to the inmate. Instead of a server and the served, we find a governor and the governed, an officer and those subject to him (Parsons, 1957, p. 115).

During the patient's hospitalization he is very likely to pass from the jurisdiction of one medical person to another, and this shift is not a result of a referral system in which the practitioner suggests another server and the patient voluntarily follows the suggestion; the patient will pass from the jurisdiction of one medical person to another because of daily and weekly medical shifts, and because of the frequency with which patients are shifted from one ward to another and medical staff from one service to another. Being members of the same organization, the patient and the doctor are both subject to decisions they do not make concerning whom they will see.[2]

Further, we must see the mental hospital in the recent historical context in which it developed, as one among a network of institutions designed to provide a residence for various categories of socially troublesome people. These institutions include nursing homes, general hospitals, veterans' homes, jails, geriatrics clinics, homes for the mentally retarded, work farms, orphanages, and old-folks' homes. Every state hospital has an appreciable fraction of patients who might better be contained in some one of these other institutions (just as these other institutions have some inmates who might better be contained in a mental hospital), but who must be retained because no space is available, or can be afforded, in these other institutions. Each time the mental hospital functions as a holding station, within a network of such stations, for dealing with public charges, the service model is disaffirmed. All of these facts of patient recruitment are part of what staff must overlook, rationalize, gloss over about their place of service.

One of the most striking problems in applying the service model to mental hospitalization has to do with the largely involuntary character of admission to a mental hospital in America. As with the medical attention required by the very young and the very old, there is an effort to employ the guardian principle and assimilate action taken by a next of kin to action taken by the patient himself. It is true that treating the very young and very old as irresponsible does not seem to be violently inconsistent with or corrupting of our continued

---

[2] In research hospitals instructive attempts have been made to deal with this problem. The role of ward physician may be strictly segregated from the role of therapist, the therapist-patient relation remaining constant, regardless of a shift in ward residence of a patient. (See, for example, Perry and Wynne, 1959, pp. 62–65.) In private general hospitals which have one or two psychiatric floors, an even closer approximation to the service relation is found: a psychiatrist in private practice may have several "beds" and will temporarily hospitalize a patient when he feels it is necessary. The house staff, typically residents, will then have the job of keeping the patient fed and quiet, and the psychiatrist will visit his patient once or twice a day, as do the doctors who make use of beds on other floors. Many of the forms of the service relationship are thereby retained; how much therapy results is a different question.

relations with them. But, though some involuntary patients do come to see the errors of their resistance to hospitalization, in general the unwilling patient's resentment seems to remain. He is likely to feel that he has been railroaded into the hospital with the help, or at least with the consent, of his close ones. While ordinarily an encounter with a server is likely to affirm the individual's belief in the rationality and goodwill of the society in which he lives, an encounter with hospital psychiatrists is likely to have an alienating effect.

The patient is not the only one, it seems, who declines to view his trouble as simply a type of sickness to be treated and then forgotten. Once he has a record of having been in a mental hospital, the public at large, both formally, in terms of employment restrictions, and informally, in terms of day-to-day social treatment, considers him to be set apart; they place a stigma on him (Schwartz, 1956). Even the hospital itself tacitly acknowledges that mental disorder is shameful; for example, many hospitals provide a code mail address so that patients can send and receive mail without having their status advertised on the envelope. Although the extent of stigmatization is declining in some circles, it is a basic factor in the life of the expatient. Unlike much medical hospitalization, the patient's stay in the mental hospital is too long and the effect too stigmatizing to allow the individual an easy return to the social place he came from.[3]

In response to his stigmatization and to the sensed deprivation that occurs when he enters the hospital, the inmate frequently develops some alienation from civil society, sometimes expressed by an unwillingness to leave the hospital. This alienation can develop regardless of the type of disorder for which the patient was committed, constituting a side effect of hospitalization that frequently has more significance for the patient and his personal circle than do his original difficulties. Here again we deal with something that does not fit the service model.[4]

Another difficulty lies in the nature of psychiatric skills themselves. It seems fair to say that the current assumption as regards functional psychotics is that the patient has developed faulty ways of relating to persons and needs to engage

[3] It seems characteristic that in medical hospitals men who are laid up will joke with the nursing staff in a self-belittling hearty way, as if to say that the body lying supine for the nurses' ministrations is so uncharacteristic of the permanent self that anything can be safely said about it. In mental hospitals, on the other hand, this easy dissociation from one's current character and circumstances is much less feasible; hence, male mental patients tend to be serious, and where self-distancing expressions are introduced, these may have psychotic-like proportions.

[4] Schneider (1947) shows how withdrawal from duties, even on medical grounds, can lead to ever-increasing isolation on the part of the sick person and increasing confirmation of his being different. The effects of separateness can then become more important than the initial causes. Operating on a somewhat similar understanding, U.S. Army research psychiatrists at Walter Reed have recently developed the notion that the more a soldier is allowed to see that he has a major psychiatric problem needful of special psychiatric treatment, the less likely is he to be quickly reassimilated into the military group in which he originally experienced his trouble. See, for example, B. L. Bushard (1958, pp. 431–443, especially p. 442): "These ends (minimization of psychiatric disability) can be accomplished through little actual, direct work with the patient himself, but do require extensive and working liaison with a variety of other agencies. Far more important than the verbal interchange with the patient is the non-verbal implication in his being seen early, listened to empathically, and restored to a duty status with dispatch. Any implication that the problem stems from remote or imponderable situations, is due to 'disease' or is based upon considerations which are not immediate and amenable to mastery, will frequently lead to the undermining of such defenses as may be still intact."

in therapeutic learning experiences to correct these patterns. But the capacity to provide a patient with this experience is not quite a technical skill, nor can it be imparted as assuredly as a technical one. Further, what skills of this kind a staff may have cannot easily be broken down into the skill-status hierarchy characteristic of other service establishments, where high-placed personnel perform the crucial brief tasks and unskilled lower levels perform routine preparatory work or merely ensure that the environment is kept benign. A ward attendant often seems to be as well equipped to offer a "good" relation to a patient as a highly trained psychiatrist, and, whether good or bad, the contribution of the attendant will impinge continuously on the patient, instead of impinging very intermittently as does the hospital psychiatrist's.[5] Menials who prepare the patient to see the psychiatrist can presumably exercise through this preparation about as much psychiatric intervention as the psychiatrist himself, the domain of face-to-face social contact being one in which every participant is equally licenced to carry and use a scalpel. This is so even though hospital administrations, operating within the medical model, give to psychiatrists the right to make crucial decisions concerning the disposition of the patient.

Operating to exaggerate the fact that little psychiatric skill is available anywhere, and where available not always distributed according to the staff hierarchy, is another issue: the usual circumspection or "functional specificity" of the server is directly denied in psychiatric service. All of the patient's actions, feelings, and thoughts—past, present, and predicted—are officially usable by the therapist in diagnosis and prescription. Current conceptions about the psychogenic character of many physical disorders even bring into the psychiatrist's domain matters otherwise apportioned to medical practitioners, with the result that the psychiatrist can indeed claim to treat "the whole person."[6] The organization of auxiliary psychiatric servers in the hospital—internist, psychologist, neurophysiologist, social worker, nursing staff—attests to the psychiatrist's diffuse mandate, feeding information to him that he alone has an official right to put together into an overall assessment of a patient. None of a patient's business, then, is none of the psychiatrist's business; nothing ought to be held back from the psychiatrist as irrelevant to his job. No other expert server with a system to tinker with seems to arrogate this kind of role to himself.

Corresponding to this diffuse diagnostic mandate of the psychiatrist is an equally diffuse prescriptive one. Incarcerating institutions operate on the basis of defining almost all of the rights and duties the inmates will have. Someone will be in a position to pass fatefully on everything that the inmate succeeds in obtaining and everything he is deprived of, and this person is, officially, the psychiatrist. Nor need the psychiatrist exercise this right according to uniform bureaucratic rulings, as a member of the civil service or the military might. Almost any of the living arrangements through which the patient is strapped into his daily round can be modified at will by the psychiatrist, provided a

[5] The milieu therapy movement presumably springs from a recognition that crucial hospital experience cannot be restricted to the therapeutic hour (when there is one) and that all personnel therefore can have an equal fatefulness for the patient. Sources here are Stanton and Schwartz, 1954; Maxwell Jones, 1953.

[6] A minor consequence of the psychogenic doctrine of physical disorders is that some mental patients are disinclined to present a claim for needed physical treatment because they fear they will be thought to be "imagining things."

psychiatric explanation is given. Again we see that the psychiatric role is unique among servers, no other being accorded such power.

In discussing the medical model in a general hospital, it was suggested that life conditions within the hospital could be divided into an inner and outer sphere: the inner sphere contains the injured area of the organism under conditions of medically indicated control that are highly responsive to the state of the injury; the outer sphere provides, in a rougher way, housing for the inner sphere. In mental hospitals this division between a therapeutic and a housing milieu can sometimes be sustained. Where medical (as opposed to psychological) intervention is employed, there can be some effort to administer the treatment under highly controlled conditions, allowing the times between treatments to be handled with less medical attention. And there are cases, as when a patient is actively suicidal or homicidal, when his whole daily round is closely managed and constitutes an inner sphere of medical control intimately adjusted to his circumstances; life conditions can thus be assimilated to treatment. Similarly, for patients of advanced neurophysiological deterioration, backward conditions seem closely adapted to the capacities of the organism: the patient's sitting all day in one place, with a vacuous expression on his face, is, in a way, an inevitable and irremedial extension of his state.

But during the earlier stages of cerebral deterioration, and during most of the life course of some organic disorders, such as epilepsy, the absolute assurance that an organic syndrome is present is by no means clearly related to the life conditions accorded the patient in the hospital. However ultimately hopeless a condition is, there are relatively few patients so deteriorated that typical backward life is an accurate reflection of and response to their capacities. As to how "normal" their living arrangements could be, there is no present agreement. Diagnosis, then, may be medical, while treatment is not, the patient being treated merely with the life available for patients of his general kind. And when we turn to functional cases, ward life ceases to be a technical response to their capacities, in the sense that bed rest is an expression of the physical state of a post-operative patient. And yet, as we shall see, mental hospital staffs do argue that the life conditions of the patient are both an expression of his capabilities and personal organization at the moment and a medical response to them.

Next I want to suggest that, compared to a medical hospital or garage, a mental hospital is ill-equipped to be a place where the classic repair cycle occurs. In state mental hospitals, and to a greater extent in private and veterans' hospitals, opportunity for observing the patient is available, but staff are often too busy to record anything but acts of disobedience. Even when staff time is available for this work, the patient's conduct on the ward can hardly be taken as a sample of his conduct off it: some conduct felt to be unacceptable on the outside does not occur here (especially when this conduct was a response to disliked persons in the patient's home environment), and other forms of misconduct overlay the old in response to the inmate's current involuntary situation. A refraction of conduct thus occurs, the walls of the institution acting like a thick and faulted prism. Unless one argues for the validity of testing persons under this particular kind of stress, the ward would seem to be the worst possible place for a server's observations.

Similarly, even where diagnostic conferences are held in regard to each patient, the effort of these meetings can be directed to agreeing on which of the legally required labels will be affixed to the case-record statement; and the timing of these meetings may have little to do with the presence or absence of an accumulation of data to act upon.

What is true of the difficulties of diagnosis in mental hospitals is even more true of treatment. As already suggested, the problem of easing the patient's attitude to the world is confused and exacerbated by the problem of easing his attitude to involuntary hospitalization. In any case, the treatment given in mental hospitals is not likely to be specific to the disorder, as it is, in general, in a medical hospital, garage, or radio repair shop; instead, if treatment is given at all, a cycle of therapies tends to be given across the board to a whole entering class of patients, with the medical work-up being used more to learn if there are counterindications for the standard treatments than to find indications for them.

At the same time, the patient's life is regulated and ordered according to a disciplinarian system developed for the management by a small staff of a large number of involuntary inmates. In this system the attendant is likely to be the key staff person, informing the patient of the punishments and rewards that are to regulate his life and arranging for medical authorization for such privileges and punishments. Quiet, obedient behavior leads to the patient's promotion in the ward system; obstreperous, untidy behavior to demotion. Interestingly enough, it is when the patient finds himself willing to improve his social conduct that the attendant is likely to bring him to the attention of the doctor as both worthy of consideration and able to profit from it, so that, as Ivan Belknap has described, the patient often gets a doctor's attention when he least needs it (Belknap, 1956, p. 144).[7]

The period in the mental hospital is a difficult one for the patient to assimi-

[7] I would like to add that since mental patients are persons who on the outside declined to respond to efforts at social control, there is a question of how social control can be achieved on the inside. I believe that it is achieved largely through the "ward system," the means of control that has slowly evolved in modern mental hospitals. The key, I feel, is a system of wards graded for degree of allowable misbehavior and degree of discomfort and deprivation prevalent in them. Whatever the level of the new patient's misbehavior, then, a ward can be found for him in which this conduct is routinely dealt with and to a degree allowed. In effect, by accepting the life conditions on these wards, the patient is allowed to continue his misbehavior, except that now he does not particularly bother anyone by it, since it is routinely handled, if not accepted, on the ward. When he requests some improvement in his lot he is then, in effect, made to say "uncle," made to state verbally that he is ready to mend his ways. When he gives in verbally he is likely to be allowed an improvement in life conditions. Should he then again misbehave in the old way, and persist in this, he is lectured and returned to his previous conditions. If instead of backsliding he states his willingness to behave even better, and retains this line for a suitable length of time, he is advanced further within the quick-discharge cycle through which most first admissions are moved up and out within a year. A point then is often reached where the patient is entrusted to a kinsman, either for walks on the hospital grounds or for town expeditions, the kinsman now being transformed into someone who has the incarcerating establishment and the law to reinforce the threat: "Be good or else I'll send you back." What we find here (and do not on the outside) is a very model of what psychologists might call a learning situation—all hinged on the process of an admitted giving-in. For this reason, patient morale on the rebellious wards seems stronger and healthier than on the discharge wards, where there is a slight air of persons having sold out to get out.

late to the medical model. A very standard complaint is: "Nothing is being done with me—I'm just left to sit." And corresponding to this difficulty is the fact that current official psychiatric treatment for functional disorders does not, in itself, provide a probability of success great enough easily to justify the practice of institutional psychiatry as an expert service occupation, as here defined, especially since the probability that hospitalization will damage the life chances of the individual is, as already suggested, positive and high.

The problem, however, is not merely that of a low probability of successful service but, for some patients, a question of the validity of applying the whole service frame of reference in the first place.

First, we must see that the discreteness of the entity in which the disorder exists is questionable. True, in cases that are organic in character, the patient encloses within himself the world in which the damage is felt and the world in which repairs, if possible, can be made. This is not so in instances of functional psychosis. Insofar as the patient's symptomatic behavior is an integral part of his interpersonal situation, the server would have to import this whole situation into the hospital in order to observe the patient's difficulty and to treat it. Instead of there being a relatively benign and passive environment and an isolated point of trouble, the figure and ground of usual service conceptions merge into one, the patient's interpersonal environment being inseparable from the trouble he is experiencing. Theoretically, it might of course be possible for a slight therapeutic change in the patient to have a benign circular effect on his environment when he gets sent back to it, and it might be possible to arrange to return him to a new environment, but in practice the patient is usually returned, when he is discharged, back into the system of which his psychotic response is a natural part.

But there is a still more fundamental issue, which hinges on the applicability of the concept of "pathology." Ordinarily the pathology which first draws attention to the patient's condition is conduct that is "inappropriate in the situation." But the decision as to whether a given act is appropriate or inappropriate must often necessarily be a lay decision, simply because we have no technical mapping of the various behavioral subcultures in our society, let alone the standards of conduct prevailing in each of them. Diagnostic decisions, except for extreme symptoms, can become ethnocentric, the server judging from his own culture's point of view individuals' conduct that can really be judged only from the perspective of the group from which they derive. Further, since inappropriate behavior is typically behavior that someone does not like and finds extremely troublesome, decisions concerning it tend to be political, in the sense of expressing the special interests of some particular faction or person rather than interests that can be said to be above the concerns of any particular grouping, as in the case of physical pathology (Szasz, 1958a).

For the patient, the application of the pathology concept to his conduct can have effects that are incompatible with the service ideal. Insofar as he feels he has acted inappropriately at all, he may see his action as part of the normal social world of intention, responsibility, and culpability—much like the initial lay perception of his troublesome conduct. To have one's behavior defined as involuntary, non-responsible, and non-culpable may be helpful in some cases, but this nonetheless involves a technical schema, not a social one, and ideally ought to disqualify the patient for any participation in the service relation even while qualifying him as an object of service. Szasz's description can be cited here:

> More precisely, according to the common-sense definition, mental health is the ability to play whatever the game of social living might consist of and to play it well. Conversely, to refuse to play, or to play badly, means that the person is mentally ill. The question may now be raised as to what are the differences, if any, between social non-conformity (or deviation) and mental illness. Leaving technical psychiatric considerations aside for the moment, I shall argue that the difference between these two notions—as expressed for example by the statements "He is wrong" and "He is mentally ill"—does not necessarily lie in any observable *facts* to which they point, but may consist only of a difference in our *attitudes* toward our subject. If we take him *seriously*, consider him to have human rights and dignities, and look upon him as more or less our equal—we then speak of disagreements, deviations, fights, crimes, perhaps even of treason. Should we feel, however, that we cannot communicate with him, that he is somehow "basically" different from us, we shall then be inclined to consider him no longer as an equal but rather as an inferior (rarely, superior) person; and we then speak of him as being crazy, mentally ill, insane, psychotic, immature, and so forth (Szasz, 1958, p. 509; Szasz, 1957c, p. 315; Szasz, 1956a).

We should not overestimate this problem, however, because, in fact, there is no great danger in mental hospitals of having one's acts consistently defined in a neutral technical frame of reference. In medicine it is possible to act as if there were no right or wrong streptococci, merely dangerous ones. In psychiatry there is a formal effort to act as if the issue is treatment, not moral judgment, but this is not consistently maintained. Ethical neutrality is indeed difficult to sustain in psychiatry, because the patient's disorder is intrinsically related to his acting in a way that causes offense to witnesses. Further, the standard way of dealing with such offenses in our society is to sanction the offender, negatively and correctively. Our whole society operates on this assumption in every item and detail of life, and without some functional equivalent it is hard to see how we could maintain a social order without it.

It is understandable, then, that even occasions set aside to demonstrate that professional non-moralistic psychotherapy is taking place in the institution will be invaded by a moralistic perspective, albeit a modified one. It is understandable that a large part of psychotherapy consists of holding the sins of the patient up to him and getting him to see the error of his ways. And in a sense, I do not see how it can or should be otherwise. The interesting point here is that psychiatric staff are in a position neither to forego the fiction of neutrality nor actually to sustain it.

When applied to the mental hospital, the service model leads to a very characteristic ambivalence of action on the part of staff. Psychiatric doctrine requires ethical neutrality in dealing with patients, for what others see as misbehavior the staff must see as pathology. The law even underwrites this position, a mental patient having the privilege of committing crimes without having to face legal action. And yet, in the actual management of patients, ideals of proper conduct must be held up as desirable, infractions inveighed against, and the patient treated as a "responsible" person, that is, one capable of a personal effort to behave himself. Psychiatric staff share with policemen the peculiar occupational task of hectoring and moralizing adults; the necessity of submitting to these lectures is one of the consequences of committing acts against the community's social order.

Given these many senses in which an expert service is not provided to the mental patient or the concept of expert service does not apply to the patient's plight, we can expect some difficulties in the interaction between institutional psychiatrist and patient, difficulties that are a necessary and natural product of mental hospitalization. The psychiatrist's training, orientation, and status commit him to approaching a mental patient civilly, in the guise of offering an expert service to a client who has voluntarily sought it. The psychiatrist must therefore assume that the patient wants treatment and has a rational mind that can come, albeit in an unskilled way, to the assistance of those who serve its possessor. The institution itself at every point affirms this service guise through the terminology used, the uniforms worn, and the terms of address employed.

If, however, the psychiatrist is to take the patient's words at face value as a report of symptoms, as in medical servicing, then the patient must be willing to respond in a very special way: a contrite admission of illness stated in modestly untechnical terms and a sincerely expressed desire to undergo a change of self through psychiatric treatment. In short, there is a psychiatric line the patient must follow if the psychiatrist is to be affirmed as a medical server.

The likelihood of an unschooled patient following the psychiatric line is not great. He may never in his life have had so many reasons obvious to him for seeing that he is not a voluntary client and for being disgruntled at his condition. He sees the psychiatrist as the person in power. In contact with the psychiatrist the patient is likely to make those kinds of demands and requests and take those stands that pull the relationship out of the service schema to, for example, that of a charge pleading with his master for more privileges, a prisoner remonstrating with an unlawful jailor, or a prideful man declining to exchange communications with someone who thinks he is crazy.

If the psychiatrist takes these complaints seriously, the relationship ceases to be the one for which he was trained. To defend his own professional role and the institution that hires him, the psychiatrist is under pressure to respond by treating these outpourings not as directly usable statements of information but rather as signs of the illness itself, to be discounted as direct information (Stanton and Schwartz, 1954, p. 200 ff). But to treat the statements of the patient as signs, not valid symptom reporting, is of course to deny that the patient is a participant as well as an object in a service relation.

The psychiatrist and patient tend to be doomed by the institutional context to a false and difficult relationship and are constantly funneled into the contact that will express it: the psychiatrist must extend service civility from the stance of a server but can no more continue in that stance than the patient can accept it. Each party to the relationship is destined to seek out the other to offer what the other cannot accept, and each is destined to reject what the other offers. In many psychiatric settings, one can witness what seems to be the same central encounter between a patient and a psychiatrist: the psychiatrist begins the exchange by proffering the patient the civil regard that is owed a client, receives a response that cannot be integrated into a continuation of the conventional service interaction, and then, even while attempting to sustain some of the outward forms of server-client relations, must twist and squirm his way out of the predicament. All day long the psychiatric staff seems to be engaged in withdrawing from its own implicit overtures.

In discussing the application of the expert service model to various trades, I suggested some standard discrepancies or strains and argued that institutional psychiatric servicing faced a very extensive set of these problems. This situation is in itself not very noteworthy; many "expert" services are sold that satisfy even less well than psychiatry the requirements of the model in whose guise they are presented, albeit few involving so many clients so sorely tried. What is analytically interesting about the mental hospital case is that doctors are involved, and so are involuntary inmates. Medical doctors in our society are exemplars of the rational, tinkering approach and ordinarily are allowed to invest their performances with great dignity and weight. Having committed much time and expense to acquiring the medical role, and expecting their daily activity to support them in the role their training has vouchsafed them, they understandably feel compelled to maintain a medical approach and the medical version of the service model. Society at large seems to back them up in this, for it is a satisfaction to us all to feel that those we exile to madhouses are receiving treatment, not punishment, under a doctor's care. At the same time, involuntary mental commitment (and often even voluntary commitment) ordinarily entails for the individual a condition of life that is impoverished and desolate indeed, often generating a sustained hostility to his captors. The limited applicability of the medical model to mental hospitals brings together a doctor who cannot easily afford to construe his activity in other than medical terms and a patient who may well feel he must fight and hate his keepers if any sense is to be made of the hardship he is undergoing. Mental hospitals institutionalize a kind of grotesque of the service relationship.

While both doctors and inmates find themselves in a difficult institutional setting, the doctors, being in control of the institution, have the greater opportunity to evolve some mechanisms for coping with their problem. Their response to the situation provides us not only with an important aspect of hospital life but also with a case history of the interplay between social models of being—in this case the expert server—and the social establishments in which there is an attempt to institutionalize these role identities.

There are some features of the hospital situation that help the psychiatrist in the difficulties of his role. The physician's legal mandate over the fate of the patient and his institutional power over some elements of staff automatically provide the authority that other servers must in part win through actual interaction with the client. Further, while psychiatric knowledge often cannot place the psychiatrist in a position to predict the patient's conduct correctly, the same nescience provides the psychiatrist with interpretive leeway: by adding *post hoc* qualifications and adumbrations of his analyses, the psychiatrist can provide a picture of what has been happening with the patient that can no more be disproved than proved, as when an unanticipated psychotic break gives rise to the interpretation that the patient now feels secure enough or strong enough to express his psychosis. To this authority that cannot be discredited, the psychiatrist can add a force derived from medical tradition, "clinical experience." Through this magical quality, the formally qualified person of longest experience with the type of case in question is accorded the final word when there is doubt or ambiguity, this person also being apt to be the ranking practitioner present.

The psychiatrist, being medically trained, can provide minor medical services to patients and can refer more difficult medical cases to the hospital's hospital. This normative function (characteristic, as suggested, of what must be done in the Army, on a ship, in a factory, or wherever large numbers are gathered to contribute to an administrative end), instead of being seen as an ancillary housekeeping service, tends to be assimilated to the central functioning of the establishment, thereby strengthening the basis in reality of the notion that mental patients receive medical-like treatment in mental hospitals. Interestingly enough, state mental hospitals sometimes are so understaffed that medically qualified personnel could spend all their time making minor medical repairs on patients and must practice psychiatry—to the extent they do—at the expense of needed medical treatment.

An obvious way for the psychiatrist to solve his role problem is to leave the state mental hospital as soon as he can afford to, often with the claim that he is leaving in order to go where "it will really be possible to practice psychiatry." He may go, especially for the last year or two of his obligatory residency, to a private hospital, perhaps of the psychoanalytically oriented kind, where there is a patient load approaching that of private practice, and where a higher ratio of patients are voluntary and "suitable" for psychotherapy. From such a hospital (or directly from the state hospital), he may go into private practice, an arrangement that may not bring his skill to many patients but will guarantee that activity is conducted in accordance with the service complex: an office, a secretary, hour-long appointments, voluntary appearance of the patient, sole control over diagnosis and treatment, and so forth.[8] For whatever reasons, this two- or three-stage job cycle is sufficiently common to constitute a standard career pattern in psychiatry.

Where the psychiatrist cannot, or does not want, to leave the state mental hospital, some other paths appear to have been established for him. He may redefine his role from that of a server to that of a wise governor, embrace the custodial aspects of the institution, and devote himself to enlightened administration. He can admit some of the weaknesses of individual therapy in the situation and move in the direction of the newer social therapies, attempting to involve the patient's kin in psychotherapy (on the assumption that the disorder resides in a family system),[9] or attempting to locate therapy in the full round of daily contacts that

---

[8] It is remarkable that the self-discipline required of the mental client if he is to allow his psychiatrist to act like any other professional man receives full and detailed justification in the psychoanalytical literature on the basis of technical therapeutic considerations. A wonderful prearranged harmony exists between what is good for the patient and what in fact the psychiatrist requires if an office profession is to be maintained. To paraphrase Mr. Wilson, what is good for the profession is good for the patient. I have found especially refreshing the discussion of the psychological importance of the patient's appreciating that the therapist has a life of his own and that it would not be good for the patient if the therapist postponed his vacation, or saw the patient in response to midnight telephone calls, or allowed himself to be physically endangered by the patient. See, for example, Witaker and Malone (1953, pp. 201–202).

[9] Faced with the doctrine that the patient may merely be the "symptom carrier" for his intimate circle, some research psychiatrists have made an effort to import whole families on to experimental residential wards. The side problems consequent upon such novel living arrangements, especially as regards the structure of family authority, are very great, and their masking effect has perhaps been underestimated.

the patient has with all levels of staff.[10] He can turn to psychiatric research. He can withdraw from patient contact as much as possible, retreating into paper work, or into psychotherapy with the lower levels of staff or with a small number of "promising" patients. He can make a serious effort to warn the patients whom he treats that his knowledge is small, but this kind of candor seems destined to fail because the medical role is defined otherwise in our society, and because the power the psychiatrist has over the patient is not readily understood as something that would be given to anyone who knew little.[11] Occasionally the psychiatrist becomes a "patients' man," agreeing with their claims as to what the institution is doing to them and voicing open criticism of the establishment to them. If he takes none of these tacks, the psychiatrist can at least become cynical about his role in the hospital, thereby protecting himself, if not his patients (Belknap, 1956, p. 200).

In addition to these modes of adaptation involving career alignments, we find adaptations of a more diffuse and more ideological kind, in which staff levels participate. It is as if the service dilemma constituted a sore spot in the hospital social system, and that around this spot intellectual energies are expended to build up a protective skin of words, beliefs, and sentiments. Whatever its source, the resulting system of belief serves to bolster and stabilize the medical-service definition of the situation. We are thus provided with an illustration in miniature of the relation between thought and social position.

Perhaps the most obvious instance of institutional ideology is found in the public relations work that is currently fairly characteristic of mental hospitals. Hallway displays, orientation booklets, institutional magazines, displayable equipment, and newer therapies—these sources of definitions of the situation await patients, relatives, and visitors, establishing the obvious claims of the medical-service line.

Further, we have in mental hospitals a collection of traditional tales whose recounting illustrates the validity of the perspective employed by staff. These stories tell of times a patient was given privileges too early, or released against advice of physicians, and went on to commit suicide or murder. Attendants have jokes to tell illustrating the animal-like nature of patients. Those staff members who attend diagnostic conferences have humorous anecdotes about patients—for example, an inmate who made a dignified claim to sanity but finally allowed that he was an agent of the FBI. There are stories of patients who begged to be kept on a locked ward, or who engaged in obvious delinquencies in order to prevent their own discharge. There are other tales of "prepatients" who displayed increasingly florid and dangerous psychotic symptoms until others were finally convinced of the illness and provided hospitalization, at which point the patients were able to relax their symptomatology, having succeeded in communicating their need for help. Finally, there are heart-warming stories of impossible patients who finally came to form a good relationship with an understanding doctor and thereafter dramati-

[10] Here the psychiatrist may explicitly admit that he must be therapist not to the individual but to the hospital social system. Psychiatric and medical training seem to equip doctors to accept the responsibility of governing a ward or hospital, freeing them from the trepidation an individual might have who had relevant training or experience for the task.

[11] For a comment on the fate of verbal modesty in the context of high hospital office, see Stanton (1958, p. 499).

cally improved. As with the other of exemplary tales, these relationship stories seem to center on proof of the rightness of the position taken by staff.[12]

The ideological or interpretative implications of management's activity seem to focus on two issues, the nature of patients and the nature of the hospital's activity, in both cases bolstering up the medical-service definition of the situation.

The key view of the patient is: were he "himself" he would voluntarily seek psychiatric treatment and voluntarily submit to it, and, when ready for discharge, he will avow that his real self was all along being treated as it really wanted to be treated. A variation of the guardian principle is involved. The interesting notion that the psychotic patient has a sick self and, subordinated to this, a relatively "adult," "intact," or "unimpaired" self carries guardianship one step further, finding in the very structure of the ego the split between object and client required to complete the service triad.

The case record plays a role here. It provides a means of systematically building up a picture of the patient's past that demonstrates that a disease process had been slowly infiltrating his conduct until this conduct, as a system, was entirely pathological. Seemingly normal conduct is seen to be merely a mask or shield for the essential sickness behind it. An overall title is given to the pathology, such as schizophrenia, psychopathic personality, etc., and this provides a new view of the patient's "essential" character.[13] When pressed, of course, some staff will allow that these syndrome titles are vague and doubtful, employed only to comply with hospital census regulations. But in practice these categories become magical ways of making a single unity out of the nature of the patient—an entity that is subject to psychiatric servicing. Through all of this, of course, the areas of "normal functioning" in the patient can be discounted and disattended, except insofar as they lead the patient willingly to accept his treatment.

The response of the patient to hospitalization can itself be nicely handled by translating it into a technical frame of reference, whereby the contribution of the hospital to the patient's trouble becomes incidental, the important thing being the internally generated mode of disturbance characteristic of the patient's conduct. Interpersonal happenings are transferred into the patient, establishing him as a relatively closed system that can be thought of as pathological and correctable. Thus an action that the patient engages in with an official of the institution that may, to the official, have an aggressive cast is translated into a substantive term like "aggressivity" that can be located well within the patient.[14] Similarly, a ward situation in which nurses do not bother to initiate contact with long-term patients (who in fact would respond to overtures) may be transferred into the patient by referring to him as "mute" (Sommer, 1959). As Szasz has suggested,

---

[12] Patients, of course, have their own set of exemplary tales almost equally discrediting of staff.

[13] The social psychology of perceived "essential" character has recently been developed by Harold Garfinkel in a series of unpublished papers, to which I am much indebted.

[14] See Money (1955, pp. 264–266). Useful examples of this translation process are found in Weinstein and Kahn (1955). The authors cite such terms as "akinetic mutism," "Anton's syndrome," "reduplicative paramnesia," "anosognosia," which have been used traditionally to refer to a patient's failure to admit his injured condition; they then describe under categories such as "displacement," "misnaming," "paraphasia," the various ways in which patients decline to respond to their situation in a civil and cooperative way, the intransigence being described as a psychophysiological by-product of brain injury, not as a social response to involuntary threatening treatment. See also Belknap (1956, p. 170).

this view has similarities to the earlier view that the mental patient has a devil or evil spirit within him that must be and need only be exorcised (Szasz, Knoff, and Hollender, 1958).

This translation process can be clearly seen in the process of group psychotherapy. In general this therapy—the principal verbal therapy patients in state hospitals receive—begins as a gripe session during which patients express demands and complaints in a relatively permissive atmosphere, with relatively direct access to a staff member. The only action on the part of the therapist that seems consistent with his obligation to the institution and his profession is to turn these demands aside by convincing the patient that the problems he feels he is having with the institution—or with kin, society, and so forth—are really *his* problems; the therapist suggests that he attack these problems by rearranging his own internal world, not by attempting to alter the action of these other agents. What we have here is a direct, although no doubt not intentional, effort to transform the patient in his own eyes into a closed system in need of servicing. Thus, to cite a relatively extreme example, I have seen a therapist deal with a Negro patient's complaints about race relations in a partially segregated hospital by telling the patient that he must ask himself why he, among all the other Negroes present, chose this particular moment to express this feeling, and what this expression could mean about him as a person, apart from the state of race relations in the hospital at the time.[15]

One of the most intimate service redefinitions of the patient's nature is to be found in the idea of the "danger mandate" characteristic of many of the tinkering services. It has been said that a medical student becomes a doctor when he finds himself in a position to make a crucial mistake.[16] Underlying this attitude is a belief that a serviceable system has organizational danger points and can therefore be greatly damaged if unskilled action is taken in these crucial, precarious matters. As already suggested, this tends to provide rational grounds for a technical hierarchy of skill and a social hierarchy of servers within any one servicing establishment.

There is a version of the danger mandate in mental hospitals. This is the view that a wrong action can greatly endanger the patient, and that the psychiatrist is in a position, due to training and skill, to take potentially dangerous actions regarding patients, actions that lesser persons in the medical hierarchy ought not to be allowed to take. Of course, in questions of prescribing drug dosage and weighing possible contraindicating side effects of physical treatment, the model here holds well enough, but the carry-over into the psychotherapeutic realm is more precarious, although often no less insisted on. It is sometimes suggested that lesser personnel, such as social workers, nurses, and attendants, ought not to engage in "amateur therapy," and certainly not in amateur "psychoanalysis." A staff psychiatrist who takes on an inmate for special sessions of psychotherapy ought not to

---

[15] The techniques employed by group psychotherapists can be studied as part of small-group indoctrination methods. For example, one commonly finds that a few patients will be well versed in the psychiatric line and reliably willing to take it. A gripe raised by a patient may then be picked up by the therapist and referred back to these patients for their opinion. They translate for the complainer, showing that his own fellows see his complaint as part of his own personality, leaving the therapist to come in with the authoritative translation, but now with some of the group polarized against the complainer. A recent discussion of these issues may be found in Frank (1959, pp. 17–39).

[16] Personal communication from Howard S. Becker.

have his work tampered with by others, especially lesser others. The wrong move during psychotherapy, it is said, can "precipitate" a psychosis, or cast the patient back into a regression from which he may never return, and exemplary tales provide evidence for this. Now while it is perfectly clear that this view fits in well with the traditional notion of a danger mandate, and while it is clear that the possession of this mandate confirms one's view of self as an expert server, it is much less clear that a purely verbal act can in fact have this effect. In any case, as previously suggested, any hospital inmate in personal therapy is likely to be undergoing, during the other 23 hours of each day, a barrage of potentially traumatic experiences, relatively uncontrolled in barbarity, that surely cloud any issue of a verbal probe going in the right or wrong direction. Moreover, given the state of psychiatric knowledge and skill, if a wrongly placed verbal shaft could cause this kind of damage, patients would be in danger indeed during the twenty-fourth hour.

Two further imputations about the patient's nature may be described, both of which again function to support the service model. When a patient is offered a discharge and declines to take it, sometimes engaging in activity calculated to assure his retention, it is commonly said that this proves he is still ill, that he is, in fact, too ill to leave. In this way a link is made between two massive aspects of the situation: being defined as ill or well, and being in or out of the hospital. There are of course many good reasons unconnected with the service model for a patient's diffidence about leaving. For example, he has already suffered the stigma of being a mental patient and in this reduced status has even poorer prospects on the outside than he did before he came in; furthermore, by the time he is ready to be discharged he is likely to have learned the ropes in the hospital and have worked himself up to a desirable position in the "ward system."

The other patient action that is rationalized in terms of the medical model is that of sudden alteration in propriety of conduct. Since the current conduct of the patient is supposed to be a profound reflection or sign of his personality organization—his psychic system—any sudden, apparently unprovoked, alteration in either a "healthy" or a "sick" direction must somehow be accounted for. Sudden changes for the worse are sometimes called relapses or regressions. Sudden changes for the better are sometimes called spontaneous remissions. Through the power of these words the staff can claim that, although they may not know what caused the change, the change can be handled within the medical perspective. Of course, this interpretation of the situation precludes one's employing a social perspective. In what is called sudden regression, the new conduct may involve no more or less illness or health than any other alignment to life; and what is accepted as spontaneous remission may be a result of the patient's not having been sick in the first place.

I am suggesting that the nature of the patient's nature is redefined so that, in effect if not by intention, the patient becomes the kind of object upon which a psychiatric service can be performed. To be made a patient is to be remade into a serviceable object, the irony being that so little service is available once this is done. And the great shortage of psychiatric staff can be seen as created not by the number of ill persons but by the institutional machinery that brings to this area the service definition of the situation.

I want now, finally, to consider the definitions that the staff maintain regarding the nature, not of the patient, but of the hospital's action upon the patient. Since the staff possess the voice of the institution, it is through these definitions that the administrative and disciplinary machinery of the hospital is presented to the patient and to the public. In brief, we find that the facts of ward management and the dynamics of the ward system are expressed in the language of psychiatric medical service.

The patient's presence in the hospital is taken as *prima facie* evidence that he is mentally ill, since the hospitalization of these persons is what the institution is for. A very common answer to a patient who claims he is sane is the statement: "If you aren't sick, you wouldn't be in the hospital." The hospital itself, apart from the therapeutic services administered by its trained staff, is said to provide a sense of security for the patient (sometimes only to be obtained by knowing that the door is locked)[17] and a release from daily responsibilities. Both of these provisions are said to be therapeutic. (Whether therapeutic or not, it is difficult to find environments which introduce more profound insecurities; and what responsibilities are lifted are removed at a very considerable and very permanent price.)

Other translations can be mentioned. Regimentation may be defined as a framework of therapeutic regularity designed to allay insecurity; forced social mixing with a multitude of heterogeneous, displeased fellow inmates may be described as an opportunity to learn that there are others who are worse off. Sleeping dormitories are called wards, this being affirmed by some of the physical equipment, notably the beds, which are purchased through hospital suppliers. The punishment of being sent to a worse ward is described as transferring a patient to a ward whose arrangements he can cope with, and the isolation cell or "hole" is described as a place where the patient will be able to feel comfortable with his inability to handle his acting-out impulses (Belknap, 1956, p. 191). Making a ward quiet at night through the forced taking of drugs, which permits reduced night staffing, is called medication or sedative treatment. Women long since unable to perform such routine medical tasks as taking bloods are called nurses and wear nursing uniforms; men trained as general practitioners are called psychiatrists. Work assignments are defined as industrial therapy or as a means through which the patient can express his reawakened capacity for assuming civil duties. Reward for good behavior by progressively increasing rights to attend socials may be described as psychiatric control over the dosage and timing of social exposure. Patients housed where treatment is first given are said to be in the "acute" service; those who fail to leave after the initial cycle of medical action are moved to what is called the "chronic service" or, more recently, "continued treatment wards"; those ready to leave are housed in a "convalescent ward." Finally, discharge itself, which at the end of a year tends to be granted to most first admissions, averagely cooperative patients or to any other patient for whom kinfolk exert pressure, is often taken as evidence that "improvement" has occurred, and this improvement is tacitly imputed to the workings of the institution. (Among the reasons for discharge of a particular patient may be ward population pressure, spontaneous remission, or the social conformity instilled in him by the disciplinary power of the ward system.) Even the concise phrases, "discharged as cured" or "discharged as improved," imply that the hospital had a hand in the curing or improving. (At the same time, failure to be discharged tends to be attributed to the difficulty of

---

[17] Of the more than hundred patients I knew in the hospital I studied, one did allow that he felt too anxious to go more than a block or so from his ward. I knew, or knew of, no patient who preferred a locked ward, except patients described by staff.

treating mental disorder and to the stubbornness and profundity of this kind of illness, thus affirming the medical model even in the face of not being able to do anything for the patient.) In fact, of course, a high rate of discharge might just as well be taken as evidence of the improper functioning of the hospital, for since little actual treatment is available, the improvement of the patient occurs in spite of hospitalization, and presumably might occur more frequently in circumstances other than the deprived ones within the institution.

Some of the verbal translations found in mental hospitals represent not so much medical terms for disciplinary practices as a disciplinary use of medical practices. Here the lore of state mental hospitals contains some exemplary tales for sociologists. In some mental hospitals, it has been said, one way of dealing with female patients who became pregnant on the hospital grounds was to perform hysterectomies. Less common, perhaps, was the way of dealing with those patients, sometimes called "biters," who continued to bite persons around them: total extraction of teeth. The first of these medical acts was sometimes called "treatment for sexual promiscuity," the second, "treatment for biting." Another example is the fashion, now sharply declining in American hospitals, of using lobotomy for a hospital's most incorrigible and troublesome patients.[18] The use of electroshock, on the attendant's recommendation, as a means of threatening inmates into discipline and quietening those that won't be threatened, provides a somewhat milder but more widespread example of the same process (Belknap, 1956, p. 192). In all of these cases, the medical action is presented to the patient and his relatives as an individual service, but what is being serviced here is the institution, the specification of the action fitting in to what will reduce the administrator's management problems. In brief, under the guise of the medical-service model the practice of maintenance medicine is sometimes to be found.

8 / A Sociopsychological Conception of the Patient

Daniel J. Levinson / Eugene B. Gallagher

What, then, is a hospitalized patient? As we have seen, this is by no means a simple question, although simple answers have often been given. We have pointed to various characteristics that can be used in forming a more embracing, systematic conception of the mental hospital patient.

There is, first, the fact that he is defined, psychiatrically and legally, as having a *serious mental illness*. He enters the mental hospital voluntarily or, more often,

Abridged from Chapter 3 of *Patienthood in the Mental Hospital* by Daniel J. Levinson and Eugene B. Gallagher. Copyright © 1964. (Boston: Houghton Mifflin Company, 1964). Reprinted by permission of the authors and Houghton Mifflin Company.

[18] I have been told of manic mental patients who were tubercular and for whom lobotomy was prescribed lest their hyperactivity kill them. This is a decision that does involve the personal service, not the maintenance, function of medicine. It may be repeated that the act itself is not the determining issue but rather the organizational context in which it is recommended.

through legal commitment, for the official purpose of having his illness treated. From this point of view he is a patient in the classic medical sense—a *client* receiving the professional services of a physician. However, unlike the autonomous client who has relatively great freedom to choose, and to change, his source of professional help, the mental patient becomes a resident within the professional organization. The client thus becomes a *client-member*, an *inmate* of a community that not only offers specific services but also makes manifold claims upon him. His membership in the hospital involves a distinctive "contract" (Durkheim, 1957; Parsons, 1957; Bidwell and Vreeland, 1963) that defines his rights and his obligations in relation to hospital authority.

Thus, in the most fundamental sense the term "hospitalized patient" refers to a category of membership, a position in the organization structure of the mental hospital.[1] Persons who occupy this position may be thought of in various ways, by others and by themselves. Several images and meanings may co-exist as features of a single, multifaceted conception of "the patient." There is a *medical model* of the patient as the carrier of a specific disease (an inner pathological process) which will hopefully be controlled or extirpated by a "definitive treatment." As we shall see, the patient who holds this view tends to regard the mental hospital as a variant form of general hospital or sanatorium, and to regard himself as a relatively passive object of medical intervention. Often, mental illness connotes breakdown of moral standards and actual or potential eruption of bizarre, antisocial behavior. In this conception, with its aura of moral deviance, the image of patient is close to that of *criminal* and the hospital is regarded as a quasi-prison serving primarily incarcerative-custodial functions. Again, the patient may be seen as a *student* engaged in various forms of learning. The conception of patient as student underlies some (though not all) forms of psychotherapy, milieu therapy, and rehabilitation programs. The emphasis here may be upon deepened emotional experience and understanding of self and others, upon new ways of coping with external stress, or upon more specific occupational and interpersonal skills.

There are other conceptions which, though less explicit, nonetheless may operate with great force. The patient may regard himself, or may be seen by others, as an inert material being molded, or an empty vessel being filled with new knowledge or new virtues. A commonly held image is that of the rebellious or improperly raised child who needs habit-training designed to eliminate improper behavior and instill greater propriety. Again, he may be conceived of as a neglected child whose prime therapeutic need is for generous doses of tender loving care, or as a confused, misinformed child in need of good advice and counsel.

A basic dimension along which these conceptions vary is in the degree to which the patient is seen as an active agent in the therapeutic-educative process. At one extreme is the view of the patient as a passive object of manipulation. Here, the

---

[1] Our present concern is restricted to the patient in the mental hospital. The concept of "patient" applies more broadly to anyone who is in some sense the recipient of "treatment" by a physician and others in the "health/illness" professions. At a more symbolic, psychological level, the term "patient" refers to anyone who *regards himself* as ill (disturbed, defective) and who engages in efforts at self-change. For a sociopsychological analysis of patienthood in this most personal form, see Erikson's study of Martin Luther (1958).

staff are regarded as working *on* patients; by means of specific treatment technologies, they produce change in patients much as a repairman fixes a machine. At the other extreme is the view of the patient as a participant being variously influenced and guided but still having an active, self-generated, responsible part. The therapeutic-educative enterprise is, from this perspective, a collaboration between patient and staff. The patient is *both an agent and an object of change.* The work of inducing change belongs above all to the patient himself. His primary task is analogous to that of the production worker in industry. The latter transforms raw materials into socially useful products. The patient's raw materials are his own personality. His task is to transform himself toward greater fulfillment of personal and societal values. From this point of view, the task of hospital staff is analogous to that of management in industry in creating conditions under which production workers can most effectively carry out their work. (Of course, if the joint efforts of patient and staff are to be truly collaborative, the direction of change must be, in part at least, a fulfillment of the patient's values, and not determined unilaterally by staff.) The main work of the patient is to engage in a process of self-healing and self-generated change. His work is in various ways and degrees facilitated or hindered by the patient himself, by staff, by other patients, and by the character of the hospital system.

Between these two extremes there are of course many intermediate steps and qualitative variations. Numerous conceptions of the patient are to be found among patients and staff in every hospital and in the outside society. In the hospital under study here, the prevailing staff orientation is relatively toward the image of the patient as active agent working collaboratively toward self-change. There are variations in orientation among individual staff members; each staff member has a repertory of conceptions including less conscious ones that may be at variance with those that are more conscious and value-syntonic. There are even wider variations among the patients, as will be shown.

Our purpose here is not to promulgate any single image of "the patient" or of the ideal staff-patient relationship. We wish, rather, to develop a theoretical framework for analysis of the patient's encounter with the hospital. In this framework, we seek to take account of the many images actually held by the persons involved. The individual patient's conceptions of himself-as-patient, and of other patients, have an important influence upon his aims and adaptations in the hospital. And the conceptions held by other patients, by staff, and by significant other persons are an important part of his psychosocial environment.

Our approach stems from a version of role theory in which "role" is used as a linking concept between "personality" and "social structure" (Levinson, 1959). The study of patienthood has been greatly neglected. Clinical investigators tend to focus narrowly on the patient's inner dynamics, especially on his psychopathology, whereas social scientists deal largely with the structure of the hospital milieu and do not take the patient as the analytic reference point. The mode of analysis presented here takes as its starting point the patient as a member of the hospital world, as an occupant of a defined position within its structure. The patient's life course in the hospital can then be seen as the progressive formation and enacting of a social role. The concept of role leads concurrently in two directions. On the one hand, it requires consideration of the opportunities and demands confronting those who occupy this social position. We refer here to role in its sociocultural sense as something external to the individual patient—a set of expectations, norms, and social influences inducing the patient to think, feel, and act in particular ways. On the other hand, role has an intrapersonal aspect: ultimately, it is the patient himself who evolves his role-definition, and he does so on the basis not only of external pressures but also of inner wishes, preferences, and conceptions. In short, a role has both *sociocultural* and *psychodynamic* aspects, and a genuine socialpsychological theory must encompass both.

Our point of departure is to regard the patient as having an organizational role and career. As in the case of other roles, such as student, aide, or executive, we ask, first, what kind of "work" it entails. What are the major tasks confronting patients in the mental hospital? These tasks are not to be defined merely as the learning of a series of required behaviors, concretely specified items in a job description. Rather, the primary tasks are to achieve viable modes of adaptation to *problematic role-issues* confronting every patient. We conceive of adaptation broadly to include the entire spectrum of conformity, deviance, innovation, withdrawal, and overt departure from the system. One may adapt by conforming to the norms of this group or that (multiple norm-systems are usually available), by seeking openly or surreptitiously to avoid the tasks and to sabotage the organizational goals involved, by efforts to redefine the tasks or the prevailing modes of dealing with them, and so on. We will come shortly to the problem of adaptation; our first concern is with the nature of the role-issues. Systematic analysis of these issues, and of the tasks they present, is one of the most difficult and most neglected problems in the study of organizational life.

We have already alluded to one major role-issue confronting the mental hospital patient—how to work toward recovery, to utilize hospital resources so he can again take his place in the outside society. This issue is, so to say, a "given," an existential reality of patienthood. Its roots lie deep both in the individual patient and in the hospital as a social organization. The sources in the patient have to do with his suffering and motivation to lead a happier or less troubled life. To the extent that the entering patient has experienced serious life difficulties, he asks of himself and the hospital, "What is the way to recovery; what can be done to facilitate my improvement?" The sources in the mental hospital stem from its commitment to society: it has a formal obligation to foster the recovery of its patients, and every patient, whatever his motivation, takes on a contractual obligation to work toward this end. There are of course wide variations in the salience of this issue. At the one extreme is the patient who voluntarily enters an "active treatment" hospital seeking inner change; in this case, "working toward recovery" is a major and valued concern of both patient and hospital. At the other extreme is the "chronic" patient in the large custodial institution. Here, both individual motivation and institutional commitment toward therapeutic-educative goals may be minimal and other role-issues assume greater prominence. The focal concerns may center much more on just "getting discharged" or on "making out" in the hospital than on "getting better."

The task of working toward recovery, though an existential given, is at the same time problematic, again for reasons involving both patient and hospital. The patient, despite his suffering, may have a vested interest in maintaining those forms of behavior that cause him and others the most difficulty. They may yield important "secondary gains." He may externalize totally the reasons for the troubles that led to his hospitalization, and thus feel no desire or obligation to work at self-change. The hospital, the staff, or the treatments offered may frighten and repel him to such a degree that he cannot regard them as resources to be used in his own behalf. Conversely, his situation in the hospital may be so gratifying (for infantile and pathological, as well as realistic reasons) that his energies are devoted more toward remaining than working for discharge to a less supportive environment. For many patients, then, this role-issue has an intense, and mixed, emotional charge.

Facilitating the patient's work toward recovery is problematic for the hospital also. Scarcity of personnel and materiel often leads to a concentration of the limited therapeutic resources in a few services. On the so-called "back wards," which house the great bulk of the patient population, therapeutic aims are secondary or entirely lacking. But the situation is complicated even when staff have the commitment and available means to pursue therapeutic goals. The efficacy of the various treatment techniques is by no means clearly established, and the choice of therapeutic intervention in any given case is itself problematic. Staff differences in treatment ideology or in preferred ways of handling a given patient may lead to rivalries and struggles in which the patient is the ultimate loser (Stanton and Schwartz, 1954). The rigidly hierarchical structure, the prison-like atmosphere, and the sheer material deprivation in many hospitals operate to counteract the therapeutic value of treatments they provide. It is ironic indeed that hospitals should, in the name of treatment, so often create a life situation that is essentially pathogenic.

More optimal conditions—in which patients are ready and able to work toward recovery, and in which the hospital plays an effective part in facilitating progress —can be brought about only to the extent that difficulties such as those mentioned above are acknowledged and resolved. Even at best, the issue remains problematic: contradictions in the patient and in his (hospital and societal) environment present continuing challenges that cannot be automatically handled by standardized procedures and institutional arrangements; they are the necessity that recurrently mothers individual inventiveness and collective negotiation.[2]

"What is the way to recovery?" is perhaps the most obvious role-issue confronting patients, the one most emphasized by professional staff, but it is certainly not the only one and is often not the most salient one. What are the other role-issues of patienthood, the fundamental tasks on which patients must work?

In an earlier study based chiefly upon naturalistic methods on field research, Pine and Levinson (1961) formulated five problematic issues in addition to the one above. The issues are:

(a) To develop a conception of self which gives meaning to the fact that one is, in an unavoidable public sense, a "mentally ill" person.

[2] Our thinking about the concept of problematic role-issues has been strongly influenced by Erikson's (1959) concept of psychosocial stages and tasks in human development. In his view, every stage in ego development can be represented in terms of a polarity such as trust-mistrust or generativity-despair. Each polarity constitutes, as it were, a developmental issue with which the person must come to terms. These issues are existential givens, and are intrinsically problematic, for reasons having to do both with the inner nature of man and with the nature of his sociocultural world.

(b) To orient oneself in the hospital community and come to terms with communal expectations and values regarding the position of patient.

(c) To adapt to the administrative decisions made by staff, particularly by doctors, about his case.

(d) To develop viable relationships with other patients.

(e) To reconcile the antithesis between security and freedom as it appears in each new stage of hospitalization.

This study is in part an outgrowth of the earlier work. Using somewhat different methods, we seek here to contribute further to the analysis of role-issues and modes of adaptation. The problematic role-issues are "constants" of patienthood— existential givens stemming both from the nature and purposes of the mental hospital and from universal human proclivities in patients. Every issue presents a task and a challenge to a patient; he must adapt to it in some way, if only to avoid it or to deny its existence. But if the role-issues are common, individual patients differ in their modes of adaptation. They differ, that is, in *personal role-definition* (Levinson, 1959). We employ this term because of its combined social-psychological relevance. It suggests that adaptation is, so to say, an individual achievement, and at the same time it requires consideration of the external influences (social pressures, norms, facilities) impinging upon the patient.

It is well to distinguish two aspects of role-definition. First, an ideational aspect, or *role-conception:* the patient adapts in part by forming a relatively conscious system of ideas (beliefs, values, attitudes, and an encompassing rationale) regarding the nature of the task and his preferred ways of dealing with it. His role-conception is his inner answer to the crucial questions (role-issues) of patienthood. Second, role-definition has a conative aspect, *role-performance:* the patient adapts also by engaging in overt behavioral strivings to fulfill, to avoid, or to redefine the tasks confronting him. The degree of correspondence between behavioral adaptation and inner conviction is variable; various factors in the situation and in the patient's personality may lead him to behave in ways that violate his inner values and preferences. Both aspects of role-definition have important affective and motivational components. In short, an individual's role-definition is a more or less (but never fully) integrated pattern of wanting, feeling, thinking, valuing, acting. To see it as comprised solely of norms, or of motives, or of actions, is unduly restricting.

What are the *determinants of role-definition?* They are to be sought both in the sociocultural character of the environment and in the patient himself. The patient is subject to powerful steering forces from the hospital community. The ward staff, the patient peer group, the administration, and other groups exert heavy role-demands upon him, indicating in ways gross and subtle how they expect "a good patient" to think, feel, and act. He is influenced by the emotional climate of the hospital and by the opportunities it provides for recreation, employment, and personal relationships. Patients in a small, affluent, psychotherapeutically oriented hospital are likely to differ in role-definition from those in a larger, poorer, and more custodial hospital.

The patient may be strongly influenced by the presence—or absence—of significant persons and groups outside the hospital. It matters whether the hospital is encapsulated from or open to the surrounding community (Greenblatt, Levinson, and Klerman, 1961; Pratt *et al.*, 1960). An important feature of patienthood in a highly segregated hospital is a sense of distance and alienation from family, friends, and work. Many patients remain in hospitals long after they are deemed clinically ready for discharge because they lack, or have been cut off from, essential social ties in society. When a patient has meaningful contact with persons in "the normal community" during his hospitalization, these persons may play a crucial part in his hospital career. Finally, he responds to the hospital in part by comparing it to the sociocultural settings (class, neighborhood, ethnic group, place of work, educational context) with which he has been familiar or to which he aspires. Thus the hospital does not operate as a monolithic, private world; outside social forces exert an influence, direct as well as symbolic, upon the patient's evolving role-definition.

While keeping in mind the importance of external demands and opportunities, we must also consider intrapersonal determinants within the patient himself. Patients differ widely, even within a single hospital, in their conceptions of patienthood and in the uses they make of it. The newly entered patient is not a *tabula rasa*. Many elements of his role-definition have already been formed. He has some conception of what mental hospitals are like, and of the varieties and causes of "mental illness." Certain kinds of treatment have meaning and value for him, while others seem frightening, inappropriate, or simply ridiculous. Some patients characteristically work on their problems by talking, others by acting. The variations in role-definition and related personality features are linked in part to class, education, religion, and ethnic background (see, among many others, Hollingshead and Redlich, 1958; Frank, 1961; Gallagher *et al.*, 1957; Miller and Swanson, 1960). When we say that a feature of personal role-definition is class-linked, we mean that, as a result of experience gained in a particular class context, the individual has developed relatively enduring personal characteristics that are reflected in his response to patienthood. The individual's class and other memberships provide significant contextual influences upon the formation of his orientation toward mental illness and patienthood. At the same time, there are individual differences within each class that lead us to investigate the relevance of more specific determinants.

The intrapersonal determinants of role-definition have their sources in various aspects and levels of personality. In studying them we take a *personological* perspective: we regard role-definition as an aspect of personality and inquire into its relation to other aspects. A brief comment will suffice here. A role-definition involves modes of thought, feeling, and behavior within a particular social context, in this case, the mental hospital. These modes of adaptation are, in part, specific to the present situation. However, the patient's role-conception and his behavioral strivings within this situation are influenced by relatively enduring features of his personality. These personality features have origins earlier in his development (including childhood as well as other periods) and gain expression in various sectors of his adult life. The more enduring, role-relevant dispositions include his core values and moral conceptions (some conscious, others partly or entirely unconscious), various elements of his ego-identity, his character traits, his unconscious wishes, fantasies, and anxieties, and the modes of defense by which they are warded off, and so on. In short, the patient's role-definition is influenced, in varying degrees, by the personality matrix within which it develops. Patients differing in personality will be differentially receptive to the multiple resources and requirements of the hospital. Thus part of our research task is to determine the nature of the *role-relevant personality dispositions* and the ways in which they influence the patient's evolving role.

Within the recently emerging interest in ego theory and dynamic social psychology, psychoanalytically oriented investigators have emphasized the need for systematic study of the ego's adaptive functions (Hartmann, 1958; Erikson, 1959; White, 1959; Rapaport, 1960). Despite the considerable interest, very little progress has yet been made. Psychoanalytically oriented clinicians tend to focus predominantly on the patient's "disorder" and to regard it largely as a derivative of unconscious processes. Progress in the development of ego theory and of dynamic social psychology will be greatly facilitated, we believe, by more focal consideration of the individual's engagement with his sociocultural environment. We must move, so to say, from the psychopathology of disease, or even the "psychopathology of everyday life," to the psychodynamics of social adaptation in the broadest sense. To do so will require a more complex and informed view both of the ego and of social reality.

Our position, then, is that the patient's role-definition is not simply taken in, swallowed whole from the environing matrix. Nor is it, on the other hand, a simple derivative or epiphenomenon produced autochthonously by unconscious conflicts and defenses. It is to be seen, rather, as a personal achievement, something the person fashions for himself in response to both external and intrapsychic influences.

9 / On Psychological Well-Being

Norman M. Bradburn

Psychological Well-Being as a Dependent Variable

If we abandon a global concept of mental health, how are we to proceed in finding a dependent variable? Let us adopt the viewpoint of a naive observer and look at ordinary individuals going about the business of conducting their lives in the best way they can. We notice several things. First, some people seem to have an easy time of it, while others have much greater difficulty in accomplishing those things they want to do in life. By difficulties, we mean a whole host of things—that they actually fail to get what they want; that in the pursuit of their goals, they cause trouble or pain to others; that they suffer from feelings of failure, unhappiness, worry, and even unpleasant physical symptoms.

Secondly, we note that almost everybody has periods in his life when he has difficulties with some or many parts of his life. We also note that there is a considerable variation among individuals, both in the degree and the duration of

Abridged from Chapter 1 of *The Structure of Psychological Well-Being* by Norman M. Bradburn. Copyright © 1969. (Chicago: Aldine Publishing Company, 1969). Reprinted by permission of the author, NORC, and Aldine Publishing Company.

these difficulties. Thus some individuals go through short periods of relatively minor difficulties, while others seem to be in trouble all the time, or at least for large periods of their lives.

Thirdly, and perhaps not quite as obviously as the previous observations, we note that these variations in intensity and duration of difficulties do not appear to be randomly distributed through society but are found to differing degrees in various groups of society. General observation, in this case supported by good empirical evidence, suggests that those whose lives are in an objective sense more difficult, such as those with marginal job skills, poor education, poor health, etc., are also to a considerable degree those who have the most difficulties in coping with life situations. Thus, we would expect to find that the experiencing of difficulties in life is not purely a function of the characteristics of the individual, but is also influenced by the characteristics of the environment in which he finds himself.

These general observations lead to some important research questions. First, how do you operationalize the concept of "difficulties in living" so that one can array individuals along some sort of dimension of intensity and investigate variations across individuals and over time? Thus, the first order of business would appear to be the development of a series of measures of the degree to which people have difficulties in life problems. Ideally, such measures would use techniques that are applicable to a large population, and can be administered by individuals with a moderate amount of training in order that studies can be conducted which involve a wide range of individuals and life situations, yet still be economically feasible.

Once such measures have been developed, some of the observations mentioned above can be studied systematically. In particular, we would be interested in differences between transitory difficulties in living which beset individuals in the ordinary course of their lives, and the more long-term problems which have been the focus of attention by those who have been primarily concerned with clinical populations. Here the type of model suggested by the Dohrenwends (1965) appears to be most appropriate. They stress the importance of differentiating between difficulties that are consequences of environmental stress, either short-term or long-term, and what might more properly be called psychological disorders in which individual reactions persist after removal of the stressful conditions or are out of proportion to the magnitude of the stress. The development of a set of operations for measuring difficulties in living and the consistent application of such measures in the framework of a distinction between responses to environmental stress and psychological disorders should lead to a series of studies in which we gain a greater understanding of the interplay between environmental factors and personality dispositions in the determination of living problems.

We noted above that the notion of difficulties in living had many meanings. How then are we to choose the most fruitful dependent variables? There are no clear-cut criteria for choosing which dependent variable is going to have the greatest payoff. Indeed, much of the art of scientific investigation lies in the choice of the variables to study, and the difference between success and failure appears to lie more in the realm of intuition and luck than in scientific competence. When one looks at the various meanings attributed to the notion of difficulties in living, one particular variable, both on a common sense basis and for historical reasons, stands out as being of primary importance—that is happiness or a sense of psychological well-being. Certainly discussions of human happiness, both concerning the best means for achieving it and whether or not it is a proper goal of human activity, have been frequent throughout history. It has not, however, played much of a part as a psychological variable in modern research. The reason for this neglect, I believe, lies largely in the influence of Freudian theory which has made psychologists particularly distrustful of self-reports of subjective feelings and sensitive to the distorting influence of defense mechanisms. The general feeling seems to be that excessive defensiveness on the one hand, or excessive self-criticalness on the other, would work to make self-reports of happiness devoid of interest as a research variable.

The neglect of happiness as a research variable may be a case of throwing out the baby with the bathwater. Wilson (1967) in reviewing the scattered literature shows that there is solid evidence that self-reports of happiness do measure something more than individual defensiveness or self-criticalness and that valid and reliable measures can be constructed. Gurin, Veroff, and Feld (1960) in a nationwide sample survey showed that self-ratings of happiness could be used meaningfully to measure levels of subjective adjustment, as well as showing how happiness ratings were related to other measures of life problems. Although the literature is not extensive, it is certainly more than encouraging that a dimension of happiness would be a rewarding place to focus attention.

Although the studies that have focused on happiness have agreed that it is possible to measure the variable reliably, there has not been agreement on its conceptual status. Specifically, there has been no agreement on whether it is an unidimensional variable or whether it is composed of several dimensions. In order for happiness to be a fruitful dependent variable in research, a conceptual framework will have to be developed which will account for some of the divergent findings and provide a model that identifies the major independent variables that influence happiness and specifies their interrelationships. Only if research is guided by some such overall theoretical framework can studies build on one another and our knowledge of the phenomenon of psychological well-being be placed on a firmer foundation.

A Theory of Psychological Well-Being

A conceptual scheme which shows promise of providing the type of orientation needed for empirical research has emerged from a pilot study that attempted to develop operational measures for problems in living (Bradburn and Caplovitz, 1964). This framework takes as its fundamental dependent variable avowed happiness or the feeling of psychological well-being. A person's position on the dimension of psychological well-being is seen as a resultant of the individual's position on two independent dimensions—one of positive affect and the other of negative affect. The model specifies that an individual will be high in psychological well-being, the degree to which there is an excess of positive over negative affect, and will be low in well-being, the degree to which negative affect predominates over positive. Thus, in many respects, the model is similar to older pleasure-pain models or utility models which view an individual's happiness or well-being in terms of the degree to which pleasure predominates over pain in his life experiences.

This particular model stems from a solid empirical base. In the pilot study mentioned above (Bradburn and Caplovitz, 1964), a cross-section of the population of four small towns was asked whether they had experienced any of several feeling states during the past week. For example, respondents were asked whether during the past week they had felt "on top of the world," "lonely or remote from other people," "bored," or "particularly excited or interested in something." The analysis of the responses indicated that individuals varied along two dimensions—one indicative of positive affect and the other indicative of negative affect. Further, it was clear that these two dimensions were independent of one another so that it was impossible to predict an individual's score on the negative dimension from any knowledge of his score on the positive affect dimension and vice versa. On the other hand, both dimensions were related in the expected direction to overall self-ratings of happiness or subjective well-being. The best predictor of the overall self-rating was the discrepancy between the two scores—the greater the excess of positive over negative affect, the higher the overall rating of psychological well-being. The independence of these two dimensions and the fact that the discrepancy score is the best predictor of overall self-ratings of well-being have been verified by further research on independent samples (Bradburn, 1969).

The fact that the discrepancy between positive and negative affect should be the best predictor of overall happiness is, of course, no departure from the usual pleasure-pain models. Where this particular model differs from the more traditional ones lies in a further finding. Analysis of the data from the pilot study, as well as from subsequent studies, indicated that not only were variations in positive and negative affect independent from one another, but that on the whole the two dimensions were correlated with different things. In the most general terms, it was found that those things which were related to the presence or absence of positive affect had no relationship to the presence or absence of negative affect, while those things which were related to the presence or absence of negative affect had no relationship to the variations in a person's position on the positive affect dimension.

Such a model, when fully developed, will add greatly to our understanding of the dynamics of psychological well-being. It suggests, on the one hand, that there are a series of forces whose presence is related to the presence of positive affect, but whose absence merely results in a lowering or absence of positive affect rather than any change in negative affect. On the other hand, there are also a series of different circumstances which contribute to the presence or absence of negative affect but which have no influence on a person's positive affect. Since an individual's overall sense of well-being is dependent on the relative balance of the two forces, we must look at those sets of forces contributing to positive affect as well as those contributing to negative affect in order to understand an individual's position along the resultant dimension of well-being.

A hypothetical example may make the implications of this model clearer. We hypothesize that if a man has an argument with his wife, he is likely to experience an increase in negative affect, but that he will not experience a decrease in his level of positive affect. If he does not have an argument with his wife, he will not experience the negative affect, but also he will not be likely to increase his positive affect. On the other hand, if he takes his wife out to dinner or to a movie, he is likely to experience an increase in positive affect, but no change in his level of negative affect. If he does not take his wife out, he will not experience the positive affect, but also he will not suffer any increase in negative affect. Similarly, if he takes his wife out but they have an argument over where they are to go, he is likely to experience an increase in both positive and negative affect. Depending on the relative severity of the argument compared with the enjoyment of the night out, the net result of such an evening might be to increase, decrease, or leave unchanged his overall sense of well-being.

Thus, knowing that a man argued frequently with his wife would not give us too much information about his overall sense of well-being (or his marital happiness, for that matter) unless we could combine this information with data on the frequency of experiences that are related to the experiencing of positive affect. Putting the two bits of information together, we would be in a better position to predict the individual's level of psychological well-being.

It should be noted here that data on the number of arguments between spouses and other experiences related to negative affect would be a good predictor of well-being if there were a strong negative correlation between things like arguments that are related to negative affect and things like going out with one's wife, which is related to positive affect. The assumption of such a negative correlation is, I believe, one of the principal reasons why most of the traditional investigations of "mental illness," which involve cases in which there is a strong predominance of negative over positive affect, have focused exclusively on this one dimension. The evidence to date, however, indicates that in fact no such negative correlation exists, at least not in the population at large. On the contrary, the correlation between the two types of experiences is nearly zero.

The model proposed here for the understanding of psychological well-being is similar to one proposed by Herzberg, Mausner, and Snyderman (1959) for work satisfaction. In their study of the determinants of work satisfaction they noted that there was a group of factors that played a role as "dissatisfiers," and another group that played a role as "satisfiers." The presence of such things as low pay, poor work conditions, and disagreements with the boss led to job dissatisfaction, but the absence of these factors did not lead to job satisfaction. Similarly, the presence of such things as challenging work, chances for self-development, and job responsibility led to job satisfaction, but their absence was not associated with job dissatisfaction. Unfortunately, data on the correlation between "satisfiers" and "dissatisfiers" was not given, but we would suspect that there would be substantial independence between the two groups.

If these two dimensions of positive and negative affect are independent of each other and related to different things, can we specify what the factors are that do influence them? While detailed knowledge of cause and effect relationships are still not worked out, certain broad outlines are reasonably clear. Negative affect appears to be related primarily to the variables that have been dealt with by the traditional "mental illness" approaches. Specifically, variations in negative affect are associated with difficulty in role adjustment such as marital problems, work dissatisfaction, and interpersonal tensions, as well as some of the more standard indicators of anxiety and worry. None of these factors, however, appears to be related to positive affect. On the other hand, positive affect appears to be related to a series of factors having to do with the degree to which one is involved in the environment around him, social contact, and active interest in the world. These factors include such things as the degree of social participation reflected in variations in organizational membership, number of friends, frequency of interaction with friends and relatives, degree of sociability and companionship with one's spouse, and exposures to life situations that introduce a degree of variability into one's life experiences. The importance of varied experience for positive affect has been noted in many different types of studies (see especially Fiske and Maddi, 1961), although the implications of much of this research has not been specifically incorporated into a general theory of psychological well-being. Recent evidence (Bradburn, 1969) indicates that variability of experience is, in fact, an important element in influencing a person's level of positive affect.

The basic model of psychological well-being as a function of the resultant of two independent dimensions of positive and negative affect, each of which is determined by an independent set of causal factors, have some interesting implications for our general understanding of some of the naive observations mentioned above. If an overall sense of well-being is viewed as a resultant of forces acting along two independent dimensions, then the effect of a particular difficulty in life on the sense of well-being will not be immediately clear. If the effect of this particular difficulty is to increase negative affect, then, other things being equal, there would be a diminution in well-being. At the same time, however, there could be an increase in factors that would increase positive affect and offset the change in negative affect, producing either no change in well-being or, if the change in positive affect were sufficiently large, even increasing the sense of well-being.

To take our example again. Evidence from the pilot study (Bradburn and Caplovitz, 1964) indicated that tensions in marriage were strongly related to negative affect. Other things being equal, an increase in marital tensions would be expected to be associated with an increase in negative affect and a concomitant decrease in overall happiness. Several other things, however, may be at work which will complicate this simple model. First, there is no telling from the change in marital tensions and change in negative affect what might be going on with the factors within or outside the marriage related to positive affect. If they should remain the same, then the simple model would be appropriate. If, however, there should be some sort of offsetting or compensating factor, such as an increase in sociability or in new experiences, we might expect an increase in positive affect which would tend to cancel out the effect of the increase in negative affect and result in no change in overall sense of well-being. The fact that there are two independent dimensions then might well help us explain the differential effect of what appears to be equal amounts of stress on different individuals. If the stress works towards changing the levels of negative affect, its total impact on well-being would be a differential function of the individual's level of positive affect. Since life is an ongoing dynamic process, we would expect that factors affecting both positive and negative experiences are continually changing and that one's sense of well-being at any particular time might be thought of as a running average of the relative strength of positive and negative affect averaged out over the recent past. Whenever we do research, we abstract from the ongoing process in an attempt to get measures of particular situations that are related to positive and negative affect, even though these do considerable violence to the richness of human life. When, as is so often the case in social sciences, our measuring instruments are rather crude, we expect a great deal of error and a considerable amount of misclassification. If our model is correct, however, we should on the whole be able to show some significant effects.

The model described here would also lead us to expect some of the group differences mentioned above. One of the well-established findings in social sciences is that those of lower education and income are less likely to be involved in the environment about them and in general lead more restricted lives. Since environmental participation and variability appear to be highly related to the presence of positive affect, we would expect that, other things being equal, there would be less positive affect among lower socioeconomic groups. There is empirical evidence that this is the case. Thus, even if there were no differential distribution of interpersonal problems of the sort that are related to negative affect, we would expect that, on the whole, there would be a lower sense of well-being among lower socioeconomic groups than among higher socioeconomic groups. If in addition there is a differential in terms of the difficulties in role adjustments of the sort that are related to negative affect, we would expect an even stronger relationship between socioeconomic status and overall well-being. It is important to note, however, that even without such differential difficulties in coping with problems, we would expect a structural effect on well-being, due to the restriction in environmental variability and social participation that is characteristic of lower socioeconomic groups.

The focusing of attention on psychological well-being as the major dependent variable in the terms of the theoretical conceptions outlined above should make it possible for studies to contribute more to one another. No matter whether one focuses on those interpersonal problems and other factors which are related to negative affect, which appears to be the concern of those who are oriented towards the more traditional problems of mental illness, or towards social participation, sociability, environmental variability, and things which appear to be more related to positive affect and seem to be the concern of those who are oriented towards positive mental health, this conception offers a model which enables each type of study to contribute toward our understanding of the basic phenomenon, which is that of happiness.

10 / "Mental Health" Reconsidered: A Special Case of the Problem of Values in Psychology

M. Brewster Smith

The signs are increasingly clear that "mental health" and its complement, "mental illness," are terms that embarrass psychologists. Many of us do not like them (cf. APA, 1959). Unable to define or to conceptualize them to our satisfaction, we use the terms in spite of ourselves, since they label the goals, however nebulous, of many of our service activities and the auspices of much of our research support. Even when we try to avoid them, we are swept along in the social movement of which they are sibboleths, and our scruples make little difference. Little wonder, then, that we and our colleagues in the other "mental health professions" seek to clear our consciences by continuing to engage in sporadic attempts to give them more precise and explicit meaning.

Having contributed from time to time to this discussion, I feel entitled to some skepticism about where it has got us. True, we have made some gains in disposing of several unprofitable ways of thinking about mental health that used to be prevalent. We have come to see that statistical notions of "normality" are no real help in giving psychological meaning to mental health and illness: they beg the question or fail to come to grips with it. We have become suspicious of the once regnant concept of adjustment, as it has fallen into disrepute at the hands of social critics and moralists (e.g., Riesman, 1950) who see it as a pseudoscientific rationalization for conformist values, and of psychological theorists (e.g., White, 1959) who are challenging the sufficiency of the equilibrium model in which it is rooted. And from many quarters we encounter the call for a more positive view of mental health than is involved in the mere absence of manifest mental disorder. Since the appearance of Jahoda's useful book (1958) that reviewed the considerable array of proposals toward such a conception of optimal human functioning, the flow of suggestions has not abated. The discussion goes on in articles, conferences, and symposia, with little evidence of consensus in the offing.

The various lists of criteria that have been proposed for positive mental health reshuffle overlapping conceptions of desirable functioning without attaining agreement—or giving much promise that agreement can be reached. The inventories repeat themselves, and indeed it is inevitable that they should, since each successor list is proposed by a wise psychologist who scrutinizes previous proposals and introduces variations and emphases to fit his own values and

From the *American Psychologist*, 1961, **16**, 299–306. Copyright © 1961. Reprinted by permission of the author and the American Psychological Association.

Adapted from a paper prepared for the Work Conference on Mental Health–Teacher Education Research Projects, Madison, Wisconsin, November 10–18, 1960. I am indebted to Barbara Biber, Robert Peck, Fred Wilhelms, John Withall, Nicholas Hobbs, Erich Lindemann, Ronald Lippitt, Ralph Ojemann, Hildegard Peplau, Carl Rogers, and the other participants in the conference for their reactions to the earlier version of the paper.—AU.

preferences. Some give greater weight to the cognitive values of accurate perception and self-knowledge (e.g., Jahoda, 1955a); some to moral values, to meaningful commitment, to social responsibility (e.g., Allport, 1960; Shoben, 1957); some to working effectiveness (e.g., Ginsburg, 1955); some to the blander social virtues (e.g., aspects of Foote and Cottrell, 1955); some to zest, exuberance, and creativity (e.g., Maslow, 1954). The terms recur, but in different combinations and with connotations that slant in divergent directions. By way of illustration, Table I gives the six headings under which Jahoda (1958) organized the proposals for mental health criteria that she encountered in her review of the literature, and Allport's most recent proposal (1960), rearranged to bring out correspondences and discrepancies in the two lists. While it is an advance that psychologists are now looking for multiple criteria of good functioning rather than seeking the single touchstone of a unitary definition of mental health, we may well ask: How are psychologists to decide what items belong in such a list? By what warrant may we assign priorities to alternative criteria? Surely we need something closer to *terra firma* on which to build our research, from which to guide our practice.

TABLE I

TWO ILLUSTRATIVE CONCEPTIONS OF POSITIVE MENTAL HEALTH
IN TERMS OF MULTIPLE CRITERIA

Jahoda (1958)	*Allport (1960)*
Attitudes toward the self	Self-objectification
Growth and self-actualization	Ego-extension
Integration	Unifying philosophy of life
Autonomy	
Perception of reality ⎫ Environmental mastery ⎭	Realistic coping skills, abilities, and perceptions
	Warm and deep relation of self to others
	Compassionate regard for all living creatures

Note. Rubrics rearranged to bring out parallels.

There is little to be gained, I think, from adding to these competing lists. Conceptual clarification, on the other hand, may be more profitable, and my attempt in the present essay lies in that direction. Starting from the now prevalent recognition that mental health is an evaluative term, that personal and social values as standards of the preferable are somehow crucially involved in any discourse about mental health, I try first to show that this intrusion of values into psychology, lamented by some, applauded by others, is entirely legitimate. But I question, secondly, whether there is any profit in the argument about which evaluative criteria for appraising human personality and behavior are to be included in a concept of mental health. Rather, I suggest that, at least in the present stage of personality theory, "mental health" should not be regarded as a theoretical concept at all, but as a rubric or chapter heading under which fall a variety of evaluative concerns. I try to show that such a view of the term may help to clear the ground for both practical and theoretical purposes.

In an earlier effort (1959) at clarification in this area, I observed that at the crux of the difficulty of assimilating "mental health" to psychology is the fact that "science has not yet learned how to deal surefootedly with values" (p. 673). Any progress toward clarity in psychological thinking about mental health, I am increasingly convinced, depends on our becoming clearer, as psychologists, about how we are to think about values. Whatever advances we make on the problem of values in this setting should also stand us in good stead in other contexts where issues of value confront psychology. The value problem is worth a close and sustained look.

Why the Search for a Value-Laden Conception of Positive Mental Health?

While evaluative criteria and judgments are involved in the notion of mental disorder, our consensus about what is *undesirable* is close enough for practical purposes that the role of values tends to remain implicit. It is when we want to talk about positive criteria of psychological functioning that we encounter the value problem head-on. A good starting point for the present discussion, then, is to ask why we ever got ourselves into this difficult, intellectually treacherous business of positive mental health. Are not the problems of mental disorder enough? Why should the mental health movement be impelled, as it has been since the days of Clifford Beers (cf. Joint Commission on Mental Illness and Health, 1961), to extend itself to concern with the "mental hygiene" of promoting positive mental health—in the absence of firm knowledge or clear guidelines?

The answer to such a question cannot be simple. But I think a generally critical onlooker from England, R. S. Peters (1960), has hit the essential point when he addressed the BBC audience thus:

> We have a highly specialized society and we are often warned that we are developing not merely two nations but a league of nations without a common culture and shared ideals. This should not surprise us; for where are such unifying ideals to be fostered? The study of literature, history, and the classics has had to be cut down to make room for the vast expansion in scientific education without which our society cannot survive, and the Church is rapidly losing the authority it once had as a source of unifying ideals. We tend to treat the doctor who looks after our bodies and the psychiatrist who advises us about our minds with more respect than we treat the priest who advises us about our souls—if we still think we have one. For they are scientists; and it is scientists who are now coming to be thought of as the repositories of wisdom about the mysteries of life.
>
> This general trend explains why the educationist sometimes inclines his ear towards a new expert, the psychologist, when he is at a loss to find new unifying educational ideals to replace the old religious ones. There is thus much talk in educational circles of "the mental health of the child," "wholeness," "integration," "adjustment," and all that sort of thing. We no longer talk of turning out Christian gentlemen; we talk of letting people develop mental health or mature personalities. Indeed in America Freud's priestly role is much more explicitly acknowledged. . . . Nevertheless the general trend is [also] with us, as is shown in the frequent references to psychological notions such as "mental health" in discussion about educational ideals (p. 46).

Discount the bias of perspective arising from Peters' assured stance in the tradition of British class education, and hold in abeyance reaction to his critical undertones: his point remains that a good many thoughtful people have turned, appropriately or otherwise, to notions of mental health in order to fill a void left by the attrition of traditionally or religiously sanctioned values. There is consumer demand for psychologists to enter the discussion of goals and aspirations for human behavior; but we had better be clear about our warrant for doing so.

The demand for a psychologically informed phrasing of objectives—for conceptions of positive mental health—comes most compellingly from those concerned with the rearing and education of children. The psychologist or psychiatrist who mainly deals with hospitalized psychotics has enough to do in trying to treat severe mental disorder and get his patients to function at some minimally adequate level; since consensus on these objectives is immediately given, the value problem hardly rises to the surface. But responsibility for the raising of children calls for positive criteria against which the success of one's efforts on their behalf can be measured. Perhaps a counselor may appropriately leave it to his adult client to set the goals for his therapy; the case can hardly be extended to the child as ward of teacher and parent—who in turn look to the psychologist for guidance.

Of course there are intellectual positions from which the responsibility appears to be minimized. If you take a Rousseau-like view that regards optimal development as the unfolding of a benign inner potential, you can at least pretend to leave goal setting entirely to the child's own nature. This doctrine of benign potentiality, which is still very much alive in educational and psychological theory (witness Maslow, 1954), strikes me as involving psychological half-truths and philosophical error. It is we ourselves, in terms of our tacit values, who single out, as optimal, one of an infinite set of possible environments for the developing child, and distinguish the way he develops in such an auspicious setting as the actualization of a naturally given potential. We ignore the infinite variety of other developmental trends that he simultaneously has the potential to actualize, many of which we would not think highly of—and ignore the silent and therefore not fully responsible intrusion of our own values involved in distinguishing one class of possible trends as self-actualizing.

Another way of minimizing responsibility for educational goal setting in terms of mental health is to accept as ultimate the values of the culture, to define the function of education as cultural transmission and, in effect, leave matters of value-choice to parents and school boards. The trouble is that this option is no longer really available, even if we prefer it. The state of affairs evoked by Peters is with us: there is no longer such a solid traditional consensus for us to fall back on. Parents and school boards too are confused and involved in the fray. Under these circumstances education can hardly avoid a complex role that combines and balances cultural transmission, on the one hand, and social criticism and reconstruction on the other. This characteristic American philosophy of education has thus become virtually a policy of necessity. It calls for clear-headedness about goals, and has tended to draw on psychology for their formulation.

Insofar as we take the requirements of education seriously, then, we cannot help trying to grapple with conceptions of optimal human functioning. We also need them in planning and assessing programs of counseling and of environmental change. In the face of a waning consensus on traditional values, we join our lay clientele in hoping that psychology can help in this endeavor. But hope does not guarantee success. The strength of our needs may head us the more rigidly down blind alleys, unless we have our wits about us.

The Value Problem

The skeptical reader imbued with the distinction between scientific objectivity, on the one hand, and the humanistic cultivation of values on the other will have balked at an earlier point, and stayed with the question: By what warrant do psychologists assume the right to posit any set of human values, as we do when we propose criteria of positive mental health? The psychologist has no more right to do so, he will say, than anyone else. Let him stick to his last, and recognize the limits of his competence. My serious rejoinder, which requires somewhat of a detour to develop, reverses this conventional view: the psychologist has *as much* right to posit values as anyone else, in some important respects more. It is time to dispel the shopworn bromide that the humanist (or moralist or philosopher) has a corner on pronouncements about values, while the psychologist (or sociologist or scientist generally) must restrict himself to facts. Things are just not that simple.

For most of us, the two sources to which everyone once looked for what were then regarded as "absolute" values—Tradition and Theology—speak only equivocally if at all. We are still suffering from the crisis of personal and social readjustment occasioned by this loss. As we regain our bearings, our nostalgia for the old illusion of Absoluteness, of givenness in the eternal scheme of things, begins to fade. But in spite of the pessimism of those who hunger after Absoluteness, we still have values, in the sense of personal standards of desirability and obligation. We see them, now, as committing choices that people make (often unwittingly) in the interplay of cultural tradition and individual experience. We see them as "relative," yes, but relative not only to culture (an exclusive focus on *cultural* relativism was the mistake of the last generation of anthropologists). They are relative also to human nature—in the diverse varieties of this nature that have emerged in human history with a degree of continuity and cumulativeness —and relative to the opportunities and limitations of human situations. Thus the warrior virtues held validity for the traditional Sioux; for the reservation Sioux they no longer make any sense (MacGregor, 1946). And one can fairly doubt whether the petty competitive values of the Alorese studied by Cora DuBois (1944) ever made much sense: she showed them to be part and parcel of a wretched and demeaning way of life that I doubt whether any Alorese would choose were some magic to give him a wider range of opportunity.

If values are social products, they rest, ultimately, on a personal commitment. Everybody, scientist or humanist or man in the street, has the right to posit values. And, since people in society are interdependent, everyone has a right to try to persuade others to his way of valuing: *de gustibus non disputandum est* may apply to tastes and preferences, but it has never prevented controversy about values, as the course of human history well reveals. We *all* have the right to dispute values, and most of us do it. The humanist and the humane scientist nevertheless have potentially different specialized roles in the argument.

Their roles arise from the peculiar nature of argument about values that follows from the basis of values in an optional personal commitment. If you want to persuade someone to value something as you do, you can follow one of at least two strategies (assuming that physical or social coercion is ruled out, which historically has unfortunately not been the case): You can, first, try to open his eyes to new ways of seeing things—increase the range of possibilities of which he is aware, create the conditions for differentiations and restructurings in his experience from which it is possible (not necessary) that, seeing things like yourself, he may come to value them likewise. Or, second, you can give him evidence that the position he takes on a particular value has consequences for other values to which he is also committed. For the fact that values rest on a personal option does not make them arbitrary in the sense of being detached from cause or consequence. If you show a person that his chosen value of racial purity conflicts with the values of the American Creed that he also embraces, he *may* reconsider it (Myrdal, 1944). Or if you show him that his prejudiced value rests causally on evasive covert tactics of defense against inner weakness, you again have a chance to win out (Adorno, Frenkel-Brunswik, Levinson, and Sanford, 1950). The *ad hominem* argument, in ill favor as it is, is fair play in this peculiar and important realm, so long as it is not taken as conclusive. Since values rest on personal option, *no* argument is conclusive, though many can be persuasive, and appropriately so.

I am thus suggesting that the humanist and the moral philosopher are especially equipped to employ the first of these strategies: drawing on the fund of human history and culture, with its stock of transmitted discriminations, they can sensitize us to differentiations and potentialities of human experience which, unaided, we could never attain individually. Our value choices are enriched and modified by this exposure. The second strategy, that of displaying the causal network in which value choice is embedded, is one for which the humane or behavioral scientist is uniquely qualified.

The old myth had it that man lost his precultural innocence when, biting the fruit of the Tree of Knowledge, he became aware of Good and Evil. In becoming modern, Man has taken a second portentous bite of the same fruit. There are alternative versions of Good and Evil, he discovers to his discomfiture, and it is up to him to choose the commitments he is to live by. From this emerging view that can no longer turn to authoritative interpretations of tradition or divine revelation to resolve questions of value, it makes no sense at all for us to encyst ourselves behind a pass-the-buck notion that we can leave value judgments to some other discipline that specializes in them. There is no discipline that has this mythical competence: the humanist and the theologian speak with no greater authority than we. We are all in it together.

The List Problem

I think I have shown the legitimacy, the clear warrant, for psychologists to concern themselves with values, as we do when we involve ourselves with mental health. But my argument gives no help at all on the other problem: what value dimensions are to get on our lists of mental health criteria, and why? If anything, it makes things more difficult. For if values are matters of a committing personal option, how are psychologists—let alone people at large—to come to agree on any particular list any more closely than the limited extent to which they already do? Even with a richer exposure to the humanistic tradition than is customary for psychologists, even with a far more adequate fund of causal knowledge than is presently available, psychological "experts" are not going to agree on the proper goals for human nature, and these are what we are talking about.

The actual situation is well typified by the experience of the Cornell Conference (National Assembly on Mental Health Education, 1960). To quote the conference report:

> Everyone at Cornell seemed to agree that the good life for all was to be desired. They split, however, on what that good life was—as they had split on the definition of mental health, and they split on who, if anyone, should have the right to try to "impose" it on others (p. 20).

The definition of mental health, of course, *involves* a conception of the good life, which nobody *can* impose on anyone else (barring "brainwashing" and physical coercion), though, at least among colleagues and equals, it is fair enough for each of us to try to persuade the rest.

But the time has come to cut the Gordian knot, to restructure the problem along more profitable lines. The place to cut, I think, is the notion that the lists we have been considering itemize criteria of some entity called "positive mental health," and are equivalent to a definition of it. Even though we may have forsaken the view of mental health as a unitary phenomenon, and may have no intention of adding up a single score across our multiple criteria, we remain beguiled by the assumption that an articulate theoretical concept or construct of mental health lurks somewhere ready to be discovered. It is the pursuit of this will-of-the-wisp that has made the procession of lists of mental health criteria so fruitless.

As we actually study effective functioning—or commit ourselves to social or educational programs that seek in various ways to promote it—our focus then becomes, not "mental health" variously indexed, but any or all of a number of much more specific evaluative dimensions of human functioning: any that we are ready to commit ourselves to take seriously as relevant and valued potential psychological outcomes of the programs that we are working with, any that we can begin to pin down in operational terms, as many of them as seem important to us and as we can feasibly cope with. Here I find myself in essential agreement with the position recently taken by Levine and Kantor (1960).

From the standpoint of research, the problem of attaining consensus on criteria is thus scaled down to the workaday dimensions we are used to: the practical difficulty of trying to convince at least some of our colleagues to study some of the same things we are studying by similar methods, so that our results can dovetail or add up. There is no reason at all why study of the causes, consequences, and interrelations of standing on various mental health dimensions has to await consensus on a common list that may never be attained—and by my personal value commitments would not even be desirable!

In the long run, it is possible that our understanding of interrelated system properties of personality may advance to a point that warrants a more theoretical conception of mental health—one related, say, to empirically based estimates of such properties as self-maintenance, growth, and resilience (cf. Smith, 1959). We are certainly still far from being able to envision such a conception except in the most schematic terms. But if it is to be attained at all, the road to it should lie through nonevaluative research on personality development and functioning, on the one hand, and, on the other, through the strategy I have just been advocating: modestly exploring the empirical correlates of valued attributes of personality.

But what of the public demands for mental health "expertise" with which we started? What implications does our analysis have for the role of the psychologist in school, clinic, or consulting room? The very fact that no simple rule book of prescribed conduct seems to follow from it gives me greater confidence in the appropriateness of the approach we have taken.

Knowing that he lacks a scientifically sanctioned single set of mental health criteria, the psychologist in his consulting or service or educational relationships will hesitate to prescribe the nature of the good life to others in the name of psychology. Since values rest on a personal option, he will find it easiest to keep a clear scientific and professional conscience when he can use his knowledge and skill to help others identify, clarify, and realize their value commitments —provided that he can reconcile them with the values that he himself is committed to. Yet his own psychologically informed personal commitments about the nature of good human functioning cannot exist in a vacuum. They may lead him to avoid or to terminate service relationships that appear to violate them, to seek relationships that promote them. When his role as teacher or therapist vests him with more direct and personal responsibility for goal setting, he will not hesitate to act in terms of his convictions about what is desirable in the relationship and of the best knowledge and wisdom he can muster. But he will seek to move such relationships in the direction of increasing the responsibility of the other party for choosing his own goals. To his colleagues in and out of psychology and to various publics, he may often appear as an advocate of particular values. But his advocacy will consist in displaying the nature of his personal commitment and of using his psychological knowledge and insight to explore the linkage between holding or attaining a value and its conditions and consequences. In a word, explicitness about values goes with responsible scientific and professional behavior, and when we are explicit about such values as truthfulness, competence, care, responsibility, creativity, we add nothing consequential by labeling them as dimensions or criteria of positive mental health.

Mental Health as a Rubric

If "mental health" is to lose its presumptive conceptual standing, what does its status become? I see it rather as a rubric, a chapter title, a label for the common concern of various disciplines involved in evaluating human functioning from the perspective of the psychology of personality. Its usefulness in this respect does not depend on its dubious status as a theoretical concept. As chapter title, "mental health" is analogous to "mechanics" in classical physics: a rubric under which we treat a number of theoretical constructs (e.g., mass, force, velocity) and the laws relating them. You do not argue very violently about where chapter boundaries should be drawn.

There remain many meaningful problems concerning the contents and organization of such a chapter, even about its name. Personally, I agree with Levine and Kantor (1960) and with Szasz (1960) that the term "mental health" is unfortunate for our present purposes, biasing the issues as it does toward a model of physical health and illness that seems quite inappropriate to the analysis of effective and disordered conduct. But with the focus shifted to specific evaluative dimensions, I do not find myself caring very much about this argument, any more than I worry about the chapter titles in a book of applied science. This is an editorial problem, not a substantive one.

As for the contents of the mental health chapter, a variety of pragmatic considerations come to mind to assist in culling, augmenting, and refining the items in the available lists. Candidates for treatment as dimensions of mental health or of goodness of psychological functioning might be expected to meet most of the following criteria, none of which seems to require elaborate justification:

1. They should be serious contenders in the arena of human values (though an impossible consensus is of course not required). The posited value should be explicit.
2. They should be capable of measurement or of inference from identifiable aspects of behavior.
3. They should articulate with personality theory (a weak requirement, since the proviso must be added immediately that personality theories will probably need to be extended and modified to make contact with value dimensions chosen on other grounds).
4. They should be relevant to the social context for which the chapter is being written. In the context of education, for instance, this is to ask: What kinds of psychological assets would we like to see the schools develop in our children? Quite different considerations would come to the fore in the context of a correctional agency.

Considerations such as these make it unlikely that the entire range of moral, esthetic, and cognitive values will vie for inclusion in the mental health chapter. But no harm is done if a venturesome soul decides to study the natural history of some utterly "unpsychological" value under mental health auspices.

A more fundamental choice concerns short vs. long versions of the chapter: in other words, minimal vs. extended conceptions of mental health. I can illustrate this choice best if I introduce at the same time a possible principle for organizing the chapter. Jahoda (1958) observed that "one has the option of defining mental health in at least two ways: as a relatively constant and enduring function of the personality . . . ; or as a momentary function of personality and situation" (pp. 7–8). Klein (1960) makes a similar point in his distinction between soundness or general stability, and well-being. We want, that is, to distinguish, on the one hand, the person's present state and behavior as an interactive resultant of his personality and features of the momentary situation that he confronts, and, on the other, the corresponding dispositions of his present personality, with situational effects discounted. Add a time dimension—here in terms of an assessment of mental health in childhood with prognosis to adulthood, since a primary ingredient of our interest in the mental health of children is the foundation it is assumed to provide for adult functioning—and minimal vs. extended views of mental health may be illustrated as in Table II.

TABLE II

ILLUSTRATION OF NARROW AND BROAD CONCEPTIONS OF MENTAL HEALTH

Mental Health of Child

Scope	Present Behavior	Present Disposition	Adult Prognosis
Minimal conception	Freedom from incapacitating symptoms	Good resistance to stress	Absence of mental disorder in adulthood
Extended conception	Momentary well-being (in specified respects)	Capacities for competent, happy, zestful, etc. child life	Capacities for competent, happy, zestful, etc. adult life

To me, this way of mapping the contents of the chapter seems clarifying. As I look at the top row, the narrow conception of the scope of mental health seems thoroughly viable. I am led to think that Jahoda (1958) may have dismissed this version too quickly, that the psychiatrist Walter Barton in his postscript to her volume was certainly right about its relevance and adequacy for the context of institutional psychiatry. But as I compare the top and bottom lines, I agree with her that the narrow version of the chapter is not in itself adequate to the evaluative concerns of education—to pick one relevant context with which psychologists are involved. And it is of course the bottom line, the extended version, that potentially expands greatly as various dimensions of good functioning are specified. Comparison of the two lines reminds me to agree with Clausen (1956) that we know very little about their relationship to one another: no longer regarding mental health as a theoretical concept, we have no particular reason to expect resistance to mental disorder to correlate with various aspects of positive functioning, but the problem calls for research. And finally, the presence of the right-hand column calls to mind how little we know about the continuities of behavior seen in evaluative terms.

So long as we grope futilely toward a *concept* of "mental health," minimal or maximal, the advantages of specificity and researchability appear to be on the side of the minimal conception. Viewing these versions as different locations of chapter boundary lines, however, we can be as specific as we want about our positively valued criteria. It may well turn out to be the case, then, that the extended version includes the valued dimensions of behavior and personality that are most responsive to our interventions. "Mental health promotion" in this sense may not be as impractical as some of us have come to assume.

Conclusion

Where has this analysis of "mental health" as a problem of values led us? It may free us, I hope, from some of the embarrassment that has motivated psychologists' attempts to treat it as a theoretical concept—attempts that have not been additive and have not made the term theoretically respectable. If we understand "mental health" not as an unsatisfactory and vague theoretical concept but as a reasonably adequate rubric or label for an evaluative psychological perspective on personality—even though the term is not of our own choosing—we can get about our business without wasting our efforts on the search for consensus on a unique set of mental health criteria when consensus is not to be had.

Under this rubric, our business, be it research or service, is properly concerned with specific valued dimensions or attributes of behavior and personality. In our focus on these dimensions we are not at all handicapped by the lack of a satisfactory conceptual definition of mental health.

Nor need we be embarrassed by the intrusion of values in our focus on various specified aspects of desirable or undesirable psychological functioning. What is to be avoided is the *surreptitious* advocacy of values disguised under presumptive scientific auspices. The lists of psychological desiderata that psychologists have continued to propose, each reflecting the value commitments of its proponent, have this drawback insofar as they are offered as "criteria of positive mental health." But there is nothing surreptitious, nothing illegitimate, in using evaluative dimensions such as those that appear on these lists to appraise behavior and personality, so long as the value position one takes is explicit. And there is much to be gained from psychological study of the empirical antecedents, consequences, and interrelations of realizing different values in the sphere of personality.

In the study of optimal human functioning, I have argued, behavioral and social scientists can put their special qualifications to work toward the clarification of values among which people must choose and of the causal relations that are relevant to value choice. From it we should not only increase our knowledge about ways and means of attaining the values we agree on; we should also bring to light factual relationships that have a bearing on our choice of what values to pursue, individually and socially. To the extent that the behavioral sciences develop in this direction, they contribute to providing a badly needed bridge between what C. P. Snow (1959) has called "the two cultures" of the scientists and the humanistic intellectuals.

Part II

ASSESSMENT
OF CASUAL FACTORS

In the search for causes of behavior labeled as mentally ill, social scientists have focused on variables related to the interpersonal milieu. A multitude of studies have been conducted to determine what social environments increase the risk of development of mental disorders. Selection of the contents of this part posed considerable difficulty. Some of the better-known large-scale studies, such as those of Srole, Leighton, Hollingshead and Redlich, Jaco, and Pasamanick, could not be included because of their length. Instead, we focused on survey articles which consider and interpret these studies while presenting newer conceptualizations and approaches to the problem.

Most space is devoted to the repeated observation that socioeconomic level is inversely related to prevalence of mental disorder. Kohn's paper summarizes numerous studies on this topic, and concludes that, regardless of the individual flaws of the various investigations, the social class studies' findings are sufficiently strong to warrant our attention. Mishler and Scotch examine some of the same studies but conclude that, in view of problems of experimental design and sampling, no conclusions should be drawn. Dohrenwend and Dohrenwend review a number of studies and agree with the trends discussed by Kohn. They offer the hypothesis that persons in lower social classes are confronted with a relatively higher number of stressors, and are thus at greater risk for the development of mental disorders. As an illustration of a typical social class study, we have

111

selected Clark's which was published in 1949. Its findings are very similar to those of studies conducted today.

In the search for an explanation of social class findings, Dunham's recent study of mental illness in Detroit reviews alternative conceptualizations. He concludes in favor of a social selection rather than a social causation hypothesis, and thus departs from the conclusions of his 1939 study of Chicago with Faris.

Two papers illustrate the use of social psychological variables in studies of causal factors. Kleiner and Parker review the findings on social class and view its relationship to mental illness in terms of discrepancies between levels of aspiration and achievement. Wechsler and Pugh relate rates of mental illness to degree of fit of the individual's personal characteristics to those of the community in which he resides. They conclude that the greater the difference between an individual and the residents of his community, the greater the risk of hospitalization for mental illness.

In addition to stress, another mediating mechanism through which the relationship of social class to mental illness can be postulated is that of the family. Mishler and Waxler's thorough review of the Bateson, Lidz, and Wynne theories discusses those aspects of interpersonal relationships which may play a role in the pathogenic family. The authors then present their systematic approach to research through the observation of interpersonal behavior within the family. Solomon and Nuttall studied the relation of rates of schizophrenia to order of birth, repeating the finding that earlier born have a higher predisposition. They also find that remission is better for the earlier born than for the later born.

To present the other side of the picture, Kringlen offers an up-to-date assessment of the role of genetic factors in schizophrenia. He concludes that although genetic factors do play a part, it is much lower than usually supposed. This is followed by Knobloch and Pasamanick's contribution concerning the influence of prenatal factors in development. It suggests that such simple mediating factors as prenatal care and diet may clarify the relationship of social class to mental retardation and other allied disorders.

This section should serve to illustrate the contradictory findings and different interpretations of the same results as well as the consistent preoccupation with social class as a variable. The mediating mechanisms which are suggested to explain the relationship, as well as the newer types of variables which are studied, should illustrate future directions for research in this area.

11 / Social Class and Schizophrenia: A Critical Review

Melvin L. Kohn

My intent in this paper is to review a rather large and all-too-inexact body of research on the relationship of social class to schizophrenia, to see what it adds up to and what implications it has for etiology.[1] Instead of reviewing the studies one by one, I shall talk to general issues and bring in whatever studies are most relevant. It hardly need be stressed that my way of selecting these issues and my evaluation of the studies represent only one person's view of the field and would not necessarily be agreed to by others.

Before I get to the main issues, I should like to make five prefatory comments:

1. When I speak of schizophrenia, I shall generally be using that term in the broad sense in which it is usually employed in the United States, rather than the more limited sense used in much of Europe. I follow American rather than European usage, not because I think it superior, but because it is the usage that has been employed in so much of the relevant research. Any comparative discussion must necessarily employ the more inclusive, even if the cruder, term.

2. I shall generally not be able to distinguish among various types of schizophrenia, for the data rarely enable one to do so. This is most unfortunate; one should certainly want to consider "process" and "reactive" types of disturbance separately, to distinguish between paranoid and non-paranoid, and to take account of several other possibly critical distinctions.

Worse yet, I shall at times have to rely on data about an even broader and vaguer category than schizophrenia—severe mental illness in general, excluding only the demonstrably organic. The excuse for this is that since the epidemio-

From pp. 155–173, David Rosenthal and Seymour S. Kety (Eds.), *The Transmission of Schizophrenia*. Copyright © 1968. (Oxford: Pergamon Press, Ltd., 1968). Reprinted by permission of the author and Pergamon Press, Ltd.

[1] The *raison d'être* of this review, aside from its being momentarily current, is in its effort to organize the evidence around certain central issues and to make use of all studies relevant to those issues. There are no definitive studies in this field, but most of them contribute something to our knowledge when placed in perspective of all the others.

For an alternative approach, deliberately limited to those few studies that meet the reviewers' standards of adequacy, see Mishler and Scotch (1963).

Dunham (1965, 1966) has recently argued for a more radical alternative; he disputes the legitimacy of using epidemiological data to make the types of social psychological inference I attempt here and insists that epidemiological studies are relevant only to the study of how social systems function. This seems to me to be altogether arbitrary.

Some other useful reviews and discussions of issues in this field have been published by Dunham (1947, 1948, 1953), Felix and Bowers (1948), Clausen (1956, 1958, 1959), Hollingshead (1961), and Sanua (1963). The present review leans heavily on an earlier paper of mine (1966), but is more complete in its coverage and represents a thorough reassessment of the field.

logical findings for severe mental illness seem to parallel those for schizophrenia alone, it would be a shame to ignore the several important studies that have been addressed to the larger category. I shall, however, rely on these studies as sparingly as possible and stress studies that focus on schizophrenia.

3. Social classes will be defined as aggregates of individuals who occupy broadly similar positions in the hierarchy of power, privilege, and prestige (Williams, 1951, p. 89). In dealing with the research literature, I shall treat occupational position (or occupational position as weighted somewhat by education) as a serviceable index of social class for urban society. I shall not make any distinction, since the data hardly permit my doing so, between the concepts "social class" and "socioeconomic status." And I shall not hesitate to rely on less than fully adequate indices of class when relevant investigations have employed them.

4. I want to mention only in passing the broadly comparative studies designed to examine the idea that mental disorder in general, and schizophrenia in particular, are products of civilization, or of urban life, or of highly complex social structure. There have been a number of important studies of presumably less complex societies that all seem to indicate that the magnitude of mental disorder in these societies is of *roughly* the same order as that in highly urbanized, Western societies. I refer you, for example, to Lin's study in Taiwan (1953), the Leightons' in Nova Scotia (1963), Leighton and Lambo's in Nigeria (1963), and Eaton and Weil's of the Hutterites (1955).[2] For a historical perspective within urban, Western society, Goldhamer and Marshall's study in Massachusetts (1953) is the most relevant; it indicates that the increasing urbanization of Massachusetts over a period of 100 years did *not* result in any increase in rates of functional psychosis, except possibly for the elderly.

These data are hardly precise enough to be definitive, but they lead one to turn his attention away from the general hypothesis that there are sizeable differences in rates of mental disorder between simpler and more complex social structures, to look instead at differences *within* particular social structures, where the evidence is far more intriguing. I do not argue that there are no differences in rates of schizophrenia among societies, only that the data in hand are not sufficient to demonstrate them (Mishler and Scotch, 1963; Dunham, 1965; Demerath, 1955). We have more abundant data on intra-societal variations.

5. One final prefatory note. Much of what I shall do in this paper will be to raise doubts and come to highly tentative conclusions from inadequate evidence. This is worth doing because we know so little and the problem is so pressing. Genetics does not seem to provide a sufficient explanation (Rosenthal, 1962a; Tiernari, 1963; Kringlen, 1964, 1964a; Kringlen, 1966), and, I take it from Kety's critical review, biochemical and physiological hypotheses have thus far

---

[2] This volume includes a valuable comparison of rates of psychosis in a variety of different cultures, from an arctic fishing village in Norway to Baltimore, Maryland, to Thuringia to Formosa to Williamson County, Tennessee.

It must be noted that although Eaton and Weil find the rate of functional psychosis among the Hutterites to be roughly comparable to that for other societies, they find the rate of schizophrenia to be low (and that for manic-depressive psychosis to be correspondingly high). There is, however, reason to doubt the validity of their differential diagnosis of schizophrenia and manic-depressive psychosis.

failed to stand the test of careful experimentation (Kety, 1960). Of all the social variables that have been studied, those related to social class have yielded the most provocative results. Thus, inadequate as the following data are, they must be taken seriously.

It must be emphasized, however, that *there are exceedingly difficult problems in interpreting the data that I am about to review*. The indices are suspect, the direction of causality is debatable, the possibility that one or another alternative interpretation makes more sense than the one I should like to draw is very real indeed. These problems will all be taken up shortly; first, though, I should like to lay out the positive evidence for a meaningful relationship between class and schizophrenia.

Evidence on the Possible Relationship of Social Class to Rates of Schizophrenia

Most of the important epidemiological studies of schizophrenia can be viewed as attempts to resolve problems of interpretation posed by the pioneer studies, Faris and Dunham's ecological study of rates of schizophrenia for the various areas of Chicago (1939) and Clark's study of rates of schizophrenia at various occupational levels in that same city (1948, 1949). Their findings were essentially as follows:

Faris and Dunham: The highest rates of first hospital admission for schizophrenia are in the central city areas of lowest socioeconomic status, with diminishing rates as one moves toward higher status peripheral areas.[3]

Clark: The highest rates of schizophrenia are for the lowest status occupations, with diminishing rates as one goes to higher status occupations.

The concentration of high rates of mental disorder, particularly of schizophrenia, in the *central city areas[4] of lowest socioeconomic status* has been confirmed in a number of American cities—Providence, Rhode Island (Faris and Dunham, 1939); Peoria, Illinois (Schroeder, 1942); Kansas City, Missouri (Schroeder, 1942); St. Louis, Missouri (Schroeder, 1942; Dee, 1939; Queen, 1940); Milwaukee, Wisconsin (Schroeder, 1942); Omaha, Nebraska (Schroeder, 1942); Worcester, Massachusetts (Gerard and Houston, 1953); Rochester, New York (Gardner and Babigian, 1966); and Baltimore, Maryland (Klee *et al.*, 1966). The two ecological studies done in European cities—Sundby and Nyhus's study of Oslo, Norway (1963) and Hare's of Bristol, England (1956a)—are in substantial agreement, too.

The concentration of high rates of mental disorder, particularly of schizophrenia, in the *lowest status occupations* has been confirmed again and again. The studies conducted by Hollingshead and Redlich in New Haven, Connecti-

---

[3] The pattern is most marked for paranoid schizophrenia, least so for catatonic, which tends to concentrate in the *foreign-born* slum communities (Faris and Dunham, 1939, pp. 82–108). Unfortunately, subsequent studies in smaller cities dealt with too few cases to examine the distribution of separable types of schizophrenia as carefully as did Faris and Dunham.

[4] There are some especially difficult problems in interpreting the ecological findings, which I shall not discuss here because most of the later and crucial evidence comes from other modes of research. The problems inherent in interpreting ecological studies are discussed by Robinson (1950), and by Clausen and Kohn (1954).

cut (1958) and by Srole and his associates in midtown, New York City (1962), are well-known examples; a multitude of other investigations in the United States have come to the same conclusion (Locke *et al.*, 1958; Frumkin, 1955; Lemkau, Tietze, and Cooper, 1942; Fuson, 1943; Turner and Wagonfeld, 1967).[5] Moreover, Svalastoga's re-analysis (1965) of Strömgren's data for northern Denmark is consistent, as are the Leightons' data for "Stirling County," Nova Scotia (1963, pp. 279–294), Ødegaard's for Norway (1956, 1957, 1962), Stein's for two sections of London (1957), Lin's for Taiwan (1953, 1966), and Stenbäck and Achté's for Helsinki (1966).

But there are some exceptions. Clausen and I happened across the first, when he discovered that for Hagerstown, Maryland, there was no discernible relationship between either occupation or the social status of the area and rates of schizophrenia (1959).[6] On a re-examination of past studies, we discovered a curious thing: the larger the city, the stronger the correlation between rates of schizophrenia and these indices of social class. In the metropolis of Chicago, the correlation is large, and the relationship is linear: the lower the social status, the higher the rates. In cities of 100,000 to 500,000 (or perhaps more), the correlation is smaller and not so linear: it is more a matter of a concentration of cases in the lowest socioeconomic strata, with not so much variation among higher strata. When you get down to a city as small as Hagerstown—36,000— the correlation disappears.

Subsequent studies in a number of different places have confirmed our generalization. Sundby and Nyhus (1963), for example, showed that Oslo, Norway, manifests the typical pattern for cities of its half-million size: a high concentration in the lowest social stratum, little variation above. Hollingshead and Redlich's data on *new admissions* for schizophrenia from New Haven, Connecticut, show that pattern, too (1958, p. 236).

There is substantial evidence, too, for our conclusion that socioeconomic differentials disappear in areas of small population. The Leightons found that although rates of mental disorder do correlate with socioeconomic status for "Stirling County," Nova Scotia, as a whole, they do not for the small (population 3,000) community of "Bristol" (1963). Similarly, Buck, Wanklin, and Hobbs (1955), in an ecological analysis of Western Ontario, found a high rank correlation between median wage and county first admission rates for mental disorder

---

[5] Relevant, too, are some early studies whose full significance was not appreciated until later. See, for example, Nolan (1917), Ødegaard (1932, esp. pp. 182–184), and Green (1939).

One puzzling partial exception comes from Jaco's study of Texas (1957, 1960). He finds the highest incidence of schizophrenia among the unemployed, but otherwise a strange, perhaps curvilinear relationship of occupational status to incidence. Perhaps it is only that so many of his patients were classified as unemployed (rather than according to their pre-illness occupational status) that the overall picture is distorted.

[6] In that paper, the data on occupational rates were incompletely reported. Although we divided the population into four occupational classes, based on U.S. Census categories, we presented the actual rates for only the highest and lowest classes, leading some readers to conclude, erroneously, that we had divided the population into only two occupational classes. In fact, the average annual rates of first hospital admission for schizophrenia, based on the population aged 15–64, were: (a) professional, technical, managerial, officials, and proprietors, 21.3; (b) clerical and sales personnel, 23.8; (c) craftsmen, foremen, and kindred workers, 10.7; (d) operatives, service workers, and laborers, 21.7. Our measures of occupational mobility, to be discussed later, were based on movement among the same four categories.

for counties of 10,000 or more population, but a much smaller correlation for counties of smaller population. And Hagnell (1966) found no relationship between his admittedly inexact measures of socioeconomic status and rates of mental disorder for the largely rural area of southwestern Sweden that he investigated.

I think one must conclude that the relationship of socioeconomic status to schizophrenia has been demonstrated only for urban populations. Even for urban populations, a *linear* relationship of socioeconomic status to rates of schizophrenia has been demonstrated only for the largest metropolises. The evidence, though, that there is an unusually high rate of schizophrenia in the lowest socioeconomic strata of urban communities seems to me to be nothing less than overwhelming. The proper interpretation why this is so, however, is not so unequivocal.

The Direction of Causality

One major issue in interpreting the Faris and Dunham, the Clark, and all subsequent investigations concerns the direction of causality. Rates of schizophrenia in the lowest socioeconomic strata could be disproportionately high either because conditions of life in those strata are somehow conducive to the development of schizophrenia, or because people from higher social strata who become schizophrenic suffer a decline in status. Or, of course, it could be some of both. Discussions of this issue have conventionally gone under the rubric of the "drift hypothesis," although far more is involved.

The drift hypothesis was first raised as an attempt to explain away the Faris and Dunham findings. The argument was that in the course of their developing illness, schizophrenics tend to "drift" into lower status areas of the city. It is not that more cases of schizophrenia are "produced" in these areas, but that schizophrenics who are produced elsewhere end up at the bottom of the heap by the time they are hospitalized, and thus are counted as having come from the bottom of the heap.

When the Clark study appeared, the hypothesis was easily enlarged to include "drift" from higher to lower status occupations. In its broadest formulation, the drift hypothesis asserts that high rates of schizophrenia in the lowest social strata come about because people from higher classes who become schizophrenic suffer a decline in social position as a consequence of their illness. In some versions of the hypothesis, it is further suggested that schizophrenics from smaller locales tend to migrate to the lowest status areas and occupations of large metropolises; this would result in an exaggeration of rates there and a corresponding underestimation of rates for the place and class from which they come.

Incidentally, the drift hypothesis is but one variant of a more general hypothesis that any differences in rates of schizophrenia are the result of *social selection*—that various social categories show high rates because people already predisposed to schizophrenia gravitate into those categories. This has long been argued by Ødegaard (1932, 1957, 1962), but with data that are equally amenable to social selection and social causation interpretations. Dunham has recently made the same point, but I think his data argue more convincingly for social causation than for social selection (1966). Intriguing though the issue is, it is presently unresolvable; so it would be better to focus on the more specific question, whether or not the high concentration of schizophrenia in the lowest socioeconomic strata is the result of downward drift.

One approach to this problem has been to study the histories of social mobility of schizophrenics. Unfortunately, the evidence is inconsistent. Three studies indicate that schizophrenics have been downwardly mobile in occupational status,[7] three others that they have not been.[8] Some of these studies do not compare the experiences of the schizophrenics to those of normal persons from comparable social backgrounds. Those that do are nevertheless inconclusive— either because the comparison group was not well chosen, or because the city in which the study was done does not have a concentration of schizophrenia in the lowest social class. Since no study is definitive, any assessment must be based on a subjective weighing of the strengths and weaknesses of them all. My assessment is that the weight of this evidence clearly indicates either that schizophrenics have been no more downwardly mobile (in fact, no less upwardly mobile) than other people from the same social backgrounds, or at minimum, that the degree of downward mobility is insufficient to explain the high concentration of schizophrenia in the lowest socioeconomic strata.

There is another and more direct way of looking at the question, however, and from this perspective the question is still unresolved. The reformulated question focuses on the social class *origins* of schizophrenics; it asks whether the occupations of *fathers* of schizophrenics are concentrated in the lowest social strata. If they are, that is clear evidence in favor of the hypothesis that lower class status is conducive to schizophrenia. If they are not, class might still matter for schizophrenia—it might be a matter of stress experienced by lower class adults, rather than of the experience of being born and raised in the lower class—but certainly the explanation that would require the fewest assumptions would be the drift hypothesis.

The first major study to evaluate the evidence from this perspective argued strongly in favor of lower class origins being conducive to mental disorder, although perhaps not to schizophrenia in particular. Srole and his associates (1962, pp. 212–222) found, in their study of midtown New York, that rates of mental disorder correlate nearly as well with their *parents'* socioeconomic status as with the subjects' own socioeconomic status. But then Goldberg and Morrison (1963) found that although the occupations of male schizophrenic patients admitted to hospitals in England and Wales show the usual concentration of

[7] Evidence that schizophrenics have been downwardly mobile in *occupational* status has been presented by Schwartz (1946), Lystad (1957), and Turner and Wagonfeld (1967).

In addition, there has been some debatable evidence that the *ecological* concentration of schizophrenia has resulted from the migration of unattached men into the high rate areas of the city. See Gerard and Houston (1953), Hare (1956), and Dunham (1965). (Dunham's data, however, show that when rates are properly computed, rate differentials between high and low rate areas of Detroit are just as great for the stable population as for in-migrants.)

[8] Evidence that schizophrenics have *not* been downwardly mobile in *occupational* status is presented by Hollingshead and Redlich (1954, 1958), Clausen and Kohn (1959), and Dunham (1964, 1965). Evidence that the *ecological* concentration of schizophrenia has not resulted from in-migration or downward drift is presented in Lapouse, Monk, and Terris (1956), Hollingshead and Redlich (1954), and, as noted in footnote 7, Dunham (1965).

cases in the lowest social class, their fathers' occupations do not. Since this study dealt with schizophrenia, the new evidence seemed more directly in point. One might quarrel with some aspects of this study—the index of social class is debatable, for example, and data are lacking for 25 per cent of the originally drawn sample—but this is much too good a study to be taken lightly. Nor can one conclude that the situation in England and Wales is different from that in the United States, for Dunham (1965; Dunham et al., 1966) reports that two segments of Detroit show a similar picture.

There is yet one more study to be considered, however, and this the most important one of all, for it offers the most complete data about class origins, mobility, and the eventual class position of schizophrenics. Turner and Wagonfeld (1967), in a study of Monroe County (Rochester), New York, discovered a remarkable pattern: rates of first treatment for schizophrenia are disproportionately high, both for patients of lowest occupational status *and* for patients whose fathers had lowest occupational status, but *these are by and large not the same patients*. Some of those whose fathers were in the lowest occupational class had themselves moved up, and some of those ending up in the lowest occupational class had come from higher class origins. Thus, there is evidence both for the proposition that lower class origins are conducive to schizophrenia and for the proposition that most lower class schizophrenics come from higher socioeconomic origins. No wonder partial studies have been inconsistent!

The next question one would want to ask, of course, is how the schizophrenics' histories of occupational mobility compare to those of normal people of comparable social class origins. Turner and Wagonfeld have not the data to answer this definitively, for they lack an appropriate control group. They are able, however, to compare the mobility experiences of their schizophrenics to those of a cross section of the population, and from this they learn two important things. More schizophrenics than normals have been downwardly mobile. This downward mobility did not come about because of a loss of occupational position that had once been achieved, but reflected their failure ever to have achieved as high an occupational level as do most men of their social class origins.

This argues strongly against a simple drift hypothesis—it is *not,* as some have argued, that we have erroneously rated men at lower than their usual class status because we have classified them according to their occupations at time of hospitalization, after they have suffered a decline in occupational position. It is more likely that a more sophisticated drift hypothesis applies—that some people genetically or constitutionally or otherwise predisposed to schizophrenia show some effects of developing illness at least as early as the time of their first jobs, for they are never able to achieve the occupational levels that might be expected of them. If so, the possibilities of some interaction between genetic predisposition and early social circumstances are very real indeed.

One direction that further research must take is well pointed out by the Turner and Wagonfeld study. The question now must be the degree to which the correlation of class and schizophrenia results from a higher incidence of schizophrenia among people born into lower class families, the degree to which it results from schizophrenics of higher class origins never achieving as high an occupational level as might have been expected of them—and *why*.

For the present, I think it can be tentatively concluded that despite what Goldberg and Morrison found for England and Wales, the weight of evidence lies against the drift hypothesis being a *sufficient* explanation. In all probability, lower class families *produce* a disproportionate number of schizophrenics, although perhaps by not so large a margin as one would conclude from studies that rely on the patients' own occupational attainments.

Parenthetically, there is another important question involved here, the effects of social mobility itself. Ever since Ødegaard's classic study (1932, 1936; Astrup and Ødegaard, 1960) of rates of mental disorder among Norwegian migrants to the United States, we have known that geographic mobility is a matter of considerable consequence for mental illness (Tietze *et al.*, 1942; Leacock, 1957), and the same may be true for social mobility (Kleiner and Parker, 1963; Myers and Roberts, 1959). But we have not known how and why mobility matters—whether it is a question of what types of people are mobile or of the stresses of mobility —and unfortunately later research has failed to resolve the issue.

The Adequacy of Indices

The adequacy of indices is another major issue in interpreting the Faris and Dunham, the Clark, and all subsequent investigations. Most of these studies are based on hospital admission rates, which may not give a valid picture of the true incidence of schizophrenia. Studies that do not rely on hospital rates encounter other and perhaps even more serious difficulties, with which we shall presently deal.

The difficulty with using admission rates as the basis for computing rates of schizophrenia is that lower class psychotics may be more likely to be hospitalized, and if hospitalized to be diagnosed as schizophrenic, especially in public hospitals. Faris and Dunham tried to solve this problem by including patients admitted to private as well as to public mental hospitals. This was insufficient because, as later studies have shown, some people who suffer serious mental disorder never enter a mental hospital (Kaplan, Reed, and Richardson, 1956).

Subsequent studies have attempted to do better by including more and more social agencies in their search for cases; Hollingshead and Redlich in New Haven (1958), and Jaco in Texas (1957, 1960), for example, have extended their coverage to include everyone who enters any sort of treatment facility— Jaco going so far as to question all the physicians in Texas. This is better, but clearly the same objections hold in principle. Furthermore, Srole and his associates (1962, pp. 240–251) have demonstrated that there are considerable social differences between people who have been treated, somewhere, for mental illness, and severely impaired people, some large proportion of them schizophrenic, who have never been to any sort of treatment facility. So we must conclude that using treatment—*any* sort of treatment—as an index of mental disorder is suspect.

The alternative is to go out into the community and examine everyone—or a representative sample of everyone—yourself. This has been done by a number of investigators, for example Essen-Möller in Sweden (1956, 1961), Srole and his associates in New York (1962), the Leightons in Nova Scotia (1963). They have solved one problem, but have run into three others.

1. The first is that most of these investigators have found it impossible to classify schizophrenia reliably, and have had to resort to larger and vaguer categories—severe mental illness, functional psychosis, and such. For some purposes, this may be justified. For our immediate purposes, it is exceedingly unfortunate.

2. Second, even if you settle for such a concept as "mental illness," it is difficult to establish criteria that can be applied reliably and validly in community studies (Dohrenwend and Dohrenwend, 1965). For all its inadequacies, hospitalization is at least an unambiguous index, and you can be fairly certain that the people who are hospitalized are really ill. But how does one interpret the Leightons' estimate (1963, p. 1026) that about a third of their population suffer significant psychiatric impairment, or Srole's (1962, p. 138) that almost a quarter of his are impaired?

Personal examination by a single psychiatrist using presumably consistent standards is one potential solution, but usable only in relatively small investigations. Another possible solution is the further development of objective rating scales, such as the Neuropsychiatric Screening Adjunct (Star, 1950a) first developed by social scientists in the Research Branch of the U.S. Army in World War II and later incorporated into both the Leightons' and Srole's investigations, but not developed to anything like its full potential in either study. The limitation here is that such scales may be less relevant to the measurement of psychosis than of neurosis.

To make significant further advances, we shall have to break free of traditional methods of measurement. Epidemiological studies still largely rely on a single, undifferentiated overall assessment. Even when such an assessment can be demonstrated to be reliable within the confines of a single study, it has only limited use for comparative studies and is questionable for repeated application in studies designed to ascertain how many new cases arise in some given period of time. At minimum, we must begin to make use of our developing capacities at multivariate analysis. One obvious approach is to try to differentiate the several judgments that go into clinical diagnoses, develop reliable measures of each, and examine their interrelationship. At the same time, it would be well to develop reliable measures of matters conventionally given only secondary attention in epidemiological research—for example, the degree of disability the individual has sustained in each of several major social roles (Clausen, 1966). A third path we might try is the further development of objective measures of dimensions of subjective state (such as anxiety, alienation, and self-abasement) thought to be indicative of pathology. All these and others can be measured as separate dimensions, and then empirically related to each other and to clinical assessments.

Whether or not these particular suggestions have merit, I think the general conclusion that it is time for considerable methodological experimentation is indisputable.

3. The third problem in community studies is that it is so difficult to secure data on the *incidence* of mental disturbance that most studies settle for *prevalence* data (Kramer, 1957). That is, instead of ascertaining the number of new

cases arising in various population groups during some period of time, they count the number of people currently ill at the time of the study. This latter measure—prevalence—is inadequate because it reflects not only incidence but also duration of illness. As Hollingshead and Redlich (1958) have shown, duration of illness—insofar as it incapacitates—is highly correlated with social class.

Various approximations to incidence have been tried, and various new—and often somewhat fantastic—statistical devices invented to get around this problem, but without any real success. Clearly, what is needed is *repeated* studies of the population, to pick up new cases as they arise and thus to establish true incidence figures. (This is what Hagnell did [1966], and it was a very brave effort indeed.) The crucial problem, of course, is to develop reliable measures of mental disorder, for without that our repeated surveys will measure nothing but the errors of our instruments. Meantime, we have to recognize that prevalence studies use an inappropriate measure that exaggerates the relationship of socioeconomic status to mental disorder.

So, taken all together, the results of the studies of class and schizophrenia are hardly definitive. They may even all wash out—one more example of inadequate methods leading to premature, false conclusions. I cannot prove otherwise. Yet I think the most reasonable interpretation of all these findings is that they point to something real. Granted that there isn't a single definitive study in the lot, the weaknesses of one are compensated for by the strengths of some other, and the total edifice is probably much stronger than you would conclude from knowing only how frail are its component parts. A large number of complementary studies all seem to point to the same conclusion: that rates of mental disorder, particularly of schizophrenia, are highest at the lowest socioeconomic levels, at least in moderately large cities, and this probably isn't just a matter of drift or inadequate indices or some other artifact of the methods we use. In all probability, more schizophrenia is actually produced at the lowest socioeconomic levels. At any rate, let us take that as a working hypothesis and explore the question further. Assuming that more schizophrenia occurs at lower socioeconomic levels—Why?

Alternative Interpretations

Is it really socioeconomic status, or is it some correlated variable that is operative here? Faris and Dunham (1939) did not take socioeconomic status very seriously in their interpretation of their data. From among the host of variables characteristic of the high rate areas of Chicago, they focused on such things as high rates of population turnover and ethnic mixtures and hypothesized that the really critical thing about the high rate areas was the degree of social isolation they engendered. Two subsequent studies, one by Jaco in Texas (1954), the other by Hare in Bristol, England (1956a), are consistent in that they too show a correlation of rates of schizophrenia to various ecological indices of social isolation. The only study that directly examines the role of social isolation in the lives of schizophrenics, however, seems to demonstrate that while social isolation may be symptomatic of developing illness, it does not play an important role in etiology (Clausen and Kohn, 1954; Kohn and Clausen, 1955).

Several other interpretations of the epidemiological evidence have been suggested, some supported by intriguing, if inconclusive, evidence. One is that it is not socioeconomic status as such that is principally at issue, but social integration. The Leightons (1963) have produced plausible evidence for this interpretation. The problems of defining and indexing "social integration" make a definitive demonstration exceedingly difficult, however, even for the predominantly rural populations with which they have worked.

Another possibility is that the high rates of schizophrenia found in lower class populations are a consequence of especially high rates for lower class members of some ethnic groups who happen to be living in areas where other ethnic groups predominate. In their recent study in Boston, for example, Schwartz and Mintz (1963; Mintz and Schwartz, 1964) showed that Italian-Americans living in predominantly non-Italian neighborhoods have very high rates of schizophrenia, while those living in predominantly Italian neighborhoods do not. The former group contribute disproportionately to the rates for lower class neighborhoods. (The authors suggest that this may explain why small cities do not show a concentration of lower class cases: these cities do not have the ethnic mixtures that produce such a phenomenon.)

Wechsler and Pugh (1967) extended this interpretive model to suggest that rates should be higher for any persons living in a community where they and persons of similar social attributes are in a minority. Their analysis of Massachusetts towns provides some surprisingly supportive data.

Other possibilities deal more directly with the occupational component of socioeconomic status. Ødegaard (1956) long ago showed that rates of schizophrenia are higher for some occupations that are losing members and lower for some that are expanding. His observation was correct, but it explains only a small part of the occupational rate differences. Others have focused on alleged discrepancies between schizophrenics' occupational aspirations and achievements (Kleiner and Parker, 1963; Myers and Roberts, 1959), arguing that the pivotal fact is not that schizophrenics have achieved so little but that they had wanted so much more. The evidence is limited.

One could argue—and I see no reason to take the argument lightly—that genetics provides a quite sufficient explanation. If there is a moderately strong genetic component in schizophrenia, then one would expect a higher than usual rate of schizophrenia among the fathers and grandfathers of schizophrenics. Since schizophrenia is a debilitating disturbance, this would be reflected in grandparents' and parents' occupations and places of residence. In other words, it could be a rather complex version of drift hypothesis. The only argument against this interpretation is that there is no really compelling evidence in favor of it; one can accept it on faith, or one can keep it in mind while continuing to explore alternatives. Prudence suggests the latter course of action.

There are other possibilities we might examine, but since there is no very strong evidence for any of them, that course does not seem especially profitable. One must allow the possibility that some correlated variable might prove critical for explaining the findings; it might not be social class, after all, that is operative here. Until that is demonstrated, however, the wisest course would seem to be to take the findings at face value and see what there might be about social class that would help us to understand schizophrenia.

Class and Etiology

What is there about the dynamics of social class that might affect the probability of people becoming schizophrenic? How does social class operate here; what are the intervening processes?

The possibilities are numerous, almost too numerous. Social class indexes and is correlated with so many phenomena that might be relevant to the etiology of schizophrenia: since it measures status, it implies a great deal about how the individual is treated by others—with respect or perhaps degradingly; since it is measured by occupational rank, it suggests much about the conditions that make up the individual's daily work, how closely supervised he is, whether he works primarily with things, with data, or with people; since it reflects the individual's educational level, it connotes a great deal about his style of thinking, his use or non-use of abstractions, even his perceptions of physical reality and certainly of social reality; furthermore, the individual's class position influences his social values and colors his evaluations of the world about him; it affects the family experiences he is likely to have had as a child and the ways he is likely to raise his own children; and it certainly matters greatly for the type and amount of stress he is likely to encounter in a lifetime. In short, social class pervades so much of life that it is difficult to guess *which* of its correlates are most relevant for understanding schizophrenia. Moreover, none of these phenomena are so *highly* correlated with class (nor class so highly correlated with schizophrenia) that any one of these facets is obviously more promising than the others.

This being the case, investigators have tended to pursue those avenues that have met their theoretical predilections and to ignore the others. In practice, this has meant that the interrelationship of class, family, and schizophrenia has been explored, and more recently the relationship of class, stress, and schizophrenia, but the other possibilities remain largely unexamined. Given the inherent relevance of some of them—class differences in patterns of thinking, for example, have such obvious relevance to schizophrenia—this is a bit surprising.

But let me review what has been done. The hypothesis that *stress* is what is really at issue in the class-schizophrenia relationship is in some respects especially appealing, in part because it is so direct. We have not only our own observations as human beings with some compassion for less fortunate people, but an increasingly impressive body of scientific evidence (Dohrenwend and Dohrenwend, in press), to show that life is rougher and rougher the lower one's social class position. The stress explanation seems especially plausible for the very lowest socioeconomic levels, where the rates of schizophrenia are highest.

There have to my knowledge been only two empirical investigations of the relationship of social class to stress to mental disorder. The first was done by Langner and Michael (1963) in New York as part of the "Midtown" study. This study, as all the others we have been considering, has its methodological defects—it is a prevalence study, and many of the indices it uses are at best questionable—but it tackles the major issues head-on, and with very impressive and very intriguing results. It finds a strong linear relationship between stress and mental disturbance, specifically, the more sources of stress, the higher the probability of mental disturbance. It also finds the expected relationship between social class and stress. So the stress hypothesis has merit. But stress is not all that is involved in the relationship of social class to mental disorder. No matter how high the level of stress, social class continues to be correlated with the probability of mental disturbance; in fact, the more stress, the higher the correlation.[9] Thus, it seems that the effect of social class on the rate of mental disorder is not only, or even principally, a function of different amounts of stress at different class levels.

In a more recent study in San Juan, Puerto Rico, Rogler and Hollingshead (1965) ascribe a more important role to stress. Theirs was an intensive investigation of the life histories of a sample of lower class schizophrenics, along with comparable studies of a well-matched sample of non-schizophrenics. Rogler and Hollingshead found only insubstantial differences in the early life experiences of lower class schizophrenics and controls; they did find, however, that in the period of a year or so before the onset of symptoms, the schizophrenics were subjected to an unbearable onslaught of stress. In effect, all lower class slum dwellers in San Juan suffer continual, dreadful stress; in addition to this "normal" level of stress, however, the schizophrenics were hit with further, intolerable stress which incapacitated them in one or another central role, leading to incapacitation in other roles, too.

The picture that Rogler and Hollingshead draw is plausible and impressive. It is not possible, however—at least not yet—to generalize as far from their data as one might like. Their sample is limited to schizophrenics who are married or in stable consensual unions. These one would assume to be predominantly "reactive" type schizophrenics—precisely the group whom one would expect, from past studies, to have had normal childhood social experiences, good social adjustment, and extreme precipitating circumstances. So their findings may apply to "reactive" schizophrenia, but perhaps not to "process" schizophrenia. In addition, for all the impressiveness of the argument, the data are not so unequivocal. Their inquiry was not so exhaustive as to rule out the possibility that the schizophrenics might have had different family experiences from those of the controls. Furthermore, the evidence that the schizophrenics were subjected to significantly greater stress is not so thoroughly compelling as one might want. Thus, the case is not proved. Nevertheless, Rogler and Hollingshead have demonstrated that the possibility that stress plays an important role in the genesis of schizophrenia is to be taken very seriously indeed. Certainly this study makes it imperative that we investigate the relationship of class to stress to schizophrenia far more intensively.

At the same time, we should investigate some closely related possibilities that have not to my knowledge been studied empirically. Not only stress, but also reward and opportunity, are differentially distributed among the social classes.

---

[9] The latter finding is in part an artifact of the peculiar indices used in this study, and reflects differences not in the incidence of illness but in type and severity of illness in different social classes at various levels of stress. At higher stress levels, lower class people tend to develop incapacitating psychoses and middle class people less incapacitating neuroses.

The more fortunately situated not only are less beaten about, but may be better able to withstand the stresses they do encounter because they have many more rewarding experiences to give them strength. And many more alternative courses of action are open to them when they run into trouble. Might this offer an added clue to the effects of class for schizophrenia?

More generally, what is there about the conditions of life of the lowest social strata that might make it more difficult for their members to cope with stress? One can think of intriguing possibilities. Their occupational conditions and their limited education gear their thinking processes to the concrete and the habitual; their inexperience in dealing with the abstract may ill-equip them to cope with ambiguity, uncertainty, and unpredictability; their mental processes are apt to be too gross and rigid when flexibility and subtlety are most required. Or, a related hypothesis, the lower and working class valuation of conformity to external authority, and disvaluation of self-direction, might cripple a man faced with the necessity of suddenly having to rely on himself in an uncertain situation where others cannot be relied on for guidance.

These hypotheses, unfortunately, have not been investigated; perhaps it is time that they were. The one hypothesis that has been studied, and that one only partially, is that lower and working class patterns of *parent-child relationships* somehow do not adequately prepare children for dealing with the hazards of life. Now we enter what is perhaps the most complicated area of research we have touched on so far, and certainly the least adequately studied field of all.

There has been a huge volume of research literature about family relationships and schizophrenia,[10] most of it inadequately designed. One has to dismiss the majority of studies because of one or another incapacitating deficiency. In many, the patients selected for study were a group from which you could not possibly generalize to schizophrenics at large. Either the samples were comprised of chronic patients, where one would expect the longest and most difficult onset of illness with the greatest strain in family relationships, or the samples were peculiarly selected, not to test a hypothesis, but to load the dice in favor of a hypothesis. In other studies, there have been inadequate control groups or no control group at all. One of the most serious defects of method has been the comparison of patterns of family relationship of lower and working class patients to middle and upper middle class normal controls—which completely confounds the complex picture we wish to disentangle. In still other studies, even where the methods of sample and control selection have been adequate, the method of data collection has seriously biased the results. This is true, for example, in those studies that have placed patients and their families in stressful situations bound to exaggerate any flaws in their interpersonal processes, especially for people of lesser education and verbal skill who would be least equipped to deal with the new and perplexing situation in which they found themselves.

Still, some recent studies have suggested respects in which the family relationships of schizophrenics seem unusual, and unusual in theoretically interesting

---

[10] See the references in Kohn and Clausen (1956), Clausen and Kohn (1960), and Sanua (1961).

ways—that is, in ways that might be important in the dynamics of schizophrenic personality development. Work by Bateson *et al.* (1956) on communication processes in families of schizophrenics (see also Mishler and Waxler, 1965) and that by Wynne and his associates (1958; Ryckoff, 1959) on cognitive and emotional processes in such families, for example, are altogether intriguing.

But—and here I must once again bring social class into the picture—*there has not been a single well-controlled study that demonstrates any substantial difference between the family relationships of schizophrenics and those of normal persons from lower and working class backgrounds.* Now, it may be that the well-controlled studies simply have not dealt with the particular variables that do differentiate the families of schizophrenics from those of normal lower and working class families. The two studies that best control for social class— Clausen's and my study in Hagerstown, Maryland (1956) and Rogler's and Hollingshead's in San Juan (1965)—deal with but a few aspects of family relationship, notably not including the very processes that recent clinical studies have emphasized as perhaps the most important of all. It may be that investigations yet to come will show clear and convincing evidence that some important aspects of family relationship are definitely different for schizophrenia-producing families and normal families of this social background.

If they do not, that still does not mean that family relationships are not important for schizophrenia, or that it is not through the family that social class exerts one of its principal effects. Another way of putting the same facts is to say that there is increasing evidence of remarkable parallels between the dynamics of families that produce schizophrenia and family dynamics in the lower classes generally (Kohn, 1963; Pearlin and Kohn, 1966). This *may* indicate that the family patterns of the lower classes are in some way broadly conducive to schizophrenic personality development.

Clearly these patterns do not provide a sufficient explanation of schizophrenia. We still need a missing X, or set of X's, to tell us the necessary and sufficient conditions for schizophrenia to occur. Perhaps that X is some other aspect of family relationships. Perhaps lower class patterns of family relationships are conducive to schizophrenia for persons genetically predisposed, but not for others. Or perhaps they are generally conducive to schizophrenia, but schizophrenia will not actually occur unless the individual is subjected to certain types or amounts of stress. We do not know. But these speculative considerations do suggest that it may be about time to bring all these variables— social class, early family relationships, genetics, stress—into the same investigations, so that we can examine their interactive effects. Meantime, I must sadly conclude that we have not yet unravelled the relationship of social class and schizophrenia, nor learned what it might tell us about the etiology of the disorder.

Conclusion

Perhaps, after so broad a sweep, an overall assessment is in order. There is a truly remarkable volume of research literature demonstrating an especially high rate of schizophrenia (variously indexed) in the lowest social class or classes (variously indexed) of moderately large to large cities throughout much of the Western world. It is not altogether clear what is the direction of causality in this relationship—whether the conditions of life of the lowest social classes are conducive to the development of schizophrenia, or schizophrenia leads to a decline in social class position—but present evidence would make it seem probable that some substantial part of the phenomenon results from lower class conditions of life being conducive to schizophrenia. It is not even certain that the indices of schizophrenia used in these studies can be relied on, although there is some minor comfort in that studies using several different indices all point to the same conclusion. Perhaps it is only an act of faith that permits me to conclude that the relationship of class to schizophrenia is probably real, an act of faith only barely disguised by calling it a working hypothesis.

This working hypothesis must be weighed against a number of alternative interpretations of the data. Many of them are plausible, several are supported by attractive nuggets of data, but none is more compelling than the most obvious interpretation of all: that social class *seems* to matter for schizophrenia because, in fact, it *does*.

When one goes on to see what this might imply for the etiology of schizophrenia, one finds many more intriguing possibilities than rigorous studies. There is some evidence that the greater stress suffered by lower class people is relevant, and perhaps that lower and working class patterns of family relationships are broadly conducive to schizophrenia—although the latter is more a surmise than a conclusion.

Finally, it is clear that we must bring genetic predisposition and class, with *all* its attendant experiences, into the same investigations. That, however, is not the only sort of investigation that calls for attention. We have reviewed a large number of hypotheses, several major conflicts of interpretation, and many leads and hunches that all cry out to be investigated. The most hopeful sign in this confusing area is that several of the recent studies have gone far beyond seeing whether the usual stereotyped set of demographic characteristics correlate with rates of schizophrenia, to explore some of these very exciting issues.

12 / Sociocultural Factors in the Epidemiology of Schizophrenia

Elliot G. Mishler / *Norman A. Scotch*

In much the same way that the schizophrenic patient is the despair of his therapist in his imperviousness to treatment, the disease entity of schizophrenia is the despair of investigators in its stubborn resistance to their efforts to understand it. Each year innumerable research reports, reviews, and conceptual anal-

From *Psychiatry*, 1963, 26, 315–343. Copyright © 1963. Reprinted by permission of the author and the William Alanson White Psychiatric Foundation, Inc.

yses appear. They represent a variety of points of view and present diverse types of data, reflecting a wide range of authors that includes psychiatrists, epidemiologists, psychologists, sociologists, anthropologists, and biological scientists. Despite this intensive effort and an increasing amount of interest in recent years, schizophrenia remains an illness about which there is little definite or reliable knowledge. Like both clinical and experimental investigations, the epidemiological study of schizophrenia has had to face serious methodological and conceptual problems that have interfered with the steady growth of empirical information and also of theoretical understanding. While these problems manifest themselves in a particularly striking way in the study of schizophrenia, they are also present in other epidemiological inquiries. We believe, therefore, that a review of the issues involved may have significance not for schizophrenia alone but for the study of other diseases as well.

In general, the social epidemiology of mental disorders is a field with a particularly high ratio of review papers to original studies. Several recent reviews are available (Clausen, 1959; Dunham, 1959; Leacock, 1957). In addition, five volumes that have appeared during the last few years include extended discussions of important methodological and conceptual issues in this area of research, with a number of these analyses focused specifically on schizophrenia (Hoch and Zubin, 1961; Milbank Memorial Fund, 1961; Pasamanick, 1959; Plunkett and Gordon, 1960; Zubin, 1961).

The surfeit of summaries, analyses, and commentaries on schizophrenia contrasts sharply with the situation described in the earlier papers, which reviewed the literature on social factors in the epidemiology of essential hypertension and rheumatoid arthritis (Scotch and Geiger, 1962, 1963; Geiger and Scotch, 1963). Another review of materials on social factors and schizophrenia is not to be undertaken lightly. This review has a three-fold objective: To summarize and evaluate findings on the relationship of schizophrenia to selected social and cultural variables; to note and compare alternative hypotheses proposed to account for these findings; and to suggest guidelines for future research. We have drawn upon other reviews whenever possible, but in comparison with them, the present review is more restricted in focus and objectives. These restrictions, deriving from certain methodological and clinical concerns that are outlined below, have permitted a more selective and systematic coverage of studies.

In many of the general articles on the role of sociocultural factors in the occurrence of mental disorders there is a broad concern with all such disorders or with all psychoses. This paper focuses solely on schizophrenia. In some instances studies not specifically concerned with schizophrenia are used as points of reference for discussion, but the interest remains in their implications for schizophrenia. The rationale for this restriction is that we do not expect the same variables necessarily to be associated with different mental disorders. While we do not hold sacred the traditional diagnostic categories of psychiatry, it seems to be most in accord with current knowledge to view schizophrenia as a clinical entity that has different characteristics from other mental illnesses.

Existing reviews tend to be neither systematic nor comprehensive in coverage. A few well-known studies are discussed by all commentators; other studies are sometimes ignored and sometimes selected for emphasis. In examining a large number of investigations we attempted to set up criteria for adequacy and relevance; we found relatively few that met these criteria. . . .

Our particular methodological viewpoint and concerns will become clear in the following sections. On the whole, we have tried to differentiate among studies in terms of the methods and procedures used for case finding and for calculating morbidity rates. We believe that this permits a comparison of different studies with each other in a meaningful and systematic way, and results in a more rigorous and precise statement of current knowledge on the relationship of particular factors to schizophrenia.

Finally, we believe that clinical considerations have not received adequate attention in studies and analyses of the epidemiology of schizophrenia. Problems of nosology and diagnosis appear to be viewed by epidemiologists primarily as sources of error. Their solutions to these problems are aimed narrowly at increasing the reliability of diagnoses. In contrast, we see them as reflecting critical and unsolved questions about the nature of the illness. These are clinical problems to whose solutions epidemiological findings might contribute, but only if there is an awareness of the nature of the issues so that relevant information may be gathered. We have endeavored to suggest how an understanding of clinical issues could play a more important role in the design and interpretation of studies in this area.

Characteristics of Schizophrenia

Extent of the Problem

It is not easy to pick a starting point for a discussion of the epidemiology of schizophrenia. If, for example, we begin by trying to estimate the frequency of its occurrence, then we must make assumptions with regard to the conceptual agreement on and diagnostic reliability of the classification among different investigators; however, as will be seen later, available evidence argues against placing much confidence in these assumptions. If we start instead with an analysis of conceptual issues or with problems in the interpretation of social differentials in rates of schizophrenia, then in the absence of information on overall rates of occurrence the reader does not have a context in which to evaluate the potential significance of the issues raised. Recognizing that there are difficulties with any scheme of organization, we will follow the pattern set in earlier papers in this series—that is, beginning with the more descriptive material, namely, information on the overall extent of the problem, before proceeding to conceptual and analytic issues.

In an instructive article focused on the problem of estimating the overall rate of schizophrenia, Lemkau and Crocetti (1958) make explicit a number of assumptions that underlie such estimates. They point out that in order to establish

> . . . the true incidence of any disease, three basic conditions must be met. First, the identification of the entity in question should be highly reliable and objective for the investigators, i.e., susceptible of replication. Second, all cases should be known, or the ratio between known and unknown cases clearly established. Third, the population from which the cases are drawn should be clearly defined and carefully enumerated (p. 68).

These are ideal conditions not met in practice with regard to other illnesses, but perhaps even less closely approximated with regard to schizophrenia.

Where there is a high degree of "variability" in diagnosis and measurement, Lemkau and Crocetti suggest that the

> . . . most reliable technique open to the medical statistician is to establish a basic minimal figure on the narrowest basis possible, and a theoretical maximum on the broadest possible basis, and to attempt to establish, by a series of inferences, that estimate of incidence least likely to be in error (p. 70).

They follow their own suggestion, and by making a number of inferences, particularly with regard to the likely numbers of unhospitalized and unknown cases of schizophrenia in the community, they arrive at the following estimates:

> In summary, it would appear that the true incidence of schizophrenia in a Western European-type society can hardly be less than 50 per 100,000, and within all reasonable probability should not exceed 250 per 100,000 per annum . . . the incidence range most likely to contain the least error in its general application to various communities in Western European-type societies is in the vicinity of 150 cases per 100,000 population per year. That is to say that the true rate for various communities in these societies can be expected to fall above as well as below this figure with equal frequency (pp. 71–72).

While one might quarrel with some of the details, the estimates arrived at by Lemkau and Crocetti reflect inferences that are reasonable and justifiable in view of what is known about schizophrenia. Their figures may be considered, therefore, as useful approximations to the true rate of occurrence of the illness. Further, as they note, considering the high level of chronicity, even the minimum estimate would entitle schizophrenia to rate as one of the major diseases of mankind.

Lemkau and Crocetti's figures include all cases of schizophrenia whether in treatment or not, hospitalized or not. Hospital admission rates for schizophrenia are not only lower but also much more variable over time and from state to state. A report of the Biometrics Branch of the National Institute of Mental Health on first admissions to state mental hospitals shows that between 1940 and 1950, ". . . the schizophrenic rate rose from 15.9 to 21.0, an increase of 32 per cent with 37 states experiencing an increase in rate and only 10 a decrease" (Kramer, Pollack, and Redlich, 1961). Their figures also show marked variability among states, with New York and Rhode Island in 1950 having age-adjusted first admission rates for schizophrenia of more than 35 per 100,000, while Virginia, New Mexico, Kansas, and Wyoming had rates of less than 10 per 100,000.

Prevalence and expectancy rates are other measures of morbidity that help to fill in the picture on the extent of the problem. The prevalence of schizophrenia —that is, the proportion of the population that would be diagnosed as schizophrenic at any one point in time—is estimated by Lemkau and Crocetti as 290 per 100,000. The several studies of admissions to mental hospitals reviewed by Norris, including estimates derived from her own investigations, suggest that the minimum "expectancy rate"—that is, the proportion of an age cohort that may be expected to be hospitalized for schizophrenia between birth and age 75—lies between 8 and 12 per 1,000 (Norris, 1959).

In summary, the proportion of the population likely to develop schizophrenia during the course of a year is about .15 per cent; those hospitalized for schizophrenia for the first time during a year constitute about .02 per cent of the population; approximately .30 per cent suffers from the illness at any one time; about 1.00 per cent of each age cohort may be expected to fall ill at some point during their lifetime.

There was a time when schizophrenia was considered to be almost entirely a disease of the young, as its early label of dementia praecox indicated. While there is a somewhat broader age range among those who develop schizophrenia than was first suspected, the view that it is primarily a disease of the younger age groups is borne out essentially in all reports. Locke and his co-workers (1958), in a recent systematic and detailed investigation of first admissions to state mental hospitals, state:

> Among white and non-white for either sex, admission rates for schizophrenia are concentrated in the ages 20–40, with the peak occurring in the 25–34 age group. This finding is consistent with findings in earlier studies as well as recent national census data. Many of these studies showed the peak age of hospitalization to occur earlier among males than females (p. 175).

Lemkau and Crocetti (1958, p. 78) also emphasize the relation of morbidity to age, pointing out that age differentials are among the most striking and consistent findings and stating that ". . . it is definitely a disease, as the older nomenclature would imply, of the younger age groups. Many more than half of the hospitalized cases—about 59 per cent—are under 35 years of age. Less than 1 per cent are over 65 years of age."

Findings with regard to sex differentials are more ambiguous. There seems to be general agreement about a somewhat later age of onset for women than men; Norris' comment (1959, p. 117) that her data "confirm the well-known finding that the exhibition of the disease is delayed in women" reaffirms the previous quotation from Locke and his colleagues. However, there is some question as to overall rate differentials. Lemkau and Crocetti (1958), for example, assert: "The morbidity of the schizophrenic disorder is about equally distributed between males and females." However, in both Norris' English study and Locke's study of Ohio mental hospitals there is evidence of a higher rate for females. The former reports annual first admission rates of 17.7 and 19.4 per 100,000 for males and females respectively for the years 1947–49; she also reports expectancy rates of 9 per 1,000 for males and 12 per 1,000 for females through their lifetime period of risk. Locke (1958) finds: "Adjustment for age does not alter the observation that the first admission rate is higher for females than for males. Indeed the ratio of age-specific male rates to female rates is usually higher only in the 15–24 group." These authors point out that pre-World War II studies had tended to show that males had higher rates than females, and speculate that the changes in ratios may reflect changes over time in patterns of hospitalization and the social role of women in society.

We have not been able to find information on the relative mortality of persons with schizophrenia vis-à-vis other populations; studies of death rates among hospitalized patients are not useful for this purpose. There appears, however, to be a widespread assumption that schizophrenics have a shorter life expectancy than the average.

The marked chronicity of the illness bears mention in concluding this section on the extent of the problem. Schizophrenics constitute about 25 per cent of all hospital admissions, but about 50 per cent of the patients in mental hospitals at any one time have this diagnosis. The median duration of hospitalization among schizophrenic patients currently in the hospital is found to be 10.8 years in the data provided by 17 Model Reporting Area States, with duration increasing markedly with age (Kramer, Pollack, and Redlich, 1961).

Sociocultural Factors

While the immediate objective of epidemiological inquiry is to determine the distribution of disease in various social and cultural groups, the ultimate aim is to increase understanding of the factors that influence the onset and course of different illnesses. An examination of the complex ideas of causation and the ways in which various types of epidemiological investigation are related to clinical and experimental studies may be found in other sources (e.g., MacMahon, Pugh, and Ipsen, 1960), and these issues need not be reviewed here. However, it seems useful to discuss briefly some alternative "frames of reference" (Clausen and Kohn, 1954) that have been proposed for interpreting associations between social and cultural variables and schizophrenia. The following discussion has benefited in particular from the analyses of the same problem by Clausen and Kohn (1954), Leighton and Hughes (1961), and Jackson (1960).

The studies discussed are concerned with the social and cultural characteristics of persons clinically diagnosed as schizophrenic. The analyses typically involve a comparison of the morbidity rates between two or more different social or cultural groups. It has been the convention to ignore similarities among groups for the purpose of theoretical interpretation and to focus on differences. Thus, the finding that many occupations have roughly equal morbidity rates for schizophrenia has not been seen as a valuable or interesting theoretical problem, while particularly high rates for one group of occupations relative to the others has been the object of considerable speculation.

In approaching the studies, one must first consider the question of artifacts—that is, the possibility that the relationship found between the social variable and the rate of schizophrenia does not reflect the "true" relationship but has arisen from errors or biases in the procedures. The main source of such artifacts lies in the diagnostic and case-finding procedures, and in the ways of computing morbidity indexes. Some concrete illustrations of these possibilities will be presented in our discussion of social class.

Another but different type of artifact is the concomitant variation between two variables that are both functions of a third. This kind of artifact is the idea underlying the two familiar hypotheses used to account for different rates of schizophrenia in different ecological areas of the city, namely, genetic or social drift. These hypotheses suggest that the association between ecological area and schizophrenia results not from the action of the social environment but from the selective migration or drift of such persons into this area.

If an empirical association is accepted as more than an artifact, then the question arises of how the social environment enters into the disease process—that is, some theoretical mechanism must be postulated. A division between indirect and direct mechanisms seems to be involved in a number of formulations. Indirect mechanisms refer to the ways in which the social environment acts to produce individuals who are particularly vulnerable to schizophrenia; direct mechanisms refer to the types of situations the culture provides that may be more or less directly "schizophrenogenic." Child-rearing practices and styles of family life are often looked upon as being particularly important in creating high vulnerability. Role transitions, severe economic deprivation, and the disruption of primary group relationships have been regarded as among the stresses that might act directly to induce illness.

Finally, the most complex question is why some individuals develop schizophrenia while others exposed to the same social environment as children and adults do not. For many writers, the answer includes some reference to biological determinants either genetically given or resulting from organic defect or damage. Often these determinants are viewed as interacting with stressful features in the social environment, so that the interpretation is framed in terms of necessary and sufficient conditions rather than in terms of a single etiological agent.

This discussion of alternative approaches to interpretation has been purposefully brief. Some of them will be discussed in more detail in our discussion of specific findings. We hope that this introduction has been sufficient to convey to the reader our belief that the process of understanding the role played by sociocultural factors in schizophrenia depends not only upon empirical study, but upon theory and interpretation as well.

Conceptual and Methodological Issues

General discussions of schizophrenia often emphasize the high level of disagreement and confusion that exists. A typical comment is that of Cameron (1944), in his review of almost 20 years ago: "Nowhere else in the field of psychopathology . . . is there less agreement on so many important points than in schizophrenia." The relative lack of change over time is underscored by a more recent paper which notes that approximately 500 papers on the etiology of schizophrenia have appeared since 1940 and ". . . these papers disagree widely with one another and reflect the fact that schizophrenia is a singularly difficult disorder to investigate" (Jackson, 1960, p. 4). Although these quotations refer to the clinical problems of nosology, diagnosis, and etiology, ignorance is equally pervasive with regard to the natural history of the illness and its response to various forms of treatment.

Thus, one could not expect a high level of consistency among the findings of different epidemiological studies. While it may not be necessary for social investigators to resolve all or most of the major clinical and theoretical issues before undertaking research, the design of their studies would benefit from an understanding of these issues and an appreciation of their relationship to methodological decisions and to the interpretation of resulting data.

The *Diagnostic and Statistical Manual of the American Psychiatric Association* (1952) describes schizophrenic reactions as follows:

> . . . a group of psychotic reactions characterized by fundamental disturbances in reality relationships and concept formation with affective, behavioral, and intellectual disturbances in varying degrees and mixtures . . . marked by strong tendency to retreat from reality, by emotional disharmony, unpredictable disturbances in stream of thought, regressive behavior, and in some by a tendency to 'deterioration' (p. 26).

In Bleuler's classic monograph (1950) we find:

> I call dementia praecox 'schizophrenia' because (as I hope to show) the 'splitting' of the different psychic functions is one of its most important characteristics . . . a group of psychoses . . . characterized by a specific type of alteration of thinking, feeling, and relation to the external world which appears nowhere else in this particular fashion (pp. 8–9).
>
> . . . The fundamental symptoms consist of disturbances of association and affectivity, the predilection for fantasy as against reality and the inclination to divorce oneself from reality (autism). Furthermore, we can add the absence of those very symptoms which play such a great role in certain other diseases such as primary disturbances of perception, orientation, memory, etc. (p. 14).

Although there is variation in emphasis and detail, writers since Bleuler tend to agree on certain symptoms as essential criteria of the schizophrenic process. These are the "blunting" or flattening of emotional responsiveness and the inappropriateness of associations, often accompanied by the use of language with private, symbolic meaning; and an inward orientation with marked indifference to, and uninvolvement with, the social environment. Persons diagnosed as schizophrenic may exhibit any or all of these symptoms to a marked, moderate, or mild degree. The general impression created in the observer of a severely ill patient is of strange, unpredictable, and unintelligible behavior. "It is as bewildering to come unprepared and untrained into the presence of a disturbed schizophrenic patient as it would be suddenly to happen on a disturbed disorganized community whose history one does not know or cannot understand" (Cameron, 1947, p. 451). However, many diagnosed schizophrenic patients may be actively psychotic only intermittently, and most of the time may display little bizarre behavior.

This brief excursion into the problem of describing the essential and critical features of schizophrenia makes it easy to understand why there is a high level of confusion and disagreement as soon as one moves to more complex issues. A disease that is defined with reference to varying degrees of impairment in any one of several major and different psychological functions—impairment which must be shown to be not attributable primarily to organic causes—is certain to create difficulties for diagnosis, theory, and research.

One would expect the reliability of diagnoses to be relatively poor. There are surprisingly few systematic studies of this problem, but this expectation appears to be borne out by the reports that are available. One recent review notes:

> It would appear from the few papers dealing with the reliability of diagnoses that variation between even experienced clinicians is so great that comparisons between groups used by different investigators are subject to large error. In one study, three psychiatrists agreed in only 20 per cent of their cases and had a majority agreement in only 48 per cent. Another study revealed that the widest disagreement occurred among the most experienced clinicians (Jackson, 1960, p. 11).

Anecdotal reports of clinical and hospital practice indicate that changes over time in administrative practices within the same institution, and differences between institutions have a marked influence on the rates of diagnosed schizophrenia (Zubin, 1961). Similarly, a significant proportion of patients diagnosed as schizophrenic at one time or in one treatment institution may have their diagnoses changed either when readmitted to the same hospital or when transferred to another hospital. One report notes that while there is higher consistency in the rediagnoses of schizophrenia than in other mental illnesses, only 50 per cent of a sample of patients diagnosed as having any "functional psychosis" on first admission received diagnoses on later admission to a different hospital that were in this same general category (Clausen and Kohn, 1959).

Conceptual agreement on the nature of schizophrenia is even more difficult to achieve than agreement at the empirical level. For many investigators, schizophrenia is a specific disease or class of diseases with specific symptoms and a specific etiological agent. There is, of course, great variety in the specific agent hypothesized. For others, it is not a specific disease but a "syndrome" in which the manifestations of ego disorganization may be quite variable from one patient to another and the responsible or predisposing factors may also be any of a multitude of stressful or traumatic disturbances (Bellak, 1958). In addition to the traditional subtypes of schizophrenia, many authors have suggested the possibility of two distinct illnesses with different etiologies, onsets, symptom pictures, and prognoses—with one group having an unfavorable and the other a favorable outcome (Vaillant, 1962).

Problems of nosology and case definition have received some discussion in the context of epidemiological research (Zubin, 1961). However, an examination of existing epidemiological studies suggests that investigators have, on the whole, been content to use as their study populations those cases diagnosed as schizophrenic in whatever institution was accessible to them as if such a diagnosis had a clear and unambiguous meaning. There has also been a general assumption that one set of findings about schizophrenia could be compared with another without examining carefully the source and meaning of the diagnosis in the different situations. There are, of course, exceptions to this over-optimistic tendency. For example, Erik Strömgren (1961) remarks: "In some cases we are suspicious from the beginning. When, for example, the word schizophrenia is used, everybody knows that the word is practically meaningless unless a detailed description is given of the sense in which the author wants to use the word" (p. 173).

It is one thing to point to these problems and quite another to derive from them some useful guidelines and principles for reviewing past work and for suggesting future research directions. Given the nature and level of disagreement on the basic features of schizophrenia and the unreliability of diagnosis, is there a meaningful way to compare findings from different studies? Given the great variety in conceptualizations and theories, how may research be oriented so as to have more direct and systematic relevance for the understanding of social factors in the etiology of schizophrenia?

We have adopted what may be termed a "fine-grained" approach to both of these questions—that is, we believe it is extremely important to specify the diagnostic and case-finding procedures in each study, as well as the other methodological procedures, in order to compare the findings of different studies with each other in a valid and meaningful way. Explicit attention to different methods may make it possible to clarify and to understand the significance of both the similarities and differences in the findings.

The specific implications of this fine-grained view will become evident in the following sections. We should like here merely to contrast it with two other approaches, one "coarse-grained" and the other involving a norm of arbitrariness. By a coarse-grained approach we refer to the collation of findings on schizophrenia regardless of the differences in methods and definitions among the studies. Here a reviewer attempts to search for an emerging consistency or pattern in the findings in spite of variance in procedures. A good example is a recent review paper where findings from community, hospital admission, and army rejection studies are used to arrive at generalizations about social variables and psychoses (Leacock, 1957). We have taken an alternate approach of restricting our comparisons to certain kinds of studies because we believe that there is already too much ambiguity involved in what is being studied.

The other alternative to the approach adopted here is a view associated with social statisticians and research epidemiologists. It begins with the standard scientific premise that all definitions are arbitrary and therefore urges that "some" definition be accepted so that investigators may get on with their work. There is an attractive simplicity to this approach, but, like Alexander's clean cut through the Gordian knot, it may destroy the phenomenon altogether. We believe that current disagreements about the nature of schizophrenia reflect basic and real issues in the attempt to understand this phenomenon. These issues should not be solved by arbitrary fiat. We believe the aim of investigations should be to clarify the nature and implications of the differences in definition and conceptualization so as to increase the understanding of schizophrenia. The critical need at the present time is not that everyone agree on "some" definition of schizophrenia, but that the several definitions be made explicit and operational.

Review of Studies

Our review of studies is divided into two major sections. The first examines investigations concerned with incidence differentials in the United States among persons with different social characteristics. We will discuss separately studies that focus on the variables of social class, social mobility, and migration. The second major section takes up comparative cross-cultural and total community studies. While no review in this field can claim to be exhaustive, we believe that the studies examined and used constitute a fairly comprehensive and representative sample of what is available.

The criteria for inclusion of studies in the review vary from section to section. The criteria are most restrictive with regard to the studies of social characteristics associated with schizophrenia. A major aim has been to determine the level of confidence that may be placed in a statement that a particular variable is associated with schizophrenia. Thus we shall be concerned with traditional and frequently asserted propositions linking schizophrenia with social class, social mobility, or migration.

With respect to the distinction between incidence and prevalence as morbidity indexes, we have adopted the position that incidence (the rate at which new cases appear during a given time period) is preferred to prevalence (the number of cases ill during a given time period) for studying the etiological role of sociocultural variables. Kramer's well-known discussion (1957) and his definition of incidence as "the fundamental epidemiologic ratio" is pointed toward clarifying the difference between the two indexes when the duration of illness is neither brief nor constant through different social groupings. As MacMahon and others (1960) have noted, prevalence may be utilized fruitfully to explore etiology only when it is considered as equivalent to incidence. Inasmuch as we believe that one problem in earlier reviews and in the proper evaluation of existing findings has been the lumping together of prevalence and incidence materials, we shall in the section reviewing epidemiological studies restrict systematic examination to those that utilize incidence. However, since there are no cross-cultural or community studies that utilize the incidence of schizophrenia as an index of morbidity, that section of the review will use prevalence data.

It is worth noting that the distinction between incidence and prevalence has received considerably more attention in studies of mental illness than in studies of physical illness, where prevalence measures tend to be the rule and have provided much of the basic data in the field. The main reason for this is that the durations of physical illnesses do not seem to be associated differentially with the basic sociodemographic variables. In the mental illnesses, while definitive data are lacking, there is enough evidence to suggest that duration is associated with such variables as social class (Hollingshead and Redlich, 1958) and marital status (Phillips, 1953) to argue against a casual use of prevalence as if it were equivalent to incidence.

While we have restricted our systematic review to incidence studies, we shall return to the question of other components of prevalence in the final section.

Some confusion exists regarding traditional ecological studies, such as the classic report of Faris and Dunham (1939) for understanding the etiology of schizophrenia. The criticisms of Thorndike (1939) and Robinson (1950) of the use of correlations between group indexes as if they validly represented correlations between characteristics in individuals has led to some misunderstanding of the meaning of the ecological findings. These critics have pointed out that high correlations between total community rates for schizophrenia and other community characteristics, such as median income of the population or median rental value of its homes, do not mean that individuals from these areas who develop schizophrenia actually have the characteristic in question. For example, Faris and Dunham showed that it was the white rather than the Negro residents of predominantly Negro areas who showed particularly high rates for schizophrenia. It is possible to show statistically that ecological and individual correlations are equivalent to each other only under very special conditions and that, on the whole, ecological correlations are likely to be higher than the corresponding individual correlations.

However, the criticism of the ecological studies on statistical grounds does not in itself suffice to dismiss these studies as spurious at the level of individual interpretation. Ecological variables have conceptual as well as operational meaning, and the problem is no different in principle from the problem of correlating occupation with schizophrenia and interpreting occupation as an index of a social class life style. If, for example, the variable "living in a high-rent census tract" is defined conceptually as an index of social aspirations, then a study of differential rates by rental value of census tracts may be interpreted in terms of psychological as well as ecological theory, and no change in statistical procedures is required to interpret it in one way rather than the other. While available ecological studies are not directly comparable for our purposes to studies using individual analyses and will therefore be used only as background in this review, nevertheless the ecological approach has a valuable role to play in epidemiological research. Some combination of ecological and individual designs would seem to be particularly powerful, a point to which we will return in the final section.

Finally, there is a great deal of controversy in the critical literature as to whether hospital admissions are valid indicators of the "true" incidence of illness. For example, Pugh and MacMahon (1962), in their recent monograph, adopt a cautious position but devote their energies to indicating the usefulness and relevance of hospital admission data. Kramer and his co-workers (1961), on the other hand, in a detailed analysis conclude that differentials in hospital admission rates are "more a function of differences in a number of external, biological, social, cultural, and environmental factors than of differences in the true incidence and prevalence of mental disorders" (p. 91). Our position in this matter has been to use data reflecting incidence whether it be a hospital admission or other treatment entry rate, but to recognize explicitly the differences among these rates in comparisons of studies and interpretations of findings.

The Incidence of Schizophrenia: Social Characteristics

SOCIAL CLASS   Two recent reviews of social class differentials in rates of schizophrenia, although superficially agreeing in some findings, suggest to us the nature and lack of clarity of accumulated findings and the difficulties associated with comparing different studies. Lemkau and Crocetti (1958), basing their remarks on explicit reference only to the early ecological study of Faris and Dunham and on the prevalence rates found in the Eastern Health District Survey of 1936, state: "There is also some evidence that socioeconomic status is a differentiating factor with a disproportionate number of cases being found in the lower socioeconomic status" (p. 81).

After reviewing many different types of English and American studies, where the sources of data vary from hospital admission records and army rejection studies to community prevalence surveys, Leacock concludes:

> Although the studies of socioeconomic status and mental illness are not strictly comparable . . . the general trend is clear and consistent enough to be meaningful. . . . Rates for schizophrenia, like rates for all mental illness, go up in situations associated with situational stress—lower socioeconomic status, living in disorganized urban areas, immigration or migration. . . (1957, p. 337).

Despite the similarity of findings, it is our contention that reports such as these do not advance the understanding of relationships between sociocultural factors and schizophrenia because they do not sufficiently differentiate among the methods and concepts used in different studies. To lump together studies of incidence and prevalence differentials, rates based on hospital admissions and surveys of untreated persons in the community, and studies using markedly different measures and conceptions of social class, is to obscure rather than clarify these relationships.

In the course of preparing this review, many studies were examined that were considered by their authors and by other reviewers to bear on the problem of social class differences in schizophrenia. We do not wish to dispute their general relevance. However, only nine studies met what we believe are minimal criteria for examining the basic hypothesis that differences in social class are associated with the development of schizophrenia. The analyses of these nine involve comparisons of the social attributes of individuals when they become ill—that is, they are studies of the incidence of schizophrenia in which the individual's own social class position rather than an ecological characteristic of his community is used as the independent variable.

Of the nine studies, eight use occupation as the measure of social class. Three of the studies include admissions to private as well as state mental hospitals. Typically, although not uniformly, the rates are age-specific or age-standardized, usually controlled for sex, and sometimes controlled for nativity or race. These specific studies, listed chronologically . . . are those of: Nolan (1917), Ødegaard (1932), Clark (1948), Frumkin (1952, 1955), Hollingshead and Redlich (1958), Locke and others (1958), Clausen and Kohn (1959), and Jaco (1960).

In view of the importance of the problem and the abundance of review articles and theoretical analyses, the relative scarcity of basic empirical studies is surprising. These nine studies cover a 35-year period. The reference populations are four states, and one large, one medium-sized, and one small city. While the census classification of occupation usually provides the basic coding categories and rank ordering, only two of the nine studies use the same number of categories in their rate comparisons. The number of categories in the different studies—2, 4, 5, 7, 8, 10, 10, 12, and 19—provides a good index of the low level of basic agreement on methods and procedures.

The most consistent finding, which emerges in eight of the nine studies, is that the highest incidence is associated with the lowest social class groupings used in each study. In six studies it is the unskilled or laborers category, in a seventh it is the unemployed, and in the eighth it is the lowest of four social classes—defined by an index of occupation, education, and residence—that produces the highest rate.

There are two important specifications to this general finding. First, when male and female rates are computed separately, the female rates are considerably higher within this lowest occupational category. For example, in one study where the highest rates of hospital admissions for schizophrenia are found for metropolitan counties with high overall hospital usage, the rate for male laborers is 106.5 and for female laborers 479.9 per 100,000 (Locke et al., 1958). Second, the rates for this category tend to be sharply higher than the rates for the adjacent occupation. The New Haven study, for example, shows rates for Class V that are twice as high as for Class IV—20 as compared with 10 on the morbidity index used (Hollingshead and Redlich, 1958).

A second, almost equally consistent finding (present in six of the studies, one of which includes admissions to private hospitals) is that the lowest rate is associated with the managerial group. This occupational group varies somewhat in definition in the different studies but usually includes proprietors of small businesses and executives of large ones. This finding is stronger among males than females, and seems to be meaningful only for metropolitan areas since too few cases exist in nonmetropolitan areas to compute rates. The differences between rates for this group and adjacent categories are not consistently large, and sometimes another group has an equally low rate.

Only the Hagerstown study reports no differences among occupations. The report focuses more on ecological distributions and social mobility and gives the occupation of patients at admission a minor and secondary role (Clausen and Kohn, 1959). Two aspects of this study restrict its value for comparison purposes. First, the small numbers of cases required that occupations be grouped into two broad classes—one including professional, technical, and managerial workers; the other including operatives, service workers, and laborers. Second, rates are not computed separately for males and females. As a result of these procedures, whether or not the differences found in other studies might also be present here cannot be ascertained.

Although all of these investigators use a similar classification of occupations as a set of empirical categories, they do not all share the same conceptual definition of this variable. Earlier writers, where they are explicit, sometimes refer to specific qualities of particular occupations as playing an etiological role in the development of mental disorders. Thus, Nolan (1917) refers to eyestrain and long hours of required concentration as occupationally linked stresses that might induce mental illness; Clark (1948) suggests among his hypotheses that "the low prestige aspect of an occupation increases the pre-schizophrenic's negative attitudes toward himself."

In more recent investigations, the specific and differentiating qualities of occupations are not mentioned. Instead, a person's occupation is used as an operational definition of his position in the general system of social stratification. Occupation is seen only as a useful index of social class, which in turn is viewed as a general style of life with clusters of values and behaviors that distinguish the members of one class from the members of other social classes.

As we have already indicated, the ecological studies do not permit direct comparison with the group of studies summarized here. It is worth noting, however, that with the rare exception of the Clausen and Kohn Hagerstown investigation, the ecological findings show the highest incidence in the poorest or most disorganized areas of the cities (Faris and Dunham, 1939; Lapouse, Monk, and Terris, 1956). There is no evidence in these studies that would contradict the relationships between social class and schizophrenia summarized here.

As indicated earlier, there are several types of alternative explanations of empirical relationships between social variables and the incidence of schizophrenia. Thus, the relationship may be viewed as an error or an artifact arising from the procedures used; both schizophrenia and class position may be thought to reflect or result from the operation of some third variable or process; different rates of remission rather than of onset may produce the associations with social variables; or, finally, social class may be interpreted as a valid etiological variable having a causative role in the development of schizophrenia. Each of these possibilities will be discussed briefly.

Among the many sources of potential error, three in particular deserve attention: The case-finding procedures are not independent of social class, the diagnostic procedures are not independent of social class, and the measurement of social class is unreliable.

It has long been recognized that the use of state hospital admissions as the sole source of data for computing morbidity rates for schizophrenia in different social groups might bias findings. This is because other psychiatric treatment resources such as private mental hospitals, psychiatric units in general hospitals, and out-patient facilities would be used disproportionately by different social groups, and these different usage patterns would be reflected in state hospital admission rates. For this reason, several of the studies have included admissions to private hospitals. This inclusion has not altered the pattern of findings. However, before this source of bias is discounted entirely, two characteristic differences between state hospital and private hospital admissions require further examination.

First, private hospitals may be less likely to diagnose their patients as schizo-phrenic because of a greater concern with the social stigma carried by such a diagnosis and a greater sensitivity to the family's resistance to this diagnosis. This would depress the schizophrenic rates for groups using these facilities—that is, the higher social class groups. Second, individuals in the higher class groups are relatively more likely to have had their illness detected early, and if hospitalized to have been released after a short period of treatment. In successive age cate-gories, a higher proportion of their admissions would then be readmissions. This factor would also tend to reduce the apparent incidence in higher class groups since incidence rates in the studies reported are based on first admissions.

Another important possibility is related to this last point—namely, that admis-sions to hospitals do not constitute a representative sample of persons becoming schizophrenic, but are a sample of those who did not recover quickly. We know that admission to a hospital comes at the end of a series of other attempts to deal with the illness. Studies of the preadmission histories of hospitalized patients indicate that a delay of several months between the onset of symptoms and hospital admission is the typical rather than unusual pattern. During this time family members may either try to deny the illness by "normalizing" the behavior (Clausen and Yarrow, 1955), or may try to adapt to the situation by developing new patterns of relationship (Sampson, 1962), or may try to cope actively with the illness through various types of professional and nonprofessional help (Cumming, 1962). While the distribution of these patterns by social class is unknown, the relatively greater availability of outpatient treatment facilities for persons in higher social classes may increase the probability of recovery or of maintenance in the community for some proportion of the schizophrenic popula-tion, and thus reduce the hospital admission rate for these groups.

There is also the possibility of bias in the diagnostic process. There is some experimental evidence that more severe diagnoses may be attached to working-class patients as compared to middle-class patients where the diagnostic informa-tion is the same for both (Haase, 1955). This is not the same, of course, as demonstrating that the lowest occupational groups are more likely to receive diagnoses of schizophrenia, but the demonstrated low reliability of diagnoses and the complex ways in which social characteristics may be used as cues to diagnosis suggest the need for further attention to this problem.

A third source of potential error lies in the measurement of the social class variable. Social researchers are aware that the reliable coding of an individual's occupation is an extremely difficult procedure requiring a number of items of information and detailed coding instructions. It is highly unlikely that adequate procedures are followed in hospital admitting offices, and the basic record information undoubtedly contains a large amount of error. This is particularly important for persons in lower-status occupations and for patients whose employment histories may show marked instability. Does one code his most recent occupation? His usual occupation? How long must he have been out of work to be listed as unemployed? These difficulties are further compounded in the occupational classification of women, and it is often unclear in reports of investigations whether their own or their husbands' occupation has been used.

Besides reflecting errors of measurement and procedure, an association between schizophrenia and social class may result from the action of some third variable— that is, the association is not evidence for a direct connection between class and ilness but may be an artifact arising from their joint attachment to another variable. Genetic and social drift are the most frequently mentioned hypotheses and suggest processes through which schizophrenics tend to accumulate in certain social groups either through breeding or geographic mobility. These interpretations have been examined in detail by Clausen and Kohn (1954). A related possibility is that the direction of the relationship is from the illness to the social class position—that is, schizophrenics have difficulty holding good jobs and tend to be downwardly mobile, so that the lower occupational groups have a disproportionately larger number of cases. Investigators have generally been aware of this problem, as indicated in the comment by Locke (1958):

> Undoubtedly additional studies are needed on the relationship of occupation to mental illness, and of mental illness as a determinant of occupation. . . . The census data and the hospital admission data employed in this study were based on the individual's latest occupational employment. Undoubtedly, studies incorporating occupational histories are needed to clarify the roles that occupation and occupational mobility play in relation to schizophrenia and other mental diseases (p. 187).

Studies of social mobility will be examined in the next section of this paper.

If the effects of artifacts and errors are removed, one may turn finally to the possibility that the variable of social class is related etiologically to schizophrenia. Earlier, we noted both indirect and direct processes: A differential vulnerability to schizophrenia produced in the early life experiences within the family in different class cultures; or differentials in levels of social and personal stress among various class groups leading to differential rates of schizophrenia. Dunham (1961) has recently evaluated the latter hypothesis:

> In this review of social structures and mental disorders, I have attempted to concentrate on the various hypotheses that purport to explain significant rate differentials in selected social structures . . . from an environmental perspective, interest is greater for the so-called functional disorders but even here the evidence is highly inconclusive for asserting with any confidence that a high rate in a given position of a social structure is a product of certain stresses, strains, and conflicts in that position (p. 258).

The role of the parental family in the etiology of schizophrenia has received considerable attention in the clinical literature. Recent reviews of research in this area indicate that interesting speculation still far outruns reliable data (Spiegel and Bell, 1959; Sanua, 1961). Studies have suffered from small and unrepresentative samples, a lack of research controls, and unreliable instruments. Despite the present limitations of family studies, it would seem that a comprehensive theory of social factors in the etiology of schizophrenia would have to include the family's influence on the patient both in his formative and later years, and the family's function as a transmitter of forces in the larger social environment. Studies which attempt to relate patients' living arrangements to their position in the social class structure are an obvious need (see Gerard and Houston, 1953).

We believe that at this time no reasonable decision can be made as to the merits of the alternative explanations of the relationships found between social class and the incidence of schizophrenia. Neither can proper weights be assigned to any set of them taken collectively. The higher rates for schizophrenia found among the lowest social class groups in the studies reviewed here may be a function of errors of measurement or may be an artifact. Before attributing an etiological role to social class, these more parsimonious though less elegant interpretations should be ruled out through systematic investigation. We shall return to some of the problems of theory and further research in the final section of this review.

SOCIAL MOBILITY   Almost as much attention has been given in theoretical discussions to the question of whether the incidence of schizophrenia is associated with downward social mobility as to the relationship with social class. It is, of course, an important variable in its own right, but it takes on increased importance in view of the finding that the lowest socioeconomic class shows the highest incidence of schizophrenia.

The usual statement of this hypothesis is that schizophrenia-prone persons tend to move down the social class structure from their point of origin. Therefore, any differentials found among social positions can more reasonably be accounted for by this process than by aspects of the social environment in which schizophrenics are located at the time of hospitalization. While it may seem equally reasonable, and more consistent with the interpretations offered of social class differentials, to invert this argument and hypothesize that one effect of downward social mobility with its attendant stress might be the development of schizophrenia, this alternative direction of the relationship is found only in the layman's theory of mental illness.

The great difficulty in a study of social mobility is to determine a meaningful base population or standard of comparison in terms of which to evaluate the social histories of schizophrenic patients. In other words, high rates of downward social mobility found among any group of schizophrenics do not permit an interpretation of the relationship until we know the mobility histories of a comparable group of nonschizophrenics.

In their original discussion of the social-drift hypothesis, Faris and Dunham (1939) try to approximate such an analysis by comparing the relative degree of concentration of older and younger patients in the areas of the city with high admission rates. They argue that older people would have had more of an opportunity to drift; not finding any age differences in concentration, they reject the drift hypothesis as being inadequate to account for their findings.

While studies meeting our criteria are rare, we are fortunate in having two recent and well-controlled investigations that are similar in design. Unfortunately, their findings do not agree.

Lystad (1957, pp. 291–292) concludes from her study in New Orleans that schizophrenic patients "show less upward status mobility than matched, nonmentally ill persons." From more intensive control analyses she suggests that this difference is present for whites, females, members of the middle class, and those with more than grammar-school education; the differences disappear among Negroes, males, lower-class members, and those with less than grammar-school education. On the basis of her findings, she stresses ". . . the importance of longitudinal studies of schizophrenic patients and controls in various subcultures of our society."

On the other hand, in a control-group study using both male and female patients matched individually for age, sex, and occupation at a point averaging 16 years before hospitalization, Clausen and Kohn (1959) report that the record of social mobility for this group of first-admission schizophrenics was "approximately equal to that of the normal controls." Fifty-nine per cent of the paired controls and 64 per cent of the schizophrenics remained in the same occupational class; 16 per cent of the controls and 8 per cent of the patients moved upward; 2 per cent of the controls and 8 per cent of the schizophrenics showed marked fluctuations over time in occupational level.

While these two studies are similar in design, comparison remains difficult. The samples, relatively small in both studies, are drawn from different cities and from different types of treatment facilities. Further, Lystad's control analyses suggest that within certain subcultural groups one might not expect differences. Finally, one study uses three and the other uses two occupational classes, and mobility manifested in the former could easily be hidden in the latter.

Two other studies, although ecological in design, deserve mention since they focus on the relationship between social mobility and the incidence of schizophrenia. Both use residential mobility as an index of social mobility. In one study, a group of first-admission white male schizophrenic patients was matched with a control group for age and residential location 25 years prior to their hospitalization; comparisons were then made between the median monthly rentals of the census tract of residence at the two points in time. No significant differences were found in social mobility between the control and patient groups. Thus, this study shows no evidence of downward social drift for schizophrenics as compared to a nonpatient population (Faris and Dunham, 1939; Lapouse, Monk, and Terris, 1956). In another study, less well-designed than those already noted, there is a suggestion of downward social drift within that subgroup of male schizophrenic patients who live in socially isolated situations. Using the average housing quality of a political ward or housing zone as a socioeconomic index, it was found that for patients living in conjugal or parental family settings at the time of admission there was little evidence of the downward mobility that might be inferred from residential instability and movement into the lower economic areas. For example, one year prior to admission 95 per cent were living in an area at the same economic level, and five years prior to admission 81 per cent were living at the same level. For patients from nonfamily settings (mostly single men), the corresponding figures were 50 per cent and 29 per cent, and there was a marked concentration of these patients in the poorer areas of the city (Gerard and Houston, 1953).

A study of social mobility requires measures of the individual's social class at two different points in time. Interpretations must take into account the previously noted sources of error and artifacts in social class studies, and must also consider problems specific to the study of social mobility. For example, the investigator's concepts and methods must be adequate for and sensitive to changes that may have taken place over time in the system of social stratification. Thus, being a school teacher today may have a different meaning for women than it did 30 years ago; many occupations did not exist less than a generation ago for which occupations at an equivalent rank must be defined in order to measure social mobility. This point underscores the importance of control-group designs in these investigations.

Studies of social mobility must also define the point of origin to which the individual's later position is to be compared. There are several alternative points that may be used—for example, the social class of the parents, the individual's first occupation on entering the labor market, the social position of his siblings, or the occupational rank of others with comparable education. Which of these is used depends upon the investigator's theory of social class and social mobility. These theories are rarely made explicit, and there appears to be an implicit assumption that all of the possible measures are equivalent in meaning and will produce the same results. This assumption is clearly not tenable.

The success of both the Lystad and Clausen and Kohn studies in using control-group designs and in tracing occupational shifts in both their control and patient samples over a long period of time is encouraging. Further studies of this type would be extremely useful. In order to make firmer statements about the relationship of social mobility to the incidence of schizophrenia, it will be necessary to obtain data on populations larger than those studied thus far. The usefulness of such studies would be markedly increased if they reflected more complex ideas about occupational shifts and mobility than are represented by measuring the amount of change up or down on a single dimension.

MIGRATION Differentials in rates of mental disorders between migrant and nonmigrant populations have also received considerable attention. In her interpretative review of studies that form the introduction to Malzberg and Lee's report (1956), Dorothy Thomas concludes:

> A variety of approaches suggest that migrants, variously defined, do indeed differ from nonmigrants, also variously defined, in respect to the incidence of mental disease; and the weight of evidence favors an interpretation that migrants represent greater "risks" than nonmigrants. But many exceptions have been noted and many ingenious attempts have been made to explain them away. Closer examination of both generalizations and exceptions shows so many inconsistencies in definitions, so few adequate bases of controls, so many intervening variables, so little comparability as to time and place, that the fundamental "cause" of the discrepancies may well be merely the nonadditive nature of the findings of the different studies (p. 41).

The problems noted by Thomas are serious, even though these studies display, on the whole, a high level of rigor and precision in procedures and analyses.

A good example of systematic and careful work is Ødegaard's early study (1932). Striking differences were found between Norwegian-born and native-born residents of Minnesota in overall rates of mental disorder, with the migrants having higher rates. Unfortunately for our present purposes, his analysis of schizophrenia differentials and migration is limited to a comparison of Norwegian-born persons in Minnesota with Norwegians in Norway—that is, a comparison of emigrants with nonemigrants. The emigrants show higher rates of schizophrenia, with the females showing the more striking difference.

Malzberg and Lee's investigation (1956) of admissions to all psychiatric hospitals in New York State in 1940–41 involves specific controls and uses three different classifications of migration status in order to make a more precise determination of the factors at work. They find that for both sexes in white and nonwhite groups, the hospital admission rates for dementia praecox are higher for both native-born and foreign-born migrants than they are for New York-born residents. Among whites, rates for native-born migrants are equal to or greater than foreign-born rates; among nonwhites, the foreign-born rates are higher. They also find that rates for all psychoses are particularly high for recent migrants (within five years prior to the census date), and especially so for nonwhites.

On the other hand, Jaco's recent study (1960), which compares native-born and nonnative-born Texans, reports no systematic differences in rates of schizophrenia between these two groups. In only one subgroup, Spanish-American females, is there any evidence that migrant rates are higher than nonmigrants as defined in this study. Jaco notes several differences between his and the Malzberg-Lee study that might account for the differences in findings: Different socioeconomic conditions between the two states and at the different time periods studied, differentials in overall rates of migration into Texas and New York, and different case-finding procedures.

Despite the inconsistency among the findings from different studies, there is a general tendency in the literature to assume higher rates for migrants. Thus Lemkau and Crocetti (1958, p. 81) state: "The most striking differentials in the rates of schizophrenia are those between age groups and between mobile and non-mobile populations . . . the more mobile populations frequently have higher rates of the disease than the non-mobile." They go on to note briefly several different interpretations of this differential: "Whether this is because of a tendency for individuals in a preschizoid stage to be migratory generally or to migrate to different cultural settings, or whether this is due to the greater stress involved in a person's living in a somewhat mobile sub-culture or a new and alien cultural milieu is not clear."

Malzberg and Lee (1956), in a qualifying note on their findings, point to a possibly important statistical artifact in migrant studies: The population turnover among migrants is relatively high and the population at risk used as the denominator in computing rates may be too low, thus artificially increasing the migrant rates.

The demographic variable of migration is closer in many ways to clinical considerations about the onset of schizophrenia than either social class or social mobility. In clinical theory, ideas of loss, of identity problems, and of lack of involvement with other people enter into discussions of the etiology of schizophrenia. The possible connection between these concepts and the social-psychological position of the migrant is an obvious one; it suggests that future studies must be as concerned with the specific environments from which the migrants come as with their place of destination. Their past and present living arrangements, whether isolated or within a family (as, for example, in the study by Gerard and Houston [1953]), and the social environments of their points of origin and destination must be examined. The evidence on social mobility would also suggest the importance of bringing together ideas and measures of both social and geographic mobility in further work.

Culture and Schizophrenia

There is a sense in which the variables already discussed, such as social class, are "cultural" as well as social. In our organization of this review we are distinguishing more between the units of study and between the directions of theorizing than between variables as either social or cultural. Whereas in the previous sections we investigated whether rates of schizophrenia varied with social class, social mobility rates, or geographic mobility rates, in this portion we begin with the characteristics of cultures and ask whether different characteristics are more or less likely to predispose persons to schizophrenia. An adequate understanding of etiological processes requires a combination of these two broad directions of work and theory; we shall return to this in the closing section of the paper.

In the following sections, we will review materials that treat the relation of "culture as a whole" to the etiology of schizophrenia. As will be seen, although several conceptual models exist as potential starting points for research and there are numerous reports of mental disorders in a great variety of societies, remarkably little systematic data have been collected that bear on the significance of cultural differences for the etiology of schizophrenia.

Several papers hypothesize ways in which culture might influence or cause mental illness (Leighton and Hughes, 1961; Jackson, 1960; Clausen and Kohn, 1954), but apparently there is very little empirical support for the hypothesized causal relationships. Such evidence as does relate culture to schizophrenia bears more on the question of content, or symptomatology, than on etiology, development, or cause of the illness. Beyond the possibility suggested in the literature that rates vary from society to society, and the implication that this *may* be a function of culture, there is no evidence relating culture in a causal manner to schizophrenia.

There are at least three broad approaches to the problem of studying and demonstrating any relationships that might exist between culture and schizophrenia: The cross-cultural or comparative approach, the study of total communities, and the study of culture change.

THE CROSS-CULTURAL APPROACH   The comparative method, while not uniquely anthropological, has been used to good advantage by anthropologists to examine the universality of various propositions concerning human behavior. It allows a certain degree of scientific control and is therefore particularly useful in the study of phenomena for which alternative methods are not feasible. Clausen (1959), in discussing such an approach to the investigation of mental disorders, has stated:

> . . . in attempting to interpret in an etiological framework any observed difference in the incidences of treated or psychiatrically observed mental illness between two population segments (whether these be social classes, ethnic groups, or subcultures), the crucial question is: do some discernible aspects of life processes in one of these segments give rise to more cases of mental illness than are produced in the other? Or, restated, if the two subcultures do differ in the amounts of mental illness produced, what are the specific

social and cultural variables or constellations of variables involved, and how do they exercise their effect (p. 496)?

While it is probably true that the comparative cross-cultural approach alone can never lead to definitive answers regarding disease etiology, it appears to be as good a starting point as any other in epidemiological studies of certain diseases. Thus the primary function of such an approach is to provide working hypotheses for further research, and possibly to better delineate the nature of the dependent variable.

A variant of the comparative approach limits the scope of inquiry by focusing on the effect of a particular variable, or set of variables, in diverse cultures. For example, one might look at the relation of social class to the prevalence of schizophrenia in a number of different settings. In this way hypotheses relating such a variable to schizophrenia may be tested and refined.

In such comparative approaches it is of course of paramount importance that the rates be accurate. The problems involved in accurate determination of rates are severe in the United States and Western Europe, but doubly so in those non-Western societies where many of these studies have been carried out. Often these comparative studies are not performed by a single investigator working in two or more different cultures; rather, they involve a comparison of a number of individual studies carried out by as many investigators. More important is the fact that diagnostic comparability is absent when findings from many different societies are assembled. This is true not only for the reasons mentioned earlier (different types of rates, different case-finding procedures, and so forth) but also because of additional questions concerning the cross-cultural applicability of designations of normal and abnormal behavior patterns.

In part for these reasons, a review of the cross-cultural literature, particularly that concerning non-Western societies, is disheartening. For example, Wittkower and his associates (1960), in a praiseworthy attempt to build a body of data, organized a "Transcultural Psychiatric Review and Newsletter," and sent questionnaires to psychiatrists and others throughout the world. They received reports from 37 respondents in 25 countries. The questionnaires cover "observed schizophrenic symptomatology, clinical subtypes, cultures and peoples to whom the observations referred, and locale of observation and psychiatric orientation of observer" (p. 855). There are no valid data on rates, either prevalence or incidence, or even on ratios of one type of illness to another, since the returns are based on estimates by the respondents derived from a variety of sources. There is thus no comparability. In the end this survey comprises what the authors call "preliminary observations" or impressions of the ratio of schizophrenia to other mental disorders, and of ratios of schizophrenic subtypes, plus impressions of the cultural effects on symptomatology and delusional content (Wittkower and Fried, 1959; see also Wittkower et al., 1960).

Recent reviews by Benedict and Jacks (1954), Benedict (1958), and Lemkau and Crocetti (1958) of existing studies on non-Western groups highlight both the lack of substantive findings and many of the methodological problems involved.

Benedict's exhaustive review includes studies of Africans, Negroes in Latin and South America, American Indians, Micronesians, Australians, Formosans, Japanese, Fijians, East Indians, and assorted immigrant groups to the United States and Canada. These studies document the noncomparability of incidence and prevalence since, with but few exceptions—such as Lin's study of Formosa (1953) —they use hospital admissions as a reflection of incidence of schizophrenia within the several populations. In fact, most of the writers devote little attention to rates but tend to be concerned with symptoms, ratios of schizophrenia subtypes, and delusional content. Thus one writer points out that his group is high in paranoids but low in catatonics, and other writers point out the reverse.

In passing, Benedict takes up the issue of the possible relativity of symptomatology, and tends to be critical of the "anthropological position" which, as he sees it, almost denies the possibility of abnormality within primitive societies (although he notes that the strength of this position within anthropology seems to wax and wane with time). He points out that the belief, no longer as popular as it once was, that schizophrenia is a disease of civilization is sheer folklore, and that while the rates reported in these studies are questionable, the fact of the existence of the disease in each of these societies is not. Additionally, Benedict, as well as the authors he reviews, asserts that not only are the forms and symptoms of the disease derived from the culture, but also there are obvious "cultural" differences in diagnosis, treatment, hospitalization, admission rates, and tolerance of behavior in the community.

Benedict points out that the majority of studies do not even attempt to deal with the question of etiology. Those that do almost uniformly offer the hypothesis of rapid culture change as the major etiologic influence. The implicit assumption is of course that in the "primitive" state there is no schizophrenia. Benedict is highly skeptical of the evidence offered in support of this position. In a few of these studies low socioeconomic status is cited as being possibly etiologically relevant.

To illustrate the difficulties in utilizing published studies for cross-cultural comparisons it is instructive to focus in some detail on what is frequently cited as one of the better studies of this type. In his review Benedict (1958) states:

> For schizophrenia among natives of West Africa we can turn to the recent study by Tooth, which is superior in most respects to any of the foregoing. Tooth, working on the Gold Coast, conducted a kind of census survey, collecting data on nonhospitalized cases through surveys by resident officers and examining as many of these cases as he could gain access to. Although he admits that his material is inadequate in many respects and describes the difficulties produced by native resistance, language handicaps, and the like, *this study must be considered the most nearly complete of any for Africa* (Italics added) (p. 698).

Both Benedict's and Tooth's caveats notwithstanding, this study is worthless for epidemiological purposes. In the first place the paper is replete with judgmental and unsubstantiated observations on African character and personality. More important for our purposes, however, are methodological shortcomings. This is a general population survey, but the findings come only from *non-hospitalized* cases in the population at large. If conclusions are to be drawn concerning, say, the distribution of schizophrenia or mental illness in general in the different areas of the Gold Coast, and if hospital populations are not included in the obtained rates, then the interpretations are subject to the artifact of possible differences in each area in the willingness to hospitalize, or keep at home, those suffering from disease. Although Tooth does warn against taking these data too seriously, he himself does nonetheless draw conclusions.

How did Tooth find his cases? He asked census enumerators and local chiefs to supply lists of names of "mad" persons. He writes: "But the reactions of Chiefs to this request were erratic and unpredictable and this part of the work furnished an interesting example of the difficulties of organizing even a comparatively *simple* [*sic!*] project through the native authority." Using such questionable methods, after two years Tooth (1950) assembled 400 cases of mental illness. He writes:

> During the period of two years covered by this report approximately 400 examples of mental illness were seen but in less than half this number was it possible to obtain anything approaching a satisfactory record of the illness. Accounts from relatives or persons who had known the subject before the onset of the illness were obtained in 173 instances and although, in many of these, the information available fell short of what is normally desirable, it was sufficient for the purposes of classification. It is with the analysis of these 173 cases that the following section is concerned.

No mention is ever again made of the 227 discarded cases, thus introducing possible biases—sex, age, tribe, and so forth—regarding which cases it is likely to get information on, and which not.

In addition, there are numerous other very considerable shortcomings as regards standards and criteria, methods of observation, and so on. What are left, then, are some characteristics of types of mentally ill Africans, with no reliable way to estimate either rates or differences in rates from tribe to tribe, area to area, sex to sex. We cite this study in some detail not as an example of a poor study, but because, according to the consensus of most reviewers, it is one of the best studies available. Since its publication, Tooth's warnings have rarely been heeded and his conclusions have tended to be accepted at face value.

Lemkau and Crocetti (1958), while reviewing much of the literature covered by Benedict, have focused almost completely on schizophrenia; they are more concerned with rates than with symptoms. They summarize their findings as follows:

> There are many descriptions in the literature of psychopathological pictures in other than Western European cultures, but most of these are anecdotal descriptions of a single case or of a group of cases with no relation to a standard population. Many are reports of cases which are clearly comparable to schizophrenia as it is known to Western psychiatrists, and, as a generalization, it may be said that psychiatrists trained in Europe and the United States seem to find cases which fit these diagnostic categories in whatever cultures they work in. As a symptom picture the disease appears to occur in every population that has been thoroughly studied, whatever its cultural background.
> The rate of occurrence is quite another matter. It is fair to say at the outset that there is no culture outside of the Western European group which has been studied as intensively. There are a great many unsupported statements in the literature that this or that culture has more or less of schizophrenia

than others. Most of these data are purely impressionistic and are frequently based on one of two equally undependable indicators: the investigator's prejudices regarding the etiology of schizophrenia or the use of inadequately gathered statistics (p. 65).

They conclude:

> In summary, there is evidence that schizophrenia, or schizophrenia-like reactions, occur in all known cultures. There is extremely little valid data on the incidence or prevalence of the disease in other than Western European-type cultures; within rough limits, rates are similar in all those which have been carefully studied (p. 66).

From the foregoing it is evident that the literature dealing with schizophrenia among primitive groups is not likely to be a particularly valuable source for rates. On the whole, the comparative cross-cultural approach has until now been of limited value with regard to an understanding of the etiology of schizophrenia.

THE STUDY OF TOTAL COMMUNITIES   The rationale for studying mental illness within "total communities" is both plausible and reasonable. Social variables can best be studied in the context of the larger cultural system in which they are found. Any given variable could have considerably different significance in different societies. Lower socioeconomic status, for example, may be critically important where the range is wide; where the range is narrow, it may be of minor importance. Thus, to study such a variable cross-culturally with the assumption that its cultural meaning and significance is *constant* may very well be unwarranted. The study of total communities would not only measure the relationship of the rate of mental illness to social class position, but also—by examining the variable in its total cultural context—would attempt to assess the meaning and importance of class membership within this community.

Additionally, a much wider range of social and cultural phenomena are surveyed in community studies than is the case when particular variables or groups of variables are selected in advance for primary or sole attention. Under the former conditions, previously unsuspected variables bearing powerfully on mental disease are more likely to impress themselves upon those conducting the study than if the focus is a priori on particular sets of variables. And while it is less likely that not-so-powerful variables will make themselves known to investigators, there is still a better chance that they will receive attention when the investigator goes into the community than if he relies simply on hospital admission data and the usual demographic indexes.

Finally, among the important advantages of community studies is the increased opportunity to study the healthy as well as the sick. Hospital studies often use control populations, but in community studies one can examine more directly how the ill and the well in the same social environment differ from each other in terms of a range of social and cultural characteristics. The answers should be productive of working hypotheses on a number of levels.

From reviewing the literature it appears that disadvantages must outweigh the advantages, since exceedingly few studies of total communities are reported. What is more discouraging is the lack of comparability of available studies, not only in terms of rates, but also in terms of the social data collected. The existing handful of community studies all rely on prevalence measures, rather than incidence. Most studies group together several different categories of mental illness and do not focus on particular disorders, since the rates for individual diseases tend to be so low that adequate numbers are not obtained unless huge populations are sampled. In some cases, traditional diagnostic categories are not used in major analyses, which means, of course, that the results are of limited value in the study of specific diseases, such as schizophrenia. Even where the diagnoses are kept separate, and the statistical procedures are rigorous, attention to social variables is superficial. In other cases, the social and cultural variables are relatively well handled, but the statistical procedures may be questioned.

It is unfortunate that in neither of the two recent elaborate community studies of mental disorder does schizophrenia receive separate attention. In the Midtown study, the primary dependent variable in the analysis of social and cultural variables is a general rating of "impairment," without reference to diagnosis (Srole et al., 1962). The Stirling County study will also emphasize general ratings of impairment and psychiatric disorder in the still-unpublished third volume, which will contain data on the distribution of levels of impairment in the several communities studied. These communities have been classified in terms of their level of social disorganization, with the prediction that the more "disorganized" communities will have higher rates of mental disorder than the "integrated" communities (Leighton, 1959; Hughes et al., 1960). Comparative studies such as this hold much promise.

The Formosan study by Lin (1953) is generally regarded as one of the better community surveys of mental disorder. Schizophrenia receives separate treatment and analysis, and Lin's methodology, especially his case-finding techniques, is impressive. Using what he calls the "census examination method" Lin carefully studied random samples from three communities in Formosa: a rural village, a small town, and an urban community. The total sample of almost 20,000 was interviewed by psychiatric teams. All cases of suspected mental abnormalities were reviewed by Lin, who was responsible for final diagnosis. Forty-three cases of schizophrenia were uncovered, yielding the following prevalence rates per 1,000: 1.8 in the rural village, 2.5 in the town, and 2.1 in the city. The differences in rates between the three communities appear negligible. However, these cases of schizophrenia tended to concentrate in the center (and most densely populated area) of *each* community (a finding in keeping with earlier ecological studies in the United States). In comparing densely populated areas with sparsely populated areas Lin found a ratio of 29:14. Lin further found that the rates were higher for females, and that they varied by social class (upper 3.5, middle 1.2, lower 4.5), though no interpretation was offered for these variations in rates. Lin did not make it clear exactly how these class categories were established, mentioning only that a number of factors—such as wealth, education, occupation, and appearance of house and furniture—were taken into consideration. Even in this careful study, the independent variables used to study the relation of schizophrenia prevalence to social factors reflect the general poverty of the field, consisting only of sex, ecological distribution, and social class.

In contrast to Lin's study, the investigation by Eaton and Weil (1955) of the mental health of the Hutterites uses somewhat questionable rates and case-finding techniques, but is quite sophisticated with regard to social and cultural factors. Essentially Eaton and Weil were interested in examining the hypothesis held by some observers that mental illness is absent in the Hutterite society, as a result of a culture and system of values that stress conformism, cooperation, and religion and devalue such "American characteristics" as aggression and competition, thought by laymen, at least, to be productive of higher rates of mental illness. Using anthropological techniques (key informants, participant observation, and so forth), the authors constructed an ethnographic description of this group, with the focus on areas of potential interpersonal difficulties. While these investigators found, in contrast to some expectation, that mental disorder was far from absent in this group, they did find a relatively low prevalence of schizophrenia, 1.1 per 1,000.

However, objections to the conclusions may be raised on at least two counts. First, the case-finding techniques represent a mixed bag. Some communities were intensively investigated, with Weil, the psychiatrist, personally examining suspected mentally ill persons; other communities were not even visited and cases were collected from hospital records, correspondence and interviews with physicians, and hearsay from Hutterite community leaders. It is difficult to diagnose an illness like schizophrenia under the best conditions, but to do it on the basis of descriptions by community leaders of the behavior of suspected individuals is highly questionable. Second, the rate used, the "lifetime morbidity rate" (all individuals alive on a given date with any history of schizophrenia), is of limited value regarding the crucial question of etiology. Kramer's comments (1957) on this problem also point to a number of important general issues that community researchers must deal with:

> In effect, this index is a determination of the proportion of a population alive on a given date who have a history of an attack of mental disorder. It should be apparent that this index is an inappropriate one to use if the focus of the research is to determine the influence of culture on the rate at which mental disorder occurs. The proportion of a population surviving to a given date with a history of a disease is a function of the incidence rate, the mortality of persons who have ever had the disease and the mortality of the non-affected population. The fact that lifetime prevalence would differ between two or more cultural groups does not mean that incidence differs. Indeed, incidence may be equal while the duration of life following attack by the illness differs. For example, there may be two primitive cultures A and B with an equal rate of incidence of mental disorders. Culture A's attitude toward the mentally ill is a protective one and everything possible is done to prolong their lives, whereas culture B's attitude is just the opposite. Thus, in A the interval between onset of illness and death would be considerably longer than in B and as a result, lifetime prevalence in A would be higher than in B (p. 838).

CULTURE CHANGE   In the study of the relationship of culture to schizophrenia, the study of culture change differs from the comparative and total community approaches in that it does not constitute a distinct methodological approach. It nevertheless deserves separate attention because of the fascination it seems to hold for a number of writers as a possible key to understanding the pathogenesis of this disease and many others. For example, Leighton and Hughes (1961) have written:

> In concluding our paper, we should like to return again to a point mentioned earlier. This is our impression that comparative study of change is one of

the most fruitful opportunities for uncovering the nature of socio-cultural factors in relation to psychiatric disorder (p. 363).

There are a number of different processes that may be used to define some aspect of culture change—industrialization, business cycles, acculturation, migration, and so on. Murphy (1961), in reviewing the literature relating social change to mental health, holds that there are two types of hypotheses in this area, one which lays the cause of disorders to the factor of change itself, the other which suggests that social change in certain circumstances combines with other elements in the situation to produce disorder. While Murphy's review deals with mental illness in general and includes only a few studies which focus on schizophrenia, his general statement is nevertheless worth noting: "There are almost as many studies which suggest that social change leads to no increase in mental disorder, or even to a decrease, as there are studies suggesting that an increase is directly traceable to such a cause" (p. 306).

With the exception of the migration studies reviewed earlier, there are exceedingly few studies dealing with the relation of culture change to schizophrenia separately from other mental disorders. For example, probably the most careful and rigorous of these studies, that by Goldhamer and Marshall (1953), deals with psychoses in general and does not treat schizophrenia separately. Nonetheless, Goldhamer and Marshall's findings deserve attention because they run so counter to what had been thought concerning the supposed influence of culture change in Western society on allegedly rising rates of psychosis. Using first admission to a variety of mental institutions in Massachusetts from the years 1840 to 1940, the authors were able ingeniously to calculate age- and sex-specific psychosis rates and found that there had been no long-term increase during the last century in the incidence of the psychoses of early and middle life.

For an example of a recent study purporting to relate culture change to changes in the rates of mental illness in the United States, with schizophrenia rates treated separately, we may turn to the paper by Wilson and Lantz (1957). Using hospital admissions (it is not clear whether they include readmissions), the writers compute rates for whites and Negroes in Virginia for the years 1920 to 1955. On the basis of these rates, they conclude: "It is felt that the fact that there is more mental illness among the Negroes of Virginia than among the whites and more mental illness among the Negroes in 1954 than in 1914 is due to segregation and to the uncertainties of the Negro race as they cross from one culture to another" (p. 31). Such a conclusion is unwarranted on at least two counts: The cases are hospital cases only, so that rates are questionable; even more important, there are no systematic measures of the independent cultural variables—these are simply crude impressions.

As expected, the situation is no better in acculturation studies of nonliterate groups. The previously criticized study by Tooth (1950) takes up the question of culture change, and is often cited in this connection as yielding negative evidence for the rôle of culture change in supposedly increasing rates of mental disorder. Of course, the methodological inadequacies of this study make it clear that any generalizations derived from it are, at best, highly questionable. Nonetheless, Tooth's interpretation is really most curious, for he finds data that would normally lead one to conclude that change does, in fact, lead to higher rates of mental disease, and interprets this data as supporting the opposite conclusion. This has not escaped Benedict's notice (1958):

> . . . he [Tooth] handles this point in a peculiarly inconsistent manner, however, and in fact suggests that the literacy rate is higher than might be anticipated among psychotics. Moreover, the incidence figures cited by him show a considerably higher value for the one relatively urbanized district (p. 698).

Finally, a study from East Africa by Carothers (1948), which attempts to demonstrate that culture change does lead to higher rates of mental illness, is also highly questionable on a number of counts, not the least of these being that the data consist of hospital admissions in a country where such admissions cannot seriously be taken to be representative, subject as they are to any number of biases.

In short, the study of culture change has not yet been productive of careful studies or substantive data. Very little has been done. But on the basis of studies of change and other diseases (for example, hypertension), and on the basis of studies of acculturation and its known psychological impact, culture change undoubtedly deserves attention.

In summarizing this section, we agree with the consensus that a relationship has not yet been demonstrated between the culture and schizophrenia. There are various possible explanations for this. Most logical, but most difficult to accept, is the possibility that no such relationship exists. More acceptable to social scientists is the likelihood that the relationship is too complex, or too distant, or both, making it extremely difficult to study. Or it may be that the methods of study have so far been inadequate. Or it may simply be that the status of the dependent variable, schizophrenia—and the numerous problems associated with it—has hindered the accumulation of such evidence.

Any or all of the above may explain the dearth of substantive evidence. There is, in addition, the important fact that few systematic studies of culture and schizophrenia have so far been reported in the literature. A number of factors inhibit such research—time, expense, the need for an interdisciplinary team, the lack of psychiatric researchers able to spend large blocks of time in the field, and so on. Further, there seems to be a widepread but insufficiently supported belief that the incidence of schizophrenia is relatively constant from one culture to another. This current belief may be a reaction to the previous belief in the rarity of the illness among primitive groups. Whatever its source, such a belief tends to dampen the enthusiasm of investigators. In sum, the number of acceptable studies that have been conducted on this question are far too few to offer even the most tentative test of the postulated relationships.

Discussion

Writing a concluding section for a review of studies of the social etiology of schizophrenia is like talking with relatives of the deceased after returning from a funeral. Other than some platitudes, there is little that can be suggested that would remedy, alleviate, or eliminate the trouble.

It is not difficult to criticize the state of the field—few studies are available, concepts and methods are unclear and unstandardized, findings are inconsistent, and speculation abounds in the absence of reliable empirical knowledge. However, it is difficult to make useful recommendations in a field where so little is tied down. How does one decide which end to secure of a billowing canvas? Or in which direction to head if there are no road markers and perhaps no roads?

Faced with this problem, critics and reviewers tend either to examine for the nth time some of the basic methodological issues or to design "ideal" studies for someone else to carry out. The interesting characteristic of the considerable existing commentary and analysis is its generally high level of quality. It is an instructive and serious literature.

One of the striking characteristics of the field is this fact of a small amount of inadequate research combined with a large amount of adequate criticism. The question arises: If we know so much why aren't we doing it? Or, if we're all so smart why aren't we rich? We believe that part of the answer lies in the narrow and restrictive definitions of epidemiologic inquiry that are implied in both the studies and the analyses. With a few noteworthy exceptions, studies in this area are simple in design and fall into the category of descriptive epidemiology. More complex designs that are closer to analytic epidemiology have not been used systematically; the separate components of the prevalence picture, particularly duration of illness, have not been explored; simple summary statistics are used with no attempt made to analyze data with more analytic multivariate techniques; finally, the hypotheses developed in the descriptive studies are not followed up through analytic and experimental studies.

We believe that the "bench-mark" data about the distribution of illness that may be accumulated through descriptive epidemiology are most meaningful when there is a body of basic knowledge about the illness itself; where such knowledge is lacking, as is the case in schizophrenia, the findings of descriptive epidemiology provide little in the way of an understanding of the illness. This does not mean that epidemiologic investigation must await the solution of the clinical questions about onset, natural history, subtypes, and remission patterns. However, in order both to accumulate information that will not be rendered obsolete or worthless by some change in psychiatric practice (such as, for example, the introduction of tranquilizers) and to contribute to the overall understanding of the illness, epidemiologic investigations should be more analytic in design and more complex in the methods and concepts used than has been true in the past.

Essentially, we believe that epidemiological investigation will come to contribute more to an understanding of schizophrenia if studies are as much concerned with limiting the range of possible interpretation of the findings as with generating the findings themselves. We do not mean that empirically minded epidemiologists should become theory-builders; however, they must build into their designs the types of controls and measuring instruments that will permit alternative and competing interpretations to be evaluated. Thus, studies of social class and schizophrenia that do not permit some comparison of social mobility and social stress hypotheses with each other will have little to contribute to an understanding of the relations between social factors and illness. Arguments between adherents of various theories tend to become sterile without the accumulation of empirical data by means of which the theories can be checked directly; on the other hand, the accumulation of descriptive statistics leads to little progress, since the different studies do not allow for meaningful comparisons if similar control variables have not been included.

Some concrete implications of these general considerations will be noted in this closing section. We will give brief attention to problems that emerge with regard to the diagnostic classification, control variables, morbidity indexes, and sociologic variables used.

As has been pointed out, the nosological and diagnostic problems hampering the study of schizophrenia are still far from solution. At this point in time, investigators must be concerned with the reliability of the diagnostic procedures used in the series of cases in their study. The use of diagnoses that appear on hospital case records without further examination of the underlying diagnostic procedures is completely inadequate. Studies that include standardized and evaluated diagnosis of cases as part of the investigation are ideal but this is not always feasible or economical. Faced with someone else's diagnosis, investigators should at least try to find out "who" this someone else is—a first-year psychiatric resident, a senior psychiatrist, a staff conference; and the basis on which the diagnosis was assigned—a half-hour admission interview, psychological tests, a month's observation on the psychiatric ward. Where both an admission and a discharge diagnosis are available, cases might be classified usefully as: Schizophrenic at admission only, schizophrenic at discharge only, schizophrenic at both admission and discharge. Obviously, none of these procedures increases the reliability of diagnosis, but they would help investigators to understand more precisely the meaning of both consistent and inconsistent findings from various studies. Further attention to the problem in this explicit way would be another pressure operating on clinical psychiatry to sharpen its diagnostic processes.

With regard to the problem of the subtypes of schizophrenia, each investigator will presumably have his own preference depending in part on the norms of the clinical subculture in which he carries out his work. We would urge that all investigators use some scheme of classification, whatever its conceptual and clinical basis, so that social variables may be related to one or two or even three types of schizophrenia rather than simply to some general category. This procedure would have several useful effects. First, it would permit an assessment of the limits or generality of influence of a particular social variable. For example: Are there social class differentials in simple as well as paranoid schizophrenia? Is there a disproportionate incidence among migrants of schizophrenics with good premorbid social adjustment as compared with those of poor premorbid social adjustment? Second, the utility of the subclassification may be determined. If all the subtypes, for example, show the same direction and degree of relationship to a range of social variables, then this would argue against the meaningfulness of the distinction used; however, if the incidence of one subtype is higher among women, but of another subtype is higher among men, then the way is open to a fuller understanding of the illness.

Our own preference is for a distinction on the order of that between good and poor premorbid patients since there is now considerable evidence that these two groups differ in terms of genetic background, social relationships, symptoms, and prognosis (Rodnick and Garmezy, 1957; Rosenthal, 1959; Phillips, 1953; Vaillant, 1962). Indicators of this distinction in hospital case records would include age of onset, premorbid social and sexual adjustment, and improvement or discharge from the hospital.

On the whole, investigators have been aware of the problems of research controls and in most studies analyses are conducted with the control of age and sex; sometimes socioeconomic and marital status are used. However, in order to test the independent effect of the variable under study, these controls are often applied in a mechanical and indiscriminate way that erases the effect of the control variable. For example, two populations will be standardized for age so as to give us rates that are comparable despite the real age composition differences between the two. Knowing that schizophrenia peaks in the under-35 age group and that the mode appears later and drops less sharply for women than for men, we think it would be more interesting and more instructive to look for relations between social variables and schizophrenia separately within under- and over-35 age groups than to obscure such possible differences by a mechanical standardization for age.

We have already discussed a number of issues concerning the index of morbidity used, the different meaning of ecological and individual correlations, and the differing interpretations dependent on whether social variables have been associated with prevalence or incidence measures. Two points merit explicit emphasis. First, attention has been almost exclusively directed toward incidence as measured by first admission to hospitals. Where chronicity is a variable and important component of the disease process—for example, there seem to be at least two types of schizophrenia that vary in terms of chronicity (Vaillant, 1962) —it is equally important to give additional emphasis to this aspect of the overall prevalence picture. Second, the relative rate for schizophrenia as compared to other major mental illnesses is a matter of great importance for an understanding of the significance of social differentials in schizophrenia itself. For example, is the overall rate for all mental illnesses relatively the same from one social group to another, with rate differentials for specific illnesses primarily a function of different diagnostic "styles"? Or are schizophrenia and the other mental illnesses related in different ways to different social variables, with the latter having specific rather than general influence? There was some early interest in these comparisons (for example, in the different ratios of schizophrenia to manic-depressive psychosis in different social classes) (Lemkau and Crocetti, 1958), and some reports contain detailed tables that permit such comparisons across a number of social variables (Jaco, 1960).

It has been particularly discouraging to the authors as social scientists to have to recognize the simplistic quality both of the social variables used in epidemiological studies and the forms of analyses into which they have been incorporated. Whereas in the investigation of almost every other problem, a relationship with social class would be the beginning of intensive analysis through a series of control and test variables, in the investigation of the epidemiology of schizophrenia it often stands for the complete analysis. In examining the social correlates of any other piece of complex behavior, the ecological and cultural characteristics of the groups in which the individuals are members would become an explicit part of the analysis through designs permitting such cross-comparisons, but in the study of schizophrenia it takes contradictions in findings to force such factors into researchers' awareness (Clausen and Kohn, 1960; Locke, 1958).

These last problems are related to the tendency to use only macrosociological variables in these investigations, such as social class or migration, and to pay little or no attention to such microsociological variables as family processes, living arrangements, or peer-group patterns. Few studies have tried to bring together micro- and macro-levels of variables; Gerard and Houston's work (1953) is a notable exception. Recent emphasis on the importance of certain family process variables (Spiegel and Bell, 1959; Jackson, 1960) suggests that it would be particularly useful if measures of these types of variables could be incorporated into more traditional epidemiological work.

Epidemiologists and statisticians have a tendency to think of theory as that vague and uncharted area of the cognitive map which will disappear as one accumulates more hard information; theorists find that the accumulated hard facts are not as relevant to the theoretical issues as might be desired; and the clinicians may be heard to complain that both the ideas and the statistics generated respectively by theorists and researchers are too abstract to be of use in understanding and dealing with the concrete phenomena of schizophrenia. We do not believe that the basic aim of understanding the etiology of schizophrenia and its ultimate prevention, control, and treatment are served well by the type of insulation that has prevailed among researcher, theorist, and clinician. Neither does it seem to us to be a plea for eclecticism to urge that theory and research findings should be relevant both to each other and to the phenomena of basic interest.

Most of the studies reviewed in this paper were carried out during the last 25 years, many of them during the past decade. The amount of useful and systematic knowledge about social factors in the epidemiology of schizophrenia is disappointingly small. However, it should be clear from the previous pages that it is within investigators' capacity to know much more. Instruments, procedures, and concepts are available that will permit organized and significant research. Whether or not much more will be known at the end of the next decade or 25 years will depend primarily on researchers' willingness to invest in these difficult undertakings.

13 / The Problem of Validity in Field Studies of Psychological Disorder

Bruce P. Dohrenwend / *Barbara Snell Dohrenwend*

For over 100 years, researchers have been reporting relations between sociocultural factors and psychological disorder. An early instance is Jarvis' finding, in 1856, that the "pauper class" in Massachusetts furnished proportionally 64 times as many cases of "insanity" as the "independent class" (Sandifer, 1962).

From the *Journal of Abnormal Psychology*, 1965, **70**, 52–69. Copyright © 1965. Reprinted by permission of the authors and the American Psychological Association.

We are grateful to Jack Elinson, Lawrence C. Kolb, and Thomas S. Langner for their helpful criticism of this paper, and to Robert J. Smith for his help with Japanese census data—AUS.

Like Jarvis, most later investigators have tried to answer questions about psychological disorder in different groups by examining the characteristics of mental patients. A classic example is the research of Faris and Dunham (1939) on the distribution of admissions to mental hospitals from Chicago which, replicating Jarvis' results, showed a heavy concentration of cases from the central slum sections. The investigators' interpretation was that social disorganization might be causing psychological disorder.

Dunham (1961) and others (e.g., Felix and Bowers, 1948; Gruenberg, 1955) have, however, pointed to the difficulty of interpreting the results of studies in which the fact of being in treatment constitutes the sole definition of disorder. Treatment rates vary, for example, with the availability of treatment facilities, and with public attitudes towards their use. Either could be responsible for spurious relations between sociocultural factors and rates of illness measured by number of cases in treatment.

Field Studies

Recognition of such problems has stimulated more than 30 attempts to count untreated as well as treated cases of psychological disorder. Excluded from this tally are studies which have reported scores measuring symptomatology, but have not indicated what is to be considered a case (e.g., Gurin, Veroff, and Feld, 1960; Langner, 1965).

Typically, the whole population in a specified geographical area has been included. In the few investigations relying on sample estimates, the n's have usually been large; for example, probability samples of 1,660 in the Midtown Study (Srole et al., 1962), and 1,010 in the Stirling County study (D. C. Leighton et al., 1963).

In most of the studies, the rates we have extracted represent prevalence during a period of a few months to a few years. Most of the exceptions, studies by Fremming (1951), by Helgason (1964), by Lin (1953), and by Rin and Lin (1962), and a summary by Strömgren (1950) of 18 small studies, counted as one study here, present lifetime prevalence rates. In addition, Hagnell (1966) gives 10 year incidence rates.

The overall results are shown in Table I. The first thing to note is the range in rates: from less than 1 per cent to over 60 per cent. What factors could conceivably account for variation of such magnitude?

Table I groups the studies according to the geopolitical area in which they were conducted, and according to whether the study site was rural or urban. These contrasts in setting do not seem to account adequately for the variation in rates. In all but one of the studies done in Asia, the rates are very low, suggesting the possibility of a difference between Western and Asian populations. However, the rate reported in the one exception (Rin, Chu, and Lin, 1967) is so high that it argues against this interpretation. There is no indication of especially low rates in Africa, since two figures reported for this area are near the top of the range found in North American and northern European studies. Moreover, within North America and northern Europe, there is no evidence that the study site is associated with the rate of disorder, since almost

TABLE I

PERCENTAGE OF PSYCHOLOGICAL DISORDER REPORTED ACCORDING TO GEOPOLITICAL AREA AND RURAL VERSUS URBAN STUDY SITE

Site	North America	Northern Europe	Asia	Africa
Rural	1.7 (Eaton and Weil, 1955)	1.1[a] (Kaila, Study II, 1942)	0.8 (Uchimara et al., 1940)	40.0 (A. Leighton et al.,[d] 1963)
	1.9[a,b] (Rosanoff, 1917)	1.3 (Brugger, 1931)	0.8[a] (Rin and Lin, Ami, 1962)	
	6.9 (Roth and Luton, 1943)	1.3 (Kaila, Study I, 1942)	0.8[a] (Rin and Lin, Taiwan, 1962)	
	18.0 (Trussel et al., 1956)	3.5[a] (Brugger, 1937)	1.0 (Lin, small town, 1953)	
	27.5 (Phillips,[d] 1966)	4.2 (Strömgren, 1950)	1.1 (Lin, village, 1953)	
	50.0+[c] (D. Leighton et al., 1963)	7.5 (Brugger, 1933)	1.2[a] (Rin and Lin, Saisait, 1962)	
	64.0 (Llewellyn-Thomas,[d] 1960)	9.0 (Mayer-Gross, 1948)	1.9[a] (Rin and Lin, Atayal, 1962)	
		11.9 (Fremming, 1951)	2.7[a] (Akimoto et al., 1942)	
		13.2 (Primrose,[d] 1962)	54.0 (Rin et al., 1967)	
		13.6[a] (Essen-Möller, 1956)		
		14.8[a] (Strotzka et al., 1966)		
		15.6[a] (Hagnell, 1966)		
		23.2 (Bremer,[d] 1951)		
		28.6 (Helgason, 1964)		
Urban	1.8[a] (Lemkau et al., 1942)	1.8[a] (Kaila, Study I, 1942)	1.1 (Lin, city, 1953)	11.8 (Gillis et al.,[d] 1965)
	2.3 (Cohen et al., 1939)	1.1[a] (Kaila, Study II, 1942)	3.0[a] (Tsuwaga et al., 1942)	45.0 (A. Leighton et al.,[d] 1963)
	3.4 (Manis et al.,[d] 1964)	15.6[a] (Gnat et al.,[d] 1964)		
	10.9 (Pasamanick et al., 1959)	20.6 (Hare and Shaw,[d] 1965)		
	23.4 (Strole et al.,[d] 1962)	33.0 (Taylor and Chave,[d] 1964)		
	32.0[a] (Cole et al.,[d] 1957)			

[a] Calculated by B. S. Dohrenwend. [b] Includes urban minority not reported separately. [c] ". . . our conclusion from all the available information is that at least half of the adults in Stirling County are *currently* suffering from some psychiatric disorder defined in the American Psychiatric Association *Diagnostic and Statistical Manual* (p. 356)." [d] Age range limited.

the full range is represented within each of four categories: North American rural, North American urban, northern European rural, and northern European urban.

Another possible explanation of differences in rates is the age range included in the study. As indicated in Table I, 13 studies covered a limited age group. In all of these, the youngest ages, in which the minimum rate is usually found (see Table III), are excluded. With one exception, the rates reported for these age-restricted studies range from moderate to high. The single exception, the study by Manis *et al.* (1964), includes the same range as the Midtown study by Srole *et al.* (1962), 20 through 59 years. The low rate reported by Manis *et al.* underlines the fact that elimination of the youngest age group is not a sufficient explanation of high reported rates.

A number of critics have argued that the factors primarily responsible for variation in rates are methodological (e.g., Blum, 1962; Pasamanick, 1962; Plunkett and Gordon, 1960). One such factor is the thoroughness of the data collection procedures. Investigators who collected data directly from the subjects, rather than relying entirely or partially on indirect sources of information, might be expected to detect more cases, as has happened with physical illness (Cartwright, 1957). On the other hand, still more thorough investigation through physical examinations might reveal organic bases of symptoms, thereby reducing rates below those reported when subjects' self-descriptions are the investigator's only source of information. Still another methodological factor which might affect rates is the conception of what constitutes a case. This conception may, as Szasz (1961) implied, have changed with time, expanding and becoming more inclusive over the years.

The effects of these methodological factors are tested in Table II by classifying the studies according to thoroughness of data-collection procedures and decade of publication. There is a general tendency for more direct contact with subjects to produce higher rates. The importance of direct contact is given further weight by the work of authors in italics in Table II, i.e., Cole, Branch, and Orla, 1957; Eaton and Weil, 1955; Rosanoff, 1917; and Roth and Luton, 1943. In each of these studies, rates found in the same population are higher among subjects with whom more direct contact was made. There is, however, no evidence that physical examination lowered the reported rates of psychological disorder. The rates yielded by the five studies which included physical examinations cover most of the range.

There is a clear tendency for rates to be higher in more recent studies. Especially notable is the increase in the 1950s and 1960s. It could be argued, of course, that rather than observing the effects of changes in the researchers' concepts, we are observing a consequence of the times we live in. However in view of statements suggesting a shift from exclusive concern with avoiding overestimation (e.g., Cohen, Fairbank, and Greene, 1939, p. 113; Lewkau, Tietze, and Cooper, 1941, p. 635; Rosanoff, 1917, p. 137) to concern with complete enumeration (e.g., Bremer, 1951, p. 12; D. C. Leighton *et al.*, 1963, p. 95), it seems premature to infer a true change in prevalence bewteen the 1940s and 1950s. Moreover, there is ample evidence from studies in which both inclusive and relatively exclusive standards were applied to the same populations that rates can be markedly affected by these standards. Essen-Möller (1956, p. 95), for

TABLE II

PERCENTAGE OF PSYCHOLOGICAL DISORDER REPORTED ACCORDING TO THOROUGHNESS OF DATA COLLECTION PROCEDURES AND DECADE OF PUBLICATION STUDY

Decade of Publication	Indirect Contact: Records and/or Informants	Directness of Contact with Subjects		
		Partial Direct Contact: Records and/or Informants, and Interviews with Some Subjects	Direct Contact	
			Interviews with All Subjects	Interviews and Physical Examination of All or Most Subjects
1910–1919		1.3 (Rosanoff, 1917)	3.6 (Rosanoff, 1917)	
1920–1929				
1930–1939	2.3 (Cohen et al., 1939)	1.3 (Brugger, 1931)	3.5[a] (Brugger, 1937)	
	4.2 (Strömgren,[b] 1950)		7.5 (Brugger, 1933)	
1940–1949	1.1[a] (Kaila, Study II, 1942)	0.8[a] (Uchimara et al., 1940)	2.7[a] (Akimoto et al., 1942)	
	1.8[a] (Lemkau et al., 1942)	1.2[a] (Kaila, Study I, 1942)	3.0[a] (Tsuwaga et al., 1942)	
	9.0 (Mayer-Gross, 1948)	6.4 (Roth and Luton, 1943)	12.4 (Roth and Luton, 1943)	
1950–1959			1.1 (Lin, 1953)	10.9 (Pasamanick et al., 1959)
	1.2 (Eaton and Weil, 1955)	2.3 (Eaton and Weil, 1955)	2.9 (Eaton and Weil, 1955)	18.0 (Trussell et al., 1956)
		11.9 (Freeming, 1951)	13.6[a] (Essen-Möller, 1956)	23.2 (Bremer, 1951)
		28.0[c] (Cole et al., 1957)	35.4[c] (Cole et al., 1957)	
1960 and after	14.8[a] (Strotzka et al., 1966)	28.6 (Helgason, 1964)	0.8[a] (Rin and Lin, Ami, 1962)	13.2 (Primrose, 1962)
			0.8[a] (Rin and Lin, Taiwan, 1962)	54.0 (Rin et al., 1967)
			1.2[a] (Rin and Lin, Saisait, 1962)	64.0 (Llewellyn-Thomas, 1960)
			1.9[a] (Rin and Lin, Atayal, 1962)	
			3.4 (Manis et al., 1964)	
			11.8 (Gillis et al., 1965)	
			15.6[a] (Gnat et al., 1964)	

TABLE II (*continued*)

Directness of Contact with Subjects

Decade of Publica- tion	Indirect Contact: Records and/or Informants	Partial Direct Contact: Records and/or Informants, and Interviews with Some Subjects	Direct Contact	
			Interviews with All Subjects	Interviews and Physical Examina- tion of All or Most Subjects
			15.6[a] (Hagnell, 1966)	
			20.6 (Hare and Shaw, 1965)	
			23.4 (Srole *et al.*, 1962)	
			27.5 (Phillips, 1966)	
			33.0 (Taylor and Chave, 1964)	
			41.0 (A. Leighton *et al.*, 1963)	
			50.0+[d] (D. Leigh- ton *et al.*, 1963)	

[a] Calculated by B. S. Dohrenwend.

[b] Eleven of the small studies summarized in Strömgren's rate were published in the 1930's, seven in the 1920's.

[c] Rates for wives are calculated for direct contact and other family members for partial contact on the basis of the statement that wives were usually interviewed; the base for each rate is the number of families interviewed.

[d] ". . . our conclusion from all the available information is that at least half of the adults in Stirling County are *currently* suffering from some psychiatric disorder defined in the American Psychiatric Association *Diagnostic and Statistical Manual* (p. 356)."

example, reported a rate of 13.6 per cent for "diagnoses constituting the main subject of most psychiatric population studies," but an average of 54.7 per cent (calculation by B. S. Dohrenwend) for whom pathology was not definitely absent. A similar contrast is offered by the figures 23.4 per cent in the impaired group, and 81.5 per cent judged less than "well" in the Midtown study (Srole *et al.*, 1962, p. 138). Another comparison with the Midtown study is provided by a recent investigation (Manis *et al.*, 1964) which used 22 symptom items taken from the Midtown interview schedule. While obtaining a distribution of responses similar to that reported by the Midtown researchers, Manis and his colleagues found that their decision to include only severe psychological disorder yielded a rate of 3.4 per cent.

The continuing importance of methodological problems is emphasized by the difficulty of comparing results even from studies carried out by the same investigators. For example, the Leightons and their colleagues (A. H. Leighton *et al.*, 1963) concluded, concerning their own studies: "the differences and similarities between the Yoruba and Stirling figures are to an unknown degree under the influence of differences in the procedures employed in the two studies" (p. 124). To complicate the problem of comparison further, various procedures used within one of these, the Stirling County study, yielded different rates of psychopathology (D. C. Leighton *et al.*, 1963, pp. 123, 127).

Problem of Validity

Given the variability of both procedures and results in attempts to assess "true" prevalence, the salient question is which, if any, among these field studies has produced valid measures of psychological disorder. Despite their deficiencies, studies restricted to treated disorder had a clear advantage. The fact that a person is in treatment usually indicates that he cannot function unaided in his customary social environments. The clinician diagnosing a patient has a "presenting problem" with which to start, so that the question he must answer is not *whether* something is wrong, but rather *what* is wrong. The diagnostic result of this analysis, moreover, can be changed on the basis of repeated observations and interviews over a course of treatment.

The investigator of untreated disorder must work without the aids to diagnosis inherent in the clinical setting. Evidence of the difficulties he faces are found in the results of the psychiatric screening attempts associated with Selective Service in the United States during World War II. The psychiatric judgments were extremely unreliable, rejection rates within the same region varying in a number of areas by a factor of three to one (Star, 1950, pp. 552, 554). Moreover, there is no evidence that among the unreliable judgments one or another was more effective, since strictness of screening procedures bore little relation to subsequent rates of separation on psychiatric grounds (Ginzberg *et al.*, 1959, Ch. 11).

Nevertheless, clinical judgment is the tool relied upon for case identification in almost all studies which include untreated as well as treated psychological disorder. In most, psychiatric diagnoses are made, and findings are presented in terms of categories such as those described in the *Diagnostic and Statistical Manual* of the American Psychiatric Association (1952). Neither the information available to the judge, nor the criteria on which the diagnoses were based are usually reported in detail in these investigations. The validity of the results is assumed to be implicit in the diagnostic process, a shaky assumption in light of the World War II experience with psychiatric screening.

A few investigators, recognizing the difficulty of placing untreated cases in diagnostic categories, have also made judgments in more general terms, such as probability of pathology (Essen-Möller, 1956; Rosanoff, 1917), likelihood of being psychiatric cases (A.H. Leighton *et al.*, 1963; D.C. Leighton *et al.*, 1963), or degree of severity ranging from "well" to "incapacitated" (Langner and Michael, 1963; Srole *et al.*, 1962). Among these relatively sophisticated investigations, the Leightons' Stirling County and Nigeria studies, and the Midtown study by Srole and his colleagues stand out. Although they differ in several aspects of their assesssment procedures, they share an important innovation. Both used structured questionnaires, thereby providing a standard, explicit set of data for psychiatric assessment. In this respect, these studies represent the methodologically most advanced epidemiological investigations of untreated and treated psychological disorder.[3] The question is whether procedures of the Midtown, Stirling County, and Nigeria studies have dealt adequately with the central methodological problem of validity.

Content Validity

Content validity involves a demonstration that the items used are a representative sample from a universe generally accepted as defining the variable to be measured (Cronbach and Meehl, 1955). In the Midtown study, the universe from which items were drawn was defined by Srole *et al.* (1962) as "the most salient and generalized indicators of mental pathology" (p. 60). Behavioral scientists selected a group of items from the Army Neuropsychiatric Screening Adjunct (Star, 1950a) and the MMPI (Dahlstrom and Welsh, 1960) "consisting principally of the psychophysiologic manifestations and those tapping the anxiety, depression, and inadequacy dimensions" (Srole *et al.*, 1962, p. 42). In addition, the psychiatrists independently contributed 40 items "bearing particularly on psychosomatic symptoms, phobic reactions, and mood" (p. 60). The final decision determining the 120 items actually included was made by the senior psychiatrist on the basis of "clinical experience" (p. 60). Thus, in the absence of systematic sampling of items, no argument can be made for the content validity of the Midtown measure of psychological disorder. The same is true of the Stirling and Yoruba studies, where items were taken from the NSA and other test sources without explicit specification of the selection procedures (e.g., A.H. Leighton *et al.*, 1963, p. 85; D.C. Leighton *et al.*, 1963, pp. 202, 205).

It is doubtful whether content validity, in the strictest sense, can be achieved in the measurement of untreated psychological disorder, since there appears to be no universe of items which experts agree on as defining the variable. Four different sources have been cited in recent studies by the relatively few researchers who related their procedures to an established diagnostic system: the Sjöbring system used at Lund University, Sweden (Essen-Möller, 1956); the system used in the Department of Psychiatry of the National Taiwan University Hospital, Taipei (Lin, 1953); the World Health Organization *International Classification of Diseases* (Primrose, 1962); and the American Psychiatric Association *Diagnostic and Statistical Manual* (D.C. Leighton *et al.*, 1963). As Clausen points out (1961, pp. 131–132), the last two differ markedly as a function of the greater emphasis placed by European psychiatrists on hypothetical constitutional determinants.

---

[3] A preliminary report of a study from Poland (Gnat, Henisz, and Sarapata, 1964) describes procedures which appear similar to those used in Midtown and Stirling County. In addition, the Polish investigators made an attempt to cross-check these procedures against clinical examinations of subsamples of respondents. Since a detailed description of its research operations has not yet been published, however, this study is not included in the following methodological analysis.

Criterion-Oriented Validity:
Concurrent and Predictive

Of the two types of criterion-oriented validity, concurrent and predictive (Cronbach and Meehl, 1955), there is no evidence in the field studies for the latter. Typically conducted at one point in time, these studies have thus far not tested their assessments of disorder against criteria of future psychiatric condition, admission to treatment, or social functioning. What evidence, then, is provided for concurrent validity?

In Midtown (Srole *et al.*, 1962), the NSA and MMPI items proposed by the behavioral scientists were tested in a study involving 139 diagnosed neurotic and remitted psychotic patients, and 72 persons judged well by a psychiatrist on the basis of a half-hour interview. The result was that "almost all the NSA and MMPI symptom questions emerged with validity confirmed" (p. 42). Twenty-two of the items included in the final questionnaire discriminated between the patient and well groups at the .01 level of significance (Langner, 1962), and the remainder of the items contributed by the behavioral scientists, at the .05 level.[4] While the Midtown psychiatrists reported that, in rating cases well or not well, they gave special weight to 8 of the 22 items which discriminated at the .01 level, they also paid special attention to 6 items which failed to discriminate at this level (p. 396). Thus, in the Midtown study, while the data from which the psychiatrists worked had been tested for concurrent validity in the manner described above, this test did not guide the use of these data by the psychiatrists.

In the Stirling County study, an attempt to identify valid items was made by administering NSA questions and items from other tests to untreated community samples and to patients diagnosed as neurotic. The selection of items included in the survey interviews, however, was not wholly determined by the results of this study (D.C. Leighton *et al.*, 1963, p. 205). As in the Midtown study, the Stirling County psychiatrists did not make use of objective scores based on these items in the judgmental assessment of psychiatric disorder.

Before considering how the psychiatrists actually used the symptom items in the Midtown and Stirling County studies, questions must be raised about concurrent validity of the items themselves. In attempts to validate these items, the patient criterion groups were homogeneous with regard to type of disorder (e.g., all neurotics in a study by Macmillan in D.C. Leighton *et al.*, 1963, Chapter VII), or unspecified as to diagnostic composition (e.g., Manis *et al.*, 1963). Moreover, the stubborn problem of well controls has not been met head-on, much less solved. For example, in Langner's (1962) study identifying 22 items which discriminated at the .01 level between patient and well groups, the fact that the well group was identified by means of clinical judgment brings the problem back to its origin, since the items can be no more valid than the psychiatrist's judgments against which they were tested.

Nor does the solution appear to lie in avoiding clinical judgments by using an unselected sample of the nonpatient population as the healthy criterion

---

[4] Thomas S. Langner, personal communication, February 1964.

group. Reports of community rates up to 64 per cent from the field studies themselves argue against such a procedure. An attempt by Manis *et al.* (1963) to cross-validate the 22 Midtown study items, using samples from patient and nonpatient populations as criterion groups, both illustrates the problem and raises another. Finding that a group of predischarge ward patients had an average symptom score lower than those of a community cross-section, and a group of college students, the authors argued that the result indicated a failure of the test since "there is little reason to believe that the mental health of these predischarge patients is equal to or better than the nonhospitalized populations" (p. 111). In the absence of independent evidence concerning the mental health of their nonpatient populations, however, it seems difficult to interpret this result. It is conceivable, though unlikely, that the predischarge ward patients are cured, while the nonpatients need treatment.

It is also possible, and perhaps more plausible, that the predischarge ward patients in the interest of "getting out" are simply less willing than nonpatients to admit socially undesirable behavior. If so, we are seeing evidence here of the impact of response style (cf. Jackson and Messick, 1962). What are the implications of such influence for the psychiatric evaluations which have relied heavily on the "face validity" of the items?

The measure of disorder in the Midtown study consisted of psychiatrists' ratings of the symptom data which ranged respondents on a scale from well through five degrees of severity of symptomatology: "mild," "moderate," "marked," "severe," and "incapacitated." Almost a quater (23.4 per cent) of the respondents were classified in the last three categories: marked, severe, and incapacitated. These are referred to collectively as "impaired," and are the "cases" in the Midtown study. Michael, one of the evaluating psychiatrists on the Midtown study, put it this way:

> The individuals in the Impaired category of mental health . . . are represented as being analogous to patients in psychiatric therapy. . . . When it is urged that the mental ratings "Marked" and "Severe" are comparable to the clinical conditions of patients in ambulatory treatment, and the rating "Incapacitated" to the clinically hospitalized, the distinction is presented . . . as an attempt to anchor our conceptualizations in relation to known degrees of psychopathology (Srole *et al.*, 1962, p. 333).

There is evidence that this claim requires scrutiny. In the Midtown sample, 40 respondents reported being current outpatients in psychotherapy at the time of the interview; 182 reported that they were expatients. The evaluating psychiatrists had full knowledge of these facts when they made their judgments. Since expatients might be expected to have benefited from treatment, it is not remarkable to find that 54 per cent of the 182 expatients in the Midtown sample were judged unimpaired. However, if respondents placed in the impaired categories indeed resemble psychiatric patients, as the Midtown researchers claim, it is hard to understand why the study psychiatrists placed 48 per cent of the 40 *current* patients in the unimpaired categories (Srole *et al.*, 1962, p. 147).

In the Stirling County study, disorder was defined in terms of judged similarity to descriptions in the 1952 *Diagnostic and Statistical Manual* of the American Psychiatric Association, rather than judged similarity to actual patients with whom the psychiatrists had had experience. The main rating was a psychiatric evaluation of "caseness" based on written summaries of symptom data collected for the most part by lay interviewers. It is described by D.C. Leighton *et al.* (1963) as "a rating of the probability that, at some time in his adult life, up to the time of the interview, the individual would qualify as a psychiatric case" (p. 53). The evidence for the validity of their conclusion "that at least half of the adults in Stirling County are *currently* suffering from some psychiatric disorder defined in the APA *Diagnostic and Statistical Manual*" (p. 356) rests largely on the study psychiatrists' blind evaluation of the likelihood that 47 former clinic patients, mostly neurotic, are cases. Of these 47, 81 per cent were rated "almost certainly psychiatric," and 11 per cent more were rated "probably psychiatric" (p. 175). Their problems, moreover, were viewed mainly as present rather than past (pp. 178–179). Thus the Stirling evaluators saw more disorder in their expatients than the Midtown evaluators saw in their current patients.

These results of the application of Midtown and Stirling County study evaluation procedures to patients and expatients suggest a number of possible interpretations: that patients get and remain sicker in Stirling County than in Midtown Manhattan; or that treatment in Stirling is less effective than in Midtown; or that Stirling methods are less able to distinguish between past and current problems; or that the definitions of cases are vastly different in the two studies; or that some combination of these circumstances has operated simultaneously. In brief, there is considerable ambiguity about the relations between the Midtown and Stirling judgmental ratings of untreated disorder.

There is, then, much to criticize and improve upon in these past attempts to investigate the criterion-oriented validity of both objective and judgmental measures of untreated disorder. There is, first of all, the absence of evidence of predictive validity, evidence that can only be supplied by prospective studies. Criterion-oriented attempts to establish both concurrent and predictive validity, however, face a common problem. Even with more attention, for example, to larger and diagnostically more heterogeneous patient criterion groups, independent criteria of "wellness," and problems of response style, there are strong reasons not to rely primarily on attempts to establish criterion-oriented validity. Foremost is the present fact that there are no generally agreed upon criteria of psychological health or disorder (cf. A.H. Leighton *et al.*, 1963, p. 264).

Construct Validity

Cronbach and Meehl (1955) have argued that when no generally accepted criteria for the variable of interest are available, and when no universe of content is fully agreed upon as defining the variable, we must become interested in construct validity. These are the circumstances of untreated psychological disorder.

In Cronbach and Meehl's formulation,

> A necessary condition for a construct to be scientifically admissible is that it occur in a nomological net, at least *some* of whose laws involve observables (p. 290).

Furthermore:

> unless the network makes contact with observations, and exhibits explicit, public steps of inference, construct validation cannot be claimed (p. 291).

As noted above, the Midtown study measure of mental health consisted of psychiatrists' ratings which ranged subjects on a scale from "well" through five degrees of severity of symptomatology: "mild," "moderate," "marked," "severe," and "incapacitated." The two rating psychiatrists (Srole et al., 1962) explained:

> Throughout the volumes of this Study, the data must be evaluated as a rating of mental health based on the rating psychiatrists' perceptions operating through a questionnaire instrument (p. 66).

Although they reported that positive responses to any of 14 specific items ordinarily precluded the classification of a subject as well, and positive responses to other items suggested various degrees of severity of symptomatology (pp. 396–397), the psychiatrists summarized their impression of the rating process:

> we used our clinical judgment to the best of our ability. It would be a mistake, however, to overlook the fact that there remain some aspects of the process which are not altogether in our awareness (pp. 62–63).

To the extent that this measurement of psychological disorder is private and hence not replicable, a claim for construct validity is precluded.

The same problem exists in the Leightons' Stirling County and Yoruba studies (1963). Although the problem of achieving public steps of inference in psychiatric evaluation concerned them, they did not attain this goal in either of these studies. Optimistically, they suggested that the development of the procedures to date:

> brings within sight the possibility that the evaluations could be done by a computer. To achieve this the steps would have to be broken down into even more specific items, and the intuitive leaps that are still allowed would have to be dissected so that their components could be identified (p. 267).

A computer program would certainly be a step toward construct validation of measures of psychological disorder. However, the construct validity of such a program could be evaluated only in relation to a nomological net. It is not clear in the work of the Leightons how such a net would be formulated. Although the Stirling County study was introduced with a theoretical volume (A. H. Leighton, 1959), the propositions in this theory are developed at a level of abstraction such that it does not make direct contact with observations. Instead, the guide for psychiatric evaluation was the American Psychiatric Association Diagnostic and Statistical Manual (1952). While this Manual often includes etiological propositions in its descriptions of nosological types, etiological inferences were avoided in the Stirling and Yoruba studies in the interest of interrater reliability. Thus, the psychiatric evaluations were removed entirely from a nomological framework within which construct validity could be evaluated.

Where, then, can we look for propositions placing psychological disorder in a nomological net? Not, it appears, to clinical experience. Unlike tuberculosis and pellagra, which are commonly cited as subjects of successful epidemiological research, psychological disorder does not constitute an etiologically defined disease entity (Clausen, 1961; Gruenberg, 1955). Instead:

> With symptoms still our primary basis for classification, we are at the same stage of knowledge about mental disease that medicine occupied a century ago with reference to the "fevers." Typhoid, malaria, and a number of other diseases, all readily distinguishable now, were lumped together (Clausen, 1961, pp. 131–132).

Recognition of this situation has led a number of investigators to avoid psychodynamic inferences and assumptions in attempting to identify untreated disorder (e.g., A.H. Leighton et al., 1963, p. 89; D.C. Leighton et al., 1963, p. 48; New York State Department of Mental Hygiene, 1959, p. 83; Srole et al., 1962, pp. 63, 134). In the absence of connections with individual psychodynamics, however, the meaning of the symptoms must emerge from the discovery of their relationships with sociocultural factors. It seems necessary, therefore, to look to the results of existing field studies for leads to a nomological network which can be used to validate the construct of psychological disorder.

Relations between Sociocultural Factors and Symptomatology

Four sociocultural factors have been studied sufficiently frequently to show a pattern of relationship to rates of judged psychopathology. These are age, sex, race, and socioeconomic status.

The age groups for which minimum and maximum rates have been reported are shown in Table III. With only four exceptions, the minimum rate was in the youngest age group reported. However, Table III does not show a consistent pattern for the age at which maximum rates were found. In five of the studies, the maximum appeared in adolescence, in ten in the middle years, and in six in the oldest age group studied. No clues to etiology seem evident in such discrepant results.

Sex comparisons, shown in Table IV, likewise do not present a clear picture. Although 16 studies reported higher rates for women and only 11 reported higher rates for men, this difference is not large enough to establish a clear trend.

There is no evidence of a trend in the studies comparing rates for whites and Negroes. Of the eight studies in Table V, four reported higher rates for whites and four for Negroes.

Against this background of inconsistent results, it is almost startling to find, as Table VI shows, that 19 of the 24 studies which present data on the relationship with social class yielded the highest rate of judged psychopathology in the lowest economic stratum. Of the remaining five, the study by Strotzka (1966), two of the early studies by Brugger (1933, 1937) and Llewellyn-Thomas' Canadian village study (1960), gave the highest rate in a middle stratum. The index of social class is somewhat problematical in the last three of these studies, however, since it is based on our grouping of the occupations reported by the authors, which may not reflect accurately the stratification in

TABLE III

MINIMUM AND MAXIMUM RATES OF PSYCHOLOGICAL DISORDER REPORTED ACCORDING TO AGE

	Minimum Age	*Minimum* %	*Maximum* Age	*Maximum* %	*% diff.*	*Author(s)*
			Maximum in adolescence			
Minimum in youngest group studied	0–5	0.03	11–15	1.88	1.85	Brugger, 1931
	0–4	0.4	10–14	4.0	3.6	Cohen *et al.*, 1939
	0–5	0.0	11–15	7.5[a]	7.5	Brugger, 1937
	0–4	2.6	10–14	11.4	8.8	Roth and Luton, 1943
	0–5	0.2[a]	11–15	14.1[a]	13.9	Brugger, 1933
			Maximum in middle years			
	0–10	0.01	41–50	2.0[a]	2.0	Uchimara *et al.*, 1940
	0–10	1.6[a]	61–70	7.2[a]	5.6	Tsuwaga *et al.*, 1942
	0–14	0.8	15–34	14.8	14.0	Pasamanick *et al.*,[b] 1959
	10–19[c]	13.9	40–49 and 50–59	28.1	14.2	Bremer, 1951
	0–15	3.2[a]	21–45	20.9[a]	17.7	Strotzka *et al.*, 1966
	15–24[c]	35.1[a]	25–34	83.3[a]	48.2	Llewellyn-Thomas, 1960
			Maximum in oldest group studied			
	20–29[c]	15.3	50–59[d]	30.8	15.5	Srole *et al.*, 1962
	16–24	15	65+	32	17	Hare and Shaw, 1965
	Under 39	46.3[a]	60+	63.7[a]	17.4	D. Leighton *et al.*,[e] 1963
	16–24[c]	27.5[a]	65+	48.1[a]	20.6	Taylor and Chave,[f] 1964
	18[c]	3.1	59[d]	26.4	23.3	Gnat *el al.*, 1964
	0–4	0.9	80+	49.1	48.2	Essen-Möller, 1956
	0–9	6.8[a]	80+	72.3[a]	65.5	Hagnell, 1966
			Maximum in middle years			
Minimum in other than youngest group studied	60+	38.1[a]	40–59	40.5[a]	2.4	A. Leighton *et al.*, 1963
	60–69	2.2[a]	70–79	5.4[a]	3.2	Akimoto *et al.*, 1942
	45–49	8.2[a]	25–29	15.7[a]	7.5	Gillis *et al.*, 1965
	30–39	23.2	50–59	39.5	16.3	Phillips, 1966
	40–44	8.7[a]	50–54	27.4[a]	18.7	Primrose, 1962

[a] Calculated by B. S. Dohrenwend.
[b] Excludes "other mental, psychoneurotic, and personality disorders" included in total rates.
[c] Youngest group reported.
[d] Oldest group reported.
[e] Results reported in A. Leighton *et al.*, 1963, p. 152.
[f] Based on survey data without supplementary physicians' reports included in total rate.

these rural areas. Only one study reported the highest rate in the highest income group.

It seems, therefore, in the face of other inconsistencies in the studies here reviewed, that a relationship of such apparent strength must command attention. The cumulative evidence it represents appears to establish the association of low socioeconomic status with a high rate of judged psychopathology as an important source of working hypotheses.

TABLE IV

RATES OF PSYCHOLOGICAL DISORDER REPORTED FOR MALES AND FEMALES

Rate for Males Higher				Rate for Females Higher			
Percentage				Percentage			
Male	Female	d	Author(s)	Male	Female	d	Author(s)
1.1[a]	1.0[a]	0.1	Kaila, Study II, 1942	1.89[a]	1.91[a]	0.02	Rosanoff, 1917
1.3[a]	1.2[a]	0.1	Kaila, Study I, 1942	3.0[a]	3.1[a]	0.1	Tsuwaga et al., 1942
11.9	11.8	0.1	Freming, 1951	1.5[a]	2.0[a]	0.5	Lemkau et al., 1942
1.4[a]	1.2[a]	0.2	Brugger, 1931	2.0[a]	2.7[a]	0.7	Eaton & Weil,[b] 1955
1.0[a]	0.6[a]	0.4	Uchimara et al., 1940	22.1	24.0	1.9	Bellin and Hardt, 1958
2.8	1.9	0.9	Cohen et al., 1939	12.3	14.9	2.6	Essen-Möller, 1956
3.4[a]	2.0[a]	1.4	Akimoto et al., 1942	27.2	30.0	2.8	Helgason, 1964
7.9	6.0	1.9	Roth and Luton, 1943	20.6	26.0	5.4	Bremer, 1951
4.5[a]	2.5[a]	2.0	Brugger, 1937	10.0[a]	16.2[a]	6.2	Primrose, 1962
41.8[a]	38.9[a]	2.9	A. Leighton et al., 1963	6.0	12.3	6.3	Pasamanick et al., 1959
9.0[a]	6.0[a]	3.0	Brugger, 1933	11.3	20.4	9.1	Hagnell, 1966
14.0[a]	9.6[a]	4.4	Gillis et al., 1965	22.6	32.2	9.6	Phillips, 1966
				8.6[a]	20.1[a]	11.5	Strotzka et al., 1966
				12.9[a]	27.5[a]	14.6	Hare and Shaw, 1965
				47.0	65.0	18.0	D. Leighton et al.,[c] 1963
				22.0	43.0	21.0	Taylor and Chave,[d] 1964
				51.8[a]	75.2[a]	23.4	Llewellyn-Thomas, 1960

[a] Calculated by B. S. Dohrenwend.

[b] Rates for both sexes are higher than the overall rate in Table I because the overall rate is for prevalence in the summer of 1951, whereas sex rates had to be calculated from data on life-time morbidity.

[c] Results reported in A. Leighton et al., 1963, p. 149.

[d] Based on survey data without supplementary physicians' reports included in total rate.

TABLE V

RATES OF PSYCHOLOGICAL DISORDER REPORTED FOR WHITES AND NEGROES

Rate for Whites Higher				Rate for Negroes Higher			
Percentage				Percentage			
White	Negro	d	Author(s)	White	Negro	d	Author(s)
1.9[a]	1.2[a]	0.7	Lemkau et al., 1942	2.2[a]	2.8[a]	0.6	Cohen et al., 1939
7.1	5.0	2.1	Rowntree et al., 1945	1.8[a]	7.0[a]	5.2	Rosanoff, 1917
7.8	4.2	3.6	Roth and Luton, 1943	11.1[a]	37.2	26.1	Hyde and Chisholm, 1944
11.2	4.6	6.6	Pasamanick et al., 1959	—	—	—	D. Leighton et al.,[b] 1963

[a] Calculated by B. S. Dohrenwend.

[b] Results reported in ridits rather than percentages.

TABLE VI

MINIMUM AND MAXIMUM RATES OF PSYCHOLOGICAL DISORDER REPORTED
ACCORDING TO SOCIOECONOMIC STATUS

	Percentage			
	Minimum	Maximum	d	Author(s)
	Minimum in highest stratum			
Maximum in lowest stratum	0.8	0.9	0.1	Hagnell, 1966[a, b]
	1.3[c]	3.2[c]	1.9	Akimoto et al.,[d] 1942
	0.7	3.7	3.0	} Cohen et al.,[e] 1939
	1.1	6.6	5.5	
	14.3[c]	20.5[c]	6.2	Hare and Shaw,[f] 1965
	19.5	27.0	7.5	Bremer,[b] 1951
	30.0	37.8	7.8	Taylor & Chave,[g] 1964
	7.3	16.6	9.3	Hyde and Kingsley, 1944
	17.4[c]	29.4[c]	12.0	Bellin and Hardt,[b] 1958
	5.0	17.0	12.0	Gillis et al., 1965
	1.6	15.1	13.5	} Gnat et al.,[h] 1964
	6.0	25.4	19.4	
	18.0	32.2	14.2	Phillips, 1966
	12.5	47.3	34.8	Srole et al., 1962
	—	—	—	Cole et al.,[i] 1957
	—	—	—	D. Leighton et al.,[j] 1963
	Minimum in a middle stratum			
	2.3[c]	2.9[c]	0.6	Tsuwaga et al.,[d] 1942
	0.8	1.9	1.1	Lin, 1953
	1.2[c]	2.5[c]	1.3	Brugger,[k] 1931
	23.9[c]	30.6[a]	6.7	Helgason, 1964
	10.3	29.7	19.4	Primrose, 1962
	Minimum in lowest stratum			
Maximum in a middle stratum	3.4[c]	5.3[c]	1.9	Brugger,[k] 1937
	45.0	54.1[c]	9.1	Llewellyn-Thomas,[l] 1960
	7.4[c]	25.7[c]	18.3	Brugger,[k] 1933
	—	22.7[c]	22.7	Strotzka et al., 1966
	Minimum in a middle stratum			
Maximum in highest stratum	6.2	13.6	7.4	Pasamanick et al., 1959

[a] Annual incidence rates. [b] Subjects divided into only two strata. [c] Calculated by B. S. Dohrenwend. [d] Distribution of population in socioeconomic strata was reported only by number of families; since Japanese census reports do not include information on family size by SES, rates were calculated on the assumption of equal family size in all four strata. Rates for socioeconomic strata are below total rate for Tsuwaga due to reduction by 12 of number of cases reported according to SES. [e] Data for whites only reported for two wards separately. [f] Males and married females only. [g] Based on survey data without supplementary physician's reports included in total rate. [h] Rates for two cities reported separately. [i] Cole et al. (1957) do not report rates but state: "Four-fifths of the families in the lower social strata contained at least one mentally ill member, while less than one-half of the upper-stratum families were thus affected" (p. 395). [j] Results reported in ridits rather than percentages. [k] Occupations grouped by B. S. Dohrenwend into three strata: high (self-employed merchants, manufacturers, and farmers, and middle level civil servants); middle (merchants, manufacturers, and farmers employed by others, and low level civil servants); and low (workers and servants). [l] Occupations grouped by B. S. Dohrenwend into three strata: high (independent business and salaried workers); middle (fishermen and farmers); and low (laborers). The maximum rate in these strata is below the overall rate because of the exclusion of two categories of persons with high rates, grouped separately by Llewellyn-Thomas; i.e., housewives, with a rate of 76 per cent, and miscellaneous, with a rate of 65 per cent.

A Theoretical Issue

A number of investigators have pointed out that the relationship between social class and psychological symptoms can be explained either as social causation, with low status producing psychopathology, or as social selection, with pre-existing psychological disorder determining social status (e.g., Dunham, 1961). The latter is, of course, compatible with the position that genetic factors are important in the etiology of psychological disorder.

In a notable advance over previous approaches, Srole and Langner in the Midtown study (Srole et al., 1962, pp. 212–213, 228–229) attempted to choose between these two interpretations by investigating parental class position, a factor clearly antecedent to the current psychiatric condition of their adult subjects. Finding a significant inverse relation between their subjects' symptomatology and the socioeconomic status of their subjects' parents, the investigators suggested that environmental deprivation in childhood is a causal factor in psychological disorder. However, they also found that the relation between parental socioeconomic status and impairing symptoms was weaker than the relation of own socioeconomic status to impairing symptoms. Moreover, subjects rated impaired were most likely to be found among people who were downwardly mobile relative to their parents, and least likely to be found among those who were upwardly mobile. Accordingly, the Midtown researchers suggested that perhaps both social causation, in the form of childhood deprivation, and social selection, in the form of intergeneration mobility, contribute to the strong inverse relation between rates of impairment and subjects' own socioeconomic status.

There are problems, however, in addition to lack of parsimony, with this explanation. Genetic predisposition could, with equal plausibility, be substituted in it for childhood deprivation. Moreover, symptoms judged psychotic appear to be an important exception. Langner, on the basis of further analysis concluded that:

> it is the adult life conditions in particular that stimulate the development of high rates of psychosis in the lower class; for the childhood conditions, at least as reported by our respondents, do not vary substantially between the classes (Langner and Michael, 1963, p. 454).

Implicit in Srole's and Langner's explanations is the assumption that impairing symptoms indicate a stable, self-perpetuating defect in the personalities of adult subjects. But what if we consider the possibility that many of these symptoms represent transient responses by normal personalities to objective, stress producing events, i.e. stressors (Dohrenwend, 1961) in the immediate environment (cf. Tyhurst, 1958, p. 161)? This hypothesis would provide a more parsimonious explanation of the array of Midtown findings concerning social status and psychological disorder. First, it suggests the possibility that the excess of cases in the lowest socioeconomic stratum is made up of normal persons reacting to unusually harsh and numerous stressors in their environment. Further, the increase in symptoms with downward mobility, and the decrease with upward mobility would be explained as consequences of changes in the number and harshness of stressors in the mobile subjects' environment. Hence, intergeneration mobility would be expected to produce a lower correlation between parental socioeconomic status and rate of impairing symptoms than between own socioeconomic status and rate of symptoms, the pattern of correlation that was found.

While this explanation in terms of contemporary stressors is parsimonious, it runs counter to the usual interpretation of symptomatology. For instance, in the Stirling County study (D. C. Leighton *et al.*, 1963), the distribution of cases according to age was intrepreted as indicating that

> these symptoms in nonpatients have the same quality of persistence that has long been recognized as an outstanding feature of psychoneurosis when seen in clinics and private practice (p. 358).

This inference was drawn, however, despite compelling evidence that some portion of the symptoms they observed were of the transient, situational variety. That is, in comparing the psychiatrists' evaluations based on interview data collected in 1952 with a general practitioner's independent diagnoses of 39 respondents about 4 years later, the authors noted that, of the 14 disagreements, 4 were due to "transient episodes of disorder" (p. 196). A fifth may also have been transient since he

> either had a better relationship to the general practitioner than to his predecessor or had actually improved, so that he changed from ill to not ill by 1958 (p. 197).

Moreover, there are strong, albeit indirect, empirical grounds for considering the possibility that the high level of symptomatology in the lowest socioeconomic stratum represents, at least in part, just such transient responses to stressors. These grounds are, first, evidence suggesting that stressors for which the individual cannot be held responsible are relatively pervasive in the lower class environment; second, observations that normal individuals exposed to stressors respond with symptoms which would ordinarily be classified as indicative of psychopathology; third, evidence of spontaneous recovery from these symptoms on removal of the stressors. Consider each in turn.

Relative Pervasiveness in Lower Class Environment of Stressors for Which Individuals Are Not Responsible

Investigators of the quality of lower class life have not generally been able to disentangle the causal web of socioeconomic disadvantage and individual ineffectiveness (e.g., Knupfer, 1947). There are, however, some facts of lower class life which seem more plausibly interpreted as stressors in the environment than as defects in the individual.

Premature deaths of children and young adults, for example, are disruptive factors in family and social life over which survivors have little control. The comparatively short life expectancy in lower class groups (Mayer and Hauser, 1950) suggests that such stressors are relatively frequent there.

Unemployment and the threat of unemployment, also suffered more frequently in the lowest stratum than in other strata (e.g., Hollingshead, 1947; Langner and Michael, 1963, pp. 386, 388), similarly appear more dependent on environmental circumstance than upon individual failure. Wide fluctuations in rates of unemployment both over time and from one place to another support this interpretation.

Moreover, some stressors are likely consequences of residence in low income areas. Such areas, for example, are the targets of bulldozers, with attendant forced relocation of low income families (e.g., Fried, 1963). And it is into low income areas that new immigrant groups must frequently move, often giving rise to problems of conflict between members of different cultures (e.g., Dohrenwend and Smith, 1962).

Responses of Normal Persons to Stressors

Reid (1961) has reviewed the literature on the relation of immediate external events to the onset of mental disorders. He found that

> the epidemiological or statistical evidence about the effect of such externals on mental disease is relatively scanty . . . much of it comes from studies done in the war (p. 197).

Striking evidence that normal individuals respond to stressors with symptoms which are found in psychiatric patients is provided by Hastings' (1944) World War II study of 150 men in the Eighth Air Force who had completed their 30 mission tour of duty without reporting sick. Since men who are predisposed to breakdown were found in another study generally to report sick before flying half this many missions (Reid, 1961, p. 202), Hastings' finding that 95 per cent of his subjects had developed symptoms of operational fatigue is particularly compelling. Hastings identifies operational fatigue as a condition which, unlike flying fatigue, is not cured by a few days rest, but can often be cured by a week and a half of therapy. It is a form of psychopathology attributed, in these cases, to the wartime flying experience rather than to previous neurotic symptoms or to family history.

Observations were also made during World War II of the responses of civilian populations to bombing. In a review of these materials, Janis (1951) concluded that repeated reports in both England and Germany indicate:

> Under conditions of severe bombing there is marked incidence of temporary emotional shock, presumably even among persons who were previously emotionally stable. Such reactions may take the form of excessive anxiety symptoms or of mild depression and apathy (pp. 96–97).

The investigators whom Janis reviewed had no direct information about the psychological condition prior to the experience of bombing of the persons whose reactions they observed. Bremer's (1951) study of a northern Norwegian village overcomes this problem. As resident physician from January 1939 to August 1945, he surveyed the entire population of 1400. When the village suffered enemy occupation and air raids, he found that 22 persons developed "war neurosis," i.e., "acquired nervous states caused by the direct effects of war," in which:

> the main syndrome was fear with its accompanying somatic conditions: starting, tremor, palpitation, precardiac pains. Add hereto in the majority of cases: fatigue, insomnia, and uncharacteristic dedolations. In a few cases the depression is extremely predominant.

In two of the women, the nervous reaction is more correctly characterized as psychotic: in the one the syndrome was one of religious-ecstatic exaltation of one or two weeks' standing; the other suffered from a depression marked by anxiety, lasting 3–4 weeks (p. 57).

There have also been some relevant studies of reactions to stressors other than those produced by war. Lindemann (1944, pp. 146–147) followed up the survivors of the Coconut Grove fire in Boston. On the basis of his observations of these cases and others who had lost a friend or relative, he emphasized the importance of the situation, and irrelevance of personal factors, as determinants of extreme grief reactions.

Nor are such reactions observed only in situations involving loss of loved persons. Fried (1963) found indications of grief and mourning, similar to those described by Lindemann, in the majority of a sample of 566 men and women who had been forced to relocate from a slum section of Boston to make way for urban renewal. Their reactions included:

> the feelings of painful loss, the continued longing, the general depressive tone, frequent symptoms of psychological or social or somatic distress, the active work required in adapting to the altered situation, the sense of helplessness, the occasional expressions of both direct and displaced anger, and tendencies to idealize the lost place (p. 15).

Finally, in a study of reactions to President Kennedy's death (Sheatsley and Feldman, 1964), 89 per cent of a national sample reported that during the 4 days following the assassination they experienced one or more of 15 physical and emotional symptoms such as "Didn't feel like eating," "Had headaches," "Had an upset stomach," "Had trouble getting to sleep," and "Felt nervous and tense." Most of these 15 items are similar to ones on which Midtown and Stirling County psychiatrists based their judgments of untreated psychological disorder (cf. Langner, 1962; D.C. Leighton et al., 1963, pp. 440–441; Srole et al., 1962, pp. 388–389).

The Reversibility of Stressor-Induced Symptomatology

If the symptoms normal persons develop when exposed to stressors disappear spontaneously on removal of the stressors, then it is clear that these symptoms indicate situationally induced response rather than self-perpetuating pathology in the individual. The weight of the evidence is that spontaneous recovery is frequent.

Thus Bremer (1951, p. 57), following the civilian cases of "war neurosis" he found in the northern Norwegian village, reports: "In all cases the prognosis was good, the symptoms disappearing when the patients were removed from the danger zone. In those who once more experienced war actions, the symptoms generally recurred."

Ginzberg and his colleagues (1959a, p. 19) studied the postwar adjustment of 534 "ineffective soldiers" systematically sampled from the men inducted in the last 4 months of 1942. An ineffective soldier was defined as "any man whom the Army discharged prior to demobilization for reasons of psychoneurosis, psychosis, inaptitude, or traits of character which made him unsuitable for retention in military service."

Relying mainly on Army and Veterans Administration records, Ginzberg and his colleagues classified types of readjustment after discharge into three major patterns: early, delayed, and unsuccessful. Early readjustment meant at least adequate civilian performance within 2 years of discharge. Delayed adjustment took longer than 2 years. Unsuccessful readjustment was indicated by failure of performance during the last 2 years for which information was available for a given soldier. The model group, 44 per cent, were judged to have made an early readjustment. Only 11.1 per cent were in the delayed readjustment category, and 19.3 per cent were judged to have made unsuccessful readjustments. For the remaining 25.6 per cent of the sample, no data were available concerning adjustment.

With regard to loss of a cherished person or home, Lindemann (1944) reported, in a follow-up of 13 bereaved victims of the fire in the Coconut Grove, that all but one were judged, after a series of psychiatric interviews, to have made a satisfactory adaptation in 4 to 6 weeks. And Fried (1963) found that the minority, 26 per cent, of the women in his sample of persons relocated from a Boston slum reported that they still felt sad or depressed 2 years later, with another 20 per cent reporting periods of 6 months to 2 years. Slightly smaller percentages were found among the sample of 316 men.

In the study by Sheatsley and Feldman (1964) of reactions to President Kennedy's assassination, interviews were done 5 to 9 days after the day of the assassination. Although 89 per cent of the sample had reported experiencing physical and emotional symptoms during the first 4 days, only 50 per cent reported that they still had at least one symptom at the time of the interview.

Some Strands in a Nomological Network

In a recent review of clinical observations about psychological disorder together with results from laboratory investigations of frustration, traumatic avoidance learning, and experimental neurosis, Wilson (1963) found common themes:

> On the one hand, the foundation for pathology is laid by a progressive state of emotional arousal that finally reaches disastrous proportions. . . . Secondly, the constant feature of the behavioral symptoms is their stereotypy and repetitiveness. Once established, the symptoms are remarkably intractable to control by external reward or punishment. . . . These . . . characteristics of behavior pathology, anchored as they are in careful experimental work, furnish substantial corroboration for . . . similar features noted . . . in the clinical literature (pp. 143–144).

Wilson's conclusion implies that the temporary, stressor-induced symptoms described in the preceding section should not be included under the rubric psychological disorder. Yet, in the absence of information as to whether the symptoms persist in the face of changed circumstances, it appears that situationally specific responses to stressors cannot be distinguished by clinicians from responses which outlive the conditions that induced them.

Faced with the problem of lack of information on persistence of symptomatology, one approach has been to interpret the symptoms relative to the setting in which they appear. Noyes and Kolb (1958) do this, for example, in suggesting that symptoms of normal battle reaction

> would be considered abnormal in a civilian setting yet are not so incapacitating as to demand removal from combat. Unless extreme, such reactions must *under the circumstances* be considered within the range of normal (p. 533, italics added).

In distinguishing here between normal and abnormal, Noyes and Kolb describe a process of social evaluation which has some interesting points of convergence with the conception of psychological disorder advanced by Wilson. Noyes and Kolb's definition suggests that symptoms are judged normal, in the particular setting of combat, when they are seen as not unduly damaging either to the military performance of the individual or to others in his group. Moreover, these authors' definition implies that when symptoms are judged harmful in these terms, it is necessary to alter the soldier's behavior, initially by removing him from combat.

Generalizing this process, we propose that psychological disorder can be defined, in part, by social judgments that the individual's reactions to a stressor in a particular social setting are harmful to him or to others in his group, and should be altered (cf. Dohrenwend, 1962, 1963; Hollingshead and Redlich, 1958, pp. 171–190). Relating this process of evaluation to Wilson's analysis, we suggest that a further condition for identification of psychological disorder is the intractable persistence of these symptomatic reactions in the face of the attempts by social agents to alter them.

These conditions can be combined into the following definition of psychological disorder as one approach to developing a nomological net:

Stressor-induced symptomatic responses, judged by the individual and/or by other social agents to be harmful to the individual and/or to others with whom he stands in social relationship, indicate psychological disorder if the symptoms continue (a) after the stressor ceases to impinge on the individual, and (b) despite sanctions directed at the individual by social agents who judge the response maladaptive.

This definition articulates within a single conceptual framework evidence concerning transient symptomatic responses to situational stressors with evidence, from both clinic and laboratory, which points to intractability to control by reward or punishment as the critical characteristic of symptoms indicative of psychological disorder.

A step toward validation of the construct, psychological disorder, could be taken, we suggest, by using this definition in tests of the proposition that the high rates of "disorder" found by field studies in the lowest stratum represent, in large part, situationally specific symptomatic reactions rather than psychological disorder as defined above. Support for this proposition would be provided by confirmation of such hypotheses as the following:

1. That a large portion of the symptomatology reported in field studies is induced by stressors in the contemporary situation.
2. That a large portion of such stressor-induced symptomatology is transient rather than persistent.

3. That transience of symptomatology varies directly with the extent to which it is defined as maladaptive.
4. That the extent to which such symptomatology is defined as maladaptive varies inversely with social class.
5. That the incidence of stressors in the contemporary situation varies inversely with social class.

Tests of these hypotheses would, we believe, provide a base from which to expand the nomological net to include crucial issues of the relative impact of genetic factors, childhood experiences, and contemporary environmental conditions on the development and course of psychological disorder.

14 / Psychoses, Income, and Occupational Prestige

Robert E. Clark

The ecological studies of Faris and Dunham (1939), Green (1939), Mowrer (1939), Queen (1940), Schroeder (1942) and Hadley *et al.* (1944) have demonstrated that in the city the distribution of all types of mental disorder shows a wide range of rates, with high rates concentrated at the center and declining in all directions toward the periphery. The ecological distributions in nine cities support this finding. Although there is not complete agreement among sociologists as to the explanation, one rather widely accepted view is that it lies more or less (*a*) in the differential composition of the populations of the various areas as to age, sex, race, nationality, occupation, social class, personality types, social types, and (*b*) in the differential physical and social experiences which persons have by virtue of the fact that they live in one area rather than in another. Most of the differences in composition of the populations of ecological areas are traditionally related to the fundamental process of competition which is, for the most part, economic competition. Through competition different types of persons become segregated. But social and physical experiences differ in accordance with the characteristics of the "natural areas" of the city.[1] These characteristics include such factors as type of social organization (or social disorganization); degree of consensus; neighborhood traditions; amount of anonymity, secondary contacts, social mobility, social isolation, etc. As illustrations of dif-

From the *American Journal of Sociology*, 1949, **54**, 433–440. Copyright © 1949. Reprinted by permission of the author and the University of Chicago Press.

[1] Of course, not all persons living in a given area react similarly to the same items in their common environment, each bringing to bear his own apperception mass, but it is assumed that the greater the number and strength of the disorganizing factors in an environment, the greater the proportion of persons who will be affected by them. It is also assumed that, since the mental-disorder rates of the various areas of the city are not distributed at random but fall into a pattern, some factor or factors associated with the ecological areas are responsible.

ferential social experiences based upon residence we can cite the articles of Faris (1934) and of Dunham (1944), respectively.

The present study is an effort to determine statistically the relationship existing between occupational psychoses rates and the ranking of occupations by income and by prestige. In general the explanations for the relationships found by statistical means are similar to *a* and *b* in the foregoing for the ecological studies except for the fact that here we are primarily interested in occupational rather than in spatial categories. These explanations, we must admit, are merely hypotheses which may explain some of the findings presented in this paper.

We may assume that the various occupational groups differ with respect to certain traits which have a bearing upon the likelihood of persons becoming psychotic. We must first recognize that there are undoubtedly a number of selective factors which determine the occupation into which a given man goes, such as constitutional differences, general intelligence (Proctor, 1920), social adjustability, personality type (Super, 1942), special aptitudes, education, cultural background, social class and/or occupation of his father (Davidson and Anderson, 1937; Centers, 1948). Some of these selective factors may at the same time be segregating men according to their likelihood of becoming psychotic. Thus the pre-schizophrenic's self-consciousness, his sensitivity, his withdrawal from normal social intercourse, his overconcern with his status and position, may prevent him from pushing himself forward occupationally and also may put him in a less favorable light when promotions are being handed out. The chronic alcoholics have been characterized (Adler, 1941; Wall, 1936; Strecker, 1942, p. 84) as dependent persons who shun responsibility. Persons with a strong need for dependency, whether alcoholic or not, would not be very likely to advance occupationally to positions of leadership. But whatever the personality of the alcoholic, his addiction to drink is not looked upon favorably by employers when they are seeking to fill positions of responsibility. The pre-paretic, who for a long period of time has suffered from syphilis, probably has been handicapped by his disease. For the general group of organic psychoses, especially those in which the organic cause has been at work for a long period of time, the lessened physical and/or mental efficiency prior to the onset of the psychosis would be reflected in reduced occupational efficiency and success. Thus we see that conditions in the etiology of some psychoses may at the same time be entering into the problem of occupational selection.

Our other assumption is that differential occupational-psychoses rates may be viewed and interpreted as the resultant of differential physical and social experiences which persons have as direct or indirect consequences of their places in the division of labor. The occupational differentials in experiences which may be related to occupational differentials in psychoses rates have never been investigated thoroughly, but they may include (1) differentials in occupational hazards of brain injuries, toxic poisoning; (2) differences in occupational roles which may or may not be desirable because of (*a*) the operations which must be performed in one's work, (*b*) the place and conditions found where one performs his work, (*c*) the prestige which one obtains from his fellow-workmen and from society at large; (3) occupational differences in income which may determine where a person will live in the city and which may cause some persons to be faced with special financial problems; (4) differences in occupational and class folkways and mores which may sanction or restrict one from engaging in such activities as intemperate use of alcohol, illicit sexual intercourse (Kinsey, Pomeroy, and Martin, 1948, pp. 349, 353–354, 430–431), which may lead to alcoholic psychoses or general paralysis; (5) differences in the way of life of the various social classes insofar as one's social class is determined by one's occupation. Some of these experiences may well be considered in the etiology of some of the psychoses. We are not implying, however, that nonoccupationally derived experiences are unimportant or that every occupationally derived experience is important in the etiology of psychoses.

It is also possible that occupational differences in psychoses rates could be due in part to nonoccupational factors which are simply correlated with occupation but which are not causally related to it. It is very difficult, however, to think of any factors associated with occupation which cannot be partially attributed to (a) occupational selection or to (b) direct and indirect differentials in occupationally derived experiences.

Let us now turn our attention to our occupational data to see whether there is some relationship between psychoses rates and the factors of occupational income and occupational prestige. Briefly, the method of study consisted in classifying 12,168 cases of male first admissions[2] to mental hospitals from Chicago into 19 large occupational groups. With the use of census data[3] as a base, age-adjusted rates[4] were calculated for each occupational group. The occupa-

[2] The data consist of 12,168 male first admissions with psychoses in the age interval 20–69 years, inclusive, from the city of Chicago during 1922–34, inclusive, to Chicago, Elgin, and Kankakee state hospitals for the insane, and to a number of local private mental hospitals. It is estimated that these data comprise 96 percent of all commitments of mental patients of the same sex and age group for the time period studied. These data were collected by W.P.A. Project 3564, carried on under the sponsorship of the Illinois Psychopathic Institute at the University of Chicago under the supervision of Miss Ethel Shanas. Funds for the machine sorting of the Hollerith cards were provided by the Social Science Research Committee of the University of Chicago. The cases were tabulated by race nativity, occupational group, type of psychosis, and age.

[3] Special data from the Bureau of the Census were obtained for the city of Chicago for the year 1930, giving a breakdown by race nativity, age, and occupation. The occupational data listed 638 different occupations, which were then classified into the same 19 occupational groups as the psychoses data. Although the year 1928 was the midyear of the study, it is not likely that the relative size of the various occupational groups would change very much by 1930 even if interpolation were feasible.

[4] The adjustment of the psychoses data for age was accomplished by applying age-specific psychoses rates by ten-year intervals for each of the 19 occupational groups to a standard population, which in this case was the age distribution of all gainfully employed males in Chicago in the 1930 census. The formulas used were:

$$(a) \quad R = \frac{S(p_s \times A_s)}{S(A_s)}, \quad (b) \quad \sigma_R = S \sqrt{\left(\frac{p_s q_s}{a_s}\right)\left(\frac{A_s^2}{A^2}\right)},$$

and

$$(c) \quad \sigma_{\mathrm{Av.}R - R_i} = S \sqrt{p_s q_s \left(\frac{1}{N_s - a_s} + \frac{1}{A_s}\right)\left(\frac{A_s^2}{A^2}\right)}.$$

In formula (a) R refers to the age-adjusted rate, p_s to the age-specific rate for a given occupational group, A_s to the number in the standard population in age-group s, and S to the summational groups were then ranked in order of increasing psychoses rates, then ranked again in terms of increasing income and prestige; and the two rankings were correlated.

It may be well to evaluate the psychoses data before presenting the findings. These data were classified by age, race nativity, occupation, and type of psychosis. How accurately are the data classified with respect to these classes?

Age

The data were sorted into, and age adjusted by, ten-year age intervals: 20–29, 30–39, 40–49, 50–59, and 60–69 years. Although smaller age intervals may be more desirable, this was not feasible because some of the occupational groups would then have had too few cases in some of the age groups. The accuracy of reporting the age of patients at time of admission is not known, but it is believed that most of the cases were placed in the proper ten-year interval.

Race Nativity

The categories here are native white, foreign white, and Negro. Country of birth may be difficult to determine accurately because of the changing of national boundaries; the problem of determining whether a patient was born in this country is easier. It is also relatively easy to distinguish between white and Negro. The total number of cases in the unknown-nativity group, aged 20–69 years, was 941, which is 5.9 per cent of the total number of cases in that age group. These data were omitted in the present study not only because they were a relatively small group and would not be likely to affect the results but also because for many of the cases in which nativity was unknown the occupation was also unknown.

Occupation

The psychoses and the census data were arbitrarily classified into the following occupational groups:

1. *Large owners, professional:* manufacturers, managers and officials, bankers, dentists, lawyers, judges, physicians, etc.
2. *Major salesmen:* commercial brokers, stock brokers, insurance agents, real-estate agents, wholesale dealers, etc.
3. *Small tradesmen:* primarily retail dealers.
4. *Office workers:* accountants, auditors, bookkeepers, cashiers, office-appliance operators, clerical workers, stenographers, typists, etc.

---

tion sign. These symbols have the same meaning in formula (b), and in addition σ_R refers to the standard error of the age-adjusted rate, q_s to ($1 - p_s$), and A is equal to $S(A_s)$. In formula (c) we have a close approximation to the standard error of the difference between the rate for a given occupational group and all occupations combined indicated by $\sigma_{Av.R - R_i}$; the number of persons in all occupations in age-group s is given by N_s; the rate for all occupations for age-group s is given by p_s; and the remainder of the symbols have the same meaning as above.

TABLE I

AGE-ADJUSTED RATES PER 100,000 MEN AGED 20–69 YEARS, INCLUSIVE, FOR
NATIVE-WHITE AND FOREIGN-WHITE MALE FIRST ADMISSIONS FOR ALL
PSYCHOSES FROM CHICAGO TO NEARBY MENTAL HOSPITALS,
1922–34, INCLUSIVE (By Occupational Group)

Occupational Group	No. Cases	Rate	Standard Error
1. Large owners professional	122	236†	22
2. Major salesmen	125	328†	30
3. Small tradesmen	200	349†	26
4. Office workers	456	581†	29
5. Policemen, firemen	113	597†	65
6. Clergy, teachers	66	624†	79
7. Engineers	70	829†	101
8. Subexecutives	179	843†	66
9. Semiprofessional	164	946	76
10. Salesmen	861	1,009†	35
11. Artists, musicians	93	1,036	109
12. Barbers, beauticians	99	1,213	125
13. Skilled workers	3,122	1,254*	23
14. Minor govt. employees	94	1,314	139
15. Domestic workers	228	1,492*	100
16. Semiskilled and unskilled workers	4,477	1,512*	23
17. Peddlers	59	1,747*	259
18. Waiters	119	2,058*	196
19. Errand and office boys	69	9,004*	1,516
All occupations	10,716	1,092	11

* This rate is significantly above the rate for all occupations.
† This rate is significantly below the rate for all occupations.

5. *Policemen, firemen:* firemen (fire department), guards, detectives, sheriffs,
   policemen, etc.
6. *Clergy, teachers:* editors and reporters, clergymen, college professors, architects, schoolteachers, trained nurses, librarians, etc.
7. *Engineers:* civil, electrical, mechanical, and mining engineers.
8. *Subexecutives:* foremen and overseers, managers of small businesses, etc.
9. *Semiprofessional:* druggists, undertakers, chemists, designers, draftsmen,
   osteopaths, photographers, veterinary surgeons, chiropractors, etc.
10. *Salesmen:* clerks in stores, commercial travelers, canvassers, salesmen, etc.
11. *Artists, musicians:* artists, musicians and teachers of music, actors, show-
    men, etc.
12. *Barbers and beauticians*
13. *Skilled workers:* inspectors, conductors, locomotive engineers, blacksmiths,
    cabinetmakers, carpenters, compositors, dyers, electricians, cranemen, ma-
    chinists, millwrights, mechanics, molders, painters, plasterers, etc.
14. *Minor governmental employees:* railway mail clerks; mail carriers; officials
    and inspectors employed by city, county, state, or federal government;
    notaries; etc.
15. *Domestic workers:* domestic and personal service, including cooks, char-
    men, cleaners, laborers, porters, servants, etc.
16. *Semiskilled and unskilled workers:* operatives of various sorts, apprentices,

filers, grinders, furnace men, laborers, deliverymen, newsboys, theater ushers, elevator tenders, janitors, etc.

17. *Peddlers:* hucksters and peddlers
18. *Waiters*
19. *Errand and office boys*

The only cases excluded by virtue of occupation were those which had no occupation listed, the retired, illicit, major politicians, soldiers and sailors, ship officers, bartenders, landlords, farmers, and students. Not included in the study because of failure to list an occupation in the hospital records were 14.7 per cent of the native whites, 13.4 per cent of the foreign whites, and 12.8 per cent of the Negroes. These race-nativity differences in percentages are not great enough to alter the relative rates of the respective race-nativity groups. It may further be assumed that, if the occupations of these rejected cases were known, most of them would fall in the unskilled occupations, where the rates are already relatively high.

Our occupational data were drawn from the face sheet of the hospital record of each patient. The question may be raised as to whether the occupation listed was the right one. This question I cannot answer except in a rough way with data collected almost ten years later from some of the same state mental hospitals by Morris Schwartz (1946). Schwartz secured employment histories from about 200 schizophrenic and manic-depressive patients. Using my occupational classification, and tabulating the Schwartz cases in each occupational group in terms of (*a*) the patient's most typical occupation and (*b*) the occupation listed on the face sheet of the hospital record, I found that out of 169 cases where the occupation was given the total errors in the tabulation of the face-sheet data were 3.5 ± 1.4 per cent. If the accuracy of hospital records did not improve between my study and that of Schwartz, it may be that the errors in recording data on the face sheet of his cases may be a fairly representative sample of the errors in mine. It is not likely that the errors would vary greatly from one type of psychosis to another, because most of the errors are not attributed to poor case histories but to the failure of the clerical staff in making the proper entry on the face sheet. There is no reason to believe that the clerical staff would be more careless with cases of one type of psychosis than with another. It does not seem likely that errors in my occupational data exceed 5 or 10 per cent, and this amount of error cannot explain the wide variation in rates.

Psychoses

Since this study is based upon all types of psychoses, the question of diagnostic error is almost nil.

The age-adjusted psychoses rates for native-white and foreign-white males show that in general the low rates are found in occupations having high prestige and high income, while the high rates are found in occupations having low prestige and low income. The age-adjusted rates for large owners, doctors, lawyers, etc.; major salesmen; small tradesmen; office workers; policemen and firemen; clergy, teachers; engineers; subexecutives; and salesmen are each significantly *below* the rate for all occupations. The age-adjusted rates for skilled workers, domestic workers, semiskilled and unskilled workers, peddlers, waiters, errand and office boys, are each significantly *above* the rate for all occupations. Except for the policemen and firemen and possibly part of the subexecutive group, those groups which have rates significantly below the average all fall into the group commonly called "white-collar workers." Without exception, the occupational groups which have rates significantly above the average are not white-collar workers. Thus low psychoses rates are associated with high occupational income and prestige, and high psychoses rates are associated with low occupational prestige and income. This does not, as we said earlier, necessarily imply any causal connection between the associated factors.

For the sake of accuracy let us compare the occupational rankings by psychoses rates with an objective ranking of occupations by income and by prestige. Occupations were ranked by prestige by combining the results of three large independent studies—those of Counts (1925), Nietz (1935), and Mapheus Smith (1943). The high agreement between these studies gives the combined results a high degree of reliability (see R. E. Clark, 1947, 1948). Also a wage-salary ranking of my 19 occupational groups was obtained by calculating the median income for each occupational group for reported income from wages and salary of $600 a year or more, as given in the 1940 census of Chicago. The results are shown in Table II. Prestige data were available for only 17 of the 19 occupational groups. The income ranking over 17 occupational groups (given in parentheses) should be compared with the prestige ranking over 17 occupational groups. The rank-order coefficient of correlation between the two series is +.85, which gives mutual support to our prestige and income rankings.

Using the occupational rankings by income and by prestige given above, we can quantify and verify our observation that psychoses rates are related to occupational income and occupational prestige by calculating rank-order correlation coefficients between psychoses rates and the factors of occupational income and occupational prestige.

For native-white and foreign-white rates combined, the correlation of occupational-psychoses rates for the nineteen occupational groups is −.83. Even when we use the ten lowest-paid occupational groups, the correlation of occupational income with occupational psychoses rates is −.85. It may be well to point out the importance of the last-given correlation coefficient. If it is argued that many psychotics in the higher income occupations are not committed to public or private mental hospitals in the Chicago area, then a correlation coefficient based upon the lower paid occupations would be expected to give a truer picture; for almost none of the persons in the lower paid occupations can afford private treatment at distant mental hospitals. However, we see that our correlation coefficient is even slightly higher for the lower paid occupational groups than it is for the entire series of occupational groups.

When we correlate occupational prestige with occupational-psychoses rates (over the 17 occupational groups) we find it to be −.75. Thus there is a real association between high income and high prestige, on the one hand, and low psychoses rates, on the other hand.

A comparison of the psychoses rates for native-whites by occupation (table not shown) reveals that for about half the occupations the native-white rates are higher and for about half they are lower than the foreign-white rates.

TABLE II

RANKING OF OCCUPATIONAL GROUPS IN ORDER OF INCREASING PRESTIGE AND INCOME

| | Rank | | |
Occupational Group	Income		Prestige
1. Errand and office boys	1		—
2. Peddlers	2	(1)	1
3. Waiters	3	(2)	2
4. Domestics	4	(3)	4
5. Barbers and beauticians	5	(4)	5
6. Semiskilled and unskilled workers	6	(5)	3
7. Salesmen	7	(6)	9
8. Skilled workers (machinists, carpenters, etc.)	8	(7)	6
9. Office employees	9	(8)	10
10. Artists, actors, musicians	10		—
11. Semiprofessional (druggists, osteopaths, etc.)	11	(9)	14
12. Small tradesmen (merchants, etc.)	12	(10)	13
13. Subexecutives	13	(11)	12
14. Policemen, firemen	14	(12)	8
15. Major salesmen (real estate, insurance salesmen)	15	(13)	11
16. Minor governmental employees (postal employees)	16	(14)	7
17. Clergy, teachers, social workers, etc.	17	(15)	16
18. Technical engineers	18	(16)	15
19. Large owners, doctors, lawyers, dentists, etc.	19	(17)	17

The psychoses rates for Negroes fall into somewhat the same pattern that we have observed for the native and foreign-born whites. This is shown in Table III. The rank-order coefficient of correlation of Negro-psychoses rates with income by occupational groups is only −.53, but this lower correlation coefficient for Negroes may be partly explained by the fact that the occupational ranking by income was based almost entirely upon data for whites. It may also be partly explained by the large standard errors of rates, which could possibly mean that the ranking was influenced by sampling fluctuations. Using the same prestige rankings as we used for whites, we obtain a rank-order coefficient of correlation of −.60 between prestige-rank and psychoses rates for Negroes by occupation.

Using the 16 occupational groups for which we have significant Negro occupational rates, we obtain a rank-order correlation coefficient of +.74 between Negro and white rates. The correlation between native-white and foreign-white rates by occupation is +.90. These coefficients indicates that many of the same social and occupational factors are operating in all the race-nativity groups.

A comparison of the 16 Negro occupational rates with the white occupational rates shows that the Negro rates are lower in only two occupational groups, namely, office workers and errand boys. If we assume that the chance that the white rate would exceed the Negro rate is 50-50 in each occupational group, the probability of the Negro rate being lower than the white rate two or fewer times out of 16 is .002. We may conclude that the Negro rates are significantly higher than the white rates. However, this difference may be partly explained by the fact that the income and prestige level of Negroes in most occupational groups is

TABLE III

AGE-ADJUSTED RATES PER 100,000 MEN AGED 20–69 YEARS, INCLUSIVE, FOR NEGRO-MALE FIRST ADMISSIONS FOR ALL PSYCHOSES FROM CHICAGO TO NEARBY MENTAL HOSPITALS, 1922–34, INCLUSIVE (By Occupational Group)

Occupational Group	No. Cases	Rate	Standard Error
1. Office workers	5	354†	178
2. Large owners, professional	5	504†	229
3. Small tradesmen	12	826†	244
4. Policemen, firemen	6	1,239	580
5. Semiprofessional	7	1,366	528
6. Salesmen	11	1,392	458
7. Semiskilled and unskilled workers	802	1,919	73
8. Skilled workers	161	1,951	173
9. Waiters	66	2,465	339
10. Domestics	265	2,501*	159
11. Artists, musicians	16	2,766	816
12. Clergy, teachers, etc	17	2,785	743
13. Barbers, beauticians	27	3,378*	722
14. Minor government employees	23	3,384*	805
15. Errand and office boys	11	4,376*	2,228
16. Peddlers	12	2,944*	1,405
All occupations	1,452‡	1,932	53

* This rate is significantly above the rate for all occupations.

† This rate is significantly below the rate for all occupations.

‡ This total includes data for occupational groups having too few cases for their rates to be significant. Major salesmen had but three cases, subexecutives but one case, and engineers but one case.

lower than that of whites, and so the occupational categories are not entirely comparable.

The findings given above indicate that the occupational-psychoses rates fall into a pattern, with an inverse relationship between psychoses rates and the fac-

TABLE IV

RANK-ORDER COEFFICIENTS OF CORRELATION CALCULATED OVER 17 OCCUPATIONAL GROUPS BETWEEN VARIOUS PSYCHOSES RATES FOR WHITE-MALE FIRST ADMISSIONS AND THE OCCUPATIONAL FACTORS OF INCOME AND PRESTIGE

Type of Psychosis	Occupational Factor	
	Income	Prestige
Schizophrenia, all types	— .71	— .81
Manic-depressive psychoses	— .02	.01
Senile psychoses and psychoses with arteriosclerosis	— .57	— .50
Alcoholic psychoses	— .78	— .92
General paralysis	— .75	— .73
Other psychoses	— .53	— .63
All psychoses	— .75	— .83

tors of occupational income and occupational prestige. Although there are variations in the rankings of a given occupational group for the various psychoses, the pattern remains the same for each type of psychosis except that of manic-depressive psychoses. This is indicated in Table IV. The rates for schizophrenia are calculated for age-group 20–49 years; the rates for senile psychoses and psychoses with arteriosclerosis for age-group 40–69; and the remainder of psychoses rates are calculated for age-group 20–69 years, inclusive. These correlation coefficients indicate that, although each psychosis has its own special etiology and can be understood only in terms of it, there appear to be some factor or factors common to all except the manic-depressive psychoses. The manner in which these factors operate is outside the scope of this paper. Their study would require the analysis of a large number of detailed case histories of mental patients and normal persons, with particular attention to occupational selection and occupational experiences, income, and prestige.

15 / Resolving Competing Hypotheses

H. Warren Dunham

The Social System and Schizophrenia: Seven Hypotheses

Anomie and/or Social Disorganization

Perhaps the oldest hypothesis and the one that enjoyed a particular prominence in contemporary social science literature between the two world wars is one that stresses anomie and/or social disorganization to account for differential distributions of various behavioral phenomena. The concept of anomie has been defined in terms of a state of normlessness, breakdown of controls, a decline in social cohesiveness, and a general decrease of consensus in social systems. But whatever the terms used, it is generally implied that with such a change in the character of order within a social system there will occur a greater frequency of more erratic, less controlled, more irresponsible, more bizarre, and more confused behavior on the part of certain persons found in the social order. The difficulty with this explanation, of course, is that it is only a partial one and actually indicates that when such a state, or states, emerges in the social order, then a greater number of persons who have been made more vulnerable by life experiences than have other persons in that social order come to official recognition. Consequently, the former are the raw recruits selected by the social order to display the more uncontrolled behavior in question. This explanation has never shown why certain persons are selected and not others; and in fact, it cannot show this because the evidence is presented in terms of correlations between certain indexes as measures

Abridged from Chapter 12 of *Community and Schizophrenia: An Epidemiological Analysis* by H. Warren Dunham. Copyright © 1965. (Detroit: Wayne State University Press, 1965). Reprinted by permission of the author and Wayne State University Press.

of conditions of the social system, the independent variable, and the rates made up of persons displaying the behavior or condition to be studied, the dependent variable.

In speaking of the concept of anomie it is impossible not to refer to Durkheim's monumental contribution (1938) to sociological theory, his classic study of suicide and his paintstaking attempt to rule out the factors that might account for rate differences in order to arrive at the true explanation, which he found in excessive individuation, insufficient individuation, and the breakdown of controls in the social order. These three sets of social causes correspond with his three types of suicide, the egoistic, the altruistic, and the anomic. But as Durkheim describes the development of these three types, the social factor acting as a causative agent becomes amorphous because he is forced to show that both social integration and lack of social integration in society become the social causes of suicide. His difficulty is finally portrayed in the necessity to refer to mixed types. Then, too, this type of study, as Durkheim's demonstrates so well, can only show the association between different conditions of society and the suicide rate. It cannot show why certain persons in a given society take suicide as a solution and other persons do not.

Again, it can be emphasized that if the anomic quality is most carefully specified then all an investigator in this area can do is to show whether certain behavior patterns occurring in the social system are highly correlated with the anomic quality. However, such correlation tells us nothing about the etiology of the behavior in question because the behavior, like the anomic quality itself, is a function of time, in which all social and other kinds of systems move. What the correlation tells us, therefore, is that there are vulnerable personalities, made that way through various experiences over the passage of time, who have a higher probability of being selected when social disorder is marked than they would have when social order prevails in a social system. The question of whether or not the anomic quality of a social system is the true selective factor would have to be investigated further because the correlation would appear to be mainly one of association and not of cause and effect.

What I have said concerning anomie applies with equal force to social disorganization, perhaps even more so, because of the vagueness of this concept. Social disorganization has been used to refer to a breakdown in the controls of the institutional structures at a specific location within the social system. Here, it is thought that because the social institutions are not functioning with a high degree of harmony, efficiency, and morale—generally measured by the more adequate functioning of comparable social institutions in some other part of the social system—inadequacy in the functioning of the institution produces maladjustments, deviant behavior patterns, and antisocial attitudes in the persons who are supposed to be controlled by the institutions. It is often found that certain kinds of socially unacceptable behavior are highly correlated with the social disorganization which is said to characterize the institutions. Now, this kind of correlation, prevalent in sociological studies, has been unproductive because of the difficulty in measuring, or deciding about, the nature of social disorganization. In addition, sociologists began to recognize that they were speaking about not a breakdown of social institutions but rather an organization and a functioning of these institutions in a manner that they neither understood nor recognized (see Waller, 1936;

Fuller and Myers, 1941, 1941a). Then, too, some began to recognize that what they were describing as social disorganization was merely a style of life unacceptable to middle class orientations (Mills, 1943). Thus, as in the case of anomie, any correlation between selected measures of social disorganization and unacceptable behavior patterns merely tended to emphasize that under certain social conditions more persons with a particular unacceptable behavior pattern came to official recognition than when social disorganization was not present. In connection with delinquency it is often said that under the auspices of certain kinds of institutional organizations, delinquents are dealt with differently than they would be if social disorganization was said to prevail. For example, one could point to the manner in which the institutions of suburbia and of the Chinatowns in America are said to handle their cases of delinquency. With the factors of anomie and social disorganization we have no explanation of the manner in which schizophrenia is distributed in the social system but may have only correlations which represent varying degrees of association.

The "Drift" Hypothesis

We turn now to the consideration of a second hypothesis: Variations in the amount of schizophrenia present in different contiguous areas are to be explained by an "unconscious" drift of persons with the disease from areas where status conditions are clear to areas where they are unclear, thus inflating the rate for the disease in certain areas to produce highly significant differences. This hypothesis, one of the oldest that has been advanced to explain the variations in the rate of schizophrenia in a given geographical area, was first suggested in the attempt to find explanations for the earlier study of the distribution of different kinds of mental disturbances in Chicago (Myerson, 1941). It was suggested primarily by psychiatrists who were oriented toward some bio-neurological explanation and wanted to explain away the rate difference as found. During the ensuing 25 years the hypothesis has had its staunch defenders as well as its staunch critics. The critics of the "drift" hypothesis, generally, try to show that "drift" could not account for such differences (see Faris and Dunham, 1939; see also Hollingshead and Redlich, 1958; Lapouse, Monk, and Terris, 1956).

Perhaps the most specific difficulty posed by the hypothesis is the image of the schizophrenic person which emerges. This image suggests that the schizophrenic is a highly incoherent, bizarre, confused, and impulsive person and that in no social situation does he know what he is doing or why he is doing it. He is seen as a very abnormal personality whose overtures are being rebuffed and rejected at every turn, repudiated by his family and permitted to drift almost in a haphazard fashion until he gets to an area where his disturbance becomes too obvious for acceptance and he is sent to one of the public mental hospitals. This image, it seems to us, is woefully inadequate and makes no allowance for the fact that in the pre-psychotic period the schizophrenic is often trying, like others, to make the most of what he has. It also fails to take account of the fact that the great majority of schizophrenics are likely to take their initial step into the disease from a family base; and it is perhaps only later that, after many treatments, trials, and failures, the full-blown schizophrenic finds himself in one of the more anonymous parts of the social structure. Further, the "drift" hypothesis by its very wording seems to deny any role for voluntary choice and selection on the part of potential schizophrenics, reserving this voluntarism only for those members of the community who are not going to break down. Because the hypothesis includes such a faulty image of the potential schizophrenic, we do not think that it can serve in any way as an explanation for rate variations of schizophrenia within different social structures.

"Mobility" Hypothesis

Another hypothesis that was early utilized to explain variations in rates of schizophrenia was found in the "mobility" concept. This hypothesis, which is related to the "drift" notion, has various facets. It apparently was suggested by the fact that rates of schizophrenia have been shown to be highly correlated with some index of mobility by area (Faris and Dunham, 1939). With such a correlation it was tied to the social disorganization hypothesis and used to support it, the notion being that a high rate of mobility is in some fashion indicative of extreme social disorganization. In my earlier study the criticism was made that many of the rates in the so-called high rate areas were spurious because they were based upon a population that turned over two or three times a year. Consequently, the population should have been doubled or trebled; this, supposedly, would bring the rates in high rate areas closer to the middle range of rates. This contention, of course, has never been proved in a systematic fashion and was partially answered, at least, by stating that, even if the population did turn over two or three times in an area, just as many cases were lost as were gained by such an area. This explanation, at least in its general form, provided no adequate explanation for the variation in the rates of schizophrenia.

The concept of mobility has much more often centered around the issue of whether schizophrenics and persons with other mental disorders are more mobile or sedentary in their habits (see Ødegaard, 1936; Malzberg, 1940; Tietze, Lemkau, and Cooper, 1942; Thomas, 1956). The findings have been contradictory here, some studies reporting a high degree and other studies a low degree of mobility among persons with mental disorders. The question has further been raised as to whether schizophrenics tend to be mobile because they are schizophrenic or whether mobility quickens, hastens, or facilitates the development of schizophrenia. Again, on any of these issues no conclusive generalization has emerged; for it has become increasingly difficult to examine this issue in a social order where such large numbers of the population are constantly on the move. In conclusion we can only say that the mobility factor *per se* has provided no significant explanation for variations in the rate of schizophrenia in social structures, nor has it been defined conclusively as a central behavioral tendency of the potential schizophrenic.

Differential Tolerance

Another hypothesis explaining rate variations for schizophrenia and other mental disorders in social structures is that of differential tolerance in the community. This hypothesis, in essence, states that a favorable and accepting attitude towards mentally ill persons in a given community is a factor serving to keep them out of a psychiatric facility and that hence they are not counted. In contrast, in a community where the attitude toward them is more unfavorable and unaccepting, they are much more likely to be hospitalized at the first sign of inappropriate behavior. This explanation has been utilized to account for the differential rates in hospital admissions in various areas and especially for the observed differential rates between rural and urban areas (Buck, Wanklin, and Hobbs, 1955a). It has also been tied to family structures by indicating that families with higher status levels are more protecting and accepting of their members than are families on lower status levels. Consequently, one would expect that the former set of families do not place their mentally sick members in psychiatric treatment as quickly as do the latter set of families. Some of our data appear to support this proposition. On the other hand, this factor of tolerance seems to be a temporary one and merely tends to lengthen the gap between the occurrence of the first symptoms and the initial entry into treatment, but does not, at least in contemporary urban society, prevent the person from eventually finding and securing treatment.

In connection with our earlier study, Mary Bess Owen (1941) was the first to call attention to the possibility of differential tolerance when she hypothesized that patients with catatonic symptoms would be less visible than patients with paranoid symptoms. She saw difference in visibility as a possible explanation for the difference in the distribution of the paranoid and catatonic schizophrenics. However, as she was unable to submit this notion to any crucial test, the entire issue still remains in doubt, although there are enough observations to indicate that under certain conditions the visibility factor may play a role in explaining rate variations in social structures. The visibility factor, however, provides no final or conclusive explanation nor is it able to show, especially in the urban situation, that it functions to keep patients out of treatment entirely. Our conclusion would be that the hypothesis cannot explain the variations in rates of schizophrenia in social structures in the urban environment.

Voluntary Segregation

Another hypothesis that has been suggested to explain variations in the incidence of schizophrenia in social structures emphasizes the concept of segregation. This hypothesis might be stated in the following manner: Potential schizophrenics voluntarily and actively select certain areas of a community for their residence in order to escape those intense involvements that come with close interpersonal relations. This voluntary segregation explains why certain areas in a city will have high incidence rates of schizophrenia in contrast to other areas. Gerard and Houston (1953), in their examination of the distribution of male schizophrenics in Worcester, Massachusetts, concluded that the high rate of schizophrenia in certain impoverished areas would be largely explained by the number of patients living alone. They further showed that schizophrenics living with their families showed definite residential stability in contrast to those not living with their families, who showed marked residential instability. They suggested that the residential instability of schizophrenics living alone was a rather conscious means of protection against involvement with disruptive family relationships. Perhaps the inference could be made, although Gerard and Houston do not make it, that the potential schizophrenic, because of his acute sensitivity, tries to escape from the closeness of intimate personal relations.

In a like manner Hare (1956a), in his study of the distribution of schizophrenic patients in Bristol, England, shows a high concentration of his cases in the poor central areas of the city. He notes that the high rates of schizophrenia in both "good" and "poor" central areas are related to the factor of living alone, thus giving support to the evidence supplied by Gerard and Houston. Hare thinks that his high rates of schizophrenia, in contrast to the low rates, are to be explained either by the process of segregation or by some undetermined causal influence operating in the environment.

In a later analysis of the Bristol data Hare (1956) organizes his data on schizophrenic and manic-depressive psychoses in order to determine whether the "attraction" or the "breeder" hypothesis best accounts for the distribution of schizophrenics in Bristol. The "attraction" hypothesis refers to the selective characteristics of an area plus the conscious tendency of some persons to segregate themselves within it, while the "breeder" hypothesis refers to the possible existence of certain social conditions in an area that would be inducive of schizophrenia. His findings give some support to both hypotheses, but he thinks that the evidence is much more weighted in terms of the former. He thus gives additional support to Gerard and Houston. His "attraction" hypothesis is the one which, in our analysis, we have labelled as "social selection."

As can readily be seen, this hypothesis avoids the unrealistic image of the schizophrenic as found in the "drift" notion and views the potential schizophrenic as a highly sensitive person actively and voluntarily attempting to select a kind of environment that will maximize his adjustment and make survival possible outside of a psychiatric facility. As related to the more general theory of social selection, it emphasizes that the element bringing about the selection is a trait of the schizophrenic personality. It attempts to pin down both the nature of the process and the specific factor accounting for the process; and in this manner provides an explanation for significant rate differentials of schizophrenia within the urban environment. Of all the hypotheses so far examined this one conforms most closely to our explanation for the variation of incidence rates of schizophrenia in the urban community, for it fits a more correct conception of the nature of the potential schizophrenic and of the factors accounting for the movement of persons within the urban environment.

Social Cohesion

Another hypothesis appearing in the literature, although not with reference to the distribution of schizophrenia but to that of the manic-depressive psychosis, centers around the concept of cohesiveness. Social cohesiveness is the opposite of anomie or social disorganization. This hypothesis states that where there is a high degree of social cohesiveness, morale, and close, accepting interpersonal relations, there will be found a high incidence of the manic-depressive psychosis. This was the idea suggested by Eaton and Weill (1955) in their study of the Hutterites' communities because they found so much more manic-depressive illness than schizophrenia in these communities. They thought that the close, integrative cohesiveness of the Hutterite community favored this disorder. This hypothesis is, as one notes, opposite to the notion of social isolation which is more likely to occur in the absence of social cohesiveness, and is mentioned here merely to point to the general, loose, and uncritical thinking that has centered around given characterizations of social organization which supposedly encourages different kinds of psychotic breakdowns. It seems to be, as in Durkheim's case, that if social disintegration does not get you, social integration must. As we have tried to show, the difficulty with both of these hypotheses is that they lack substantial evidence and are largely afterthoughts in the search for an adequate explanation of differential rates of schizophrenia in various social structures.

"Size of the City" Hypothesis

Another hypothesis that has recently been suggested to explain significant differential incidence rates of schizophrenia in large cities comes from the study of the distribution of first admissions of schizophrenics to public and private hospitals in Hagerstown, Maryland (Clausen and Kohn, 1959). In this city, the investigators found that rates of schizophrenia tended to approach parity for different socio-economic areas in the city. This finding, at marked variance with the studies of the distribution of schizophrenics in large cities, suggested the hypothesis that as the size of a city increases the rate of schizophrenia in the various areas become more sharply differentiated. This hypothesis, which is clearly on a social level of analysis, throws sharply into focus the question as to whether there are any real differences in the incidence rate of schizophrenia in various social structures and population groups. When differences are found they are to be accounted for by a combination of the size of the urban community and the tendency of schizophrenics to collect in certain areas as a result of a social selection process.

These investigators have taken note of the fact that in the study of the distribution of schizophrenia in smaller cities in the 1930's, the real differences were not as marked as in the large city of Chicago (Faris and Dunham, 1939; see also Schroeder, 1942). The investigators further note that the class structure in Hagerstown is not as highly differentiated as that of the larger cities and, as a consequence, socio-economic differences in areas are not as sharp as in a larger city. They note further that the family residences in the community seem to be much more stable than is the case in larger cities and, consequently, there is perhaps a greater mixture of the families of different status in the same areas than would be the case in the larger cities. All of these speculations caused the investigators to favor the "size of the city" hypothesis; and in so doing they clearly paved the way for a more complete statement of the social selection theory, in which variations in the incidence of schizophrenia in social structures are considered a product of demographic differences in populations and not a result of the operation of social and cultural factors in certain areas and their absence in other areas. These investigators have attempted to come to grips with the very issue which has been the focus of attention in the present study. It should be noted, however, that although their hypothesis accounts (only) for the fact that significant rate variations of schizophrenia occur in some cities and not others, it does not account for those significant variations that do seem to occur in the larger cities.

In the consideration of these seven hypotheses we have not found one that completely explains the rate differences in schizophrenia which occur in the large metropolitan cities. The one that comes closest to the hypothetical explanation that we favor centers around the notion of segregation because here an attempt has been made to indicate the process involved as well as the factor that accounts for the process. We turn now to a more detailed examination of the social selection hypothesis and the selective factors which we think are at work.

Social Selection

As we have indicated above, a precise statement of the social selection hypothesis should include a statement of the process involved and the initiating factor or factors that help to get the process under way. The innumerable studies noting variations in the distribution of schizophrenia by sex and age contain nothing which provides any evidence that these factors have any bearing upon the distribution of schizophrenia in the urban community. In the case of our own data, we have already shown that the age and sex distributions for schizophrenics in our two subcommunities are comparable to those of the other studies and give no evidence that these are important factors in the selection. In fact, it is interesting to note that the age distribution of our schizophrenics is quite similar, after intensive screening, to the distribution before intensive screening. In much the same vein, the sex distribution for our schizophrenics has shown no variation in these two subcommunities year after year.

If we turn to the factor of race, again we find no indication that this plays any significant role in the spread of schizophrenia in the community. While the number of non-white schizophrenics turned up in Cass represents about 50 per cent of our total cases in this subcommunity, and the non-white population represents about one-third of the total, we do not attach any significance to this discrepancy. Rather, we find that as various residential areas opened up to the non-whites during the fifties, they moved into these areas largely on a family basis regardless of whether the families contained potential schizophrenics or not. This was true in all the areas of Detroit where the non-white population pressed in. We can find no evidence that race is the factor involved in the selective process.

While Gerard and Houston (1953) infer that the trait of sensitivity in the schizophrenic may be the selective factor involved, and perhaps it does operate to cause certain persons to select a particular residential area, we cannot tell from our data how significant it is. In our judgment, however, sensitivity is not a central factor because we do not think that it can ever be established that persons with a certain personality trait will predominate over others with an opposite trait in a given residential area. On the contrary, we suspect that there is much more likely to be a random distribution of persons possessing a given trait in the urban environment. While, as we have indicated, we have no evidence on this specific point, our general knowledge of urban community life points to a lack of plausibility with respect to this factor. The same argument can be given with respect to the idea of proneness to psychosis; for if there was any evidence that psychotically-prone persons tended to collect in certain areas of the urban community, we would expect to find a much sharper variation in the rates than we actually do. Actually we find no subcommunity in the city completely free of schizophrenic cases in a given year. The three-to-one ratio which seems to exist between high- and low-rate areas is in line with the evidence reported from other studies; and while these differences are in most cases statistically significant, they do not point to the collection of potential schizophrenics in specific areas.

The hypothesis of social selection is not new but has been favored less by investigators in this country than in Europe. This is partially due to the constant search for etiological factors in the social process to the neglect of the selective character of the social process that sorts and sifts persons by residence, occupation, education, and institutional affiliations.

Studies Utilizing Social Selection

In Europe, Ødegaard has been one of the strong advocates of the social selection hypothesis. In his earlier study of the migration of Norwegians to the United States he explained their higher rate of mental illness in the United States as compared to Norway by pointing out that psychiatrically vulnerable persons were more likely to migrate (Ødegaard, 1936). In his recent study of mental disorder in the various occupational groups of Norway he concluded that social selection versus environmental stress provides the most telling explanation for the highest rate of psychosis among seafaring men (Ødegaard, 1956). This rate among the seamen held for all psychotic groups with the exception of psychoses with epilepsy, psychoses with mental deficiency, and manic-depressive psychosis, three groups where the seamen have the second highest rate. Ødegaard regards this finding as best explained by social selection as well as secondary selection which takes place when certain men around the age of thirty leave seafaring to seek other occupations. By this process the unstable and psychopathic types tend to remain among the seamen. He thinks that the evidence for social selection is most apparent for schizophrenia, epilepsy, and mental deficiency. Contrary to this, he finds no evidence that social stress and protection are valid for explaining the distribution of psychosis in the Norwegian occupational structure. Ekblad (1948) also provides support for Ødegaard's study by pointing to the higher rates of psychopathy and schizophrenia among his sample of seamen as compared to a sample of non-seamen in naval training.

The hypothesis of social selection has been frequently utilized by investigators in dealing with such special social structures as the army, merchant marine, or prison. In Winston's study (1935) of psychoses in the army, her question, "Does mental disease act as a further selective factor in the already highly selective military group?" points clearly to the hypothesis of social selection. She does not find any evidence that mental disease increases in the army, but she does find that numerous psychological misfits are weeded out eventually so that mental disease decreases as length of service in the army increases. This finding introduces a selective factor different from Ødegaard's finding (1956) on mental disorders among the merchant seamen, in that the army actively eliminates those persons who cannot adjust to army life while the seamen are able to make a voluntary choice to separate themselves from the service. Sims (1946), in a study of non-commissioned officers in the British army and prisoners of war, has also pointed to the selective process for explaining the differences in the incidence of mental disorders in the various groups. He calls attention also to the aspect of the selective process where the elimination of recruits in basic training lowers the incidence of those who get to combat areas.

We have referred to these studies to show how the social selection hypothesis has been applied to rate differentials of specific psychoses in selected social structures. In general, the studies show that social selection is primarily a process that functions outside of the individual to relegate him to a certain position in the social structure. In the research cited, the factors external to the person appear much more telling in relation to selection than do any action of the person himself. This is especially noticeable in Winston's study of psychoses in the army although much less telling in Ødegaard's study of the occupational structure in Norway; for, in this example actions which a person takes to enter an occupational category must be correlated with how the structure disposes of, and deals with, his application. Thus, in the Ødegaard study we have something analogous to our own problem of formulating the proposition that will most adequately explain variations in the distribution of schizophrenics within the class and community structure of the urban community.

It is to be recalled that several findings were quite telling with respect to the differential distributions of schizophrenics in our two subcommunities in Detroit. We found that when the factor of mobility was taken into account, the rate differential for schizophrenia was reduced although there was still a difference. We found further that better than 60 per cent of the schizophrenic cases found in both subcommunities had started from the inner city. We further reported a much more marked residential stability, as measured by moves of residence within four years, in Conner-Burbank as compared with Cass. We further reported that utilizing two measures of stress, the discrepancy between the nativity of the father and that of the patient, and overcrowdedness, showed no differences with respect to schizophrenia in our two subcommunities. Like Ødegaard's analysis of stress factors, ours casts much doubt on any *objective* stress-measure as a plausible explanation for variations in the incidence rates of schizophrenia in our two subcommunities.

Life Chances and the Incidence of Schizophrenia

These findings point to both the factor and the process that would seem to determine the spread of schizophrenia within the urban community. We emphasize that the mobility pattern accompanying the residential changes typical of our urban communities is the central process involved, and the initiating factor is the differing life-chances present in the family at the birth of the potential schizophrenic. While we emphasize the initiating factor of life-chances because, as a concept, it encompasses a number of elements present in families, we recognize that there are other factors emanating from this general condition of life-chances —the needs of the person with respect to health, job, family, housing, schooling for children, location of friends, residence of the family of orientation, avoidance of certain social and ethnic groups, and perhaps other factors—that play a role in initiating and facilitating the movement of persons in the urban community. *We concluded therefore that the selective process was one that operated through a social necessity for maintaining a balance between the needs of persons and the central characteristics of social organization and that the initiating factor was the life-chances of the family at the birth of a potential schizophrenic. This process and initiating factor should be central for explaining the incidence of schizophrenia in any geopolitical unit of society in the United States.*

Conclusions

In this examination of the several hypotheses on the social system level that have been advanced to explain rate differentials of schizophrenia in different types of social structures, we have been concerned with pointing out the deficiencies which make it difficult for them to do the task for which they are designed. On our side, while we realize that we have added little to the more general form of the social selection hypothesis, we do think that we have presented evidence that serves to specify the factors involved in social selection. We have tried to point to the selection process at work and the specific factor that operates in its initiation. We have thus arrived at a much more exact explanation than heretofore attempted of the differential incidence of schizophrenia within the urban community.

In this study it has been our considered opinion that the distribution of schizophrenia—and perhaps, other types of psychoses—in social structures must find an explanation on the social system level of analysis. Thus, any significant findings on the level of the case or on the level of interpersonal relations should provide more adequate insights into the factors that lie behind the distribution of schizophrenia in geographical space in the society that characterizes the United States. This latter statement means that differential distributions of this disorder in other cultural settings may find explanations with respect to other initiating factors and processes and underlines the notion that differing social and cultural conditions will require different explanations of the way a mental disorder—and, particularly, schizophrenia—is distributed in a given population.

We have purposely ignored the innumerable hypotheses of a social-psychological nature which have tried to pin down factors in the area of interpersonal relations which purport to have an etiological significance for the development of schizophrenia. We have ignored hypotheses centering upon such concepts as social isolation, role confusion, role strain, minority group status, mental conflicts, and frustration because they are inappropriate to the task at hand. This is not to say that they have no significance; it is only to say that they cannot be useful here because our materials and observations have been made on another level. We would hasten to add, however, that the chief difficulty with all of these hypotheses is that of establishing, with respect to the person with a schizophrenic syndrome, a specific relationship between a quality of status or interpersonal relations acting as an independent variable and the production of schizophrenia acting as a dependent variable. When two investigators suggest "that the important factors here may not be social status *per se* but frustration, which may be at least partially caused by a discrepancy between actual and desired group membership" (Kleiner and Tuckman, 1961, 1962), one is certainly conscious of the big gap between the emotional condition of frustration and the appearance of schizophrenic symptoms. Especially is this true when the sort of frustration described by the investigators is so prevalent in American society and, in fact, might be described as one of its general characteristics, considering the emphasis upon striving and ambition in the American culture. One or more of these hypotheses will continue to be posed for investigation in the coming years; but unless we can develop an adequate methodology, we will probably not advance much further with respect to specifying how sociocultural factors operate in the development of schizophrenia. There is no simple terrain here; the best lead, in my judgment, would be to study the manner in which different persons who are physically, mentally, and emotionally handicapped deal with their interpersonal relations. Such studies should be made in the initial stages of the developing handicap if this is possible, for they might provide clues of how various techniques of handling interpersonal relations may be quite pathological for the person under a given set of particular cultural conditions. This is one direction that research of the future might take in dealing with interpersonal elements on the social-psychological level.

In this chapter we have examined in some detail the hypotheses advanced for explaining the differential incidence rates of schizophrenia in social structures. We have attempted to show that they are on theoretically solid grounds because they try to effect explanations of epidemiological observations on the level on which they are made and organized. While the assumptions underlying each hypothesis vary considerably, they all represent variations of the more general one of social selection. We find this hypothesis to be the most satisfactory for accounting for the differential incidence of schizophrenia in social structures.

16 / Social Structural and Psychological Factors in Mental Disorder: A Research Review

Robert J. Kleiner / Seymour Parker

In both the professional and the popular literature, one frequently encounters the idea that excessive goal striving and frustration because of failure to reach desired goals are responsible for mental illness. Merton (1949), for instance, has stimulated considerable research in this area by his suggestive work concerning the relationship of anomie, status striving, and deviant behavior (e.g., crime, mental illness, alcoholism, etc.). Also some of the theorizing and experimental research of Lewin, Festinger, and their associates (1944) on the determinants of goal-striving behavior is related to this problem.

This paper attempts to review some of the research on the relationship of status position, status mobility (and inconsistency), and mobility orientation (i.e., discrepancy between achievement and aspiration) to mental illness. Although work on the periphery of this problem is considerable, the connection among these phenomena has been insufficiently explored. These independent variables link both sociological and psychological factors to each other and to mental disorder. Most of the studies in this field correlate *either* one or the other of these concepts with mental disorder. In reviewing the literature, the authors were impressed with the need to bring together in one review some of the disparate findings, and to suggest the possible interrelationship of the data. This attempt also provides an opportunity to discuss some of the methodological problems that arise in this research.

The central theme of the review will be the relationship between goal-striving behavior and mental disorder. The first of the variables mentioned above, status position, is intimately related to various aspects of goal striving. The position an individual has achieved will affect the nature of his aspirations, will limit his potential for social mobility, and will affect his perception of his chances of obtaining his goals. The second variable, status mobility, is related to the social distance a person has moved, from a point of time in the past, to his present level of achievement. One may assume that the individual who has experienced a high degree of upward status mobility feels successful and is thus psychiatrically relatively healthy. On the other hand, it is also possible that status mobility is accompanied by shifting reference groups and concomitant interpersonal disturbances. In addition, status inconsistency refers to the extent to which an individual occupies different status positions along several status continua (e.g., high rank for education and low rank for occupation). High inconsistency may be assumed to lead to differential acceptance and role expectations by valued reference groups. This, in turn, may result in feelings of rejection, frustration, and maladjustment. The final independent variable, mobility orientation, is a major source, and probably a more direct measure, of frustration. Although the review will be limited to the above-mentioned variables, there is no implication that they represent either the only, or the most important, factors in mental disorder.

"Mental illness" is difficult to define. However, without defining the term, we may still delimit the kinds of data to be included under this rubric. The studies to be reviewed embrace mental illness and emotional instability as diagnosed by judgments of qualified medical and non-medical personnel, making use of clinical interviews, psychological tests, and scores on questionnaire check-lists of psychosomatic and neurotic symptoms. Although "casting such a wide net" raises many problems of its own, the existing level of knowledge concerning the nature and limits of "mental illness" (and mental health) does not warrant a constriction of the definition to include only medically diagnosed cases. In addition to the problem of inadequate knowledge of the nature of these disorders, recent studies by Leighton, Srole, Pasamanick, and others, show that large numbers of undiagnosed and untreated "cases" exist in the community population, raising questions about the generalizing value of incidence and prevalence studies of medically diagnosed cases.

Status Position and Mental Disorder

The research findings concerning the relationship between socio-economic status and mental illness are both numerous and confusing. Despite the contradictory nature of the evidence, there is an increasing tendency in the relevant literature to assume that an inverse relationship between status position and mental disorder has been firmly established (Cassel, 1966; Dohrenwend, 1966; Roman and Trice, 1967; Turner and Wagonfeld, 1967). Confusion is sometimes compounded by failure to distinguish between incidence and prevalence studies. Incidence is generally defined as the number of *new* cases appearing within a given interval of time, while prevalence refers to *all* cases active during a given interval. Prevalence rates, which include re-entries (or re-admissions), continuations, and first admissions, provide valuable information with regard to the frequency of disease in general. When interest is focused on etiological factors, however, incidence studies are superior because the new case is closer in time to the precipitating conditions.

A number of studies have indicated that a high *incidence* of schizophrenia is associated with low socio-economic status. Faris and Dunham (1939), in their studies of the distribution of mental hospital first admissions in the Chicago area during the 1930's, found that the low status areas of the city sent much larger proportions of their residents to the mental hospitals than did those areas designated as middle or upper status. Although schizophrenia conformed to this pattern, manic-depressive psychoses showed a relatively uniform distribution throughout the various status groups. Similar findings have subsequently been reported for a number of different areas. Tietze, Lemkau, and Cooper (1941) found that high rates of schizophrenia in Baltimore were associated with lower class status. Manic-depressive disorders were slightly more common in upper class groups. The earlier findings in Chicago (with respect to both types of disorders) were also confirmed in a subsequent study in that city by Clark (1949). Kaplan, Reed, and Richardson (1956) reported a higher incidence of undifferentiated hospitalized psychoses in a lower and lower middle class area of Boston than in an upper and upper middle class section. The inverse relationship between the incidence of schizophrenia and social class was also found in England and Wales (Morris, 1959).

Hollingshead and Redlich (1958) carefully studied treated mental disorder in New Haven. Incidence rates revealed a slightly different picture than the studies previously mentioned. While rates for all psychoses, and schizophrenia specifically, showed an inverse relationship with social class, the statistical significance can be explained in terms of the heavy concentration in Class V. Neurosis, on the other hand, showed no relationship to social class. This significant concentration of schizophrenia in Class V is also noted by Goldberg and Morrison (1963).

Clausen and Kohn (1960) found no relationship between the incidence of schizophrenia and socio-ceonomic position in a small city in Maryland. Jaco (1960) reported a curvilinear relationship between the incidence of all psychoses and social status in the state of Texas. Incidence rates were high among those who had the lowest and the highest occupational and educational statuses, and were low among those in medium status positions. This pattern was obtained for whites, Negroes, and Spanish-Americans. Using occupation as the status measure, this pattern was also obtained for psychotics and neurotics by Parker and Kleiner (1966) in a study of the Philadelphia Negro population. Using other status indices, it was found that income yielded an inverse relationship, while education showed a W-shaped curve. The rate differences with the different status measures suggest the questions of whether status indices should be combined at all and, if so, with what weights. Kleiner, Tuckman, and Lavell (1959) showed that Catholics in Pennsylvania (1951–1956) had significantly higher incidence rates of schizophrenia than Protestants, despite the similarity of their status positions (as measured by occupation and education). These investigators (1960) also found no relationship between occupational status and incidence of schizophrenia among Negroes (in Pennsylvania, 1951–1956). Finally, Dunham (1965) reported no systematic relationship between social class and schizophrenia. Incidence studies in Australia (Cade, 1956), Norway (Bremer, 1951; Ødegaard, 1956), and in England (Stein, 1957) also failed to confirm the inverse relationship between status and schizophrenia, manic-depressive psychoses, or psychoneuroses. The research cited in this section indicates that the stability of socioeconomic position in predicting mental disorder is open to question. However, further conceptual clarification, both of the independent variable of status position and the dependent variable of mental disorder, is necessary before a definitive conclusion can be reached.

In a report of *prevalence* rates, Hollingshead and Redlich (1958) found that rates of treated (undifferentiated) psychiatric illness were highest in the lowest social class (Class V). However, patients were actually under-represented in Classes I through IV (Hollingshead and Redlich, 1958). Furthermore, this under-representation increased from Classes I to IV. If socio-economic status and treated psychiatric illness were inversely related, under-representation should have decreased. There were no significant differences in morbidity rates of Classes I through IV; the reported inverse relationship was due to a marked over-representation of patients in Class V. While the prevalence of psychoses was inversely related to status position, neurotic disorders varied directly with socio-economic status. In examining the separate components of prevalence (i.e., incidence, re-entry, and continuations), it was found that these two relationships could be largely accounted for by one of these elements—continuations. Clearly, continuations represent a poor measure of etiological relevance.

All of the previously mentioned studies deal with diagnosed mental disorder. It is generally recognized that many undiagnosed "cases" do not come to the attention of the medical profession and continue to live in the community. Because of the possibly biased picture presented by hospital statistics, there is widespread interest in whether the inverse relationship would be confirmed in studies of the distribution of mental disorder outside the mental hospital. Attempts to answer this question must deal with the complex problem of how to identify mental disorder in the general population. It is impossible to diagnose even a sample of the community population by accepted psychiatric diagnostic procedures—hence the development and use of various questionnaire methods designed to obtain information on such things as psychosomatic and other psychopathological symptoms (Macmillan, 1959). In an extensive prevalence survey of the non-hospitalized population in an area of New York City, Srole et al. (1962) reported that, when the severity of psychiatric disturbance was considered, the usual inverse relationship was found. High status individuals had fewer representatives in the "impaired" group and more in the "well" group. In a preliminary study, Rennie et al. (1957) found that 75 per cent of the entire community sample showed "significant" (pathological) anxiety. The proportion of anxious individuals was about the same in the lower, middle, and upper status groups. It is interesting that when all the respondents were classified according to diagnostic "types," the "psychotic type" was inversely related to class status, the "neurotic type" was directly related, and the "neurotic type with prominent symptoms" varied independently of class position.

Still another prevalence study of psychiatric disorder in a representative sample of the non-hospitalized population was conducted in Baltimore by Pasamanick et al. (1959). The majority of respondents were examined by (nonpsychiatric) physicians and a diagnosis arrived at by clinical evaluation procedures. When the population was divided into five status groups, it was found that, except for the lowest group, psychotic disorders generally decreased as income increased. The exception was explained by the fact that Negroes, who had lower rates of psychoses than their white counterparts, were concentrated in this group. For neurotic disorders, there was a U-shaped curve, the rates being high in the low status group, declining in the middle status group, and rising once more in the highest status group. There was a direct relationship between the prevalence of psychosomatic complaints and economic status. Primrose (1962) failed to find any significant relationship between prevalence of psychoses or neuroses and social class in a community in northern Scotland. Character disorders, however, showed a greater concentration in the lowest status group. A combination of neuroses and "some" character disorders revealed a U-shaped distribution—higher prevalence rates both in the highest and lowest classes.

Several investigators attempted to determine incidence rates in nonhospitalized populations. Hyde and Kingsley (1944) gathered statistics on a large number of inductees rejected by the armed services for psychiatric reasons. The number of psychiatric rejections varied inversely with the economic status of the communities from which the inductees came. Kaplan, Reed, and Richardson (1956) reported the rates of non-hospitalized psychoses to be greater in an upper class community. This conclusion was based on information gathered from "sophisticated" informants in the community. Lin (1953) also failed to confirm the inverse relationship between mental disorder and socioeconomic status in three Formosan communities.

Sewell and Haller (1959) administered a questionnaire to 1,462 elementary school children. This instrument was designed to explore the relationship between class position (of the family) and symptoms of nervousness and anxiety. The children were placed either in an upper or lower status group. Lower status students scored higher than those in the upper group, both for nervous symptoms and general anxiety. This finding seems consistent with Auld's comprehensive review (1952) of the literature dealing with the relationship of status position and neurotic symptoms as gauged by the Rorschach, the T.A.T., the M.M.P.I., and other psychological tests. He noted that almost all of the studies showed either a significant inverse relationship or a tendency in this direction. In no study was there a direct relationship between class and neuroticism. Three more recent large scale studies have been concerned with the issue of untreated prevalence. Leighton et al. (1963) found that high status communities had more low symptom individuals than low status communities. However, this inverse relationship was not obtained when status was analyzed *within* any given community; no systematic relationship was found in these analyses. In a study of automobile workers in Detroit, Kornhauser (1965) showed that men in low status (manual) occupations had higher levels of neurotic symptoms than skilled workers. Finally, Parker and Kleiner (1966) have shown an inverse relationship between status (i.e., occupation, income, and education) and psychoneurotic symptoms in an untreated community population.

The findings summarized above indicate that for diagnosed schizophrenia, manic-depressive psychoses, total psychoses, and psychoneuroses, there appears to be no consistent relationship between illness and status position. This conclusion holds for both incidence and prevalence studies. In regard to the distribution of neurotic and psychosomatic symptoms in untreated community populations, the above-mentioned conclusion received additional support. However, some of the more recent findings suggest a greater prevalence of symptoms in the lower status groups.

Studies of the prevalence of psychiatric symptoms in general community populations by means of symptom check-lists were originally undertaken to avoid the limitations of rates based on treated illness. The latter were thought to be affected by artifacts such as attitudes toward psychiatry and the availability of treatment facilities. Consequently, it was believed that if we knew the amount of treated *and* untreated pathology in a community, this summation would represent the total "iceberg." However, Dohrenwend (1966) has shown that this procedure may not be valid. His findings indicated that different population groups exhibited stylistic differences in their expressions of psychological stress. He, therefore, raised the question of "under what conditions does symptomatic expression of psychological stress become evidence of underlying personality defect." These findings cast doubt on the assumption that illness represented by diagnosed pathology and the "illness" represented by symptom scores fall on a single continuum. These two conditions may represent two qualitatively different phenomena. In another study, Jackson (1965) found that individuals showing different patterns of status incongruity manifested their stress differently (e.g., somatically or politically). Additional support for this argument was reported by Parker and Kleiner (1966). They noted that, for each of three measures of status, the curves representing rates of diagnosed pathology were different from the curves for symptom scores in a general community population. The findings of these three studies suggest that adding undiagnosed "cases" and diagnosed cases together creates new problems.

An overview of the results presented in this section indicates that the relationship between status and mental disorder is by no means a simple one and may be complicated by varying definitions of mental disorder, different case-finding methods, and the nature of the class system in the community being studied. In a recent article on social status, Jackson (1962) concluded that the components of social status commonly used (e.g., education, occupation, etc.) were experienced psychologically as "separate and distinct status dimensions in America today." This investigator raised serious questions about the advisability of determining an over-all status rank by averaging the various disparate status ranks of an individual. It is possible that, even if the same components of status position are used and the same weights assigned to them (which is not usual), the psychological meaning and social concomitants of a given status position may vary in different types of communities. The finding of Clausen and Kohn (1960) that the usual inverse relationship did not hold for a small urban community is suggestive in this regard. The studies reported by Pasamanick and his associates (1959), and by Kleiner, Tuckman, and Lavell (1960) indicate that the status dimension, as it applies to mental disorder, may operate differently for whites and Negroes. Further exploration of this phenomenon necessitates a more precise delineation of the character of the populations and the communities in which the findings are made, and an understanding of the more subtle intervening variables in these gross epidemiological relationships.

A study pertinent to this problem of intervening variables was reported by Tuckman and Kleiner (1962). These investigators found that, by applying an index of discrepancy (between education as an indicator of aspiration, and occupation as an indicator of achievement) to various social groups, they could predict rates of schizophrenia with greater accuracy than by using conventional criteria of social status position. In addition, their method provided an explicit theoretical rationale for the predictions, clearly related to the unifying theme of this review. The paper by Tuckman and Kleiner suggested a relationship between a high aspiration-achievement discrepancy and mental disorder. If this intervening variable is pertinent to the discussion of status position and mental disorder, it is important to establish a link between status positions and the discrepancy. A number of studies enable us to do this. Gould (1941) found that, in a sample of 81 college students, those from a lower socioeconomic background tended to have higher discrepancies between actual performance and aspiration on experimentally created tasks. Empey (1956) reported that, while the absolute occupational status aspirations of lower class senior high school students were lower than those either of the middle or upper class, their *relative* occupational aspirations (i.e., distance between their fathers' occupations and their own occupational aspirations) were higher than either of the two other groups. The authors of this review carried out two early studies in which the concept of aspiration-achievement discrepancy was employed directly to determine its relation to mental disorder. They reported (Kleiner and Parker, 1962) that a low status group with a high rate of mental illness also showed greater goal discrepancies than a high status group with a low rate of illness. Possibly, inconsistencies in previously mentioned studies relating status position to mental disorder can be accounted for by this social-psychological intervening variable (i.e., goal-striving discrepancy). In a second paper (Kleiner and Parker, 1965), the authors found that native-born Philadelphia Negroes had a higher rate of mental illness than in-migrants from the South. The native-born, who had the higher rate, also occupied higher status positions and showed larger goal-striving discrepancies than the in-migrants.

In summary, the studies reviewed in this section point to the potential value of the discrepancy between achievement and aspirations as an intervening social-psychological variable between status position and mental disorder. Considerable research has been done along these lines, and these studies will be more fully reviewed in a later section.

Status Mobility and Mental Disorder

This section deals with changes in the status level of an individual from a baseline of the status position of his parental family, or of his own adult status at an earlier point in time. Research in this area has been concerned mainly with two questions: (1) Can the high rates of mental disorder, often reported for the lower socio-economic groups, be explained by the "downward drift" of sick individuals into a lower socio-economic position? This question is concerned with mobility as a manifestation of "social selection." (2) To what extent is social mobility (including considerations of direction and degree) related etiologically to mental disorder? This is concerned with the "social causation" hypothesis.

With regard to the first question, if the high rates in the lower class can be explained on this "downward drift" basis, then the experiences associated with lower class life per se, might have little relevance for mental disorder. This question has been discussed many times since the early study of Faris and Dunham (1939). Tietze, Lemkau, and Cooper (1941) reported that the inverse relationship between schizophrenia and social class could not be explained by mobility into the lower socioeconomic class. Using "place of residence" as a criterion of status position, Lapouse (1956) also found evidence that "for first admissions of schizophrenics to state hospitals from Buffalo, the concentration in the low economic areas is not the result of downward drift from higher areas. Nor is there any evidence that the concentration in the poor areas is the result of a recent migration into those areas of mobile men who live alone." More recent studies by Hollingshead and Redlich (1955), Clausen and Kohn (1959), and Kornhauser (1965) also fail to support the social selection concept.

Although there is impressive evidence tending to refute the "downward drift" hypothesis, other studies tend to support it. Lystad (1957) found that schizophrenic patients tended to be significantly more downwardly mobile than a comparable group of nonmentally ill individuals. In their study of a non-hospitalized population in New York City, Srole and his associates (1962) reported that a relatively high proportion of the interviewees having severe psychiatric symptoms have been downwardly mobile. Further analyses of these same data by Langner and Michael (1963) confirmed Srole's conclusion that the downwardly mobile were characterized by the poorest mental health, and the upwardly mobile by the least mental impairment. Nonmobile individuals fell between these two groups. This finding applied to "psychotic types" but not to "neurotic types." The latter, in fact, were most often upwardly mobile and least often downwardly mobile. In contrast to Hollingshead and Redlich and other studies above, the data analyzed by Srole, and by Langner and Michael, depended on symptom inventory scores in a general community population. Furthermore, their measures of status position used to determine social mobility also differed. Jaco (1959) investigated social mobility in communities yielding different rates of mental disorder and noted more downward mobility (compared to achievement of the parental generation) in communities with high rates of mental illness. In studies carried out in England, Morris (1959) and Goldberg (1963) reported a heavy concentration of schizophrenic patients in the low status group but noted that the fathers of these patients were more randomly distributed throughout all classes. More recent studies (Turner and Wagonfeld, 1967; Dunham, Phillips, and Srinivasan, 1966; Parker and Kleiner, 1966) in the United States all show a disproportionately large number of downward mobile individuals among the mentally ill relative to "normal" controls.

The weight of the evidence presented thus far clearly shows that the mentally ill are characterized by higher rates of downward mobility. One may ask to what extent is upward mobility related to mental disorder? Srole's findings (1962) indicate the least impairment for the upward mobile. However, Hollingshead and Redlich (1954) noted that although there was no significant relationship between mobility and mental disorder, most of the patients who did change social position were, in fact, upward mobile. Hollingshead, Ellis, and Kirby (1954) explored mobility and diagnosis at two different status levels. At the lower status level they found no relationship between mental illness and mobility, but at the higher status position neurotics were more upwardly mobile than non patients, and schizophrenics were the most upwardly mobile of all groups. Of considerable interest to this discussion is the study by Parker and Kleiner (1966) of a Negro population. Their data indicated the downward mobile had the highest rates of illness while the upward mobile had the lowest. However, when controlling for status position, they showed that *both* the downward mobile at the low end of the scale and the upward mobile at the high end had significantly higher rates than their respective status peers. Thus, the two studies using status controls report that upward mobility is associated with mental disorder at the upper end of the scale. Clearly, status controls are necessary in studies of mobility.

There has been considerable theorizing to the effect that individuals who have experienced social mobility are more prone to be confused as to their reference groups and their self-identity, thus experiencing concomitant interpersonal difficulties (Blau, 1956). Ruesch (1946) and Ruesch, Jacobson, and Loeb (1948) reported that people who had been "social climbers" tended to be more subject to chronic psychosomatic disorders than those who had not been socially mobile, or who had been downwardly mobile. Sorokin (1927), Warner (1937), and Lipset and Bendix (1963) speculated that high social mobility in our society was related to disturbed interpersonal relationships and mental illness. This explanation seems to account for findings relating social mobility to various forms of deviant behavior such as racial prejudice, high concern over health, and radical political voting behavior (Greenbaum and Pearlin, 1953; Litwak, 1956; Lopreato, 1967). Three additional studies (Lane and Ellis, 1967; Parker and Kleiner, 1966; Kleiner and Parker, 1969) determined directly the social-psychological correlates of the mobility experience. Lane and Ellis found that lower class youth entering a high status university felt isolation and personal strain. In the other studies, high goal-striving stress, poor integration with reference groups, and low self-esteem characterized the upward mobile at the high end of the occupational scale *and* the downward mobile at the low end relative to their respective non-mobile peers.

It has been suggested in the literature that status inconsistency is psychologically disturbing, since social roles and expectations associated with one status position may conflict with those of another (Hughes, 1945; Lenski, 1954). Using this assumption, Lenski (1967) predicted, and found (in four separate countries), that high status inconsistency was associated with radical political voting. Jackson and Burke (1965) showed that particular patterns of inconsistency were associated with different types of deviant reactions. Although the authors of this review reported (Parker and Kleiner, 1966) that status inconsistency was not significantly related to mental disorder, a particular pattern of inconsistency (i.e., high education and low occupation) was so related. As discussed earlier, this pattern was associated with a high aspiration-achievement discrepancy.

The literature summarized above strongly suggests that downward mobility is associated with mental disorder. Other studies, particularly those using status controls, have also shown that upward mobility is associated with mental disorder. It can be concluded that a wide variety of deviant behavior, including mental disorder, is associated with social mobility regardless of direction. Studies have also been cited that show some of the social psychological variables that intervene in this association. An issue that has consistently been raised in the literature concerns social selection and social causation. Social selection would be considered operative if it could be shown that individuals drifted into a status position because of prior mental illness. This widely held view is used to explain the high concentration of downward mobile individuals in psychiatric populations. On the other hand, social causation would attempt to explain high rates of mental disorder in a given class as being due to socialization experiences in that class. The concentration of downward mobile individuals at a given class level is often used to affirm social selection and deny social causation. However, the assumption that illness is prior to mobility is an unwarranted inference. It is also possible to hypothesize that mobility was prior to and etiologically related to mental illness. Myers and Roberts (1959) emphasize that the Class III patients relative to Class III controls experienced more upward social mobility, higher goal-striving stress, and social rejection prior to their illness. As noted previously, Parker and Kleiner found that mental illness was associated with downward mobility at the low end of the scale, and upward mobility at the high end of the scale. It is very difficult to entertain the hypothesis that people "drifted" up because of prior mental illness. It was also found that both types of mobility were associated with similar stress-provoking factors (e.g., high goal-striving stress, poor integration with reference groups, etc.). These same factors were highly associated with the upward and downward mobile groups in the non-psychiatric community population. These findings suggest the distinct possibility that social mobility and the associated stress factors are both antecedent to illness. The evidence presented does not resolve the question of temporal priority. The resolution of this question awaits relevant longitudinal studies.

Mobility Orientation and Mental Disorder

The research in this area is primarily concerned with the discrepancy between achievement and aspiration and its relation to mental illness. This discrepancy will be referred to as "mobility orientation." Assertions in the literature about the relationship of mobility orientation and mental disorder are usually based on clinical experience. Such well-known clinicians as Horney (1937) and Kardiner (1951) emphasize that our society makes status achievement an important element in self-evaluation and self-esteem. Failure to achieve desired goals leads to feelings of worthlessness, and, in some cases, to mental disorder. Kardiner found, in his study of Negroes, that achievement striving was an important etiological factor in the middle class psychopathology, but not in that of the lower class. Studies of mental illness in immigrant populations also maintain that the discrepancy between expected (and desired) and actual achievement frequently leads to mental disorder (Weinberg, 1953, 1955; Last, 1960).

Hollingshead, Ellis, and Kirby (1954) investigated this problem in New Haven and found that the mentally ill, both in the lower and middle class, had large discrepancies between their occupational and educational achievements and their aspirations in these areas. These authors concluded that vertical mobility striving and frustrations in both classes were significant in schizophrenia and neurosis, and that these factors merited intensive investigation. Myers and Roberts (1959) studied intensively a small sample of psychiatric patients and their families and found that equally large discrepancies existed between the aspirations and achievements of patients both in Class III (middle) and Class V (lower). However, the authors felt that these discrepancies were psychologically significant only in Class III because, while patients in this class spent a great deal of energy striving to narrow the gap between their achievement and aspirations, Class V patients appeared to be more reconciled to the low probability of achieving their aspired goals. In Class III, the prevailing belief was that if a person worked diligently, he would be successful; therefore, the failure of a middle class individual to reach his goals led to a drop in self-esteem and to feelings of depression.

Related to the finding of differences in emphasis on achievement striving between Class III and Class V individuals are studies of the importance of this factor in various psychiatric diagnostic groups. Controlling for class, schizophrenic patients showed higher discrepancies compared to their siblings than did neurotics (Myers and Roberts, 1959). Becker (1960) compared the achievement-related characteristics of a small group of manic-depressive patients to a comparable number of normal controls. The psychiatric patients placed significantly more emphasis than normal controls on achievement values. Since manic-depressive psychosis is significantly associated with middle class status, this indirectly confirms the findings of Myers and Roberts. However, the patients did not score higher than the controls in "need for achievement," as measured by the T.A.T. The author concluded that in manic-depressive patients the high achievement values and conformity behavior seemed to have as a goal the gaining of approval of others rather than satisfying internalized standards. Eysenck and Himmelweit (1946) compared goal-striving behavior of two groups of psychiatric patients—those who manifested affective symptoms (i.e., introvert-dysthymic group) and hysterics. They found a marked tendency in the affective group to neglect the reality of their past achievement performance and to be dominated instead by subjective factors. The affective group tended to depreciate their past performances and to over-value (unrealistically) their future possibilities. In his intensive social psychological study of the "schizophrenic type," Weinberg (1955, 1960) found that the inability of such patients "to assess their own limitations and/or limitations of a given situation in which they participated was one direct contributing factor in their subsequent breakdowns." He also noted their deep need for approval, leading to intense over-compensatory aspirations. Dunham (1959) confirmed this in a study of catatonic schizophrenia.

Hinkle and Wolff (1957) found, in a large sample (of predominantly working class persons), that those individuals who were most frustrated in their aspirations, and disappointed in their accomplishments, also had the highest incidence of illness and showed more disturbances of mood, thought, and behavior than those who came nearer to reaching their aspirations. Sewell and Haller (1959) also found a direct relationship between achievement frustration and psychiatric symptoms in a study of 1,462 elementary school children. On the California Test of Personality, lower class children scored as more maladjusted than children in the middle class, and also had significantly more concern over achievement. In addition to showing a direct relationship between concern about achievement and symptoms of maladjustment, this study tended to question the frequently reported finding that socialization in lower socio-economic groups results in a reduction of achievement striving and achievement anxiety (Davis, 1947; Hyman, 1953; Hollingshead and Redlich, 1958). The authors of this review (Parker, Kleiner, and Taylor, 1960) found (for Negro and white populations) that when occupational achievement was controlled, groups with higher educational achievement yielded relatively higher rates of schizophrenia than those with less education. Assuming educational achievement to be an index of level of aspiration, it was inferred that the discrepancies were larger for those with high rates of schizophrenia. In their study of the Negro community, Parker and Kleiner (1966) found the discrepancies for income and occupational goals to be lower in a psychiatric population. However, for self-selected areas of goal striving, their discrepancy scores were larger.

The studies in this section suggest that mobility orientation is a significant factor in mental disorder. In addition, the data indicate that larger discrepancies between achievement and aspiration may be more prevalent among individuals in lower socioeconomic groups. However, Myers and Roberts showed that middle class individuals were more psychologically involved and more optimistic concerning their aspirations. This pointed to the need to consider the individual's subjective probability of goal attainment and the importance of the goal area to him. These variables are suggested by the level of aspiration theory of Lewin, Festinger, and their associates (1944).

Using this level of aspiration theory, the authors of this paper (Parker and Kleiner, 1966) constructed a composite index consisting of the discrepancy between level of aspiration and achievement, subjective probability of success, and the valence of this goal; this index was considered a measure of goal-striving stress. Subsequent analyses showed that the mentally ill had higher goal-striving stress than the community population in all areas of goal striving. The data derived from this measure was then used to explain the correlations between several social-structural variables (e.g., social mobility and migration) and mental disorder.

Small Group Studies of Achievement-Related Behavior and Mental Disorder

The studies reported in this section are concerned mainly with small group research, using experimentally created tasks. Although some of these studies were carried out with medically diagnosed psychiatric cases, others employed various measures of maladjustment and anxiety.

A large body of research indicates that persons showing some evidence of maladjustment also tend to select experimentally created tasks that have either a very high or very low probability of being successfully completed. The discrepancies between their actual performances and their aspirations tend to be either extremely high or low (but predominantly high) compared to more "normal" subjects (Atkinson, 1957). In a study of the achievement behavior of a group of college students, Atkinson et al. (1960) found that individuals who had high needs to avoid failure (as determined by the T.A.T.) tended to avoid tasks having intermediate risks and selected those having either high or low probabilities of success. In a group of 50 neurotic patients, Louis Cohen (1954) attempted to determine the relationship between goal-setting behavior and feelings of self-rejection as determined by the Rorschach Test. He found that both very high and very low goal settings were significantly related to a high degree of self-rejection. A low degree of self-rejection was related both to medium-high and medium-low settings. On the other hand, self-acceptance was found to be associated with low positive or low negative aspirations. Atkinson (1954a) showed that those with high aspirations also had large discrepancies between their actual and their ideal self-images.

Individuals in need of psychotherapy also had large discrepancies between their perceptions of what they were and what they would like to be (Turner and Vanderlipp, 1958; Butler and Haigh, 1954). Pauline Sears (1941) found a definite relationship between various personality traits and achievement behavior on experimentally created tasks. Students who had negative discrepancies (i.e., goal levels lower than past performances) tended to find it anxiety-provoking to admit that they were striving for more than they were able to achieve. These students had very low tolerance for failure. Consequently, after even one failure, they quickly dropped their levels of aspiration to points below their previous perform-ances and aspired goals were relatively confident and secure. Those with high positive discrepancies also had high fears of failure but were able to admit failure without too much damage to their self-esteem. Klugman (1948) investigated the relationship between aspiration on contrived tasks and emotional stability in a group of 30 native-born white subjects. His results indicated that the more stable subjects tended to have narrower ranges of discrepancy between attainment and aspiration than did the less stable ones. Those who were more emotionally stable tended to be flexible and to shift their goals moderately in response to their previous attainments. However, those in the less stable group were more inclined either to maintain their aspirations rigidly, or to show extreme changes. Mahone (1960) attempted to apply some of the findings reported above to a situation in which the respondent was asked to select socially relevant goals instead of an aspiration on a contrived laboratory task. He administered vocational interest questionnaires and anxiety scales to a sample of 135 college students. As pre-dicted, he found that those students who had high "debilitating anxiety" were unrealistically high in their occupational aspirations. In addition, these individuals were least accurate in placing themselves in rank order of achievement in their class. They had difficulty in giving a realistic estimate of their own abilities.

Many of the laboratory experiments with individuals showing definite psycho-pathology indicate that these individuals are characterized by relatively high discrepancies. Himmelweit (1947) compared psychoneurotic individuals with normals and found that the former had high "D" scores (i.e., discrepancy scores). Jost (1955) noted that the same was true of schizophrenic patients, as compared to a normal group. Children diagnosed as emotionally disturbed showed higher discrepancy scores than did their normal peers (Ferguson, 1958). Such high dis-crepancy scores between aspiration and achievement on laboratory tasks were also found in those with multiple psychosomatic symptoms (Klugman, 1947, 1948), asthma (Little and Cohen, 1951), and peptic ulcer (Raifman, 1957).

The evidence cited above points to a tendency for emotionally disturbed sub-jects either to over- or under-aspire, compared to those who have made a better adjustment. The dominant tendency in these studies, however, is for over-aspiring in the maladjusted and pathological groups. Generally, two lines of reasoning have been advanced to explain this phenomenon. One argument is that mal-adjusted subjects have high anxiety and high fear of failure, compared to others. They attempt to minimize anxiety by selecting a task that is so easy that they cannot fail, or one which is so difficult that failure would be no cause for self-blame (Atkinson, 1957). The other explanation advanced is that the high level of anxiety experienced by maladjusted subjects prevents them from accurately evaluating their own abilities relative to the realistic difficulties in reaching cer-tain goals (Mahone, 1960).

Although most of the studies in the field support the idea that maladjusted sub-jects select either very high or very low levels of aspiration, not all research in the area confirms this finding. The level of aspiration may be a function of personality type. Chance (1960) selected a group of maladjusted (as determined by the

M.M.P.I.) college students and divided them into depressives and repressors. She hypothesized that the former would under-aspire because they would tend to minimize their past achievements. On the other hand, the repressors, who generally denied their failure, would tend to over-aspire. After subjecting both groups to an experimentally contrived failure situation, she found that students of the depressive type lowered their aspirations considerably; however, the repressors maintained their old goals or reduced them only slightly. Davids and White (1958) studied 30 normal children and a matched sample of 30 who were diagnosed as emotionally disturbed. Prior to the experience of experimental success or failure, the disturbed children showed larger discrepancies between achievement and aspiration on the tasks. After experimentally produced success, both the normals and the disturbed group increased their aspirations; the increase for the normals was higher. After experimentally produced failure, the disturbed group decreased their aspirations significantly more than the normals did. In addition, the disturbed children showed much more heterogeneity in their responses after failure than did the normal children. These results indicate that the maladjusted group only selected (relatively) extreme aspirations after a failure situation.

The hypothesis has been advanced, with some supporting evidence, that schizophrenics are minimally responsive to external environmental stimuli in their achievement behavior, and tend to raise or lower their aspirations indiscriminately either after success or failure situations (Hausmann, 1933). Olson (1958) investigated this question, using a sample of 45 male schizophrenics between the ages 20–40 and a comparable group of normal subjects. This investigator was interested in the reactions of the two groups to three kinds of experimentally created situations. In one situation, the investigator approved their performances by telling them that they had done well, better than others, etc. In the second situation, he told them that their performances had been poor. With the third group, he remained neutral and gave neither positive nor negative reactions. There was no way for the subjects in this situation to evaluate their performances realistically. After mild disapproval of their performances, the subsequent achievement of the normals improved, but that of the schizophrenics remained relatively the same. Members of the ill group showed the greatest subsequent improvement after their performances were approved by the investigator. This study lends little support to the idea that schizophrenics are not responsive to external environmental stimuli. It also shows that praise is a more effective enhancer for these individuals than even mild disapproval. Thus, there is some evidence for hypersensitivity to failure among disturbed subjects.

The research reviewed in this section shows that the "emotionally disturbed" are not uniform in the goal-oriented behavior. There is considerable variation among personality types and diagnostic categories. Little is known at this point about the applicability of the theory concerning achievement behavior in "real life" situations. Assuming that it is revelant, an interesting methodological problem arises. In previous sections of this paper, we reviewed research concerned with the etiological relevance of achievement-related behavior for mental illness. For example, attempts were made to see whether the magnitude of the discrepancy between achievement and aspiration was related to mental illness. However, some of the small group research suggests the possibility that the size of this discrepancy may arise as a defense against emotional disturbance rather than act as a cause of it. Achievement-related behavior may be relevant *both* as a cause and an effect of mental disorder. It is thus crucial for any research in this area to determine carefully the temporal relationship between the onset of mental illness and changes in achievement-related behavior. Only in this way will it be possible to separate the role of achievement behavior either as an antecedent or as a consequence of mental disorder.

Conclusions

Although the present state of the research on status position and mental disorder does not permit firm generalizations, it seems likely that the social psychology of goal-striving behavior provides an encouraging possibility for a unifying thread. Notwithstanding the conceptual and methodological problems in this area of endeavor, the empirical studies focusing directly on mobility orientation, and the inferences that were drawn from related research, justify this belief.

The methodological problems characterizing these studies have been discussed at various points in the review. These problems, which apply both to the dependent (i.e., mental disorder) and the independent (i.e., sociological and psychological) variables, make comparisons of the different studies difficult and limit the extent to which generalizations can be made. Some problems result from a lack of clarity or a lack of consensus concerning the nature of the concepts used, while in other cases the difficulty is not conceptual clarity, but rather the use of different operational definitions for a given construct. Epidemiological studies frequently commit the "ecological fallacy" by contrasting the modal characteristics of whole communities or groups rather than individuals. The fallacious assumption consists in attributing the modal characteristic of a group to all individuals making up that group, thus possibly yielding spurious conclusions.

One of the most serious methodological problems encountered in this review stems from the concept of "mental disorder." Because of varying definitions of this condition and a limited understanding of the factors involved, either in its etiology or current dynamics, there is a need for research to help clarify and delineate this concept.

Another problem besetting attempts to compare the various studies in the field arises from variations in case-finding methods. In some instances, the investigator does not provide a full and precise explanation of the methods he uses. Where such explanations *are* furnished, it is frequently not valid to compare results; the same inferences and the same conclusions should not be made from incidence and prevalence studies. In addition, it may not be valid to assume that diagnosed mental disorder lies on the same continuum as psychophysiological or psychoneurotic reactions obtained from a symptom checklist. The considerable variations in findings of studies using the different case-finding methods suggest further their incomparability.

The present status of our knowledge of mental disorder may limit its usefulness as a variable in sociological research. It is necessary to pursue further research on appropriate models of the pathological processes involved in order to define variables that are genotypically homogeneous. It is possible, for example, in lieu of a medical model, to define mental illness in terms of role malfunctioning.

While the use of mental disorder as a research variable presents considerable problems, the variables mentioned in this review also present some methodological difficulties. In a previous section we questioned the advisability of averaging the ranks of the various status components to obtain a mean status position. It is also possible that the psychological meaningfulness of using such a procedure varies according to the nature of the population (e.g., racial composition) or the community being studied (e.g., rural or urban community).

Another problem associated with the concept of status position and its relationship to mental disorder arises from the question of which point in a patient's career should be used to determine his achievement. The review of studies exploring the drift hypothesis indicated limited agreement about the relative social mobility of psychiatric patients and normal control groups. It is clear that, at least in some instances, the status distribution of patients will differ, depending on whether the investigator has chosen the achievement level at the time of entering treatment, or another point in time that would be a closer approximation to the patient's pre-morbid achievement. If the aim is to focus on the etiological factors in mental disorder, rather than on its effects, it is important to use the latter point.

With regard to mobility orientations, studies have utilized various methods of determining the level of aspiration. Some investigators asked their subjects about the goals they expected to reach, while others inquired about the desired goals. Research shows that the expected and the desired goals are quite different. It is sometimes felt that expected goals will be more realistic and psychologically meaningful than desired goals. However, it may also be true that expected goals represent a painful compromise and will fail to give a true picture of a subject's degree of striving and frustration. Although the discrepancy between aspiration and achievement has proven to be useful, it appears that considering the additional concepts of probability and valence of success provides a more powerful approach.

This review has brought into clear relief some of the theoretical and methodological problems in the sociological and psychological studies of psychopathology. There has been little effort to utilize theoretical schemes to explain inconsistencies. Despite the methodological problems noted above, we are impressed with the agreement of the findings on the relationship between mobility orientation and mental disorder. This points to the importance of exploring further social psychological concepts as intervening variables. They can serve to further our understanding of the relationship between sociological variables and mental disorder and also help to explain apparent inconsistencies in the data.

17 / Fit of Individual and Community Characteristics and Rates of Psychiatric Hospitalization

Henry Wechsler / Thomas F. Pugh

Epidemiological methods are used to localize determinants of the distribution of non-infectious as well as infectious disease (MacMahon, Pugh, and Ipsen, 1960). Descriptive studies of mental disease using these methods have indicated, with respect to personal characteristics, that older persons have higher rates of hospitalization for mental disorders than younger persons; single persons, higher rates than married persons; and persons of lower occupational or socioeconomic status, higher rates than persons from middle or upper social classes (Malzberg, 1940; Dayton, 1940; Jaco, 1960; Hollingshead and Redlich, 1958). Prior indications that foreign-born persons and native-born persons who move within the United States have higher rates than others (Malzberg and Lee, 1956) are no longer as consistent, but there are indications that the increasingly mobile non-white population in the United States has had progressively higher rates of psychiatric hospitalization (Pugh and MacMahon, 1962).

A prototype of studies focused on place of occurrence, rather than on personal characteristics, is that of Faris and Dunham (1939) in Chicago in 1930–1931 which indicated that higher rates of schizophrenia occurred among people living in the central areas of the city where there were lower socioeconomic neighborhoods than in the peripheral areas where the neighborhoods had higher socioeconomic status.

Such studies, dealing with the spatial distribution of mental disorders, have been strongly criticized. First is the criticism that the properties of an area do not necessarily indicate the properties of the individuals who become ill in it (Clausen and Kohn, 1954). To avoid this problem requires simultaneous consideration of the characteristics of the individual and those of the community in which he resides. Second is that the findings may reflect a selective migration of persons with psychiatric disorders rather than the operation of etiologic factors. Thus, the problem of "drift" (Gerard and Houston, 1953; Lapouse, Monk, and Terris, 1956) should be considered in the interpretation of the findings of such studies.

The study presented here is based on the idea that ready availability of a peer group facilitates the formation of interpersonal relationships and that its relative lack hampers the formation of such relationships. The latter situation is assumed to be associated with a greater degree of stress and social isolation than the former and to be more conducive to the production of mental disorders.

Although the formulation is familiar, the present study avoids the two prob-

From the *American Journal of Sociology*, 1967, 73, 331–338. Copyright © 1967. Reprinted by permission of the authors and the University of Chicago Press.

lems just cited by considering both the type of community and the type of person as they interact in influencing rates of hospitalized mental disorder and by having, as well, a built-in examination of the influence of "drift."

Specifically, the hypothesis tested is that people with a particular personal characteristic who are living in communities where the characteristic is less common should have a higher rate of psychiatric hospitalization than people with the characteristic living in communities where it is more common—that is, people who do not "fit" in a community should have a higher rate than those who do.

Rates based on "fit" with respect to age, marital status, place of birth, and occupation provide four general areas for testing the hypothesis. These are shown in Table I. Within the four areas, fifteen tests of the hypothesis were made.

TABLE I

TESTS OF THE "FIT" HYPOTHESIS

Population Group	Higher Rates in Towns with	Lower Rates in Towns with
1. Age		
a. Younger persons (15–34)	Fewer young persons	More young persons
b. Medium-aged persons (35–54)	Fewer medium-aged persons	More medium-aged persons
c. Older persons (55 and over)	Fewer older persons	More older persons
2. Marital status		
a. Married	Fewer married persons	More married persons
b. Single	Fewer single persons	More single persons
c. Widowed, separated, and divorced	Fewer widowed, separated, and divorced	More widowed, separated, and divorced
3. Place of birth		
a. Massachusetts	Fewer Massachusetts born	More Massachusetts born
b. U.S., not Massachusetts	Fewer U.S., not Massachusetts born	More U.S., not Massachusetts born
c. Foreign born	Fewer foreign born	More foreign born
4. Occupation		
a. Professional	Fewer professionals	More professionals
b. Craftsmen	Fewer craftsmen	More craftsmen
c. Clerical and sales	Fewer clerical and sales	More clerical and sales
d. Operatives	Fewer operatives	More operatives
e. Service workers and	Fewer service and laborers	More service and laborers
f. Unknown	Fewer unknown	More unknown

Method

All first admissions to inpatient care in licensed Massachusetts mental hospitals, fifteen years of age and older, during the three-year period from October 1, 1958, to September 30, 1961, are included. These comprise 24,934 patients admitted for the first time to a universe of twenty-nine hospitals (thirteen state, twelve private, and four Veterans Administration).

The patients were categorized as to their place of residence in the 351 cities and towns in Massachusetts at the time of initial hospitalization. Information was also recorded on age, marital status, birthplace, and, for males, occupation.

Special tabulations from the U.S. Bureau of the Census (1962) provided the following data on the population of each of the 351 cities and towns as of April 1, 1960: (1) age, (2) marital status, (3) place of birth, (4) occupation for males. These tabulations were needed because population data in detail are not routinely published by the Bureau of the Census for individual minor civil divisions. The tabulations obtained gave age and marital status simultaneously; this permitted adjustment for one when the other was being examined. The tabulations of place of birth and occupation permitted adjustment for age. Simultaneous adjustment for place of birth, occupation, and marital status was not possible with the material obtained.

Because of the extremely high rates of psychiatric hospitalization among residents of the city of Boston compared to rates in the other cities and towns, and because of its very large size, Boston was eliminated from the analyses presented.

The remaining 350 cities and towns were grouped with respect to each of the four variables listed (age, marital status, place of birth, and occupation—males) into the 56 (16 per cent) with the highest proportion, the 238 (68 per cent) with the intermediate proportion, and the 56 (16 per cent) with the lowest. For example, when the "fit" hypothesis was tested for young persons (those between the ages of fifteen and thirty-four), towns were grouped into the 56 with populations having the highest percentages of young persons, the 238 with the intermediate percentages, and the 56 with the lowest. Thus, the towns were arranged separately into three groups for each of three ages, into three for each of three marital status groups, into three for each of three nativity groups, and into three for each of six occupations. In addition to providing material for fifteen tests of the "fit" hypothesis, these groupings of towns also generated forty-eight comparisons of the possible influence of the groupings which did not bear directly on the hypothesis.[1]

Adjustment for differences in the marital status composition of the populations was made when rates were calculated for town groups according to age; adjustment for differences in age composition was made when rates were calculated for towns grouped with respect to the marital status, place of birth, and occupation of their populations. The adjustment for age used seven ten-year intervals (15–24, 25–34, . . . , 75+) and that for marital status used three categories (married; single; and widowed, separated, and divorced).

The general formula for the adjusted rates is the familiar $(O \div E) \times R$, where O is the observed number (first admissions to mental hospitals), E the expected number, and R the rate for all persons, without respect to any characteristic other than their inclusion in the study. The expected number (of first admissions) is the sum of the numbers obtained by applying category-specific rates to the same categories of the population at risk of such admission. Confidence limits were obtained by use of the formula: $R \times \dfrac{(O \pm M\sqrt{O})}{E}$, where M equals 1.960 for the

[1] $([3 \times 3] + [3 \times 3] + [3 \times 3] + [6 \times 6]) = 63$; and $63 - 15 = 48$.

.05, 2.576 for the .01, and 3.291 for the .001 probabilities of statistical significance, respectively.

Findings

The findings which follow compare the rate in towns with a high proportion of the population having the characteristic being examined with the rate in towns having a low proportion of the characteristic.

TABLE II

RATES OF FIRST ADMISSION TO MASSACHUSETTS MENTAL HOSPITALS BY AGE (IN YEARS) IN TOWNS WITH DIFFERENT AGE COMPOSITIONS*

Towns Grouped by Percentage of Population	Rates per 100,000 Population per Year for Persons in Specified Age Groups		
	15–34	35–54	55 and Over
A. Young (age 15–34)			
Low	**198.1**	222.4	218.1
Medium	182.6	218.5	219.5
High	**147.6**	223.1	210.6
B. Medium age (35–54)			
Low	182.0	**256.0**	231.8
Medium	178.7	215.9	216.7
High	163.5	**193.4**	205.3
C. Older (55 and over)			
Low	**115.6**	**180.5**	**178.4**
Medium	185.1	222.4	221.0
High	**192.9**	**227.8**	**219.6**

* Rates adjusted for marital status. Rates having statistically significant differences between towns grouped as low and high are in boldface.

Age (Table II)

A. Younger persons (15–34 years) had a higher rate of first admission to mental hospitals in towns where there was a low proportion of young persons than in towns where the proportion was high (p <.001).

B. Medium-aged persons (35–54 years) had a higher rate in towns where there was a low proportion of medium-aged persons than in towns where there was a high proportion of them (p <.001).

C. However, persons in the older age groups (55 years and over), as well as the younger and medium ages, each had a lower rate in towns that had a low proportion of older persons than in towns where the proportion was high (p <.001, <.01, and <.05, respectively).

Marital Status (Table III)

A. Married persons had a higher rate in towns that have a low proportion of married persons than they did in towns where the proportion was high (p <.001). And, conversely, married persons had a lower rate in towns

TABLE III

RATES OF FIRST ADMISSION TO MASSACHUSETTS MENTAL HOSPITALS BY MARITAL STATUS IN TOWNS WITH DIFFERENT MARITAL STATUS COMPOSITION*

Towns Grouped by Percentage of Population	Rates per 100,000 Population per Year for Persons in Specified Marital Status Groups		
	Married	Single	Widowed, Separated, and Divorced
A. Married			
Low	**194.3**	269.7	283.5
Medium	166.4	263.6	269.4
High	**144.0**	241.8	293.8
B. Single			
Low	149.4	262.8	274.3
Medium	163.7	264.3	274.2
High	199.0	267.3	277.6
C. Widowed, separated and divorced			
Low	145.1	**158.2**	276.3
Medium	177.5	266.0	274.8
High	171.6	**285.1**	276.5

* Rates adjusted for age. Rates having statistically significant differences between towns grouped as low and high are in boldface.

  that had a low proportion of single persons than in towns with a high proportion (p <.001).

 B. No statistically significant difference is found for single persons in towns grouped according to the proportion of single persons.

 C. Both married and single persons had higher rates in towns that had a high proportion of widowed, separated, and divorced persons than in towns with a low percentage (p <.01 and <.001, respectively).

 D. No difference is found for widowed, separated, and divorced persons in towns grouped according to the proportion of widowed, separated, and divorced.

Place of Birth (Table IV)

 A. Massachusetts-born persons had a higher rate in towns where there was a low proportion of them than in towns where there was a high proportion (p <.001).

 B. Persons born in the United States outside of Massachusetts had a higher rate in towns where they were in low proportion than in towns where the proportion was high (p <.01). In harmony with this finding—since the foreign-born formed a small fraction of the total population while the other two components were both large—persons born in the United States outside of Massachusetts had a lower rate in towns where the proportion born in Massachusetts was low (p <.01).

TABLE IV

RATES OF FIRST ADMISSION TO MASSACHUSETTS MENTAL HOSPITALS BY
PLACE OF BIRTH IN TOWNS WITH DIFFERENT PLACE-OF-BIRTH COMPOSITIONS[*]

Towns Grouped by Percentage of Population	Rates per 100,000 Population per Year for Persons in Specified Place-of-Birth Groups		
	Massachusetts Born	U.S., Non-Mass. Born	Foreign Born
A. Massachusetts born			
Low	**224.9**	**154.1**	190.6
Medium	212.1	186.6	214.2
High	**188.7**	**206.0**	173.2
B. U.S., non-Mass. born			
Low	212.9	**191.7**	207.4
Medium	203.3	182.0	209.1
High	183.9	**143.5**	186.7
C. Foreign born			
Low	**163.8**	136.3	163.9
Medium	186.2	169.6	195.1
High	**239.7**	194.4	216.0

[*] Rates adjusted for age. Rates having statistically significant differences between towns grouped as low and high are in boldface.

C. Foreign-born persons, however, as well as those born in Massachusetts and in the United States outside of Massachusetts, each had a lower rate in towns where the foreign-born population was in low proportion than in towns where it was high. In two instances out of the three—for the rate of the Massachusetts-born and that of persons born elsewhere in the United States—the difference is statistically significant (p $<.001$ and $<.01$, respectively).

Occupation (Table V)[2]

A. Professional workers had higher rates in towns where there was a low proportion of them than in towns where their proportion was high (p $<.01$).
B. Clerical and sales workers had a higher rate where there was a low proportion of them than in towns where the proportion was high, but the difference is not statistically significant. An additional finding with towns so grouped is that both craftsmen and persons with unknown occupations had lower rates in towns with a low proportion of clerical and sales workers than in towns with a high proportion (p $<.001$ and $<.05$, respectively).
C. Craftsmen had a higher rate in towns where they were in low proportion than in towns where their proportion was high (p $<.01$). An additional finding with towns so grouped is that operatives had higher rates in towns with a low proportion of craftsmen than in towns with a high proportion.
D. Operatives had a higher rate in towns where they were in low proportion than in towns where their proportion was high (p $<.01$).

[2] This analysis is restricted to males aged 25–64 years.

TABLE V

RATES OF FIRST ADMISSION TO MASSACHUSETTS MENTAL HOSPITALS BY OCCUPATION IN TOWNS WITH DIFFERENT OCCUPATIONAL COMPOSITIONS (MALES, AGES 25–64 YEARS)*

Towns Grouped by
Percentage of
Population   Rates per 100,000 per Year for Persons in Specified Occupational Groups

	Professional	Clerical and Sales	Craftsmen	Operatives	Service and Laborers	Unknown
A. Professional						
Low	**197.9**	206.7	163.4	198.1	506.4	459.9
Medium	148.9	202.1	175.7	202.0	505.7	486.1
High	**134.2**	205.0	132.0	246.2	475.9	424.0
B. Clerical and Sales						
Low	172.7	334.9	**70.4**	184.4	427.4	**192.8**
Medium	156.9	202.4	175.3	194.1	497.5	468.9
High	142.8	203.3	**162.8**	250.3	533.7	**512.7**
C. Craftsmen						
Low	141.1	227.2	**209.5**	**266.7**	547.8	527.8
Medium	155.1	199.4	174.9	200.8	506.2	469.2
High	154.4	199.5	**111.7**	**174.4**	410.3	380.3
D. Operatives						
Low	146.5	219.5	138.4	**289.3**	498.5	365.8
Medium	149.8	207.4	174.2	207.1	514.6	479.5
High	186.9	152.2	160.6	**171.2**	453.7	543.7
E. Service and laborers						
Low	127.3	162.0	105.0	183.4	477.6	346.8
Medium	154.5	209.9	179.1	207.2	523.8	484.8
High	192.7	188.9	132.3	160.7	352.7	485.1
F. Unknown						
Low	**99.4**	**122.2**	**129.1**	132.5	281.6	1558.7
Medium	149.6	200.5	162.4	206.0	509.1	500.8
High	**185.1**	**243.6**	**220.0**	204.6	517.7	353.3

* Rates adjusted for age. Rates having statistically significant differences between towns grouped as low and high are in boldface.

E. Service workers and laborers had a higher rate in towns where there was a low proportion of them than in towns where their proportion was high, but the difference is not statistically significant.

F. With towns grouped according to the proportion with unknown occupation, the rate for persons of unknown occupation was high where there was a low proportion of persons of unknown occupation and low where the proportion was high ($p < .01$). The rates for all categories of workers with known occupation, however, were lower when there was a low proportion of workers of unknown occupation than when the proportion was high ($p < .01$ for professionals, $< .05$ for clerical and sales, $< .001$ for crafts, and $< .01$ for service workers and laborers. Although not statistically significant for operatives, the difference is in the same direction).

Summary of Findings

The findings give substantial support to the "fit" hypothesis studied—namely, that people with a particular characteristic, who are living in areas where the characteristic is less common, should have higher rates of hospitalization for mental disorder than people with that characteristic who are living in areas where the characteristic is more common. Within the fifteen tests of the hypothesis, the rates were in the predicted direction in eleven; and in the eleven the difference in nine was statistically significant. Specifically, the hypothesis was borne out in a convincing fashion for people with the following characteristics who are living in towns grouped according to the proportion of the population having that characteristic: (1) younger (15–34 years), (2) medium age (35–54), (3) married, (4) Massachusetts-born, (5) born elsewhere in the United States, (6) professional workers, (7) craftsmen, (8) operatives, and (9) persons of unknown occupation.

Rates in a direction opposite to that proposed by the hypothesis occurred in one statistically significant instance out of the fifteen tests: when towns were grouped according to the proportion of older persons (55 years and over). However, the phenomenon was a general one. Rates for all three age groups were significantly lower in towns with low percentages of old people. Similarly, rates for Massachusetts- and United States-born persons were significantly lower in towns with low percentages of foreign-born, and rates for married and single persons were significantly lower in towns with low percentages of widowed, separated, and divorced persons.

Neither agreement nor disagreement with the hypothesis was observed when towns were grouped by the percentages of single persons.

An unexpected but interesting finding involved persons of known occupation who are living in towns grouped by the proportion having unknown occupation. Here, people with known occupation had a lower rate in towns where the percentage of unknown occupation was low than in towns where the percentage was high. Also unexpected were the significantly lower rates among craftsmen and men with unknown occupation in areas where the proportion of clerical workers was low.

Interpretation and Discussion

Although the findings of the present study appear consistently to support the "fit" hypothesis, interpretation of the results should take the following considerations into account.

The Index of Mental Illness

The index was initial psychiatric hospitalization. Thus, findings may reflect patterns of mental hospital use and not "true" rates of illness. Rates of first admission to inpatient care, however, measure incidence rather than prevalence and thus avoid the complicating variable of duration of illness.

Simultaneous Consideration of Individual and Community Characteristics

Research on the spatial distribution of mental illness is justly criticized when it assumes that patients coming from a certain region necessarily have personal characteristics similar to those of the bulk of the residents in it. Here the problem is absent because of the simultaneous consideration of the characteristics of the region and of its patients. The fact that there was a negative relationship between risk of hospitalization and similarity to other residents of towns indicates that patients from an area were not representative of the population of that area— that is, the patients and the towns did not "fit."

The Drift Hypothesis

This hypothesis states that persons becoming mentally ill, or who have certain characteristics predisposing them to become ill, gravitate toward lower socio-economic neighborhoods. Were this hypothesis to be supported by the data presented here, one would expect the rate of professional workers in areas where there are relatively many service workers and laborers to exceed the rate of professional workers in areas where there are relatively many professional workers, since professional workers have the highest median income and service workers and laborers the lowest (U.S. Bureau of the Census, 1962). Similarly, one would expect the rates of clerical and sales workers and of craftsmen to be higher in areas with relatively many service workers and laborers than in areas with relatively many professional workers. In none of these cases does examination of Table V show significant difference in such a direction.

Etiologic Interpretations

If this study has significance with respect to the etiology of mental disorders, then thought about mechanisms which might explain the findings is important. Is it that persons living in areas where fewer residents are similar to them are under special stress from social isolation, and thus at a greater risk of mental disorders? Or is it that persons living in communities where more are similar to them are somehow protected from stress by being provided with enough peer relationships to decrease risk of mental disorders?

Without respect to etiology, a study similar to this one would be useful in determining whether the current situation of desegregation in the United States follows the pattern of the "fit" hypothesis. Do Negroes living in predominantly white areas have a higher rate of psychiatric hospitalization than Negroes in segregated areas? If this is the case, more strenuous efforts toward providing social supports for Negroes moving into predominantly white neighborhoods would seem mandatory.

18 / Sibling Order, Premorbid Adjustment and Remission in Schizophrenia

Leonard Solomon / *Ronald Nuttall*

Several clinical theorists have maintained that in schizophrenia the characteristic defense against anxiety is social withdrawal. In addition, many of the symptoms of communicative disorder represent symbolic attempts to achieve disaffiliation (Arieti, 1955; Bateson *et al.*, 1956). Schacter (1959) has demonstrated that earlier-born female sibs tend to be more affiliative under anxiety-provoking situations than are later-borns. Schacter has interpreted the earlier-born sibs' preference for the affiliative mode as reflecting the fact that as children they were exposed to more inconsistent nurturance patterns than were the later-borns. As adults the earlier-borns express a greater need for dependency and social approval, and these needs can be satisfied through different modes of affiliation. Closely related to the concept of affiliative tendencies is the question of the patient's history of friendships and social adjustment before he entered the hospital. This area of "premorbid" social adjustment in schizophrenia has been the subject of relatively extensive research.

The two major scales used in research on premorbid adjustment have been the Elgin Prognostic Scale (EPS) (Wittman, 1941) as revised by Becker (1955, 1959) and the Phillips (1953) Prognostic Rating Scale (PRS). Both scales are designed to enable a rater to score a series of dimensions of premorbid adjustment based on an analysis of case history material. A combined set of items from these two scales have been factor analyzed by Nuttall and Solomon (1965) and seven simple structure oblique factors were retained. These premorbid factors and the prognostic scales from which they were derived have traditionally been used to operationally define the distinction between the so-called "process" and "reactive" schizophrenic (Solomon and Zlotowski, 1964). The *process* schizophrenic is characterized by a premorbid history of social isolation, insidious onset and emotional unresponsiveness; the *reactive* is characterized by a relatively normal premorbid social adjustment with a sudden and dramatic onset of psychosis under stressful conditions (Vaillant, 1964). We view these seven factors as constituting an improved multidimensional measure of premorbid adjustment and the syndromes of process and reactive schizophrenia.

The first three of these factors are linked by the common conceptual thread of a general tendency to affiliate with, or disaffiliate from, others. These factors are: 1) social withdrawal, 2) inadequate heterosexual relationships, and 3) social undesirable and uncooperative ward behavior. Previous research by Nuttall and Solomon (1965) has shown that these factors are differentially significant as a function of the social class of the patient. From Schacter's hypothesis that the

Abridged from the *Journal of Nervous and Mental Disease*, 1967, **144**, 37–46. Copyright © 1967. Reprinted by permission of the authors and the Williams & Wilkins Co.

earlier-born sibs express a greater need for dependency and social approval through affiliative responses, it can be predicted that these three premorbid adjustment factors dealing with affiliative relationships are related to sibling order in schizophrenia. Moreover, we may expect an interaction by social class.

Method

Administration and Sample

As part of a broader program of research relating factors of premorbid adjustment to behavioral measures in schizophrenics, the case histories of a sample of 291 male schizophrenic patients were selected from five mental hospitals, four of which are in the Boston area. The criteria used for the selection of the case histories, demographic characteristics of the sample and details of the rating procedure and factor derivation are fully presented in an earlier study (Nuttall and Solomon, 1965). More than one-half of the case histories were drawn from the Massachusetts Mental Health Center (MMHC) and McLean Hospital, and one-third were drawn from Boston State Hospital. MMHC and McLean have a disproportionate number of upper social class patients. We made a deliberate effort to secure a high proportion of younger, first admission patients for purposes of possible research follow-ups. This is reflected in the distributions on age at testing (median = 28 years) and total time in hospital where over one-third of the sample had been hospitalized for less than one year and only one-third for over four years at the time of the rating.

Method of Analysis

Birth order depends on both the size of the sibship as well as the ordinal position within the sibship. A second-born child is in the last half of a two-child sibship, in the middle of a three-child sibship, and in the first half of a four-child sibship. Frequently a chi-square analysis is used to compare first-half *vs.* last-half sibs or to compare first-born with last-born sibs (Caudill, 1963; Schooler, 1961, 1964).

The chi-square is relatively insensitive, however, since it lumps together all possible types of variation from expectation. A more powerful test has been developed for dealing with birth order data. This test was devised by Keeping (1952) and has been used by Smart (1963) in a study of birth order and alcoholism. Keeping's normal deviate test relies on the assumption that the sum of birth ranks is normally distributed. This assumption of equal frequencies of first-, second-, and third-born people from three-child families, for example, is valid except insofar as there are differences in the death rates and sex ratios of these birth orders. (These differences are unlikely to be large enough to invalidate the use of the statistic for the present sample.) The expected value of the sum of ranks is given by

$$E(X_s) = N_s(s+1)/2$$

and the variance of the sum of ranks [$V(X_s)$] is given by

$$V(X_s) = N_s(s_2 - 1)/12$$

where s is the size of the sibship, N_s is the number of subjects from sibships of size s, and X_s is the sum of the birth ranks of these N_s people.

The difference between the observed total birth rank (X_s) and the expected total birth rank $[E (X_s)]$ for each sibship is then calculated.[1] Both the deviations $[E (X_s) - X_s]$ and the variances $[V (X_s)]$ are summed across all sibship sizes. The sum of the deviations when divided by the square root of the sum of the variances yields a normal deviate. The significance of any single sibship (or group of sibship sizes) can be evaluated by the normal deviate resulting from dividing the deviation (or sum of deviations) by the square root of the sum of the respective variances. Of course such an analysis is only appropriate when the hypothesis is framed before examining the data for the respective sibship sizes.

The Keeping normal deviate test cannot be easily used when the birth rank is being compared with a continuous variable. In order to relate the birth rank with the continuous variables of premorbid adjustment factor scores, a correlational method was used. Since the meaning of birth rank cannot be understood without relating it to sibship size, product-moment correlations between premorbidity factor scores and birth rank were run *within* each sibship size. The sibship sizes ranged from one to 18 with relatively few patients in each sibship size above six. The birth ranks, therefore, for patients from sibships of size seven and above were coded as follows: 1 = first born; 2 = upper middle; 3 = middle middle (occurs only for odd size sibships); 4 = lower middle; and 5 = last born. In order to inspect the correlations for birth rank per se (across sibship sizes) the correlations were averaged using Fisher's r to z weighting method as described in McNemar (1962). There was no attempt made to correct for the restriction in the range of variance (which would increase the size of the rs) as a function of sibship size.

Results

Keeping's normal deviate test (Table I) reveals a significant tendency ($p <$ .001) for *earlier*-born sibs to be over-represented in the present sample of male resident schizophrenics. Table I indicates that the greatest preponderance of early-born sibs are from sibship sizes three, four, and six. Furthermore, for the total sample there were more than twice as many first-born as last-born sibs ($p < .001$) and almost twice as many older sibs as younger sibs ($p < .001$).

Social Class and Sibling Order

To examine the relationship of social class to sibling order we used Duncan's Population Decile Scale of Occupations (1961) as the measure of social class. The total sample of 291 patients was divided into three groups: 1) patients whose fathers had occupations in the ninth or tenth decile ($N = 108$); 2) patients whose fathers had occupations in the fifth through eighth decile ($N = 112$); and 3) those whose fathers had occupations in the lowest four deciles

---

[1] This test assumes that only one sib of a sibship is represented in the sample of families. While our own sample has *no* family represented by more than one sib, this assumption is likely to be violated in the population at large, since the incidence rate for sibs of schizophrenic patients is much higher than for the general population (Kallman, 1956).

($N = 71$). The occupation of the father was used in determining social class for two reasons: some of the patients had entered the hospital before completing their education and were still part- or full-time students and others may have "drifted down" in their occupations due to the effects of mental illness.

TABLE I

PREVALENCE OF SCHIZOPHRENIC MALES BY BIRTH ORDER FOR EACH SIBSHIP SIZE FOR TOTAL SAMPLE OF 291 PATIENTS

Size of Sibship	\multicolumn{10}{c}{Birth Order}									N_s†	X_s†	$E(X)_s$†	$X_s -$ $E(X_s)$	$V(X_s)$†
	1st	2nd	3rd	4th	5th	6th	7th	8th	9th	10th or more				
1	22										22	22	22	0	0.00
2	33	17									50	67	75	−8.0	12.50
3	28	35	13								76	137	152	−15.0	50.67
4	18	14	11	2							45	87	112.5	−25.5	56.25
5	7	3	10	4	6						30	89	90	−1.0	60.00
6	5	5	3	6	3	0					22	63	77	−14.0	64.17
7	2	2	1	2	1	1	2				11	42	44	−2.0	44.00
8	2	2	0	1	1	1	4	0			11	49	49.5	−0.5	57.75
9	2	0	1	3	1	0	0	1	3		11	57	55	+2.0	73.33
10 or more	1	3	1	1	3	0	0	1	1	2*	13	78	84.5	−6.5	165.67
							Sums				291	689	761.5	−70.5	584.34

* One of these cases is the 14th of 17 children, the other is 18th of 18 children.

† Key: N_s = observed number of affected individuals who are members of size s.

X_s = sum$_r$ rN_{rs} = sum birth ranks or scores for sibships of size s.

$E(X_s) = [N_s(s + 1)/2]$ = expected value of birth ranks for sibships of size s.

$V(X_s) = [N_s(s^2 − 1)/12]$ = variance of sum birth ranks (X_s) for sibships of size s.

$p < .002$ (earlier-born siblings are over-represented in the sample.)

$$\text{Keeping's Normal Deviate} = z = \frac{\text{sum } [X_s − E(X_s)]}{\text{square root sum } [V(X_s)]} = \frac{-70.5}{24.173} = -2.916.$$

Three separate Keeping tests were done for the three social class groupings. In all three social class groupings, the earlier-born patients predominated. However, the strength of association between birth order and prevalence of schizophrenia is significant ($z = -3.797$, $p < .001$) only for the highest social class grouping ($z = -0.937$) and for the lower class grouping ($z = -0.663$), the earlier-born siblings did not significantly predominate. The difference sum $[X_s − E(X_s)]$ of the Keeping test was partialled by social class groupings. Sixty-six per cent of the total sample difference sum is due to the high social class group, yet the high social class group comprises only 37 per cent of the total sample.

Premorbid Adjustment Factors and Sibling Order

The relationships between premorbid factors and birth rank for each family size provide direct tests of our major hypothesis: namely, that the premorbid factors are related to birth rank. On the whole, the data provide partial support for this view. Only undesirable ward behavior (Factor 3) and insidious onset (Factor 5) are significantly correlated with birth rank. Factor 3 is essentially a "postmorbid" measure of initial social adjustment to ward life. A patient high on this factor tends to be untidy in appearance, reluctant to work, and relatively asocial on the ward; contrastively, the low scorer is likely to be neat, sociable, and a cooperative ward worker. Our data indicate that later-born patients tend to be high (poor premorbid) on undesirable ward behavior.

Factor 5 tapped the dimensions of insidious onset *vs.* acute stress. A patient high on this factor is likely to have had a psychotic onset in the absence of identifiable precipitants, whereas a low scorer had an acute onset and social and/or personal stresses. The younger sibs were more likely to have an insidious onset without an identifiable precipitant. In general then, for the two case history factors of insidious onset (Factor 5) and undesirable ward behavior (Factor 3), which did significantly correlate with sibling rank, the later-born patients were more likely to be at the poor premorbid end.

At the item level, only three items yielded correlations with birth rank which were significant at better than the .01 level. Phillips 2B and Elgin N tap the presence of precipitating stress (Factor 5) and the Phillips 3A reflects interest in personal appearance (Factor 3). There were no significant correlations between total Phillips PRS or Becker EPS scales and sibling rank.

Relative Chronicity and Sibling Order

Data on the relationship between sibling rank and outcome in terms of length of hospitalization were examined. Three indices were used to measure outcome: 1) total months since first admission, 2) total months spent in a mental hospital, 3) per cent of time spent in hospital since first admission. Each index of outcome significantly correlated with sibling rank (p < .001). These correlations reflect the fact that later-born sibs are more likely to become chronic patients whereas earlier-borns recover more rapidly. The relationship between chronicity and birth order appears to be particularly pronounced for family sizes two, three, and five. The correlations between age and birth rank was also positive, but smaller (+ 15).[2] There was no significant relationship between birth rank and age at first admission.

Discussion

Sibling Rank and Incidence of Schizophrenia

A major finding of the present study was that among resident male schizophrenics earlier-born sibs are significantly over-represented, the explanation for which probably lies in the fact that many patients from very high social class families were included in the sample. Schooler (1964) in a study of 127 male patients admitted to Spring Grove State Hospital, Maryland, found no significant overall relationship between birth order and hospitalization. However, significant

---

[2] In order to check the possibility that the correlations between length of hospitalization and sibling rank were not in part an artifact of age, we computed partial correlations. The effect of age is trivial. The partial correlations (with age controlled) for sibling size two through seven respectively are: .54, .24, .00, .33, −.12, and .24. Only one of these partial correlations differs from the first order correlation by more than ±.03. In sibship size six, the difference is −.08, which is not significant.

associations were obtained when the sample was differentiated by social class as measured by the Hollingshead rating of the father's occupation. The only social class grouping in Schooler's study that is comparable to that of our own was the lower class group.[3] For this group our findings were consistent (i.e., first-borns as contrasted with last-borns are significantly over-represented).

Our results are also consistent with those obtained by Rao (1964) and Caudill (1963) who likewise based their studies upon resident male schizophrenic samples. Rao has reported a study done in India in which he analyzed the sibling rank of 2,227 consecutive male admissions with a diagnosis of schizophrenia. The age range was 15 to 45, and the maximum sibship size was eight. He found a significant over-representation of earlier-born siblings, particularly pronounced for the *first*-borns. Rao believes this reflects special cultural stresses placed upon the first-born son.

Caudill's study was based upon a sample of 156 male schizophrenic patients admitted in 1958 to four psychiatric hospitals in the Tokyo area. Finding a significant over-representation of eldest sons, Caudill also attributes his findings to the differential nature of social roles assigned within the family. Only the eldest son is expected to assume his father's role, to support his parents, and to live in the same home with them. Thus one social explanation for our finding may pertain to the differential family pressure placed upon the first-born child who is male. We would expect pressures (e.g., for achievement and responsibility) to be particularly pronounced in the upper social class where there is both property and family tradition to uphold. Clearly other explanations, such as the possibility that parents are willing to maintain later-born and especially youngest sons at home for longer periods during a schizophrenic illness, must be considered.

Birth Order and Premorbid Adjustment

The finding that earlier-born sibs are more likely to have had an acute onset (Factor 5) and to show cooperative and affiliative ward behavior (Factor 3) provides partial support for the notion that earlier-born sibs are more likely to be characterized as having had a good premorbid adjustment. Langfeldt (1939), Kant (1941), Zubin (1961), and more recently Vaillant (1964) have cited the variables of acute onset with identifiable precipitants as having high prognostic significance. Our own previous research (Nuttall and Solomon, 1965) indicated that Factor 3 was the most consistent and overall the most powerful predictor of chronicity. Jenkins and Gurel (1959), in interpreting the prognostic significance of ward behavior, state, "it does not appear to be the severity of the symptoms which influence the duration of hospitalization so much as does the extent to which (these) symptoms isolate the psychotic patient from those about him."

[3] Schooler (1961) found a disproportionately greater number of first-born male patients from lower social class families as contrasted with an over-representation of last-born males from middle class families. He reports no relationship for his upper class sample. It should be noted that there are a number of crucial differences between Schooler's sample and that of our own. Fifty-four per cent of our sample consists of patients from two private hospitals; namely the Massachusetts Mental Health Center and McLean Hospital. Schooler's sample has no social class grouping that is comparable to the special upper class group in our sample drawn largely from the tenth decile of the Duncan Scale. Since our lower class sample was drawn largely from Boston State Hospital, it would most closely approximate the lower class sample in Schooler's study, which was also drawn from a state hospital.

The finding that earlier-born sibs are more likely to be sociable and cooperative in the ward setting may simply reflect their achievement of a higher level of social competence and adaptability. This finding may also be related to the notion that earlier-born sibs have a greater need for attention and social approval from authority figures. Several studies using male samples have indicated that earlier-born sibs are more likely to volunteer as experimental subjects (Suedfeld, 1964) and are more susceptible to social influence (Sampson, 1962). If the earlier-born (especially the first-born) has a greater need for social approval, then he will be more strongly motivated to fulfill new sets of role requirements in a ward culture (Factor 3). One may view the need for social approval as an affiliative disposition and a factor which contributes to the development of social competence. The fact that earlier-born sibs are *less* likely to become chronic patients suggests that they have developed higher levels of social competence in other areas.

Birth Order and Etiology of Schizophrenia

If schizophrenia were due to purely genetic causes, one would expect the incidence of schizophrenic offspring to be randomly distributed across sibling ranks. This expectation is based upon the notion that, since each successive child is drawing his genes from the same gene pool (biological parents), each sib has an equal chance to draw any schizophrenic genes, should they exist. Our research findings dealing with birth rank and the prevalence of hospitalized schizophrenics are inconsistent with the genetic explanation.

An alternative hypothesis is that a biological stress factor might explain the birth order relationship. Thus, the larger number of previous children or the advanced age of the mother may leave the later-born child with a biological predisposition for schizophrenia. In this regard the literature which deals with birth order and its relationship to congenital syndromes which include a mental component is pertinent. MacMahon and Sowa (1961), in summarizing this literature, indicate that significant relationships have been found for mental deficiency and mongoloidism with both maternal age and parity. Lilienfeld and Pasamanick (1956), controlling for maternal age, found a significant increase in the incidence of mental retardates with increasing birth rank. This effect was present in each of several maternal age groups. An association with maternal age was also present but not clearcut when parity was held constant. If we assume that schizophrenia is a congenital disease with a mental component, we would expect to find schizophrenia to occur with greater than chance frequency among later-born sibs. Our results, as well as those of Caudill (1963) and Rao (1964) based upon male schizophrenic samples, do not lend support to the biological stress hypothesis for schizophrenia taken as an undifferentiated entity.

Brackbill and Fine (1956) have proposed that the process form of schizophrenia reflects an organic and/or biochemical deficit, whereas the reactive type is primarily psychogenic in origin and precipitated by acute social stress.[4] On this basis one would predict that process schizophrenia (as a congenital disease

---

[4] Recent research on the attention dysfunction (Orzack and Kornetsky, 1966) and cortical arousal in different types of schizophrenics lend considerable support to this point of view (Gromoll, 1961; Venables, 1964; Venables and Wing, 1962).

with a mental component) would occur with greater frequency among later-born sibs who are exposed to greater biological stress. If we assume that first- (and earlier-) born males are subject to a more acute pattern of familial and societal stresses (particularly among the upper classes), then our results, both with respect to prevalence and remission, are consistent with Brackbill and Fine's theory.

An alternative hypothesis is that later-born male sibs who are schizophrenic are more likely to be treated or maintained at home. It would be useful to examine the relationship between birth order and schizophrenia in an untreated sample drawn from the general population. Our ratio of earlier-born to later-born schizophrenics may not reflect their true proportions in the general population.

Future research will also require the development of measurement techniques for assessing the severity of social as distinguished from biological stressors in the life history of the patient.

19 / Family Interaction Processes and Schizophrenia: A Review of Current Theories

Elliot G. Mishler / Nancy E. Waxler

Many investigators have been concerned with whether specific features of family life are associated with the etiology and development of schizophrenia. Both personality characteristics and social attributes of parents have been objects of considerable research and speculation since the pre-World War II period; the well-known notion of the schizophrenogenic mother was one of the products of this early line of inquiry. (Reviews of much of this work may be found in Sanua, 1961, and Spiegel and Bell, 1959.) During the past decade there has been a noticeable shift in the focus of attention among students of this problem. Interest is now centered on the whole family as a unit for study and conceptualization and, in particular, on the patterns of interaction and communication among the members of the family.

This has been an exciting development accompanied by an array of new concepts and hypotheses about schizophrenia, suggestive of new techniques of treatment and productive of a growing body of research. It seemed to us both appropriate and timely to attempt a review and comparative analysis of current theories relating family processes and schizophrenia.[1] While many investigators have con-

From the *Merrill-Palmer Quarterly*, 1965, 11, 269–315. Copyright © 1965. Reprinted by permission of the authors and *Merrill-Palmer Quarterly*.

[1] A recent paper by Meissner (1964) also attempts a review and critique of these and other theories of family relationships. The two papers overlap in the territory covered but differ considerably in point of view and in the framework used for the comparative analysis of these theories.

tributed to this development, three groups of investigators have had a major influence on the shape and direction of current thought and research; these are the research groups led by Gregory Bateson, Theodore Lidz, and Lyman Wynne. We shall place particular emphasis on their formulations.

Our intent is both expository and analytic. We wish to clarify each theory's basic concepts, and compare their respective foci and levels of conceptualization. We have a special interest in how well the theories might serve as guides for research and will therefore be concerned with the degree of precision and testability of the various hypotheses. Experimental approaches to the study of family interaction have seemed to us to have a special relevance for these new formulations, and we shall refer at a number of points to the methods and findings of experimental studies of patient families. We hope that this review of these theories and methods will permit a specification of particularly critical areas for further work.

It will be seen below that the several theories differ from each other in a number of important ways—from their descriptive terms to their assumptions about schizophrenia; in whether they focus on difficulties in communication or affective relationships; in the degree of their concern with social roles or personality dynamics. While we have tried to preserve the flavor and the essential conceptual concerns of each theory, our primary interest has been in comparing them with each other. This has been done by contrasting the answers that each gives to a minimum set of basic questions with which any serious and systematic theory of family process and schizophrenia must be concerned. Taken together, answers to these questions would permit a relatively complete account of the specific conditions under which schizophrenia develops. This paper is organized around this set of questions.[2]

1. What are the patterns of family interaction that are related to the development of schizophrenia?
2. What is schizophrenia, and what are the psychological mechanisms through which family patterns of interaction enter into the development of the schizophrenic process?
3. How do these interaction patterns persist over time, that is, what individual and family functions are served that help to maintain the schizogenic forms of interaction?
4. What are the preconditions for these patterns of interaction? That is, what are the social and personal attributes of family members that are associated with the development of these processes?

---

[2] Response to an earlier draft of the paper has called our attention to a special problem of comparative analysis of theories that are still in process of development. In brief, the theorists felt that we did not emphasize sufficiently the fact that their formulations were presented over a period of time and that their theories are not finished statements but theories "in process." We do not believe that there is a completely satisfactory solution to this problem since any attempt at analysis involves the use of standard dimensions for comparison and requires an assumption that a theory at any point in time is to be taken seriously as it is stated at that point in time. We have tried, however, to remain sensitive to what we see as the basic thrust and direction of each theory and to give primacy to the most current statements in our interpretations of their work. The reader is asked to bear in mind this historical and developmental aspect of the theories discussed.

Only the theories associated with Bateson, Lidz, and Wynne will be examined in detail. However, other formulations will be referred to at points in the discussion where they may provide further understanding of the various issues.

Before presenting detailed analyses in terms of the outline of critical questions listed above, it may be useful to the reader unfamiliar with one or another of the theories to have brief résumés of each of them in which the major concepts and special emphases may be seen in overall view.

Résumés of Theories

Bateson Group

The general theory of this group of investigators is often identified with the idea of the *double bind*. While this one concept does not do full justice to the complexity of the theory, it nevertheless mirrors in microcosm many of the latter's important aspects. The *double bind* is defined as a special type of learning context from which the growing child cannot escape; a context where he is subjected to incongruent messages that require him to deny important aspects of his self or his experience. The necessary ingredients are: repeated experience between two or more persons where one of them, i.e., the victim, is confronted with two incongruent negative injunctions, for example, "I order you to disobey me." Negative injunctions could be expressed in the affective quality of statements or be implicit in the situation of interaction as well as being expressed directly in verbal content. Punishment is expected to follow either choice in this conflict situation; a third negative injunction is present that prohibits the child from attempting to escape from the situation. Repeated exposure to such situations results in the individual's stripping his own messages of meaning since punishment can be avoided only by preventing the other person from understanding his response. Eventually, he behaves as if he had lost the ability to discriminate the true meanings of his own and others' messages, that is, he manifests schizophrenic behavior.

It is important to note that these hypotheses about schizophrenia derive from a proposed general model about human behavior where communication is viewed as equivalent to human behavior rather than as only one aspect among others. Further, there is a special focus in this theory on the equilibrium of the family state, that is, on the ways family members maintain stability in their communication with each other by developing rules governing who says what to whom in what contexts.

Originally, the theory was arrived at deductively, that is, by considering the nature of schizophrenic communication and "deducing" a set of requirements in the family that would lead to this form of pathological communication. Since that beginning, the formulation has developed through observations and analyses of family therapy sessions and, more recently, experimental studies of family behavior.

Lidz Group

While an explicit focus on the family as the unit of theoretical and empirical interest distinguishes this group's formulation, there is, nevertheless, a close resemblance to familiar psychodynamic traditions of theorizing about personality development and psychopathology. In many ways, this theory is a direct extension and application of orthodox psychoanalytic concepts to the family triad. There is a central concern with age-sex structure of the family. A critical etiological feature for schizophrenia lies for these theorists in the blurring of age and generation boundaries; parents behave inappropriately for their sex and age with respect both to each other and to their child and the child therefore learns inappropriate behavior. The consequence is that identity development for the child is distorted, and it is in the distortion of adequate identity development that the theory locates the psychological basis for schizophrenia. Empirically two types of schizogenic families are distinguished—one, organized around a central, dominating, pathological figure, usually the mother, and referred to as "skewed"; a second pattern of "schism" where the relationship is characterized by chronic hostility and mutual withdrawal. Different processes in the development of schizophrenia for males and females are postulated and related to the different problems of identity development in each of these types of families. The entire family is seen as pathological, and patterns of irrational thinking and unrealistic views of the outside world are taught to the developing child. Finally, the dramatic quality of family relationships is described more explicitly here than in the other theories; both murderous and incestuous wishes, reciprocated by parents, threaten to break out of control during adolescence and are seen to play an important part in the schizophrenic breakdown.

Empirical work of the Lidz group has centered on an extensive investigation of a small sample of hospitalized schizophrenic patients and their families; information has been gathered largely through diagnostic and therapeutic interviews.

Wynne Group

This theory is closer to that tradition in social psychological theory about socialization and personality development that gives prominence to the concept of an individual's identity as the link between the person and his culture. Within this general orientation, special attention is given to the impairment of ego functioning and its associated thought disorders in schizophrenia. In Wynne's formulation, an adequate identity and a healthy, well functioning ego require not only a stable and coherently meaningful environment but an opportunity to test out and to select as part of one's own individual identity a variety of roles during the course of development. The families of schizophrenics do not provide such a stable environment—in role structure they are either too rigid or too loosely and ambiguously structured, a lack of true complementarity is concealed under a façade of "pseudo-mutality," communication and interaction are disjointed and fragmented, irrational shifts in the focus of attention prevent real continuity of interaction. Pressures to maintain this façade and to deny or to avoid the recognition of the basic meaninglessness of the relationships force the child to conform to the family system; the imposition of sanctions isolates him effectively from other sources of socialization. There is a general guiding hypothesis that the thought disorder in schizophrenia derives from the disordered patterns of interaction in the family.

Observation of families in family therapy situations were the major source of early formulations. More recently, emphasis has shifted to the systematic analysis of both psychological test protocols and family interactions within a "predictive" research strategy, that is, an attempt to predict from parental characteristics to presence and type of schizophrenia in the child.

Interaction Patterns in Schizogenic Families

If social interaction is defined broadly to include consistent ways in which persons act toward and respond to each other, then each theory under review gives a central place to the influence of certain types of intrafamilial interaction on the development of schizophrenia. However, the theories also differ markedly from each other, at the general level of the aspect or dimension of interaction with which each is concerned, and specifically in the particular types of distortion of normal interaction that are seen as critical and distinctive in schizophrenogenic families. Their similarities and differences in these respects will be explored in this section.

The Bateson group's felicitous phrase, *the double bind,* has gained wide currency although its precise intended meaning seems not to be as well understood as its general usage would suggest. (See the comments by Watzlawick, 1963.) In part, its success as a term may reflect its surface relationship to the popular notion of a "bind" as a troubled and self-defeating interpersonal relationship. The difficulty is that a "bind" is a term with a vague referent rather than a precise definition of a particular type of relationship. If it is assimilated to this familiar and unclear concept, the new concept of the *double bind* loses both the formal precision that entered into its original formulation as well as its specific properties.

In their first comprehensive statement of a "communicational theory of the origin and nature of schizophrenia"—that is, a theory that centers the etiology of schizophrenia in parental communication to the child—Bateson and his co-workers (1956, pp. 253–254) specified the following necessary ingredients of a double bind situation: "1. Two or more persons. . . . 2. Repeated experience. . . . 3. A primary negative injunction. . . . 4. A secondary injunction conflicting with the first at a more abstract level, and like the first enforced by punishments or signals which threaten survival. . . . 5. A tertiary negative injunction prohibiting the victim from escaping from the field. . . ." These five elements exemplify in concrete form one of the ways in which the abstract idea of the double bind becomes manifest as a system of interaction.

In addition to this general formulation of a communication pattern consisting of conflicting injunctions, there is specification of three other features of the double bind that in this theory are necessary conditions for the development of schizophrenic reactions. In a sense, these are different types of "tertiary negative injunctions"—first, the fact of conflicting injunctions is denied; second, the child cannot escape from the situation; third, he is not permitted to "metacommunicate," that is, he can neither comment upon nor point to the contradictory nature of the communication. Of these "other features of the context" also to be mentioned, Bateson (1959, p. 133) states: ". . . there is, or appears to be, an absolute prohibition upon calling attention to the parents' incongruity in any overt way. . . . Neither the parents nor the patient is able to act as if fully aware of the incongruities. There is also a prohibition upon escaping from the field and, in addition, an insistence on the part of the parents that the patient respond. There shall be no non-responding and no not-caring and all these prohibitions are linked together. After all, to leave the field or to express 'not caring' would be to point the finger at the incongruities."

In the earlier paper (Bateson *et al.*, 1956, p. 259), he and his co-workers provide a good example of a double bind in describing a situation involving a schizophrenic patient and his mother:

> A young man who had fairly well recovered from an acute schizophrenic episode was visited in the hospital by his mother. He was glad to see her and impulsively put his arm around her shoulders, whereupon she stiffened. He withdrew his arm, and she asked, "Don't you love me any more?" He then blushed, and she said, "Dear, you must not be so easily embarrassed and afraid of your feelings."

The mother's communication includes conflicting sets of messages, putting her son in an impossible dilemma: "If I am to keep my tie to mother I must not show her that I love her, but if I do not show her that I love her, then I will lose her."

This is a "damned if you do and damned if you don't" situation for the child, who is trapped by the incongruent demands and forbidden to call attention to his predicament. Such a patient is, to apply here a statement made elsewhere by Bateson (1960, p. 477f), "faced with the dilemma either of being wrong in the primary context or of being right for the wrong reasons or in the wrong way. This is the so-called double bind. We are investigating the hypothesis that schizophrenic communication is learned and becomes habitual as a result of continual traumata of this kind."

The idea of incongruity is pervasive in the writings of members of this group of investigators. It is defined by example and implication and refers essentially to the lack of consistency between different aspects, levels, or elements of a message. Incongruity in communication may take any of a variety of forms. For example, the affect conveyed by tone of voice may differ from the literal meaning of the words, as in sarcasm or in joking hostility; the message may be inappropriate to its context, as in gallows humor; or the gestures may contradict the verbal content, as in the previous example of a double-bind situation between a patient and his mother; incongruity may result from denying or negating any of the elements of a message.

Such incongruities are involved in many forms of human discourse including humor and poetic metaphor. The problem lies with those special types of incongruity, i.e., double binds, where the individual is threatened with punishment whichever aspect of the incongruent message he chooses to respond to and where there is the underlying "prohibition upon comment." Bateson and his group generalize their views by referring them to Russell's theory of logical types where basic paradoxes are explored that result from the proposition that a class cannot be a member of itself.[3] If we understand them correctly, they are suggesting that

---

[3] Historically, interest in Russell's theory of logical types preceded work on schizophrenia; the schizophrenic was seen as a person who manifested special difficulties in the classification of messages. The original article on the theory of schizophrenia was ". . . a product of deduc-

the analogue to resolving logical paradoxes, by recognizing that two different levels of abstraction are involved, is the act of metacommunicating or commenting upon the incongruity between parts of a message. Where this last is forbidden, the incongruency cannot be resolved and the person receiving the messages remains trapped.

As a formal statement of relationships among levels of meaning, the double-bind hypothesis and its associated ideas is viewed as applicable to all types of social and cultural systems. (See, for example, the comments on cultures caught in double binds in Bateson, 1959.) However, within the narrow frame of family interaction the hypothesis as originally stated focused attention primarily on dyadic interaction, particularly between mother and child, in the etiology of schizophrenia—with the emphasis placed on the problems faced by the growing child "caught" in the double bind. More recently, there has been increased emphasis on the active role of the "victim" in maintaining this system.

While he uses the same basic paradigm of the double bind and its insoluble paradoxes, Haley (1963), in further developing the original formulation, gives more emphasis to the whole family unit as an interacting system. In so doing he suggests some of the parameters of a social system within which double binds may be adaptive responses. He points to the importance of the struggle for power and control in these families and suggests that a primary issue in all human relationships has to do with "who" is going to set the rules for the relationship. He defines the family as a self-corrective social system in which behavior is governed, regulated, and patterned by internal processes where family members set limits to each other's behavior. Haley (1963, p. 160) stresses the need for complex models of such systems, since ". . . two levels of governing processes must be included: (a) the error-activated response by a member if any member exceeds a certain range of behavior, and (b) the attempt by family members to be the metagovernor, i.e., the one who sets the limits of that range."

As in all families, members of schizogenic families govern each other's behavior by imposing sanctions and other correctives when their rules and prohibitions are violated. The difference in these families, according to Haley, lies in the collective denial that anyone is setting the rules, that is, that anyone is the metagovernor. In this respect he notes:

> Typically in these families the mother tends to initiate what happens, while indicating either that she isn't, or that someone else should. The father will invite her to initiate what happens while condemning her when she does. Often they suggest the child take the lead, and then disqualify his attempts. . . . The family "just happens" to take actions in particular directions with no individual accepting the label as the one responsible for any action (Haley, 1959, p. 366). . . . The family of the schizophrenic would seem to be not only establishing and following a system of rules, as other families do, but also following a prohibition on any acknowledgment that a family member is setting rules. Each refuses to concede that he is circumscribing the behavior

---

tion more than of observation, for we had hardly looked at the families of schizophrenics. It was hypothesized that given a learning organism which communicates like this then this sort of learning context (i.e., one involving conflicts in levels of communication) would have led to his communicating like this" (Jay Haley, personal communication).

of others, and each refuses to concede that any other family member is governing him (Haley, 1959, p. 372).

Haley points out that the act of communicating inherently involves defining one's relationship with the other person; that is, to communicate is to set rules at some level with regard to the nature of the behavior that is to take place in the relationship. Within schizogenic families, the members attempt to avoid defining their relationships to each other by negating or disqualifying any or all elements of their messages. These elements are listed as: "(1) I (2) am saying something (3) to you (4) in this situation" (Haley, 1959a, p. 325). A person may deny that he is the person speaking, may contradict one message with another, may refuse to acknowledge whom he is addressing. For example, Haley describes the husband whose wife asks him to do the dishes, responding with: "I would like to do the dishes, but I can't. I have a headache." By this response, the husband indicates that *he* is not defining the relationship by this refusal; after all it was the headache which prevented the dishwashing, not he. In a sense, these different ways of denying elements of a message appear to be varieties of double binds. Haley seems to be suggesting that the double bind is an adaptive response in a family whose members refuse to acknowledge that they are setting rules for each other's behavior, and as a consequence interaction is oriented toward denying any responsibility for the nature of their relationships.

Among other theorists concerned with the etiological role of family interaction processes in the development of schizophrenia, both Searles and Laing have described mechanisms that emphasize types of incongruity similar to those described in the Bateson-Haley formulations. Searles (1959) outlines six "modes of driving the other person crazy," each of which tends to activate various areas of the person's personality in opposition to each other. These modes are: pointing out areas of the other's personality, of which he may be unaware, that are inconsistent with his ideal or actual self-image; stimulating the person sexually in settings where attempts at gratification would be disastrous; simultaneous or rapidly alternating stimulation and frustration; relating to the other simultaneously on two unrelated levels, for example, sexual advances during an intellectual-political discussion; switching erratically from one emotional wavelength to the other while discussing the same topic; switching topics while maintaining the same emotional wavelength, for example, discussing life and death issues in the same manner as trivial happenings.

While each of these is a concrete example of a pair of conflicting messages and therefore stands as an instance of that one ingredient of the double bind, Searles' treatment of the "binding" nature of these interactions focuses on the mutual satisfaction of needs rather than on the formal structure of the interaction.

Laing discusses "confirmation" of the self as a process through which individuals are recognized, acknowledged, "endorsed" by others—"the crux seems to be that it is a response by the other that is *relevant* to the evocative action, . . . a direct response, in the sense at least of being 'to the point,' or 'on the same beam' or 'wavelength' as the first person's initiatory or evocatory action" (Laing, 1961, p. 89). His discussion of the lack of true confirmation in the families of schizophrenics bears obvious similarities to the general idea of the double bind, but differs in the stress Laing places on the experiencing self as the object of the incongruous act. Thus, ". . . there is minimal genuine confirmation of the parents by each other and of the child by each parent, separately or together, but there may not be obvious disconfirmation. One finds, rather, interactions marked by pseudoconfirmation, by acts which masquerade as confirming actions but are counterfeit . . . the schizogenic potential of the situation seems to reside largely in the fact that it is not recognized by anyone; or, . . . this knowledge is not brought out into the open" (Laing, 1961, p. 91). This tangential failure to "endorse" the other's experience is evident in the incident reported by Laing (1961, p. 93) where a little boy runs to his mother with a worm in his hand and says, "Mummy, look what a big fat worm I have got." To which the mother responds, "You are filthy. Away and clean yourself immediately."

There are several problems that deserve brief mention in concluding this summary of the Bateson group's formulation of critical interaction processes in the families of schizophrenics. First, there is a lack of precision and clarity in their writings that presents serious difficulties for an accurate understanding of the types of interaction sequences that do and do not fall within the definition of the double bind. From the way the concept is used, it sometimes appears that all communication sequences may be interpretable, at some level of analysis, as double binds, and, if this be so, the concept loses all usefulness. This ambiguity regarding the generality of the concept also obscures its specific relationship to related formulations. For example, the relations between the original double-bind hypothesis and Haley's later analyses of family rules has not been made explicit and remains unclear.

Two important problems do not receive attention in the writings of this group. One is that, in emphasizing the structure of communicative acts, the possibility is ignored that the critical influence of the double bind may reflect the substantive nature of the conflict presented. For example, if the conflict embodies deep and important intrapsychic conflicts (perhaps love vs. hate, or dependence vs. autonomy) or centers around significant family norms, then this may be more important than if the conflict concerns more trivial issues. Laing (1961, p. 90) makes the same point: "It may be that there are some areas of a person's being for which there is a more crying need for confirmation than others. It may be that there are some forms of disconfirmation which may be more actively destructive of the person's developing sense of himself than others, and which could therefore be schizogenic." However, this view is not shared by the Bateson group. Jackson writes that they "have not been impressed" by the need to include content in their analysis since they find a particular style of interaction manifesting itself irrespective of the content discussed. "The act itself alerts the participants that there is conflict and in itself constitutes a kind of psychological trauma, whatever the substantive issue."[4]

Second, there is the question of whose perspective is being used in determining the presence of incongruency or of disqualification. While the theory appears to refer to the perspectives of participants in the interaction, case materials and interpretations tend to reflect observers' viewpoints as to what are considered congruent or incongruent messages. This is a difficult problem for research and analysis, since messages an observer judges to be incongruent with reference to

[4] Don D. Jackson, personal communication.

general external standards may carry with them implicit meanings, developed in the culture of that particular family, that makes the messages congruent to the family members. While either the internal or external perspective could provide useful bases for interpretation, the differences between them are of critical importance and criteria for making the appropriate judgment require a more explicit statement than they have so far received.

There are many contrasts between the Bateson group's formulation and that of Lidz and his co-workers to whom we now turn. One of the most noticeable differences is the less formal and less abstract quality of the latter's statements; there is marked emphasis on the content of the pressures and conflicts as well as on their structure. Also, the point of reference of the theory shifts away from the level of communicative acts to the level of interpersonal role relationships.

The age and sex axes of role differentiation have a critical place in the Lidz analyses of different types of schizogenic families, and specific distortions in what they consider to be normal parent-child role relationships play a key role in their interpretations of the development of schizophrenia. The influence of Talcott Parsons' sociological formulation of family role structure is explicitly acknowledged. Thus, Lidz (1963, p. 53) writes that there are certain "requisites" for a marital relationship if it is to provide for the harmonious development of its offspring: "What appears to be essential can be stated simply. . . . The spouses need to form a coalition as members of the parental generation maintaining their respective gender-linked roles, and be capable of transmitting instrumentally useful ways of adaptation suited to the society in which they live."

This ideal model of a normal family, implied in the above quotation, pervades much of the work of these investigators. They find two deviant types of marital relationships in the family backgrounds of schizophrenic patients, one of which appears empirically to be associated with schizophrenia in female children and the other in male children. In the first pattern, designated as *marital schism*, there is a "state of severe chronic disequilibrium and discord . . . [and] recurrent threats of separation. . . . Communication consists primarily of coercive efforts and defiance or of efforts to mask the defiance to avoid fighting. There is little or no sharing of problems or satisfactions. . . . [There is] chronic 'undercutting' of the worth of one partner to the children by the other. The tendency to compete for the children's loyalty and affection is prominent. . . . Absence of any positive satisfaction from the marital relationship (excluding the children) is striking. . . . Mutual distrust of motivations is the rule . . ." (Lidz *et al.*, 1957a, p. 244). In the second pattern, called *marital skew*, the couples achieve a state of relative equilibrium in which the continuation of the marriage is not constantly threatened. However, ". . . family life was distorted by a skew in the marital relationship . . . the rather serious psychopathology of one marital partner dominated the home" (Lidz *et al.*, 1957a, p. 246).

Their emphasis on the concrete substance of underlying conflicts, and on the strength of both the hostile and seductive elements in the situation, has led this group to explore the different implications for the development of schizophrenia of these two types of pathogenic marital relationships. They find that schizophrenic girls are more likely to have had a "schismatic" background; each parent in this open conflict situation seeks the support of the daughter. The boys with schizophrenia, on the other hand, are more likely to come from "skewed" situations which tend to have dominant mothers and passive fathers.

In neither of these types of marital relationship is there true "role reciprocity" which Lidz and his group see as one of the requisites for a successful marriage. They note (Lidz *et al.*, 1957a, p. 243) that ". . . role reciprocity requires common understanding and acceptance of each other's roles, goals, and motivation, and a reasonable sharing of cultural value orientations." This lack of role reciprocity is associated with distortions in role-appropriate behaviors for the different age-sex groups within the family. Thus distinctions between the generations are not observed, the normal parental coalition is not maintained, and children become involved in the parental conflicts, with each parent competing for the child's support.

A schismatic family that includes many of these elements is thus described by Lidz:

> Mr. Nussbaum remained away from home as much as possible, and turned to his daughter [the patient] for the affection and admiration he could not gain from his wife. At times, he seemed to be spiting his wife by the alliance with the girl. He became very seductive toward the daughter, sleeping with her when she became anxious at night, and cuddling her to sleep until she began, during adolescence, to express fears of becoming pregnant. The child's problems became a major concern to both parents, but also a source of mutual recrimination. The mother sought to devote herself to her daughter's care when she became increasingly difficult during adolescence, but would lose patience and go into rages in which she would tell the girl that she wished she were dead. The mother, fairly typically, lacked empathy for her daughter, and because of her inconsistent behavior and the father's devaluation of her formed an unacceptable model, while the father seductively substituted the daughter for his wife. Thus the patient was at times a scapegoat and at other times a divisive influence (Lidz *et al.*, 1963, p. 10).

Lidz attaches much significance to the notion of role reciprocity, but it is not given a more precise definition than that implied in the quotation in the preceding paragraph. While Spiegel's (1959) analysis of family equilibrium and disequilibrium in terms of complementary role expectations is referred to as an explicit source, there are some differences in Lidz's use of the concept and some special problems associated with these differences. First, his idea of role-appropriate behavior involves the use of an assumed model of normatively correct family role behavior. Spiegel's original formulation leaves room for much interfamilial as well as subcultural variation in role expectations; Lidz, on the other hand, tends to neglect these variant patterns. Spiegel also provides for the possibility that strain and tendencies toward disequilibrium may exist with complementary role expectations, whereas equilibrium and role reciprocity appear to be viewed as synonymous in Lidz's formulation.

Associated with the general blurring of sex-generation roles in the families of schizophrenics is a preoccupation with and anxiety about incestuous feelings and behavior. "In our studies, we have noted the central moment of incestuous impulses, and our studies of their families revealed that these were not simply regressive symptoms of the patient, but that one or both parents was also caught in incestuous ties to the patient. . . . There is a reciprocity to these impulses of the patient that provokes panic lest loss of their own self control might lead to actual incest" (Lidz, 1963, p. 72).

These types of interpersonal relationships are viewed as "abnormal" family environments in which it is difficult for children to learn and behave in ways appropriate to their age and sex during the course of development. As a further consequence, these relationships predispose toward irrationality and distortions in thinking. Lidz (1963, p. 96) has described it as ". . . a strange family milieu filled with inconsistencies, contradictory meanings, and denial of what should be obvious. Facts are constantly being altered to suit emotionally determined needs. The children . . . learn that meanings are not primarily in the service of reality testing. . . . The acceptance of mutually contradictory experiences requires parological thinking. Such environments provide training in irrationality." Lidz (1963, p. 101) also points to a tendency for these families to be isolated from their social and cultural environments, noting for example, ". . . that the patients were habitually exposed to conflicts and meanings deviant from the shared communicative meanings of the culture. . . ." Opportunities for reality testing that would be provided by more contact with the normal world outside the family are restricted, and internal irrational patterns in the family are further reinforced.

Generally speaking, this formulation has both the flavor and vocabulary of traditional psychoanalytic theory—but as applied to the family rather than the individual as the unit of description and analysis. For example, as we shall see below, incestuous and hostile wishes, as well as difficulties in the successful resolution of the Oedipal situation figure prominently in their analyses of why these particular family patterns appear to be conducive to schizophrenia. This psychoanalytic toning of the theory is also evident in their treatment of social roles. While there is frequent reference to the concept of social role and to the notion of the family as a social system, the real dynamic sources of interaction in this theory lie in the personality structures of the individuals. Thus, the difficulties in establishing a harmonious marital relationship with true role reciprocity are attributed to the psychological problems brought to the marriage by husband and wife. Further, while pathogenic family backgrounds are described by such system terms as schism and skew, these family types appear empirically to be related to different types of parental personalities—a cold, punitive mother with a seductive father in the former; a dominant, seductive mother and a passive father in the latter. In attempting to predict the likelihood of a schizophrenic outcome, it appears that we have to depend on an understanding of the psychodynamics of the parents; to the extent that this is necessary, the analysis of the family as a social system is superfluous.

Unfortunately, there is much vagueness and ambiguity in Lidz's use of the social role concept. Sometimes, particularly in the early papers, it refers simply to stable ways of interacting that reflect personality, such as the "dominant mother" role. At other times, roles are normatively defined modes of "appropriate" behavior, that is, differentially appropriate for specified age and sex categories. In general, the complicated relationships between personality, role, and interaction are not specified; at times they appear to be used as different names for the same thing.

In general, Lidz's formulations are weakest when considered critically from the point of view of evaluating his theory as a set of coherent and rigorously defined concepts and abstract propositions. Concepts are borrowed from sociology, psychoanalysis, and theories of language development; these concepts have not yet been welded together into a unified system. On the other hand, the strength of this group's approach lies in their emphasis on those powerful concrete parameters of family life, namely, the differentiating axes of age and sex. This has been associated with their discovery of different types of family structures in the developmental histories of male and female schizophrenics; such distinctions are not made systematically by other investigators.

The theory of schizophrenic development proposed by Bowen and Brodey deserves mention at this point, since it has marked similarity to that of Lidz as well as an important difference in the conception of family roles. The similarity is evident in such things as the description by Bowen and Brodey of their study families as having marked conflict, "emotional divorce" between the parents, an overadequate mother with a peripherally attached father (Bowen, 1959, 1960)—a pattern closely resembling Lidz's schismatic group. There is also an emphasis on the psychodynamic sources of the marital role relationships. The difference lies in the etiological significance attributed by Bowen and Brodey to the structure of the role relationships rather than to its content. The important factor for them is the extremity and rigidity of the role structure. The tendency in these families as they describe them is for the roles to become polarized, for example, for an omnipotent-helpless polarity to develop (Brodey, 1959). Behavior is then molded into conformity with these extreme and stereotyped role definitions. While a high degree of rigidity in role structure is evident in the case descriptions given by Lidz, this feature does not enter into their formulations as a significant variable. As with Lidz, there is some difficulty with the Bowen-Brodey formulations in separating personality pathology in the parents from the pattern of role polarization as etiological influences in the development of schizophrenia.

Wynne and his co-investigators at the National Institute of Mental Health are also concerned primarily with the quality and structure of role relationships within the family, rather than with the particular content of these relationships. Their emphasis is on the family system as the unit of conceptualization rather than on dyadic or triadic relationships within the family. Thus, their objective is to develop an interpretation of schizophrenia "that takes into conceptual account the social organization of the family as a whole" (Wynne et al., 1958, p. 205). The rationale for this approach, stated in an early paper, is made explicit in the general hypothesis underlying their work: "The fragmentation of experience, the identity diffusion, the disturbed modes of perception and communication, and certain other characteristics of the acute reactive schizophrenic personality structure are to a significant extent derived, by processes of internalization, from characteristics of the family social organization, . . . also internalized are the ways of thinking and of deriving meaning, the points of anxiety, and the irrationality, confusion, and ambiguities that were expressed in the shared mechanism of the family social organization" (Wynne et al., 1958, p. 215).

The definition of schizophrenia and the psychological mechanisms involved, that are implicit in the above statement of rationale, will be examined in later sections of this paper. At this point we wish to review the specific properties of family social organization that are thought to be significant by the NIMH group.

In a number of papers dealing with the relationships between schizophrenic thinking disorders and family transactions, Wynne and Singer have described what they believe to be the main features differentiating the families of young adult schizophrenics from other families. They note that these are the features that "work" empirically in the sense that they permit predictions of whether and what type of schizophrenia is present in the offspring on the basis of information about parental patterns of behavior and cognition. A recent statement refers to the four main features of these families as follows:

> . . . first and foremost, *patterns of handling attention and meaning* [that interfere with the child's capacity for selective attention and purposive behavior]; second, styles of relating, *especially erratic and inappropriate kinds of distance and closeness;* third, *underlying feelings of pervasive meaninglessness, pointlessness and emptiness;* and fourth, an *overall structure of the family* in which members have collusively joined together in shared maneuvers which deny or re-interpret the reality or existence of anxiety-provoking feelings and events. These shared maneuvers, including what has been called pseudo-mutuality and pseudo-hostility, tend to encompass the experience of the growing child and cut off or render anxiety-laden, experiences with peers and the broader culture. This kind of family structuring, previously described as the "rubber fence" phenomenon, reduces or negates the corrective influence which extra-familial contacts could otherwise have and heightens the impact of the disturbed intra-familial environment (Wynne and Singer, 1964, p. 10).

Major attention has been given in their recent work to the first of the four features—patterns of handling attention and meaning in the family. The "transactional thought disorders" in schizophrenic families are evident in communications that are fragmented, blurred, poorly integrated, and disjunctive. The assumption here is that these "familial transactions and maneuvers would be especially likely to disrupt and impair the development of an offspring's capacity to focus attention and to think sequentially and adaptively" (Singer and Wynne, 1965).

Transactional thought disorders, represented in the communication and the interaction of the whole family, are classified along the same amorphous-fragmented continuum as are individual thought disorders. Amorphous patterns of interaction in these families are exemplified by vague drifting of a discussion through shifts in the object of attention, blurring of meaning by using uncertain referents, and irrelevant meanings. Singer and Wynne (1965) describe an amorphous response to a TAT story given by the parent of a schizophrenic that might be considered an example of how this parent interacts with his child: "A father began a story about a young boy wanting to go out with his friends instead of practicing his violin. He was reminded of a movie about an older fellow who went joy-riding with his friends. After a lengthy, aimless story, he concluded: 'And so, into the sunset.'" Fragmented patterns of interaction and communication consist of such characteristics as intrusion of primary process, using odd vantage points for communications, such as peculiar spatial or temporal positions, and crypticness; each of these modes of communication results in poorly integrated messages. For example, one parent's complete response to a Rorschach card was, "If you read stories of Cossacks, that's self-explanatory."

These styles of communicating meaning are assumed to be characteristic of the family as a whole, not simply the thought patterns of one parent. Further, it is hypothesized that these ". . . styles of attending, perceiving, thinking, communicating and relating used in family transactions are likely to have promoted the cognitive development of the offspring in certain directions, either by serving as models for identification or by eliciting complementary behaviors" (Singer and Wynne, 1965).

The second general feature of the schizophrenic family included in the summary listing given above has to do with styles of relating, especially with erratic and inappropriate kinds of distance and closeness. Here the maintenance of proper distance refers both to cognitive and affective functions, both to distance from people and distance from ideas or objects. Schizophrenic family patterns seem to be characterized by "fluctuating and variable cognitive sets and relational distances. . . . The distance taken is often inappropriately close or remote and when an alteration in 'focal distance' is made, which in normals occurs smoothly and unnoticed, it is disjunctive and awkward" (Singer and Wynne, 1965). For example, the mother of a schizophrenic child related to the psychologist in much the same way she probably related to her child. "[She] limited herself to describing the Rorschach cards as symmetrical, and as 'reproductions,' [and] seemed remote both from the card and the tester. Suddenly she asked the tester what brand of lipstick she was wearing" (Singer and Wynne, 1965). These shifts in affect and style of relating make for confused expectations in the child and provide odd and fragmented models for identification.

These modes for handling meaning and the styles of relating, in Wynne's theory, seem to serve as defenses against underlying feelings of pervasive meaninglessness, pointlessness and emptiness. Feelings of meaninglessness are defined as subjective states, "in which purposes, wishes, aspirations, interpersonal relationships, work, and other activity are felt by the person himself to be without point, without direction, without leading to decisive satisfaction or dissatisfaction, to clear success or defeat, to genuine mutuality or total alienation or separation."[5] These feelings are not continuously present and manifest to family members but rather are similar to repressed or unconscious material in the sense that family members attempt to defend themselves against their recognition.

Finally, the overall structure of the schizophrenic family is characterized by shared maneuvers that serve to deny or reinterpret the reality of anxiety-provoking feelings, and apparently, of the underlying meaninglessness of the relationships. Wynne uses the concepts of pseudo-mutuality and pseudo-hostility to describe these structural patterns. Pseudo-mutuality is defined by contrasting it both with mutuality or a relationship of true complementarity, and with non-mutuality or a situation without reciprocal obligations. Complementarity is lacking in pseudo-mutual relationship, but the façade of mutuality is maintained

---

[5] Lyman Wynne, personal communication.

energetically: ". . . in describing pseudo-mutuality, we are emphasizing a predominant absorption in fitting together, at the expense of the differentiation of the identities of the persons in the relation. . . . In pseudo-mutuality emotional investment is directed more toward maintaining the *sense* of reciprocal fulfillment of expectations than toward accurately perceiving changing expectations" (Wynne *et al.*, 1958, p. 207).

In illustration, Wynne quotes one mother whose desperate preoccupation with harmony at all costs is obvious. "We are all peaceful. I like peace even if I have to kill someone to get it. . . . A more normal, happy kid would be hard to find. I was pleased with my child! I was pleased with my husband! I was pleased with my life. I have *always* been pleased. We have had twenty-five years of the happiest married life and of being a father and mother" (Wynne *et al.*, 1958, p. 211).

The negative counterpart of pseudo-mutuality is pseudo-hostility. It differs from the former in defining a state of chronic conflict and alienation among family members, but this difference is seen as unimportant and superficial. What is important is that both states are fixed, rigid, and "pseudo." Both are viewed as collective defenses, permitting family members to maintain some semblance of a life together without having to confront directly the essential and pervasive "meaninglessness" of their life as well as their underlying fears of separation, hostility, tenderness, or intimacy.

These qualities of family relationship are associated with family role structures that are either rigid and stereotyped or loosely and ambiguously structured. The specific type of structure, whether rigid or ambiguous, may be associated with the specific subtype of schizophrenia developed (a point to which we shall return), but either structure creates difficulties for the development of appropriate personality-role and role-role relationships. The sources of these difficulties are as follows: Deviation is not permitted from prescribed and simple "formulas" for behaving; distinctions are not made between the person and his role. This "blurring" of boundaries between individual and role results in the family's being experienced by the developing child as all-encompassing of the self; there is no identity separate from one's role within the family.

A number of mechanisms are described through which deviations from the family's rigid role structure are either excluded from recognition or reinterpreted, thus preserving the illusion of harmony and mutuality. Among these are family myths and legends that stress the catastrophic consequences of divergence from the rigidly-defined roles; a bland and indiscriminate approval of each other's actions preserving a façade of harmony and peace; the denial of contradictions in one's own or others' behavior; a stress on secrecy and a concomitant concern with prying into other persons' private experiences; and, a formalization or ritualization of normal family experiences. Reinforcing these processes is the lack of adequate articulation between the family and the larger social system —so that ". . . family members try to act as if the family could be a truly self-sufficient social system with a completely encircling boundary" (Wynne *et al.*, 1958, p. 211). This "continuous but elastic" boundary is referred to as a "rubber fence."

In his attempt to characterize the patterns of interaction in these families, Wynne employs concepts at several different levels of analysis. Thus, the structure of role relationships is described as falling along a continuum from rigidity to amorphousness, the affective quality of relationships varies from pseudo-mutual to pseudo-hostile or fluctuates from close to distant, and interpersonal communication shows degrees of fragmentation or amorphousness. Further, the structure of role relationships is seen as a collective defense against recognizing the underlying "meaninglessness" of the relationship. The strategy of research and theory formation seems to be to view each of these as independent dimensions and to determine whether and how they are empirically associated with each other. Thus, no *a priori* claim is made that pseudo-mutuality is theoretically required by rigid roles, or that fragmentation is a function of pseudo-mutuality. Rather than deriving the connections among these different levels from systematic theory, the aim is to accumulate relevant data and work toward empirical generalizations of the conditions under which these different patterns are found together.

The preceding review of how these different theories approach the problem of schizophrenia suggests some of the difficulties of comparing them to each other in a systematic way. While they share an emphasis on family interaction, the conceptual foci vary markedly as do the particular dimensions of interaction they isolate as significant. It is tempting—but we believe deceptive and not particularly useful—to consider double binds as illustrative of fragmented communication, or pseudo-mutuality as the affective quality of a skewed marital relationship. The formulations differ from each other in more serious and significant ways than in the labels they apply to phenomena. They point to different phenomena, and these differences merit clarification before an attempt is made to reduce them to one comprehensive theory.

Some of these differences will become more evident in the following sections, but a few may be noted here. First there is the question of conceptual focus—of how "sociological," "psychological," or "interactional" the different theories are. It seems to us that Wynne and Haley in focusing on family roles and norms are most sociological in their analysis. Lidz's use of role terms, as we have noted before, is not systematic and his primary emphasis on personality and motive places him at the psychological pole of theorizing. Bateson is concerned neither with roles nor motives but with a different unit of analysis entirely, namely, the communicative act. Both Haley and Wynne, of course, are also interested in communication but always within its context of the role structure. These varied conceptual foci permit the different theories to avoid direct confrontation at a theoretical level. Empirical comparison of the theories with each other is, for this reason, an extremely difficult and complex problem.

A further point of difference refers to the concrete relationship that the theories tend to focus upon. Bateson's use of the double bind in its specific application to schizophrenia is dyadic in emphasis; for example, one of the stated essential ingredients is two persons. One consequence is that the family tends to be viewed as consisting of a set of dyadic relationships. In Lidz, the stress is also on the dyad, in this instance the marital relationship; however, it is a dyadic relationship that has an effect on a third person, that is, the developing child. Finally, in Wynne and Haley, the concepts refer to the whole family as the unit for analysis and theory without concern for any specific role player or players.

Both of these points on the different emphases of the several theories must be qualified by noting that over time each theory has tended to become more comprehensive and more eclectic. Wynne's view has already been referred to regarding the independence of the different levels—role, interaction, and psychological functioning. Lidz, for whom ". . . every area of interaction in these families was found to be faulty in some respect . . ." (Lidz and Fleck, 1964, p. 4) views each separate area of deficiency or failure—parental nurturance, appropriate role structure, and the transmission of culturally instrumental techniques—as related to a specific problem in development. And he suggests that the severity of the illness may be related to how extreme and generalized the deficiencies are. In Bateson's formulation, the distinctions between levels are erased through the use of the highly abstract model of communicative behavior as a general framework for describing all behavior.

Since each of the theories is concerned with the same basic phenomena, this "strain toward comprehensiveness" gives recent statements of the Wynne, Lidz, and Bateson groups a stronger appearance of similarity than was evident in early statements. However, it has seemed to us that the differences in emphasis outlined in this section, and detailed further in the following ones, remain and are important determinants of both the research and theoretical directions still being pursued by the different groups.

The Schizophrenic Process

The distinctive feature of the theories we have been discussing lies in their emphasis on the critical role in the development of schizophrenia played by particular interaction patterns and family role relationships. In this section we shall be concerned with the accounts given by each of the theories about the ways in which this family environment leads to schizophrenia in the child. Several different questions are involved, and the theories vary in the degree of explicitness and detail with which they attempt to answer them. How is schizophrenia defined? What are the psychological mechanisms through which a person becomes schizophrenic? What distinguishes the prepsychotic schizophrenic personality structure from the psychotic schizophrenic? What are the precipitating events for a psychotic breakdown?

In discussing "overt" schizophrenia or the "identified" schizophrenic in the family (thus distinguishing this from the endemic "covert" schizophrenia in these families), Bateson (1960, p. 487) states:

> The more serious and conspicuous degree of symptomatology is what is conventionally called schizophrenic. . . . [They] behave in ways which are grossly deviant from the cultural environment . . . characterized by conspicuous or exaggerated errors and distortions regarding the nature and typing of their own messages (internal and external) and the messages which they receive from others. . . . In general, these distortions boil down to this: that the patient behaves in such a way that he shall be responsible for no metacommunicative aspects of his messages. He does this, moreover, in a manner which makes his behavior conspicuous.

Elsewhere (Bateson, 1959, pp. 133–134) the typical schizophrenic message is described as a "stripping of all explicit or implicit metacommunicative material . . ." and the "boundary of sanity is, however, crossed when the subject uses these tricks of communication in situations which the common man—one hesitates to say the 'normal'—would not perceive as the schizophrenic seems to perceive them."

For Bateson, distinguishing between "overt" and "covert" schizophrenia is an explicit problem, because the ways in which schizophrenic patients communicate appear (in terms of his theory) to be only exaggerations of forms of communication that are pervasive in their families. On the whole, while he is not clear on this matter, Bateson would appear to make the distinction between overt and covert schizophrenia a function of the severity and extent of these forms of communication. The identified schizophrenic behaves this way "conspicuously" and in "normal" situations; the other members of his family are more selective and restrained.

Bateson's views about schizophrenia as an "illness" are outlined in his introduction to an autobiographical account of a schizophrenic psychosis, *Perceval's Narrative* (1961). In a sense, he turns the whole question of illness on its head —by proposing that the symptoms of schizophrenia are adaptive responses of an individual to an underlying illness, in much the same way that fevers and other somatic symptoms are recognized in medicine today as the body's response to primary pathology. While he does not explicitly connect these observations with his other views on the role of the overt schizophrenic within the family, it appears as if the "pathology" to which the psychosis is a response refers to the distorted patterns of family relationships. In this context, the schizophrenic psychosis is conceived to have a potentially curative function and a normal course that may end with the remission of symptoms, a course that may be aided or hindered by the forms of therapeutic intervention attempted. As he has stated in the introduction referred to (Perceval, 1961):

> [This is] . . . one of the most interesting characteristics of the strange condition known as schizophrenia: that the disease, if it be one, seems sometimes to have curative properties . . . we are today familiar with the fact that many of the so-called symptoms of organic disease are the efforts that the body makes to correct some deeper pathology. . . . The dynamics of the curative nightmare are, however, quite obscure. It is one thing to see the symptom as a part of a defense mechanism; it is quite another to conceive that the body or the mind contains, in some form, such wisdom that it can create that *attack* upon itself that will lead to a later resolution of the pathology (pp. xi–xii). . . . Once precipitated into psychosis the patient has a course to run. . . . Once begun, a schizophrenic episode would appear to have as definite a course as an initiation ceremony—a death and rebirth—into which the novice may have been precipitated by his family or by adventitious circumstances, but which in its course is largely steered by endogenous process (p. xiv).

Haley approaches the problem of defining the nature of schizophrenia within the context of an attempt to develop an interactional description of schizophrenia, in contrast to either the classic psychiatric or psychodynamic approaches. Expanding upon a basic theme that persons cannot avoid dealing with the problems of the definition and control of their relationships with others (since all communication presupposes rules about "who" is permitted to say "what" to "whom," "when," and "where"), Haley proposes that there is, however, one way by which a person can avoid defining a relationship and that way is by negating or disqualifying his communications. It is not easy to "strip" one's messages of their metacommunicative meanings; Haley suggests that it requires various types of denial and distortion of one's responsibility for messages. He notes:

> When everything a person says to another person defines the relationship with that person, he can avoid indicating what sort of relationship he is in only by denying that he is speaking, denying that anything is said, denying that it is said to the other person, or denying that the interchange is occurring in this place at this time. . . . It seems apparent that the list of ways to avoid defining a relationship is a list of schizophrenic symptoms. . . . The various and seemingly unconnected and bizarre symptoms of schizophrenia can be seen to have a central and rather simple nucleus. If one is determined to avoid defining his relationship, he can do so only by behaving in those ways which are describable as symptoms of schizophrenia. . . . The differences from the normal lie in the consistency of the schizophrenic's behavior and the extremes to which he goes (Haley, 1959a, pp. 326–327).

Thus, schizophrenic behavior is viewed both as purposeful, in that the individual is attempting through his behavior to avoid committing himself to a particular definition of his relationships with others, and as unavoidable, since the only solution open to someone caught in a double bind is to respond in kind. In the end he gives up the attempt to discriminate meanings in the messages of others and attempts only to ensure that others will not find "meaning" in his own messages. It is not clear whether Bateson, Haley, and others in this group view the schizophrenic patient as having lost the capacity to discriminate or whether it is simply that he ceases to respond in terms of normally discriminated meanings. Their descriptions focus on his behavior rather than on his internal states. His behavior is "learned" in the sense that all human communicative behavior is learned. The learning context, however, is the rather special one where he is punished by withdrawal of love, abandonment, or hostility for alternative and more adequate responses to the double bind.

Haley considers the overt psychotic phase of schizophrenia "an intermittent type of behavior" occurring in situations of a particular kind of stress: ". . . when the patient is staying within the rules of his family system, he is behaving 'normally.' However, when he is required to infringe the rules, and at the same time remain within them, he adapts by schizophrenic behavior" (Haley, 1960, pp. 466–467). By "normal," Haley means normal for the patient's family in the sense that he is qualifying his statements in ways that are similar to that of his parents. Faced with the possibility of having to infringe a family prohibition, "[as] when (1) two family prohibitions conflict with each other and he must respond to both, (2) when forces outside the family, or maturational forces within himself, require him to infringe them, or (3) when prohibitions special to him conflict with prohibitions applying to all family members" (Haley, 1959, p. 369), the schizophrenic behaves in a unique and actively psychotic way; that is, he displays incongruence at all levels of communication. These conflicting prohibitions may occur when the patient is in treatment and involved with both his mother and therapist, or they may occur with greater frequency at certain times, such as in adolescence.

In the formulations of Bateson, Haley, and their co-workers, schizophrenia as an active psychosis is intermittent and specific to the "identified" patient in the family. The schizophrenic process as a form of communication, however, is continuous and generalized to all family members. Thus, any member of the family might become an "overt" schizophrenic if faced with the conflict of infringing and staying within the family prohibitions. In another aspect of his analysis, which we shall discuss in the next section, Bateson also hypothesizes that these families require only one "overt" schizophrenic and that his existence serves to stabilize the family.

There are many contrasts between the views outlined above and those of Wynne and his collaborators regarding the nature of and basic processes involved in schizophrenia. In overview, the Wynne group sees schizophrenia as the result of an individual's failure to develop a clear and stable ego identity—a failure reflecting a faulty family environment that prevents the individual from developing the necessary ego capacities and strengths for normal personality development. Within this general approach, they have centered their specific research and conceptual analyses on the thought disorder aspects of schizophrenia. "We have stressed the desirability of focusing research upon those aspects of schizophrenia which have seemed central and primary, rather than peripheral and secondary, that is, upon *structural* features, particularly the formal thinking disorders, rather than the content of the disturbance" (Wynne and Singer, 1963a, p. 200).

In their general formulation, the process of schizophrenic development is contrasted explicitly with a model of normal personality development. An assumed basic requisite for normal development is the establishment of an adequate ego-identity. This, in turn, is viewed as dependent upon a family environment with a clear and organized role structure where the focus of attention in interaction is consistent and unambiguous. In other words, the family system must be a learning environment that permits both appropriate identification and reality testing. With explicit acknowledgment to Erikson's formulations, Wynne conceives of an adequate and healthy identity as consisting not only in the sum of different role components, but as involving the selective integration of various role components into a unique personal identity.

The learning environment constituted by the role structure and interaction processes in families of schizophrenic patients, described in the previous section of this paper, permits neither adequate reality testing nor opportunities for the flexible integration of roles into the developing self. For example, the rigid role structure combined with the norm of pseudo-mutuality force the child to act out the form of a role but not to grasp its substance. The role cannot be adequately integrated as a part of his self since the required actions do not correspond to inner feelings and needs. Thus, in describing the process of internalization of the family role structure, Wynne *et al.* (1958, pp. 215–216) state: ". . . roles and role behavior in intense pseudo-mutual relations come to be largely dissociated from subjective experience. Such roles are not integrated into the functioning of an actively perceiving ego, but come to govern the person's behavior in an automatic 'reflex' fashion, having the quality of 'going through the motions.' These patterns of role behavior . . . in a general sense are internalized into the personality, although they are not under the jurisdiction of an actively discriminating ego."

Further, because the patterns of interaction are either amorphous or fragmented, in ways described previously, a stable and coherent "focus of attention" is lacking that would permit adequate reality testing and the development of rational and ordered thought. In formulating the link between the type of thought disorder present in schizophrenia and patterns of family interaction, the concept of "focal attention" (borrowed from Schachtel) is given a prominent place. "In schizophrenia, as we are formulating it, there is an impairment or defect of those ego structures which involve the various aspects of focal attention . . . the failure of the capacity to focus and maintain a major set in the face of intrusiveness from both external and internal stimuli" (Wynne and Singer, 1964, p. 7). The family patterns of handling attention and meaning, described above as lying along the continuum from amorphous through fragmented styles of interaction, are seen as "directly related to the development of capacities for focal attention in offspring."

While these distorted modes of thinking and patterns of rigid role performance are inadequate and inappropriate from the point of view of the general culture, they nevertheless permit the individual to function adequately within his family until adolescence. At this point in his life, both his inner drives and the expectations of society require an independent and secure ego identity if the individual is to participate fully on the wider social scene. Acute schizophrenia, in this theory, occurs in the context of an identity crisis. This crisis derives from the societal requirement that the individual move out of the rigid family role structure and behave as an independent and flexible person. This is an insoluble problem for the child since he can no longer remain completely within the family but cannot meet adequately the new demands. The schizophrenic reaction is his solution.

Wynne and Singer also distinguish between types of schizophrenics—those with primarily amorphous and those with primarily fragmented thought disorders. Although mentioned occasionally, such distinctions are not used systematically by other theorists. They suggest (Wynne and Singer, 1965) that these differences may be rooted in different family structures: "In using this differentiation-integration formulation for classifying schizophrenia, we shall group global, predominantly undifferentiated forms of functioning under the heading of 'amorphousness.' Failures of hierarchic integration, after some degree of clear differentiation has been achieved, we shall call 'fragmentation.' Along a continuum these represent, in our formulation, different varieties of cognitive disorganization or thought disorder." They also suggest (Wynne and Singer, 1962, p. 71) that these types of schizophrenic thought disorders may be associated respectively with different family types whose interaction characteristics correspond to the amorphous-fragmented patterns of cognitive disorganization: ". . . One of the implications of the work is that patterns of the families of schizophrenics need to be considered as heterogeneous in order to link them successfully with the heterogeneity of schizophrenic offspring."

Given the pervasiveness of thought disorder within these families, should all members be viewed as schizophrenic—perhaps covert schizophrenics as in Bateson's formulation? Wynne does not deal explicitly with this question and does not distinguish between thought disorder as part of the active psychosis and thought disorder as part of a more general schizophrenic-type process. It appears as if he starts with the schizophrenic patient as a "given" and then attempts to define and describe his characteristic ways of thinking. Thus, in a sense, the patient has been diagnosed as schizophrenic on other grounds and features of his cognitive styles are then examined to determine if there are consistencies in this area of his behavior. In this connection we find the following view expressed:

> . . . it should be clear that we do *not* regard the patterning of attentional and thinking disorders as basically transitory states which come and go in response to temporary stresses whether induced by psychological disturbance, drugs, fatigue, etc., but as underlying enduring forms or styles of functioning. To be sure, psychological or physiological stresses may facilitate the emergence into view of the disorders, but more fundamentally they are the relatively stable, built-in pattern in which an individual functions in a considerable variety of circumstances, experimental and clinical (Wynne and Singer, 1964, p. 9).

Wynne's formulations have been developed on the basis of data derived from family therapy, experimental studies, and the use of a predictive method. The latter has been particularly prominent in the recent work (Wynne and Singer, 1963). Essentially, in this method an attempt has been made to predict whether and what type of schizophrenic illness is present in an offspring (typed in terms of style of thinking) on the basis of an analysis of data from other members of the patient's family; this data has usually been projective test material, but excerpts of parental interaction have also been used. They believe that the systematic use of this method has moved them toward ". . . greater precision in differentiating and defining concepts and greater attention to the processes and methods by which data are assessed" (Wynne and Singer, 1964, p. 3). Associated with the increased use of this method in their work has been increased attention to psychological processes in the development of schizophrenia, and less emphasis than there was in the early papers on the patterning of roles within these families.

The view of schizophrenia presented by Lidz and his co-investigators is similar in many respects to that of Wynne and his NIMH group. Thought disorder is paramount in the definition of the illness: ". . . the critical characteristics that distinguish this category of mental illness concern the disturbed symbolic processes without degradation of the intelligence potential. The core problem . . . : disordered concept formation, concretistic thinking, mislabelled metaphor, impaired categorical thinking, intrusions of primary process material, derailment of association, etc." (Lidz, 1963, p. 91). Further similarities with Wynne lie in Lidz's view of schizophrenia as primarily a disease of adolescence and in the emphasis placed both on the lack of an adequate identity and on the learning of paralogic and distorted ways of thinking as major components of the schizophrenic developmental process.

However, the problems of identity formation in adolescence and the consequences for the child are specified very differently. Rather than locating the source of identity problems in either a poorly or rigidly articulated role structure, as Wynne does, Lidz sees the basic problem as consisting in a lack of adequate identity models within the family. He distinguishes between concrete problems in development for boys and girls. However, he notes that in both cases the essential difficulty is the same, that is, how to form a sex-appropriate identity in the presence of the faulty identity model provided by the parent of the same sex. For the girl, the mother is cold, aloof, and hostile; for the boy, the father is passive and inadequate. In both cases the opposite sex parent is engaged in undercutting his or her spouse and in making seductive overtures to the child. This blurring of generation boundaries and the lack of proper adult models, results in an inadequate, weak ego identity: ". . . these parents fail to provide a satisfactory family milieu because they cannot form a coalition as members of the parental generation maintaining their appropriate sex-linked roles, or transmit instrumentally valid ways of thinking, feeling, and communicating suited to the society into which the child must emerge. The child who grows up in a family lacking in these fundamentals has confused and confusing models for identification, has difficulty in achieving a sex-linked identity, in overcoming his incestuous attachments, and in finding meaningful and consistent guides for relating to others . . ." (Lidz et al., 1963, p. 3).

At adolescence, rather than an identity crisis of the kind described by Wynne, the acute onset of a schizophrenic psychosis is precipitated by the fear of loss of control over either incestuous or hostile impulses. The threat of being overwhelmed by these drives, of being unable to control them, forces the child to adopt a schizophrenic response where either the perception of his own needs is altered radically or he abandons rational ways of behaving. Or as outlined by Lidz (1963):

> [The] progression of the erotically toned child-parent attraction to an incestuous bond threatens the existence of the nuclear family, prevents the child from investing energy into extra-familial socializing channels, and blocks his emergence as an adult. . . . His conscious avoidance of incest becomes necessary because of defective family structure and role confusion, the personalities of family members become further distorted because spontaneous interaction becomes impossible, role conflict inevitable, and crippling defenses necessary (p. 73). . . . Confronted by an untenable conflict and unable to find a path into the future, the schizophrenic patient withdraws from the demands of society and reality by breaking the confines imposed by the meanings and logic of his culture which, in turn further isolates the patient. The condition tends to become self-perpetuating, because the patient ceases to test the instrumental utility of his concepts and no longer seeks the consensus of meanings required for living cooperatively with others (p. 92).

Essentially this is a description of a psychosis that develops when a weak ego can no longer manage its inner drives. Contributing to the choice of a schizophrenic pattern in this conflict is the fact that the child's background has been deficient in rational problem solving. His learning environment was one where irrationality and denial were pervasive. He thus has little in the way of either internal or external resources that can be drawn upon at the time of acute crisis.

The problems of development outlined above are linked by Lidz to general deficiencies in parental nurturance patterns and the failure of the familial environment to provide an adequate socialization context for normal personality development. In recent papers, equal attention has been directed to "defects in transmitting the communicative and other basic instrumental techniques of the culture to the child" (Lidz and Fleck, 1964, p. 5). The acquisition of language is seen as primary to the acquisition of other adaptive skills for participation in the culture:

> The foundations of language are established within the family. Whether the child gains trust in the utility and validity of verbal communication as a means of understanding and collaborating with others, or learns that words are in the

service of fantasy rather than of problem solving, or are a means of avoiding recognition of the obvious, or are used to blur or obfuscate, depends upon the nature of the intrafamilial communications. The topic is crucial to the study of schizophrenia and extremely complex. Here, we can only assert that these families in which schizophrenic patients grew up fail to inculcate consistent or instrumentally valid meanings (Lidz and Fleck, 1964, p. 20).

The critical role in the onset of schizophrenia assigned by Bateson, Wynne, and Lidz to the stressful period of adolescence is in agreement both with epidemiological findings on age differentials in rates of schizophrenia (see, for example, Locke *et al.*, 1958, p. 175; Mishler and Scotch, 1963, p. 318) and with the views of many other investigators of family relationships in schizophrenia. There are some differences, however, in the nature of the particular stresses that are judged to be important. For example, the conflict between dependence and independence is stressed by such workers as Lu (1961, 1962), Bowen (1959, 1960) and Brodey (1959). They suggest that the groundwork for the particularly intense conflict experienced by the individual who becomes schizophrenic is prepared by parents who overtly stress independence and achievement in one context, but foster dependence in another context, sometimes at a covert and sometimes at an overt level. At adolescence there is either a sudden demand for adult responsible behavior, failure to meet this demand, and consequent schizophrenic withdrawal; or the individual is faced with insoluble and conflicting demands to be both dependent and independent and resolves his dilemma by a schizophrenic breakdown.

From this discussion, certain contrasting emphases are evident among these theorists in how they define schizophrenia and see its development. Wynne sees schizophrenia as essentially a problem in identity development with associated cognitive difficulty; the psychosis is an exaggerated form of a relatively enduring cognitive style. Bateson, on the other hand, views schizophrenia as an inability to label and respond accurately to messages, which inability has developed from particular types of learning situations. While the manifestations of the psychosis in distorted patterns of communication are exaggerations of previous patterns, the psychosis is for Bateson a symptom of the individual's struggle for psychological health. Lidz seems to combine problems of sex-role identification with the learning of distorted and maladaptive ways of thinking in his characterization of the nature of the illness; schizophrenia is seen as a "deficiency" disease, i.e., the end result of a long family history of failures in adequate enculturation.

These different formulations of the schizophrenic process correspond in many ways to the theorists' different descriptions of patterns of family structure and interaction that were presented in an earlier section. Thus, in seeing schizophrenia as a problem in identity development, Wynne tends to describe the socializing environment in terms of inadequate role relationships, i.e., a rigid or ambiguous family role structure. These relationships prevent healthy role identifications and at the same time provide a confusing learning environment that interferes with the development of a stable identity. If, on the other hand, schizophrenia is seen as a problem of distortions in communication, as Bateson sees it, then the developmental context tends to be described in terms of situations where one is punished for responding to messages as if they contained clear and definite meaning. There are both gains and losses from a degree of internal consistency of point of view within each theory. Obviously, there must be some form of correspondence between the descriptions of interaction patterns and the schizophrenic process if the former are to be etiologically related to the latter. However, it is also obvious that if the theories are to provide comprehensive accounts of the etiology of schizophrenia, then additional concepts must be introduced which may stretch this fabric of consistency. Lidz and Wynne have been moving toward more comprehensive statements. For example, both are concerned with cognitive and affective aspects of personality, and with developmental sequences and processes, as well as with family interaction processes. The relationships between the different types and levels of concepts is not always clear in their work and the gaps between levels tend to be bridged by implicit assumptions rather than by empirical findings. We shall return to this general problem in the concluding section of this paper.

The Persistence of Interaction Patterns

The previous two sections were devoted to the central questions with which these theories are concerned, namely, what are the special characteristics of interaction in the families of schizophrenics, and how do they lead to schizophrenia. While answers to these two questions constitute the core of each of the theories with respect to the etiology of schizophrenia, there are two other questions that are of interest in their own right and also throw additional light on the similarities and differences among the several approaches that we have been comparing. These are: first, what accounts for the persistence in these family patterns? Second, what are the predisposing background factors for the development of these interaction patterns and the schizophrenic solution? We will discuss the first question in this section and the second in the following one.

While the level and focus of description vary among the several theories under review, there appears to be general consensus about characterizing these families as in states of chronic distress. This does not imply that there is continual and manifest dissatisfaction and unhappiness. In Wynne's analysis, as one example, a family may avoid the overt expression of underlying and pervasive tension by a retreat behind a façade of harmony. However, if such a solution were adopted it would be considered in all of these formulations as inherently unstable and unsatisfying in the same sense that neurotic defenses are considered unsatisfying in analyses of personality dynamics. That is, the defenses may be necessary to avoid overwhelming anxiety and further disintegration, but serious costs are involved. Thus, the presumed cost for the family of a retreat behind a harmonious façade to the posture of Wynne's pseudo-mutuality in role relationships is the denial of reality and the loss of personal identities for all family members.

Nevertheless, despite the distress and lack of mutual satisfaction, it appears that these families persist and their members persist in dealing with each other over and over again in the same ways. Bateson (1961, p. 104) points explicitly to the stability of the system despite its pathogenicity, in that "these families, in a gross sense, continue as families. The statement, 'this is a closely intercommunicating system,' continues to be true in spite of the very considerable unhappiness of the members. . . ."

Given this paradox—of relationships that persist despite the distress they occasion—it is important to ask how the system maintains itself. Or, more precisely, it is important to ask how each of the theories attempts to answer the question. What functions are presumed to be served by these patterns of interaction, at both an individual and group level, that might account for their persistence?

In the approach of Bateson and his co-workers, functions served for the family as a social unit receive attention. In his analysis of the "steady state" of these families, Bateson (1959, p. 128) writes that, "first and foremost that which is characteristic is a very tough stability . . . homeostasis. . . . When the identified patient begins to get well, we observe all sorts of subtle pressure being exerted to perpetuate his illness. . . . It is not that at all costs the identified patient must be kept confused; rather it seems as if the patient himself is an accessory—even a willing sacrifice—to the family homeostasis."

How does the theory attempt to account for this "tough stability"? We could not find an explicit attempt to provide an explanation. However, in general discussions of this problem of homeostasis, two broad hypotheses are proposed that would seem to be relevant to this question of why the patterns persist—one at the level of group and the other of individual dynamics. At the level of group dynamics, Bateson suggests that these are families that do not permit stable coalitions. He views coalitions as requisites for viable solutions to the recurrent problems faced by such social units as families. In the absence of viable solutions, family members cannot achieve stable and adequate self-identities; they are "continually undergoing the experience of negation of self." This hypothesis at the level of the family as a social group is connected with a hypothesis at the individual level to account for the persistence of unsatisfactory interaction patterns. This is the belief on the part of family members, presumably derived from the self-negating experience, that the self can actually be destroyed: "In fact, the double-binding interaction is a sort of battle around the question of whose self shall be destroyed and the basic characteristic of the family, which is shared by all the relevant members, is the premise that the self is destroyed or can be destroyed in this battle—and *therefore* the fight must go on" (Bateson, 1959, p. 136). In outline, this proposes that in families, stable coalitions are necessary for successful problem solving and successful problem solving is necessary for the development of adequate self-identities. In the absence of this pattern, the double bind becomes persistent and pervasive as a mode of communication, apparently because it permits individuals to avoid the complete destruction of the self that they believe would follow an unambiguous expression of real feelings and beliefs.

Haley attempts to account for these persistent patterns of mutually destructive activity by proposing a conceptual model that he believes has particular appropriateness for the analysis of interaction processes. His point of departure is the ". . . peculiar sensitivity of people to the fact that their behavior is governed by others" (Haley, 1959, p. 371). Central to his approach are the two ideas that human communication can be classified into several message levels and that social groups are self-corrective, governed systems. "If a family confines itself to repetitive patterns within a certain range of possible behavior then they are confined to that range by some sort of governing process. No outside governor requires the family members to behave in their habitual patterns, so this governing process must exist within the family. . . . When people respond to one another they govern, or establish rules, for each other's behavior. . . . Such a system tends to be error-activated. Should one family member break a family rule, the others become activated until he either conforms to the rule again or successfully establishes a new one" (Haley, 1959, p. 373). This analogy of an error-activated system is proposed as a model for describing all families. The special characteristic of the family of the schizophrenic is that it is "not only establishing and following a system of rules, as other families do, but also following a prohibition on any acknowledgement that a family member is setting rules. Each refuses to concede that any other family member is governing him" (Haley, 1959, p. 372). Haley's model has obvious similarities to traditional sociological conceptualizations of social systems where behavior is mutually regulated by shared norms (i.e., rules) and where social control is exercised through the imposition of sanctions when deviant behavior occurs (i.e., error-activated responses to rule breaking).

The view that the double bind interaction pattern may persist because it serves a defensive psychological function is noted though not stressed by Bateson. For example, a child may have a special significance for the mother such that her anxiety and hostility are aroused when she is in danger of intimate contact with the child. In order to control her anxiety, she tries to control her distance from the child by giving incongruent messages, that is, messages that reject but simultaneously deny the rejection. Haley also points to the potential psychological function of the double bind but formulates its general aim as the maintenance of a fluid and undefined relationship; the basic anxiety in this instance would seem to be that in entering into defined relationship one must acknowledge that one is setting rules for governing the relationship.

Whether the specific defensive function is to allay anxiety about intimacy or the fact of a relationship itself, the Bateson-Haley formulation gives the child an active role in the maintenance of the pathological interaction. This results from the specific reward-punishment schedule in this type of learning context. The child is led to respond to incongruent messages with incongruencies of his own; only this type of response is rewarded since it serves to maintain the mother's denial, while other behaviors of the child are met by punishment and the threat of abandonment or the withdrawal of love.

The views set forth by Searles (1958, 1959) are relevant here, since he also sees the child as actively involved in the maintenance of the special forms of interaction in these families and relates this to the child's perception of the mother's intrapsychic conflicts and needs. However, he ascribes this involvement to different sources than Bateson. Starting from the perspective that there are "positive feelings in the relationship between the schizophrenic and his mother," he suggests that the child stays within the relationship out of compassion and love for the mother, with the related concern that were he to leave her or to change the mother would be "annihilated" or "go crazy." Thus, he argues that the child is not kept in the relationship by "hateful" double binds, but remains in it so that he will not hurt the mother.

The problem of why these unsatisfying interaction patterns persist receives less explicit stress in the work of Lidz and his co-workers, although at the same time they seem to give more attention in their descriptive accounts to states of disturbance and conflict in these families. In their model of family social organization the marital role relationship serves the function of maintaining each partner's emotional equilibrium; different types of marital roles are seen as deriving from individual differences in intrapsychic needs and conflicts. As we understand the implications of this view, however distorted or abnormal the role relationship in a schizogenic family may appear to an observer, it persists because it serves tension-reducing functions for both partners. There is an obvious relationship between this formulation and their general psychodynamic approach noted earlier.

The child appears to be "recruited" into the system, that is, taught appropriate but pathological behavior, in order to help stabilize the system. In other words, he is not permitted to work out a role for himself that would threaten the existing parental role pattern, whether it be a relationship of marital schism or marital skew, since that would threaten the emotional equilibrium of one or both parents. He is permitted to take any of a number of positions within the structure—as a mediator, as a scapegoat, as an ally of one or the other parent—but any role must be consistent with the ongoing relationship and in this way his actions serve to maintain the system.

We have noted previously two other characteristics of these families that are reported by Lidz which would seem to be of further help in maintaining their basic relationship patterns. These are the pervasive atmosphere of irrationality within the family and the associated isolation of family members from the common culture. The effects of this atmosphere on the child are to restrict drastically his ability to perceive and communicate appropriately in the world outside the family. The distortions of perception and communication on the part of the parents, in the service of their own rigid defense systems, are transmitted to the child who finds these forms of perceiving and behaving necessary if he is to maintain his position within the family. He is forced into a more complete dependence on the family and into patterns of behavior that are consistent with the emotional requirements of the parents.

One problem in interpreting Lidz's position on this general question is that he sometimes discusses the social organization of the family as if only the normal family had a stable organized form, defined by a condition of effective role reciprocity, while the pathology of the schizogenic family is treated as if in itself it constituted a state of disorganization. (For example, see Lidz, 1963, pp. 39–76.) However, at other times the characteristic patterns found in the schizogenic family, such as schism and skew, are clearly recognized as stable and persistent; they are simply less harmonious and more conflictful forms of family organization than that of full role reciprocity. This lack of consistency in his conceptual analysis of the idea of the family as a social organization has resulted in a lack of attention to the problem of the persistence of pathological patterns. In particular, the functional analysis has been restricted to the individual level and there has been no analysis of the functions served for the family as a social unit.

As we noted in an earlier section, Wynne and his team of NIMH investigators view pseudo-mutuality as a collective defense against a recognition of the underlying and pervasive meaninglessness of family members' experience and of their relationships with each other. The interaction patterns associated with the pseudo-relationships appear to persist for the same reason that personality defenses persist, namely, they are effective in reducing overwhelming anxiety. As a result, considerable energy and affect is invested in the defensive pattern, and other alternatives are excluded.

In this theory, there seems to be a general but implicit assumption that social systems like families maintain themselves through complementary role expectations. Sanctions are imposed if behavior is not consistent with the normative definitions of the group; the imposition of the sanctions serves to perpetuate accepted behaviors. The pseudo-relationships in the schizogenic family are like this, only more so. The respective roles are stereotyped and rigid; deviations or failures in role performance are either denied or reinterpreted. The similarity between this and Haley's formulation of the family as an error-activated system is evident. However, while Haley separates rule-setting activity from the rules themselves and proposes that it is the rule-setting activity that is denied, Wynne has emphasized the denial of violations of the rules.

In addition to this mutually regulative process of complementary role expectations, Wynne suggests that one consequence of the rigid role structure is that each family member develops a strong personal investment in maintaining things as they are. This comes about because the system does not permit a separation of their personal identities from their family roles. This is clearest in the case of the child. Wynne argues that the development of an adequate ego identity requires a socializing environment where the individual is free to step back from and reflect upon his role, to try out different ways of carrying out his role, to select and reintegrate aspects of his several different roles into his own distinctive identity. Where there is little tolerance for not fitting completely into a role and where emphasis is placed on the rigid maintenance of a façade of relationships, there is neither the proper atmosphere nor appropriate opportunities to engage in the type of role-playing experience through which the identity can be separated from the family role system. Since there is no self as distinct from the role, the role must be carried out in an exact way, or there would be no self. The same general function is served for the parents, whose identity problems derive from their own backgrounds. In order to retain any sense of self, each parent must invest great energy in maintaining the set of rigid family roles since underneath these "identities" there is only a frightening "meaninglessness."

Among these theorists, Wynne is closest to the tradition of social psychology that is equally concerned with group and personality dynamics. His formulations, therefore, share with Lidz an interest in the personality dynamics underlying an individual's behavior in his social roles and with Haley a sociological emphasis on norms and sanctions as group regulatory mechanisms. The inclusion of both levels of analysis leads, we believe, to a somewhat different orientation to the problem of persistence. Whereas for both Lidz and Haley, the fact of persistence has a passive or responsive quality—the patterns serve personality needs or continue through the operation of an error-activation mechanism—for Wynne, persistence is an active state. Family members struggle to maintain their existing relationship patterns and resist pressures to change. It should be noted that Bateson's views are also "dynamic" with reference to this problem and this may be related to his focus here on issues of personality development similar to Wynne's focus on identity, namely, the issue of the self and the possibilities of its destruction.

The general answer given by the several theories to the question of why particular patterns of social relationships and interaction persist is that they serve defensive functions at both an individual and group level. In attributing persistence to the functional significance of the behaviors and relationships, the theories are consistent with traditional conceptual models in the social and behavioral sciences that attempt to account for the repetitive "ongoingness" of both social and personality systems. One of the problems with such functional explanations, however, is that they lead us to infer the motives or needs in whose service the resultant behaviors are presumed to function. In Bateson, Lidz, and Searles the line of inference leads to the personality structures of the parents and, in particular, to a pathological level of anxiety when faced with problems of intimacy and control in normal parent-child relationships. In Haley and Wynne, emphasis is given to inferred group processes for maintaining or restoring stable relationships. It is important to point out that these individual and group processes are inferred from the observed patterns of interaction, and, while they are used as hypothetical explanations, as presently stated they are not useful for purposes of prediction.

Predisposing Factors in the Development of Schizophrenia

What personal and social characteristics of the parents are associated with the types of interaction patterns that are postulated as schizogenic? Are there specific attributes that make involvement in these interaction patterns more likely for one child rather than another in the family? Do certain combinations of parent-child traits increase the likelihood that these patterns will develop around a particular child? Each of the theories proposes answers to these questions by specifying predisposing factors, or "sorting" variables, that serve to make certain families and children more vulnerable than others to the postulated schizogenic processes.

There is general reference in each of the theories to the preexisting personality pathology of one or both parents or the existence of a "difficult" interpersonal relationship between them (or a combination of these). For example, Lidz notes that a distorted marital role pattern, either "schismatic" or "skewed," is the family environment into which the child is born. He also points to their findings (Lidz et al., 1963, pp. 2–3) that half of the fathers and half of the mothers have serious personality disturbances: "All of the families were seriously disturbed. The difficulties pervaded the entire family interaction. . . . We have noted the severe psychopathology of the fathers as well as the mothers, and we have found that these families were either schismatic . . . or were 'skewed' in that the serious personality disturbance of one parent set the pattern of family interaction." The emphasis in this theory is on the distortion of the "normal" role patterns resulting from and associated with personality pathology in one or both parents—"the fathers, as are so many of the mothers, are so caught up in their own problems that they can rarely satisfactorily fill the essentials of a parental role" (Lidz et al., 1957, p. 342).

Wynne gives little attention to the problem of predisposing background factors. While in general he seems to locate the determinants of interaction patterns in the parental role relationship, he also views the personality characteristics of the parents as among the determinants of role patterns. Bateson's discussion of these factors is also sketchy. Nevertheless, he appears to give more weight to the personality of the mother than to the parental role relationship in the initiation of the double bind; once it begins, however, other factors maintain it. For example, the mother's anxiety may be aroused when she is threatened by the possibility of a close interpersonal relationship. She tries, therefore, to develop a particular style of interaction—that is, the double bind—that will protect her from a "close" relationship with the child. The specific role of the father and his relationship to the mother in the development of the family's interaction pattern is left unstated. It is further suggested by Bateson (1960, p. 485f) that the pathological interaction patterns develop over time through a process of mutual reinforcement among family members: ". . . It seems that in schizophrenia the environmental factors themselves are likely to be modified by the subject's behavior whenever behavior related to schizophrenia starts to appear. . . . The symptomatic behavior of the identified patient fits with this environment and, indeed, promotes in the other members those characteristics which evoke the schizophrenic behavior." In other words, while the process may start with the mother's attempts through double binds to defend herself against anxiety, the factors involved in its origin are considered less important than the process through which in time the child and other family members come to behave toward each other in similar ways.

The question of the increased or special vulnerability of a particular child comes down in large part to the question of why not all of the children in these families are schizophrenic. One solution to this problem is to propose that all the children "really" are schizophrenic but only one of them shows manifest symptomatology, usually because of the particular patterning of stressful circumstances in some situation or at some point in time. As we pointed out earlier in discussing Bateson's distinction between covert and overt schizophrenia, he tends to adopt this position. "If the family is schizophrenogenic, how does it happen that all of the siblings are not diagnosable as schizophrenic patients? . . . In the schizophrenic family there may be room for only one schizophrenic" (Bateson, 1960, p. 486). This last point is related to the more general equilibrium theme we have found in this theory; the particular type of homeostasis in these families is achieved by one and only one of its members being overtly schizophrenic. In other contexts, it is suggested that while genetics may play a role in deciding which of several siblings shall be the schizophrenic, the particular attributes of the child "selected" to be the overt schizophrenic may be less important determinants than the nature of the mother's emotional conflicts; the latter determine which child will be focused upon as "special" and threatening to her defenses. For example, in some instances male children may be special in this sense and thus be more vulnerable; in other instances it may be female children.

While Wynne is more specific in mentioning the types of biological characteristics that may be important—such as the sex of the child, place in the birth order, activity pattern at birth, or physical features—his general view is that the significance of the characteristic depends upon the psychological situation of the parents rather than upon what the concrete characteristic may be. Variations in significance reflect some "fit" between the parents' intrapsychic makeups and the attributes of the child. In their discussion of etiology, Wynne and Singer propose a "transactional and epigenetic view of development" where interactions between parents and offspring depend at each phase on the outcome of previous phases. In this context, they stress the necessity of considering the kinds of transactions the parents will make together as a team and the ways in which their "role fit and emotional meshing" give different meaning to such concrete characteristics of the child as sex, or place in the sibling order (Wynne and Singer, 1964, pp. 13–20).

Lidz and his co-workers have focused more directly than other theorists on the problem of specific predisposing factors. In their work the most significant attribute for the selection of one rather than another sibling for schizophrenia appears to be the sex of the child. This follows from two general assumptions in the theory: (a) the developmental tasks of male and female children differ from each other, and (b) schizophrenia occurs in a context of familial role relationships that do not permit the child to complete his or her normal cycle of development. Specifically, the male child is particularly vulnerable in the "skewed" type of family where there tends to be a passive, weak father and a seductive, engulfing mother. Thus, the male child's opportunity for normal identity development will be markedly impaired. In "schismatic" families, on the other hand, it is the female child who is most vulnerable. Here, the marital role relationship typically reflects an aloof and devalued mother with a grandiose and narcissistic father. In these families, the developmental tasks for the female child are most difficult and the chances of developing a normal and adequate identity are reduced. (It should be noted that the association described between marital role type and the pathology of the particular parents is reported as a trend; there are instances where mothers are dominant and grandiose in the schismatic families and fathers are dominant in the skewed types.)

Among other theorists, Lu has been specifically concerned with differences between schizophrenics and their non-schizophrenic siblings in the relative intensity both of the contradictory demands made by the parents and the attempts by the child to fulfill the demands. She notes (Lu, 1962, p. 229) that the ". . . process of such parents' preschizophrenic interaction and emotional entanglement seems to begin as early as the period of the patient's birth and infancy." Two sets of unusual circumstances are described which may lead mothers to pay more attention to or give more protection to the preschizophrenic child; the child has special characteristics or the birth occurs at a time of particular frustration and tension within the family. Bowen and Brodey's formulation is similar to Wynne's in stressing that the preschizophrenic child in some sense "matches" an area of personality conflict. For example, a sickly child or one who may need extra help and nurturance has a mother with strong unresolved conflicts around dependency needs; the non-schizophrenic child does not "match" these needs and therefore can remain somewhat outside of the entangling involvment (Brodey, 1959).

In focusing on the differences among the theories in the predisposing factors they specify, we have given insufficient stress to certain general themes that are common to all of them. For example, in each of the theories the parents of schizophrenics are seen as immature people, anxious and conflicted, and tending to use primitive mechanisms of defense. The marital relationship is unsatisfying and distorted; role relationships are rigid; ways of meeting each other's needs are disturbed and pathological; there is a state of chronic disequilibrium in the family. The child who becomes schizophrenic is "weak" to begin with; he may have a physical handicap, be ill in infancy, have severe eating problems, or in some way be defined quite early as needing special attention. There is also reference to, although not systematic examination of, the possibility of exceptional stress at the time of the child's birth or early infancy such as extreme financial pressure, illness in the family, or sudden shifts in place of residence.

Both Bateson and Wynne are explicit about the transactional nature of the process and point out that the selected child comes to act as required and in turn elicits special types of response from others. Wynne and Singer (1962, p. 61) point out how this approach differs from certain traditional points of view: "Each offspring clearly has an impact upon the rest of the family, including the parents, so that the offspring alter and help shape the family system from which they in turn derive some of the personality characteristics and forms of functioning. Our viewpoint thus differs from those psychodynamic theories which have sometimes implied that particular kinds of psychological trauma have a unidirectional effect upon a passively receptive child or that 'schizophrenogenic' mothers or parents have one-way victimizing effects upon their offspring."

Associated with this transactional approach is a general recognition that none of the specific or general predisposing factors is *the* cause of schizophrenia. Rather, the several factors are viewed as setting the stage for schizophrenia by increasing the vulnerability both of the family and of the selected child to the development of the schizogenic process.

Discussion

It would be relatively easy, as anyone could confirm who has read papers by Bateson, Lidz, Wynne, and their co-investigators, to detail a long list of criticisms of these theories. Some specific criticisms have been noted explicitly at appropriate points in preceding sections. Other criticisms have been implicit but presumably evident; for example, our persistent concern with whether we had fully understood the meaning of one or another concept is obviously related to what we feel to be an unnecessarily high level of ambiguity and imprecision in their writings. The basic aim of this review, however, is not to score points but to clarify as best we can the meanings of these theories so as to achieve a fuller understanding of the implications of their work for research and theory on the role of family interaction processes in personality development. In this last section, therefore, rather than reviewing previous criticisms or listing new ones, we wish to draw attention to some of the important new directions in theory and research that are suggested by the body of work summarized in this paper. Our emphasis will be on shared characteristics of the different theories, rather than upon the differences stressed in previous sections. Thus, we shall be treating the theories as different expressions of a general approach to the study of family interaction.

Taken collectively, there are two major contributions that these theories may make to our general understanding of personality and social processes. First, their serious and sustained effort to focus on the family group as the unit of observation and conceptualization marks an important advance over traditional approaches to both normal and pathological personality development. Second, through specific concepts like the *double bind, fragmentation,* and *pseudo-mutuality* they have alerted us to important phenomena in family life and other interpersonal relationships that have heretofore been neglected by other investigators.

The potential significance of this focus on the total family unit cannot be over-stressed. It would be inaccurate to draw the implication that information should now be collected about the husband of the schizophrenogenic mother; this would miss the point. The more accurate implication is that information must now be collected about relationships and transactions among family members; the latter, as we know from a long history of work in small group studies, cannot simply be reconstructed on the basis of knowledge of the personal attributes of the several family members. The introduction of this new level of conceptualization leads toward more complex models of causation, as, for example, in Wynne's "epigenetic transactional" approach. At the same time, it points to simple mechanisms at a concrete behavioral level through which personality is shaped by intrafamilial social processes. Because these mechanisms are specified in terms of observable behavior, they are more open to empirical study than the abstract propositions that have heretofore constituted much of social interaction theory as it has been applied to problems of socialization.

The implications of these theories are not restricted to the area of personality development but extend to our understanding of processes at work in other types of groups. Analyses of problem solving, training, therapy, and work groups could benefit from attention to the forms of interaction isolated in these family studies. At the level of individual behavior, some of the persistent styles of interaction might transfer from the family to other group settings, and the conditions under which such transfer did or did not take place would be an interesting area of investigation. At the level of group dynamics, since all groups face the same types of problems that are described as facing families—the development and reinforcement of norms, the control of affect, the differentiation of roles—the mechanisms observed in these family studies can serve as hypotheses in studies of other groups.

There is no need to multiply examples of how these theories alert and sensitize us to important aspects of interpersonal relationships. We have implied throughout that these phenomena are open to systematic investigation because they have been formulated in behavioral terms. This will permit the introduction of rigorous methods of study that have been developed in experimental studies of *ad hoc* groups. This latter complex of methods—including experimental procedures and techniques of quantitative coding of interaction—would seem to be particularly appropriate to the further study of the processes reported by clinical observers of these families. Several investigators have already recognized the potential value of linking these two traditions of experimental social psychology and the clinical study of the schizogenic family. An overview of these recent developments will help to underscore our general point that we may be approaching a confluence of these two traditions and that such an event would be of value for both of them.

We have selected five studies for brief comment to serve as examples of this direction in research. In these studies, the focus of analysis is the difference between families with diagnosed schizophrenic members and other types of families. This is clearly only a first step in assessing the hypothesized etiological function of these patterns of interaction.[6] Farina's (1960) experiment is the first reported of this type. He compared interaction between parents of male schizophrenics and parents of male tuberculosis patients in order to investigate patterns of dominance and conflict. Using the "revealed difference" technique to generate

---

[6] It is recognized by many observers of the characteristics of schizogenic families that they bear a close resemblance to characteristics reported of other "disturbed" families, such as families of homosexuals, autistic children, children with school phobias, etc. Clearly one of the tasks of future research is to specify in detail the relationship between family structure and particular disturbances in the child. Meissner's review (1964) includes references to studies of these varied types of families.

parental interaction (Strodtbeck, 1954), he scored tape recordings on certain aspects of the structure of interaction (who speaks first, number of interruptions, etc.). He found a higher degree of conflict between the parents of schizophrenics than between parents in his tuberculosis control group. He also found systematic differences between parents of patients with good premorbid histories ("reactive" schizophrenics) and those with poor premorbid histories ("process" schizophrenics). For example, mothers of poor premorbid patients showed high dominance, but in good premorbid families fathers tended to be dominant. Caputo's (1963) study of interaction between parents of chronic schizophrenics was concerned with similar questions. He used parents of "normal" sons as a control group, and tested the hypothesis of role reversal in schizogenic families, that is, that mothers would play a dominant role and fathers an expressive role. He also predicted unilateral patterns of hostility, from wife to husband, in these families. Using the "revealed difference" procedure and a modified Interaction Process Analysis category system (Bales, 1950) to code tape recordings, he found that none of these hypotheses was supported by the data.

It is less important at this stage of research and knowledge that the results of these two studies are somewhat inconsistent with each other than that together they suggest modifications in theory and method regarding interaction in these families. For example, Farina's findings point to the need for careful discrimination in theory and research between types of schizophrenia. Findings from both studies indicate the need for several coding systems at different levels to measure important concepts such as power and conflict that appear repeatedly in the clinical and theoretical literature. Perhaps consistent conflict patterns in these families are manifested in their styles of interaction and would be evident in an "interruptions" code such as Farina's, but not manifested in verbal content and would not be found in a verbal content code such as that used by Caputo.

Frances Cheek's (1964a) experiment takes into account some of the previously mentioned design problems and her results raise the question of consistency between parental values and parental behavior. This is the first reported experimental study of schizophrenic family interaction in which the patient was actually present in the discussion and the first to compare families of male and female patients. Cheek's hypotheses center on the distribution of affect and power; she used a modified Bales system to code tape recordings. Examples of her findings are: in interaction with husband and child, mothers of male schizophrenic children show greater hostility and greater tension than mothers of females; in contrast with mothers of normal children, schizogenic mothers are more withdrawn and cold. A comparison of expressed values with observed behavior showed that mothers of schizophrenics who report high values on support and permissiveness in child training do not show this behavior in their interaction; in contrast mothers of normals report that they value giving support and being permissive to children and actually behave this way in family discussions.

In these experiments indexes of types of interaction are based on an average rate of participation over some period of time. However, the theories previously discussed, particularly Bateson's and Wynne's, stress the transactional nature of relationships and thus are more concerned with sequences of interaction. Haley's (1964) experiment is focused on the kind of ordered pattern of communication that may be characteristic of schizophrenic families. Comparing interaction in a set of "disturbed" families with normal families, Haley showed that when "who follows whom" patterns are compared with random sequences, the "disturbed" families tended to show a more rigid sequential pattern than the normal families. He interprets this difference as reflecting the normal family's ability to be more flexible and to change patterns in accord with the requirements of the situation.

In an experimental study now in process, the present authors have attempted to take into account some of the design and measurement problems present in earlier investigations (Mishler and Waxler, 1964). The design includes families of male and female patients with good and poor premorbid histories as well as comparable normal control families. As an important additional control, parents are observed in interaction with a well sibling of the patient as well as with the patient himself. Family discussions are generated through the "revealed difference" procedure and typescripts of the discussions are multiple-coded with the use of a number of independent coding systems. This study will permit the analysis of sequences as well as average scores and will allow for a determination of whether parental interaction patterns are child- or family-specific.

We believe that the general approach illustrated by the several studies reviewed above holds great promise. It opens up to systematic investigation the range of interpersonal relationships in natural groups which has until now been studied almost exclusively either through self-report questionnaires or qualitative case study procedures. Of equal importance, in constructing general theories about personality and group process, we will no longer be limited to findings from studies of artificial *ad hoc* groups but will be able to draw upon well-controlled studies of natural groups.

One aim of this review when we began was to derive crucial hypotheses through comparison of the several theories that would permit an empirical assessment of their relative validity. As we learned more about the theories, our conviction was reinforced that they each contained hypotheses and concepts that led easily into empirical study. We have emphasized particularly the appropriateness of experimental methods for this. However, it also became clear, as we have suggested at a number of points in the body of the paper, that the theories cannot be compared directly with each other in ways that would permit a critical empirical test of differential hypotheses. It is always evident that the theories refer to the same general phenomena, viz., schizophrenic patients and their parents. However, this is a level of similarity equivalent to asserting the similarity of Van Gogh, Monet, and Andrew Wyeth because they have all painted landscapes.

The analogy to artists is helpful in understanding a major source of the difficulty in achieving a systematic comparison of the different theories. They are less like scientific theories than artful constructions or coherent accounts arrived at independently through different perspectives and methods of conceptualization. Their value for other investigators, like that of art, lies in giving us a new way of looking at the world. Techniques and methods are available for systematic empirical study of the processes they have observed and reported. There is some likelihood that, guided by this new view of the phenomenon, such studies will result in an increased understanding not only of schizophrenia but of normal human behavior as well.

20 / Schizophrenia in Twins: An Epidemiological–Clinical Study

Einar Kringlen

By and large, investigations of twins have shown much higher concordance figures for monozygotic than for dizygotic twins with respect to schizophrenia and manic-depressive psychosis. However, in a previous study (Kringlen, 1964a) the present author found no significant difference in concordance rates between monozygotic and dizygotic schizophrenic males. As the sample in that study was small, a more comprehensive study has been conducted, in which all twins recorded in the Norwegian birth register from 1901 to 1930 have been checked against the Central Register of Psychosis. This has provided a relatively large and, what is more important, an unselected sample of psychotic twins. In this paper I shall present some of the findings of this investigation.

The study had three principal aims: First, to obtain true concordance figures for all types of functional psychoses; second, to study a larger sample of discordant pairs in order to clarify the crucial environmental factors; and, third, to study problems pertaining to nosology. To solve the first problem, that of concordance rates, special attention had to be paid to sampling. To throw some light upon the other two problems, the life histories of discordant pairs were investigated.

The Rationale of the Twin Method

There are two principal questions that may be asked in genetics: *What* is inherited? *How* is it inherited? The first question can be answered by studying twins, and the second by genealogical studies. In the latter type of studies, an attempt is made to follow certain traits or illnesses from generation to generation, and the incidence of the traits in each generation is calculated. It is regrettable that many research workers have started with the second question. It has been taken for granted that the illness—for instance, schizophrenia or manic-depressive psychosis—is a hereditary disease.

Monozygotic twins are held to be identical in inherited characteristics; hence all differences between them have to be attributed to the environment, in the widest sense of that term. Dizygotic twins, on the other hand, from a genetic point of view are siblings who are accidentally born at the same time. Differences between dizygotic twins may, therefore, be due both to hereditary and to environmental factors.

In the so-called "classical twin method," developed in the 1920's, monozygotic

From *Psychiatry*, 1966, 29, 172–184. Revised. Copyright © 1966. Reprinted by permission of the author and the William Alanson White Psychiatric Foundation, Inc.

and dizygotic pairs of twins are compared statistically in respect to their concordance for the trait and the illness in question. A pair is called concordant if both twins have the same illness—for instance, schizophrenia—and discordant if one is sick and the other is not sick—that is, if one is schizophrenic and the co-twin is not schizophrenic.

Selection of the Sample

In Norway, local clergymen have long been entrusted with the task of reporting all births to the Central Office of Vital Statistics. All twin births are registered regardless of whether only one or both survives. These birth lists are recorded in such a way that it is relatively easy to pick out the twin births and establish a twin register. In doing this, I selected the period 1901 to 1930, on the following grounds: The twins born in this period would now be in the 35 to 64 age group, so that most of them have passed the risk period of schizophrenia. If a younger age group were taken, there would be fewer cases, and disputable corrections for age would have to be made. If an older population were selected, problems would be encountered because many would have died by now and it would be difficult to get the necessary background data. There was another factor of some importance: namely, the psychosis register was started in 1916, and so twins hospitalized for a psychosis after the age of 15 would appear in this register. Thus, a sample of approximately 50,000 twins, or 25,000 pairs of twins, both monozygotic and dizygotic, was obtained. According to the Weinberg differential method, about 28 per cent of these twins should be monozygotic (Stern, 1960).

The next step was to check the twin register against the National Register of Psychosis.[1] All psychiatric hospitals must report annually all patients diagnosed as psychotic, and, in practice, they also report many cases of neurosis, psychopathy, and mental deficiency. Two important questions arise here. Are all the seriously psychotic hospitalized? How complete is the reporting? These questions will be discussed later on.

The checking of the twin register against the Register of Psychosis resulted in 519 pairs of twins, 35 to 64 years of age, one or both of whom at one time or another in their lives had been hospitalized for a psychosis. Excluding the few cases registered of neurosis, psychopathy, oligophrenia, alcoholism, and organic psychoses left a sample of 422 pairs of twins, in which one or both had been hospitalized at some time because of "functional" psychosis—schizophrenia, manic-depressive psychosis, or reactive psychosis.

The superintendents of psychiatric institutions in Norway were then approached with a request for the case histories of the patients involved. All of the hospitals were willing to let me use their case material. Although the case histories often mentioned that the patient was a twin, in only a few cases was it possible to have a reasonable assurance of the diagnosis of zygosity. I myself summarized the case histories. Such items as "hereditary tainting," date of onset, and the actual clinical picture were, for the most part, fairly well described, but the information about family background and life history was often meager.

[1] This Register was under the jurisdiction of the Ministry of Health during the first years of its existence; since 1937 Professor Ørnulv Ødegaard of Gaustad Psychiatric Hospital has been in charge of it.

Next came the tedious job of trying to trace the twins. First an attempt was made to use the addresses given in the case records, but many of the patients had been hospitalized several years earlier and had since then moved and/or married. Therefore, I had to rely largely on the population registers, local registers containing such data as the addresses and the birth dates of the entire population. I obtained permission from the Central Statistical Bureau to use these general registers and found them most helpful in tracing the twins.

After I had located the index case, I approached him and explained my scientific goals, asking for his cooperation in answering my questions. To establish a preliminary diagnosis of zygosity, I asked: Was the identity of the twin confused with that of the co-twin when they were children? Were they as alike as two drops of water? Or were they only as similar as siblings are likely to be? At the same time the twin was asked to give the names and addresses of the parents, the co-twin, and other siblings. Several pairs were excluded at this point because it was learned, for instance, that the co-twin had died before the age of 15. In most of these cases, the twin had died directly after birth. The sample was now reduced to 342 pairs of twins, or about 400 index cases.

All pairs of the same sex were then asked to visit their private physicians for blood samples to be taken. Since very few responded to this request, in most cases I had to visit the twins myself to get the blood samples. Some of these twins were extremely uncooperative. For example, there was one twin who had never been hospitalized but who was very defensive and secretive. A blood sample had been taken from her twin sister, but this sample was, of course, without any value if the co-twin's blood was not obtained. I called at her home five times; but twice she was either absent or disinclined to let me in, and the other three times she simply refused to permit me to take a blood sample. During the course of my visits to obtain blood samples I had to play various roles, ranging from that of an aggressive salesman to that of a beggar and, sometimes, that of a psychiatrist.

I succeeded in getting blood samples for 71 per cent of the sample group. The rest consisted of pairs of twins in which one or both had died, had left the country, or could not be located (19 per cent), or absolutely refused to give blood (10 per cent). However, rather reliable information was obtained about the similarities and dissimilarities existing in the doubtful group. Sixty pairs of the 75 pairs considered to be monozygotic have been blood-typed.

Blood tests were done on venous blood at the Institute of Medical Genetics, University of Oslo, without any knowledge of the clinical zygosity diagnosis. The following blood and serum systems were used: ABO, MNS, P, Rh, Le, Fy, Kell, Gm, and Gc. Juel-Nielsen and his co-workers (1958) have shown that 98 per cent of all dizygotic twins can be classified by means of the ten most common serological systems.

Psychiatric Investigation of the Family

I investigated as many as possible of the families of the monozygotic twins. First I studied personally both twins, and next, where it was possible, their siblings and parents. To obtain reliable information about the twins, I interviewed as many of their siblings as I could, and in the course of this it was relatively easy to investigate the siblings themselves. I succeeded in investigating personally 63 families of monozygotic twins, including about 160 siblings.

Forty-two pairs of dizygotic twins of the same sex were also studied personally, but not their families. The rest of the dizygotics were investigated on the basis of hospital records.

The home visit part of the study was highly interesting, but also very strenuous, as the twins and their families were geographically distributed over the whole country.

Information about the families was obtained through semistructured interviews. In studying the identical twins, I was especially interested in the life-history differences from early childhood on. As far as the siblings were concerned, attention was focused on the adult life and mental health status. Each twin was asked to describe his co-twin; and each sibling was asked to describe the other siblings and the twins. In this way the data were constantly corrected and supplemented. However, some families were extremely difficult to study, being inclined to see the interviewer as a policeman, a Gestapo agent, rather than as a psychiatric researcher. In one family in particular this attitude was displayed by all family members except one brother. They were silent and secretive, and all I could get from them was "I don't know. . . . There is no difference between us. . . . We are very much alike, all of us." And, in a way, they were right. They said they had never been nervous; they were all right. Only the one brother could give me a more colorful picture.

Therefore, in some cases, I had to seek information from other sources, asking help of the family doctor or other relatives. I point out here the indirect ways in which some of the information was obtained in order to show how unreliable part of the data may be. Of the personally investigated "monozygotic families," about 70 per cent can be classified as cooperative, 25 per cent as less cooperative, and 5 per cent as extremely uncooperative. All global personality, social functioning, and symptomatology evaluations are subjective. All the items of knowledge obtained from the hospital case histories, from schools, from doctors and hospitals, and from my own personal interviews were transferred to punchcards for analysis by computer.

While the home visits were a strenuous undertaking, from a psychiatric point of view they were very useful. They yielded information regarding the subjects' living conditions which would have been difficult to obtain by any other method. I was often able to speak with husbands and wives of the twins or siblings, who frequently were rather objective and ready to report symptoms—for instance, mild paranoid ideas, jealousy, excessive drinking, or drug abuse—which the subject might have been apt to deny. A visit to a remote farm, isolated, small, and poor, would give me a much more accurate picture of the subject's life than any hospital record could convey.

These home visits, however, were not without their tragic and sometimes comical aspects. I remember especially one family in Bergen in which there had been four offspring, including a pair of twins, both schizophrenic. One had died young; the second, showing signs of severe deterioration, was in a mental hospital. In talking to their sister, who was disabled by severe neurotic troubles, including headaches, depressions, and anxiety, I gathered that the youngest living brother had received a rather good education, but was a failure. The sister asked me not to contact him, since she was afraid that my visit might precipitate a nervous breakdown. I regretted not seeing him, for I wondered whether he was a schizophrenic or just lazy by nature, and some months later when I returned to Bergen I again called on the sister and asked her to agree to my interviewing him, promising to be very careful and not ask too many questions. This time she consented. I found his name, which was a quite unusual one, in the telephone directory, and when I phoned a boy answered and said that his father had gone to the country, and he gave me the address. I jumped into my car and took off, working my way through the Saturday afternoon crowds bound for an island near Bergen, and after driving for two hours, came to the farm where the man was staying. I was told that he was down at the fiord repairing his boat. I went down and introduced myself and asked whether he was MM. He said yes, he was. I then said that I was studying twins and knew that he had two twin brothers. "No," said the man. A bit startled, I thought to myself, "Brother, you are a real schizophrenic." Then I changed my approach and became extremely "psychiatric," repeating, "Yes, you have two twin brothers." At this he became angry, made a fist while standing in the boat, and said, "No, man. Can't you understand that I have no twins in my family and that I never have had any?" Curious paranoid ideas, I thought. We looked at each other for a few seconds. Really not knowing what to do next, I said, "Aren't you MM?" "Yes," he replied. A new silence. Then a light dawned on the man, and he became very angry indeed. "Now I understand," he said. "This is the second time this man has caused me trouble!" He then told me about his alter ego, a man who had the same name, but who was not in the telephone directory. All the same, the wrong MM was able to give me some information. "This man," he said, "caused me trouble some years ago. I paid for him the year they changed the tax system in Norway, because the income tax agencies mixed us up." I asked him some questions, and he gave a rather thorough report on the other man's personality.

It was evening by then, and I drove back to Bergen, obtained the mystery man's address, and went to his home, but no one was there. The house looked rather poor for one of his profession, which seemed to confirm the impression of failure I had gotten from his sister. Even more anxious to meet him, I went back to my hotel to learn that my plane had just left for Oslo. On Sunday morning, I went to see the man again, but he was still away. This time I could wait no longer and had to leave for Oslo without meeting my quarry.

Classification

Three types of classification were used principally: the classical type based on psychiatric diagnosis—for example, schizophrenia, reactive psychosis, and manic-depressive illness; the one based on syndrome—for example, depression, excitement, paranoid symptoms, obsessions, and so on; and a global-evaluation diagnosis based mainly on symptomatology, personality, and social functioning. This mental health rating scale ranges from 1 to 7, from "normality" to severe deteriorated schizophrenia. My approach has been a phenomenological one with emphasis on description, and with an effort to avoid too many inferences.

TABLE I

ZYGOSITY OF SAMPLE, IN COMPARISON WITH EXPECTATIONS ACCORDING TO WEINBERG'S METHOD*

	Male	Observed Female	Total	Expected Total
Monozygotics	37	38	75	90
Dizygotics, same sex	65	66	133	126
Unknown zygosity, same sex	6	4	10	
Dizygotics, opposite sex			126	126
Total pairs	108	108	342	342

* See Weinberg's differential method as described in Stern (1960).

Results

Table I presents a comparison of the zygosity of the twins observed with the expected numbers according to Weinberg's method. The 126 pairs of twins of opposite sex are without further ado dizygotics. Roughly speaking, there ought to be the same number of dizygotics of the same sex. According to Weinberg's differential method, the number of monozygotics is then obtained by subtracting the dizygotics from the total of all twins. There are fewer twins in this group found to be monozygotics than expected. (It is assumed that schizophrenia, reactive psychosis, and manic-depressive illness are equally distributed in all twin groups.) This means that some of the pairs supposed to be dizygotic and/or some pairs in the unknown group are probably monozygotic. The difference is, however, not significant at the 5 per cent level (the observed difference is 1.9 times its standard error).

In all previous twin studies dealing with psychoses there has been an excess of female pairs, most likely due to shortcomings in sampling. In the present twin series there is practically the same number of male and female pairs of the same sex, as shown in Table I.

TABLE II

CONCORDANCE FOR ALL TYPES OF FUNCTIONAL PSYCHOSES*

	Number of Pairs	Concordant	Discordant	Per cent Concordant
Monozygotics	75	18	57	24%
Dizygotics, same sex	131	8	123	6%
Unknown zygosity, same sex	10	0	10	0%
Dizygotics, opposite sex	126	8	118	6%

* These figures are arrived at by checking the twin register against the Register of Psychosis. The figures are without age correction.

Table II gives an overall picture of the concordance rates, with the three main diagnostic groups—schizophrenia, reactive psychosis, and manic-depressive psychosis—lumped together. The concordance rates are significantly different for monozygotics and dizygotics, but the difference is less than usually reported.

The concordance figures for "strict"—that is, strictly defined—schizophrenia plus the group of so-called schizophreniform psychoses are presented in Table III.

TABLE III

CONCORDANCE FOR SCHIZOPHRENIA AND SCHIZOPHRENIFORM PSYCHOSES, BASED ON HOSPITALIZED CASES*

	Number of Pairs	Concordant	Discordant	Per cent Concordant
Monozygotics	55	14	41	25%
Dizygotics, same sex	90	6	84	7%
Unknown zygosity, same sex	6	0	6	0%
Dizygotics, opposite sex	82	8	74	10%

  * See Langfeldt (1939).

The term "schizophreniform" is used in a descriptive clinical sense. This group comprises psychoses, usually with an acute onset, with a clearcut precipitating factor and a good prognosis. The symptoms may, however, be quite similar to typical schizophrenia. Patients belonging to this group will in most countries, including the United States and England, be classified as schizophrenic. The figures are based on hospitalized cases. During the personal investigations I learned that three of the co-twins in the monozygotic group had been psychotic, but not hospitalized. If these are included, the concordance figures are raised to 31 per cent.

TABLE IV

CONCORDANCE FOR SCHIZOPHRENIA AND SCHIZOPHRENIFORM PSYCHOSES, BASED ON FURTHER PERSONAL INVESTIGATION

	Number of Pairs	Concordant	Discordant	Per cent Concordant
Monozygotics	55	21	34	38%
Dizygotics, same sex	90	9	81	10%

Table IV shows the concordance figures when a rather wide concept of concordance is used, and is based on personal investigation as well as hospitalization. A pair is grouped as concordant if the index case has a diagnosis of schizophrenia or schizophreniform psychosis and the co-twin has either the same diagnosis or a diagnosis of reactive psychosis or borderline. (There is no "cross-over" to typical manic-depressive psychosis.) Personal knowledge was utilized for half of the schizophrenic dizygotic group of the same sex. The opposite-sexed dizygotics were not personally investigated.

As the table clearly shows, even if a rather wide concept of concordance is used, the concordance rates are still low. There is some increase for both the monozygotics and the dizygotics.

TABLE V

CONCORDANCE FOR "STRICT" SCHIZOPHRENIA, BASED ON HOSPITALIZED CASES

	Number of Pairs	Concordant	Discordant	Per cent Concordant
Monozygotics	45	12	33	27%
Dizygotics, same sex	69	3	66	4%
Dizygotics, opposite sex	64	3	61	5%

Table V gives the concordance rates for typical schizophrenia, excluding so-called schizophreniform psychoses. Regardless of school of thought, most clinicians should be able to agree on a diagnosis of schizophrenia for these cases. The findings are based on hospitalized cases. The result of the personal investigation will not change these figures significantly; only one discordant pair in the monozygotic group would be reclassified as concordant.

As shown in Table I, the number of males and females in the sample is nearly the same. Concordance rates for monozygotic male and female pairs are compared in Table VI, which shows no significant difference between the sexes.

TABLE VI

CONCORDANCE OF MALE AND FEMALE PAIRS OF MONOZYGOTIC TWINS FOR SCHIZOPHRENIA AND SCHIZOPHRENIFORM PSYCHOSES*

	Number of Pairs	Concordant	Discordant
Male	31	13 (7)	18 (24)
Female	24	8 (7)	16 (17)
Total	55	21 (14)	34 (41)

* The figures in parentheses are based on hospitalized cases.

The numbers based upon clinical assessment—employing a wide concept of concordance, and calling a pair concordant if, for instance, the index case is typically schizophrenic and the co-twin severe borderline—show a tendency toward higher concordance rates for male twins, 42 per cent, against 33 per cent for female, but statistically nonsignificant. Based on hospitalized cases, the concordance figures are lower for male twins, 23 per cent, against 29 per cent for female.

In previous studies there is a considerable difference between the concordance rates for women and those for men, the latter being markedly lower. This is apparent in the studies of Luxenburger (1928, 1934, 1936), Rosanoff and his co-workers (1934), and Slater (1953). Kallmann (1946) and Inouye (1961) did not give breakdowns of their concordant and discordant pairs by sex. Tienari (1963) studied only male pairs. Probably sampling errors and psychological factors influence the sex-concordance ratios. This problem is discussed in detail by Rosenthal (1962), who favors the psychological hypothesis.

In the main, the concordance figures for schizophrenia in dizygotic twins are not significantly different from those of previous studies—namely, 4 to 10 per cent. The figures for monozygotics, on the other hand, are considerably lower than usually reported—namely, 25 to 38 per cent, according to whether the concordance rates are based on hospitalized cases or personal investigations, and whether a wide or a strict concept of schizophrenia is employed.

The difference in concordance rates for monozygotic and dizygotic twins with respect to schizophrenia is statistically significant, thus supporting a genetic factor in the etiology of schizophrenia, but the genetic factor seems to be much weaker than it is usually considered to be.

Discussion of Methodology

The sources of error in this study should be of a minor nature, but still they should be examined and their implications discussed.

Sources of Error Due to Sampling

As mentioned earlier, this study should have this advantage: The material is large and unselective. There is good reason to believe that practically all clearcut schizophrenics sooner or later will be hospitalized in Norway. However, I have data that show that this assumption is but roughly true. Of the siblings and co-twins found to have been psychotic by personal investigation, about 20 per cent were not in the Register of Psychosis, either because they had never been hospitalized or because of unsatisfactory reporting. This source of error, however, is of minor degree, as the following calculations clearly show: If one assumes that the probability of being hospitalized and reported to the Register of Psychosis is 80 per cent ($p = 0.8$) and that members of a concordant pair are admitted or reported independently, then the probability of being in this sample is 0.8 for a discordant pair and 0.96 for a concordant pair. That is, the probability that either of two outcomes will occur is the sum of their probabilities minus the probability that both will occur together; thus, for a concordant pair: $p = 0.8 + 0.8 - (0.8 \times 0.8) = 0.96$. This will lower the concordance figures by about 3 per cent in the monozygotic group and by about 1 per cent in the dizygotic group, if based on the figures in Table II. Hence, from a sampling point of view, the concordance figures in this study represent maximum figures because concordant pairs will have a greater chance of appearing in this sample than discordant ones.

TABLE VII

"TEXTBOOK" CONCORDANCE FOR SCHIZOPHRENIA IN MONOZYGOTIC AND DIZYGOTIC TWINS ACCORDING TO VARIOUS INVESTIGATORS

	Monozygotics		Dizygotics	
	Number of Pairs	Concordance	Number of Pairs	Concordance
Luxenburger (Germany, 1928)	17	67%	33	0%
Rosanoff and others (U.S.A., 1934)	41	67%	101	10%
Essen-Møller (Sweden, 1941)	7	71%	24	17%
Kallmann (U.S.A., 1953)	268	86%*	685	15%*
Slater (England, 1953)	41	76%*	115	14%*

*Corrected for age.

Sources of Error Due to Doubtful Zygosity Diagnosis

According to the Weinberg differential method (Stern, 1960), one would expect to find 90 identical pairs in my sample of 216 pairs of the same sex. I observed only 75. This means that some of the pairs supposed to be dizygotic and/or some pairs in the unknown group are probably monozygotic. Since all except two pairs in this doubtful group are discordant pairs, this would have the effect of lowering the concordance figures of the monozygotic group. Such an assumption is also reasonable from another point of view. The zygosity diagnosis of the doubtful cases is based upon answers to such questions as the following: Were you and your co-twin "mixed up" as children? and Were you and your co-twin as alike as two drops of water? Cederløf and his co-workers (1961) have shown that the diagnosis of monozygosity can be nearly 100 per cent correct when based upon such simple questions. This means that there is no reason to believe that the pairs in the group that are supposed to be identical are not. The diagnosis of dizygosity, however, is not made with the same certainty when these questions are used. The same authors found that 88 per cent of the total number of serologically discordant twin pairs were diagnosed as dizygotic.

From a sampling point of view, about 15 pairs of twins of doubtful zygosity should probably be monozygotic. On the assumption that more than 88 per cent of the dizygotics are correctly diagnosed by the questionnaire and interview method, less than five pairs classified as dizygotics should be monozygotics.

On this basis it seems reasonable to conclude that the concordance rates from a zygosity point of view have to be lowered in monozygotics and increased in dizygotics. It is evident, however, from the figures presented that this source of error due to doubtful zygosity diagnosis is negligible.

Sources of Error Due to Risk Period

When a discordant pair of twins has not passed the risk period of the illness under discussion, correction should be made for age. For instance, a pair discordant for schizophrenia who are 20 years of age should be followed for about 25 years to see whether they remain discordant. In the twin population under consideration some have not passed the risk period. The observed concordance figures will, hence, from this point of view, represent minimal figures. In this paper I have dealt especially with schizophrenia. If the generally accepted risk period of 15 to 45 is used, it will be found that most of the schizophrenics have passed the risk period and that all are older than 34 years, at which age more than 60 per cent of potential schizophrenics have developed the illness (Strømgren, 1938; Ødegaard, 1946). In my opinion, one has to take into account the correlation of the age of onset of the psychosis, the length of time the co-twin has been well before and/or after the illness of the proband, and the clinical evaluation of the co-twin (Kringlen, 1964a). In the broad schizophrenic group of this study, 10 discordant pairs are in the 35 to 45 age group, and 5 of these are more than 40 years of age. According to Kallmann (1946), monozygotic twins become concordant for schizophrenia at roughly the same age. He reports, in fact, that 89.4 per cent of the concordant pairs had an interval of onset of less than eight years. In the present sample all of the schizophrenics in the discordant group, in the 35 to 45 age group, had been sick for at least eight years. Clinically the chance of the development of schizophrenia in the nonschizophrenic co-twin seems minimal, since the eight indicated above showed good social adjustment and mental stability. In conclusion, it might be said that, taken together, the probabilities of schizophrenia developing in these are minimal from all angles, and correction for age is unnecessary. The same applies to the dizygotic group.

Discussion of Previous Studies

In most of the more comprehensive earlier studies, the concordance rates found for schizophrenia were much higher for uniovular than for biovular twins. I would now like briefly to examine the previous studies more critically. It is not unusual to find the information presented in Table VII in psychiatric textbooks, or in review articles about the etiology of schizophrenia. It has to be conceded that the picture is remarkably uniform. However, Table VIII shows a picture that is far more varied.

TABLE VIII

CONCORDANCE FOR SCHIZOPHRENIA IN MONOZYGOTIC TWINS ACCORDING TO VARIOUS INVESTIGATORS

Luxenburger (Germany, 1928)	67%
Luxenburger (Germany, 1934)	33%
Luxenburger (Germany, 1936)	52%
Rosanoff and others (U.S.A., 1934)	61%*
Essen-Møller (Sweden, 1941)	0-71%
Kallmann (U.S.A., 1953)	69% (86%)†
Slater (England, 1953)	65% (69%)*†
Inouye (Japan, 1961)	60% (76%)†
Tienari (Finland, 1963)	0%

* Modified by the present author.
† Figures in parentheses are corrected for age.

Luxenburger was the first to stress the importance of the sampling procedure. Starting with patient material obtained mostly from hospitals in Bavaria, he studied parish registers to locate the twins. His 1928 material includes consecutive admissions as well as the resident hospital populations. Hence, it is evident that this sampling procedure was very good. His zygosity data, seemingly as accurate as they could have been in those days, were obtained mainly by Siemens' "similarity method" (1924). This is a practicable method for distinguishing between monozygotics and dizygotics, based upon a systematic comparison of twin pairs and measurement of their degree of resemblance with respect to a number of morphological traits supposed to be genetically determined. However, several uncertainty factors were connected with the calculation of the concordance rates in Luxenburger's material. To be safe, perhaps one should say that his concordance figures for male monozygotics are from 30 to 70 per cent and for female monozygotics 30 to 90 per cent. Noteworthy is Luxenburger's revised and extended 1934 material, in which he found a much lower concordance rate for monozygotic pairs than in his first material. In a third study Luxenburger found a concordance rate of 52 per cent (1928, 1934, 1936).

Essen-Møller (1941) used Luxenburger's method as a starting point in his study of birth registers. His material comprised only consecutive hospital admissions. His schizophrenic group included four female and three male uniovular pairs. With the use of the term schizophrenia in its strictest sense, no concordance was found in any of the cases, but some of the co-twins had had lighter psychoses without hospitalization, which might be described as reactive transient episodes. If these are regarded as cases of schizophrenia, the concordance rates become higher, 14 per cent to 71 per cent. In his 1963 article, Essen-Møller explicitly states that, in fact, no clearcut instances of schizophrenia could be found among the co-twins.

As to the other three studies, those of Rosanoff, Kallmann, and Slater, certain shortcomings appear in the sampling procedure. They did not start with a study of the birth registers as Luxenburger and Essen-Møller had done. Consequently, one might expect to find a relatively higher number of concordant than of discordant cases. All these authors, moreover, collected their material chiefly from among chronic hospital inmates. Rosenthal (1961) suggests that there are many indications that this will give a higher concordance rate than would have been obtained with consecutive admissions.

Kallmann (1946, 1953) started out with a chronic hospital population and later included consecutive admissions. His data are based on reports from the staffs of mental hospitals in the state of New York, not on birth registers. Since his sampling is unsystematic, he is bound to have a preponderance of concordant cases. That his data are not representative is easily confirmed by referral to Rosenthal's studies. From a Scandinavian point of view, his concept of schizophrenia is exceedingly broad. My objection to this latitude in the diagnosis of schizophrenia is not rigid. No psychiatric diagnoses are right or wrong. Like most definitions, one may be more convenient than another. My criticism of Kallmann is not aimed at his concept of schizophrenia as such, but at his failure to describe its implications. That the concordance rate will be higher with such diagnostic procedures is not surprising, since many pairs will be classified as concordant even if the clinical picture of the members of the pairs is highly different. One must assume, for instance, that by these diagnostic procedures a pair of twins in which one presents marked schizophrenic deterioration while the other has massive neurotic symptoms (panneurotic) but no psychotic traits would be classified as concordant. A pair in which one has schizophrenic dementia while the other is unaffected but has previously had a transient reactive psychosis again would be classified by Kallmann as concordant.

The establishment of zygosity in Kallmann's work was based partly on his personal observations. He used Siemen's "similarity method" and made no serological tests, rendering the diagnosis less definite than it would have been if a blood workup had been included.

With reference to computation of concordance, one has to make a correction for age if the pair is not past the period of risk as to schizophrenia. It should be noted that Kallmann's original concordance figure for schizophrenia in monozygotic twins was 69 per cent. The often cited figure of 86 per cent was arrived at by using Weinberg's short method for calculation of the morbidity risk of the nonaffected co-twin. This crude method is highly disputable, in particular with regard to twin studies, since Weinberg counts on no risk up to 15 years of age, half risk from 15 to 44 years of age, and full risk after 44. Slater (1953, p. 54) categorically states that application of this method on his own material gives figures that have little meaning. I am in accordance with Slater, who maintains that one has to take into account both correlation of age at onset of the psychosis and the length of time the co-twin has been well before and/or after the illness of the proband, and, I would add, if possible, also the clinical evaluation of the co-twin.

It is hard to form an accurate idea of the sources of error in Kallmann's work, but it seems likely that all of them tend to give rather high concordance rates. This is fairly certain with regard to his sampling procedure, psychiatric diagnosis, and employment of the Weinberg statistical method. Whether the tendency is the same when it comes to establishing the zygosity diagnosis is hard to decide.

Rosanoff and his collaborators (1934) used samples from a resident hospital population, and the establishment of twinship was made by inquiry. These authors used the similarity method in zygosity diagnosis. They arrived at various degrees of concordance. In my opinion the concordance figures should be 61 per cent, not 67 per cent as is frequently stated. I would also like to point out the marked difference in concordance rates for males and females, 42 per cent and 78 per cent, respectively.

Slater (1953) sampled a resident hospital population and established twinship by mailed inquiry. He also did not use a serological confirmation of the zygosity diagnosis. According to Rosenthal (1962) one should expect a preponderance of concordant cases by this sampling method. Like Luxenburger and Rosanoff, Slater found higher concordance rates for the female than for the male pairs. Of 11 male monozygotic pairs only 5 (45 per cent) are classified as concordant.

Inouye (1961) did not explain how he collected his twin material, but he explicitly stated that the sampling was not systematic. Both twins were alive in all 72 pairs. Zygosity was established by the similarity method in combination with serological tests. The author dealt especially with diagnostic and nosological problems.

In general, then, the concordance rates indicated in these previous works have to be regarded as maximal. I would also like to stress that there is a considerable difference between the rates for women and those for men, the latter being markedly lower. This is apparent in the studies of Luxenburger, Rosanoff and co-workers, and Slater. Kallmann and Inouye did not break down their concordant and discordant pairs by sex. Probably sampling errors and psychological factors influence the sex-concordance ratios. Theoretically the difference might also be due to different penetrance in the two sexes.

A recent study by Tienari (1963), dealing with a population of twins, all males, born in Finland between 1920 and 1929, is, in my opinion, the best study thus far from a methodological point of view. In Tienari's study zygosity was established on the basis of a number of variables, including the results of a battery of serological tests. Although a few of the 16 probands were not typical schizophrenics, a sample of 12 to 13 monozygotics, all of them discordant as to schizophrenia, is a remarkable finding.

I have only two minor reservations, which the author himself points out: Not all of Tienari's pairs were past the period of schizophrenic risk, and there was a relatively high loss of cases. It is noteworthy that Tienari failed to find a single monozygotic pair concordant for schizophrenia. This must have been more or less fortuitous, since it is generally known that concordant pairs do exist. The dizygotic group included 1 to 3 concordant pairs.

I shall try to speculate on why Tienari did not find even one concordant monozygotic pair. In his initial material, he had 2,288 pairs of twins, all males. He excluded from this 1,147 pairs, in most instances because either one or both of the twins had died before 1957. Now, the question is: Was this last group composed primarily of concordant cases? The answer is not certain, but it is my hypothesis that Tienari lost, for the most part, concordant pairs.

Until recently, tuberculosis was the principal cause of death in psychiatric institutions, where its incidence was much higher than among the general population. The chances of dying of tuberculosis were much higher in a mental institution than on the outside. Hence with his material Tienari was more apt to lose the concordant pairs than the discordant pairs. It should be remembered, moreover, that the deaths of concordant twins are not wholly unrelated events, since such twins are thrown together much of the time, which increases the chance of their infecting each other.

I find some support for this hypothesis in my own data. Where one or both of the twins had died, five of the eight monozygotic pairs of twins were concordant, while three were discordant. One would have expected it to be the other way round. However, I must stress that, even if this hypothesis does apply to Tienari's material, it does not detract from the significance of his figures.

My general conclusion is that the earlier studies probably contained many sources of error, the most important of which resided in the sampling techniques that gave results in which the genetic factor was overestimated. Perhaps it should be added that these earlier studies were made at a time when one of the leading questions was whether schizophrenia and other "functional" psychoses were organic or hereditary diseases, and when only a very few psychiatrists seriously believed that they were determined by psychogenic factors. After all, it is only within the last 10 to 15 years that the psychogenetic hypotheses have become popular in psychiatric circles. (In the United States a more functional view of schizophrenia has been prevalent since the teachings of Adolf Meyer in the 1920's.)

One may, of course, wonder whether Scandinavian twins are different from twins in other countries. Is the mutual relationship of twins far more intense in other countries? There are up to now no data to answer this question, but I personally feel that differences in sampling methods, in the psychiatric diagnostic fashion, and in the zygosity diagnosis, to name the more important sources of errors, are sufficient to explain the variability in concordance figures. For a more detailed critical review readers are referred to the studies by Rosenthal (1961, 1962), Tienari (1963), and Kringlen (1964a).

It should also be noted that criticism has been leveled against the assumption, which is implicit in the classical interpretation of twin data, that the environments of monozygotic and dizygotic twins are alike, somatically and psychologically. I shall postpone discussion of this difficult problem until I can present data which hopefully can throw some light on it.

In the investigations so far, this pattern seems consistent: *The more accurate and careful the samplings, the lower the concordance figures.* In the present study of an unselected sample of 342 pairs of twins, 35 to 64 years of age, where one or both at some time in their lives had been hospitalized for a "functional psychosis," the concordance figures for schizophrenia were found to be 25 to 38 per cent in monozygotics and 4 to 10 per cent in dizygotics. These concordance rates support a genetic factor in the etiology of schizophrenia; however, the genetic factor does not play as great a role as has been assumed.

21 / Prospective Studies on the Epidemiology of Reproductive Casualty: Methods, Findings, and Some Implications

Hilda Knobloch / Benjamin Pasamanick

We first became interested in the influence of prenatal factors during the course of a longitudinal study of Negro child development in New Haven (Pasamanick, 1946). In a group of Negro infants born during one of the middle war years we found adaptive behavioral development proceeding at rates normal for white infants according to the Gesell developmental techniques. Not only was this finding contrary to previous published studies, but also no explanation of the disparity could be found in environmental associations such as the education or geographic origin of the parents, number of siblings, quality of housing, or skin color. However, when the growth curves were examined we noted (also contrary to previous findings) that from birth the subjects were progressing according to the best available white rates in both weight and height.

On the basis of this we hypothesized that the mothers of these infants had received an adequate prenatal diet because of wartime rationing, and because of employment opportunities that bettered their economic status. This hypothesis was supported by further examinations of the children, continued into their eighth year of life (Knobloch and Pasamanick, 1953). At seven years of age, the subjects had a mean intellectual functioning equal to that of the mean white scores as measured on the Stanford-Binet and Arthur performance tests (E. Nash, H. Nash, Knobloch, and Pasamanick, unpublished data).

At this time we would not wish to overemphasize the contribution of prenatal diet to the parity of Negro and white infants in this study. We have found in two additional and larger representative groups of postwar Negro infants that they are identical to white infants in behavioral development. However, it would appear likely that prenatal diet did play a role in the comparable physical growth rates; it may also have played some role in maintaining the intellectual function-

Abridged from the *Merrill-Palmer Quarterly*, 1966, 12, 27–43. Copyright © 1966. Reprinted by permission of the authors and *Merrill-Palmer Quarterly*.

ing of the group as a whole at white rates into the school years (Pasamanick, 1962).

In two areas of behavioral development, language and gross motor behavior, we did find significant differences from the white norms. The lowered language scores found at two years of age were shown to be due to impaired verbal responsiveness, possibly a result of inhibition caused by a white examiner, while verbal comprehension remained unimpaired (Pasamanick and Knobloch, 1955). It may also indicate the beginning of the loss of verbal ability seen in lower-class children, attributable to decreased verbal stimulation by the relatively less articulate, less well-educated lower-class mother. During the course of another study to be described later, we found that the seeming acceleration in gross motor behavior that had also been described by other investigators was not present (Knobloch and Pasamanick, 1959b). Motor behavior of white and Negro infants at the midcentury is comparable and is significantly accelerated over the norms established a decade or two ago. This may be due to changes in childrearing methods, but no definitive explanation is available at this time.

The retrospective studies discussed elsewhere (Pasamanick and Knobloch, 1966) indicated the potent association of prematurity, as defined by a birth weight of 2500 grams or less, with a number of clinical conditions which might be attributable to brain damage. A somewhat better test of the hypothesis was deemed possible through the prospective investigation, in which the dependent variable of the retrospective studies became the independent variable and the independent, in turn, became the dependent examined repeatedly through time (Pasamanick, 1952a). It was thought that by examining the children periodically it would not only be possible to confirm the previous findings but that abnormal neurologic signs and symptoms more readily found during infancy would indicate that the psychologic, neurologic, and social difficulties found later were truly associated with damage to the brain (Knobloch and Pasamanick, 1959a).

Some 12 years ago we entered upon such a study in which the independent variable was prematurity. In this study a socioeconomically stratified sample of 500 prematurely born children delivered in one year in Baltimore and their full-term matched controls were followed from birth. A detailed description of the study design and analysis has already been published (Knobloch and Pasamanick, 1956; Knobloch et al., 1955), but some of the findings of the Gesell Developmental Examination given at 40 weeks of age are germane to our present discussion.

When adjustments were made for differences between the whites and non-whites in the distribution of birth weights, no significant differences were found between the races in the incidence of neurologic and intellectual defect (Knobloch et al., 1956). However, as was predicted by our hypothesis, the incidence of abnormality increased as the birth weight decreased. The frequency of serious neurologic abnormality was significantly higher in the prematures than in the controls, and there was a high negative correlation of intellectual potential with degree of prematurity. Of the infants with birth weights under 1500 gm., 44 per cent had an abnormal condition of sufficient magnitude to cause serious concern about the prognosis for future development. The comparable incidence for the rest of the premature group was 8.6 per cent, and for the full-term infants, 2.6 per cent.

In addition, significantly more of the prematures exhibited the syndrome of "minimal damage." This syndrome describes a group of children who in infancy show distinct and definite deviations in neurologic patterning, but in whom clinical experience indicates that complete compensation for the neurologic abnormalities will occur with maturation. According to the hypothesis these children— found among both prematures (16.3 per cent) and controls (10 per cent)—are the ones who should exhibit at a later date the integrational defects seen in behavior and learning disorders.

We have had occasion to do an item analysis of the 46 individual neurologic patterns investigated in our study of prematures; it has given us a clinical picture of what may be a fairly specific entity, and it is now being tested by further studies (Knobloch and Pasamanick, 1959c). Unfortunately, most of these neurologic items are difficult or impossible to secure on a retrospective historical basis in clinical practice. They include such items as substitutive patterns, excessive extension in and abruptness of release, difficulty in retaining, maldirected reaching, increased tendon reflexes, hypertonicity, and so on. However, some of the behavior patterns that can be secured by anamnesis (such as sucking and feeding difficulties, and excessive startle), and which are as discriminating as the neurologic items, deviate in the same direction.

On re-examination at three years of age, most of our expectations of behavioral difficulties in those infants in whom some degree of neurologic impairment was found were confirmed (Knobloch and Pasamanick, 1962). Difficulties in achieving bowel and bladder control, organization of behavior, maturity, discrimination, judgment, exploitation, emotional stability, attention, perseveration, irritability, restlessness, crying, scatter, and overall quality of integration were all found to be statistically significantly present. These are signs and symptoms reported in known brain-damaged children. These children are now of school age and follow-up by others indicates persistent difficulties.

Some of our findings in studies on perception in known brain-injured, school-age children may provide an explanation of the sources of difficulty in minimally brain-injured individuals, as well as a basis for some objective diagnostic measures. While studying different measures of visual perception—including light thresholds (Mark and Pasamanick, 1958a), a critical flicker fusion (Mark, Meier, and Pasamanick, 1958), asynchronism and apparent movement thresholds (Mark and Pasamanick, 1958)—we found, in addition to threshold differences, significant intra-individual response variability. These studies were strengthened by threshold measurements in other sense modalities, including the proprioceptive. The findings are probably related to the so-called "scatter of function" referred to in intelligence testing. It is possible to hypothesize, therefore, that organic dysfunction readily manifests itself in a lack of consistency of one sort or another. Indeed, it is easy to conceptualize how increased variability in the relatively simpler primary functions, such as light perception, may actually give rise to dysfunction in processes such as conditioning and memory, as well as in more complex behavior patterns.

The large numbers involved in this prospective investigation permitted us to examine more closely the entire question of racial and social variables determining intellectual development, i.e., enter upon the vexing and vital nature-nurture controversy (Pasamanick, 1963; Knobloch and Pasamanick, 1961). The distribution of general developmental quotients was made representative of the infant population of Baltimore by adjusting for difference in birth weight, race, and economic status in the infant sample. At 40 weeks of age, the mean general developmental quotient was 105 and 104 for the white and nonwhite controls respectively (Knobloch and Pasamanick, 1959). It is noteworthy that the distribution of the general developmental quotient was not affected by differences in the education of the parents or by economic status. Essentially the same findings were noted in the 1,000 infants in our Columbus sample. At approximately three years of age, however, distinct racial differences were observed. In the first 300 of the 1,000 children in the Baltimore study the mean developmental quotient for the whites rose significantly to 111 while that for the nonwhites fell to 97.

A closer scrutiny of the distributions is quite illuminating. When the infant distributions are compared with those found on Stanford-Binet testing in older children, it is quite apparent that the latter is much broader and closer to a normal distribution. Two points about this widening are important. First, relatively little increase occurred at the upper range of the I.Q. scale compared with the marked increase in the percentage of older children who had I.Q.s under 85. In addition, in the infant group there was a sharp, abrupt rise at a level of 90, while in the older group this curve was relatively smooth, and the increase started at a lower level in the 50 to 55 I.Q. range. When we examined the distribution at three years of age by socioeconomic status, we began to note some of the possible causes for these differences (Knobloch and Pasamanick, 1961a). In the Negro group, in contrast to what was found during infancy, the children from lower-status families go down, the upper nonwhite and lower white groups remain unchanged, and the upper white group goes up. In accordance with their socioeconomic circumstances, Negroes are lowest, lower-class whites are intermediate, and upper-class whites are highest. We now begin to see the divergence in functioning by status, which we know from the literature increases with age and experience (Knobloch and Pasamanick, 1960).

The significance of the data offered is dependent upon the reliability and validity of the methods used. Much as we are tempted to enter upon a discussion of the meaning and utility of infant developmental methods, time forbids. Suffice it to say that in our hands, and now replicated by others, the levels of reliability of the quantitative judgments made are surprisingly similar to those on the Stanford-Binet at school ages (Knobloch and Pasamanick, 1960). Test-retest correlations, using different examiners or a number of examiners observing the same examination, give correlations above 0.9, depending upon the examiner, the nature of his training, and the circumstances of the examination. Examiners examining the same child at different times achieve correlations only slightly below 0.9. Predictability, in terms of correlations between early and late examinations, averages approximately 0.5 in a number of different samples, the maximum difference in ages being almost seven years (Knobloch and Pasamanick, 1962).

Findings of the tests of reliability and prediction help support some of the hypotheses advanced for the determinants of intelligence. Sources of variance lay in the immediate circumstances of examination and physical state, such as illness, emotional distress, or learning, and in the long-term biological and sociopsychological experience. For example, infants who recovered from seizures tended to go up in score; children who developed seizures went down. Children with obvious signs of brain damage tended on the whole to do worse with time;

environmental and test factors increased in complexity and proved detrimental to performance. The major source of variation in prediction was initial performance. The performance of those infants at the lower end of the curve (there largely because of brain damage) could be predicted best. The highest correlation, 0.75, was encountered in the damaged group between the 40-week and 3-year examinations. (Our most recent and highest correlations are over 0.6 between infancy and seven years with 0.9 for a group of retarded children of the same ages.) Correlations fell as the scores rose, particularly the scores at the older ages. This is understandable on the basis of the data previously presented, inasmuch as family circumstances were more and more influential in determining the intellectual functioning of the developing child (Knobloch and Pasamanick, 1961a).

A parenthetical note apropos maternal deprivation and the effects of hospitalization might be inserted at this point. In the study referred to in the introduction of this report, we found that in addition to a linear positive relationship of maternal tension to degree of brain damage there was a similar direct relationship of brain injury to illness (Knobloch et al., 1959). This was accompanied by a significantly higher rate of hospitalization that could be related directly to the amount of cerebral injury. It should be apparent by now that the psychologic effects of early hospitalization may not be simply a result of maternal deprivation but may contain within the complex mother-child system the additional variable of brain injury in a significant number of the cases. The interactions between behavioral dysfunction in the infant as a symptom of minimal cerebral injury and maternal tension, illness, hospitalization, and psychologic injury, eventually followed by further dysfunction and tension, should be considered as possible causes of behavioral difficulties later in childhood. Further, since a large number of children exhibit no significant difficulties after hospitalization, we must consider the possibility that it may be largely those children having some brain injury, with a consequent lowering of thresholds to stress, who are affected by hospitalization during infancy.

Considerable strength was added to this impression by an additional test applied to the data. Since it was possible that the mothers might have been tense because of the prematurity of their children rather than their developmental difficulties, mothers of neurologically normal prematures were compared with mothers whose premature children were judged to be abnormal. The former were found to be no more tense than the mothers of normal full-term infants; concomitantly, if the full-term control was abnormal, the proportion of tense mothers was comparable to that found in the mothers of the abnormal prematures. These findings indicate quite clearly that it was the infant's abnormality which made the mother tense rather than its prematurity.

Another aspect of the concept that some childhood difficulties are the result of organic dysfunction rather than of maternal problems may be present in the frequently puzzling failure of infants to thrive. This infantile growth failure—when not obviously due to infections, organ inadequacy such as renal malformation, or other overt organic impairment—has frequently been attributed to maternal deprivation or lack of affection. We have now seen a sizable number of these diagnostic problems and have found that neurologically, developmentally, and in respect to a history of prematurity and prenatal maternal complications of

pregnancy, they resemble the host of brain-injured children we have been studying. This should not have occasioned any surprise, when we recall that it has
been known and documented in numerous reports that many overtly brain-
damaged children who have mental deficiency or cerebral palsy also exhibit
failure to grow normally even under the best environmental circumstances.
The mechanisms remain obscure; it may be, in some instances, merely another
sign of disinterest or nonresponsiveness to stimuli, this time food or the feeding
situation. On the other hand, it may be more complex and intrinsic to the structural dysfunction. It is now well known that various central nervous system activities on the cortical and subcortical levels which involve voluntary and visceral
functioning, including neural control of the endocrines, must be integrated for
normal physical growth. Impairment of any of these functions could be a cause
of infantile growth failure and consequent maternal distress. In any event, this
clinical phenomenon might seriously be considered for possible inclusion as another constituent of the continuum of reproductive casualty. We have recently begun an investigation to test this hypothesis.

Failure to thrive physically is not infrequently encountered in institutions for
prolonged infant care. It is possible that in a portion of these cases this failure is
attributable to the lack of stimulation in these institutions which generalizes to
feeding situations. On the other hand, we know that infants in these institutions,
who stem almost wholly from the lowest socioeconomic circumstances and are
frequently illegitimate and otherwise deprived and neglected, are those at greatest
risk of prenatal exposure to precursors of brain damage and thus to be found in
greater numbers in infant care institutions. The most likely explanation for many
of the cases is a lowering of thresholds to environmental difficulties following
upon minimal brain injury, aggravated by inadequate or faulty sensory and social
stimulation and eventually resulting in retardation or distortion of behavioral development and growth.

The same series of events must be considered in explaining many of the difficulties in individuals who come from poor social and economic backgrounds. For
instance, the reported incidence of behavioral difficulties in adopted children may
not be due wholly to adoption mismanagement but rather to the spiralling effects
of the variables discussed above. It must be remembered at all times that the
majority of children in institutions, in adoptive homes, or indeed in lower socioeconomic circumstances are unimpaired, further supporting the concept that some
intervening but not independent variable as brain injury may be involved.

By this time it should be quite apparent that if, in a country so well supplied
with the necessities of life, sources of protection, and stimulation as ours, the few
stressful factors discussed are apparently sufficient both to produce major differences in racial and social groups and to serve as partial explanations for the
variance in intellectual performance in these groups, then inhabitants of less-
advantaged nations must suffer from these factors to enormous degrees. A number
of additional factors which have been shown to be associated with mortality
and morbidity in offspring, such as prenatal infection or heavy maternal work
and postnatal nutrition and illness in the child, all largely socioeconomically determined, have not even been touched upon. Because of the state of political and
governmental organization of the disadvantaged areas, very little reliable information is available to indicate the terribly destructive and retarding effects of

poverty and deprivation (Knobloch and Pasamanick, 1962a). Here and there hints of the effects come to hand from which we can extrapolate to behavioral effects.

For instance, the high neonatal and child mortality rates probably indicate that a proportionately large number remain alive who have minor crippling of the central nervous system. Surely family incomes of a few dollars a year for literally millions of individuals must take their toll organically and psychologically, prenatally and postnatally. Prematurity, as one of the best indices of prenatal inadequacy and as an index of postnatal impairment in functioning, varies quite significantly in this country by race and class and differs even more widely abroad, where great numbers fall below the thresholds apparently necessary to produce healthy, well-functioning offspring. For instance, a study from India reported that prematurity rates could rise precipitously from 9 per cent in the higher groups to 31 per cent in the lowest segments of the population (more than twice that of the lowest groups in this country) (Kulkarni et al., 1959). Conversely, in some of the Scandinavian countries the incidence of prematurity has been reduced to 3 per cent, and in one clinic in Copenhagen, with additional attention being paid to prenatal care, it has even been reduced to well below 2 per cent. The difference in birth weights between Japanese-Americans born in the United States and Japanese born in Japan is easily related to differences in socioeconomic status in the two countries.

An important experimental study by Tompkins and Wiehl (1954) supporting the epidemiologic observations of the effects of dietary supplements demonstrated in over 1,500 patients the relationship between protein and vitamin intake and nutritional state and the development of toxemia and the incidence of premature birth. The highest incidence of severe or moderate toxemia occurred in patients who were 15 per cent or more underweight at the start of pregnancy. (Our most recent data indicate that it is the severe toxemias which apparently produce prematurity and brain damage.) Those patients who had protein and vitamin supplements had an incidence of toxemia of 0.6 per cent, and all the cases were mild. Those who had either protein or vitamin supplements had an incidence of 2.2 per cent, while the group with no dietary supplementation had an incidence of toxemia almost eight times as great (4.7 per cent). There was also a significant increase in premature separation of the placenta, which is associated with toxemia and fetal damage.

The clearest effect of the nutritional supplementation was seen in infants whose birth weights were less than 5½ pounds and whose gestation periods were less than 39 weeks. With full supplementation of protein and vitamins the prematurity rate was 3 per cent. If proteins alone were given, it was 4.3 per cent, if vitamins alone, 5.6 per cent, and in the absence of any dietary supplement, 6.4 per cent. If the mother was underweight at the start of pregnancy and had less-than-average weight gain, or a weight loss, the incidence of prematurity was 23.8 per cent. This was reduced to less than 2 per cent by protein and vitamin supplements in mothers with good pregravid nutrition. In considering the effect of diet it is important to note that in this study the protein supplementation increased the total intake to 100 grams or more per day. This is considerably higher than the recommended 70 grams of protein and is a distinct increase over the usual diet of the lower socioeconomic group.

Data such as these indicate the determinants of normal and aberrant behavior, including intelligence, which are implicated in the changes over time and in the differences between racial and social groups.

We have striven to indicate that we view determinants of behavior as consisting of the interactions among the biological and sociocultural facets of human existence. The biological determinants serve primarily to establish the physiological limits and the floor of potential in the organism. The sociocultural factors, on the other hand, are like the soil in which the plant is nurtured. By enrichment or impoverishment, human behavioral potential can be made to blossom or wither, to achieve its limits or to fall far short of them.

The findings point to the overwhelming importance of the factors of prenatal maternal health, preschool stimulation, and later educational effort which are the major foci in the anti-poverty programs for children today (Pasamanick, 1952). These programs should be geared to the elimination and modification of such results of poverty and deprivation as malnutrition, infection, and other forms of stress, prenatally in the mother and postnatally in the child. In addition, it seems apparent to us that psychosocial deprivation, faulty stimulation, and inadequate education in childhood require fully as much attention, if not more, in preventive programs. Hopefully, some of these programs would be established on a controlled experimental basis so that the hypotheses offered could be tested definitively and the activities improved continuously (Pasamanick, 1959).

Part III

THE SOCIAL CONTEXT
OF TREATMENT

Most of the selections in this part seek to provide a systematic analysis of the influence of a variety of "micro" social systems upon the career of the mental patient—from the prepatient to the expatient phase. They elucidate the role of social class, the culture of the psychiatric institution, the family, the community, and the small face-to-face group from the perspective of their psychological meaning to the patient. The social psychological analysis seeks to specify the joint influence of these social systems upon the disordered personality. In fact, there is no single integrated "social psychological model" or theory of the treatment of mental disorder. There is rather a sizable and growing body of theory, observation, and experimentation regarding institutional, familial, and face-to-face group pressures which affect the patients' participation in the treatment process.

Grob provides a historical analysis of the "career" of one state mental hospital. He documents the manner in which broad social forces, such as new immigrant populations and industrialization, shape the culture of the mental hospital. Hollingshead and Redlich trace the role of social class membership in determining the prepatient's pathways to and in psychiatric treatment. Levinson and Gallagher reveal the existence of personality orientations (e.g., authoritarianism) which vary as a function of social class membership. These authors illuminate the manner in which the patient's class orientation and the staff's treatment values are mutually selective and often reinforcing.

The papers by Caudill *et al.* and Goffman provide a vivid picture of what it feels like to become a mental patient. Whereas Goffman generates a searing indictment of the latent functions of the mental hospital, Caudill *et al.* emphasize the positive functions of the ward society for the hospitalized patient.

Kelman conceptualizes group therapy in terms of social influence process. Redl introduces several social phenomena which occur in group therapy situations but which are, as yet, inadequately dealt with by current theories.

The papers by Raush *et al.*, Atthowe and Krasner, and Ellsworth *et al.* seek to assess the nature and effectiveness of treatment programs. While these three papers represent differing theoretical approaches, they contribute to the development of technologies for evaluating the relative efficacy of innovations in treatment programs.

Some of the negative effects of institutionalization, such as prolonged absence from work, loss of contact with family, and the "readjustment" to a community after discharge, can be avoided by a "partial hospitalization" scheme (e.g., Day Hospital, Community Day Centers, or Halfway House). The secondary effects of institutionalization are particularly pronounced for lower class patients, since their skills and jobs are more marginal. Kramer's paper provides a description of "partial hospitalization" and how it fits into a program of rehabilitation.

The bulk of social psychological research has been done within the boundaries of an institution. Systematic social psychological studies of the prepatient or expatient career phase are sparse. Wechsler's paper provides a vivid description of the structure, values, and group processes of Recovery, Inc., a voluntary expatient organization.

The final paper by Solomon serves to evaluate the contributions to this section and raises a number of unresolved research questions.

22 / The State Mental Hospital in Mid-Nineteenth-Century America: A Social Analysis

Gerald N. Grob

Webster's Dictionary (1949) defines a hospital as an "institution in which patients or injured persons are given medical or surgical care" (p. 400). Thus a mental hospital is ostensibly an institution treating persons suffering from various forms of mental illness. In this sense there is little difference between a general and a mental hospital; the latter is simply a specialized version of the former. Similarly, the function of the psychiatrist is precisely the same as that of the general physician or specialist; namely, to diagnose the nature of the illness and to prescribe appropriate remedies.

In reality, of course, a mental hospital is *not* like any other hospital, nor is mental illness like other illnesses. Although the psychiatrist historically regarded himself as a medical specialist dealing with a physical illness in the conventional sense of the word, he always had difficulty in presenting convincing evidence to corroborate this assumption. Thus the belief that mental disease was somatic in nature—a natural consequence of psychiatry's medical origins—remained largely unproven for much of the nineteenth and twentieth centuries. With the exception of syphilis, no disease entity down to 1920 was identified in terms of its etiology and symptomological manifestations and then correlated with structural lesions and changes. Psychiatric research was in most cases a nosological catalogue of disease classifications based on outward behavioral symptoms—a catalogue that tended to change rapidly from time to time.

Yet a mental hospital is a functioning institution. It separates patients by various criteria; it treats some patients and offers custodial care to others; it has all of the characteristics of a complex social organization, including a hierarchy of authority, specialization, and the like. But if its identity is not always determined by medical and scientific factors, what does determine it? In dealing with this question, this article will offer as a case study the development of Worcester State Hospital (Massachusetts) in the quarter of a century following its opening in 1833. The reason for selecting this particular hospital is not difficult to understand, for Massachusetts was the pioneer in establishing a comprehensive system of public mental hospitals; its experiences served as a model for the rest of the nation.

Abridged from the *American Psychologist*, 1966, **21**, 510–523. Copyright © 1966. Reprinted by permission of the author and the American Psychological Association.

Origins

Like most institutions that arise in response to the needs of society, the mental hospital grew out of a specific cultural milieu and reflected the unique characteristics of its indigenous environment. The history of Worcester State Hospital is particularly revealing in this respect. The institution was a logical outgrowth of a number of historical trends and ideas current in 1830, the year in which it was established by an act of the Massachusetts legislature. What factors, therefore, were responsible for its founding?

First, the urbanization of Massachusetts had caused the informal mechanisms for the care of mentally ill persons to break down. The concentration of population in relatively small areas also led to a greater public awareness of "queer" or deviant behavior. Consequently, there were demands that special provision be made for the mentally ill not only to protect the general public but to provide as well for the care and welfare of such persons.

Second, the changing intellectual climate during the eighteenth century was to prove a decisive factor not only in softening popular antipathy toward the insane,[1] but also in reforming the custodial and prisonlike institutions of that period. The rise of experimental science and the emphasis on empiricism led to demands that mental disease be approached from a more naturalistic point of view. . . . Not only did the feeling become widespread that the conquest of disease was momentarily pending, but also that mental illness was no longer an object of pessimistic despair. . . .

Third, a vigorous reform movement had been set in motion in the United States by the resurgence of Christianity about 1800 in an event known to historians as the "Second Great Awakening." The Awakening had the immediate effect of weakening the Calvinistic emphasis on the essential depravity of human nature and the inability of men to save themselves. In place of such pessimistic tenets, Protestant leaders substituted the idea of a loving and benevolent God whose first concern was the happiness of his creatures. . . . When the belief in the free individual was fused with the millennial vision of a society performing a divine mission and eradicating all evidences of evil, Evangelical Protestantism was transformed into a radical social force seeking the abolition of the restraints that bound the individual and hindered his self-development. Thus, many ministers and laymen began to work actively to destroy the evil institutional restraints that imprisoned the individual. All persons, they maintained, were under a moral law that gave them a responsibility for the welfare of their fellow man. As a result of the teachings of Evangelical Protestantism, virtually dozens of reform movements sprang forth during the first half of the nineteenth century, including movements to better the condition of the insane, the inebriate, the blind, the deaf, the slave, the convict, and other less fortunate members of society.

Finally, the traditional interpretation of mental disease—that it was a de-

---

[1] No doubt some readers will be offended at the constant use of the terms "insane" and "insanity" as opposed to "mentally ill" and "mental illness." Although the former two have acquired an odious connotation, they were perfectly good terms in the past. My usage, therefore, is a historical one and is not intended to imply any derogatory connotation. After all, it is probable that the word "mental illness" itself will in the future be looked down upon with the same disfavor as "insanity" is at present.

moniacal possession resulting from a compact with Satan or a punishment inflicted upon the individual for his sins—was being modified as a result of the work of Philippe Pinel in France, William Tuke in England, as well as many others. The work of Pinel was of particular importance, since it provided reformers with ammunition to support their contention that mental illness was neither of supernatural origins nor was it incurable. While Pinel's contributions to psychiatric theory were not of critical importance, his contributions to therapy easily made up for his theoretical deficiencies. Because he rejected the idea that insanity could occur only in conjunction with physical lesions, he made room for a psychologically oriented therapy, which heretofore had been a theoretical impossibility.

Kindness was the fundamental ingredient in Pinel's therapeutic approach. Seeking to gain the patient's confidence and instill in him a sense of hope, he developed what became known as "moral treatment" (which in contemporary psychiatry corresponds to milieu therapy). Moral treatment involved the creation of a total therapeutic environment: social, psychological, physical. It assumed that insanity was a curable disease, given understanding, patience, kindness, and proper treatment. . . . "Moral treatment," Esquirol (1960, p. 519), one of Pinel's most famous students, wrote, "is the application of the faculty of intelligence and of emotions in the treatment of mental alienation." Implied in this new therapy was the more active participation of the patient in the therapeutic process prescribed by the physician. Thus each individual could be considered separately in terms of his unique needs. Advocates of moral treatment also placed great emphasis on providing mentally ill persons with a new environment in order to break patterns associated with the patient's past history. Such an emphasis was quite natural, since most physicians were influenced by associationist or sensationalist psychology, as well as faculty psychology and phrenology (which at this time was a scientific psychology that combined a theory of localized brain functions with a behavioristic faculty psychology)—all of which, directly or indirectly, involved the influence of the physical environment over the individual's mental state.

Surprisingly enough, much of the leadership in the movement to reform the condition of the insane in the early nineteenth century was provided by middle- and upper-class laymen. The establishment of the Worcester hospital, for example, resulted from the work of Horace Mann, who later achieved a national reputation as a great educational reformer. Indeed, many of the early mental hospitals were run by laymen rather than physicians. Perhaps the unspecialized nature of society made it easier for laymen to assume such positions of leadership. Most of these laymen were broadly educated and thoroughly versed in the scientific knowledge of their day. Having also been influenced by the optimistic and humanitarian currents that had grown out of the Enlightenment, they sought to eradicate the evil remnants still existing within society.

The Therapeutic Hospital

The opening of the Worcester hospital in 1830, then, represented a new chapter in the history of the care and treatment of mental illness in the United States. At this time the establishment of a comprehensive hospital system based on rational therapeutic principles, and open to all regardless of social or economic class, lay in the future. Most insane persons were confined to jails, houses of correction, and poorhouses, living amidst conditions that almost defy the imagination. A number of private and public institutions had been founded after the War of 1812, but all were small and catered largely to upper- and middle-class patients able to pay for their upkeep.

Like so many institutions, the initial success of the Worcester hospital was due largely to the efforts of its leader. Samuel Bayard Woodward, the first superintendent, was a man of unusual ability. His achievements at Worcester were of such high order that his professional colleagues elected him in 1844 as the first president of what is today the American Psychiatric Association. . . . He had been born in Connecticut in 1787 and had studied medicine under the tutelage of his physician father. As a young boy he had been influenced by the Second Great Awakening that swept through Connecticut. Influenced by a liberalized Congregationalism stripped somewhat of its Calvinistic pessimism, Woodward developed a strong sense of social idealism and warm humanitarian concerns that led him to accept a religious obligation to improve the condition of his fellow man; he consistently rejected a life devoted merely to the pursuit of material goods. Consequently, he was active in reform movements throughout his career.

Rejecting a supernatural interpretation of mental disease, Woodward began with the assumption that it was a somatic disease, not unlike other diseases. . . . Most of Woodward's contemporaries believed that mental illness was always a consequence of physical damage or malfunctioning. The general direction of medical thought in the nineteenth century, leading to a localized pathology that identified specific disease entities by correlating lesions with symptoms, also influenced psychiatry by tending to discourage a psychological approach in favor of a somatic one.

Although holding to a somatic pathology, Woodward accepted modifications that permitted a psychologically oriented therapy. For example, he adhered to a form of Lockean psychology, for he believed that knowledge came to the mind only through the senses. If the senses (which were physical organs) became diseased, then false impressions would be conveyed to the mind, leading in turn to faulty thinking and abnormal behavior. Such a psychology was eminently suited to therapy, both physical and psychological. . . . If the physician could manipulate the environment, he could thereby provide the patient with new and different stimuli. Thus older and undesirable patterns and associations would be broken or modified and new and more desirable ones substituted in their place.

Finally, Woodward found in phrenology a means of connecting mind with matter. . . . Its supporters believed that anatomical and physiological characteristics directly influenced behavior. . . . From phrenology Woodward took the idea that the normal and abnormal functioning of the mind was dependent on the physical condition of the brain. . . .

The causes of insanity, Woodward believed, included intemperance, ill health, religious excitement, masturbation, domestic affliction, loss of property, fear of poverty, personal disappointment, as well as the pressures of an industrial and commercial civilization (which he regarded as unnatural) upon the individual. Having grown to maturity in a staunch New England middle-class Protestant home, he tended to make the standards of his own class applicable to all of society.

Conceiving of insanity in predominantly naturalistic and somatic terms, it is not surprising, given his faith in progress and generally optimistic outlook, that Woodward believed the disease to be as curable as, if not more curable than, other somatic illnesses. If derangements of the brain and nervous system produced the various types of insanity, it followed that the removal of such causal abnormalities would result in the disappearance of the symptoms and therefore the disease. The prognosis for insanity thus was quite hopeful. Woodward, however, did add one important qualification to his theory; namely, that the sooner the mentally ill were brought to the hospital for treatment, the better the chances for recovery.

In caring for his charges, Woodward relied on various forms of therapy; in this sense he was a pragmatic eclectic. But above all, he was a confirmed believer in moral therapy. While susceptible to many interpretations, moral therapy meant kind, individualized care in a small hospital with occupational therapy, religious exercises, amusements and games, kind treatment, and in large measure a repudiation of all threats of physical violence and an infrequent resort to mechanical restraint. In brief, the new therapy implied the creation of a healthy psychological environment for the individual patient as well as the group.

On the other hand, Woodward never neglected medical treatment. He was concerned about the general health and well being of the patient as well. Thus he used medication for specific symptoms as well as tonics to improve the general condition of the individual. He also relied extensively on narcotics such as morphine and opium; their purpose was to quiet the patient and thus make him amenable to moral treatment.

After the patient's health had been cared for, Woodward then brought moral treatment into play. He insisted on a regular living regime, a substantial though simple diet, emphasis on personal cleanliness, occupational therapy, religious exercises, amusements, and sports. The staff was required to treat all patients with kindness and respect. Rejecting the idea of confining patients, Woodward permitted a high proportion of them complete freedom to walk about the grounds or go into the city without supervision.

In its early days the hospital had about 120 patients, all of whom were on an intimate basis with the superintendent. There seems little doubt that Woodward, working with a relatively homogeneous group of patients—many of whom were Protestant and literate—developed extraordinarily close relationships with many of them. Not all patients, on the other hand, received the same or equal treatment. To a certain extent middle- and upper-class patients or those with more formal education were accorded special privileges. Similarly, the method of classifying patients and wards served indirectly to differentiate patients on the basis of class. By refusing to force patients to associate with persons whom they found distasteful, Woodward implicitly permitted a homogeneous grouping whereby persons of the same social, economic, and educational status tended to come together. Finally, advanced and violent cases of insanity, which occurred with a high frequency among lower-class inmates who had previously been confined in jails and almshouses for long periods of time, received the least attention. Undoubtedly the wide social and educational differences between such patients and the physician contributed to their partial inability to communicate in a meaningful manner with each other.

How successful was Woodward in treating patients in this way? "*In recent cases of insanity* [persons ill for 1 year or less]," Woodward remarked, "*under judicious treatment, as large a proportion of recoveries will take place, as from any other acute disease of equal severity*" (Woodward, quoted in *Worcester State Lunatic Hospital Annual Report*, 1835, p. 35). According to Woodward's figures, 2,583 cases were admitted to the hospital between 1833 and 1846. During this same period 2,215 were discharged, of which 1,192 were listed as recovered. When the fact is taken into consideration that those who were discharged as stationary represented largely old and chronic cases, Woodward's figures regarding the chances of recovery of new and recent cases become even more imposing, particularly by contemporary standards.

Were Woodward's claims valid, or was he guilty of a form of unconscious self-deception? Fortunately, one of Woodward's successors in the late nineteenth century decided to undertake a follow-up study of persons discharged from the hospital as recovered on their only admission or on their last admission. This study, which took nearly 20 years to complete, traced the history of over 1,000 individuals throughout their lives. The results proved highly informative. By 1893 no less than 1,157 persons had been included in the study. Complete information had been gathered on 984, of whom 317 were alive and well at the time of reply, while 251 had remained well until their death and had never again entered a mental hospital. In other words, nearly 58 per cent of those discharged as recovered had not had a relapse. The results are even more impressive when the fact is taken into consideration that the survey included friends, relatives, ministers, and employers of former patients, all of whom were asked to give their impression of the individual concerned. It is therefore possible to infer that the familial atmosphere of the hospital, coupled with the kind, humane, and optimistic attitude of Woodward toward his charges, produced a psychological climate within the hospital which had a beneficial effect upon its inmates.

From the Therapeutic to the Custodial Hospital

At this point an obvious question emerges. If the Worcester, along with other early nineteenth-century mental hospitals, were so successful in treating patients, what was responsible for the regression that clearly took place in the second half of the century as well as in the twentieth century when most state hospitals were transformed into custodial rather than therapeutic institutions? While the answer to this question is extremely complex and must include attention to psychiatric theory and practice, it is also clear that part of the answer lies in the rapidly changing social, intellectual, and economic environment of mid-nineteenth-century America. To illustrate this latter point, I should like to focus on the post-Woodward era from 1846 to 1855 as an illustrative case study.

When Woodward retired from the superintendency, the trustees of the hospital selected as his successor George Chandler, a former assistant to Woodward who had become head of the Asylum for the Insane at Concord, New Hampshire. While the trustees may not have realized it at the time, they had set an important precedent; in the future—with only a single exception—the super-intendency was occupied by individuals who had spent most of their profes-sional careers at the hospital, and who had been elevated to the position by virtue of the seniority they had acquired. Indirectly this practice of inbreeding was to prove a potent factor in the hospital's history. Since superintendents came up from the ranks and were often isolated from external influences, they often had difficulty in viewing the needs facing the hospital dispassionately and at a distance. By and large, they tended to follow along paths that had been laid out by their predecessors. Consequently, many problems faced by the hospital were intensified, for older routines and practices often proved ill adapted to new situations. . . .

Chandler's primary interests . . . lay in standards and routines of hospital management. These interests, however, did not spring from any defects in char-acter or callousness to suffering. Like most persons attracted to a career in psychiatry at this time, he too was motivated by a desire to help the mentally ill. But the situation that he found himself in by the late 1840s and 1850s was unlike that of the 1830s. By Chandler's time the hospital was facing a crisis as a result of the pressure of rising admissions, a pressure that it could not resist because of the legal system under which it functioned.[2] The internal growth of the hospital, a response to these external factors, created an entirely new set of circumstances. No longer was Chandler able to run the hospital in a loose and informal manner as Woodward had done. With 400 to 500 patients the problems of social organization and adjustment were much more complex. The theory of moral treatment provided few answers or guidelines, for it was based (according to Chandler) on a direct and personal relationship between doctor and patient. Since no theoretical framework existed that could harmo-nize or rationalize an individualistic therapy with a collective social system having different objectives, the tendency was for the demands of the social system to outweigh the requirements of therapy. Thus Chandler found himself in an unen-viable dilemma; his concern for the welfare of his patients was conflicting with the larger goal of maintaining order in a complex social institution.

Chandler's difficulties were compounded even further by outside pressures. The hospital, for example, played a dual role, one therapeutic, the other cus-todial. As long as it remained small, it was relatively easy for the superintendent to combine both of these roles. The hospital's growth, however, made this more difficult. Increasingly the superintendent found himself confronted with the responsibility of having to sacrifice one of these goals in order to achieve the other. Given a choice, therapeutic considerations might well have been domi-

---

[2] The increasing pressure on the hospital resulted from a variety of influences. First, the existence of a mental hospital meant that jails and almshouses were not the only places for the confinement of insane persons. Families that had once been reluctant to send loved ones to substandard institutions were now more willing to consider the possibility of institutionalization. Second, the growing urbanization made it more and more difficult to care for the mentally ill in the community. Deviant behavior in densely populated areas not only posed greater problems than in rural areas, but it was also less likely to be tolerated. Third, the establishment of a mental hospital increased societal awareness of mental disease, and undoubtedly some who had been considered quaint or odd were now looked upon as insane. Finally, the rapid growth in population, which was partly associated with industrialization and partly with the tremendous increase in immigration from Ireland, was accompanied by a proportionate increase in the number of mentally ill persons.

nant. But the superintendent could not only be concerned with the welfare of his patient; he had to take into account the demands of society for protection against those who ostensibly menaced the community. As more and more lower-class patients entered the hospital, the public clamor for adequate protection increased sharply. Consequently, therapeutic considerations receded into the background.

Under this set of circumstances Chandler's immersion in administrative problems was hardly surprising. An intricate social institution like a mental hospital required formal mechanisms to ensure order and efficiency; formal mechanisms, in turn, often defeated the aims of moral treatment, which was based on the ability of the physician to manipulate the environment of the individual and group as the need arose. Custodial considerations merely reinforced administrative concerns, for custody required a tight and efficiently run institution governed by rational and clearly defined procedures.

Chandler's immersion in administrative psychiatry was by no means atypical. By the middle of the nineteenth century, American psychiatry had become identified with hospital management. Leading psychiatrists, with a few exceptions, were concerned with problems of administration, organization, architectural standards, occupational therapy, efficient heating and ventilating systems, and the like. Few undertook, as did their European counterparts, any basic research; the pages of the *American Journal of Insanity,* the outstanding psychiatric periodical of this period, are notable only for the lack of articles embodying the results of original research. While French, German, and to a lesser extent, British physicians were performing autopsies, correlating symptoms with pathological anatomy, studying the nervous system, and trying to observe the course and development of identifiable disease entities, their brethren across the Atlantic remained aloof from such concerns. In this respect American physicians were representative of their milieu, for during the nineteenth century there was little basic research in either science or medicine in the United States. Americans were an intensely practical breed; they were most interested in concrete results. American doctors, for example, excelled in applied research of immediate utility, such as surgery. There were practically no studies that combined clinical-pathological approaches, and as late as 1860 Oliver Wendell Holmes could ridicule science as having no value for actual medical practice.

The development of administrative psychiatry was accompanied by other internal changes in the profession. The emphasis on management techniques fostered a narrow specialization that made alienists less receptive to outside criticism, help, or advice. The ensuing professionalization of psychiatry opened a chasm between lay reformers and physicians. The greater their sense of professionalism, the less were psychiatrists willing to listen to others or to take advantage of advances in related fields. The coalition of reformers and physicians that had been so influential in founding mental hospitals, developing a more humane therapy, and modifying public attitudes, had been broken.

The transformation of the psychiatrist into an administrator also had a subtle effect upon psychiatric theory and practice. A comparison of Woodward's views on etiology with those of Chandler's, for example, offers a good case in point. Ostensibly Chandler's ideas of etiology were approximately the same as those of his predecessor. Yet Woodward's psychiatric theories had been developed within a broad religious framework that emphasized above all the responsibility of the individual for the welfare of those less fortunate than himself. Thus feelings of sympathy and compassion tempered and softened his attitudes. Although he frequently warned that immoral acts (masturbation, intemperance, etc.) played a part in etiology, he never condemned or treated harshly patients whose illness had resulted from improper acts. On the contrary, such persons were worthy of the aid and sympathy of any true Christian.

Chandler, however, lacked Woodward's religious commitment. . . . When large numbers of Irish paupers entered the hospital, he was unable to accept them in the way that he accepted natives. His awareness of class and cultural differences was more distinct because of the absence of the religious fervor that had universalized rather than particularized humanity. Thus in discussing etiology, he began by dividing the causes of insanity into two general classes, the moral or psychological and the physical. Both were usually involved in bringing on mental disease. The leading causes of insanity involved behavior that deviated from the standards of the average middle-class New Englander. Thus intemperance, which by this time was often associated with the alien Irishman as contrasted with the sober and upright native citizen, was singled out as a major cause of mental disease.

Like Woodward, Chandler was probably influenced by phrenological thought, for he placed considerable emphasis upon the inculcation of proper living habits as early in life as possible, so as to permit the brain to develop in a normal manner. . . . They included, among other things, avoidance of certain behavior patterns that would lead hereditary predispositions to become operative, and a regime that was balanced between physical and mental labor. Chandler was also influenced by an incipient anti-intellectualism. He felt that overcultivation of bookish or intellectual qualities was wrong; hence long confinement in school or among books was dangerous to mental health. Not surprisingly, he argued that farmers and mechanics had provided New England with its healthiest individuals; urban areas were indebted to these groups for their active and successful population. Finally, Chandler maintained that the ambitions of many children were being overstimulated by the allurements of success in the free and open competition of the marketplace, and insanity resulted when their hopes were not fulfilled. His norm, in other words, was an individual who was neither poor nor rich, who did not overvalue physical or mental labor, who knew his place in life and did not overstep its boundaries, who avoided excesses in either drinking or religion—an individual, to put it another way, who came from a middle-class, Protestant background. In large measure Chandler's views on the etiology of insanity were derived principally from his own moral, ethical, religious, and philosophical ideas.

The dissimilarities between Chandler and Woodward had significant implications for therapy at the hospital. Under Woodward moral treatment was administered with enthusiasm and optimism. Probably few patients remained completely immune to the charged and dynamic atmosphere at the hospital in its early days. Chandler, on the other hand, was dealing with a more heterogeneous and much larger group of patients. Considerations of order and efficiency could not be ignored; they tended to limit the degree of innovation and the flexibility that moral treatment required. What happened was not that moral treatment was abandoned; rather it was institutionalized and forced into a regular and predictable pattern, with a consequent loss of its inner spirit and drive.

Chandler was by no means unaware of what was happening at the hospital. When queried by a legislative investigating committee in the late 1840s, he made known his preferences for a small rather than a large hospital in no uncertain terms. His ideal of a small hospital—an ideal shared by most persons at this time—however, was becoming obsolete because of the continuous pressure of new admissions. By 1852 the average number of patients exceeded 500, and the strain upon the hospital's facilities became almost unbearable. At this time the medical staff still consisted of the three physicians that it had nearly a decade before: the superintendent and two assistant physicians. The former spent most of his time on administrative duties; responsibility for caring for the patients fell upon the latter. Since the two assistants were responsible for a number of tasks, including the preparation of all medical prescriptions, they were unable to devote their undivided energies to the care and treatment of patients.

The growth of the hospital had other effects as well. First, the increase in the size of the patient population forced the superintendent to place greater reliance upon attendants and nurses. At that time no formal training was available for nonprofessional personnel; as a result inexperienced persons were normally hired. Since salaries were low, there was a high turnover rate, averaging close to about 40 per cent per year.

The inexperience of nurses and attendants, however, was not the critical variable in explaining the declining success of moral treatment. Much more important was the intangible change in atmosphere at the hospital. The transfer of many of the psychiatrist's functions to a low paid, inexperienced, nonprofessional staff with low morale had an adverse effect upon inmates. By and large, nurses and attendants were not motivated by altruistic concerns (as the high turnover rate indicates), nor did they view their occupation in terms of a calling to help those less fortunate than themselves. Outwardly moral treatment remained constant; inwardly there was a shift in its complexion and spirit, leading to a deterioration of its effectiveness.

Although Chandler and others were aware of the problem, the thought of training attendants and nurses and giving them greater responsibility for the welfare of the patient was never seriously considered. In this respect Chandler reflected the growing belief of his profession that treatment was the sole prerogative of the physician; at best laymen were useful auxiliaries. Since mental illness, like smallpox and other organic diseases, was something that a patient had, responsibility for his care and treatment had to remain within the hands of the psychiatrist. The doctor-patient relationship was an inviolate one that precluded the intrusion of a third party. Although psychological factors entered into etiology and therapy, the patient was still viewed as a passive agent who was active only in the sense that he followed or complied with the directions of the physician; his status was not that of an equal partner. Given such a medical model, it is easy to understand the failure to employ attendants and nurses in a deliberate and meaningful manner—a failure that remained constant for most of the nineteenth as well as the twentieth century.

Second, the growth of the hospital led to greater reliance upon physical restraint. With more patients, the need for formal mechanisms of ensuring order became greater. Under such conditions, the easiest way of ensuring order was to keep violent or hard-to-manage patients under some form of restraint. Such restraint usually took one of two forms. Extremely difficult patients were confined in solitary rooms, where they required little or no attention. Other patients were confined by straps and waistbands.

There is little doubt that the use of restraints eased the burdens of the staff and permitted the hospital to maintain a high degree of order. In this respect the goals of restraint had changed sharply since the 1830s. To Woodward restraint was partly therapeutic; it was intended to protect and quiet violent and dangerous patients, who could then be brought within the range of moral treatment. Under Chandler the institutional setting had so changed that his use of restraint also undermined moral treatment. Neglected and ignored, restrained patients at best remained in a stationary condition; at worst they became even further demented. Furthermore, the hostility of physicians toward patients who upset the hospital's routine contributed to the deterioration in the condition of such inmates. It does not require much imagination to conceive of a patient's reaction when a physician could describe the case in the following words, which were not at all unusual: "No improvement in this degraded woman—is wholly lost to shame and has no more regard to exposing herself than a dumb beast" (p. 105).[3]

By the 1850s restraint at the hospital was quite common. In this respect Chandler was following practices that were sanctioned by the overwhelming majority of American superintendents. Generally speaking, restraint was more common in the United States than in England or on the continent. In England its use had been severely restricted by the work of John Conolly and others. In the Pinelian tradition of humanistic psychiatry, Conolly advocated a therapeutic system that involved attitudes of respect, kindness, patience, understanding, and truthfulness on the part of the staff toward the inmates, and an almost total elimination of restraint. The nonrestraint system, however, never made very much progress in the United States, largely because a burgeoning population so taxed hospital facilities that superintendents used it as an administrative device to maintain order. "Restraints and neglect may be considered synonymous," Conolly (quoted in Deutsch, 1937, p. 221) had written in perceptive words, "for restraints are merely a general substitute for the thousand attentions required by troublesome patients."

In the third place, the character of therapy, both medical and moral, was transformed as the Worcester hospital grew in size. Between 1834 and 1853 the doctor-patient ratio rose from 1:58 to 1:140. Consequently, physicians devoted less time to each case. The manuscript case histories offer striking corroboration of this generalization. During Chandler's years in office the case histories became more fragmentary and uninformative than they had been under Woodward. Sometimes the physician in charge would not enter any statements about his patient for a 3- to 5-year period, and when he did so his remarks tended to be cursory and superficial.

---

[3] Entry of November 3, 1851, Case No. 3260, Case Book No. 24, p. 105, Record Storage Section, Worcester State Hospital, Worcester, Massachusetts.

Other aspects of patient care also deteriorated. Since the hospital authorities were handling larger numbers of patients, they found Woodward's precedent of relying on drugs a useful one. The practice of ensuring a manageable patient population, however, tended to become an end in itself. Unlike his predecessor, Chandler did not regard it primarily as a prelude to other forms of therapy. Drugs were useful and necessary because they facilitated the management of a large patient body with a minimum of trouble. Thus while the use of drugs, including morphine and opium, remained more or less constant between 1833 and 1855, the underlying rationale changed considerably. Similarly, occupational therapy became more haphazard during the later period. As the hospital increased in size, work was assigned more to meet the needs of the hospital than the needs of the patient. In 1853 the trustees estimated that only one-quarter of the patients were employed in the summer and one-fifth in the winter. The hospital, in other words, was custodial for more than three-quarters of its patients.

Finally, the hospital's growth increased the influence of ethnic, religious, and class factors in determining care and treatment. During the 1840s and 1850s the rise in the number of patients had resulted partially from an influx of immigrants into Massachusetts, especially from Ireland. Quite naturally, the Irish began to constitute a higher proportion of the population at the hospital. In 1846 only 12 Irish patients had been admitted; by 1854 this figure had risen to 96. Chandler considered this to be an important development, and in 1855 he included in his annual report a table that specifically singled out the Irish at the hospital in the previous decade.

Chandler's action in identifying the Irish was hardly unusual. The overwhelming majority of them were Catholic, and Massachusetts since its founding had been a center of no-Popery sentiment. In the seventeenth century the General Court had actually passed a number of laws intended to prevent the migration of Catholics into the province and to make impossible the propagation of their religion. As long as the number of Catholics had remained insignificant, the strong feelings against them were quiescent. But as the impact of Irish immigration became more pronounced, public hostility increased in virulence. After 1830 anti-Catholicism became a movement of national significance.

But antipathies toward the Irish were not solely a result of religious friction. On the contrary, their economic condition also played a role in arousing hostility. Prior to their arrival in large numbers, the economy of the Bay State was oriented toward small-scale skilled enterprises rather than large-scale unskilled ones. Generally speaking, poverty, and pauperism were of no great importance, for broad occupational diversity minimized the impact of changes within a particular trade or occupation. By the 1840s, on the other hand, the economy of Massachusetts was beginning to change as the movement toward industrialism accelerated. In this development the Irish played a crucial role, for they contributed the necessary cheap and unskilled surplus labor without which industrialization would have been impossible.

The economic transformation of Massachusetts soon created problems that had few precedents. For the first time in their history Bay Staters were confronted with the problems of slums, poverty, and pauperism that accompanied industrialization. Since the Irish—more than any other group—were associated with these developments, they bore the major share of the blame. To middle-class natives the abject poverty of the Irish—exemplified by the slum areas in which they congregated—was destroying the beauty and homogeneity of American society and burdening the more thrifty and prosperous classes with a rising tax bill to care for the impoverished and improvident. Still others feared the competition of Irish laborers willing to work for low wages. Above all—especially as the newcomers developed a sense of group consciousness—native citizens became aware of the differences that separated the two groups. Slowly but surely the older tradition of anti-Catholicism merged with the more recent fear of the changes that were transforming the Bay State, giving rise to strong feelings of distrust and even hatred.

The ethnic, social, and economic tensions that divided Massachusetts society had an important influence over conditions among the mentally ill, for they exacerbated existing class differences in institutional care and treatment. Increasingly the argument was heard that the public burden of supporting foreign-born paupers, including insane persons, was fast becoming an unbearable strain. "This is only the beginning of troubles," commented the influential *Boston Medical and Surgical Journal,* one of the leading medical journals in the United States, upon the subject of the foreign insane,

> for the new hospital that is to be reared will soon be in their possession also. Never was a sovereign State so grievously burdened. The people bear the growing evil without a murmur, and it is therefore taken for granted that taxation for the support of the cast-off humanity of Europe is an agreeable exercise of their charity (Editorial, 1852, p. 537).

The charge that foreign paupers, including the insane, were the single largest group supported by the state was quite true. The state auditor estimated that during the 10 years ending in 1851 nearly 2,500 out of a total of 3,722 insane state paupers were Irish. Since most Irish immigrants came from lower-class backgrounds—indeed, many were nearly destitute upon their arrival on American shores—it was not surprising that when mental illness struck they were completely dependent upon public charity.

As the proportion of Irish patients at the hospital increased, public attitudes toward the mentally ill began to undergo a subtle transformation. Many Americans began to draw invidious distinctions between the native insane and the Irish insane. The former were still treated with compassion and sympathy; but the latter were the objects of a growing hostility. The older and still dominant New England natives not only were reluctant to extend their hopeful attitudes toward insanity to include lower-class Irish immigrants, but they actually believed that the Irish constituted a separate race whose members were not as responsive as native Americans to therapy when afflicted with mental disease.

The hostile feelings toward foreigners in general and the Irish in particular had a considerable impact over their treatment within the hospital. Most staff physicians reflected to some extent the popular anti-Catholic feelings then prevalent, and undoubtedly these feelings influenced their relationships with patients. Equally if not more significant was the fact that the Irish were drawn almost exclusively from lower-class backgrounds. They worked at unskilled jobs; they received low wages; they congregated in slums; they provided a disproportionate share of paupers; they had little if any formal education; and they tended to band together and to develop a strong sense of group consciousness and cohesion. To the physicians—most of whom came from middle-class homes and had been reared in a Protestant-dominated culture—the Irish, by virtue of their lower-class character, appeared as social undesirables who were responsible for many of the evils that afflicted American society. Rather than being the victims of an impersonal system, the Irish were the cause of all problems. Thus they were poor not because they came from an impoverished environment, but because they were unable to assimilate and adjust to the demands of American ideals.

Chandler's attitude toward the Irish is a case in point. Although he claimed that he made no distinctions between patients who came from different ethnic and economic backgrounds, there is evidence to show that care and treatment were partly dependent upon social and economic status and ethnic origin, both of which were closely related. Chandler, for example, admitted that he was more successful in dealing with native-born patients than with foreign ones, although he laid responsibility for this situation at the latter's doors. As he reported in 1847:

> Most of the foreigners are Irish. The want of forethought in them to save their earnings for the day of sickness, the indulgence of their appetites for stimulating drinks, which are too easily obtained among us, and their strong love for their native land, which is characteristic with them, are the fruitful causes of insanity among them. As a class, we are not so successful in our treatment of them as with the native population of New England. It is difficult to obtain their confidence, for they seem to be jealous of our motives; and the embarrassment they are under, from not clearly comprehending our language, is another obstacle in the way of their recovery (Chandler, quoted in *Worcester State Lunatic Hospital Annual Report*, 1847, p. 33).

There is little doubt that the ethnic and social backgrounds of the professional staff indirectly played an important role in determining patient care at the hospital. Though physicians may not have been aware of their hostile attitudes, it is quite probable that patients toward whom this antipathy was directed would be suspicious and uncommunicative. The mutual distrust hardly could have been conducive to successful therapy, which usually required a close and trusting relationship between doctor and patient. Chandler's observation that he had trouble in communicating with foreign patients was quite true, but not for the reasons he gave. Since he and others usually approached foreign pauper patients with an air of condescension and dislike, patients tended to reciprocate in kind. A superficial perusal of the case histories proves this point. Most of the descriptions of foreign paupers at the hospital are marked by feelings of revulsion on the part of the physician. One Irish female, to cite only one example out of many, was described in 1854 in the following terms: "This girl is much of the time noisy and troublesome. Has nymphomania and exposes her person. . . . Is vulgar and obscene." A month later there is a similar description: "There has been no perceptible change in her condition or habits. Is noisy destructive violent and vulgar. Almost constantly excited. Screaming and tearing her clothes" (p. 240).[4] Middle-class native patients, on the other hand, received considerably more attention and sympathy.

---

[4] Entries of October 3, November 3, 1854, Case No. 4710, Case Book No. 28, p. 240, Record Storage Section, Worcester State Hospital, Worcester, Massachusetts.

Conclusion

. . . Looking in retrospect at the development of the state mental hospital, it is possible to make some broad generalizations. Because a "scientific psychiatry" often proved more of a dream than a reality, the development of the mental hospital was often determined—perhaps unconsciously—by external and internal social, psychological, economic, and intellectual influences. Moral treatment, for example, which had enjoyed great success during the first half of the nineteenth century, was not based on a systematic theory nor had it grown out of controlled experimentation. On the contrary, it developed out of the humanitarian and religious concerns of the period. Moral treatment was based on the assumption that there would be a close relationship between the therapist and patient—a relationship made possible by the fact that both probably came from the same ethnic, economic, and religious backgrounds and environment, and shared a common cultural heritage.

After 1850, as patients from diverse ethnic, religious, and economic backgrounds entered the hospital, moral treatment became less and less successful. Because psychiatrists were never fully aware of the important part that their own attitudes played in their professional rationale and ideology, they were unprepared to cope with the heterogeneous patient population that accompanied the new urban and industrial society. . . . Some psychiatrists attributed their inability to help patients coming from low socioeconomic backgrounds to the fact that such individuals had inherent character defects that not only explained their impoverished straits, but also their lack of response to therapy. Others accused the legislature of not appropriating sufficient funds. . . . But whatever the reasons offered, it was evident that most psychiatrists no longer adhered to the belief that mental disease, irrespective of a patient's background, was a largely curable malady.

. . . When psychiatrists were confronted with the decline in the effectiveness of moral treatment, they began to adjust their theoretical approach in the light of their experiences. Up to the middle of the nineteenth century they had accepted the role of psychological factors in etiology and treatment. After this time, however, they began to revert to an outright and explicit somaticism. But a strictly somatic approach—which was reinforced by the direction taken by nineteenth century scientific and medical theory—usually led to therapeutic nihilism.[5] After all, if the basis of insanity was physical, of what use would be a psychological therapy? . . .

The rise of the custodial hospital was related to other influences as well. One such influence was the growing sense of professionalism among psychiatrists. . . . Specifically, professionalism involved not only a monopoly of special skills, but the creation of a subculture that gave members of a specialty both a common experience which facilitated communication within the group and excluded all non-specialists, including, of course, laymen. The establishment of a professional

---

[5] This statement is a *historical* one and is not intended to prove or to disprove the thesis that mental illness is or is not somatic or psychological in nature. It is only to state that for the nineteenth century, as well as for a good part of the twentieth, somaticism ran hand in hand with pessimism. A psychological approach, however, often—though not always—implied optimism and therefore therapy.

psychiatric subculture—with its explicit and implicit system of values and norms —resulted in the erection of a barrier between psychiatrists and other groups. The founding of the present-day American Psychiatric Association in 1844 was one indication of this development, since one of the major purposes of this organization was to define standards that would govern therapy, administration, and management. By insisting that special skills and knowledge were required for treating mental illness, psychiatrists were able to justify the exclusion of all other persons having no formal training and instruction in this specialty.[6]

Undoubtedly the creation of a psychiatric community and the establishment of minimum standards permitted the adoption of more rigorous guidelines to govern care and treatment of the mentally ill. On the other hand, professionalism had adverse effects as well. Indeed, professionalism resulted in the exclusion of those laymen whose work had been responsible for much of the élan and drive— to say nothing of the material success—that had characterized the early efforts to aid the mentally ill in the first half of the nineteenth century. Professionalism also tended to isolate psychiatrists from those social and humanitarian influences that might have tempered the pessimistic outlook of late nineteenth and early twentieth century psychiatry. Having rejected as subjective and unscientific such affective sentiments as humanity, love, compassion, psychiatrists found their own supposedly objective and scientific approach barren because of the ambiguities that marked their efforts to define and identify the essential attributes and nature of mental disease. Last, professionalism, when combined with intellectual isolation, deprived psychiatry of some of the insights of other disciplines and approaches that might have been useful in dealing with some of the philosophical and scientific problems growing out of mental illness.

Other forces contributed to the custodial-like nature of the mental hospital. If the hospital's existence could not be justified by the number of patients that it cured, then its *raison d'être* had to be rationalized in custodial terms. Indeed, much of the support that the mental hospital received was predicated on the assumption that it provided protection against groups that menaced the safety and security of society. The easiest way to get appropriations was to appeal to the legislature for funds with which to provide accommodations to care for the growing number of chronically deranged individuals. . . .

Far from merely reflecting certain scientific and medical currents, the mental hospital as well as psychiatry both emerged out of the interaction of complex social, intellectual, and economic forces.

[6] It should be noted that the increasing professionalization of psychiatry was matched and paralleled by professionalization in other specialties in medicine as well as in virtually every field of the sciences and arts. Indeed, the growth of professionalism was closely related to other societal determinants such as urbanization, industrialization, the rise of the mass communication media, rationalization, the availability of organizational techniques, and the development of accreditation procedures, particularly in the universities and professional schools.

23 / The Treatment Process

August B. Hollingshead / Fredrick C. Redlich

The Psychotic Patients

We will now examine the clinical histories of the 1,442 psychotic patients in the study to learn if their class positions are determinants in where and how they are treated. The where phase of the analysis will be developed in four separate but related steps. First, we will investigate which treatment agencies are utilized by what classes when psychotic individuals come under the care of psychiatrists for the first time. Second, we will see if the 51 per cent of psychotic patients who have had at least one previous course of psychiatric care are now utilizing the same treatment agency as in their first episode. This analysis will be made to see if patients with a history of a previous treatment shift from one kind of agency to another when they re-enter treatment. The third step in the examination of the treatment records of the psychotics will be focused on where the patients are being treated now. Finally, we will explore the possibility that the use of treatment agencies is influenced by the kind of mental disorder the patient has, rather than by his class position.

The statistical procedures used to test the treatment hypothesis on the psychotic patients are essentially the same as those we followed with neurotic patients, but the emphasis is different. This is dictated by the differential use of treatment facilities in these diagnostic groups. For example, 87 per cent of the psychotics are hospitalized in state and Veterans Administration hospitals. This means that the more rigid tests of *Hypothesis 3*[1] are limited to psychotic patients in public hospitals. Whereas, among the neurotics the large concentration of patients treated by private practitioners indicated that the most rigid statistical tests of the treatment hypothesis should be focused on the patients of the private practitioners. The very fact that so many psychotic patients are in state hospitals presents a unique opportunity to subject *Hypothesis 3* to a critical test. There are hundreds of patients in the state hospitals who are being treated, presumably for their illnesses, in relatively similar ways. If the factor of class status is linked to the kinds of treatment these patients receive, we shall conclude that the hypothesis under examination is valid.

Agency of First Treatment

Information on the agency where psychotically disordered individuals receive their first psychiatric treatment will give us some insight into what agencies are available to whom. It also will tell us if class status is correlated with the utiliza-

Abridged from Chapter 9 of *Social Class and Mental Illness: A Community Study* by August B. Hollingshead and Fredrick C. Redlich. Copyright © 1958. (New York: John Wiley & Sons, Inc., 1958). Reprinted by permission of the authors and John Wiley & Sons, Inc.

[1] *Hypothesis 3* postulated that the type of psychiatric treatment a patient receives is connected with his position in the class structure.

TABLE I

PERCENTAGE OF PSYCHOTICS TREATED FOR THE FIRST TIME IN SPECIFIED
TYPES OF PSYCHIATRIC AGENCIES—BY CLASS

Treatment Agency	Class			
	I–II	III	IV	V
State hospital	7.7	39.7	77.5	89.0
Military or V.A. hospital	0.0	5.5	6.2	3.2
Private hospital	67.3	39.7	5.2	0.6
Public clinic	1.9	8.9	9.0	6.8
Private practitioner	23.1	6.2	2.2	0.5
$n =$	52	146	581	663

$$\chi^2 = 610.43, 12 \, df, p < .001$$

tion of therapeutic agencies. The data essential to provide an answer to these
facets of the treatment process are given in Table I.

The most striking impression gained from an examination of the percentages in
Table I is the confirmation of our common sense expectation that the higher
classes turn to private hospitals, whereas the lower classes go to the state hospitals. The different percentages tell us, in a way, what kinds of treatment facilities are relied upon by different classes when a psychotic illness strikes. For
examples, all class I psychotics received their first psychiatric treatment in private
hospitals or from private practitioners, and only four class II's were treated first
in a state hospital. . . . The state hospital, for classes I and II, is a taboo institution to be utilized only as a "last resort." Entry into the state hospital is the
antithesis of what high-status persons should do when mental disturbances occur.

Class III exhibits a distinctly different pattern of where its psychotic members
are first treated. Some two out of five patients go to private hospitals, but an equal
proportion go to state hospitals. A third pattern of response to psychosis is
observable in class IV, in which some three out of four go directly to state hospitals and private hospitals; only 2 per cent are cared for by private practitioners.
Class V turns to the state hospitals in some nine out of ten cases. The 1 per cent
who are treated first either in private hospitals or by private practitioners are as
distinct exceptions as the four persons in class II who went to the state hospital.
It is by chance that four class V persons had their first psychiatric contact in a
private hospital, but it is not chance that they entered the same hospital and that
none of them stayed longer than six days. Three of the four were employees of
the Community Hospital at the time they became psychotic. The house staff of
the Community Hospital referred them to the University psychiatric hospital.
They were kept there for a few days and then transferred to the state hospital.
The fourth patient was admitted to the psychiatric hospital from her home upon
the advice of a general practitioner, but when the family became aware of the
economic burden entailed, the woman was taken to the state hospital.

The data summarized in Table I demonstrate that class status is correlated
with the utilization of different types of treatment agencies when persons become
psychotically disturbed. The use of private mental hospitals is related directly to
the higher class positions, whereas reliance upon the state hospitals is connected
with the lower classes. . . .

Treatment Agency, Diagnosis, Type of Therapy, and Class

Hypothesis 3 can be tested stringently by holding both diagnosis and treatment agency constant and making comparisons between class position and the principal form of therapy prescribed for patients. Unfortunately, from the perspective of statistical methodology, when the data are analyzed with treatment agency, diagnosis, principal form of therapy, and class position interacting, the number of patients in any one cell of the tables is too small for reliability. To meet this problem, we grouped treatment agencies into three categories: (1) private practitioners and private hospitals, (2) clinics, and (3) public hospitals. The data on patients in each of these groups of treatment agencies were then analyzed with diagnosis held constant. The findings on this series of analyses are presented in subsequent paragraphs.

Private Practitioners and Private Hospitals

No significant relationship appears between class position and the principal forms of therapy administered by private agencies in any diagnostic group. This finding is a product of three sets of factors: First, practically no class V psychotics are treated by private practitioners and none are treated in private hospitals. Second, patients treated by private practitioners, irrespective of their class position, tend to receive individual psychotherapy. Custodial care is not applicable to the patients of private practitioners. Third, the patients treated in private hospitals and by private practitioners represent a relatively narrow range of class positions. These considerations practically eliminate the possibility of a significant relationship between class position, diagnostic group, and the type of therapy administered. In sum, if a class I, II, or III psychotic patient is treated in a private agency, irrespective of his diagnosis, he is likely to receive individual psychotherapy. Nevertheless, 14 per cent of the affectives and 27 per cent of the schizophrenics in private facilities are treated by an organic therapy. This is of interest because current psychiatric folklore holds that organic therapy, especially electroconvulsive therapies, are significantly helpful in many of the affective disorders; the same body of theory denies that there is a similar degree of benefit by any known therapy except possibly prolonged intensive psychotherapy for the schizophrenic psychoses. Incidentally, only two-thirds of the schizophrenics but 76 per cent of the affective patients in these agencies are being treated by psychotherapy. In each disorder, psychotherapy is concentrated in classes I, II, and III; both diagnosis and therapeutic theory are subordinate to class position.

Clinics

So few psychotic patients are treated in the clinics that no reliable statement can be made about interrelationships among diagnostic groups, therapy, and class position. No seniles or organics, and only one affective, are treated here. The 11 schizophrenics treated in the clinics all receive psychotherapy. Of the 36 alcoholics treated in the clinic, 34 receive individual psychotherapy, and the remaining 2 receive an organic therapy.

Public Hospitals

Schizophrenic patients are the only psychotic group large enough (60 per cent of all psychotics in public hospitals) to enable us to test *Hypothesis 3* with both diagnosis and treatment agency controlled. Nevertheless, so few of the schizophrenic patients are in classes I and II (1.5 per cent) that patients in these classes have to be combined with class III in the chi square tests. This requirement increases the severity of the test of assumed relationships between class status and the kind of treatment prescribed for the patients. If significant relationships do appear between class status and the principal form of psychiatric therapy prescribed, we may conclude that class position is a true variable operating in the treatment process within the public hospitals in the one diagnostic group that is large enough to enable us to analyze the data with some measure of reliability.

TABLE II

PRINCIPAL FORM OF THERAPY ADMINISTERED TO SCHIZOPHRENIC PATIENTS IN STATE AND VETERANS ADMINISTRATION HOSPITALS—PERCENTAGE BY CLASS

Type of Therapy	I–II*	III	IV	V
Psychotherapy	16.7	12.1	9.6	8.5
Organic therapy	25.0	53.6	50.6	33.8
Custodial care	58.3	34.3	39.8	57.7
$n =$	12	66	322	376

$$\chi^2 = 27.14, 4\ df, p < .001$$

* Classes I–II were combined with class III in the computation of χ^2.

Table II shows that a significant association does not exist between class position and the type of therapy prescribed for schizophrenic patients in the public hospitals. Only a small proportion of the schizophrenic patients receive psychotherapy but the class I–II patients receive it twice as frequently as the class V patients. The proportion receiving organic therapy varies unevenly from class II to class V, with classes III and IV receiving more than the adjacent classes. On the other hand, custodial care is prescribed for the highest proportion of the cases in classes I–II and in class V. The reader should remember there are only seven persons in class I–II, whereas there are 217 in class V. Moreover, every class I–II patient has been ill for a long time and has experienced two or more previous hospitalizations. All these patients are "burned out." The state hospital is indeed the "end of the road" for them. By way of contrast, 64 per cent of the patients in class V who are receiving custodial care have had no previous treatment. . . .

Summary and Conclusions

This chapter has been focused on a series of tests of the proposition that class status is a significant factor in the treatment of mentally ill patients. We have found real differences in *where, how,* and *how long* persons in the several classes have been cared for by psychiatrists. The many statistical tests made, even under the most rigid controls, demonstrate the validity of *Hypothesis 3*.

The data presented lead to the conclusion that treatment for mental illness depends not only on medical and psychological considerations, but also on powerful social variables to which psychiatrists have so far given little attention. It is certainly true that not enough psychiatrists are trained to handle patients in the way good psychotherapy prescribes, and that the process of psychotherapy in particular is complex, not easily mastered, and inevitably costly. This cost . . . with the exception of a few clinics, is assumed only rarely by third parties for those who cannot afford to pay themselves. Here, however, we want to point out that we controlled economic factors by dealing with treatment agencies separately and still found that distinct class differences prevail within agencies. Psychotherapeutic methods and particularly insight therapy are applied in disproportionately high degrees to higher status neurotic patients being treated by private practitioners. Organic therapies tend to be applied most often to neurotics in classes III and IV. Among the psychotic patients treatment differences among classes are most marked for the schizophrenics contributing, in no small part, to the large number of chronic patients in class V who remain in state hospitals year after year. Class as a factor in the length of treatment is also marked in the affective disorders. The bulk of these patients receive organic therapy, that is, electroconvulsive treatment. This suggests that if, for a given disorder, there is a treatment available which is relatively effective, inexpensive, and technically simple, class differences may be reduced, but not eliminated.

This lack of availability becomes enhanced when the social and cultural backgrounds of the patients differ from that of the psychiatrists. This should not be interpreted to mean that the lower class patients are not able to participate in or benefit from any kind of psychotherapy, but we believe that obstacles which have their roots in certain aspects of the social structure are quite formidable. Such practice is not just a social injustice; even if the lower class patient were to be given the same opportunity, much effort in research and therapy will have to be exerted before the situation will change. It is deeply rooted in certain habits of therapist and patient and their social value systems. A number of lower status patients are treated in mental hygiene clinics and in hospitals of the Veterans Administration. Yet we have serious doubts that the application of insight therapy to patients is effective unless considerable modifications of therapeutic techniques are undertaken. Any changes in technique and orientation must consider the phenomenology and dynamics of social stratification. Finally, on the basis of our data, we think that new approaches are indicated in order to bring psychotherapy to lower class patients with mental and emotional disorders. This may point to group therapy, new techniques for certain groups, such as adolescents and children, and the use of less expensive personnel, such as social workers and clinical psychologists in carrying out certain aspects of psychological intervention, for which they are trained.

We wish to reiterate that value differences between high status psychiatrists and lower status patients are a serious obstacle in psychotherapy, even if psychiatrists were to widen their cultural and social horizons and learn to understand the class IV and V patient. The mere suggestion of the existence of such a bias may offend psychiatrists who, like most professional practitioners, do not like to think in terms of social differences. Nevertheless, a number of different social and cultural factors operate on the psychiatrist, the patient, his family, and the community to produce the relationships reported here. Relevant factors include differential evaluation of psychiatrists by different classes, the attitudes of patients toward psychiatrists, and the ability of the persons in various classes to pay for psychiatric care. Another major factor is the different ways members of the several classes conceive of the nature and treatment of mental disorders. Finally, differing perceptions create communication problems for both the doctor and the patient. Needless to say, the practices we have highlighted in the preceding tables and charts are not the result of deliberate policy, but the unanticipated consequences of complex and tacit sociocultural and psychosocial processes of expectancies and role assignments. Powerful social processes keep many psychotic patients, particularly schizophrenics, in public mental hospitals; neither the family and community nor the hospital facilitate rehabilitation. However, they substantiate the assumption we built into the research design, namely, that latent social factors besides claimed medical criteria are influential in the determination of who is treated *where, how* and for *how long.* . . .

24 / The Relevance of Social Class

Daniel J. Levinson / Eugene B. Gallagher

Social Class and Patient "Career"

Typical attitudes toward mental illness at different class levels are associated with differences in the way patients are admitted to hospitals (and clinics), diagnosed, treated, assigned rooms and granted privileges, and moved along the course of patienthood. We use the term "career" to indicate that there is coherence and meaning in the unfolding of these events and provisions. "Career" embodies the notion of continuity over time. It also accents what the hospital "does to" the patient: how it grades and classifies him; and how it educates him in various career contingencies—gaining privileges, receiving desirable forms of treatment, attaining discharges, and the like.[1]

One reason why lower-class persons have an exaggerated fear of mental illness is that such patients rarely receive good psychiatric care or fare as well in psychiatric institutions as patients from higher classes. The New Haven research provides abundant evidence that this is so: regardless of psychopathology, lower-class patients receive less favorable treatment than higher-class patients. For example, the Myers and Schaffer (1954) study of a New Haven psychiatric clinic showed a connection between a patient's social class and the amount of training

Abridged from Chapter 11 of *Patienthood in the Mental Hospital* by Daniel J. Levinson and Eugene B. Gallagher. Copyright © 1964. (Boston: Houghton Mifflin Company, 1964). Reprinted by permission of the authors and Houghton Mifflin Company.

[1] The career concept has been best expounded and illustrated by Goffman (1961). See also Roth (1963).

of the clinic therapist assigned to him. There, all patients received psychotherapy; but higher-class patients usually received it from skilled staff members, while lower-class patients more often had therapy with inexperienced medical students.

This finding deals with a fairly subtle difference, of which the patient himself may be unaware, in the treatment of outpatients. For inpatients, the difference between higher- and lower-class careers tends to be more obvious. Lower-class patients are likely to delay entering a hospital until their outside social relationships have been severely damaged; they are likely then to enter a public hospital which is ill-equipped and understaffed. Once in the hospital, they are more likely to receive organic treatment (such as electric shock) or minimum custodial care than psychotherapy. Further, their hospital stay may be prolonged, partly because of severe pathology at admission, partly because of inadequate treatment, partly because their families have limited physical and emotional resources for dealing with a member now defined as mentally ill. The career of the higher-class patient is, in these several respects, a smoother and more advantaged one, since as a rule he has earlier and more effective treatment.

In speaking thus of careers, we do not wish to focus unduly upon patient passivity or inactivity; the mental patient is, contrary to the strict etymology of "patient," not simply a passive sufferer. His attitudes, as delineated above, are important. Indeed, there is a degree of fit between his attitudes toward psychiatry and the career he experiences under psychiatric auspices.

The Measurement and Distribution of Social Class

Our measure of social class is the Hollingshead (1957) Two-Factor Index of Social Position (ISP). The Index assigns to a patient a score based upon his educational attainment and the prestige of his occupation. Education and occupation scores are weighted in the proportion of 4 to 7 and then combined. ISP scores range from 11, the highest possible social status, to 77, the lowest possible status (note that *low* numerical score signifies *high* status).

After a patient's ISP score has been determined, it is used to assign him to a social class. Four cutting points are inserted into the 11–77 range, yielding five social class levels. We use *social class* to divide the sample into distinct status groups. We use *ISP score* to represent social status in correlational analysis.

A sketch of the five classes, as they appear in our sample of 100 patients, is useful here. There are four patients in Class I. All have graduated from college. Their occupations are computer programmer, physicist, certified public accountant, and veterinarian. Class II has 16 representatives in the sample, most of whom have completed at least part of college or had other education following high school. In this group, there is an advertising copywriter, a women's reformatory official, a high school teacher, and an insurance agent. There are relatively more Class I and II patients in this hospital, with its good reputation and active treatment program, than in most public hospitals. For statistical purposes we combine Classes I and II into a single category, I-II, comprising 20 per cent of our sample.

Class III, the "lower-middle" class, has 38 patients and is the largest in our sample. Most Class III patients have completed high school. Their jobs include liquor salesman, hardware salesman, cake decorator, and nurse's aide.

Class IV, the "upper-lower" class, has 28 patients. Some have completed high school, most have not. Their jobs include hosiery inspector, shoe salesman, designer in a garment factory, and oil burner repairman. Classes III and IV together, 66 per cent of our sample, comprise the broad stratum of the "common man." It is the largest segment of the population, in the hospital and outside. It includes the lower reaches of white-collar work as well as many skilled and semi-skilled blue-collar occupations in factories, warehouses, and the like.

Our sample contains 14 Class V patients. Almost none have finished high school, and some have only a few years of schooling. One Class V patient works in a laundry; others work as domestics, porters, or janitors. Their jobs are unskilled and often transient. Many Class V jobs have the additional quality of social undesirability, because they place the worker in difficult or hazardous working conditions, or expose him to dirty, messy materials and to moral temptation.

The social class distribution of patients in a mental hospital is an important characteristic in its own right. It is also a useful tool in comparative analysis of the structure and functioning of different hospitals. Siegel et al. (1962) have compared this hospital with Hillside Hospital in Glen Oaks, New York, and with Menninger Hospital in Topeka, Kansas. Hillside and this hospital have predominantly "common man" populations, whereas Menninger has a heavy preponderance of higher-class patients. The modal status of patients is a significant feature of a hospital, with many implications for its functioning. It affects the scope and major emphases of the formal treatment program, the emotional atmosphere of the ward, the complex of rules and privileges which govern patient life, and the quality of relationships between patients and staff. Its influence is largely implicit or unacknowledged. As a collective or group characteristic, modal patient status operates in a pervasive background fashion, belonging, as it were, to the institution's "unconscious."

We suggest that modal patient status affects not only the separate constituents of hospital functioning, as cited above, but also their patterning. Without attempting a detailed analysis, let us briefly compare the typical large public hospital with the small private hospital.

In large state hospitals, the patient population is mainly lower class. The staff-to-patient ratio is small, and the chances are slight for patients to form meaningful relationships with staff. However, of the several staff roles, the attendant or aide is likely to know the patient best and to play a significant, potentially therapeutic part in the patient's life (see Rowland, 1939; Belknap, 1956).[2] This relationship is facilitated in large part by the similarities in social background between attendant and patient. Psychiatrists are few in number and tend to have little immediate contact with patients; their role is primarily administrative. Such hospitals have recently shown increasing interest in milieu therapy, especially in training attendants and other ward personnel in psychodynamics and group therapy. Through this, hopefully, personnel may turn to therapeutic advantage their already considerable ability to communicate with patients.

---

[2] The attendant-patient relationship is based on the exigencies of hospital life. The patient offers conforming behavior and deference, in return for privileges which the attendant controls. This relationship thus has the mechanical aspect of exchange, rather than an affective tone of spontaneity and warmth; it is not real friendship. Nevertheless, it involves a measure of mutual respect and accommodation from each party.

The situation is quite different in small private hospitals. The patients are mainly upper or upper-middle class. The staff-to-patient ratio is much more favorable, and patients can have close contact with many categories of staff. However, treatment responsibility and prerogatives are centered in the psychiatrist. Psychotherapy is, as a rule, the major mode of treatment, and is well suited to the modal qualities of the patient body, which is usually well-educated, articulate, and intraceptive. In private hospitals where somatic methods such as electric shock are relied upon heavily, treatment is still centered in the psychiatrist who acts in his more "medical" capacity. A parallel exists between the "psychiatrist-centered" treatment emphasis and the pressures created by the high modal social status of patients. The patients orient primarily to the psychiatrist (and conversely he to them), among the several staff groupings, as their status equal. Some patients, at the extreme, may attempt to distort relationships with him in a "friendship" fashion, basing their claims upon shared high status; at a greater extreme, they may attempt to "use" him as a provider of services. Further, since many patients at such institutions are present in voluntary status, they can, if dissatisfied, prematurely terminate their hospitalization. The hospital administration, sensitive to this condition, may protect the individuality of the patient to an excessive, pathology-reinforcing degree. Where nurses and attendants are perceived as socially subordinate, there may be little awareness, on the part of either staff or patients, of their therapeutic potentialities.

By comparison with the public hospital patient, the patient in the exclusive private hospital is more a client and less an inmate. He has the client's independence, which as we have seen may be abused. But, his autonomous strivings for self-change are likely to find more ample reinforcement in the treatment process, particularly in hospitals which stress psychotherapy. Also, if he seeks to utilize the environment for self-learning and construction of new social skills, his efforts will find response in the more diversified opportunities afforded by the hospital.

The *modal* status of patients in a hospital has implications for the situation of the *individual* patient. How does modal patient status affect the role-conceptions, treatment provisions, and social adaptation of the individual patient? We cannot answer this question here, but we can briefly illustrate its relevance. The Class I patient in an exclusive private hospital can mingle with other patients from his class, whose educational experiences, social outlooks, and values are similar to his own. The same patient in a public hospital finds himself in a quite different situation. Most patients on his ward are of modest means and less educated; social relationships may be difficult for him. Class II or III patients are to be found in both public and private hospitals. Again, we suggest, it makes a difference for them which kind of hospital they enter. An important component of this difference lies in the modal patient status of the hospital. . . .

Social Class and Personality

We shall examine the relationship of social class to authoritarianism, the personality syndrome that has emerged most clearly as a determinant of role-conception. There is considerable evidence that authoritarianism is more prevalent in the lower and lower-middle classes than at higher status levels. This correlation is of moderate strength, and it appears consistently in different studies. Janowitz and

Marvick (1953), using data from an authoritarianism scale administered to several national samples, found more "high authoritarian" individuals in the less-educated portion of the samples than in the better-educated portion. Similar results are reported when socio-economic position is taken as a status index, independent of education. Lipset (1959), in his cross-national compilation of research on politico-social attitudes, says that ". . . authoritarian predispositions . . . flow more naturally from the situation of the lower classes than from that of the middle and upper classes in modern industrial society. . . ." He cites several elements in the lower- and working-class situation which contribute to authoritarianism—low education, little reading, low participation in political and voluntary associations, work in socially isolating conditions, economic insecurity, and rigid, hierarchical family patterns.

Hollingshead and Redlich (1958) describe numerous features of lower-class life in New Haven which are components of the authoritarian syndrome. Consider this passage (p. 176): "In Class V, where the demands of everyday life are greatest, awareness of suffering is perceived less clearly than in the higher levels. The denial, or partial denial, of the existence of psychic pain appears to be a defense mechanism that is linked to low status. Also, Class V persons appear to accept physical suffering to a greater extent than do persons in higher status positions. This may be realistic and in keeping with the often hopeless situations these people face in day-to-day living. In Classes I and II, by way of contrast, there is less willingness to accept life as unalterable."

From this description it seems that lower-class persons commonly hold uncritical, submissive, hopeless attitudes toward their lot. They have little concern with the psychological side of life, and a relative lack of awareness of the inner world of motivation, subjective experience, intrapsychic process, fantasy, and aspiration. This quality of *anti-intraception* is crucial both as a leading element in authoritarianism and as an element which differentiates lower-class from middle- and upper-class ways. In the higher classes, there is a wider margin of economic and psychological security, wherein self-awareness and sensitivity to the motivations of others can be cultivated. Social horizons, life experience, and education are broader, and this facilitates a more tolerant, non-authoritarian outlook.[3] Time perspectives into past and future are longer, permitting a more intraceptive grasp of meaning and cause in human affairs.

In another field of study, Miller and Swanson (1960) give evidence that lower-class parents are on the average more authoritarian in their modes of child-rearing—more punitive in discipline, less affectionate and permissive—than are middle-class parents. Also, boys and girls receive the greatest differential in parental treatment among lower-class families (Bronfenbrenner, 1958). As one moves up the social ladder, parental treatment of the two sexes becomes more similar. Sharp differentiation of sex roles is indicative of general exaggerated concern with sex; such concern is another component of the authoritarian syndrome (Levinson and Huffman, 1955).[4] That it is greater on the lower social levels

---

[3] In a study which attempts to define, conceptually and empirically, the "tolerant personality," Martin and Westie (1959) found that tolerant subjects had a higher mean level of educational and occupational status than prejudiced subjects.

[4] These authors mapped out an ideology of family life—of husband-wife, parent-child relations, and other family issues—which expressed the essential structure of authoritarianism.

lends additional support to the notion of high authoritarianism among working- and lower-class persons.

We expect that these findings about class differences will hold for patients as well. Our hypothesis: *Lower-class patients will be high on authoritarianism, higher-class patients will be low.* In correlational terms, this prediction calls for a significant correlation between ISP and F. This hypothesis was supported in our earlier study of patients, which yielded a significant ISP-F correlation of .38 (Gallagher, Levinson, and Erlich, 1957).

Our present study yields a moderately strong correlation of .53 between ISP and F. A strong trend of association is discernible in Table I. The 20 patients in Classes I and II have an F Mean of 34.6; this is almost 20 points lower than the

TABLE I

THE RELATION OF SOCIAL CLASS TO AUTHORITARIANISM (F SCALE)

Social Class	N	F Scale Mean	S.D.	Per cent who are Low on F*
I–II	20	34.6	9.9	80
III	38	42.1	11.1	53
IV	28	46.4	10.8	43
V	14	54.1	9.4	14
Total sample	100	43.5	12.1	50
Analysis of variance: F ratio = 9.88				
	$p < .001$			
Correlation of ISP and F = .53				

* Low on F: in lower half of distribution for total sample.

Class V Mean of 54.1. Classes III and IV are intermediate with Means, respectively, of 42.1 and 46.4. Thus the "middles" on status (the "common man" classes) are also middle, but highly diverse, on authoritarianism. It can also be seen that the proportion of low-F patients (those in the lower half of the total F distribution) declines steadily from Class I–II to Class V.

Analysis of variance on F shows a highly significant ratio of between-class to within-class variance. However, along with sizable between-class differences in F, it is noteworthy that patients in each class show considerable dispersion around the class mean. In Class III, for example, the Standard Deviation is 11.1. Only in Class V do we find an extreme restriction of variability around a relatively extreme mean. The Class I–II patients are predominantly in the low half of the F distribution; however, their mean of 34.6 is hardly extreme, and it would be unwarranted to conclude that most Class I–II patients are markedly low F-scorers.

In summary, we have shown, first, that patients show substantial class differences in personality; and second, that there is considerable heterogeneity in personality within each class. The second finding is scarcely surprising; more surprising would be the discovery of a high degree of uniformity within classes,

---

Prominent in this ideology (and in a scale devised to measure it) is an extreme emphasis upon differences between the sexes—in interests and values, social obligations, and psychological make-up.

or of a true "class personality." Social class, as an agency of socialization and personality formation, has an impact which is pervasive and insistent, threading its way through the individual's material environment, his social relationships, and his general attitudes—but still, the impact of class is uneven and attenuated. Some individuals are more tightly integrated than others into social situations typical of their class. Mental patients may well be *less* class-integrated, on the average. Also, social class must divide its influence upon personality with other powerful forces, such as family structure, educational systems, role-models, economic stresses, mass communications, multiple pathological or health-promoting stimuli and processes, many of which may operate with more impact and immediacy than social class.

We acknowledge, then, the intra-class variation in authoritarianism, and grant it theoretical status co-equal with the social class differences in authoritarianism. . . .

The Relevance of Social Class in Hospital Life

We have given primary emphasis thus far to social class as an aspect of the patient's extra-hospital world—the world of social acceptance, occupational prestige, consumption standards, neighborhood desirability, and so forth, which the patient largely but not entirely leaves behind on entering the hospital. Hospitalization in *any* mental hospital has a status-externalizing and status-leveling effect. Witness the fact that whereas hospital staff is stratified into several finely-graded status hierarchies, every patient is simply "patient"—and only that.

To a considerable extent, the patient is urged into a temporary redefinition of himself: psychologically, he is urged to regard himself as sick and in need of care; socially, he is to some extent deprived of an habitually recognized social class position (even if it be a lowly one). Further, his various other social identities—regional, religious, ethnic, and the like—become neutralized and submerged (though not completely erased, except in the case of the chronic patient whose extra-hospital identity may become totally lost). The patient is characteristically viewed by staff in an all-enveloping framework drawn from medicine and psychiatry which pays scant attention to his socio-cultural flavoring. He may be seen variously as a biological-neurological disease process; as an abstract set of psychodynamics; as a "troubled person" who has not yet learned to communicate; or in still other guises. These varied perspectives have in common one feature: an *a*-cultural bias, which is usually more implicit than explicit.

Although the process of redefinition is among the existential givens of patienthood, its scope and penetration may vary. The social structure and climate of the hospital can greatly modify and influence it, selectively urging patients to discard undesirable or pathogenic identity elements while at the same time reinforcing other, more socially desirable, ego-syntonic elements. Certain themes from the outside even receive special emphasis, in the interest of preserving continuity between outside and inside culture. Mental hospitals operated by religious orders, for example, give prominent play to religious imagery and rites. Social class may also have prominence in certain hospitals. Such might well be the case in exclusive private hospitals where, despite the mishap of illness, one's upper-class identification is affirmed by association with similarly-placed patients and through treatment by distinguished experts. Social class is underscored also in those mental hospitals where some patients are "paying" patients and others are "charity" patients. . . .

In presenting their findings on social class distinctions in the mental hospital, social scientists can scarcely avoid the intimation of gross inequity within the institution (and not all wish to avoid it). It is difficult to select a reasonable standard for evaluating such findings. For example, few people would be shocked to learn that architects or portrait artists deal mainly with upper-class clients. Yet it is a revelation to learn that the psychiatric profession deals mainly with upper- and upper-middle-class patients, that lower-class foreign-born patients are more likely than others to receive shock treatment, and so on. These revelations bring in their wake proposals for reform: for broadening the training of psychiatrists and increasing their exposure to the "common man"; for devising psychotherapies less dependent upon verbal procedures; for increasing the supply and upgrading the skills of non-psychiatric professionals such as psychologists, nurses, and social workers; and for leveling treatment costs through prepayment insurance. There are widespread, strong pressures in our society for more uniform access to psychiatric treatment. Residual barriers such as social class are receding, but nonetheless remain powerful.

Additional Approaches
to Study of Social Class Influences

We have conceptualized social class as an "external" influence upon patient role-conception. We have also discussed the ways in which class and status, as a theme in the culture of the hospital itself—and particularly in the situation of the patient—may be accentuated or diminished. In these respects, our concern has been with social class as an "objective" characteristic of the patient. We have virtually ignored the domain of *subjective* status—how the patient regards his social status, its functions for him, and related questions. Status exists "inside" the patient as well as in the social system.

We suggest that the inner sense of one's status may have important implications for patient role-conception and adaptation to the hospital. Status has various aspects which are subjective and intensely personal. People have status aspirations and strivings, private ambitions, fantasies of elevation and degradation, achievement motivations, and fears of success. One's self-concept, whether he be inside or outside a mental hospital, includes sense of status as a crucial ingredient. From a narrowly clinical viewpoint, status is frequently regarded as merely "social"—as an extrinsic, happenstance appendage of the psyche which has no bearing upon intrapsychic constellations. Or status may be regarded solely as a designation of external life-chances—material advantages or deprivations—which make reality more favorable or burdensome but, again, do not alter intrapsychic forces.

In theoretical terms, however, it is possible to view status as a more integral and constitutive part of the personality, closely tied to self-esteem. In this sense, one's primitive, less-conscious feelings of potency, prowess, competence, desirability, uniqueness have the significance of "high status." Actions and wishes in accord with central moral conceptions mean high status. Sheer good fortune or misfortune also can contribute to the internal sense of high or low status. A fuller conceptualization and exploration of status as part of personality seems particularly germane in the sociopsychological study of mental patients. Many patients view their lives, their prospects and accomplishments, unrealistically—by a lamp which casts a glow too exalting or too demeaning. Further, it is not uncommon for patients to disavow or subjectively to suspend their previously accepted social status.

Erikson's (1959) notion of the "moratorium" is applicable here. Younger patients sometimes place themselves, so to speak, in a deep freeze, totally suspending the customary props and forms of existence in a desperate effort to discover what they themselves are at bedrock—their primal essences and mainspring impulses. There is, we suggest, a complex interplay here between psychological forces within the patient and the inducements and pressures supplied by the hospital. The hospital attempts to provide a safe haven wherein the patient is freed of involvements and responsibilities in the outside world of status-striving, family ties, and the like. Corresponding forces exist within the patient, as implied in the concept of the moratorium; the patient acts *less* but thinks and feels *more* in relation to his sexual, social, religio-ethnic, and occupational identity.

We suggest that, paradoxically, the moratorium and search for self-redefinition can achieve its greatest depth in those environments where social pressures are most subtle and least coercive, and where the patient's commitment is most nearly voluntary. The severity of a self-imposed moratorium may far exceed any externally-imposed mortification or stripping rituals. The ultimate case is that in which patienthood is a pure seeking for self-change, impelled by an inner sense of defect or suffering, and without institutional coercion. Here, we might say, status means human dignity. Status becomes subjectivized and simplified, consisting primarily of one's sense of capacity for enduring and surmounting the unacceptable in himself and others. Further work could well incorporate these more complex aspects of status and relate them to patienthood in the hospital. . . .

25 / The Moral Career of the Mental Patient

Erving Goffman

Traditionally the term *career* has been reserved for those who expect to enjoy the rises laid out within a respectable profession. The term is coming to be used,

From *Psychiatry*, 1959, **22**, 123–142. Copyright © 1959. Also from pp. 125–169 of *Asylums: Essays on the Social Situation of Mental Patients and Other Inmates* by Erving Goffman. Copyright © 1961. (Garden City, N.Y.: Doubleday & Company, Inc., 1961). Reprinted by permission of the author, the William Alanson White Psychiatric Foundation, Inc., and Doubleday & Company, Inc.

however, in a broadened sense to refer to any social strand of any person's course through life. The perspective of natural history is taken: unique outcomes are neglected in favor of such changes over time as are basic and common to the members of a social category, although occurring independently to each of them. Such a career is not a thing that can be brilliant or disappointing; it can no more be a success than a failure. In this light, I want to consider the mental patient.

One value of the concept of career is its two-sidedness. One side is linked to internal matters held dearly and closely, such as image of self and felt identity; the other side concerns official position, jural relations, and style of life, and is part of a publicly accessible institutional complex. The concept of career, then, allows one to move back and forth between the personal and the public, between the self and its significant society, without having overly to rely for data upon what the person says he thinks he imagines himself to be.

This paper, then, is an exercise in the institutional approach to the study of self. The main concern will be with the *moral* aspects of career—that is, the regular sequence of changes that career entails in the person's self and in his framework of imagery for judging himself and others.[1]

The category "mental patient" itself will be understood in one strictly sociological sense. In this perspective, the psychiatric view of a person becomes significant only in so far as this view itself alters his social fate—an alteration which seems to become fundamental in our society when, and only when, the person is put through the process of hospitalization.[2] I therefore exclude certain neighboring categories: the undiscovered candidates who would be judged "sick" by psychiatric standards but who never come to be viewed as such by themselves or by others, although they may cause everyone a great deal of trouble;[3] the office patient whom a psychiatrist feels he can handle with drugs or shock on the outside; the mental client who engages in psychotherapeutic relationships. And I include anyone, however robust in temperament, who somehow gets caught up in the heavy machinery of mental hospital servicing. In this way the effects of being treated as a mental patient can be kept quite distinct from the effects upon a person's life of traits a

[1] Material on moral career can be found in early social anthropological work on ceremonies of status transition, and in classic social psychological descriptions of those spectacular changes in one's view of self that can accompany participation in social movements and sects. Recently new kinds of relevant data have been suggested by psychiatric interest in the problem of "identity" and sociological studies of work careers and "adult socialization."

[2] This point has recently been made by Cumming and Cumming (1957, pp. 101–102). "Clinical experience supports the impression that many people define mental illness as 'That condition for which a person is treated in a mental hospital.' . . . Mental illness, it seems, is a condition which afflicts people who must go to a mental institution, but until they do almost anything they do is normal." Leila Deasy has pointed out to me the correspondence here with the situation in white collar crime. Of those who are detected in this activity, only the ones who do not manage to avoid going to prison find themselves accorded the social role of the criminal.

[3] Case records in mental hospitals are just now coming to be exploited to show the incredible amount of trouble a person may cause for himself and others before anyone begins to think about him psychiatrically, let alone take psychiatric action against him. See Clausen and Yarrow (1955a); Hollingshead and Redlich (1958).

clinician would view as psychopathological.[4] Persons who become mental hospital patients vary widely in the kind and degree of illness that a psychiatrist would impute to them, and in the attributes by which laymen would describe them. But once started on the way, they are confronted by some importantly similar circumstances and respond to these in some importantly similar ways. Since these similarities do not come from mental illness, they would seem to occur in spite of it. It is thus a tribute to the power of social forces that the uniform status of mental patient can not only assure an aggregate of persons a common fate and eventually, because of this, a common character, but that this social reworking can be done upon what is perhaps the most obstinate diversity of human materials that can be brought together by society. Here there lacks only the frequent forming of a protective group-life by expatients to illustrate in full the classic cycle of response by which deviant subgroupings are psychodynamically formed in society.

This general sociological perspective is heavily reinforced by one key finding of sociologically oriented students in mental hospital research. As has been repeatedly shown in the study of nonliterate societies, the awesomeness, distastefulness, and barbarity of a foreign culture can decrease in the degree that the student becomes familiar with the point of view to life that is taken by his subjects. Similarly, the student of mental hospitals can discover that the craziness or "sick behavior" claimed for the mental patient is by and large a product of the claimant's social distance from the situation that the patient is in, and is not primarily a product of mental illness. Whatever the refinements of the various patients' psychiatric diagnoses, and whatever the special ways in which social life on the "inside" is unique, the researcher can find that he is participating in a community not significantly different from any other he has studied.[5] Of course, while restricting himself to the off-ward grounds community of paroled patients, he may feel, as some patients do, that life in the locked wards is bizarre; and while on a locked admissions or convalescent ward, he may feel that chronic "back" wards are socially crazy places. But he need only move his sphere of sympathetic participation to the "worst" ward in the hospital, and this too can come into social focus as a place with a livable and continuously meaningful social world. This in no way denies that he will find a minority in any ward or patient group that continues to seem quite beyond the capacity to follow rules of social organization, or that the orderly fulfillment of normative expectations in patient society is partly made possible by strategic measures that have somehow come to be institutionalized in mental hospitals.

The career of the mental patient falls popularly and naturalistically into three main phases: the period prior to entering the hospital, which I shall call the *prepatient phase;* the period in the hospital, the *inpatient phase;* the period after discharge from the hospital, should this occur, namely, the *expatient phase.*[6] This paper will deal only with the first two phases.

[4] An illustration of how this perspective may be taken to all forms of deviancy may be found in Lemert (1951, pp. 74–76). A specific application to mental defectives may be found in Perry (1954, p. 68).

[5] Conscientious objectors who voluntarily went to jail sometimes arrived at the same conclusion regarding criminal inmates. See, for example, Hassler (1954, p. 74).

[6] This simple picture is complicated by the somewhat special experience of roughly a third of ex-patients—namely, readmission to the hospital, this being the recidivist or "repatient" phase.

The Prepatient Phase

A relatively small group of prepatients come into the mental hospital willingly, because of their own idea of what will be good for them, or because of whole-hearted agreement with the relevant members of their family. Presumably these recruits have found themselves acting in a way which is evidence to them that they are losing their minds or losing control of themselves. This view of oneself would seem to be one of the most pervasively threatening things that can happen to the self in our society, especially since it is likely to occur at a time when the person is in any case sufficiently troubled to exhibit the kind of symptom which he himself can see. As Sullivan (1956, pp. 184–185) described it,

> What we discover in the self-system of a person undergoing schizophrenic changes or schizophrenic processes, is then, in its simplest form, an extremely fear-marked puzzlement, consisting of the use of rather generalized and any-thing but exquisitely refined referential processes in an attempt to cope with what is essentially a failure at being human—a failure at being anything that one could respect as worth being.

Coupled with the person's disintegrative re-evaluation of himself will be the new, almost equally pervasive circumstance of attempting to conceal from others what he takes to be the new fundamental facts about himself, and attempting to discover whether others too have discovered them.[7] Here I want to stress that perception of losing one's mind is based on culturally derived and socially engrained stereotypes as to the significance of symptoms such as hearing voices, losing temporal and spatial orientation, and sensing that one is being followed, and that many of the most spectacular and convincing of these symptoms in some instances psychiatrically signify merely a temporary emotional upset in a stressful situation, however terrifying to the person at the time. Similarly, the anxiety con-sequent upon this perception of oneself, and the strategies devised to reduce this anxiety, are not a product of abnormal psychology, but would be exhibited by any person socialized into our culture who came to conceive of himself as some-one losing his mind. Interestingly, subcultures in American society apparently differ in the amount of ready imagery and encouragement they supply for such self-views, leading to differential rates of *self*-referral; the capacity to take this disintegrative view of oneself without psychiatric prompting seems to be one of the questionable cultural privileges of the upper classes.[8]

For the person who has come to see himself—with whatever justification—as mentally unbalanced, entrance to the mental hospital can sometimes bring relief, perhaps in part because of the sudden transformation in the structure of his basic social situations; instead of being to himself a questionable person trying to maintain a role as a full one, he can become an officially questioned person known to himself to be not so questionable as that. In other cases, hospitalization

[7] This moral experience can be contrasted with that of a person learning to become a mari-huana addict whose discovery that he can be "high" and still "op" effectively without being detected apparently leads to a new level of use. See Becker (1955, pp. 40–41).

[8] See Hollingshead and Redlich (1958, p. 187, Table VI), where relative frequency is given of self-referral by social-class grouping.

can make matters worse for the willing patient, confirming by the objective situation what has theretofore been a matter of the private experience of self.

Once the willing prepatient enters the hospital, he may go through the same routine of experiences as do those who enter unwillingly. In any case, it is the latter that I mainly want to consider, since in America at present these are by far the more numerous kind.[9] Their approach to the institution takes one of three classic forms: they come because they have been implored by their family or threatened with the abrogation of family ties unless they go "willingly"; they come by force under police escort; they come under misapprehension purposely induced by others, this last restricted mainly to youthful prepatients.

The prepatient's career may be seen in terms of an extrusory model; he starts out with relationships and rights, and ends up, at the beginning of his hospital stay, with hardly any of either. The moral aspects of this career, then, typically begin with the experience of abandonment, disloyalty, and embitterment. This is the case even though to others it may be obvious that he was in need of treatment, and even though in the hospital he may soon come to agree.

The case histories of most mental patients document offense against some arrangement for face-to-face living—a domestic establishment, a work place, a semipublic organization such as a church or store, a public region such as a street or park. Often there is also a record of some *complainant*, some figure who takes that action against the offender which eventually leads to his hospitalization. This may not be the person who makes the first move, but it is the person who makes what turns out to be the first effective move. Here is the *social* beginning of the patient's career, regardless of where one might locate the psychological beginning of his mental illness.

The kinds of offenses which lead to hospitalization are felt to differ in nature from those which lead to other extrusory consequences—to imprisonment, divorce, loss of job, disownment, regional exile, noninstitutional psychiatric treatment, and so forth. But little seems known about these differentiating factors; and when one studies actual commitments, alternate outcomes frequently appear to have been possible. It seems true, moreover, that for every offense that leads to an effective complaint, there are many psychiatrically similar ones that never do. No action is taken; or action is taken which leads to other extrusory outcomes; or ineffective action is taken, leading to the mere pacifying or putting off of the person who complains. Thus, as Clausen and Yarrow have nicely shown, even offenders who are eventually hospitalized are likely to have had a long series of ineffective actions taken against them (Clausen and Yarrow, 1955a).

Separating those offenses which could have been used as grounds for hospitalizing the offender from those that are so used, one finds a vast number of what students of occupation call career contingencies.[10] Some of these contingencies in the mental patient's career have been suggested, if not explored, such as socioeconomic status, visibility of the offense, proximity to a mental hospital, amount of treatment facilities available, community regard for the type of treatment given

---

[9] The distinction employed here between willing and unwilling patients cuts across the legal one, of voluntary and committed, since some persons who are glad to come to the mental hospital may be legally committed, and of those who come only because of strong familial pressure, some may sign themselves in as voluntary patients.

[10] An explicit application of this notion to the field of mental health may be found in Lemert (1946).

in available hospitals, and so on (for example, Myers and Schaffer, 1954; Lemert, 1951, pp. 402–403; U.S. Bureau of Census, 1941, p. 2). For information about other contingencies one must rely on atrocity tales: a psychotic man is tolerated by his wife until she finds herself a boy friend, or by his adult children until they move from a house to an apartment; an alcoholic is sent to a mental hospital because the jail is full, and a drug addict because he declines to avail himself of psychiatric treatment on the outside; a rebellious adolescent daughter can no longer be managed at home because she now threatens to have an open affair with an unsuitable companion; and so on. Correspondingly there is an equally important set of contingencies causing the person to by-pass this fate. And should the person enter the hospital, still another set of contingencies will help determine when he is to obtain a discharge—such as the desire of his family for his return, the availability of a "manageable" job, and so on. The society's official view is that inmates of mental hospitals are there primarily because they are suffering from mental illness. However, in the degree that the "mentally ill" outside hospitals numerically approach or surpass those inside hospitals one could say that mental patients *distinctively* suffer not from mental illness but from contingencies.

Career contingencies occur in conjunction with a second feature of the pre-patient's career—the *circuit of agents*—and agencies—that participate fatefully in his passage from civilian to patient status (e.g., Hall, 1948). Here is an instance of that increasingly important class of social system whose elements are agents and agencies, which are brought into systemic connection through having to take up and send on the same persons. Some of these agent-roles will be cited now, with the understanding that in any concrete circuit a role may be filled more than once, and a single person may fill more than one of them.

First is the *next-of-relation*—the person whom the prepatient sees as the most available of those upon whom he should be able to most depend in times of trouble; in this instance the last to doubt his sanity and the first to have done everything to save him from the fate which, it transpires, he has been approaching. The patient's next-of-relation is usually his next of kin; the special term is introduced because he need not be. Second is the *complainant*, the person who retrospectively appears to have started the person on his way to the hospital. Third are the *mediators*—the sequence of agents and agencies to which the prepatient is referred and through which he is relayed and processed on his way to the hospital. Here are included police, clergy, general medical practitioners, office psychiatrists, personnel in public clinics, lawyers, social service workers, school teachers, and so on. One of these agents will have the legal mandate to sanction commitment and will exercise it, and so those agents who precede him in the process will be involved in something whose outcome is not yet settled. When the mediators retire from the scene, the prepatient has become an inpatient, and the significant agent has become the hospital administrator.

While the complainant usually takes action in a lay capacity as a citizen, an employer, a neighbor, or a kinsman, mediators tend to be specialists and differ from those they serve in significant ways. They have experience in handling trouble, and some professional distance from what they handle. Except in the case of policemen, and perhaps some clergy, they tend to be more psychiatrically oriented than the lay public, and will see the need for treatment at times when the public does not (Cumming and Cumming, 1957, p. 92).

An interesting feature of these roles is the functional effects of their interdigitation. For example, the feelings of the patient will be influenced by whether or not the person who fills the role of complainant also has the role of next-of-relation—an embarrassing combination more prevalent, apparently, in the higher classes than in the lower (Hollingshead and Redlich, 1958). Some of these emergent effects will be considered now.[11]

In the prepatient's progress from home to the hospital he may participate as a third person in what he may come to experience as a kind of *alienative coalition*. His next-of-relation presses him into coming to "talk things over" with a medical practitioner, an office psychiatrist, or some other counselor. Disinclination on his part may be met by threatening him with desertion, disownment, or other legal action, or by stressing the joint and explorative nature of the interview. But typically the next-of-relation will have set the interview up, in the sense of selecting the professional, arranging for time, telling the professional something about the case, and so on. This move effectively tends to establish the next-of-relation as the responsible person to whom pertinent findings can be divulged, while effectively establishing the other as the patient. The prepatient often goes to the interview with the understanding that he is going as an equal of someone who is so bound together with him that a third person could not come between them in fundamental matters; this, after all, is one way in which close relationships are defined in our society. Upon arrival at the office the prepatient suddenly finds that he and his next-of-relation have not been accorded the same roles, and apparently that a prior understanding between the professional and the next-of-relation has been put in operation against him. In the extreme but common case the professional first sees the prepatient alone, in the role of examiner and diagnostician, and then sees the next-of-relation alone, in the role of advisor, while carefully avoiding talking things over seriously with them both together.[12] And even in those nonconsultative cases where public officials must forcibly extract a person from a family that wants to tolerate him, the next-of-relation is likely to be induced to "go along" with the official action, so that even here the prepatient may feel that an alienative coalition has been formed against him.

The moral experience of being third man in such a coalition is likely to embitter the prepatient, especially since his troubles have already probably led to some estrangement from his next-of-relation. After he enters the hospital, continued visits by his next-of-relation can give the patient the "insight" that his own best interests were being served. But the initial visits may temporarily strengthen his feeling of abandonment; he is likely to beg his visitor to get him out or at least to get him more privileges and to sympathize with the monstrousness of his plight—to which the visitor ordinarily can respond only by trying to maintain a hopeful note, by not "hearing" the requests, or by assuring the patient that the medical authorities know about these things and are doing what is medically best. The visitor then nonchalantly goes back into a world that the patient has learned is incredibly thick with freedom and privileges, causing the patient to feel that his next-of-relation is merely adding a pious gloss to a clear case of traitorous desertion.

[11] For an analysis of some of these circuit implications for the inpatient, see Deasy and Quinn (1955). An interesting illustration of this kind of analysis may also be found in Gowman (1956). A general statement may be found in Merton (1957a).

[12] I have one case record of a man who claims he thought *he* was taking his wife to see the psychiatrist, not realizing until too late that his wife had made the arrangements.

The depth to which the patient may feel betrayed by his next-of-relation seems to be increased by the fact that another witnesses his betrayal—a factor which is apparently significant in many three-party situations. An offended person may well act forbearantly and accommodatively toward an offender when the two are alone, choosing peace ahead of justice. The presence of a witness, however, seems to add something to the implications of the offense. For then it is beyond the power of the offended and offender to forget about, erase, or suppress what has happened; the offense has become a public social fact (Riezler, 1943). When the witness is a mental health commission, as is sometimes the case, the witnessed betrayal can verge on a "degradation ceremony" (see Garfinkel, 1956). In such circumstances, the offended patient may feel that some kind of extensive reparative action is required before witnesses, if his honor and social weight are to be restored.

Two other aspects of sensed betrayal should be mentioned. First, those who suggest the possibility of another's entering a mental hospital are not likely to provide a realistic picture of how in fact it may strike him when he arrives. Often he is told that he will get required medical treatment and a rest, and may well be out in a few months or so. In some cases they may thus be concealing what they know, but I think, in general, they will be telling what they see as the truth. For here there is a quite relevant difference between patients and mediating professionals; mediators, more so than the public at large, may conceive of mental hospitals as short-term medical establishments where required rest and attention can be voluntarily obtained, and not as places of coerced exile. When the prepatient finally arrives he is likely to learn quite quickly, quite differently. He then finds that the information given him about life in the hospital has had the effect of his having put up less resistance to entering than he now sees he would have put up had he known the facts. Whatever the intentions of those who participated in his transition from person to patient, he may sense they have in effect "conned" him into his present predicament.

I am suggesting that the prepatient starts out with at least a portion of the rights, liberties, and satisfactions of the civilian and ends up on a psychiatric ward stripped of almost everything. The question here is *how* this stripping is managed. This is the second aspect of betrayal I want to consider.

As the prepatient may see it, the circuit of significant figures can function as a kind of *betrayal funnel.* Passage from person to patient may be effected through a series of linked stages, each managed by a different agent. While each stage tends to bring a sharp decrease in adult free status, each agent may try to maintain the fiction that no further decrease will occur. He may even manage to turn the prepatient over to the next agent while sustaining this note. Further, through words, cues, and gestures, the prepatient is implicitly asked by the current agent to join with him in sustaining a running line of polite small talk that tactfully avoids the administrative facts of the situation, becoming, with each stage, progressively more at odds with these facts. The spouse would rather not have to cry to get the prepatient to visit a psychiatrist; psychiatrists would rather not have a scene when the prepatient learns that he and his spouse are being seen separately and in different ways; the police infrequently bring a prepatient to the hospital in a strait jacket, finding it much easier all around to give him a cigarette, some kindly words, and freedom to relax in the back seat of the patrol car; and finally, the admitting psychiatrist finds he can do his work better in the relative quiet and luxury of the "admission suite" where, as an incidental consequence, the notion can survive that a mental hospital is indeed a comforting place. If the prepatient heeds all of these implied requests and is reasonably decent about the whole thing, he can travel the whole circuit from home to hospital without forcing anyone to look directly at what is happening or to deal with the raw emotion that his situation might well cause him to express. His showing consideration for those who are moving him toward the hospital allows them to show consideration for him, with the joint result that these interactions can be sustained with some of the protective harmony characteristic of ordinary face-to-face dealings. But should the new patient cast his mind back over the sequence of steps leading to hospitalization, he may feel that everyone's *current* comfort was being busily sustained while his long-range welfare was being undermined. This realization may constitute a moral experience that further separates him for the time from the people on the outside.[13]

I would now like to look at the circuit of career agents from the point of view of the agents themselves. Mediators in the person's transition from civil to patient status—as well as his keepers, once he is in the hospital—have an interest in establishing a responsible next-of-relation as the patient's deputy or *guardian;* should there be no obvious candidate for the role, someone may be sought out and pressed into it. Thus while a person is gradually being transformed into a patient, a next-of-relation is gradually being transformed into a guardian. With a guardian on the scene, the whole transition process can be kept tidy. He is likely to be familiar with the prepatient's civil involvements and business, and can tie up loose ends that might otherwise be left to entangle the hospital. Some of the prepatient's abrogated civil rights can be transferred to him, thus helping to sustain the legal fiction that while the prepatient does not actually have his rights he somehow actually has not lost them.

Inpatients commonly sense, at least for a time, that hospitalization is a massive unjust deprivation, and sometimes succeed in convincing a few persons on the outside that this is the case. It often turns out to be useful, then, for those identified with inflicting these deprivations, however justifiably, to be able to point to the cooperation and agreement of someone whose relationship to the patient places him above suspicion, firmly defining him as the person most likely to have the patient's personal interest at heart. If the guardian is satisfied with what is happening to the new inpatient, the world ought to be.[14]

Now it would seem that the greater the legitimate personal stake one party has in another, the better he can take the role of guardian to the other. But the

---

[13] Concentration camp practices provide a good example of the function of the betrayal funnel in inducing cooperation and reducing struggle and fuss, although here the mediators could not be said to be acting in the best interests of the inmates. Police picking up persons from their homes would sometimes joke good-naturedly and offer to wait while coffee was being served. Gas chambers were fitted out like delousing rooms, and victims taking off their clothes were told to note where they were leaving them. The sick, aged, weak, or insane who were selected for extermination were sometimes driven away in Red Cross ambulances to camps referred to by terms such as "observation hospital" (see Boder, 1949, p. 81; Cohen, 1954, pp. 32, 37, 107).

[14] Interviews collected by the Clausen group at NIMH suggest that when a wife comes to be a guardian, the responsibility may disrupt previous distance from in-laws, leading either to a new supportive coalition with them or to a marked withdrawal from them.

structural arrangements in society which lead to the acknowledged merging of two persons' interests lead to additional consequences. For the person to whom the patient turns for help—for protection against such threats as involuntary commitment—is just the person to whom the mediators and hospital administrators logically turn for authorization. It is understandable, then, that some patients will come to sense, at least for a time, that the closeness of a relationship tells nothing of its trustworthiness.

There are still other functional effects emerging from this complement of roles. If and when the next-of-relation appeals to mediators for help in the trouble he is having with the prepatient, hospitalization may not, in fact, be in his mind. He may not even perceive the prepatient as mentally sick, or, if he does, he may not consistently hold to this view (e.g., see Yarrow *et al.*, 1955; Schwartz, 1957). It is the circuit of mediators, with their greater psychiatric sophistication and their belief in the medical character of mental hospitals, that will often define the situation for the next-of-relation, assuring him that hospitalization is a possible solution and a good one, that it involves no betrayal, but is rather a medical action taken in the best interests of the prepatient. Here the next-of-relation may learn that doing his duty to the prepatient may cause the prepatient to distrust and even hate him for the time. But the fact that this course of action may have had to be pointed out and prescribed by professionals, and be defined by them as a moral duty, relieves the next-of-relation of some of the guilt he may feel.[15] It is a poignant fact that an adult son or daughter may be pressed into the role of mediator, so that the hostility that might otherwise be directed against the spouse is passed on to the child.[16]

Once the prepatient is in the hospital, the same guilt-carrying function may become a significant part of the staff's job in regard to the next-of-relation (Cumming and Cumming, 1957, p. 129). These reasons for feeling that he himself has not betrayed the patient, even though the patient may then think so, can later provide the next-of-relation with a defensible line to take when visiting the patient in the hospital and a basis for hoping that the relationship can be reestablished after its hospital moratorium. And of course this position, when sensed by the patient, can provide him with excuses for the next-of-relation, when and if he comes to look for them.[17]

Thus while the next-of-relation can perform important functions for the mediators and hospital administrators, they in turn can perform important functions for

[15] This guilt-carrying function is found, of course, in other role-complexes. Thus, when a middle-class couple engages in the process of legal separation or divorce, each of their lawyers usually takes the position that his job is to acquaint his client with all of the potential claims and rights, pressing his client into demanding these, in spite of any nicety of feelings about the rights and honorableness of the ex-partner. The client, in all good faith, can then say to self and to the ex-partner that the demands are being made only because the lawyer insists it is best to do so.

[16] Recorded in the Clausen data.

[17] There is an interesting contrast here with the moral career of the tuberculosis patient. I am told by Julius Roth that tuberculosis patients are likely to come to the hospital willingly, agreeing with their next-of-relation about treatment. Later in their hospital career, when they learn how long they yet have to stay and how depriving and irrational some of the hospital rulings are, they may seek to leave, be advised against this by the staff and by relatives, and only then begin to feel betrayed.

him. One finds, then, an emergent unintended exchange or reciprocation of functions, these functions themselves being often unintended.

The final point I want to consider about the prepatient's moral career is its
peculiarly *retroactive* character. Until a person actually arrives at the hospital
there usually seems no way of knowing for sure that he is destined to do so,
given the determinative role of career contingencies. And until the point of hospitalization is reached, he or others may not conceive of him as a person who is
becoming a mental patient. However, since he will be held against his will in the
hospital, his next-of-relation and the hospital staff will be in great need of a rationale for the hardships they are sponsoring. The medical elements of the staff
will also need evidence that they are still in the trade they were trained for.
These problems are eased, no doubt unintentionally, by the case-history construction that is placed on the patient's past life, this having the effect of demonstrating that all along he had been becoming sick, that he finally became very sick,
and that if he had not been hospitalized much worse things would have happened
to him—all of which, of course, may be true. Incidentally, if the patient wants
to make sense out of his stay in the hospital, and, as already suggested, keep alive
the possibility of once again conceiving of his next-of-relation as a decent, well-
meaning person, then he too will have reason to believe some of this psychiatric
work-up of his past.

Here is a very ticklish point for the sociology of careers. An important aspect of
every career is the view the person constructs when he looks backward over his
progress; in a sense, however, the whole of the prepatient career derives from
this reconstruction. The fact of having had a prepatient career, starting with an
effective complaint, becomes an important part of the mental patient's orientation,
but this part can begin to be played only after hospitalization proves that what
he had been having, but no longer has, is a career as a prepatient.

The Inpatient Phase

The last step in the prepatient's career can involve his realization—justified or
not—that he has been deserted by society and turned out of relationships by
those closest to him. Interestingly enough, the patient, especially a first admission,
may manage to keep himself from coming to the end of this trail, even though
in fact he is now in a locked mental hospital ward. On entering the hospital, he
may very strongly feel the desire not to be known to anyone as a person who
could possibly be reduced to these present circumstances, or as a person who
conducted himself in the way he did prior to commitment. Consequently, he may
avoid talking to anyone, may stay by himself when possible, and may even be
"out of contact" or "manic" so as to avoid ratifying any interaction that presses a
politely reciprocal role upon him and opens him up to what he has become in
the eyes of others. When the next-of-relation makes an effort to visit, he may be
rejected by mutism, or by the patient's refusal to enter the visiting room, these
strategies sometimes suggesting that the patient still clings to a remnant of relatedness to those who made up his past, and is protecting this remnant from the
final destructiveness of dealing with the new people that they have become.[18]

[18] The inmate's initial strategy of holding himself aloof from ratifying contact may partly
account for the relative lack of group-formation among inmates in public mental hospitals, a

Usually the patient comes to give up this taxing effort at anonymity, at not-hereness, and begins to present himself for conventional social interaction to the hospital community. Thereafter he withdraws only in special ways—by always using his nickname, by signing his contribution to the patient weekly with his initial only, or by using the innocuous "cover" address tactfully provided by some hospitals; or he withdraws only at special times, when, say, a flock of nursing students makes a passing tour of the ward, or when, paroled to the hospital grounds, he suddenly sees he is about to cross the path of a civilian he happens to know from home. Sometimes this making of oneself available is called "settling down" by the attendants. It marks a new stand openly taken and supported by the patient, and resembles the "coming out" process that occurs in other groupings.[19]

Once the prepatient begins to settle down, the main outlines of his fate tend to follow those of a whole class of segregated establishments—jails, concentration camps, monasteries, work camps, and so on—in which the inmate spends the whole round of life on the grounds, and marches through his regimented day in the immediate company of a group of persons of his own institutional status (see Goffman, 1957).

Like the neophyte in many of these "total institutions," the new inpatient finds himself cleanly stripped of many of his accustomed affirmations, satisfactions, and defenses, and is subjected to a rather full set of mortifying experiences: restriction of free movement; communal living; diffuse authority of a whole echelon of people; and so on. Here one begins to learn about the limited extent to which a conception of oneself can be sustained when the usual setting of supports for it are suddenly removed.

While undergoing these humbling moral experiences, the inpatient learns to orient himself in terms of the "ward system" (Belknap, 1956, p. 164). In public mental hospitals this usually consists of a series of graded living arrangements built around wards, administrative units called services, and parole statuses. The "worst" level involves often nothing but wooden benches to sit on, some quite indifferent food, and a small piece of room to sleep in. The "best" level may involve a room of one's own, ground and town privileges, contacts with staff that are relatively undamaging, and what is seen as good food and ample recreational facilities. For disobeying the pervasive house rules, the inmate will receive stringent punishments expressed in terms of loss of privileges; for obedience he will eventually be allowed to reacquire some of the minor satisfactions he took for granted on the outside.

---

connection that has been suggested to me by William R. Smith. The desire to avoid personal bonds that would give license to the asking of biographical questions could also be a factor. In mental hospitals, of course, as in prisoner camps, the staff may consciously break up incipient group-formation in order to avoid collective rebellious action and other ward disturbances.

[19] A comparable coming out occurs in the homosexual world, when a person finally comes frankly to present himself to a "gay" gathering not as a tourist but as someone who is "available" (see Hooker, 1956, esp. p. 221). A good fictionalized treatment may be found in Baldwin (1956, pp. 41–63). A familiar instance of the coming out process is no doubt to be found among prepubertal children at the moment one of these actors sidles *back* into a room that had been left in an angered huff and injured *amour-propre*. The phrase itself presumably derives from a *rite-de-passage* ceremony once arranged by upper-class mothers for their daughters. Interestingly enough, in large mental hospitals the patient sometimes symbolizes a complete coming out by his first active participation in the hospitalwide patient dance.

The institutionalization of these radically different levels of living throws light on the implications for self of social settings. And this in turn affirms that the self arises not merely out of its possessor's interactions with significant others, but also out of the arrangements that are evolved in an organization for its members.

There are some settings which the person easily discounts as an expression or extension of him. When a tourist goes slumming, he may take pleasure in the situation not because it is a reflection of him but because it so assuredly is not. There are other settings, such as living rooms, which the person manages on his own and employs to influence in a favorable direction other persons' views of him. And there are still other settings, such as a work place, which express the employee's occupational status, but over which he has no final control, this being exerted, however tactfully, by his employer. Mental hospitals provide an extreme instance of this latter possibility. And this is due not merely to their uniquely degraded living levels, but also to the unique way in which significance for self is made explicit to the patient, piercingly, persistently, and thoroughly. Once lodged on a given ward, the patient is firmly instructed that the restrictions and deprivations he encounters are not due to such things as tradition or economy —and hence dissociable from self—but are intentional parts of his treatment, part of his need at the time, and therefore an expression of the state that his self has fallen to. Having every reason to initiate requests for better conditions, he is told that when the staff feels he is "able to manage" or will be "comfortable with" a higher ward level, then appropriate action will be taken. In short, assignment to a given ward is presented not as a reward or punishment, but as an expression of his general level of social functioning, his status as a person. Given the fact that the worst ward levels provide a round of life that inpatients with organic brain damage can easily manage, and that these quite limited human beings are present to prove it, one can appreciate some of the mirroring effects of the hospital.[20]

The ward system, then, is an extreme instance of how the physical facts of an establishment can be explicitly employed to frame the conception a person takes of himself. In addition, the official psychiatric mandate of mental hospitals gives rise to even more direct, even more blatant, attacks upon the inmate's view of himself. The more "medical" and the more progressive a mental hospital is—the more it attempts to be therapeutic and not merely custodial—the more he may be confronted by high-ranking staff arguing that his past has been a failure, that the cause of this has been within himself, that his attitude to life is wrong, and that if he wants to be a person he will have to change his way of dealing with people and his conceptions of himself. Often the moral value of these verbal assaults will be brought home to him by requiring him to practice taking this psychiatric view of himself in arranged confessional periods, whether in private sessions or group psychotherapy.

Now a general point may be made about the moral career of inpatients which has bearing on many moral careers. Given the stage that any person has reached

---

[20] Here is one way in which mental hospitals can be worse than concentration camps and prisons as places in which to "do" time; in the latter, self-insulation from the symbolic implications of the settings may be easier. In fact, self-insulation from hospital settings may be so difficult that patients have to employ devices for this which staff interpret as psychotic symptoms.

in a career, one typically finds that he constructs an image of his life course—past, present, and future—which selects, abstracts, and distorts in such a way as to provide him with a view of himself that he can usefully expound in current situations. Quite generally, the person's line concerning self defensively brings him into appropriate alignment with the basic values of his society, and so may be called an *apologia*. If the person can manage to present a view of his current situation which shows the operation of favorable personal qualities in the past and a favorable destiny awaiting him, it may be called a *success story*. If the facts of a person's past and present are extremely dismal, then about the best he can do is to show that he is not responsible for what has become of him, and the term *sad tale* is appropriate. Interestingly enough, the more the person's past forces him out of apparent alignment with central moral values, the more often he seems compelled to tell his sad tale in any company in which he finds himself. Perhaps he partly responds to the need he feels in others of not having their sense of proper life courses affronted. In any case, it is among convicts (Heckstall-Smith, 1954, pp. 52–53), "wino's" (Bain, 1950, pp. 141–146), and prostitutes that one seems to obtain sad tales the most readily.[21] It is the vicissitudes of the mental patient's sad tale that I want to consider now.

In the mental hospital, the setting and the house rules press home to the patient that he is, after all, a mental case who has suffered some kind of social collapse on the outside, having failed in some over-all way, and that here he is of little social weight, being hardly capable of acting like a full-fledged person at all. These humiliations are likely to be most keenly felt by middle-class patients, since their previous condition of life little immunizes them against such affronts; but all patients feel some downgrading. Just as any normal member of his outside subculture would do, the patient often responds to this situation by attempting to assert a sad tale proving that he is not "sick," that the "little trouble" he did get into was really somebody else's fault, that his past life course had some honor and rectitude, and that the hospital is therefore unjust in forcing the status of mental patient upon him. This self-respecting tendency is heavily institutionalized within the patient society where opening social contacts typically involve the participants' volunteering information about their current ward location and length of stay so far, but not the reasons for their stay—such interaction being conducted in the manner of small talk on the outside.[22] With greater familiarity, each patient usually volunteers relatively acceptable reasons for his hospitalization, at the same time accepting without open immediate question the

---

[21] Apparently one of the occupational hazards of prostitution is that clients and other professional contacts sometimes persist in expressing sympathy by asking for a defensible dramatic explanation for the fall from grace. In having to bother to have a sad tale ready, perhaps the prostitute is more to be pitied than damned. Good examples of prostitute sad tales may be found in Mayhew (1862). For a contemporary source, see Rolph (1955, esp. p. 6): "Almost always, however, after a few comments on the police, the girl would begin to explain how it was that she was in the life, usually in terms of self-justification." Lately, of course, the psychological expert has helped out the profession in the construction of wholly remarkable sad tales (see, for example, Greenwald, 1958).

[22] A similar self-protecting rule has been observed in prisons. Thus, Hassler (1954, p. 76), in describing a conversation with a fellow-prisoner: "He didn't say much about why he was sentenced, and I didn't ask him, that being the accepted behavior in prison." A novelistic version for the mental hospital may be found in Kerkhoff (1952, p. 27).

lines offered by other patients. Such stories as the following are given and overtly accepted.

> I was going to night school to get a M.A. degree, and holding down a job in addition, and the load got too much for me.

> The others here are sick mentally but I'm suffering from a bad nervous system and that is what is giving me these phobias.

> I got here by mistake because of a diabetes diagnosis, and I'll leave in a couple of days. [The patient had been in seven weeks.]

> I failed as a child, and later with my wife I reached out for dependency.

> My trouble is that I can't work. That's what I'm in for. I had two jobs with a good home and all the money I wanted.[23]

The patient sometimes reinforces these stories by an optimistic definition of his occupational status: A man who managed to obtain an audition as a radio announcer styles himself a radio announcer; another who worked for some months as a copy boy and was then given a job as a reporter on a large trade journal, but fired after three weeks, defines himself as a reporter.

A whole social role in the patient community may be constructed on the basis of these reciprocally sustained fictions. For these face-to-face niceties tend to be qualified by behind-the-back gossip that comes only a degree closer to the "objective" facts. Here, of course, one can see a classic social function of informal networks of equals: they serve as one another's audience for self-supporting tales —tales that are somewhat more solid than pure fantasy and somewhat thinner than the facts.

But the patient's *apologia* is called forth in a unique setting, for few settings could be so destructive of self-stories except, of course, those stories already constructed along psychiatric lines. And this destructiveness rests on more than the official sheet of paper which attests that the patient is of unsound mind, a danger to himself and others—an attestation, incidentally, which seems to cut deeply into the patient's pride, and into the possibility of his having any.

Certainly the degrading conditions of the hospital setting belie many of the self-stories that are presented by patients; and the very fact of being in the mental hospital is evidence against these tales. And of course, there is not always sufficient patient solidarity to prevent patient discrediting patient, just as there is not always a sufficient number of "professionalized" attendants to prevent attendant discrediting patient. As one patient informant repeatedly suggested to a fellow patient:

> If you're so smart, how come you got your ass in here?

The mental hospital setting, however, is more treacherous still. Staff has much to gain through discreditings of the patient's story—whatever the felt reason for such discreditings. If the custodial faction in the hospital is to succeed in managing his daily round without complaint or trouble from him, then it will prove useful to be able to point out to him that the claims about himself upon which he rationalizes his demands are false, that he is not what he is claiming

---

[23] From the writer's field notes of informal interaction with patients, transcribed as near verbatim as he was able.

to be, and that in fact he is a failure as a person. If the psychiatric faction is to impress upon him its views about his personal make-up, then they must be able to show in detail how their version of his past and their version of his character hold up much better than his own.[24] If both the custodial and psychiatric factions are to get him to cooperate in the various psychiatric treatments, then it will prove useful to disabuse him of *his* view of their purposes, and cause him to appreciate that they know what they are doing, and are doing what is best for him. In brief, the difficulties caused by a patient are closely tied to his version of what has been happening to him, and if cooperation is to be secured, it helps if this version is discredited. The patient must "insightfully" come to take, or affect to take, the hospital's view of himself.

The staff also has ideal means—in addition to the mirroring effect of the setting—for denying the inmate's rationalizations. Current psychiatric doctrine defines mental disorder as something that can have its roots in the patient's earliest years, show its signs throughout the course of his life, and invade almost every sector of his current activity. No segment of his past or present need be defined, then, as beyond the jurisdiction and mandate of psychiatric assessment. Mental hospitals bureaucratically institutionalize this extremely wide mandate by formally basing their treatment of the patient upon his diagnosis and hence upon the psychiatric view of his past.

The case record is an important expression of this mandate. This dossier is apparently not regularly used, however, to record occasions when the patient showed capacity to cope honorably and effectively with difficult life situations. Nor is the case record typically used to provide a rough average or sampling of his past conduct. One of its purposes is to show the ways in which the patient is "sick" and the reasons why it was right to commit him and is right currently to keep him committed; and this is done by extracting from his whole life course a list of those incidents that have or might have had "symptomatic" significance.[25] The misadventures of his parents or siblings that might suggest a "taint" may be cited. Early acts in which the patient appeared to have shown bad judgment or emotional disturbance will be recorded. Occasions when he acted in a way which the layman would consider immoral, sexually perverted, weak-willed, childish, ill-considered, impulsive, and crazy may be described.

[24] The process of examining a person psychiatrically and then altering or reducing his status in consequence is known in hospital and prison parlance as *bugging*, the assumption being that once you come to the attention of the testers you either will automatically be labeled crazy or the process of testing itself will make you crazy. Thus psychiatric staff are sometimes seen not as *discovering* whether you are sick, but as *making* you sick; and "Don't bug me, man," can mean, "Don't pester me to the point where I'll get upset." Sheldon Messenger has suggested to me that this meaning of bugging is related to the other colloquial meaning, of wiring a room with a secret microphone to collect information usable for discrediting the speaker.

[25] While many kinds of organization maintain records of their members, in almost all of these some socially significant attributes can only be included indirectly, being officially irrelevant. But since mental hospitals have a legitimate claim to deal with the "whole" person, they need *officially* recognize no limits to what they consider relevant, a sociologically interesting license. It is an odd historical fact that persons concerned with promoting civil liberties in other areas of life tend to favor giving the psychiatrist complete discretionary power over the patient. Apparently it is felt that the more power possessed by medically qualified administrators and therapists, the better the interests of the patients will be served. Patients, to my knowledge, have not been polled on this matter.

Misbehaviors which someone saw as the last straw, as cause for immediate action, are likely to be reported in detail. In addition, the record will describe his state on arrival at the hospital—and this is not likely to be a time of tranquility and ease for him. The record may also report the false line taken by the patient in answering embarrassing questions, showing him as someone who makes claims that are obviously contrary to the facts:

> Claims she lives with oldest daughter or with sisters only when sick and in need of care; otherwise with husband; he himself says not for 12 years.
>
> Contrary to the reports from the personnel, he says he no longer bangs on the floor or cries in the morning.
>
> . . . conceals fact that she had her organs removed, claims she is still menstruating.
>
> At first she denied having had premarital sexual experience, but when asked about Jim she said she had forgotten about it 'cause it had been unpleasant.[26]

Where contrary facts are not known by the recorder, their presence is often left scrupulously an open question:

> The patient denied any heterosexual experiences nor could one trick her into admitting that she had ever been pregnant or into any kind of sexual indulgence, denying masturbation as well.
>
> Even with considerable pressure she was unwilling to engage in any projection of paranoid mechanisms.
>
> No psychotic content could be elicited at this time.[27]

And if in no more factual way, discrediting statements often appear in descriptions given of the patient's general social manner in the hospital:

> When interviewed, he was bland, apparently self-assured, and sprinkles high-sounding generalizations freely throughout his verbal productions.
>
> Armed with a rather neat appearance and natty little Hitlerian mustache this 45-year-old man who has spent the last five or more years of his life in the hospital, is making a very successful hospital adjustment living within the role of a rather gay liver and jim-dandy type of fellow who is not only quite superior to his fellow patients in intellectual respects but who is also quite a man with women. His speech is sprayed with many multi-syllabled words which he generally uses in good context, but if he talks long enough on any subject it soon becomes apparent that he is so completely lost in this verbal diarrhea as to make what he says almost completely worthless.[28]

The events recorded in the case history are, then, just the sort that a layman would consider scandalous, defamatory, and discrediting. I think it is fair to say that all levels of mental hospital staff fail, in general, to deal with this material with the moral neutrality claimed for medical statements and psychiatric diagnosis, but instead participate, by intonation and gesture if by no other means, in the lay reaction to these acts. This will occur in staff-patient encounters as well as in staff encounters at which no patient is present.

In some mental hospitals, access to the case record is technically restricted

---

[26] Verbatim transcriptions of hospital case record material.

[27] Verbatim transcriptions of hospital case record material.

[28] Verbatim transcriptions of hospital case record material.

to medical and higher nursing levels, but even here informal access or relayed information is often available to lower staff levels.[29] In addition, ward personnel are felt to have a right to know those aspects of the patient's past conduct which, embedded in the reputation he develops, purportedly make it possible to manage him with greater benefit to himself and less risk to others. Further, all staff levels typically have access to the nursing notes kept on the ward, which chart the daily course of each patient's disease, and hence his conduct, providing for the near-present the sort of information the case record supplies for his past.

I think that most of the information gathered in case records is quite true, although it might seem also to be true that almost anyone's life course could yield up enough denigrating facts to provide grounds for the record's justification of commitment. In any case, I am not concerned here with questioning the desirability of maintaining case records, or the motives of staff in keeping them. The point is that these facts about him being true, the patient is certainly not relieved from the normal cultural pressure to conceal them, and is perhaps all the more threatened by knowing that they are neatly available, and that he has no control over who gets to learn them.[30] A manly looking youth who responds to military induction by running away from the barracks and hiding himself in a hotel room clothes closet, to be found there, crying, by his mother; a woman who travels from Utah to Washington to warn the President of impending doom; a man who disrobes before three young girls; a boy who locks his sister out of the house, striking out two of her teeth when she tries to come back in through the window—each of these persons has done something he will have very obvious reason to conceal from others, and very good reason to tell lies about.

[29] However, some mental hospitals do have a "hot file" of selected records which can be taken out only by special permission. These may be records of patients who work as administration-office messengers and might otherwise snatch glances at their own files; of inmates who had elite status in the environing community; and of inmates who may take legal action against the hospital and hence have a special reason to maneuver access to their records. Some hospitals even have a "hot-hot file," kept in the superintendent's office. In addition, the patient's professional title, especially if it is a medical one, is sometimes purposely omitted from his file card. All of these exceptions to the general rule for handling information show, of course, the institution's realization of some of the implications of keeping mental hospital records. For a further example, see Taxel (1953, pp. 11–12).

[30] This is the problem of "information control" that many groups suffer from to varying degrees (see Goffman, 1959). A suggestion of this problem in relation to case records in prisons is given by Peck (1950, p. 66):

"The hacks of course hold all the aces in dealing with any prisoner because they can always write him up for inevitable punishment. Every infraction of the rules is noted in the prisoner's jacket, a folder which records all the details of the man's life before and during imprisonment. There are general reports written by the work detail screw, the cell block screw, or some other screw who may have overheard a conversation. Tales pumped from stool pigeons are also included.

"Any letter which interests the authorities goes into the jacket. The mail censor may make a photostatic copy of a prisoner's entire letter, or merely copy a passage. Or he may pass the letter on to the warden. Often an inmate called out by the warden or parole officer is confronted with something he wrote so long ago he had forgotten all about it. It might be about his personal life or his political views—a fragment of thought that the prison authorities felt was dangerous and filed for later use."

The formal and informal patterns of communication linking staff members tend to amplify the disclosive work done by the case record. A discreditable act that the patient performs during one part of the day's routine in one part of the hospital community is likely to be reported back to those who supervise other areas of his life, where he implicitly takes the stand that he is not the sort of person who could act that way.

Of significance here, as in some other social establishments, is the increasingly common practice of all-level staff conferences, where staff air their views of patients and develop collective agreement concerning the line that the patient is trying to take and the line that should be taken to him. A patient who develops a "personal" relation with an attendant, or manages to make an attendant anxious by eloquent and persistent accusations of malpractice, can be put back into his place by means of the staff meeting, where the attendant is given warning or assurance that the patient is "sick." Since the differential image of himself that a person usually meets from those of various levels around him comes here to be unified behind the scenes into a common approach, the patient may find himself faced with a kind of collusion against him—albeit one sincerely thought to be for his own ultimate welfare.

In addition, the formal transfer of the patient from one ward or service to another is likely to be accompanied by an informal description of his characteristics, this being felt to facilitate the work of the employee who is newly responsible for him.

Finally, at the most informal of levels, the lunchtime and coffee-break small talk of staff often turns upon the latest doings of the patient, the gossip level of any social establishment being here intensified by the assumption that everything about him is in some way the proper business of the hospital employee. Theoretically there seems to be no reason why such gossip should not build up the subject instead of tear him down, unless one claims that talk about those not present will always tend to be critical in order to maintain the integrity and prestige of the circle in which the talking occurs. And so, even when the impulse of the speakers seems kindly and generous, the implication of their talk is typically that the patient is not a complete person. For example, a conscientious group therapist, sympathetic with patients, once admitted to his coffee companions:

> I've had about three group disrupters, one man in particular—a lawyer [sotto voce] James Wilson—very bright—who just made things miserable for me, but I would always tell him to get on the stage and do something. Well, I was getting desperate and then I bumped into his therapist, who said that right now behind the man's bluff and front he needed the group very much and that it probably meant more to him than anything else he was getting out of the hospital—he just needed the support. Well, that made me feel altogether different about him. He's out now.

In general, then, mental hospitals systematically provide for circulation about each patient the kind of information that the patient is likely to try to hide. And in various degrees of detail this information is used daily to puncture his claims. At the admission and diagnostic conferences, he will be asked questions to which he must give wrong answers in order to maintain his self-respect, and then the true answer may be shot back at him. An attendant whom he tells a version of his past and his reason for being in the hospital may smile disbelievingly, or say, "That's not the way I heard it," in line with the practical psychiatry of bringing the patient down to reality. When he accosts a physician or nurse on the ward and presents his claims for more privileges or for discharge, this may be countered by a question which he cannot answer truthfully without calling up a time in his past when he acted disgracefully. When he gives his view of his situation during group psychotherapy, the therapist, taking the role of interrogator, may attempt to disabuse him of his face-saving interpretations and encourage an interpretation suggesting that it is he himself who is to blame and who must change. When he claims to staff or fellow patients that he is well and has never been really sick, someone may give him graphic details of how, only one month ago, he was prancing around like a girl, or claiming that he was God, or declining to talk or eat, or putting gum in his hair.

Each time the staff deflates the patient's claims, his sense of what a person ought to be and the rules of peer-group social intercourse press him to reconstruct his stories; and each time he does this, the custodial and psychiatric interests of the staff may lead them to discredit these tales again.

Behind these verbally instigated ups and downs of the self, is an institutional base that rocks just as precariously. Contrary to popular opinion, the "ward system" insures a great amount of internal social mobility in mental hospitals, especially during the inmate's first year. During that time he is likely to have altered his service once, his ward three or four times, and his parole status several times; and he is likely to have experienced moves in bad as well as good directions. Each of these moves involves a very drastic alteration in level of living and in available materials out of which to build a self-confirming round of activities, an alteration equivalent in scope, say, to a move up or down a class in the wider class system. Moreover, fellow inmates with whom he has partially identified himself will similarly be moving, but in different directions and at different rates, thus reflecting feelings of social change to the person even when he does not experience them directly. As previously implied, the doctrines of psychiatry can reinforce the social fluctuations of the ward system. Thus there is a current psychiatric view that the ward system is a kind of social hothouse in which patients start as social infants and end up, within the year, on convalescent wards as resocialized adults. This view adds considerably to the weight and pride that staff can attach to their work, and necessitates a certain amount of blindness, especially at higher staff levels, to other ways of viewing the ward system, such as a method for disciplining unruly persons through punishment and reward. In any case, this resocialization perspective tends to overstress the extent to which those on the worst wards are incapable of socialized conduct and the extent to which those on the best wards are ready and willing to play the social game. Because the ward system is something more than a resocialization chamber, inmates find many reasons for "messing up" or getting into trouble, and many occasions, then, for demotion to less privileged ward positions. These demotions may be officially interpreted as psychiatric relapses or moral backsliding, thus protecting the resocialization view of the hospital, and these interpretations, by implication, translate a mere infraction of rules and consequent demotion into a fundamental expression of the status of the culprit's self. Correspondingly, promotions, which may come about because of ward population pressure, the need for a "working patient," or for other psychiatrically irrelevant reasons, may be built up into something claimed to be profoundly expressive of the patient's whole self. The patient himself may be expected by staff to make a personal effort to "get well," in something less than a year, and hence may be constantly reminded to think in terms of the self's success and failure.[31]

In such contexts inmates can discover that deflations in moral status are not so bad as they had imagined. After all, infractions which lead to these demotions cannot be accompanied by legal sanctions or by reduction to the status of mental patient, since these conditions already prevail. Further, no past or current delict seems to be horrendous enough in itself to excommunicate a patient from the patient community, and hence failures at right living lose some of their stigmatizing meaning.[32] And finally, in accepting the hospital's version of his fall from grace, the patient can set himself up in the business of "straightening up," and make claims of sympathy, privileges, and indulgence from the staff in order to foster this.

Learning to live under conditions of imminent exposure and wide fluctuation in regard, with little control over the granting or withholding of this regard, is an important step in the socialization of the patient, a step that tells something important about what it is like to be an inmate in a mental hospital. Having one's past mistakes and present progress under constant moral review seems to make for a special adaptation consisting of a less-than-moral attitude to ego-ideals. One's shortcomings and successes become too central and fluctuating an issue in life to allow the usual commitment of concern for other persons' views of them. It is not very practicable to try to sustain solid claims about oneself. The inmate tends to learn that degradations and reconstructions of the self need not be given too much weight, at the same time learning that staff and inmates are ready to view an inflation or deflation of a self with some indifference. He learns that a defensible picture of self can be seen as something outside oneself that can be constructed, lost, and rebuilt, all with great speed and some equanimity. He learns about the viability of taking up a standpoint—and hence a self—that is outside the one which the hospital can give and take away from him.

The setting, then, seems to engender a kind of cosmopolitan sophistication, a kind of civic apathy. In this unserious yet oddly exaggerated moral context, building up a self or having it destroyed becomes something of a shameless game, and learning to view this process as a game seems to make for some demoralization, the game being such a fundamental one. In the hospital, then, the inmate can learn that the self is not a fortress, but rather a small open city; he can become weary of having to show pleasure when held by troops of his own, and weary of having to show displeasure when held by the enemy. Once he learns what it is like to be defined by society as not having a viable self,

[31] For this and other suggestions, I am indebted to Charlotte Green Schwartz.

[32] In the hospital I studied there did not seem to be a kangaroo court, and so, for example, an engaging alcoholic, who managed to get two very well-liked student nurses sent home for drinking with him, did not apparently suffer much for his betrayal of the desires of the peer group.

this threatening definition—the threat that helps attach people to the self society accords them—is weakened. The patient seems to gain a new plateau when he learns that he can survive while acting in a way that society sees as destructive of him.

A few illustrations of this moral looseness and moral fatigue might be given. In state mental hospitals currently a kind of "marriage moratorium" appears to be accepted by patients and more or less condoned by staff. Some informal peer-group pressure may be brought against a patient who "plays around" with more than one hospital partner at a time, but little negative sanction seems to be attached to taking up, in a temporarily steady way, with a member of the opposite sex, even though both partners are known to be married, to have children, and even to be regularly visited by these outsiders. In short, there is license in mental hospitals to begin courting all over again, with the understanding, however, that nothing very permanent or serious can come of this. Like shipboard or vacation romances, these entanglements attest to the way in which the hospital is cut off from the outside community, becoming a world of its own, operated for the benefit of its own citizens. And certainly this moratorium is an expression of the alienation and hostility that patients feel for those on the outside to whom they were closely related. But in addition, one has evidence of the loosening effects of living in a world within a world, under conditions which make it difficult to give full seriousness to either of them.

The second illustration concerns the ward system. On the worst ward level, discreditings seem to occur the most frequently, in part because of lack of facilities, in part through the mockery and sarcasm that seem to be the occupational norm of social control for the attendants and nurses who administer these places. At the same time, the paucity of equipment and rights means that not much self can be built up. The patient finds himself constantly toppled, therefore, but with very little distance to fall. A kind of jaunty gallows humor seems to develop in some of these wards, with considerable freedom to stand up to the staff and return insult for insult. While these patients can be punished, they cannot, for example, be easily slighted, for they are accorded as a matter of course few of the niceties that people must enjoy before they can suffer subtle abuse. Like prostitutes in connection with sex, inmates on these wards have very little reputation or rights to lose and can therefore take certain liberties. As the person moves up the ward system, he can manage more and more to avoid incidents which discredit his claim to be a human being, and acquire more and more of the varied ingredients of self-respect; yet when eventually he does get toppled—and he does—there is a much further distance to fall. For instance, the privileged patient lives in a world wider than the ward, made up of recreation workers who, on request, can dole out cake, cards, table-tennis balls, tickets to the movies, and writing materials. But in absence of the social control of payment which is typically exerted by a recipient on the outside, the patient runs the risk that even a warm-hearted functionary may, on occasion, tell him to wait until she has finished an informal chat, or teasingly ask why he wants what he has asked for, or respond with a dead pause and a cold look of appraisal.

Moving up and down the ward system means, then, not only a shift in self-constructive equipment, a shift in reflected status, but also a change in the calculus of risks. Appreciation of risks to his self-conception is part of everyone's moral experience, but an appreciation that a given risk level is itself merely a social arrangement is a rarer kind of experience, and one that seems to help to disenchant the person who has it.

A third instance of moral loosening has to do with the conditions that are often associated with the release of the inpatient. Often he leaves under the supervision and jurisdiction of his next-of-relation or of a specially selected and specially watchful employer. If he misbehaves while under their auspices, they can quickly obtain his readmission. He therefore finds himself under the special power of persons who ordinarily would not have this kind of power over him, and about whom, moreover, he may have had prior cause to feel quite bitter. In order to get out of the hospital, however, he may conceal his displeasure in this arrangement, and, at least until safely off the hospital rolls, act out a willingness to accept this kind of custody. These discharge procedures, then, provide a built-in lesson in overtly taking a role without the usual covert commitments, and seem further to separate the person from the worlds that others take seriously.

The moral career of a person of a given social category involves a standard sequence of changes in his way of conceiving of selves, including, importantly, his own. These half-buried lines of development can be followed by studying his moral experiences—that is, happenings which mark a turning point in the way in which the person views the world—although the particularities of this view may be difficult to establish. And note can be taken of overt tacks or strategies—that is, stands that he effectively takes before specifiable others, whatever the hidden and variable nature of his inward attachment to these presentations. By taking note of moral experiences and overt personal stands, one can obtain a relatively objective tracing of relatively subjective matters.

Each moral career, and behind this, each self, occurs within the confines of an institutional system, whether a social establishment such as a mental hospital or a complex of personal and professional relationships. The self, then, can be seen as something that resides in the arrangements prevailing in a social system for its members. The self in this sense is not a property of the person to whom it is attributed, but dwells rather in the pattern of social control that is exerted in connection with the person by himself and those around him. This special kind of institutional arrangement does not so much support the self as constitute it.

In this paper, two of these institutional arrangements have been considered, by pointing to what happens to the person when these rulings are weakened. The first concerns the felt loyalty of his next-of-relation. The prepatient's self is described as a function of the way in which three roles are related, arising and declining in the kinds of affiliation that occur between the next-of-relation and the mediators. The second concerns the protection required by the person for the version of himself which he presents to others, and the way in which the withdrawal of this protection can form a systematic, if unintended, aspect of the working of an establishment. I want to stress that these are only two kinds of institutional rulings from which a self emerges for the participant; others, not considered in this paper, are equally important.

In the usual cycle of adult socialization one expects to find alienation and mortification followed by a new set of beliefs about the world and a new way of conceiving of selves. In the case of the mental hospital patient, this rebirth does sometimes occur, taking the form of a strong belief in the psychiatric perspective, or, briefly at least, a devotion to the social cause of better treatment for mental patients. The moral career of the mental patient has unique interest, however; it can illustrate the possibility that in casting off the raiments of the old self—or in having this cover torn away—the person need not seek a new robe and a new audience before which to cower. Instead he can learn, at least for a time, to practice before all groups the amoral arts of shamelessness.

26 / Postscript to "The Moral Career of the Mental Patient"

Erving Goffman

From Autumn 1954 to the end of 1957 I was a visiting member of the Laboratory of Socio-environmental Studies of the National Institute of Mental Health in Bethesda, Maryland.* During those three years I did some brief studies of ward behavior in the National Institutes of Health Clinical Center. In 1955–56 I did a year's field work at St. Elizabeths Hospital, Washington, D.C., a federal institution of somewhat over 7,000 inmates that draws three-quarters of its patients from the District of Columbia. Later additional time for writing up the material was made possible by an NIMH grant, M-4111(A), and through participation in the Center for the Integration of Social Science Theory at the University of California at Berkeley.

My immediate object in doing field work at St. Elizabeths was to try to learn about the social world of the hospital inmate, as this world is subjectively experienced by him. I started out in the role of an assistant to the athletic director, when pressed avowing to be a student of recreation and community life, and I passed the day with patients, avoiding sociable contact with the staff and the carrying of a key. I did not sleep in the wards, and the top hospital management knew what my aims were.

It was then and still is my belief that any group of persons—prisoners, primitives, pilots, or patients—develop a life of their own that becomes meaningful, reasonable, and normal once you get close to it, and that a good way to learn about any of these worlds is to submit oneself in the company of the members to the daily round of petty contingencies to which they are subject.

From pp. ix–xi of *Asylums: Essays on the Social Situation of Mental Patients and Other Inmates* by Erving Goffman. Copyright © 1961. (Garden City, N.Y.: Doubleday & Company, Inc., 1961). Reprinted by permission of the author and Doubleday & Company, Inc.

* Goffman's evaluation of his own motives provides insight into the research process. Additional comments by the Editor are presented in the final paper of this part.

The limits, of both my method and my application of it, are obvious: I did not allow myself to be committed even nominally, and had I done so my range of movements and roles, and hence my data, would have been restricted even more than they were. Desiring to obtain ethnographic detail regarding selected aspects of patient social life, I did not employ usual kinds of measurements and controls. I assumed that the role and time required to gather statistical evidence for a few statements would preclude my gathering data on the tissue and fabric of patient life. My method has other limits, too. The world view of a group functions to sustain its members and expectedly provides them with a self-satisfying definition of their own situation and a prejudiced view of non-members, in this case, doctors, nurses, attendants, and relatives. To describe the patient's situation faithfully is necessarily to present a partisan view. (For this last bias I partly excuse myself by arguing that the imbalance is at least on the right side of the scale, since almost all professional literature on mental patients is written from the point of view of the psychiatrist, and he, socially speaking, is on the other side.) Further, I want to warn that my view is probably too much that of a middle-class male; perhaps I suffered vicariously about conditions that lower-class patients handled with little pain. Finally, unlike some patients, I came to the hospital with no great respect for the discipline of psychiatry nor for agencies content with its current practice.

I would like to acknowledge in a special way the support I was given by the sponsoring agencies. Permission to study St. Elizabeths was negotiated through the then First Assistant Physician, the late Dr. Jay Hoffman. He agreed that the hospital would expect pre-publication criticism rights but exert no final censorship or clearance privileges, these being lodged in NIMH in Bethesda. He agreed to the understanding that no observation made about any identified staff person or inmate would be reported to him or to anyone else, and that as an observer I was not obliged to interfere in any way whatsoever with what I could observe going on. He agreed to open any door in the hospital to me, and throughout the study did so when asked with a courtesy, speed, and effectiveness that I will never forget. Later, when the Superintendent of the hospital, Dr. Winifred Overholser, reviewed drafts of my papers, he made helpful corrections regarding some outright errors of fact, along with a useful suggestion that my point of view and method be made explicit. During the study, the Laboratory of Socio-environmental Studies, then headed by its originating director, John Clausen, provided me salary, secretarial help, collegial criticism, and encouragement to look at the hospital with sociology in mind, not junior psychiatry. The clearance rights possessed by the Laboratory and its parent body, NIMH, were exercised, the only consequence I am aware of being that on one occasion I was asked to consider a substitute for one or two impolite adjectives.

The point I want to make is that this freedom and opportunity to engage in pure research was afforded me in regard to a government agency, through the financial support of another government agency, both of which were required to operate in the presumably delicate atmosphere of Washington, and this was done at a time when some universities in this country, the traditional bastions of free enquiry, would have put more restrictions on my efforts. For this I must thank the open- and fair-mindedness of psychiatrists and social scientists in government.

27 / Social Structure and Interaction Processes on a Psychiatric Ward

William Caudill / *Fredrick C. Redlich*
Helen R. Gilmore / *Eugene B. Brody*

The individual who enters a mental hospital finds himself placed in a number of new social situations, all of which influence his behavior and treatment. The patient's relationship to his therapist, both in its administrative and therapeutic aspects, has received the most study. This holds true where the course of treatment is through insight psychotherapy (Fromm-Reichmann, 1947, 1950), and also where it involves a structuring of the patient's social milieu by prescribing how hospital personnel shall react to him (Adams, 1948; Menninger, 1937; Sullivan, 1931). More recently, the influence on the patient of the overall social structure of the hospital has been investigated (Bateman and Dunham, 1948; Rowland, 1938, 1939), as well as the structure of certain types of wards (Devereux, 1944, 1949), and the social processes at work in the split social field existing between patients and staff (Hyde and Solomon, 1950; Schwartz and Stanton, 1950; Stanton and Schwartz, 1949, 1949a, 1949b; Szurek, 1947).

For information on a third social influence, the interpersonal relationships of patients with each other, we must, however, rely largely on patients' autobiographical accounts of their experiences (Beers, 1921; Boison, 1936; Hillyer, 1926; Kindwall and Kinder, 1940; King, 1931; Peters, 1949). Despite the importance of this area of life in the mental hospital, it has, beyond an occasional astute reference (Noble, 1941), received little systematic attention and no methods have been developed for pursuing such a problem. The problem becomes a particularly crucial one when thought of in terms of the effect on each other of those less disturbed neurotic and psychotic patients who remain intact, and utilize many of their social personality characteristics and interaction techniques.

Because it is so important a variable, we wished to make a study of this area of social influence in the lives of patients despite the recognition of the many difficulties which would be encountered in obtaining adequate data. Although we are fully aware of the importance of unconscious determinants of interpersonal behavior, the present study has concerned itself primarily with a definition of the social reality in which the patients find themselves. Before field work was begun, an outline was made of the most pertinent problems to be explored: 1) The interpersonal relations on the ward between patients and patients, patients and nurses, and patients and physicians. 2) The social psychological processes involved in becoming a patient after admission, and ceas-

From the *American Journal of Orthopsychiatry*, 1952, **22**, 314–334. Copyright © 1952. Reprinted by permission of the authors and the American Orthopsychiatric Association.

ing to be a patient as the time of discharge approached. (3) The value and belief systems of the patient group, and the general attitudes to life in the hospital centering around both administration and therapy. (4) The difficulties experienced by the patients as a group in communicating with the various levels of the staff hierarchy, and the reflection of these difficulties in the operation of the control and decision-making functions invested in the staff.

Two methods were used in gathering data: Initially, in order to determine some of the social and therapeutic problems of life in a mental hospital as seen through the eyes of the patients, we decided to have an observer undergo the experience of being a patient. Known only to two senior members of the staff, he was admitted to the less disturbed ward of the hospital and, upon being assigned to one of the psychiatric residents for therapy, he followed a course of treatment for two months.[1] Secondly, after a turnover in the patient population, the same observer acted as an assistant in the activities program for several months. This paper will present material only from the first set of observations, but the major points emphasized here were found to hold true for both of the patient populations.

Neither of the methods used was completely satisfactory. In the first, the observer, by living on the ward, was in a position to experience the full round of life and to interact with the patients as people. Coupled with these advantages there were, however, disadvantages. While to our knowledge no discernible harm was done to the therapeutic progress of any of the patients, it was recognized that this might have occurred. We were also mindful of other ethical considerations, of the personal strain on the observer in undergoing psychotherapy, and of the fact that the observer's identification with the patients would inevitably result in some degree of subjectivity in the data. A partial check on such biasing was provided by having the observer include in his daily record many of his own emotional reactions to the events of hospital life. As the observer had going-out privileges after his first week of treatment, he left the hospital each afternoon for a few hours and used this time to work up his material. Despite its disadvantages, the first method provided a rich body of data concerning many problems, hitherto only incompletely recognized, which were faced by the patients as a social group in their life on the ward. The second method, while allowing the observer to be known, had the disadvantages of restricting his participation to specific ward activities which were essentially isolated from the flow of day-to-day life. It might be feasible to work out an alternative procedure whereby a known observer could live on the ward on a 24-hour-a-day basis.[2]

The observations were carried out in a small private mental hospital connected with a psychiatric training center. Treatment of the patients was primarily

---

[1] Upon admission to the hospital, the observer told his therapist that he had recently been compulsively trying to finish the writing of a scholarly book, but felt that he was not getting ahead; worry over his work drove him to alcoholic episodes ending in fights; he was withdrawn and depressed, and had quarreled with his wife who had then separated from him. Beyond these fictions, the observer gave a somewhat distorted version of his own life in which he consciously attempted to suppress his own solutions to certain problems and to add a pattern of neurotic defenses.

[2] The methodological aspects of the study will be reported later in detail.

through dynamically oriented psychotherapy. Each patient was assigned to a psychiatric resident who was under the supervision of a physician-in-charge. The resident assumed direct responsibility for most of the management and for the therapeutic care of his patients. Apart from routine contacts on rounds, a patient usually saw his therapist for one hour a day, five days a week. The remainder of a patient's schedule was worked out very sketchily, as only a limited recreational and activities program was available.

The hospital was divided into three wards. Two of these were locked wards located on the second floor where the more severely disturbed psychotic patients were treated. The third was a less disturbed ward on the first floor which accommodated both male and female patients, most of whom were diagnosed as suffering from various types of severe psychoneuroses. This paper will be concerned only with the patients on this last ward, in which each sex occupied a separate wing containing eight private rooms, a four-bed dormitory, and a living room. Men and women intermingled in the two living rooms except at mealtime.

As the average stay in the hospital was over two months, the patient population was quite stable during the period in which the observations were made. All told, there were 12 male and 15 female patients on the ward, most of whom were between 20 and 35 years of age. The majority came from upper middle class homes, although there were a few from upper lower, lower middle, and upper class backgrounds. Three were Jewish; two were Catholic; the rest were Protestant. There was one Negro patient.

Observations

From the moment the observer left his room on his first day in the hospital and joined the patient group at the evening meal, he felt pressure upon him to act in certain ways.[3] As he took his food tray from the cart, he was told by several patients that they had been unable to eat during their first meal at the hospital. As a consequence, he only toyed with his food. During the meal he mentioned that he should write some letters, and was told, "You can't be very sick if you are going to write letters." He feebly parried this by saying that he probably would not get an answer anyway. After the supper trays had been removed by a nurse, and the therapists had made their evening rounds, the group asked him if he played bridge, and was overjoyed to find that he did. After several rubbers, it seemed expected of him that he would retire to his room, and he did so. At ten o'clock he heard a nurse ask the group to go to their rooms, but two of the patients later returned to the living room and he overheard them discussing their problems for several hours until he fell asleep.

Although he would have been unable to categorize them so neatly at the time, there had been, even in his first day's experience, pressures exerted on the observer by the other patients for adherence to certain attitudes in four areas of life—toward the self, toward other patients, toward therapy and the therapist, and toward nurses and other hospital personnel.

[3] The observer also, of course, felt pressure upon him in his first contacts with nurses, his therapist, and other members of the staff. These are not discussed here, however, because the major focus of this paper is upon the relationships developed by patients with each other.

Pressures for Attitudes Toward the Self

On the second day, following a conference with his therapist, the observer expressed resentment over not having going-out privileges to visit the library and work on his book—his compulsive concern over his inability to finish this task being one of the factors leading to his hospitalization. Immediately two patients, Mr. Hill and Mrs. Lewis,[4] who were later to become his closest friends, told him he was being "defensive"; since his doctor did not wish him to do such work, it was probably better "to lay off of it." Mr. Hill went on to say that one of his troubles when he first came to the hospital was thinking of things that he had to do or thought he had to do. He said that now he did not bother about anything. Mrs. Lewis said that at first she had treated the hospital as a sort of hotel and had spent her therapeutic hours "charming" her doctor, but it had been pointed out to her by others that this was a mental hospital and that she should actively work with her doctor if she expected to get well.

The observer later saw such pressure applied time and again to other patients, and he came to realize that the group attempted to push its members toward a middle ground where they would not, as in his case and that of Mrs. Lewis, attempt to deny the reality of the hospital. On the other hand, pressure was also brought to bear on those patients who went to other extremes by engaging in too much immature acting-out behavior, who regressed too far, or who denied the emotional basis of their illness. For example, one day shortly after his arrival, the following incident, thereafter to be repeated almost exactly each day, occurred:

> Dr. Johnson came by on evening rounds and Mr. Davis made a great fuss, taking him down the hall and swearing violently at him. After Dr. Johnson had left, Mr. Davis stormed back to the table saying that Dr. Johnson told him that by such actions he was trying to destroy all the patients on the ward. But, Mr. Davis continued, all that he wanted out of life was to be a pants presser; he did not want any of that intellectual stuff. Mr. Brown and Mr. Hill told Mr. Davis that he only created these scenes when his doctor showed up; he did not need to do this as he was all right and quiet at all other times. Mr. Davis admitted this.

Equally, the patients sympathized with Mr. Brown when he periodically took to his bed and requested that he be cared for, but they also told him that he was resisting leaving the hospital and that ultimately he would have to go out and get a job. Also, while Mr. Anderson and Mrs. Smith were positive that their ills were "purely physical," and continually attempted to convince others of this, the patients only smiled and pointed out that the doctors would not allow people to come "just for a rest," and that everyone in the hospital had emotional problems.

The patients felt certain that their doctors had as one of their major aims the requiring of patients to give up their "defenses." As the patients interpreted most of their ordinary social activities as defenses, the problem was phrased by Mr. Hill when he said that his doctor kept telling him he had to give up all his defenses but that he could not see this, as what would he have left?

[4] All names appearing here are pseudonyms.

Pressures for Attitudes toward Other Patients

During his first few days in the hospital the observer was frequently told, "You cannot really refuse anything people ask of you around here," and he saw this belief put into action in many small ways. He was also told many stories of recent dramatic incidents, such as that of a recent suicide and what a swell person the patient had been; and he was introduced to what might be called the folklore of the group concerning stories of bizarre and rather humorous behavior on the part of previous patients, such as that of the patient who had been brought in nude upon a stretcher screaming that she expected a telephone call from a producer in Hollywood, and who later did receive the call. Late one night a patient upstairs created a violent and noisy commotion which awakened a number of patients who congregated in the hall. The observer was told, in the warmest terms, of this patient's personal sexual problems and, at the same time, of what a nice person he really was. It was to be noted that such incidents and stories were often treated humorously, but they were almost never treated negatively. The gossip and backbiting that might be expected to develop in a closely confined group were far overshadowed by an emphasis on the positive qualities of a person and a suspension of the direct expression of judgment in other areas.

The patients felt that many of the ordinary conventions and social gestures of the outer world were made temporarily meaningless by hospital life. On one occasion the observer, who had been asked if he cared to go downtown, said he would like to do so if his friend did not mind waiting until he changed his clothes. The friend laughingly chided him to the effect that he had forgotten where he was, that in the hospital one had all the time in the world. On the other hand, small courtesies and expressions of approval that would be carried out almost unconsciously in the outer world often became conscious problems. If one overheard, and enjoyed, a patient playing the piano, should one applaud the performance, or would such approval call forth a neurotic response? Would others overreact and feel hurt if several patients wished to go to a movie alone and did not freely extend the invitation to the entire group? Such problems as these formed part of the belief that one was not free to release oneself fully in the hospital, and that it was very difficult for an individual to satisfy his need to be alone at times.

Although acquaintances among the patients would be made on the basis of similar backgrounds and interests, and much time was spent in gossiping about the social characteristics of others, these activities lacked the invidious overtones they would have carried in the outer world. Along with this went a muting of outer-world distinctions on the basis of race, ethnic group, or social class—it was as if the patients had agreed that such categories had little meaning in a hospital. Such an orientation of one's behavior was made easier by the commonly held belief that since none of the group expected to see the others again, it was not necessary to relate one's outside status to life on the ward.

While there was a suspension of the direct expression of judgment, and a much greater tolerance of wide ranges of behavior than would have been true in social situations on the outside, there were limits to such behavior even in the patient group. For example:

> One evening a number of the patients had brought in several kinds of cheese, rye bread, and Coca Cola, which they were sharing with the group. Mr. Davis, whose behavior was characterized by aggressive, adolescent outbursts of ranting toward his therapist, immediately began to grab large amounts of the food in a very ill-mannered way. The three women to whom the food belonged became angry and gave Mr. Davis a severe tongue-lashing, calling him "an ill-bred, emotionally immature kid," etc. However, one of the women shortly brought the group together again by saying, "Well, what the hell, we are all in the same boat in this place, so don't worry about it, it's all right." Unity was re-established, the food was shared, and the group then proceeded to get a great deal of enjoyment out of playing a crossword-puzzle game introduced by Mr. Davis.

It was almost as if whenever, within the hospital setting, a disagreeable episode took place, the unity of the group, and its tolerance, had of necessity to reassert itself. Beyond the suspension of judgment, it was also noted that patients expected others to support and sustain them in their activities and roles even if this meant ignoring some of the rules of the hospital:

> Mr. Brown very cleverly made stuffed cloth animals which he sold to the other patients at slightly above cost. There was a rule against patients' selling articles to each other; the nurse in charge had spoken to Mr. Brown about this several times, and the patients knew that in buying the animals they were going against the wishes of the hospital. Nevertheless, they felt that it was more important to support Mr. Brown in a productive activity that gave him pleasure than to obey a rule that they thought had little meaning in this case.

Beyond the simple supporting of others, it quickly became apparent that a type of therapy—characterized by sympathetic listening and the making of suggestions —would be carried out among close acquaintances. For example:

> Mr. Davis and Mr. Wright were close friends. When Mr. Wright went out with his wife one night, Mr. Davis sat up until 1 A.M. waiting for him in order to see how he would be feeling. On the other hand, the next day Mr. Davis was stirring up a great storm over trying to get out of the ward because he had received some letters from his wife that made him want to leave. Mr. Wright took Mr. Davis to his room, talked to him, got him a glass of milk, and calmed him down. Such scenes were repeated daily between these two patients; after one particularly bad period, Mr. Davis jokingly said that Mr. Wright was going to send him a bill for consultation services since Mr. Wright had sat up and talked with him all night.

Pressures for Attitudes toward Therapy and Therapists

When, on the morning of his second day, the observer attributed his sick stomach to the colorless, liquid sedative that he had been given the night before, the patients told him that this had been paraldehyde, that it was given to alcoholics, and was one of the most powerful sedatives used in the hospital. This led to a discussion of the nature of each other's problems which concluded with the agreement that every case was different and that one could not generalize. Partly because of this attitude, there was a strong feeling that a patient should keep his actual relations with his therapist, and what went on during his conference hours, separate from his life on the ward. However, while the patients often adopted the pose that "the conferences weren't helping very much," they would privately discuss their progress with their closer friends, and felt they had to hold to the belief that one's doctor was competent in his therapeutic capacity; one must cooperate with him in order to make any progress and should not question his authority.[5]

The patients believed that therapy was "somehow psychoanalytical," that one had "to go back into childhood," and that therapy went on "24 hours a day." One evening a group of 11 patients were discussing the lack of activities in the hospital, and they came to the conclusion that it was part of a conscious plan by the staff to increase the intensity of "24-hour-a-day" therapy. The matter was summed up when one patient said he thought that therapy in the hospital was better than having a psychoanalysis on the outside, because in the latter case your hour of therapy was sandwiched between many other activities, whereas in the hospital you could work on your problems all the time.

Not infrequently, many patients despaired of the seemingly endless one-way talk involved in psychotherapy. They felt that they were repeating the same story over and over again until it lost all emotional feeling and became rote. They felt that their doctors never told them anything in their conferences. They were concerned about the end goal of therapy, feeling that this was kept concealed and that they never seemed to be moving toward whatever it was. Somewhat fatalistically, they felt that the doctors took "a long-range view" and did not think of the financial expense involved.[6] While they had to believe that psychotherapy was helpful, they were disturbed because few patients seemed to get better, or to leave the hospital as "cured." Since the patients all shared in such frustrations and doubts, the group was tolerant of occasional aggressive outbursts about one's doctor in his therapeutic capacity, and sanctioned criticism and caricature of the staff's behavior as this manifested itself in attending to administrative duties, making rounds, or in unexpected meetings outside of the hospital.

The patients generally agreed that while they all shared some similar experiences in their conferences, there were also great differences depending on the individual patient and doctor. The characterizations made by the patients of the doctors' personalities seemed to be a blend of projection by the patient of his problems onto the doctor, and a very astute, intuitive grasp of the doctor's own emotional or social problems. For example:

> Mr. Hill and Mr. Davis got into a discussion about the differences in their conferences. Mr. Hill said that Dr. Black worries more than he does. He said that they both sit and frown at each other and look worried. Mr. Hill said that he would say something and then sit and worry about it, and Dr. Black would look at him with a worried expression and say, "What do you think that

---

[5] From the patient's viewpoint, the therapist was a benign, omnipotent authority beyond whom the patient could not look. Actually, in most instances, the therapist was a psychiatric resident who had to discuss his cases with a supervisor before coming to any major decisions. The patient, however, was not aware of this, and was puzzled by what often appeared to be indecision, arbitrariness, and withholding of information on the part of the therapist. This is one aspect of the whole problem, which cannot be discussed here, of the blocking of the free flow of communication between the various sharply defined strata of the hospital hierarchy due, in part, to the highly formalized nature of interpersonal relationships across these strata.

[6] In the opinion of some senior staff members there was a lack of awareness of the patients' economic problems and definite resistance on the part of the residents to recognize these.

means?" They would then sit in silence and worry together for a while. Usually about that time the sounds of an explosion would occur in the next office and it would be Mr. Davis screaming and swearing at the top of his lungs at Dr. Johnson. Mr. Hill said that one day Dr. Black had inadvertently laughed at something Mr. Davis was shouting at Dr. Johnson in the next office, and then Dr. Black was confused and embarrassed toward Mr. Hill over the effect his laughter might have had on the conference hour.

Pressures for Attitudes toward
Nurses and Other Hospital Personnel

As the observer was playing bridge on his second day, a nurse came by and said to one of the players, "I bet you are beating them at this game, I'll bet." After she had left, Mr. Davis commented that she had "treated us like seven-year-olds." Shortly, another nurse did essentially the same thing. At another time, the staff, without consulting the patients, decided to give them a Valentine party. Many of the patients did not wish to go, but did so anyway as they felt that they should not hurt the feelings of the student nurses who had organized the party. The games introduced by the nurses were on a very childish level; many of the patients felt silly playing them and were glad when the party was over and they could go back to activities of their own choosing.

The patients knew that the nurses, particularly the students, sat around in the living rooms "in order to get material for their reports," and hence the patients felt that the nurses were fair game for occasional kidding. For example:

> A nurse was listening to a conversation between Mrs. Lewis and Mr. Brown. So Mrs. Lewis joked with Mr. Brown by saying, "You didn't come in and say good night to me last night." Then she turned to the nurse and said, "You know, Mr. Brown is in and out of my room all night long." Mr. Brown smiled and said, "Yes, of course, that's true."

While the patients ignored the fact that the nurses overheard many of their conversations, there was a definite feeling in the group that one should not inform on another patient in answer to a direct request for information from the nurse:

> During the night, Mr. Sullivan had had an anxiety attack and had been taken care of by Mr. Brown, who wrapped him in a blanket and rubbed his temples until he went to sleep. When Mr. Sullivan awakened again, another patient read to him for several hours. The night nurse, of course, must have observed this behavior. Nevertheless, when a student nurse asked at breakfast the next morning how late Mr. Sullivan had been up, none of the group of male patients would answer her.

Since there was little of what is ordinarily thought of as "nursing" to be done on the first-floor ward, the patients utilized the nurses to a considerable degree for domestic or routine service purposes—the nurses served the meals, called cabs, mailed letters, etc. A number of the nurses said that they preferred to work on the locked wards where they felt that there was more "real" nursing. They were ambivalent about their domestic role on the first floor and communicated this feeling to the patients by occasional casual remarks such as, at mealtime, "Be sure and leave a tip for the waitress."[7]

---

[7] The role of the psychiatric nurse on a ward of neurotic patients is vaguely defined and includes many varied services of which traditional medical nursing is probably the least important.

Life on the Ward

One of the observer's strongest impressions during his first day on the ward was the feeling of boredom and ennui existing among the patients, several of whom told him that "tomorrow would be just another day with nothing to do but sit around, or play bridge and ping-pong." Actually, as there were few organized activities or secondary types of therapy available, the patients, for the most part, utilized each other to develop a social life. Bridge was played interminably, endless numbers of crossword puzzles were worked cooperatively, while the daily cryptogram in the newspaper was copied out and the patients avidly competed for the solution.

The staff tended to look upon the games and activities of the patients as "fads," in the sense of a passing fashion or fancy. They were much more than this, as they provided simple settings for realistic role taking and helped to bind the group together. The considerable quantity of food the patients brought in from the outside to share with others served much the same function.[8] Snacks, such as *salami*, cheese, pumpernickel, popcorn, and Coca-Cola, lent a zest lacking in the crackers and chocolate milk provided by the hospital twice a day as "nourishment." Despite the frequent tacit disapproval of the nurses, the consumption of these snacks was usually made into a social rite which complemented the evening-at-home atmosphere the patients created in the living rooms. The social stimulus value of these evening gatherings was heightened by the interaction of small friendship groups which were supported by the patients because they increased the potential for social participation and conversation in the group. Such activities provided reassurance for the patients that they could still, in some measure, interact on an adult level, and also represented a partly conscious resistance to those aspects of the hospital routine which were unduly "infantilizing."

The patients noted that the lack of activities, and the restraint placed on their freedom of action in many areas of life, both by the hospital and the pressure of the patient group, resulted in a great overemphasis on words, and the talking about rather than carrying out of actions. This symptom was labeled "diarrhea of the mouth." For much the same reasons, new physical objects on the ward assumed an importance all out of proportion to that they would have had in the outer world. A new couch placed in the men's living room became a focus of attention and topic of conversation for over a month; while previously the patients had distributed themselves in both living rooms during the evening, they now all congregated on the men's side.

The patients sense the vagueness of the nurse's role and act out toward her more than toward the physician. When, in addition to her other duties, the nurse has to assume a policing function, and may be denied at times a humane maternal role, the relationship between nurse and patient may easily become difficult and antitherapeutic. We became increasingly aware of this problem in the course of the study, but more detailed observations will have to be carried out before theoretical conclusions or practical recommendations can be made.

[8] This social function of food must be distinguished from the need gratification obtained by a particular patient in the giving of food. Both Mrs. Jones and Mr. Anderson constantly proffered food to other patients and this technique of social participation, which was the only one they had, was intimately related to their personality dynamics. The patients were more or less aware of this personal meaning of food for Mrs. Jones and Mr. Anderson, but they took the food and utilized it for the purpose of increasing group social interaction.

Given the situation in the hospital, the patient group, if it wished a social life, had no choice but to turn inward and, so far as possible, to develop the potentialities of its members. This is what happened, and the resulting social structure is best seen in terms of the implementation of the values of the patient group through the role and clique system that operated in the life on the ward.

Value and Role Systems

As the sorts of pressures that have been discussed were felt by the observer, he came gradually to realize that the attitudes held by the patients were formed into a pattern of values, some of which were verbalized, while others might be inferred from the consistency of behavior. This *value system* might, in summary form, be stated as follows: 1) Toward oneself. (a) A patient should not deny the reality of being in the hospital for therapeutic purposes, (b) should give up his "defenses," and (c) should try to bring himself to a middle ground where he neither engaged in extreme regressive behavior nor attempted to carry on life as if the hospital did not exist. 2) Toward other patients. (a) A patient should suspend judgment and attempt to see all sides of a person, (b) sustain and support others, and (c) if requested, try actively to help them with their problems by doing a sort of therapy with them. 3) Toward therapy and the therapist. (a) A patient should try to believe in the ability and competence of his doctor, (b) cooperate in working with him, and (c) feel that treatment on a "24-hour-a-day" basis in the hospital was better than therapy received in the outer world. 4) Toward nurses and other personnel. (a) A patient should try to be thoughtful and pleasant, and (b) cooperate by abiding by the rules of the hospital up to the point where either the demands of the nurses became unreasonable, or the rules conflicted with a more important value toward other patients.

This value system of the patient group was translated into action by ascribing to each new member what may be called the *role of a patient*. This role required that one act in accordance with the complex of values and behavior patterns expected of every patient as described above. In addition, each individual played a *personal role* rooted in his background outside the hospital; that is, he presented himself as a certain kind of person to the patient group. The individual patient, then, had the task of integrating his personal role with the role of a patient; or, at least, seeing to it that the values and behavior characteristic of his personal role did not directly conflict with those of the patient role.[9]

If a patient would accept and play the ascribed role of a patient, especially as it entailed mutual tolerance and responsibility for others, then the group would, in turn, support the patient in his personal role. Particularly this was true if the personal role of the patient served some positive function in the group. For example, Mr. Brown's imitations of the doctors, nurses, and other patients were a real source of catharsis for the group; and Mr. Davis's immature explosions toward the staff provided vicarious satisfaction for others,[10] while his expertness at bridge and at solving cryptograms was a source of recreation.

---

[9] These ideas on the social dynamics of the role system in the patient group owe much to Linton's discussion (Linton, 1936, 1949) of ascribed and achieved statuses and roles. (Linton has verbally indicated he now prefers the term "acquired" rather than "achieved.")

[10] In psychoanalytic terms, much of what would be considered primitive instinctual "anti-

The integration of one's personal role with that of the patient role often required that an individual make a conscious effort to channel his personal abilities and resources into the helping of others. For example, Mrs. Lewis was a fashionably dressed woman who purposely went out of her way to help Miss Wood with her clothes; Miss Wood, in her turn, had considerable competence in massage and provided this service for a number of the women patients.[11] The group went so far as to try to establish a function for a patient's personal role if one did not seem self-evident, and through this process the observer's library work and interest in music were drawn into the orbit of the group by having him obtain books and record albums for others.

It was possible to set up a continuum on the basis of the degree of success achieved by the patients in the integration of their personal roles with the role of a patient. The nature of such an integration had a great deal to do with the place occupied by a patient in the total structure of the group.

One extreme was represented by Mr. Hill, whose personal role coincided almost completely with what was expected of him in the role of a patient. He was a passive, nonthreatening person who was very sensitive to group approval and pressure; he had good social techniques and skills for relating to others, and a nice dry sense of humor which he utilized a great deal but never in such a way as to hurt other patients. He was always willing to sustain any activity of the group and was receptive when others came to him for support or therapy. On the other hand, he frequently sought out other patients to ask their advice. While it would be difficult to speak of "leadership" among the patients because, owing to the nature of their situation in the hospital, there were few goals toward which the group as a whole might have been led, Mr. Hill represented the most highly pivotal person on the ward, with whom all of the patients acknowledged some ties.

The other extreme was represented by Miss Ford, whose personal role conflicted in almost all respects with what was expected of her in the role of a patient. Since she felt a need to belong to the patient group, this conflict of roles was a source of anxiety for her. She said that she thought of the hospital as "just like college" and treated her doctor as a professor who would hand her the answers to her problems. She stated that she wanted nothing to do with anyone else's troubles, and hence she made little effort to support other patients. She openly expressed anti-Semitism, was aggressive and hostile to the Negro patient, and was snobbish and class-conscious. Indeed, while she continually tried to participate socially, most of her conversation was derogatory of others. As a consequence, she incurred the hostility of the group and was rejected and isolated

---

social" behavior in the outer world became "social" behavior in the hospital because of the wider range of tolerance and suspension of judgment among the patients. Seen in this way, a mental hospital ward is not only, in the traditional sense, a place where the patient should be free, if need be, to regress with some degree of comfort, but it is also a place where primitive instinctual forces are themselves enmeshed and utilized in the subculture and role system of the patient group. Thus, psychotherapy carried out in the hospital must not only contend with such forces due to regression, but also with such forces supported by a social system.

[11] While such behavior forms a large part of the patients' lives in the hospital, it receives, owing to its undramatic nature, less emphasis in the nurses' reports and the therapists' conversations than do the more dramatic instances of aggressive and destructive neurotic behavior, or that behavior which is precipitated more by frustrations inherent in the hospital situation.

because, although she wished to belong to the patient group, she would not carry out its values and responsibilities. Hers was a very different type of isolation from the occasional self-imposed withdrawal of Mrs. Gray, which was respected by the patients, or from the complete isolation imposed on himself by Mr. Reed. Though physically present on the ward, Mr. Reed never entered the social field of the patients, who held an entirely neutral attitude toward him and scarcely recognized his existence.

Most of the patients interacting in the group fell somewhere between the extremes sketched above. Their personal roles did not completely coincide with the role of a patient, but they did accept the society's values and in turn received support. It cannot be said that the place occupied by a patient in the group structure was entirely what might have been expected from his previous psychodynamic history. Mr. Hill was much more highly rewarded for his type of behavior in the patient group than he would have been in the outer world, where he would have been marked as too passive a person. On the other hand, Miss Ford would probably not have been so rigidly censored for her nonsupportive and often hostile behavior by the outer world. This does not mean that she would have exhibited less anxiety, or found life easier, on the outside as the hospital still served as a refuge. It is indicated, however, that the nature of a patient's social integration into the group will affect his therapeutic progress, and both Mr. Hill and Miss Ford, for opposite reasons, experienced more than ordinary difficulty in ultimately leaving the protection of the hospital environment—the former because of his overdependence on the group, the latter because she received too little support.

A further aspect of the social structure of the patient group lay in its encouragement of various types of cliques, one of which was the boy-and-girl team. For example, Mr. Brown and Miss Gaynor spent a great deal of their time together and often joked about the amusing incidents that happened in town when clerks would mistake them for man and wife; they formed a unit in the "evenings at home" held by the group in the living rooms, where Mr. Brown would work on his cloth animals and Miss Gaynor would knit. Once, when Mr. Brown and Miss Gaynor gave a popcorn party for the group, Mrs. Gray jokingly said that all they needed were "His" and "Her" aprons. Such romantic attachments were approved so long as they remained flirtatious and casual because they served to increase social interaction, which was one of the main sociological functions of the clique. If, however, such attachments went beyond this point, they were frowned upon because any behavior which might lead to serious social consequences was felt as threatening by the group.[12] In general, if a clique, for whatever reasons, became so interested in itself that it drew away from the group, this was felt as a social loss and pressure was applied to bring it again into the wider social field.

A second function of the clique, examples of which have already been given, was to act as a mutual therapy group; a third was to provide opportunities to let off steam and thus act as a safety valve since it was not always easy for a patient to maintain a constant attitude of tolerance and support toward all other patients; while a fourth function became operative when a patient felt disturbed and

---

[12] We realize, of course, that sexual behavior, as well as other behavior, is not only influenced by forces in the social field, but also by powerful genetic and dynamic variables.

wished to draw away from the group, but did not want to isolate himself completely. The last two functions of the clique can be seen in the following example:

> The clique of Mr. Hill, Mr. Porter, and Mrs. Lewis frequently joked with each other in an aggressive manner they never used toward other patients. Mrs. Lewis felt free to call Mr. Hill a "fathead"; Mr. Porter kidded Mr. Hill about torturing himself; and Mr. Hill told Mr. Porter that he seemed to work endlessly on his book, and should just give up academic life. At another time, when the three of them were alone, Mr. Hill told how he disliked Miss Ford, and Mrs. Lewis spoke of how Mrs. Jones hounded and tagged after her. Mr. Hill said that this place stifled him; the boredom got on his nerves. He expressed resentment about the four-bed ward in which he slept, saying that Mr. Sullivan kept the radio on all the time, Mr. Owens was always doing push-ups, and Mr. Miller's only topic of conversation was his "dear old mother." Mr. Hill went on to say that he felt guilty because he had made himself scarce from Mr. Davis today, but that being around Mr. Davis every other day was enough.

Another type of clique, restricted to a predominantly social function, was formed, especially among the women, on the basis of similarity in background outside the hospital. There was a clique of young adolescent girls; a second composed of those women who like to sew, cook, and follow other domestic pursuits; while a third consisted of those women with interests in literature, music, art, and fashion. There was occasional friction between these cliques as, for example, when Miss Ford was attempting to move into one of the women's groups:

> Supper being over, Mrs. Lewis came back to the men's side quite furious and angry. It seemed that there was a "plot" instigated by Miss Ford to break up the group of women who usually ate together at the larger table in the women's living room. Before the meal was served, Miss Ford and Miss Gaynor had spread their knitting paraphernalia over half of the larger table and had said those places were reserved. Miss Ford commented rather pointedly to Mrs. Gray, Mrs. Peterson, and Mrs. Lewis about "you intellectuals who play Sark and do crossword puzzles while we sit around and do knitting." Mrs. Lewis said that Mrs. Gray and Mrs. Peterson were really working themselves up to "jumping down Miss Ford's throat" if she continued behavior of this kind.

In general, the women remained separated in small cliques, whereas the men formed a single, loosely integrated group that functioned with little discord. Many patients remarked on the fact that the women's side seemed to be in a state of constant minor turmoil in contrast to the relative peace reigning among the men.

From the patients' point of view, the purpose of the group structure just described was, first of all, to develop among themselves the opportunities for social activities otherwise lacking in the hospital environment by maximizing the number of interpersonal relationships and roles available to an individual, while at the same time trying to keep any serious social consequences of these relationships at a minimum; and, secondly, to provide the members of the group with as supportive and ego-sustaining a milieu as was possible without coming into conflict with the staff or the routine of the hospital.[13] Nevertheless, conflicts did arise

---

[13] The role and clique structure of the patient group not only functioned, in a general sense, to provide a social life and personal support for its members, but also helped individuals to

because the staff, both doctors and nurses, seemed unacquainted with many aspects of life in the patient group, and dealt with each individual as a separate entity in administrative details as well as in therapeutic matters. In part, this was due to the fact that there was no channel provided by which the patients, as a group, could voice their desires to the staff. If a group of patients wished to make a request, this could be done only by each patient's taking the matter up, as an individual, with his therapist. For example:

> A number of the patients had been trying to arrange suitable facilities for listening to music. Their general request was that the hospital either repair the broken phonograph in the living room, or allow another machine—kept in the occupational therapy shop and available only during the time that other pa-tients were using the jig saw, etc.—to be brought on the ward, where it would be more accessible and the surroundings were more conducive to listening. The occupational therapist, however, refused the latter part of this request. Since there was no channel whereby the group could express their desires, the patients who were most interested in music approached their therapists and the nurses on an individual basis. This they did for several weeks. At about this point, the patients' therapists began to use the conference hours to inquire as to the personal meaning music had for the individual patients. Six weeks after the patients made their initial requests, the phonograph in the living room was repaired. The patients were pleased, bought record albums, and formed a music clique. On the afternoon the phonograph was returned, a group of six patients were listening to music at the time the therapists made their rounds, but none of the doctors made a social remark about the pleasure of having the machine in working order.

As a result of this situation, the emphasis placed by the staff upon those aspects of the patients' day-to-day behavior that were brought to their attention was almost solely upon the meaning of this behavior in terms of the patients' indi-vidual psychodynamic histories, and seldom was any attention focused on factors inherent in the immediate group situation. When, for example, their doctors attempted to separate the boy-and-girl team of Mr. Brown and Miss Gaynor for therapeutic reasons, they did not fully realize that they were also modifying the place occupied by these two patients in the social group, and hence indirectly affecting the lives of all the patients. Further, since in this case administrative as well as therapeutic control was in the hands of the same doctor, Mr. Brown and Miss Gaynor would be denied permission by their therapists to attend a movie outside the hospital with other patients on one evening, and the next morning would be placed in the position of having to discuss the psychodynamic impli-cations of their desires with the same therapists.

The lack of a channel of communication, and an insufficient separation between administration and therapy, increased the mutual isolation of patients and staff. Both patients and staff structured their actions in accordance with a set of values and beliefs, but because the values and beliefs of each group were only incom-

---

meet a number of special situations by making available a sympathetic and understanding audience to which a patient could bring his doubts and problems concerning: 1) the visits of friends and relatives, 2) the finding of part-time temporary employment while still in the hospital, 3) the awkward incidents that sometimes occurred during excursions downtown, and 4) the final task of preparing oneself to leave the hospital for good.

pletely known or understood by the other, the two groups viewed one another in terms of stereotypes which impeded an accurate evaluation of social reality. Such a situation, when coupled with alternating periods of permissive and restrictive administrative control, probably helps to account for the mood swings in the patient group. One week a general air of depression would prevail, at other times the ward had the atmosphere of a hotel, while again a feeling of rebellion would come over the entire group.

Discussion

This paper has emphasized the point that psychoneurotic patients on a less disturbed ward of a mental hospital should not be thought of as an aggregate of individuals, but as a group which tries to meet many of its problems by developing a shared set of values and beliefs translated into action through a system of social roles and cliques. Some of the problems faced by the patient group in ordering the interaction of its members would seem to have been due directly to the factor of emotional illness. Since all of the members were emotionally disturbed, they had all experienced a high level of anxiety during their life in the outer world over the inability to play certain required social roles without introducing extraneous behavior stemming from neurotic conflicts.[14] The particular patient group reported on here recognized this problem and provided for it by its values of suspension of judgment and support. In so doing, the patients were acting in ways very similar to those noted by Rowland (1938) for the patients on the less disturbed wards of another mental hospital where interaction was characterized by "small, closed friendship groups," having "a maximum of insight and sympathetic interpenetration," with a "rigid control of affect in terms of group standards."

The patient group also sensed that because of hospitalization, an individual was not only relieved from playing roles in those areas of life where he experienced particular difficulty, but was also cut off from playing those roles in other areas of life which furnished him with some measure of self-esteem. Since few substitutes for these latter roles, in the form of short-range realistic goals and activities, were provided in the hospital, the patient group attempted to meet this problem by increasing opportunities for role taking through utilizing the personal attributes of the patients.

Many other problems of the patient group arose, however, because the patients and staff lived, as Rowland (1939) has expressed it, "in two entirely separate social worlds, yet . . . in the closest proximity." While the staff exercised control over the patients, they did not give recognition to the patient world as a social group, but rather, they interpreted the behavior of the patients almost solely in individual dynamic-historical terms. The patient group, thus lacking an adequate channel of communication to the staff, protected itself by turning inward, and by developing a social structure which was insulated as much as possible from friction with the hospital routine. Nevertheless, such friction did occur, and the subsequent frustration led to behavior on the part of the patients which, although it

[14] This is, of course, part of the problem of parataxic distortion discussed by Sullivan (1947).

overtly resembled neurotic behavior arising from personal emotional conflicts, was, in fact, to a considerable extent due to factors in the immediate situation.[15] Such phenomena are similar to the "increased agitation and dissociative behavior" observed by Stanton and Schwartz (1949b) when two staff members with power over a patient disagree as to how the case should be handled. Stanton and Schwartz conclude:

> If our hypothesis is correct that the patient's dissociation is a reflection of, and a mode of participation in, a social field which itself is seriously split, it accounts for the sudden cessation of excitement following any resolution of this split. . . . In other words, the phenomena are not completely "autistic" in the sense that they are not derived entirely from the patient's past history or from an unconscious which is isolated from reality.

Some aspects of the above situation seem almost inevitable in the nature of the hierarchical hospital structure. It is necessary to exercise some degree of control over patients; they will be cut off from the positive as well as the negative aspects of their outside life by hospitalization, and some frustration due to close living will occur in any institutional setting which must, by its nature, restrict the personal liberty of its members. If this is true, then some of the behavior of the patients is due to the nature of the situation rather than to their condition of emotional illness, and such behavior should be shared by groups living in other settings which have some *structural* similarities in common with mental hospitals. Sullivan asks this question in his discussion in the Stanton and Schwartz (1949) material when he says: "Is this a pattern which is a function of the particular larger group setting, or is it one that has relatively wide validity? . . . Is it to be seen in essential rudiments among the complements of a naval vessel, among the population of a penitentiary, in any hospital which has a relatively chronic patient population, [or] on the wards of most mental hospitals only . . . ?"

A review of the work done on behavior in such settings would seem, at least tentatively, to answer this question in the affirmative. A group of less disturbed patients in a mental hospital would seem to represent one point on a continuum of types of groups all of which share some structural characteristics—e.g., membership in these groups is transitional, positive goals for the members other than their successful removal from the group are mostly lacking, and control is largely

---

[15] The occurrence of such phenomena would seem to make it essential that a systematic understanding be gained of that behavior by patients on the ward which is attributable more to factors in the immediate social situation, and of that behavior which is attributable more to factors in their psychodynamic histories. Once such understanding is gained it would then be possible to investigate a second and very complex problem. This second problem concerns the effect of the patient group on the course of individual behavior that has its main inception in repetitive neurotic patterns. In the hospital the individual is protected from many of the realistic consequences that would follow his actions in the outer world, and he encounters a somewhat different system of rewarding and punishing responses from his fellow patients than he would from persons in ordinary life. Thus, while the patient's action is initially rooted in a repetitive conflict, the behavior flowing from this conflict is carried out in a different social reality than has heretofore been the case, and this may significantly influence the dynamic course of the behavior. The question is how the patient's behavior, set within the context of group interaction, should be met by the staff, given the knowledge that such behavior is both psychodynamically determined and affected by, and itself affects, the immediate social structure of the entire patient group on the ward.

authoritarian. Despite other great differences, such as voluntary or involuntary entrance and helping or punishing aims, these characteristics tend to be shared by groups in mental hospitals (Dembo and Haufmann, 1935), tuberculosis sanitariums (Mann, 1930; Todd and Wittkower, 1948), orphanages (Goldfarb, 1943), displaced persons camps (Boder, 1949; Friedman, 1949), wartime posts relatively free from danger (Greenson, 1949; Heggen, 1946), and under various conditions of imprisonment (Bettelheim, 1943; Bluhm, 1948; Haynor and Ash, 1939; Jacobson, 1949; Weinberg, 1942). In general, the accounts of behavior in these types of settings all stress the phenomena, so many of which are noted in hospitalized mental patients, of apathy and depersonalization, regression, denial of reality, attempts to maintain threatened self-esteem, increased wish-level and fantasy, and the formation of stereotypes concerning those who control the authority and power.

For example, the previously emotionally mature, female political prisoners observed by Jacobson (1949) exhibited, as did many of the patients discussed in this paper, initial feelings of depersonalization and denial of reality; a seeming regression to adolescence with its heightened affect lability; an increased, but unstable, sensitivity to aesthetic and intellectual stimulation; and a strong upsurge of oral cravings. Also, Jacobson's prisoners and the patients showed, as a sort of group reaction formation, increased morality and superego severity, great concern over the welfare of other members, and a constant effort to control irritability.

Such similarities in behavior as are sketched above for the various types of settings would seem to be in line with the experimental results and theoretical conceptualizations of Lewin, Lippit, White and others (French, 1941; Lewin, 1937; Lippitt, 1939; Lippitt and White, 1947) as to the direct effect on behavior of differences in social climate.

Beyond this the patient group seemed to develop certain types of behavior shared with all human groups whether they be, as Homans (1950) has pointed out, a bank wiring room in an industrial plant, a street-corner society, or a Polynesian community. Since social life is never wholly utilitarian, the patients were acting like any human group when they tended to overelaborate their interaction beyond the point required by the purely practical problems of the environment in which they found themselves. This tendency, noted by Linton (1936) and detailed by Homans (1950), accounts, in part, for the fact that the bank wiring employees restricted their output in accordance with their own norms and helped each other on piecework even though this was forbidden by management; similarly, the patients supported the activities of others even if this meant going against a rule of the hospital.

Research stemming from the observations discussed here might lead to an investigation of the following problems: 1) Further studies of the value systems of patient groups, and of the roles by which these values are implemented. 2) An exploration of the somewhat separate value systems of the various communication- and mobility-blocked strata of the hospital staff hierarchy. 3) A detailed analysis of interaction processes between the groups making up the hierarchy in light of the differences in values that might be found to exist. 4) Related to the foregoing problems, a study of what happens to reports on patient behavior, in terms of distortions, omissions, and additions, as these reports are channeled upward through the hospital strata to the point where decisions are made, and then down again.

A review would also seem to be indicated of the important question of whether neurotic patients who are still able to function in some areas of life should be admitted to a hospital beyond the need for diagnostic studies. It is quite possible that a great many neurotic patients now admitted to our hospitals would fare better in ambulatory treatment than in a hospital setting. At the same time, many neurotic patients must temporarily be removed from the anxiety-provoking setting of the home in order to facilitate therapeutic progress. This dilemma raises many theoretical and practical problems, and would seem to call for research on other types of environmental settings that might be more conducive to the successful psychotherapeutic treatment of such patients.

There are many questions of ward management to which this study has drawn attention. Our main emphasis, however, has been on a theoretical investigation of basic problems of social structure and interaction processes. Much further study is needed before well-founded, practical applications can be made.

28 / Postscript to "Social Structure and Interaction Processes on a Psychiatric Ward"

William Caudill

... this book is about the second of two studies I did in the same hospital.* In the first (Caudill *et al.*, 1952) I acted as a patient, and my identity was concealed. The second and fuller study (1958), reported on here, was begun a year and a half later, and in it I presented myself openly as a research anthropologist. From the published accounts of both studies the reader may judge which was the more successful. In the report of the first study (Caudill *et al.*, 1952) mention has already been made of the ethical problems posed by such a study, along with the suggestion of the feasibility of alternative procedures. I have no wish to rationalize my actions in this earlier study. I did it, and I learned much from it. I do not recommend others' doing it because I feel the price is too high. The ethical questions here are rather tricky—some of the purposes of almost any research project on human behavior are concealed from the subject, client, or patient, and this is too involved a topic for a preface. Certainly one factor, however, is how comfortable—morally and emotionally—a person is about the matter of concealment. Once in the situation, I felt decidedly uncomfortable.

* Caudill's evaluation of his own motives provides insight into the research process. Additional comments by the Editor are presented in the final paper of this part.

I believe I was naïve when I undertook the task of living as a patient. I had no strong opinions pro or con about the method. I did have a strong desire to learn by experience what life was like on the wards, and it was this rather than any wish to pry into secrets that provided my motivation. And yet the aura of the forbidden clings to such a study, and while I did not knowingly have such wishes, perhaps these were there unknowingly. Much is made of concealment these days, what with hidden role players in the experiments being carried out in several of the social sciences, and the question of the degree of frankness to be maintained with the patient in the sound recording of interviews and other material in psychiatry. Subsequent to my own experience with concealment, I have been somewhat startled at times at the aplomb with which plans for concealment in experiments and interviews are proposed as a matter of course. In my own case, whatever other factors were involved, I was taking the role, in a sense, for real.

What I learned from the concealed study had less to do with "facts" and more to do with "feelings." I became sensitive to such things as the difference in the meaning of "time" for the patient on the ward in contrast to the time kept by the busy staff member. I became aware of the immediate importance for patients of their communication with each other—during the day, at night, from one ward to another. On the whole, the experience taught me much about hospital life, and if, in reporting on the second study in this book, I have convincingly portrayed some aspects of the life of patients, it is in part because of the earlier study when I was, for a time, in the situation myself.

After the first study I was concerned about the one-sidedness of my work. I felt I knew a good bit about the organization of life on the wards, but very little about the operation of the hospital at the staff level. Besides, as I have said, I felt uncomfortable about the concealed study and wished to find out if similar data could be obtained more openly. More generally, I was eager to determine if scientific procedures could be worked out for studying the entire system of the hospital over time. I therefore decided to do the second study upon which this book is based. In this I hoped to correct the one-sidedness of the earlier study and to check my own observations and those of other investigators.

During the second study I spent a great deal of time with the various groups of staff and patients as they went about their life in the hospital. I believe I was able to work out methods of observation, interviewing, and analysis—as presented in the following pages—which provided data equal in richness to those of the earlier study. In addition, the methods of the second study yielded a wider range of data over which it was possible to exercise a high degree of control. Personally, I feel more satisfied, both intellectually and emotionally, with the material in this book (1958).

29 / The Role of the Group in the Induction of Therapeutic Change

Herbert C. Kelman

Psychotherapy can be regarded as a social influence situation in which the patient's relationship to the therapist is the primary vehicle for the production of therapeutic change. In individual psychotherapy, the situation is so arranged as to maximize the probability that the patient's interactions with the therapist will facilitate desirable changes in his attitudes, values, and action-tendencies. In group psychotherapy, the patient's relationships to his fellow-patients and to the group as a whole become additional vehicles for the production of therapeutic change. In choosing between group and individual therapy, one has to keep in mind, of course, that while the patient-group relationship may serve to strengthen forces toward change, it may also bring certain counterforces into play, thus reducing the potentiality for change contained in the dyadic relationship. Whether or not group therapy seems to be indicated, given these competing forces, will depend on the characteristics of the patient, the nature of his problems, and the current status of his general treatment program. Group therapy will be resorted to when there is reason to believe that the combination of therapist and group will make for a more effective influence situation and facilitate the occurrence of the particular changes that are desired.

My use of the term "social influence" does not carry any value connotations whatsoever. It will become clear, as I proceed, that I use the term very broadly to refer to any change in a person's behavior that is induced by another individual or a group. The induction may take many forms: for example, the influencing agent may exert pressure, offer suggestions, attempt persuasion, serve as a model, or make available new information; all of these would be subsumed under the term "social influence," without ignoring, of course, the importance of the qualitative differences between them. In describing psychotherapy as a social influence situation, then, my purpose is not at all to expose it as a manipulative process. Rather, it is my purpose to make it accessible to a social-psychological analysis of influence processes, based on theoretical and empirical exploration of a variety of laboratory and field situations. While psychotherapy constitutes a very unique kind of interaction situation, it is nevertheless continuous with other social situations in which changes in behavior and personality are induced. An application to this situation of some of the concepts that have been developed in the study of other influence situations may, therefore, provide a different perspective for viewing psychotherapy and perhaps offer some new insights.

From the *International Journal of Group Psychotherapy*, 1963, **13**, 399–432. Copyright © 1963. Reprinted by permission of the author and the *International Journal of Group Psychotherapy*.

A Framework for the
Analysis of Social Influence

Specifically, I would like to apply to the therapy situation a theoretical framework for the analysis of social influence with which I have been working over the last few years (Kelman, 1961). This framework has generated a number of specific hypotheses that have been tested experimentally (e.g., Kelman, 1958); and it has also been used in the interpretation of attitude changes found in an intensive field situation (Bailyn and Kelman, 1962). The starting point of this framework is a distinction between three processes whereby influence can be accepted: compliance, identification, and internalization.

Compliance can be said to occur when an individual accepts influence from another person or from a group in order to attain a favorable reaction from the other, that is, to gain a specific reward or avoid a specific punishment controlled by the other, or to gain approval or avoid disapproval from him. Identification can be said to occur when an individual accepts influence from another person or a group in order to establish or maintain a satisfying self-defining relationship to the other. In contrast to compliance, identification is not primarily concerned with producing a particular effect in the other. Rather, accepting influence through identification is a way of establishing or maintaining a desired relationship to the other, as well as the self-definition that is anchored in this relationship. By accepting influence, the person is able to see himself as similar to the other (as in classical identification) or to see himself as enacting a role reciprocal to that of the other. Finally, internalization can be said to occur when an individual accepts influence in order to maintain the congruence of his actions and beliefs with his value system. Here it is the content of the induced behavior and its relation to the person's value system that are intrinsically satisfying.

Each of these three processes is characterized by a distinct set of antecedent conditions and a distinct set of consequents. These are summarized in Table I. Very briefly, on the antecedent side, it is proposed that three qualitative aspects of the influence situation will determine which process is likely to result: (1) the basis for the importance of the induction, i.e., the nature of the predominant motivational orientation that is activated in the influence situation; (2) the source of power of the influencing agent, i.e., the particular characteristics that enable him to affect the person's goal achievement; and (3) the manner of achieving prepotency of the induced response, i.e., the particular induction techniques that are used (deliberately or otherwise) to make the desired behavior stand out in preference to other alternatives. Thus, compliance is likely to result if the individual's primary concern in the influence situation is with the social effect of his behavior; if the influencing agent's power is based largely on his means-control (i.e., his ability to supply or withhold material or psychological resources on which the person's goal achievement depends); and if the induction techniques are designed to limit the individual's choice behavior. Indentification is likely to result if the individual is primarily concerned, in this situation, with the social anchorage of his behavior; if the influencing agent's power is based largely on his attractiveness (i.e., his possession of qualities that make a continued relationship to him particularly desirable); and if the induction techniques serve to delineate

TABLE I

SUMMARY OF THE DISTINCTIONS BETWEEN THE THREE PROCESSES*

	Compliance	*Identification*	*Internalization*
Antecedents:			
1. Basis for the *importance of the induction*	Concern with social effect of behavior	Concern with social anchorage of behavior	Concern with value congruence of behavior
2. Source of *power of the influencing agent*	Means control	Attractiveness	Credibility
3. Manner of achieving *prepotency of the induced response*	Limitation of choice behavior	Delineation of role requirements	Reorganization of means-ends framework
Consequents:			
1. Conditions of performance of induced response	Surveillance by influencing agent	Salience of relationship to agent	Relevance of values to issue
2. Conditions of change and extinction of induced response	Changed perception of conditions for social rewards	Changed perception of conditions for satisfying self-defining relationships	Changed perception of conditions for value maximization
3. Type of behavior system in which induced response is embedded	External demands of a specific setting	Expectations defining a specific role	Person's value system

* Reprinted by permission of the publisher (Kelman, 1961, p. 67).

the requirements of the role relationship in which the person's self-definition is anchored (for example, if they delineate the expectations of a relevant reference group). Internalization is likely to result if the individual's primary concern in the influence situation is with the value congruence of his behavior; if the influencing agent's power is based largely on his credibility (i.e., his expertness and trustworthiness); and if the induction techniques are designed to reorganize the person's means-ends framework, his conception of the paths toward maximization of his values.

On the consequent side, the framework proposes that the changes produced by each of the three processes tend to be of a different nature. The crucial difference in nature of change between the three processes is in the conditions under which the newly acquired behavior is likely to manifest itself. Behavior accepted through compliance will tend to manifest itself only under conditions of surveillance by the influencing agent, i.e., only when the person's behavior is observable (directly or indirectly) by the agent. The manifestation of identification-based behavior does not depend on observability by the influencing agent, but it does depend on the salience of the person's relationship to the agent. That is, the behavior is likely to manifest itself only in situations that are in some way or other associated with the individual or group from whom the behavior was originally adopted. Thus, whether or not the behavior is manifested will depend on the role that the individual takes at any given moment in time. While surveillance is irrelevant, identification-based behavior is designed to meet the other's expectations for the person's own role performance. The behavior, therefore, remains tied to the external source and dependent upon social support. It is not integrated with the individual's value system, but rather tends to be isolated from the rest of his values, to remain encapsulated. In contrast, behavior accepted through internalization depends neither on surveillance nor on salience but tends to manifest itself whenever the values on which it is based are relevant to the issue at hand. Behavior adopted through internalization is in some way, rational or otherwise, integrated with the individual's existing values. It becomes part of a personal system, as distinguished from a system of social-role expectations. It becomes independent of the original source and, because of the resulting interplay with other parts of the person's value system, it tends to be more idiosyncratic, more flexible, and more complex. This does not imply complete consistency, nor does it mean that the behavior will occur every time it is relevant to the situation. Internalized responses will, however, at least come into play whenever their content is relevant and will contribute to the final behavioral outcome, along with competing value considerations and situational demands.

I hope that this brief review is sufficient to give the flavor of the three processes of influence. Clearly, the ultimate aim of therapy, at least of insight therapy, is the development of new attitudes, new self-images, and new patterns of interpersonal relationships at the level of internalization. However, as I shall attempt to show, all three processes are typically involved in the therapeutic interaction, and all three are necessary to the production of therapeutic change. Even when internalized change takes place at the conclusion of therapy, compliance and identification serve as ancillary processes: changes at these other levels represent preliminary steps that make internalization possible. Sometimes, as shall be discussed below, changes produced in therapy may not proceed to internalization but remain fixated at the level of compliance and identification.

Changes Within and Outside of the Therapy Situation

Before spelling out the way in which the three processes enter into the production of therapeutic change, I would like to make a further distinction between two phases of behavior change to which the therapeutic relationship must address itself. Very simply, these are changes in the patient's behavior *within* the therapy situation and changes in the patient's behavior *outside* of the therapy situation (cf. Kelman, 1952).

First, the therapist and the group have to exert influence on the patient's behavior within the therapy situation in order to be certain that the patient will engage in the therapeutic process and thus open himself up to the therapeutic potential of the situation. The model of the therapy situation that I have in mind here is that of a situation so set up that the patient is both freed and forced to overcome his resistances and to think and talk about things he ordinarily avoids; the greater freedom allows him to *experience* certain feelings in the therapy situation and to express these feelings as he experiences them; as he engages in this process, corrective emotional experiences in the therapy situation become possible, i.e., experiences marked by the simultaneous occurrence of intense feelings and the examination of these feelings. To make the occurrence of this process possible and likely, the therapist and the group must influence the patient to shed his resistances, to allow himself to experience certain threatening feelings, to express these feelings as he experiences them, and to examine them as he expresses them. In short, they must induce changes in the patient's behavior within the therapy situation so that he will increasingly meet the requirements of the therapeutic process.

But, obviously, changes in the patient's behavior within the therapy situation are not enough. To be effective, therapy must produce changes in the patient's behavior outside of therapy, in his daily life and in his interactions with the people that form his customary milieu. The therapy situation itself helps to unfreeze existing attitudes and behavior patterns and to extend the patient's repertory, to bring out new behaviors and emotional experiences around which new insights can be built. But the pay-off of such corrective emotional experiences comes when the insights derived from them are transferred to real life. Thus, there is a second phase of behavior change to which the therapist and the group must address themselves: they have to exert influence on the patient's behavior outside of the therapy situation. This must be done in order to make certain that he will apply the therapeutic insights to those situations in which his actions are self-defeating, his perceptions distorted, and his interpersonal relationships unrewarding.

According to the usual model of therapy, the therapist does not intervene in the patient's real-life situation in any direct way. The only point at which he enters into the patient's life is during the therapeutic interactions themselves. Nevertheless, therapist and group do exert influence on the patient's real-life behavior by encouraging him (implicitly or explicitly) to try out new patterns, by providing him with a frame of reference for analyzing his own behavior, and by reviewing with him some of his attempts to apply therapeutic learnings to his interactions outside. I am speaking here of ways of influencing the patient's outside behavior while he is still in therapy. Needless to say, if therapy has been successful, its effects will continue to manifest themselves after it has been terminated, as the person applies both the process and the insights he derived from therapy to more and more of his life experiences. This would presumably happen to the extent that internalization has taken place. My concern at the moment, however, is not with these self-activated changes in the patient's behavior that represent the aftermath of effective therapy but with the direct influence on the patient's behavior outside of the therapy situation *while therapy is still in progress*. While most therapists do concern themselves with extra-therapy behavior, there are differences in how much they emphasize it and how explicit they are about it. In some therapeutic approaches, the emphasis is placed entirely on the interaction in the therapy situation proper. Real-life matters are regarded as almost irrelevant. In other approaches, there are deliberate attempts to bring in real-life experiences, to encourage transfer from what happens in therapy to what happens outside (e.g., to encourage the patient to try out new behaviors), to review the patient's attempts to apply new insights—in short, to use the therapeutic situation as a *deliberate* training facility for real life.

It should be noted that these two phases of change may also represent competing demands. The very features of the therapeutic situation and of the techniques employed by the therapist that are most conducive to unfreezing old behavior and "getting out" new behavior *during* the therapy sessions may, at the same time, interfere with the generalization of this behavior. For example, the more isolated the therapy situation is from real life, the more it is structured as a playful situation which "doesn't really count," the more likely it is that the patient will feel free to experience and express emotions that he finds too threatening in the outside world. By the same token, however, it will be more difficult to generalize what he learns in this situation to real life, where the threatening features are present in full force and where everything does count. Similarly, to the extent that the therapist encourages a view of the therapy situation as the predominant focus of the patient's life, to the requirements of which all other life requirements must be subordinated while therapy is in progress, he will increase the power of the therapeutic situation for controlling the patient's behavior within it. This kind of emphasis may prevent a diffusion of transference, a premature acting-out in real-life contexts, or an escape from the analysis of the person's own neurotic problems to an examination of the reality problems of his environment. At the same time, however, by keeping the therapy situation "pure," one reduces its power to induce changes in the patient's behavior outside of therapy. Thus, a major challenge in all forms of psychotherapy is to find the proper balance between forces toward change in within-therapy behavior and forces toward change in extra-therapy behavior. In this connection, there may be some interesting differences between group and individual therapy. Group therapy may be less powerful in the unfreezing of old behavior and the "getting out" of new behavior, but it may be more powerful in the generalization of therapeutic insights to real life. I would not want to push this proposition too far, without considerable qualification, but it may represent one major dimension of difference.

I would like to propose that compliance, identification, and internalization play a part in each of the two phases of behavior change with which therapy is concerned, i.e., changes within and changes outside of the therapy situation, and contribute to the achievement of a therapeutic effect. In the remainder of this paper, I shall try to show how each process enters into the induction of therapeutic change. Looking first at the patient's behavior within the therapy situation, I shall take the three processes in order and, for each, discuss (1) what type of patient behavior, relevant to a therapeutic outcome, is induced by that particular process; (2) what the therapist's role is in the induction of this particular behavior; and (3) what the group's role is in the induction of this behavior, i.e., how it may reinforce (or possibly reduce) the therapeutic potential of the situation. I shall then proceed to present a parallel analysis of the patient's behavior outside of the therapy situation.

I should mention here my assumption that, even in group therapy, the therapist is of necessity the primary influencing agent, although the group can make some powerful and unique contributions to the process.

Influence Directed to Behavior
within the Therapy Situation

The influence attempts directed to the patient's behavior within the therapy situation are summarized in Table II. It is proposed that three types of patient behavior have to be induced within the therapy situation in order to facilitate therapeutic change, and that these correspond, in the main, to the three processes of influence.

TABLE II

TYPES OF INFLUENCE INVOLVED IN THE PRODUCTION OF
THERAPEUTIC CHANGE

A. PROCESSES OF INFLUENCE DIRECTED TO THE PATIENT'S BEHAVIOR
WITHIN THE THERAPY SITUATION

	Type of Patient Behavior Induced by This Process	Therapist's Role in the Induction of This Behavior	Group's Role in the Induction of This Behavior
Compliance	Engagement in the therapeutic work (obeying the "basic rule")	Trainer	Sanctioning agents
Identification	Commitment to the therapeutic situation	Accepting, permissive, expert listener	Facilitating agents; comparison reference group
Internalization	Occurrence of corrective emotional experiences	Transference object	Interaction objects; role reciprocators

Engagement in the Therapeutic Work

If the therapeutic business is to be transacted effectively, the patient must engage in the therapeutic work. He must be trained, as it were, to produce some kinds of behavior and to eschew others in the therapy situation. If he fails to do so, he does not provide the necessary openings for therapeutic interventions and makes it impossible for corrective experiences to emerge. Thus, in analytically oriented therapy, the patient must allow himself to experience certain feelings despite strong resistances to them and he must express these feelings; he must be trained to talk, to free-associate, to obey the "basic rule."

Almost invariably some degree of compliance is necessary at this stage of therapy. The patient, of course, brings a certain amount of self-activated motivation to the situation, based on his desire to benefit from therapy. Nevertheless, the resistances to engaging in the therapeutic work are so strong that some extraneous motivation has to be brought into play, at least at the beginning. This motivation derives from the patient's desire for the therapist's approval and the avoidance of his disapproval. The patient's concern with a favorable reaction from the therapist constitutes a potent force in overcoming his strong resistances and getting him to proceed with the therapeutic work.

The therapist's role in this part of the process is essentially that of a *trainer,* who responds to the patient's productions in such a way as to increase the probability that what he considers therapeutically relevant material will emerge. Analysts and particularly nondirective therapists would not like to think of themselves as engaging in such deliberate training. But they do—and in fact have to— train the patient, even if they are unaware of it. The therapist often, in subtle ways, directs the patient; he approves of some things and disapproves of others. The patient picks this up and tailors his subsequent productions accordingly. For example, in analytic therapy, the therapist makes the patient uncomfortable about his resistances by confronting him with them, interpreting them, etc., until they gradually become less frequent. Also, he encourages certain kinds of contents, in contrast to other kinds, by responding to them, showing interest in them, and building interpretations around them. Patients learn to give the therapist what he seems to want. In nondirective therapy, the therapist shows approval by reflecting, reacting to a particular line, and picking up some contents while neglecting others. The research on verbal conditioning (cf. Greenspoon, 1955; Krasner, 1958) has shown that in *nontherapeutic* situations, individuals are responsive to slight cues of approval, such as the sound of "mm-hm." Since the therapist's reactions are so much more important to the patient and since the patient finds himself in a relatively ambiguous situation in which he is searching for guidelines for his behavior, it seems more than reasonable to assume that he will be sensitive to subtle cues of approval or disapproval emanating from the therapist. The work of Murray (1954, 1956) is consistent with this assumption.

I do not want for a moment to equate this part of the process with the therapeutic process as a whole. My view of therapy, as should be clear from everything I have said and will say, is completely inconsistent with the notion that it is all "just a matter of verbal conditioning." I am only proposing that the kind of training I have described, which is based primarily on the therapist's ability to supply or withhold approval in this ambiguous, anxiety-laden, and delicate interpersonal situation, represents an essential step which mediates therapeutic change. Inducing the patient to experience feelings and to talk about them is a prerequisite for the occurrence of therapeutically relevant events. Moreover, inducing the patient to talk about the particular contents and in the particular language that are required by the therapist's theory provides the terms within which this particular therapist can become useful to the patient. While compliance, then, is strictly a mediating step, it may happen that a patient becomes fixated at that level, i.e., that he adopts the language overtly and superficially and does not go beyond that. He says all the right words, even though they do not correspond to his actual feelings and are not used in an attempt to develop more appropriate labels for his behavior. Typically, this represents an elaborate form of resistance to the therapeutic process rather than a way of bringing it forward. By complying with the letter rather than the spirit of the therapist's requests, the patient avoids real engagement in the situation. Overcompliance, as a matter of fact, may represent a form of hostility.

Turning to group therapy, in what way does the group contribute to this part of the therapeutic process, to inducing the individual group member to engage in the therapeutic work? The group members can serve as additional *sanctioning agents* who can apply various kinds of pressure on the individual patient to conform to the requirements of the situation and engage in the therapeutic work. If the requirements to express one's feelings, to say what is on one's mind, etc., are adopted as part of the group's norms, the training process that I have described can be considerably reinforced and speeded up. The group has powerful techniques at its disposal for controlling the behavior of individual members and maximizing their conformity. Desirable behavior can be rewarded by praise, encouragement, support, or by giving the individual visible signs that he is a valued member of the group and that his status is secure and may, in fact, be enhanced. Undesirable (nonconforming) behavior can be discouraged by direct criticism, ridicule, ostracism, loss in status, and other signs of rejection. Small-group studies, both in the laboratory and in industrial settings, have provided demonstrations of the group's power to control member behavior through the selective application of encouragement and pressure. This clearly represents a potentially powerful source of influence.

A group's ability to induce compliance to its norms depends on its control over resources that are important to the individual. In the case of therapy groups, the resources that are at stake are not of a material but of a psychological nature. A member will be likely to comply with the group's demands to the extent that he depends on this particular group as a source of acceptance and approval. It can be assumed that for most patients this dependence will be rather high for two reasons: first, because they are likely to be low in self-esteem and thus need external support to bolster it; second, because they are likely to lack close interpersonal relationships and involvements in rewarding group interactions. For many patients the therapy group may fulfill a unique function, not by virtue of the therapeutic process that it sets in motion, but simply by virtue of the sustained and meaningful social relationships that it makes possible for them, thus filling a void in their daily lives. It can be assumed that the group's control over this particular type of patient will be especially strong. One might also predict that this type of patient would be most likely to remain fixated at the level of compliance. To the extent that remaining a member in good standing of this group and obtaining immediate satisfactions that derive from group membership satisfy major needs for him, he may be both more motivated to protect his status in the group and less motivated to get deeply involved in the therapeutic process itself: he already has what he most wants, provided the group continues to accept him.

The group's ability to induce compliance also depends, of course, on some of the characteristics of the group. For example, if the group has built up the sanctioning function by actively encouraging and approving conforming behavior and actively discouraging and punishing nonconformity to its norms, its means-control over the individual member will be stronger. Means-control depends not only on the extent to which the group controls important resources, but also on the perceived probability that it will use this control to insure compliance. A group that actively uses this sanctioning function can make an important contribution to the therapeutic business by inducing the patient to engage in the therapeutic work. It must be kept in mind, however, that the group's power in this regard is a double-edged sword. It can be used for the furtherance of the therapeutic process, but it can conceivably also be used for resistance to it. In experimental and industrial groups it has been found that group pressure can be very effective in inducing members to conform to a particular standard of productivity. This, however, may take the form of increasing *or decreasing* an individual's level of productivity, depending on the particular nature of the group standard (Coch and French, 1948; Schachter *et al.,* 1951; Berkowitz, 1954). Similarly, in group therapy, if group norms develop that encourage resistance to the therapeutic process, the group may strengthen antitherapeutic forces. Frank (1957) points out that this is unlikely to happen, because the therapist himself is the only stable source of norms for the group. Be that as it may, it is still necessary for the therapist to concern himself with the nature of the group norms that develop. He cannot leave this entirely to chance, but must bring his unique influence to bear in such a way that the group norms will support engagement in the therapeutic work rather than resistance to it.

Commitment to the Therapeutic Situation

The sanctions applied by the therapist and the group may be powerful instruments in inducing the patient to conform to the therapeutic norms, but their effectiveness depends on the patient's motivation to remain in therapy. If this motivation is low, then he will simply remove himself from the situation as soon as the level of anxiety created by the experience and disclosure of his feelings becomes too high. If the patient, then, is to continue in therapy long enough so that he can get to the point of having corrective emotional experiences, he must develop a commitment to the therapeutic situation as one that is potentially beneficial to him and for which it is worth making certain sacrifices. This attitude of commitment is particularly essential since, for most patients, therapy is a strange and ambiguous situation, which violates many of their initial expectations and whose benefits are by no means clear to them. Even under the best of circumstances, it takes some time for any beneficial effects to become apparent, and the patient needs this sense of commitment to sustain him in the interim.

There is another sense in which commitment to the therapeutic situation is essential. The patient must come to view it not only as a situation which is beneficial to him in the long run, but also as one that is safe for him in the "short run." When he is asked to conform to the therapeutic norms by exposing himself and expressing his feelings without censorship, he is placed in a very difficult situation. He runs the risk of criticism, rejection, and condemnation after he has divested himself of his defenses and laid himself bare before others. If the patient is to feel free to engage in the therapeutic process and talk about himself, then he must regard the situation as one in which he is safe from attack and condemnation and in which he can afford to relax his customary protective mechanisms. In short, then, if the patient is to engage himself in the therapeutic process and open himself to the possibility of therapeutic experiences, he must develop a commitment to the situation: an attitude of trust and a willingness to accept its terms, based on his conviction that he will be protected in his situation and that he will benefit from it.

These attitudes to the therapeutic situation, I propose, are induced primarily through the process of identification with the therapist. A patient typically establishes a relationship to the therapist that provides him with a more satisfying self-definition than the one with which he entered therapy. Through his relationship to the therapist, the patient's self-esteem is enhanced: he comes to see himself as a person who is worthy of attention and acceptance. Moreover, as a consequence of this relationship, he gradually loses his sense of hopelessness about his fate and sees himself as a person who is successfully moving toward a resolution of his conflicts. It is as part of this satisfying self-defining relationship to the therapist that the patient's commitment to the therapy situation as a whole develops. Trust in the therapy situation and acceptance of its terms represent the expectations that circumscribe the patient's role in this reciprocal relationship. To the extent that the patient wishes to maintain this relationship, he will tend to adopt the attitudes expected for his role within it. Freud's (1950) concept of the conscious component of positive transference refers, essentially, to this process of commitment to the therapy situation through identification with the therapist.

The therapist's contribution to this process consists in offering the patient a relationship that will enhance his self-esteem and his feeling of hope. He accomplishes this largely by adopting, as his part of this reciprocal relationship, the role of an *accepting, permissive, expert listener*. Most schools of therapy stress that an essential part of the therapist's role is to communicate to the patient a full understanding and unconditional acceptance of him. Regardless of what the patient may reveal about himself, the therapist does not judge or condemn him. Rogerian therapy places primary emphasis on the attitude of acceptance conveyed by the therapist and regards it as not only a necessary, but actually a sufficient, condition for therapeutic change (Rogers, 1957). In analytically oriented therapy, the emphasis is not so much on acceptance of the patient as a person as it is on permissiveness in the sense of reassurance that no feeling the patient might express and no revelation he might make will lead the therapist to condemn or reject him (cf. Menninger, 1958). Despite differences in emphasis, most schools of therapy do view some form of acceptance as a necessary part of the therapeutic relationship, as Fiedler's (1950, 1950a) research tends to demonstrate. This aspect of the therapist's role, which tends to enhance the patient's self-esteem and provide him with a more satisfying self-image, certainly forms part of the basis of the patient's identification with the therapist.

A second feature of the therapist's role, which greatly contributes to inducing a commitment to the therapy situation in the patient, is the therapist's apparent expertness and related characteristics designed to inspire faith in his ability to help the patient. Frank (1959) has provided a most illuminating discussion of the variety of factors that promote this kind of faith in the therapist and of the way in which faith enters into the therapy process. The main point in the present context is that, to the extent that the therapist inspires faith, the patient's relationship to him reduces his sense of helplessness and enhances his feeling of hope. The resulting identification with the therapist, in turn, increases the patient's commitment to the therapy situation and to his own role requirements within it.

In most forms of therapy, this part of the therapeutic process is regarded as a means to therapeutic experiences, not as an end in itself. In analytically oriented therapy, in particular, positive transference is important only in that it provides motivation for the patient to continue with the therapeutic work despite its painfulness, and in that it creates an atmosphere in which the patient feels safe and free to examine his feelings. As a matter of fact, analysts, like Menninger (1958), stress the necessity of limiting the amount of satisfaction that the patient derives from his relationship to the therapist: it must be sufficient to keep him in the situation, but not so much as to make it an end in itself and thus reduce the patient's motivation to engage in the therapeutic process. Even Rogerians, who put primary emphasis on acceptance, do not regard this as the end of therapy. They merely regard it as the limit of the *therapist's* contribution, but this is only a means to the therapeutic process itself, which is essentially the patient's own responsibility. It often happens, however, that the therapeutic process becomes fixated at the level of identification, that establishing a self-defining relationship to the therapist becomes an end in itself rather than a step that mediates the occurrence of corrective, insight-producing experiences. This is the kind of outcome that is sometimes referred to as a "transference cure," which has similar dynamics to placebo cures and faith healing, as described in detail by Frank (1959, 1961). Such an outcome may, in fact, be quite meaningful therapeutically, depending, of course, on the criteria one uses. The opportunity of establishing a relationship with the therapist—by giving the patient something to hold on to, someone in whom he can have faith, on whom he can depend and on whose acceptance he can count—may help to stabilize the patient's self-concept, provide him with a sense of identity (even if it is a borrowed identity), and thus change the whole balance of his life. Thus, solely on the basis of the relationship to the therapist, without any special insight or working-through, the patient may manifest changes in his self-attitudes and, related to these, an increase in general feeling of comfort and symptomatic relief.

Now let us turn to group therapy and examine the way in which the group contributes to this part of the therapeutic process, to inducing the patient's commitment to the therapy situation and to his own role requirements within it. Other group members serve, in various ways, as *facilitating agents* who make it easier for the individual patient to continue with the therapy process and to take the risks of self-revelation. The patient's relationship to the group typically provides him with a more satisfying self-definition because it enhances his self-esteem and lowers his sense of helplessness. In these respects, the group does not merely reinforce the effects of the therapist but makes certain unique contributions that the one-to-one relationship to the therapist cannot offer.

First, the group can help to overcome the patient's feeling of isolation, which is, of course, a central problem for many neurotic patients. The very feeling of belonging to a group is in itself a source of self-esteem (Frank, 1957), which is further bolstered by the experience of intimacy and support from others. Of particular importance is the fact that this is a group of individuals with similar or related problems (cf. Beck, 1958), which gives the patient the reassuring feeling that his situation is not unique and unprecedented. The presence of shared problems and a common fate increases the likelihood of identification with the group, which in turn increases the patient's commitment to the therapy situation as a whole.

A second contribution of the group to a more favorable self-definition of the individual patient is based on its acceptance of him, despite his "obvious deficiencies, lack of status, and intimate revelations" (Beck, 1958). Needless to say, such acceptance enhances the patient's self-esteem as well as his feeling that he can somehow be reclaimed. While acceptance from the group is not as predictable nor as unconditional as that from the therapist, when it does occur it is likely to have a powerful impact. For here is acceptance not by a professional, who has been trained to take this role and is being paid for it, but by the person's own peers who, despite their deviancy, are more representative of society at large.

A third contribution of the group in the present context is based on the fact that it can serve as a *comparison reference group* for the individual patient, i.e., as a group that he can use as a standard for comparison in evaluating his own fate and his own progress. By comparing himself to others whose situation resembles his own, the patient can gain a certain degree of hope and encouragement. His difficulties seem less devastating when he can use a group of fellow-patients as his reference group, rather than his associates from his daily environment (cf. Beck, 1958). Moreover, as other patients show progress, the patient's optimism about his own situation may (at least up to a point) be enhanced.

In short, by relieving the patient's sense of isolation and deviance, by offering him support and acceptance by his peers, and by providing him with encouraging points of reference, the group can greatly enhance his commitment to the therapy situation. The increased self-esteem and hope generated by his relationship to the group help in motivating him to continue therapy and in freeing him to express himself despite the risks this entails.

The satisfying self-definitions that patients derive from their relationship to the group have not only a direct but also an indirect facilitative effect on their commitment to the therapy situation. These and other satisfactions provided by the group contribute to the general cohesiveness of the group, i.e., "the resultant of all the forces acting on all the members to remain in the group" (Cartwright and Zander, 1960, p. 74). Numerous studies have shown that the greater the cohesiveness of a group, the greater its ability to induce change in the members, not only at the level of public conformity but also at the level of private belief. That is, the more cohesive the group, the more likely are the members to accept the attitudes that it prescribes—which, in the case of therapy groups, would include a favorable attitude to the therapy situation. Among the potential sources of cohesiveness in the therapy groups, Frank (1957) mentions the extent to which the group provides direct satisfaction for some of the members' needs and promises future satisfactions, the extent to which members find that they can be mutually helpful to each other, the extent to which the group provides rewards for successful performance, and the extent to which mutual attraction of members develops.

If the group is highly cohesive, there is, of course, the possibility that the individual patient will become committed to the group per se rather than to the therapeutic process. In that case, the patient would remain fixated at the level of identification with the group: that is, the satisfying relationship to the group would become an end in itself rather than a means to further self-examination and insight-producing experience. As I pointed out earlier, such an outcome may be therapeutically quite meaningful in that it may, by enhancing the patient's self-esteem, restore the balance of his life situation. Typically, however, it would be up to the therapist to make sure that the patient's relationship to the group serves as a spur to the therapeutic process rather than as a subsitute for it.

There is another danger inherent in group therapy to which the therapist must always remain alert. The facilitative effect of the group is predicated on the assumption that the group will accept the individual member as he is. If the member is confronted, however, with condemnation and rejection, the experience may be antitherapeutic, his commitment to the therapy situation may be reduced, and he may eventually withdraw from the situation completely. This does not mean that acceptance of others has to be complete. As a matter of fact, there is some experimental evidence (Dittes and Kelley, 1956) to the effect that, under certain circumstances, the member who is not fully accepted in the group is more likely to become committed to its norms than the one whose acceptance is very high. Moreover, criticisms and attacks from the group may on occasion initiate therapeutically useful experiences (Frank, 1955, 1957). There must, however, be an underlying atmosphere of acceptance and support by the group, so that the patient will not regard an occasional attack as complete rejection, and so that there will be the definite prospect that, as he changes his behavior, acceptance will be restored. It is up to the therapist to foster an atmosphere of mutual acceptance as part of the normative structure of the group and to step in to protect the individual patient when this norm is seriously violated.

Occurrence of Corrective Emotional Experiences

The experience and expression of feelings in the therapy situation, which are encouraged through deliberate training by the therapist and identification with him, are designed to provide opportunities for the occurrence of "corrective emotional experiences" (Alexander and French, 1946). Such experiences are based on the manifestation, right in the therapy hour, of the distorted, self-defeating, and troubling attitudes that the patient brings to his real-life relationships. The conditions for a corrective emotional experience are present if the feelings the patient experiences when he expresses these attitudes in the therapy situation are as real and intense as they are under usual circumstances. The difference between the therapy situation and other situations is, of course, the fact that in therapy he is able, and in a way forced, to examine these feelings as they occur, which he cannot do in real life. With the help of the therapist, the patient can thus begin to see his attitudes in their true light, he can recognize their distorted and self-defeating aspects, and he can gain some understanding of their origins. Typically, the therapist is able to confront the patient with the inappropriateness of his attitudes by reacting in ways that violate the patient's expectations. A clear disconfirmation of a clear expectation provides the raw material for re-examination of the patient's unrealistic attitudes and inappropriate feelings.

The essence of a corrective emotional experience is the fact that the patient's examination of his attitudes and behavior patterns occurs simultaneously with their actual manifestation at a real-life level of emotional intensity. He examines his attitudes and behavior while he is still experiencing the relevant feelings, which makes this more than a mere intellectual exercise. The unique value of psychotherapy is that it makes this simultaneous occurrence of real feelings and their examination possible. Outside of therapy, situations in which strong feelings occur are precisely those in which examination of these feelings—stepping aside and observing one's self objectively—is impossible. When a person does examine his behavior objectively, it is generally after he has gained some distance from it and it has been drained of its emotional intensity.

Corrective emotional experiences can form the basis for internalized changes in the patient's conceptions of the self and of interpersonal relationships. As a result of these experiences, and the therapist's interpretations, the range of information that is available to the patient becomes widened. He gains new insight, a new understanding of the attitudes that he characteristically brings to his interpersonal relationships, of the behavior patterns that result from them, and of the expectations of others' reactions that generally guide him. Out of these new insights, more realistic attitudes and expectations can develop. We can speak of internalized changes here because corrective emotional experiences represent a re-examination of the patient's attitudes and behavior in the light of his own value system. The changes that emerge from such experiences are presumably integrated with his value system: the patient abandons self-defeating attitudes and behavior patterns and, instead, learns to see himself and others and to behave interpersonally in ways that are more likely to maximize his own values.

Sometimes, a series of corrective emotional experiences may lead, not only to changes within an existing value framework, but actually to changes in basic values themselves, that is, the patient may come to adopt new values that are more realistic for him. Ideally, however, even when this happens, there would be some continuity between the new values and his self-system. Values communicated by the therapist would serve as catalysts and models in the re-examination of the patient's values, but the patient would not simply take them over *in toto*. He might adopt the therapist's values in modified form, in ways that meet his own needs, temperament, and life history. It may, of course, happen that a patient simply takes over the values of the therapist. This would be a case of therapy having been fixated at the level of identification. A genuine corrective emotional experience, however, implies a confrontation between the patient's current attitudes and behavior and his own value system. Changes resulting from such an experience should, therefore, be changes at the level of internalization.

As has already been noted, compliance and identification are usually necessary before such corrective experiences can occur. Often, the three processes represent sequential steps in the therapeutic process. The patient starts out by complying: he follows the basic rule and engages in the therapeutic work, at least in part, for short-range rewards at the beginning stages of therapy. Identification then enters in, in two ways: the patient must get some satisfaction out of the relationship to the therapist as such, in order to continue in therapy; and, if the therapeutic situation is to offer some novelty, he must be able to take over the therapist's point of view, at least on an experimental basis. As he continues to engage in the therapeutic process, corrective emotional experiences can occur and internalized changes can be built on them.

The therapist contributes to this part of the therapeutic process by confronting the patient with the distorted and self-defeating character of his attitudes and behavior, by offering interpretations, and in other ways encouraging the patient's examination of himself. There is another important contribution, however, that the therapist makes to this part of the therapeutic process: he is frequently the *object* of a corrective emotional experience. One of the major sources of emotional experiences in therapy is the patient's relationship to the therapist. In the context of this relationship, the patient can feel anger, dependency, anxiety about loss of love, sexual attraction, and a whole host of other emotional reactions. Feelings toward the therapist are the most likely to be experienced at their full intensity because they are immediate and directly related to the present ongoing situation. Thus, these feelings are most likely to form the basis of corrective emotional experiences. Essentially, then, the therapist serves as *transference object*, if we use this term more broadly than in its strictly psychoanalytic meaning. In part, it can be assumed that the patient transfers to the therapist attitudes and feelings that are irrelevant to the present situation, that are merely repetitions of patterns based on childhood relationships or of patterns carried over from the patient's present interpersonal relationships outside of the therapy situation. In part, the patient's attitudes and feelings toward the therapist may represent direct reactions to the therapist as a person or to the role that he enacts. Even though the therapist tries to be neutral, he does reveal his personality and attitudes in some ways, and these may stimulate some of the patient's characteristic patterns. Moreover, neutrality as such is also a definite role which can elicit some of the patient's interpersonal reactions. For example, the patient may interpret the therapist's neutrality as lack of interest and lack of concern for him, and he may proceed to manifest his characteristic patterns for situations thus interpreted. Regardless of whether the patient's emotional reactions to the therapist are based "purely" on transference or whether they are based on the patient's interpretation of the realities of the situation, they reveal some of the patient's characteristic patterns of interpersonal behavior at a realistic level of emotional intensity and thus provide current material for corrective experiences.

In group therapy, the group has a special contribution to make to this part of the therapeutic process. The group situation provides many possibilities for stimulating the patient's habitual interpersonal reactions, which can then be examined and form the basis for corrective emotional experiences (cf. Frank and Ascher, 1951; Beck, 1958). The great advantage of the group over the individual therapist in this regard is that it makes available a wide range of *interaction objects* to the patient, thus increasing the chances that the attiudes and patterns that trouble him in real life will come into play during the therapy hour. In individual therapy the possibilities are limited. The therapist is only one person, and moreover a person who enacts a very special and unusual role, marked as it is by affective neutrality (Beck, 1958). This does not mean that he fails to arouse emotional reactions, particularly since the opportunity for transference is ever-present, but in the group the opportunities are much more extensive. For one thing, there may be a wide range of social statuses represented: members are likely to vary in sex, age, social class, education, occupation, family position, etc. Thus, there are more opportunities for the patient's unrealistic and inappropriate attitudes to be stimulated in the therapy situation. For example, if a patient has problems in his relations with women, or with authority figures, or with peers, it is likely that these will manifest themselves as he interacts with the group members who represent these statuses. Moreover, the group is likely to represent a range of personality styles, interpersonal patterns of behavior, and general attitudes. Thus, again, it offers many opportunities for stimulating the patient's characteristic reactions. If, for example, his neurotic attitudes are most likely to be aroused when he deals with people who are more aggressive than he is, or more confident than he is, etc., chances are that the group will make such interactions available.

A third reason why there is likely to be more stimulation of habitual patterns in the group situation is that it brings into play a wider range of current issues that generate emotions at a real-life level of intensity. The patient is involved in a real group situation, even though this is an atypical group. This situation, like other group situations, is marked by competition for the leader's attention, struggles for power and status within the group, attempts at saving face and making a good impression, requests for help and offers of help, and so on (cf. Varon, 1953). This range of interpersonal issues with which the group members are constantly concerned is likely to stimulate the patient's characteristic attitudes and behavior patterns at a high level of intensity and make them available for examination. The stimulation provided by the here-and-now issues of group interaction is further enhanced by the fact that these bring into play a variety of informal roles and interpersonal patterns, distributed over the members of the group. This happens partly because these situations elicit characteristic behavior patterns that patients bring to their interpersonal relationships (cf. Frank *et al.*, 1952), and partly because the inherent dynamics of group functioning make some degree of role differentiation necessary. Thus, as any given patient deals with the real and current interpersonal issues activated by the group situation, he is confronted with a range of role behaviors on the part of other group members that can serve to instigate, complement, and reciprocate his own reactions.

In sum, one of the major advantages of group therapy is that it provides numerous opportunities for eliciting affect-laden reactions on which corrective emotional experiences can be based. The group accomplishes this by generating significant current issues around which interactions can occur, and by offering each patient a wide range of interaction objects—varying in social status, characteristic interpersonal behavior, and informal group role—capable of bringing out his habitual attitudes and behavior patterns. Thus, the patient's reactions to a wide variety of interpersonal stimuli become directly available for examination at the very moment that they are occurring. The range of possibilities is further extended by the fact that the patient can have some vicarious corrective emotional experiences by observing the behavior of others and its interpretations and applying these to his own case. While this is clearly not at the same level of emotional intensity as a corrective experience in which he himself is the main actor, his identification with the other patient may give the experience an emotional impact. Such experiences may be useful forerunners to more direct corrective experiences for which the patient may not yet be ready. In the group situation there is, thus, a ready-made mechanism for graduating the intensity of the experience. Furthermore, corrective emotional experiences in a group situation typically involve supporting actors in addition to the main one. While one patient's reactions may be the focus in a given situation, the examination of his reactions may also reveal how others have elicited it and contributed to it. Patient B may thus learn something from patient A's corrective experiences, particularly about his own stimulus value and the effect he has on others.

This leads us to another special contribution that the group can make to the analysis of corrective emotional experiences. When the patient manifests a troublesome interpersonal attitude or behavior pattern, he can be confronted not only with the distorted and self-defeating character of the behavior itself but also with the reactions it elicits in others. In individual therapy, such confrontation is limited. The therapist does not react spontaneously, but tends to remain neutral. He can only inform the patient of the kind of reaction this behavior is likely to elicit in others. In group therapy, the reactions of others are present here and now. They are produced spontaneously by fellow-patients, can be observed directly by the patient and the therapist, and thus constitute part of the experience available for analysis. The other patients can also confirm and support the therapist's interpretations by describing their own reactions to the patient's maneuvers. The patient is thus able to obtain a fuller and more dramatic picture of the nature and meaning of his behavior, since he is immediately confronted with the impact it has on others. For example, he can be shown convincingly that the way he reacts to an offer of help is calculated to alienate others at a time when he most needs them. Similarly, his distorted perceptions of others can be examined effectively since these others are personally present. For instance, he may act on the assumption that others will disdain him if he reveals too much dependency; this expectation can be refuted by the way others in fact react to him and by the way they describe their own reactions in subsequent examination of the relevant event.

The fact that, in group therapy, the reactions of others are included in the corrective emotional experience not only provides a fuller picture of the patient's characteristic behavior for analysis but also increases the similarity between the event in the therapy hour and the real-life situations in which the patient experiences difficulty. The patient's ability to build on this experience, to relate it to his daily life, to find examples that fit what he has just learned, and to note how his interpersonal behavior in daily life prevents maximization of his values is therefore increased. The process thus initiated may lead to internalized changes in the patient's conceptions of himself and of interpersonal relations that go beyond the therapy situation.

The group's ability to stimulate and enhance the realism of corrective emotional experiences depends, in large part, on the heterogeneity of its composition. The opportunities for such experiences will increase if the members of the group represent a range of social statuses and personality types, thus providing a variety of potential interpersonal stimuli. At the same time, however, there must be enough homogeneity in the group so that it can constitute a reasonably representative social unit. If the cultural backgrounds of the members are extremely varied, it is less likely that complementary patterns will mesh and characteristic reactions will be elicited. Similarly, the reactions of others who are clearly from a different milieu do not have as much of an impact on a patient who is confronted with them. In short, then, from the point of view of maximizing opportunities for corrective emotional experiences, there should be as much heterogeneity as possible, within the limits of the range of people with whom the patient is likely to interact in his daily life. Of course, other considerations have to enter into the determination of group composition. From the point of view of increasing the patient's commitment to the therapy situation, as discussed above, a certain degree of homogeneity is necessary: the patient must see the other group members as similar to himself and sharing some of his problems. Here too, however, complete homogeneity is neither necessary nor desirable. Optimally, there should be a communality of fate in some important respects but differences in personality, background, and so on.

These requirements can generally be met by including in the same group patients with a variety of neurotic symptoms. Even in those cases, however, in which it is considered desirable to maintain homogeneity of symptoms because of the special nature of the problems engendered by these symptoms, e.g., in groups of alcoholics, it would be best to aim for heterogeneity in all respects other than the defining symptom.

The group therapist's responsibility with respect to this part of the therapeutic process is to serve, as it were, as the director of the corrective emotional dramas that the patients act out. He must be alert to the interactions between the patients in order to guide them and use them as bases for corrective experiences. In this connection, it is important for the therapist to be sensitive to the dynamics of the group process itself, so that he will be aware of some of the immediate forces that determine the patients' behavior and the here-and-now issues with which they are concerned. Group therapists do not always take into account the character of the group as an actual functioning unit in which meaningful interactions are going on. Yet, these interactions offer some of the best opportunities for insight-producing confrontations.

Influence Directed to Behavior
Outside of the Therapy Situation

Changes produced within the therapy situation certainly have an important bearing on the patient's behavior outside. Thus, changes resulting from corrective emotional experiences, insofar as they are internalized changes, should, by their very nature, be generalized to the patient's interpersonal relationships in daily life. Similarly, some of the changes produced by identification with the therapist or the group may go beyond the therapy situation: they may enhance the patient's self-esteem and faith sufficiently to help him through a critical period, at which point his normal coping mechanisms can again come into play. In the course of the therapy situation itself, however, there are also *direct* attempts at exerting influence on the patient's behavior outside of therapy. Here again, all three processes of influence may be involved. This part of the argument is summarized in Table III. I am proposing that three types of extra-therapy behavior must be induced in the patient during therapy in order to facilitate therapeutic change, and that these correspond, in the main, to the three processes of influence.

Experimentation with New Actions

Generalization of therapeutic learnings to the patient's real-life situations requires, first of all, that he experiment with new behaviors. Only as he tries to change his actions in interpersonal situations can he become fully aware of the unrealistic nature of his earlier attitudes and gain the necessary confidence to reorient his characteristic patterns. Such experimentation, of course, continues to take place after the patient has terminated therapy, but it is important that it begin while therapy is still in progress. At that point, the patient's experimentation can be based on therapeutic experiences that are still fresh in his mind; it can be brought back to the therapy situation for further review; and it can be carried out under conditions of greater protection, i.e., with the support of the

TABLE III

TYPES OF INFLUENCE INVOLVED IN THE PRODUCTION OF
THERAPEUTIC CHANGE

B. Processes of Influence Directed to the Patient's Behavior
Outside of the Therapy Situation

	Type of Patient Behavior Induced by This Process	Therapist's Role in the Induction of This Behavior	Group's Role in the Induction of This Behavior
Compliance	Experimentation with new actions	Imaginary interlocutor	Anticipated audience
Identification	Adoption of the therapist's and/or group's standpoint for viewing the self and interpersonal relations	Role model; norm setter	Normative reference group
Internalization	Generalization of therapeutic insights to specific real-life situations	Auxiliary reality tester	Representatives of society

therapist and the group and the assurance that the patient can always turn to them in the event of failure.

Typically, experimentation with new behavior develops out of corrective emotional experiences and represents attempts to generalize new insights to specific real-life situations (see "Generalization of Therapeutic Insights to Specific Real-Life Situations," below). Such experimentation, however, usually does and should begin earlier in the course of therapy. It is sometimes possible to induce a small but significant change in the patient's interpersonal behavior simply by pointing out to him that other actions are possible and socially acceptable and encouraging him to try them. Such changes can occur with very little prior insight, but they can become an important source of subsequent insight: after having tried out the new behavior, the patient will be in a better position to examine the causes for his earlier difficulties and the possibilities for overcoming them. Moreover, such experimentation, if successful, may increase the patient's self-esteem and commitment to the therapy situation as a potentially useful experience. For these reasons, there is therapeutic value in inducing the patient to experiment with new behaviors outside—on a limited, graduated basis—even during the early stages of therapy. At that time, the induction leans heavily on the side of compliance.

What typically happens is that the patient reviews some of his interpersonal relationships and reveals their troublesome character. As he does so, he may be confronted with explicit or implicit suggestions to change his approach in some of the specific situations that he describes. For example, if he discusses the fact that his mother-in-law constantly criticizes him and he always gets upset by these experiences, he may be told: "Next time your mother-in-law criticizes you, why don't you try to stand up to her?" Or, more likely, the encouragement to try out new behavior will be implicit. For example: "It is interesting that you never stand up to your mother-in-law when she nags at you." Along with these suggestions, the expectation is communicated (again, usually implicitly) that carrying out the suggested experimentation will produce approval by the therapist or the group, and failure to do so, disapproval. Often, the patient will react to this kind of suggestion by committing himself to trying out a new approach. When that happens, he can expect further disapproval for failure to carry out his commitment. The patient's concern with approval and disapproval may, thus, motivate him in part to carry out the suggested behaviors.

The therapist's role in this part of the therapeutic process is that of an *imaginary interlocutor*. When the patient finds himself in real-life interpersonal situations that he has discussed in a therapy session, the therapist tends to be represented as a third party with whom he engages in imaginary conversation. The knowledge that he will have to report his behavior in the next session increases the likelihood that he will live up to the therapist's expectations and to his own commitment to try out new actions. Even when a particular situation has not been specifically discussed with the therapist, the patient's behavior is likely to be influenced by the anticipated reaction of the therapist to the subsequent report of this behavior. A patient may spontaneously experiment with new behavior because (on the basis of earlier statements and reactions by the therapist) he expects the therapist to approve it. Similarly, a patient may refrain from engaging in certain behaviors that he knows or thinks are disapproved by the therapist, because he would rather not be in a position of having to report them. Thus, the requirement of reporting to the therapist everything that happens in the patient's life extends the range of the therapist's surveillance and his training function to events outside of the therapy situation proper.

The group's role with respect to this part of the therapeutic process serves to reinforce that of the therapist. Just as the group can use its sanctioning function to induce conformity within the therapy situation, it can extend this function, to some degree, to extra-therapy behavior. The group represents, in essence, an *anticipated audience* to whom the patient must report on his behavior outside of therapy. Experimental research by Zimmerman and Bauer (1956) has shown that the way in which people organize and remember experiences is partly determined by the groups to whom they expect to report on these experiences. It seems reasonable to propose, in line with their theoretical notions, that the groups to whom the individual expects to report on his experiences will also influence the very experiences he allows himself to have. In other words, there will at least be some tendency to tailor his experiences so that their report will meet with the approval of the anticipated audience. This mechanism is likely to be operative in group therapy, and thus to increase the likelihood that the patient will experiment with new behaviors that the group has encouraged him to try or that he has reason to believe will meet with the group's approbation. The group's ability to influence the patient in this direction should depend on the very same factors that determine its ability to influence the patient's engagement in the therapeutic work within the therapy situation. There is also the possibility of antitherapeutic effects if the group reinforces defensive ways of handling the patient's real-life difficulties.

To the extent that the patient's changes in his behavior outside of therapy are tied strictly to the approval of the therapist or the group, their effect will be limited. They will tend to persist only as long as direct surveillance by the therapist or the group continues. The expectation, of course, is that this experimentation with new behavior will facilitate and be tied in with subsequent insights.

Adoption of the Therapist's and/or Group's Standpoint

In the course of therapy, the patient is induced not only to experiment with new behaviors in real life but also to adopt a new frame of reference for viewing his own behavior and his relations with others. Thus, for example, he may accept the assumption that much of his interpersonal behavior is defensive in nature; or that his difficulties originate in his own attitudes rather than in an unfriendly environment; or that he is ineffective because he is caught up in neurotic interactions, not because he has a weak character. As he reacts to various baffling situations in his daily life, which previously he had been unable to understand, he can now bring this new point of view to bear on them. He is now able to see some of his problematic interpersonal patterns in a new light and to formulate them in a new language. Essentially, he has learned a new conceptual scheme or a new ideological system from which he derives hypotheses that he can apply to his behavior outside of therapy. The adoption of some new frame of reference of this sort is essential if the patient is to have corrective emotional experiences in therapy and to carry over the insights derived from these experiences to his real-life situations. The therapeutically induced viewpoint helps to shake loose his original, and generally unproductive, way of looking at things and makes him aware of new possibilities. Moreover, it provides him with a language in terms of which he can account for what is happening and formulate new insights. It also provides a vehicle for bringing real-life experiences back to the therapeutic hour, where their interpretation can be further discussed and refined. Adoption of this frame of reference, then, is not a therapeutic end in its own right, but it represents an important conceptual tool for developing and communicating about new insights.

Typically, this new frame of reference is originally adopted through the process of identification with the therapist. I have already discussed the bases for identification with the therapist and the way in which such identification produces commitment to the therapy situation, i.e., a taking over of the therapist's attitudes toward the situation. For similar reasons and in a similar manner, the patient gradually tends to adopt the therapist's standpoint in viewing himself and his interpersonal relationships. He takes over the therapist's attitudes, including the therapist's attitudes toward the patient himself, as his own. He thus comes to formulate and judge his own behavior and the behavior of others with whom he interacts in the terms that the therapist would use.

The therapist's obvious function with respect to this part of the therapeutic process is that of a *norm setter:* he communicates the normative expectations that the patient would have to meet (outside of the therapy situation, not only within it), if the patient-therapist relationship is to be maintained. These normative expectations include the adoption, at least on a trial basis, of the therapist's ideological viewpoint. There is, however, a perhaps even more important function that the therapist performs with respect to this part of the process, namely, that of a *role model.* Typically, the therapist is attractive to the patient not simply as a partner in a reciprocal role relationship but also as an object for emulation, since he so clearly possesses all the attributes that the patient himself lacks: recognized status, knowledge about human behavior, control over the current situation, apparent mental health. The patient is motivated to become like the therapist and, in the process, to adopt the therapist's language, attitudes, and values, particularly as they relate to matters of immediate concern. Thus, he takes over the therapist's role and looks at himself and others from its vantage point. In group therapy, of course, there is a ready-made arena where this identification with the therapist can play itself out: the patients can take on the therapist's role vis-à-vis each other, and in fact they are often helpful to each other in doing so.

Ideally, the adoption of the therapist's standpoint through identification with him represents only a transitional stage in therapy. It is therapeutically very important because the patient must find some new way of looking at things and must have some framework that he can apply to specific situations and in terms of which he can formulate specific new insights. Taking over the therapist's framework represents the only economical solution to this problem during the early stages of therapy. As therapy proceeds, however, and the patient manages to loosen his habitual ways of looking at things and to acquire new insights, he should no longer be dependent on the therapist as an ideological fountainhead. He should be able, at that point, to become more selective with respect to the therapist's standpoint, to accept it not as a total system but as a source of useful hypotheses. He would then modify the therapist's standpoint to suit his own value system; he would accept parts of it and reject others in the light of his own experiences and his attempts to maximize his own values.

Thus, the challenge confronting the therapist is to induce an identification that contains the seeds of its own dissolution. It seems to me that such an outcome is most probable if the emphasis is on encouraging the patient to adopt a certain *process* of looking at himself and the world, rather than a certain set of specific formulations. What should ideally remain from the patient's identification with the therapist is the process of self-examination, based originally on emulation of the therapist—a process that involves splitting his ego and observing his own behavior from the outside, the way the therapist would observe it. Adoption of the therapist's standpoint in that sense would enable the patient to carry on the therapeutic process outside of therapy, even after therapy has been terminated, and would mediate internalized changes as the patient examines his own behavior in specific real-life situations.

It is, of course, possible for the therapeutic relationship to become fixated at the level of identification. The patient may adopt the therapist's values as his own and build a whole philosophy of life on the therapist's standpoint (or at least on his interpretation of the therapist's standpoint). Thus, for example, he may take over psychoanalysis as a total ideology, a way of life, a cause. There are some striking similarities between this type of ideological conversion and some of the effects observed in the "brainwashing" situation where the adoption of "the people's standpoint" and of Marxist ideology are induced (cf. Lifton, 1956; Frank, 1959). Needless to say, there are vast differences in the goals and procedures of the two situations, and ideological conversion in therapy stems largely from the needs of the patient rather than the wishes of the therapist. Nevertheless, therapists can profit from studying the conditions under which brainwashing occurs and seeing in what parallel ways they may inadvertently be structuring the therapeutic situation so as to make ideological conversion a likely outcome. Generally, the changes produced under these circumstances will persist as long as the patient is able to maintain, in some way, the relationship to the therapist or some substitute for it: the patient may remain in therapy for a long time, or return to it repeatedly; or he may build a substitute into his daily life, for example, by establishing active ties with the mental health movement. As long as these relationships persist, they may lend stability to the patient's self-concept and represent a meaningful, if limited, form of improvement.

The group can contribute to this aspect of the therapeutic process by incorporating the therapist's standpoint—the new frame of reference for seeing one's self and one's interpersonal relationships, induced by the therapist—into its normative structure. To the extent that the patient uses the therapy group as a relevant *"normative" reference group,* he will be motivated to live up to its expectations, not only within the therapy situation but also outside of it, and, accordingly, to adopt the standpoint that the group supports. The likelihood that the patient will identify with the therapy group and that it will serve as an imporant reference group for him is quite high in view of the group's special contribution to his attainment of a more favorable self-definition, as discussed above. The more cohesive a group becomes, the more likely the patient is to adhere to its norms even in the absence of direct surveillance.

The primary value of the group in the present context, then, is that it can use its considerable power in support of the adoption of the therapist's standpoint. This support may make a great deal of difference, since the therapist's standpoint tends to fly in the face of the conventional norms prevalent in the patient's own social milieu (cf. Beck, 1958); despite strong identification with the therapist, the patient is usually subject to normative pressures to reject his deviant ideology. Under these circumstances, the availability of a reference group that supports and prescribes these norms, even though it is an atypical group as far as society at large is concerned, reduces the conflict engendered by the therapist's standpoint and provides the consensual validation necessary for its adoption. The assumption in all of this is, of course, that the group will develop norms in support of the therapist's standpoint rather than in opposition to it. The latter possibility cannot be completely dismissed, although it is not a likely development. While group members may occasionally support each other in their resistance to the therapist's influence (cf. Bennis, 1961), the group is not likely to develop this resistance into a definite, normatively prescribed standpoint that opposes the therapist's standpoint. A therapy group of neurotic patients typically lacks the independent power to accomplish this. To induce a particular standpoint, the group would have to be cohesive, but, as Frank (1957, p. 61) points out, the therapy group "can develop cohesiveness only by incorporating the standards of the therapist." Nevertheless, it must be kept in mind that lack of support from the group (even in the absence of a normatively structured opposition) can reduce the therapist's effectiveness. The therapist must, therefore, encourage the group to incorporate his standpoint into its normative structure.

Generalization of Therapeutic
Insights to Specific Real-Life Situations

The ultimate goal of psychotherapy is achieved when the patient generalizes therapeutic insights to specific situations in his daily life. He addresses himself to interpersonal situations in which he has problems, situations in which he is in-effective, self-defeating, and uncomfortable. He examines these situations from the point of view of his own contributions to them, the attitudes and expectations that he brings to them, the elements of distortion and unrealism with which he approaches them, and the kind of interaction patterns in which he typically becomes involved. In this examination, the patient applies the insights he derived from corrective emotional experiences in the therapy situation to the real-life situation with which he is now confronted.

The significance of this part of the process lies in the fact that insights are applied to *specific* situations. That is, the patient does not merely adopt some general formulation about himself and interpersonal relationships which he then carries with him into his real-life situations (which is the part of the process discussed in the preceding section). Rather, he goes a step beyond that and in-volves himself in a more active and idiosyncratic process, not just taking over and expounding an explanatory system and a language but deliberately applying them in a concrete and unique situation. If this application is to be meaningful, it must be based not merely on the general formulations that the patient has learned but on the specific personal insights that he has had in the course of his therapeutic experiences. Moreover, it must involve a consideration of the special character-istics of the life situation to which the insights are generalized. If the process takes this form, then it represents a continued testing and evaluation of the therapeutic learnings as they are applied to real-life experiences, and probably some modification in them in the light of new data. Any changes produced by this process are likely to be at the level of internalization: they should be inde-pendent of the patient's relationship to the therapist and integrated with his own value system.

As has already been mentioned, this is the type of process that should go on after therapy has been terminated; adoption of the process of self-examination is perhaps the most valuable carry-over from therapy to the patient's subsequent daily life. This process, however, begins while the patient is still in therapy. Typically, a corrective emotional experience within the therapy situation itself is followed by an attempt to apply the insights derived from this experience to some of the patient's troublesome relationships outside of therapy. That is, the patient is encouraged to examine some of his real-life relationships in the light of the new insight so that he can gain a better leverage on them. Experimentation with new behavior is often tied to this process. Thus, following a corrective emotional experience, the patient would be encouraged to generalize the insights derived from it to real-life situations and to plan new behavior accordingly. In subsequent therapy sessions, the patient's attempts to apply the new insights and to experi-ment with new behaviors can be brought back for further review. The generaliza-tion of therapeutic insights can be facilitated in the therapy situation itself by reviewing, particularly in the aftermath of a corrective emotional experience, both the patient's current behavior outside of therapy and his attempts at changing his behavior.

The therapist contributes to this part of the therapeutic process by taking the role of an *auxiliary reality tester*. As the patient examines his current behavior outside of therapy, the therapist can help him reality-test by calling attention to the points at which his perceptions and expectations of others are likely to be distorted and by making him aware of the reactions that his behavior is likely to generate in the people with whom he interacts. When the patient plans new behavior outside of therapy, in the light of his new insights, the therapist again can help him reality-test by anticipating the kinds of reactions that his behavior is likely to produce in others. Similarly, when the patient brings back to the therapy session reviews of his attempts at trying out new behavior patterns, the therapist can help in the interpretation of the effects that this behavior produced in others and in the explanation of the reasons for these effects. The therapist's usefulness as an auxiliary reality tester is based on his role of an objective outside observer who is generally wise, knowledgeable about human relations, and familiar with social reality and the prevailing cultural norms. Nevertheless, the therapist's contribution to this part of the process is limited. He can only speak about social reality, indirectly, on the basis of the patient's reports and of his own estimation of the social situations to which these reports refer.

In group therapy, the group is in a unique position to make a special contribution to this aspect of the therapeutic process. The group "is more like society in miniature" (Frank and Ascher, 1951, p. 127). It can facilitate reality testing by bringing society, to a certain extent, directly into the therapy situation. Despite the fact that the group members are in some sense social deviates themselves, they are, in general, sufficiently close to the cultural norms to serve as adequate *representatives of society.* Thus, as the patient examines his current behavior outside of therapy, he can reality-test his interpretations immediately and directly by turning to his fellow-patients. They can inform him about their probable attitudes and reactions if they had been his partners in the situations about which he is reporting. To the extent that they come from a similar milieu and represent a wide range of social roles within it, they should be able to give him a reasonably accurate picture of the social reality that he faces. In fact, they are more likely to give him an accurate picture than he would obtain in real-life situations, since the therapy group operates in terms of the norm of honestly stating what is on one's mind.

When the patient entertains the possibility of trying out new behavior in the light of his new insights, the group can again be very useful by helping him anticipate the reactions that this behavior is likely to produce in the real world. As representatives of society, they can remind him of the social expectations that circumscribe this behavior; they can point out the unrealistic features of his expectations; and they can inform him whether he underestimates or overestimates the negative effects that the planned actions are likely to produce. The group situation provides the patient with the opportunity to engage in an anticipatory practice session, a dry run of the behavior that he will try out in real life. This allows him to reality-test the new behavior under conditions that are both realistic and protective: failure in this situation is not as devastating as it would be outside, since in the therapy group the patient does not "play for real" and he knows that he is in a supportive environment.

Finally, when the patient brings back to the group reports of his experimentation for subsequent examination, he can again benefit from the group's reaction. In the group situation, there is the opportunity for a fairly realistic re-enactment of the real-life experience that the patient has reported. The other group members can indicate directly how they would have reacted if they had been the other participants in the interaction. As a result, the patient can gain a fuller understanding of the adequacy of his expectations and of the social effects of his new behavior. He can see more clearly and dramatically where he has succeeded and where he has failed.

Conclusion

An analysis of the influence processes involved in group therapy has been presented, and their role in the production of therapeutically relevant changes in the patient's behavior, both within the therapy situation and outside of it, has been described. The analysis was based on a theoretical framework for the study of social influence in general, which was applied here to the special circumstances of the therapy situation. My assumption throughout was that, even in group therapy, the therapist is and must be the primary influencing agent. I tried to point out, however, that there are a variety of very important, unique, and powerful contributions that the group can make to the production of therapeutic change. At the same time, one must remain aware of the possibility that, under certain circumstances, the group may impede or weaken the therapeutic process. It is up to the therapist to make sure that the potentials for therapeutic change that are inherent in the group are maximized and that its possible antitherapeutic effects are minimized. Moreover, the influence processes that characterize the group situation and the varying potentialities of the group have to be taken into account deliberately in the composition of the group and in the decision, for any given individual, as to whether group therapy is the indicated form of treatment.

The kind of systematic analysis that I have offered here may seem arbitrary in that it makes sharp distinctions between changes inside and outside the therapy situation and between different stages and the influence processes that are relevant to them. Needless to say, I do not assume that these neat separations are possible in the actual situation. They are made only for analytic purposes. I hope that they will prove useful by yielding certain implications for the practice of group therapy. It seems to me that this kind of approach may (1) point to some of the features of the group therapy situation that have to be manipulated in order to strengthen its potential for change; (2) help to locate those features that have potentially antitherapeutic effects; and (3) help to provide some criteria both for the selection of patients who can benefit from this experience and for the composition of therapy groups so as to maximize their ability to produce therapeutic changes.

30 / Psychoanalysis and Group Therapy: A Developmental Point of View

Fritz Redl

In a nutshell, it seems to me that the following four phenomena constitute the "facts of group life" that emerge clearly in therapy groups but that our present model of personality is not flexible enough to explain: first, the phenomenon of "contagion and shock effect"; second, the power of "group-psychological role suction"; third, the tax-imposition and tax-exemption powers of group structure and group code; and fourth, the action-threshold impact of spatial designs and of things.

It will not be easy to present enough of a description of what I refer to as "group-psychological facts" to convince you that I am not talking about what we already know anyway, that the phenomena I have in mind really contain some core as yet hard to explain. It fills me with horror that my short and colorful illustrations may be interpreted as if they were meant to be adequate evidence for what I am trying to prove. So let me make sure it is understood that what I say from here on in only illustrates a special angle I am trying to convey. I think I have some proof for it, but I cannot, of course, unpack anything as complex as "evidence" in the few pages that remain.

The Phenomena of Contagion and Shock Effect

This concept poses the following challenge to our psychoanalytic theory: Freud rightly opposed Le Bon's explanation of some group phenomena on the basis of his concept of "imitation" and showed, as we all know, how much more complex what looks like simple imitation really is, when viewed in the light of such concepts as identification. On the other hand, Freud directed his remarks primarily at "imitation" events as they were expected to occur in specific types of leader-related group. He left untouched a wide range of group situations we have since run into. I too am well aware that much "imitative" behavior in groups follows exactly Freud's formula. Yet under certain circumstances, one individual may "pick up" behavioral cues from other individuals in the group in a situation lacking any of the conditions Freud postulates—when there is neither libidinous nor any other type of dependency of the acting individual on the one whose behavior he seems to "imitate" and when nevertheless the impact of this other individual seems "coercive" to the "actor" in question. This goes beyond what we can easily explain.

EXAMPLE   In a mess hall in a camp for deliquency-prone children, a boring performance on the violin is being given by an otherwise group-acceptable staff member. Most of the "tougher kids" try hard to remain still because they want to play fair with the guy who is playing the fiddle way over the heads of everybody. Suddenly, a little kid—the low man on the totem pole, with obviously no status in anybody's book—can't take it any longer. Out of the sheer desperation of his boredom he climbs up the fireplace bricks and swings head down from the rafters above. Two minutes later half the crowd is up there too. How did he do it? I don't mean scaling the wall; I mean the incredible feat of an otherwise powerless individual to sway the whole group into behavior its members really tried hard to avoid.

EXAMPLE   In an early session of a relatively new therapy group, most group members are resisting the therapist's frantic attempts to "pull them in" and are reacting to everything that is said with nearly tangible emanations of a deeply hostile silence. Suddenly one group member—and, in this case again, one without any traceable sign of status or role in the group—"warms up" naïvely, without being aware of the chance he really takes, and starts to talk and to react cooperatively to the therapist's attempts at discussion. All of a sudden the "ice" seems to be broken, and the whole group is coming through with the goods. What gave this person the power to force them to drop their resistance and "do as he did"? What made it possible for the others to drop their resistance just because they saw somebody else act that way?

EXAMPLE   A therapy group of adults is well under way, and a pretty good over-all atmosphere has developed by now. The group has been well at work on whatever the theme of its major discussion happens to be. Suddenly, one group member, through undeniable evidence of her deep-seated resistance and defense against anything the group or the therapist may be doing, spreads such an aura of "hostile silence" around that everybody else dries up in the process. What is the source of the power of that person to reinforce the otherwise well-relating group members' defenses and resistances by merely oozing hostility and defense? She is not admired or loved; she has no other status or power weapons at her disposal. Why should the other group members freeze up just because of the hostility from that one unimportant corner of the room?

The phenomenon of "shock effect" is equally hard to explain. In this specific instance, I mean by it the impact of one member of a group that forces new intensities of defense on another group member against the very impulsivity he allows himself to indulge in.

EXAMPLE   The setting is a cabin of primarily delinquency-oriented thieves. Grouped with them by mistake is a child with a long history of stealing which was more on a neurotic basis and which this child, as a result of previous therapy, had already tried hard to conquer in himself. Is the delinquency of the rest going to make him steal again? Guaranteedly not. However, the contrary pathology is going to emerge: Our youngster will be severely threatened, his only partially overcome internal conflict will be revived, and he will have to produce a double dose of "reaction formation" against his previous symptom trend. He will become a goody-goody or tattler, or he will be so plagued by newly evoked neurotic symptoms like anxiety, sleep disturbances, and whatnot that his stay in the group will be inadvisable. How is it that the overtly visible behavior of the other kids, whom our youngster neither loved nor liked nor selected as "identification objects," could throw him into such an internal revival of his conflict, and that the mere visualization of their behavior started all this off in him?

In short, under certain conditions the very visualization of behavior by others is enough to start off either a chain of the same behavior or a heavy load of "defenses against it" in the individual who perceives it—all without the specific libidinous and identification-related processes we usually assume.

QUESTION. How is it that others can have such influence on behavioral production in a child, and, even worse, how does that child perceive the precise basis for the behavior of the others?

The Power of "Group-Psychological Role Suction"

Here I limit the term "role" to those situations in which certain performances basic to the need gratifications of a group are demanded by someone in it. Please let me get away with this heuristic oversimplification of the role concept, for it is all too obvious that any fertile discussion of a concept as involved as that of group roles cannot be attempted now.

Most teachers with some experience have observed that sometimes the nicest kids, who are quite friendly and pleasant in individual interaction, become a pain in the neck when they hit the group. They may turn into clowns, little rebels, rabble-rousers, or the ones who "tattle" on others' mischief. Sometimes a teacher remarks that, in this special group, an otherwise wild and unruly kid seems eager for chores and jobs, accumulating with glee before the teacher knows it all the janitorial chores classroom life has to give away. Or he may say that, whenever things get tight, you can "bet" on Johnny to come through with a good and appropriate joke that makes everybody laugh and relax or express his relief that Mary invariably yells "shut up" to the rest of the noisy crowd just a moment before he, the teacher, would have to do it. Group therapists, in recent years, have also produced ample evidence for the analogous trend among adults. Terms like "therapist's little helper," "group scapegoat, self-appointed," "isolate," "underdog," "defender of the underdog," "group admonisher," and "umpire" have recently entered the standard vocabulary of this field.

Most of this poses no special problem. In fact, psychoanalysts, more than most other people, find it easy to discover just why such individuals play such roles in groups. I have no quarrel with this. My only request is let's not stop there: It is not enough. Our usual explanation fits a large number of cases, but it does not hold true all along the line. We usually assume that the given individual has strong conscious or unconscious needs in that direction and has finally either forced them on this group or has used the group's inability to defend itself against him to allow himself behavior he otherwise might not have enough opportunity for.

Two facts seem to puncture this otherwise quite plausible explanation: First, some people do not use groups indiscriminately to live out their individual pathologies or personality needs. They seem to reserve some role acting for some groups only and do not show much of it in the rest of their lives. If that is so, I should like to know just what it is in that group that seems to bring out "the worst" or "the best" in them. Assuming the real cause is a basic need to act that way anyway, just what sets it off—or pushes it back—in specific group situations? Obviously, it must be a property of the group they are in, regardless of their own motivations. If so, what is it?

The second challenge is this: Although many a "clown" or "therapist's little helper" may be sufficiently explained on the basis of his personal pathology, I don't think this is true for all. Granted that nobody would do anything that he lacks the latent capacity to do, the push from within by no means always explains precisely what evokes the behavior. I think I have seen situations in which Johnny's need to tattle was among the least vehement forces in the child, when, in fact, it belonged to trends heavily opposed by his own superego. Only in certain group situations, for instance, when panicked by a too frightening lack of control within the group, would he assume the "tattler's role." Far from using the group to satisfy his tattling greed, he actually, with great disgust within himself, performed the salutary task for the sake of the group, for otherwise the group would soon have gone to pieces or things would have gotten out of hand. And not every kid who yells "shut up" when the group gets too noisy is a conceited egotist or a namby-pamby teacher's pet. Some really yell "shut up" just in time and in just the right way, because their own perceptions of group processes show them that the group is helpless, that some behavior has to be terminated, that nobody else seems ready to do it, so maybe they had better, for somebody must.

In all these cases—and I wouldn't care if you could convince me that they are few compared with the other type, for even one would be enough to get my theoretical visor up—it seems to me that something like "role suction" emanating from the dynamic events within the group itself is just as relevant in explaining behavior as is whatever we know about inner needs. If so, what is it, how can I nail it down, and what theoretical constructs do I need to explain the fact that the transition of a mild wish into open behavior can be influenced by something as "superficial" and intangible as a dimly perceived group need? A tracing, no matter how thorough, of the history of the youngster's individual readiness for such action certainly would not suffice.

The Tax-Imposition and Tax-Exemption Powers of Group Structure and Group Code

We know what a superego is made of and the source of its value content. We also know that, by the time kids reach their postlatency years or become adults, most of that process has long been under way, and the basic structure of the various individual superegos must be well established, on whatever level.

If any changes are to be made, we know they will require new libidinous relationships toward important "parent surrogate" figures in a person's life, which he will then ward off because of his fear of resexualization of the original wishes and so forth and that, on the basis of such renunciation of original drive wishes, he will incorporate ego ideals or superego content into his own superego. It takes all that to bring about a modification in superego content.

How does it happen, then, that under certain circumstances a group of youngsters suddenly lives way above or way below their usual level of operation? And I mean it does so without any of the basic, analytically assumed conditions but by the sheer force of situations that are difficult to assume to be powerful enough to account for all that.

EXAMPLE   Delinquent gang, moved into the camp setting and kept together. No need to describe what it takes to survive with them and to make them survive with one another and with the rest of the camp. Suddenly, somebody thinks of some especially well-advised "project," which happens to catch the fancy of the kids. For about a week, with no other personal changes having occurred in the individuals, this group abandons its collective warfare against society and operates on a high level of reliability and work orientation, and its members even develop temporary changes in their superego functions. Individuals feel guilty if they do anything that endangers their project; they feel ashamed if caught slacking behind the effort expected; they stop stealing, raiding, destroying—their normal side enterprises; they live as though they have changed. The termination of the project, of course, terminates this whole episode, and concomitant work with the individuals makes it clear that no lasting changes in their superegos have yet occurred. Yet what is the source of the power of the group atmosphere created by that specific project to influence their superegos even to the point of production of appropriate guilt feelings, and how is it that something like group organization around a program is able to produce such atmospheric changes to begin with?

EXAMPLE   A group of otherwise respectable adults, well oriented in their values, find themselves at a convention in a hotel in somebody else's town. How is it that a wide range of behavior suddenly becomes "tax exempt from guilt feelings" for the duration, while their individual superegos apparently emerge undamaged after their return home? How can solid agents like superegos and basic processes like appropriate guilt feelings be modified by changes as seemingly simple as geography and group-organizational pattern?

By the way, the very power of therapy groups to bring about some changes in individuals at times when their individual readiness for such changes is seriously in doubt has impressed us in many a case. Those of us with longer experience with many groups will also remember that we must keep in mind how many changes that turn up within the confines of a patient's group life may be limited to the very condition of his being immersed in the over-all value pattern of that specific group and that we must question whether we have a group-psychological process on our hands or a real personality change before we let him out as cured.

By the way, what constitutes a real change anyway, and, come to think of it, is some of this perhaps also at work when we predict what will happen when a patient leaves the two-person group of the individual therapy room?

The Action-Threshold Impact
of Spatial Designs and Things

This issue seems to be a new one, not faced either by psychoanalysis in general or by group therapy, although both have pointed to it with ample illustrations. After we have said all there is to say in our capacity of analytically oriented group therapists on the basis of such concepts as transference, countertransference, and libidinal cathexis, we are sometimes astounded by the incredible impact "simple facts" can have on the behavior of people in a group. We know now, for instance—as nursery-school teachers have always known—that occasionally the simple geography of a seating order may make or break a group session or may actually be a decisive factor in the formation of or failure to form a subgroup or in what shading the member-leader relationship will assume. We have also developed, without theoretical astonishment and sheerly for our survival as practitioners, a holy respect for issues as "superficial" as the size of the room in which we hold our sessions, the presence or absence of water faucets, the privacy or the heavy traffic of the terrain, or whether or not a recorder—although visibly unused —stands around on the table. Anyone who tries group therapy with body-restless adolescents or children will willingly add to this inventory a variety of "gadgets" that had better be left out, or else. That baseball bat, for instance, is okay when we take them out for a game, but, leave it around on the table or a chair while the group is supposed to sit down for a serious discussion of an incident its members are all really eager for, and you know what will happen in spite of their "readiness" for the discussion.

In short, it seems that a variety of properties of space, timing, and equipment or anything that can be used as a prop for anything else has a latent power over the behavior of people, which our psychoanalytic theory does not seem to me to explain sufficiently. Only those who deal with the borderline cases of psychotics and delinquent "actor-outers" have, even in their individual therapy, conceded that power, although conceding it is a far cry from being able to explain it. All of us seem to have forgotten what Freud had to say in his initial insistence on the conditions for analytic therapy. If the emotional interaction between therapist and patient by means of words, thoughts, and emotions is the main current through which treatment takes place, why should such little issues as a prone or upright position, a couch versus a chair, an exit or an entrance or the sound-proofness of a room be deemed so important?

I think we were able to neglect all this for so long because we had learned how to control such factors efficiently in individual therapy with certain types of neurosis. In individual therapy with children, it was already harder, and, the moment we invited other patients into the room—individuals who might become live props for one another—the impact of spatial arrangements, gadgets, and props could no longer be ignored.

My question is how do we know just which spatial arrangements, time sequences, and physical properties of the therapy environment will assume such dramatic importance, and why? How can a silly thing like a baseball bat lying in the wrong place elicit open behavior that might otherwise have been fantasied but not acted out?

This, by the way, seems to me to be the crucial challenge to our over-all theoretical design: We have paid ample respect to the ego's role as a watchdog on the threshold between the conscious and the unconscious. I don't think we have studied thoroughly enough another function that certainly belongs in the description of a well-functioning ego, its power to decide which fantasy, emotion, urge, should remain just that and which should be allowed access to the muscular machinery and therefore find entrance into the realm of behavior that can be called "acted out."

31 / The Interpersonal Behavior of Children in Residential Treatment

Harold L. Raush / Allen T. Dittmann / Thaddeus J. Taylor

This report[1] is concerned with the interpersonal behavior of a small group of disturbed children and with changes in their behavior over a period of a year and a half in a residential treatment program. In general, the study was exploratory, oriented toward description and a search for order in complex behavioral events, toward the evaluation of behavioral change in treatment, and toward the evaluation of a method for observing and coding interpersonal behavior.

Toward Description

The source of data was spontaneous behavior as it appeared in the daily activities of six "hyperaggressive" or "acting-out" boys. To some extent, then, the paper presents a naturalistic study of the social behavior of a small group of children. Studies of small groups have mostly centered on the social interactions of adults in task-oriented situations (Bales, 1950; Hare, Borgatta and Bales, 1955), whereas interest in the social behavior of children has generally focused on specific variables in relation to more or less specific hypotheses (Baldwin, 1955). The work of Barker and Wright (1957) on the ecology of children's behavior in a small Midwestern town is an exception to the trend. The methods of the present study differ from those of Barker and Wright—a difference in part guided by doubts about the usefulness of a level of approach that is so strictly phenomenological. But there is a major shared value orientation: that it would be useful to have objective and manageable descriptions of the quality, frequency, and intensity of everyday behavior for all sorts of groups and for all sorts of situations. Such a statement is not an exhortation to random empiricism. Description is not necessarily atheoretical, and an interest in descriptive patterns of everyday behavior is not necessarily antithetical to the testing of hypotheses about specific variables. To some extent, there is, however, a question of order. Anthropologists, for example, have learned that one cannot legitimately interpret specific actions in isolation from other actions or in isolation from patterns within a culture, and they have learned how misleading isolated hypotheses may prove when contextual information is lacking. Adequate psychological descriptions of the everyday behavior of various subgroups, theoretically or pragmatically defined, would

Abridged from the *Journal of Abnormal and Social Psychology*, 1959, 58, 9–26. Copyright © 1959. Reprinted by permission of the authors and the American Psychological Association.

[1] Among the people, other than the authors, who have been involved in this study at one time or another, special note should be made of the contributions of Donald S. Boomer and D. Wells Goodrich. They were not only contributors to the observation and coding processes, but the procedures and methodology used here owe much to them. Fritz Redl, Chief of the Child Research Branch, and the Child Care Staff made the study possible by their cooperation.

constitute a step toward the formulation of specific hypotheses. Such descriptions would also constitute a step toward a general ethology of human behavior.

The group under study was small, and it was a rather special one in the sense that it was selected for a particular syndrome to which considerable social interest accrues in relation to delinquency and which is recognized as difficult to treat clinically. As a group, it was not task-oriented, nor had it come together through the common interests of its members. The environment was also a special one—even if only because psychiatric institutions are not typical of children's living arrangements. Because of the selection process, the children were rather homogeneous, and they lived together under the protection, supervision, and control of a professional staff in the rather homogeneous environment of the institution. The limitations of the present study are, however, perhaps not so much in the special characteristics of the subjects or of their environment, but rather in the lack of comparative data.

Toward Evaluation of Change

The second aim is toward the evaluation of treatment change, not as measured by ratings or by tests, but rather as manifested in the interactions of everyday life. It was, of course, expected that the children would show some improvement in their overt interpersonal relations. Findings of improvement would be consistent with clinical impressions about most of the children. But long-term clinical work has its hazards, one of which is that changes, if and when they occur, are often so gradual that an awareness of the similarities and contrasts between the then and the now is easily lost or distorted. A more formal method would exercise a discipline on both clinical wishes and clinical doubts, while perhaps also pointing to areas and problems which were less clinically obvious.

Clearly, the study is not definitive in relation to treatment of the "acting-out" child or in relation to any of the specific variables that enter into the residential treatment situation. Critical tests of treatment benefits can most relevantly be made outside the framework of a therapeutically focused environment; critical tests would involve variables in addition to those overt aspects of interpersonal behavior which are investigated here; and finally, critical tests would involve adequate controls. What can be fruitfully investigated is whether a group of children change systematically in their ordinary interactions. Given evidence of such changes, examination may be made of their relevance to treatment aims. From the viewpoint of therapeutic concerns, the possibilities of favorable modification in the behavior of a clinically difficult subgroup might be shown, and perhaps the clinical worker may be encouraged in his efforts.

Toward Evaluation of the Method

At the least, a method for evaluating interpersonal behavior and behavioral change was studied. The method involved multiple observations of children in naturalistic settings and the coding of these observations by a scheme which was originally devised for studying the group behavior of adults (Freedman et al., 1951; Leary, 1957). A partial proof of the method lies in its success or failure in demonstrating expected phenomena. That is, one aspect of the study is related to a question of construct validity (Cronbach and Meehl, 1955). To the extent that the approach achieves the differentiations that might reasonably be expected of it, the method offers promise for investigations of other groups in other environments.

Method

The Children and the Institution

The six boys were the total patient population of a hospital ward which they entered when they were from 8 to about 10 years old. There was—and still is— no diagnostic category into which they fit easily. In general, their pathology and their actions were beyond the realm of the typical childhood neuroses, yet at the same time they did not represent childhood psychoses. The behavior of the children was characterized by such overwhelming aggressiveness that they could not be tolerated by community, schools, foster parents, or parents. Four boys had been referred to courts for destructive behavior, and three of these had been sent to a reformatory shortly before their admission. The two children who had not come to the attention of the courts had been excluded from several schools because of their antisocial actions. There was usually a history of multiple contacts with social agencies, but outpatient clinical treatment and special school programs seemed to be of little use, at least in the long run, in these cases. None of the boys were "gang" delinquents. Their problems seemed rather a function of intense personality disturbances with a marked deficiency in ego controls, particularly where aggression was concerned. They were children such as Redl and Wineman (1957) have described, children often called hyperaggressive or "acting-out," although neither of these terms is ideal. All six were physically healthy, and so far as could be judged from psychological and psychiatric examinations, they were of normal intelligence and showed no evidence of gross brain damage. They came from socioeconomic milieux ranging from lower-lower through lower-middle class, with two children from lower-middle class homes and the rest lower in socioeconomic status.

Throughout the time of these investigations, the children lived on the ward. Their program was planned intensively and minutely. All were seen approximately four hours weekly in psychotherapy; their schooling, which took place adjacent to the ward, was with specially trained and experienced teachers and clinicians; ward programming and the handling of clinical problems of daily living were closely planned and organized, again by people with considerable experience with disturbed children. Most of all, considerable time and effort were devoted to the coordination and integration of the various levels of treatment. This brief description, though markedly oversimplified, is relevant for interpreting the results of the study.

The present report examines the interpersonal behavior of the children at two phases. When the initial series of observations was made, two of the children had been at the institution between three and four months, and the other four had been there nine or ten months. One may suppose, then, that they knew each other fairly well and that they were familiar with the general pattern of living within the ward. Their ages, at the start of the study, ranged from 8 years, 11 months, to

10 years, 11 months, with the median age at 10 years. The second series of observations was made some 18 months later.[2]

The Observations

In each phase of the study, each of the six children was observed twice in each of six settings. There were, thus, a total of 144 observations, 72 in each phase. A number of observers were involved, but each single observation was made by a single observer.[3] The observer would go over to the ward or to the gym or to the outdoor play area, for example, to observe a particular child according to his assignment of children and settings. He would concentrate on that particular child, trying to follow as much as was possible the transactions between this child and other children or adults. But he would also try to note what went on among the other children within the locus of observation. The observer did not take notes; he would gauge the length of his observation to the amount of the specific activity that he could remember. This meant that the time period of observation was highly variable. If there was, for example, an extremely rapid interplay of behavior, the observation time might be as brief as several minutes; on the other hand, it might extend, if the interchanges were few and far between, to as much as 20 minutes or a half hour. The mean time for an observation was about 8 minutes. An analysis of variance indicated that differences in observation time allotted to either individual children or to different settings were not significant.

After leaving the setting, the observer would immediately dictate onto tapes or Audograph discs a factual, descriptive report of his observation. Observers were cautioned to focus on interaction, to be as specific and concrete as possible, and to avoid psychological terms and inferential conclusions. In general, observer training required only several practice trials.[4] The protocols of the observations resemble those obtained by Barker and Wright (1957), though their descriptions were undoubtedly more fully detailed.

The Settings

Different situations—for example, even different games—exert a pull for different behaviors, and they differ in the kinds of behavior they sanction, positively encourage, or inhibit (Redl and Wineman, 1957). The opportunity rarely exists to study behavior in a representative variety of settings, to relate behavior to what Brunswik (1947) has called "the ecology of environmental events." A residential treatment center provides such an opportunity. The design of the study utilized a *somewhat* representative sampling of the kinds of activities around which the children lived their lives so as to allow investigation of the relevance of different settings for interactive behaviors. This aspect of the study will not be discussed here, but the settings should be noted: (a) breakfast—an early morning observation; (b) snacks in the period just before the children went to bed at night; (c) other mealtimes; (d) structured game activities, ranging from cards to

---

[2] The first series was completed within a month; the second series took some five months to complete.

[3] In addition to the authors and others already mentioned, Joseph H. Handlon and Jeston Hamer served as observers.

[4] The problems of making formal observations in an on-going clinical operation and the methodological issues in pretesting the approach are complex matters. Discussions of these questions by A. T. Dittmann and by D. W. Goodrich are in preparation.

basketball;[5] (e) unstructured group activities where the specific external task structure was minimal—for example, social conversations; and (f) an arts-and-crafts period. Since one phase of the study occurred during the summer, when school was not in session, this last setting was utilized as an approximation to an instructional situation. Since selection was in terms of kind of activity, the data are not representative of time as a time sample would be; the nature of the settings did, however, insure that various times of the day were included. Relevant settings omitted from the study were psychotherapy, other two-person group situations, where the presence of an observer might be intrusive, and school situations other than arts and crafts.

The Coding Scheme

The search for methods for describing human interactions and the problems involved in extant approaches have been reviewed by Heyns and Lippitt (1954). The present need was for a scheme (a) applicable to a wide variety of situations, (b) relevant for the study of personality and individual behavior patterns, (c) suitable for dealing with the behavior of both children and adults, and (d) relatively comprehensive. The approach initially described by Freedman *et al.* (1951), and discussed in detail by Leary (1957), was used.

The scheme (Fig. 1) is based on two polar coordinates. One is along the dimension of affection: love (affiliate, act friendly) to hate (attack, act unfriendly). The other axis is concerned with status: dominate (command, high status action) to submit (obey, low status action). Each action of one person toward another is coded by letter into one of 16 categories along the periphery of the circle in accordance with its blending of the two coordinates. The words below the letters are simply examples of the kinds of actions that might be coded at that position. In practice, coding was generally a compromise between the words representing the categories and the position relative to the two axes, but in cases of doubt the position was utilized rather than the words.[6]

As in the Bales scheme (1950), the attitude taken by the coder is that of the "generalized other." The question he attempts to answer via his categorization is, "What is this person doing to the other? What kind of relationship is he attempting to establish through this particular behavior?" (Heyns and Lippitt, 1954, p. 91). For example, when a child says, "Wasn't that a good movie we saw last night?" he is generally not coded J (Fig. 1), although J can include asking someone's opinion; he is rather coded M, which is simple affiliation. Or when a child says to another, "I can kick better than you," rather than simply stating an opinion P, he is usually establishing a dominant, slightly hostile relationship B, although within some contexts such a statement might involve more of an aggressive element than one of status differentiation and so might be coded D. The statement, "I don't want to play with you," may represent active rejection C, whiny complaining F, or very passive withdrawal H, depending on the context and on the quality with which it was said.

In addition to the categorization described above, a form of "intensity" coding

---

[5] Behaviors specific to the game itself—for example, passing a ball, playing a card, or claiming one's turn—were not coded or considered in the analyses to follow.

[6] Practical coding problems were sometimes resolved by double codings, but such solutions are not wholly adequate.

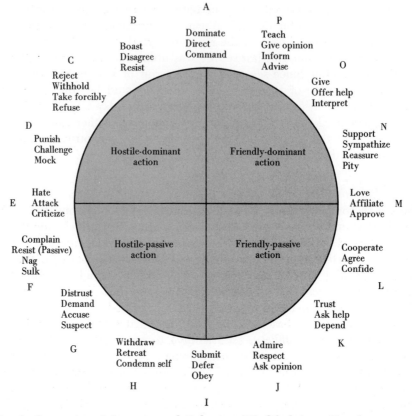

Fig. 1. Categories of Interpersonal Behavior (Modified from Freedman et al., 1951 and Leary, 1957, p. 65)

was employed simultaneously. Each interaction was also coded as to whether the behavior was (*a*) uninvolved—for example, a very casual "Hi" or a casual ignoring of another's statement or request, (*b*) involved and appropriate, or (*c*) involved and inappropriate—either an overly intense behavior or a behavior that is qualitatively inappropriate such as responding to an affectionate gesture with an attack. These latter codings are rather crude, and the aspects of involvedness, appropriateness, and intensity are confounded. Recognizing these limitations, we can still make use of these categories over a wide sampling of behavior, and in point of fact, they do add another useful dimension to our findings.

Coding was done from tapes or typescripts of the dictated observations. Each observation was coded by at least two coders working together. The coders read the protocol (or listened to the tape) line by line, coding each interaction in terms of the person behaving (the specific child or adult), the intepersonal quality and "intensity" of the behavior, and the person toward whom the behavior was directed. Thus, one may obtain in chronological sequence the interactions of any given child toward any other child or adult, and also the behavior of others, children or adults, towards him.[7]

---

[7] Freedman *et al.* (1951, p. 155) present some data on interrater agreement in coding verbal behavior of adults. Adequate assessment of reliability is made difficult by the fact that there

Results and Discussion

In the discussion that follows, the basic source of material was, for each child, the 24 protocols—12 in each phase—in which he served as the central focus for observation. For analyzing qualitative changes, the interactions of individual children were distributed into the four quadrants of the circle (Fig. 1); frequencies at the midpoints (M, I, E, and A) were divided evenly between the two adjacent quadrants with any remaining odd entry randomly assigned.[8] Further data from individual segments of the 16-category scheme are noted occasionally, where this would seem to provide clarification. The approach to analyzing the reaction of others to individual children is commented on later.

The statistical method employed was chi square which, though it fails to take into account the continuity postulated in the circle scheme, involves few assumptions as to the nature of the data. The indices suggested by Leary (1957, pp. 68–71), while mathematically more elegant, would seem to require assumptions even beyond those of ordinal classification. The data for each child were analyzed independently in order to avoid confounding. Where individual chi squares for

---

is no baseline for evaluating correlational indices with data scored in this fashion. Rank order correlations between codings from protocols of independent observers of the same events and between pairs of coders of the same protocols are invariably high, but they are likely to be somewhat spurious, since there is some doubt that correlations between random protocols are of zero order. Dittmann (1958) discusses a number of aspects of the reliability of the system. Considering agreement between two pairs of coders working with the same material, Dittmann notes that item-by-item agreement, analogous to test item reliability, is far greater than chance expectancy, but he also notes that there remain appreciable discrepancies. When, however, the single interactions are grouped to form a profile for an observation, a situation analogous to test reliability, discrepancies between independent pairs of coders are far smaller than could be expected by chance. Similarly, the protocols from independent observers of the same events yield smaller differences than could be expected by chance. A recent check by the present authors compared different observers who observed the same children in matched, rather than identical, settings—a situation analogous to alternate forms. Differences, which might have resulted from observer variations or from lack of equivalence in the matched settings or from both, were well within chance limits. Furthermore, a series of observations made approximately two months apart with the same children also failed to yield significant differences.

Clearly, none of these results allows a statement about level of reliability comparable to the usual Pearson r. The significant item-by-item agreement, together with the failure to find evidence of bias in the sources tested, and together with the finding of consistent individual differences, discussed below, would, however, seem to warrant the conclusion reached by Dittman (1958). The conclusion is that reliability is adequate for grouped data—such as the individual profiles considered in the present study—although it may not be adequate for the analysis of single sequences.

There remains a question of possible bias occurring between the two phases of the study, and the only answers at present are indirect ones. First, the scheme seems fairly objective; second, raters have been aware of the problem, and their continued sensitivity to the possibility of bias has probably served to reduce that possibility; third, the data yield negative as well as positive results, whereas a bias would be likely to operate more consistently. It is recognized that such answers are incomplete. A more definitive check, which has awaited the presence of uncontaminated raters for whom protocols can be adequately disguised, is currently in process.

[8] For the early phase observations, the median was 98 interactions for a child toward other children (range 62 to 141), and the median was 89 interactions toward adults (range 66 to 143). In the observations made 18 months later, the median number of interactions toward children was 77 (range 53 to 89); toward adults, it was 69 (range 61 to 98).

each child are summed to yield a total estimate of group change, the formula is the sum of chi squares in one direction minus the sum of chi squares in the other direction. Since there are no rational bases for expected distributions of behavior—any assumption that behavior should be distributed equally into each category is obviously untenable—total marginal distributions for individual children were used in obtaining theoretical values. Significance tests are reported for two-tailed distributions, for although some expectations are rather obviously directional in studying behavior change for this group of children, we were at this stage interested in exploring both sides of any coins which seemed worth examining.

Changes in Interactions Toward Adults

HOSTILE-DOMINANT INTERACTIONS   Figure 2 presents for each of the children the percentage of his total responses toward adults which were coded as hostile-dominant at each of the two phases. The category represents active forms of aggressive behavior. Included are such interactions as actively refusing to comply with adult requests, making boastful demands on adults, threatening or challenging adults, attempting to "argue down" an adult, poking unfriendly fun at an adult, ordering adults around in a boastful or unfriendly manner, and any attack on the adult in his role of authority with the attempt to negate or degrade the authority component. Difficulties in authority relationships were prominent in the case records of all six boys prior to their admission. In one sense, the chief symptoms which entered into their selection were their consistent failure to accept the roles that adults define for children and their active rebellion against adult authority.

In the early phase, the mean percentage of hostile-dominant interactions toward adults was 28. This proportion is, of course, difficult to evaluate without control studies of more normal pre-adolescents in a comparable environment. For the clinical staff, however, it is a patent understatement to say that the amount of active hostility shown by these children was high.[9] In the later phase, the mean percentage of hostile-dominant responses toward adults dropped to 11. Over the year and a half between the two phases, each of the children changed in the expected direction. The shift was examined for each child separately by chi square—comparing frequencies of hostile-dominant vs. all other behavior toward adults over the two phases. The changes were significant for one child at $p <$ .001, for two children at $p <$ .01, for one child at $p <$ .02, and for two children at $p <$ .20. The sum of the individual chi squares was 44.23, which with 6 df (one for each two-by-two table) indicates a change at a level of confidence well beyond .001.

HOSTILE-PASSIVE INTERACTIONS   Hostile-passive modes of expressing hostility were, in general, less prominent in the relations of the children with adults than were the more dominant forms of aggression discussed above. Such behaviors as whining and complaining in relation to adults, accusing adults of punitive behavior or attitudes, demanding something of an adult in such a way as to imply that the adult is an ungiving monster, sulky withdrawal from interaction, tearful refusals—these constituted a mean of 14 per cent of the behavior toward adults in the earlier phase (Fig. 3). A year and a half later, the mean percentage had

---

[9] Preliminary data from control studies confirm staff impressions.

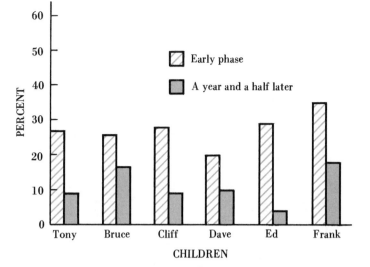

Fig. 2. *Changes in Proportions of Hostile-Dominant Interactions by Children to Adults*

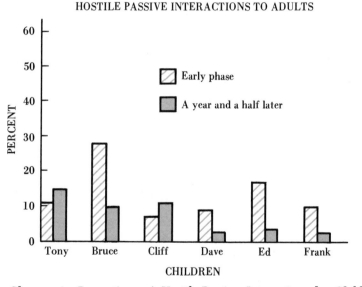

Fig. 3. *Changes in Proportions of Hostile-Passive Interactions by Children to Adults*

dropped to 8. Four of the six children showed a decrease in passive expressions of aggression—one at $p < .01$, one at $p < .02$, one at $p < .10$, and one at $p < .20$; two children showed an insignificant increase ($p < .50$ in both cases). The sum of the four chi squares in the expected direction minus the two chi squares in the contrary direction is 17.62, which with 6 *df* is significant at a confidence level beyond .01. Thus, it would seem that while the magnitude of decrease in passively hostile interactions toward adults was significant, the change was not nearly as great as in the case of dominant expressions of hostility.

FRIENDLY-PASSIVE INTERACTIONS It is interesting that despite the fact that these were hyperaggressive children, selected because of their unmanageability, the modal response toward adults was in the friendly-passive category (Fig. 4).

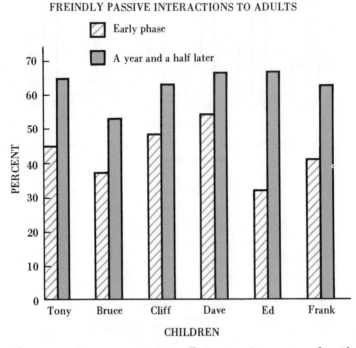

Fig. 4. *Changes in Proportions of Friendly-Passive Interactions by Children to Adults*

Even in the earlier phase, friendly-passive behaviors made up the greatest proportion of interactions with adults for each of the children with a mean of 43 per cent. Examination of the total interactions toward adults of all six children when each was in the primary focus of observation indicates that in the earlier phase the three highest ranking of the 16 categories (Fig. 1) were affiliative behaviors (M), cooperative behaviors (L), and help-seeking behaviors (K), which produced respectively 15, 14, and 12 per cent of all interactions toward adults.[10] This phenomenon, rather than indicating that the children were not "really" hyperaggressive, would seem to point in two directions. First, these are children and their behavior in many ways must resemble that of other children of their age. Second, each interaction in these analyses carries a single weight, and while this arrangement serves its purposes, it is unlikely that the recipient, for example, is equally impressed by one friendly "hello" as by a single attack of murderous rage.

[10] Active resistance or disagreement (B) was next with 10 per cent.

The relatively high frequencies of friendly-passive behaviors do not negate the difficulties in living with these children. The problem is that there are no units for effectively gauging the psychological impact of an action on the recipient.

By the time of the later period, the percentage of friendly-passive interactions with adults had risen to a mean of 63 per cent. Each of the children showed an increase in such responses—one at $p < .001$, two at $p < .01$, one at $p < .05$, one at $p < .10$, and one at $p < .30$. The sum of the chi squares is 45.37, which with 6 df is significant at a confidence level well beyond .001. Further consideration of the specific nature of the changes appears below.

FRIENDLY-DOMINANT INTERACTIONS It is difficult to know what to expect in the friendly-dominant area, both in proportions and in actual changes. In contrast with the situation for aggression and dependency, there has been little theoretical or research interest in such children's behaviors as sympathizing with or reassuring adults, offering help to adults, and teaching or advising adults. One might guess that such actions are perhaps not very appropriate as a major aspect of the relations of pre-adolescent boys with adults. For the present group, friendly-dominant responses constituted a rather small proportion of behaviors toward adults. The values in Fig. 5 and the mean values—16 per cent in the

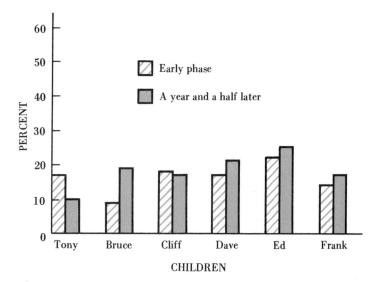

FRIENDLY DOMINANT INTERACTIONS TO ADULTS

Fig. 5. Changes in Proportions of Friendly-Dominant Interactions by Children to Adults

early and 18 per cent in the later phase—are somewhat spuriously high because the major contributory entry was from affiliative responses (M), which in the analyses were distributed equally between friendly-dominant and friendly-passive interactions.[11] Only for one child, Bruce, did the change between the two phases

[11] The total of the three categories, N, O, and P, contributed 7 per cent to the total number of interactions in each of the two phases, whereas M contributed 15 per cent and 21 per cent to the early and late phase, respectively.

approach significance ($p < .10$), and here it was almost wholly a function of the increase in affiliative responses (M). The sum of the four chi squares showing increase minus the two showing descrease was 2.95, which is not significant ($p < .90$).

THE "INTENSITY" DIMENSION   Most of the children's behavior was considered by the coders to be appropriate and involved. In the early phase, this "intensity" category comprised a mean of 75 per cent of the children's action toward adults (Fig. 6). Only 9 per cent of the behavior in this period—a mean for the six children—was coded as inappropriate and involved, that is, as being overly intense or qualitatively inappropriate to the circumstances. Uninvolved interactions yielded a mean of 16 per cent of the behaviors in this phase; these included such actions as silent rejections of adult requests, subtle provocations, as well as token gestures of acceptance or affiliation, and the term *uninvolved* is not very adequate.

In any case, the proportions of appropriate-involved interactions increased in the later phase from a mean of 75 per cent to a mean of 86 per cent. Each of the children changed in the expected direction. Comparing the frequencies of appropriate-involved behaviors with the summed frequencies of the other two categories over the two phases yielded chi squares at confidence levels of $p < .01$ for one child, $p < .05$ for two children, $p < .20$ for two children, and $p < .90$ for the sixth child (two-tailed tests). The sum of the chi squares was 21.19, which with 6 df is significant at $p < .01$. Five children showed a decrease in inappropriate-involved behavior; the means went from 9 per cent to 4 per cent. All six children showed a decrease in uninvolved actions toward adults, the means dropping from 16 per cent to 10 per cent. The raw frequencies are in some cases too small to warrant statistical analysis, but the trends seem obvious.

SUMMARY COMMENTS ON CHANGES IN INTERACTIONS WITH ADULTS   Over the year

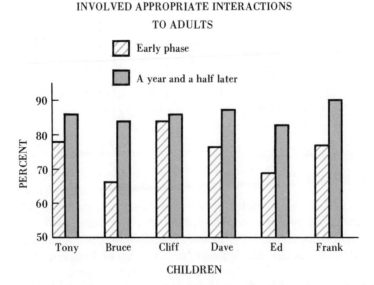

Fig. 6. Changes in Proportions of Appropriate-Involved Interactions by Children to Adults

and a half the children changed considerably in their behavior toward adults. Primarily, they lessened their attempts to dominate adults aggressively, and they increased their friendly and compliant associations with adults. Passive expressions of hostility also decreased, and in general, behavior became more appropriate, but these latter changes, while statistically significant, were less striking.

It is obvious that improvement occurred in overt behavior toward adults. During the period of the study, however, the boys had not only been under an intensive residential treatment program, but they had also grown older. Where so little is known in any systematic way about the interpersonal behavior of normal children and about developmental changes in such behavior, there is the perplexing question that is often put as an issue between maturation and learning (or treatment). The question is a complex one, since social maturation can never be divorced from considerations of the particular environment involved and its indulgences, tolerances, and demands. For example, the treatment of children, in order to be adequate, must take growth and development into account. Conversely, maturational phenomena will be influenced by the environmental medium in which they occur. In the present situation, one may legitimately ask: Are the changes necessarily to be attributed to the treatment program together with growth and development, or are they, perhaps, primarily a function of normal development within a *somewhat* benign environment? No definitive answer can be given without control studies, and there are manifold problems even so. There are, however, some partial cues in the data which indicate that the treatment, in a broad sense, is a critical factor. Thus, while one might *possibly* expect decreased aggression and decreased dominance in relation to adults as part of a "normal" growth process, though the argument would be tenuous, one would not expect to find much increase in trusting, dependent relations with adults. It is interesting that out of the 16 possibilities (Fig. 1), the category that showed the greatest shift was K, which deals with requesting, depending, and asking-help behavior, and that the percentage of responses in this category went from 12 per cent of all behaviors toward adults in the early phase to 24 per cent in the later phase. In frequency of responses, K shifted from third to first rank. It would seem that this was not a maturation phenomenon—that is, it is unlikely that children either become increasingly dependent or increasingly admit their dependency on adults with age. One may speculate that the evidence points to the dissolution of a defensive layer so that dependency emerges; such a speculation dovetails with the impressions of the psychotherapists that oral themes became very prominent in the later phases of psychotherapy with these children. The critical question about what factors in the treatment program contributed to change can unfortunately not be answered by a study such as this, but some further issues in the process of change will be considered below in the discussion of behaviors directed toward each of the children.

Changes in Interactions Toward Peers

We turn to the behavior of the children toward their peers, again considering each child when he was the focal subject for observation, but now investigating changes in the behavior that he directed toward other children. The discussion can be briefer in this section because some of the contextual material has already been presented.

HOSTILE-DOMINANT INTERACTIONS   Figure 7 presents for each child at the two phases the percentage of his actions which were hostile-dominant in orientation toward other children. In both phases the means are higher than was the case for behavior toward adults—39 per cent as compared to 28 per cent in the early

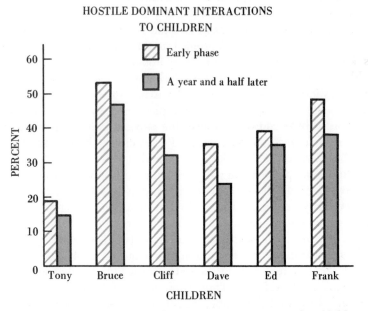

Fig. 7. *Changes in Proportions of Hostile-Dominant Interactions by Children to Peers*

phase, and 32 per cent as compared to 11 per cent in the later phase. Five of the six boys were in the early period more dominantly aggressive toward their peers than toward adults, and all six showed this trend in the later period. That is, aggressive attempts at dominance were, as might be expected, more readily expressed toward peers than toward the higher status adults.

All six of the children showed expected decremental changes over the 18 months. While this directional consistency for six cases is significant at a confidence level of $p = .03$ by a simple two-tailed binomial test, none of the individual changes reached statistical significance, and the sum of the individual chi squares was also nonsignificant. Thus, in contrast to the marked shifts between the two phases in proportions of hostile-dominant interactions toward adults, the changes in interactions with peers were, at the most, slight.

HOSTILE-PASSIVE INTERACTIONS   Although four of the six children showed a decrease in hostile-passive behaviors (Fig. 8), in no case was the change significant. One child, Clif, increased in passive expressions of aggression toward the others, and the shift was significant by chi square at $p < .001$. For this child, both passive resistance (F) and withdrawal (H) increased over the year and a half. His overall proportion of hostility rose somewhat, though not significantly, since a slight decline in hostile-dominant interactions did not compensate for the increased passive hostility. The situation thus points to the possibility of a slight deterioraton in peer relationships for this child over the period of the study. The mean percentages of hostile-passive responses for the six children are the same in the

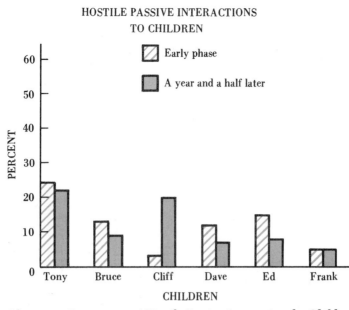

Fig. 8. Changes in Proportions of Hostile-Passive Interactions by Children to Peers

two phases, 12 per cent, and the sum of the chi squares for the positive change direction minus those in the negative direction is, although opposite to the direction of improvement because of Clif's contribution, not significant.

FRIENDLY-PASSIVE INTERACTIONS Just as active aggression was more characteristic in response to peers than to adults, so friendly-passive interactions, at the opposite side of the circle, were less characteristic in peer relationships than in relationships with adults. In the early phase, friendly-passive actions made up 43 per cent of the responses to adults and 24 per cent of the responses to other children; in the later period, the respective percentages were 63 and 29. In behavior toward adults, Categories M, L, and K (Fig. 1) held the three highest ranks for response frequencies in each of the two phases, based on the total number of responses of all children in each phase. In behaviors toward peers, M (affiliative responses) and L (cooperative responses) were at Ranks 1 and 4.5 in the early phase and at Ranks 1 and 2.5 in the later phase. But the position of K (trusting, dependent, help-seeking responses) was quite different in relations with peers. In the early phase, only 2 per cent of all responses were coded K, a ranking of 14 in a triple tie; in the later phase, only 3 per cent of all responses were coded K, a ranking of 11.5 in a quadruple tie. Thus, unlike the case in relation to adults, dependency responses among the children occurred relatively infrequently, and they showed rather little shift between the two times of study.

Four boys showed gains in the proportions of friendly-passive behaviors toward peers (Fig. 9), and for two of them the change was significant by chi square at $p < .05$. None of the other shifts were statistically significant; the sum of the four chi squares in the expected direction minus the two in the opposite direction was 8.87 which, with 6 df, yields a confidence level of $p < .20$.

FRIENDLY-DOMINANT INTERACTIONS One might expect the friendly-dominant mode of interaction to be more characteristic of relations among children than from children to adults, and such an expectation appears to be legitimate. In the

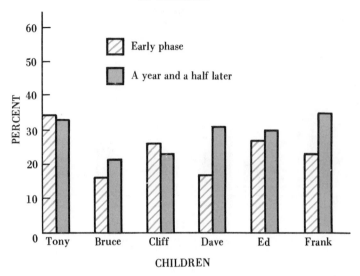

FRIENDLY PASSIVE INTERACTIONS
TO CHILDREN

Fig. 9. Changes in Proportions of Friendly-Passive Interactions by Children to Peers

early phase, an average of 26 per cent of the children's responses to peers were friendly-dominant in orientation in contrast to the average of 16 per cent in responses to adults; in the later phase, the two averages were 28 per cent and 18 per cent, respectively. The category M again constituted a major source of data for the quadrant, and that the values are not deceiving is shown by the fact that Categories N, O, and P yielded 15 per cent of all responses toward children in each of the two phases and 7 per cent of all responses toward adults in each of the two phases.

Figure 10 shows four of the six changes to be in the direction of an increase in friendly-dominant behaviors toward peers, but none of the changes in either direction is significant; neither is the sum of the chi squares.

THE "INTENSITY" DIMENSION   The distributions of responses toward peers are strikingly similar to the distributions of responses toward adults in the three-category "intensity" classification. In the early phase, the mean proportions of interactions toward children were 74 per cent appropriate-involved (as compared to 75 per cent for behavior toward adults), 16 per cent uninvolved interactions (as compared to 16 per cent for behavior toward adults), and 9 per cent inappropriate-involved interactions (as compared to 9 per cent for behavior toward adults). In the later phase, the three means are, respectively, 84 per cent, 11 per cent, and 5 per cent as compared to 86 per cent, 10 per cent, and 4 per cent in behavior toward adults.

Figure 11 shows the shifts in the proportions of appropriate-involved behaviors for each of the children. All changes were in the expected direction of increase. For one child the change was significant at $p < .02$, for another at $p < .05$, and for a third at $p < .10$; for the other three children there is less conclusive evidence of change. The sum of the chi squares is 15.85, which, with 6 df, is significant at a level of $p < .02$. Decreases in inappropriate-involved and in uninvolved actions

FRIENDLY DOMINANT INTERACTIONS
TO CHILDREN

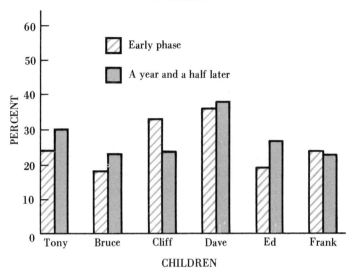

Fig. 10. *Changes in Proportions of Friendly-Dominant Interactions by Children to Peers*

INVOLVED APPROPRIATE INTERACTIONS
TO CHILDREN

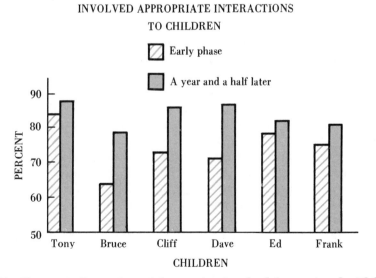

Fig. 11. *Changes in Proportions of Appropriate-Involved Interactions by Children to Peers*

toward peers seem by inspection to be less consistent than they were in behavior toward adults.

SUMMARY COMMENTS ON CHANGES IN INTERACTIONS TOWARD PEERS   Certainly, the evidence of change in relations with peers is much less than in the case of relations with adults. The only general change in peer directed action that warrants much confidence was the increase in the relative proportion of appropriate behavior. In other aspects, the directions were similar to those for behavior toward adults—toward a decrease in dominant aggressive actions and toward an increase in friendly compliant actions—but the shifts over the year and a half were, for the most part, unimpressive.

To the question of why changes in relations to adults were so much more striking than were changes in peer relations, no clear answer can be given. There is the possibility that interpersonal behavior with peers was less disturbed than that with adults. Control studies would be required to confirm or disaffirm this statement. There is also the possibility that changes occur earlier in the treatment process in relation to adults than in relation to peers. Such an hypothesis would be reasonable though not necessary on the basis of clinical evidence that the difficulties of these boys developed out of primary relationships with parental figures. Perhaps, with these primitive children, some resolution of earlier relationship problems must occur before the genetically more advanced problems of peer relationships can be met. Follow-up studies and studies of other clinical groups would be useful here. There is also a possibility that the observation method and the instrument are less potent for gauging peer interactions than for interactions of children toward adults.

What can be said about the specific nature of reciprocal action? Obviously, nothing definitive, but there are some cues. Let us look, for example, at Tony's relations with the other boys during the early phase. Tony was the least dominantly aggressive and the most passively aggressive of the children. Complementarily, Tony received the greatest proportion of dominant aggression and the lowest proportion of passive aggression from his peers. While Tony initiated the highest proportion of friendly-passive responses to other children, he received the lowest proportion of such responses from peers but the second highest proportion of friendly-dominant behaviors. In contrast to Tony, Frank "sent" a high proportion of dominantly aggressive and a low proportion of passively aggressive behaviors toward the other boys and received from them a high proportion of passive-hostile and a relatively low proportion of dominant-hostile responses. But, as seems true for reciprocality in change, patterns of complementariness in action are not equally clear for all children.

That passive aggression evokes dominant aggression and that dominant aggression evokes passive aggression is not unexpected. What is more interesting is a tendency in the data for passive aggression to evoke friendly-dominant behavior, and for dominant aggression to evoke friendly-passive behavior. The evidence is obviously meagre and the indications are not wholly consistent, but it would seem that hostile oriented actions were not always met with counter-hostility. Do "successes" maintain the behaviors? If so, how is the alternative cycle of reciprocal aggression to be counteracted?

Summary

An exploratory study was made of the interpersonal behavior of six hyper-aggressive boys in residential treatment. Each child was observed twice in six life settings and his interactions with both peers and adults were noted. The observations were repeated after a year and a half in the treatment program.

Over the year and a half the interpersonal behavior of the children shifted considerably. The major changes were in the relations of the children with adults. Here, there was primarily a decrease in hostile-dominant behavior and an increase in friendly-passive behavior. The appropriateness of behavior increased both in relations with children and with adults. The patterns of change were consistent with treatment aims, and they seemed, at least in part, a function of the treatment program.

Group similarities and individual differences among the children were noted, and patterns of reciprocality in behavior between children and adults and among children were explored. In relations with peers, the children received about the same amount of aggression as they expressed. They received less aggression from adults than they expressed toward them. Changes in patterns of behavior toward others were accompanied, in general, by reciprocal changes in the behaviors of others, both adults and children.

The study demonstrates (a) that systematic observation and coding of the interpersonal behavior of a small group of children in naturalistic settings can yield tenable descriptions, orderly relationships, and some tentative hypotheses about interpersonal processes, (b) that hyperaggressive children can change in residential treatment in a direction consistent with therapeutic aims, and (c) that the mode of observation described here, together with the scheme for coding interpersonal behavior (Freedman et al., 1951; Leary, 1957), has some measure of utility.

32 / A Preliminary Report on the Application of Contingent Reinforcement Procedures (Token Economy) on a "Chronic" Psychiatric Ward

John M. Atthowe, Jr. / *Leonard Krasner*

Although investigators may disagree as to what specific strategies or tactics to pursue, they would agree that current treatment programs in mental hospitals are in need of vast improvement. Release rates for patients hospitalized five or more years have not materially changed in this century (Kramer et al., 1956). After five years of hospitalization, the likelihood of release is approximately 6 per cent (Kramer et al., 1956; Morgan and Johnson, 1957; Ødegaard, 1961); and, as patients grow older and their length of hospitalization increases, the possibility of discharge approaches zero. Even for those chronic patients who do leave the hospital, more than two out of every three return within six months (Fairweather

From the *Journal of Abnormal Psychology*, 1968, **73**, 37–43. Revised. Copyright © 1968. Reprinted by permission of the authors and the American Psychological Association.

et al., 1960). There is certainly need for new programs of demonstrated efficiency in modifying the behavior of long-term hospitalized patients.

In September, 1963, we began a research program in behavior modification which was intimately woven into the hospital's ongoing service and training programs. Our objective was to create and maintain a systematic ward program within the ongoing social system of the hospital. The program reported here involves the life of the entire ward, patients and staff, plus others who come in contact with the patients. The purpose of the program was to change the chronic patients' aberrant behavior, especially that behavior judged to be apathetic, overly dependent, detrimental, or annoying to others. Our goal was to foster more responsible, active, and interested individuals who would be able to perform the routine activities associated with self-care, to make responsible decisions, and to delay immediate reinforcement in order to plan for the future.

The Ward Population

An 86 bed, closed ward in the custodial section of the V.A. Hospital in Palo Alto was selected. The median age of the patients was 57 and more than one-third were over 65. Their overall length of hospitalization varied from 3 to 48 years with a median length of hospitalization of 22 years. Most of the patients had previously been labeled as chronic schizophrenics; the remainder were classified as having some organic involvement.

The patients fell into three general performance classes. The largest group, approximately 60 per cent of the ward, required constant supervision. Whenever they left the ward, an aide had to accompany them. The second group, about 25 per cent, had ground privileges and were able to leave the ward unescorted. The third group, 15 per cent of the patients, required only minimal supervision and could probably function in a boarding home under proper conditions if the fear of leaving the hospital could be overcome.

In order to insure a stable research sample for the two years of the project, 60 patients were selected to remain on the ward for the duration of the study. The patients selected were older and had, for the most part, obvious and annoying behavioral deficits. This "core" sample served as the experimental population in studying the long-term effectiveness of the research program, the token economy.

The Token Economy

Based on the work of Ayllon and his associates (Ayllon, 1963; Ayllon and Azrin, 1965; Ayllon and Houghton, 1962; Ayllon and Michael, 1959) and the principle of reinforcement as espoused by Skinner (1938, 1953), we have tried to incorporate every important phase of ward and hospital life within a systematic contingency program. The attainment of the "good things in life" was made contingent upon the patient's performance.

If a patient adequately cared for his personal needs, attended his scheduled activities, helped on the ward, interacted with other patients, or showed increased responsibility in any way, he was rewarded. Our problem was to find rewards that were valued by everyone. Tokens, which could in turn be exchanged for the things a patient regards as important or necessary, were introduced. As stated in the manual distributed to patients (Atthowe, 1964):

> The token program is an incentive program in which each person can do as much or as little as he wants as long as he abides by the general rules of the hospital, *but,* in order to gain certain ends or do certain things, he must have tokens. . . . The more you do the more tokens you get.

Cigarettes, money, passes, watching television, etc., were some of the more obvious reinforcers; but, some of the most effective reinforcers were idiosyncratic, such as sitting on the ward or feeding kittens. For some patients, hoarding tokens became highly valued. This latter practice necessitated changing the tokens every 30 days. In addition, the tokens a patient still had left at the end of each month were devaluated 25 per cent, hence the greater incentive for the patient to spend them quickly. The more tokens a patient earned or spent, the less likely he would be to remain apathetic.

In general, each patient was reinforced immediately after the completion of some "therapeutic" activity; but, those patients who attended scheduled activities by themselves were paid their tokens only once a week on a regularly scheduled pay day. Consequently, the more independent and responsible patient had to learn "to punch a time card" and to receive his "pay" at a specified future date. He then had to "budget" his tokens so they covered his wants for the next seven days.

In addition, a small group of 12 patients were in a position of receiving what might be considered as the ultimate in reinforcement. They were allowed to become independent of the token system. These patients carried a "carte blanche" which entitled them to all the privileges within the token economy plus a few added privileges and a greater status. For this special status, the patient had to work 25 hours per week in special vocational assignments. In order to become a member of the "elite group," patients had to accumulate 120 tokens, which entailed a considerable delay in gratification.

The token economy was developed to cover all phases of a patient's life. This extension of contingencies to all of the patient's routine activities should bring about a greater generality and permanence of the behavior modified. One criticism of conditioning therapies has been that the behavior changed is specific, with little evidence of carry over to other situations. In this project we incorporated plans to program transfer of training as well as behavior change per se. As a major step in this direction, token reinforcements were associated with social approval.

The attainment of goals which bring about greater independence should also result in strong sustaining reinforcement in and of itself. Our aim has been to support more effective behavior and to weaken ineffective behavior by withdrawal of approval and attention and, if necessary, by penalties. Penalties comprised "fines" of specified numbers of tokens levied for especially undesirable behavior or for *not* paying the tokens required by the system. The fines can be seen as actually representing a high token payment to do something socially undesirable, e.g., three tokens for cursing someone.

Method

The research program was initiated in September of 1963 when the senior author joined the ward as the ward psychologist and program administrator. The remainder of 1963 was a period of observation, pilot studies, and planning. Steps were taken to establish a research clinic and to modify the traditional service orientation of the nursing staff. In January, 1964, the baseline measures were begun. The baseline or operant period lasted approximately six months and was followed by three months in which the patients were gradually prepared to participate in the token economy. In October, 1964, the token economy was established, and, at the time of writing is still in operation. This report represents results based on the completion of the first year of the program.

The general design of the study was as follows: A six-month baseline period, a three-month shaping period, and an eleven-month experimental period. During the baseline period, the frequency of particular behaviors was recorded daily and ratings were carried out periodically. The shaping period was largely devoted to those patients requiring continual supervision. At first, the availability of canteen booklets, which served as money in the hospital canteen, was made contingent upon the amount of scheduled activities a patient attended. It soon became clear that almost one-half of the patients were not interested in money or canteen books. They did not know how to use the booklets, and they never bought things for themselves. Consequently, for six weeks, patients were taken to the canteen and urged or "cajoled" into buying items which seemed to interest them (e.g., coffee, ice cream, pencils, handkerchiefs, etc.). Then all contingencies were temporarily abandoned, and patients were further encouraged to utilize the canteen books. Next, tokens were introduced but on a non-contingent basis. No one was allowed to purchase items in the ward canteen without first presenting tokens. Patients were instructed to pick up tokens from an office directly across the hall from the ward canteen and exchange them for the items they desired. After two weeks, the tokens were made contingent upon performance and the experimental phase of the study began.

Within a reinforcement approach, we have utilized the principles of successive approximation in gradually shaping the desired patient behavior. Once the tokens were introduced, shaping procedures were reduced. It would be impossible to hold reinforcement and shaping procedures constant throughout the experimental period or to match our ward or our patients with another ward or comparable group of patients. Consequently, a classical statistical design does not suit our paradigm. It is much more feasible, in addition to reducing sampling errors, to use the patients as their own controls. Therefore, we first established a baseline over an extended period of time. Any changes in behavior from that defined by the baseline must be taken into account. The effects of any type of experimental intervention become immediately obvious. We do not have to rely solely on the inferences teased out of statistical analyses.

Other than an automatic timer for the television set, the only major piece of equipment was the tokens. After a considerable search, a durable and physically safe token was constructed. This token was a 1 3/4" × 3 1/2" plastic, non-laminated, file card which came in seven colors varying from a bright red to a light tan. Different exchange values were assigned to the different colors. The token had the appearance of the usual credit card so prevalent in our society.

Whenever possible, the giving of the tokens was accompanied by some expression of social approval such as smiling, "good," "fine job," and a verbal description of the contingencies involved, e.g., "Here's a token because of the good job of shaving you did this morning."

Results

There has been a significant increase in those behaviors indicating responsibility and activity. Figure 1a shows the improvement in the frequency of attendance at group activities. During the baseline period, the average hourly rate of attendance per week was 5.85 hours per patient. With the introduction of tokens, this rate increased to 8.4 the first month and averaged 8.5 during the experimental period, except for a period of three months when the reinforcing value of the tokens was increased from one to two tokens per hour of attendance. Increasing the reinforcing value of the tokens increased the contingent behavior accordingly. With an increase in the amount of reinforcement, activity increased from 8.4 hours per week in the month before to 9.2 the first month under the new schedule. This gain was maintained throughout the period of greater reinforcement and for one month thereafter.

Thirty-two patients of the core sample comprised the group activity sample. Nine patients were discharged or transferred during the project, and the remaining patients were on individual assignments and did not enter into these computations. Of the 32 patients, 18 increased their weekly attendance by at least two hours, while only 4 decreased their attendance by this amount. The probability that this is a significant difference is .004, using a sign test and a two-tailed estimate. Eighteen per cent of those patients going to group activities

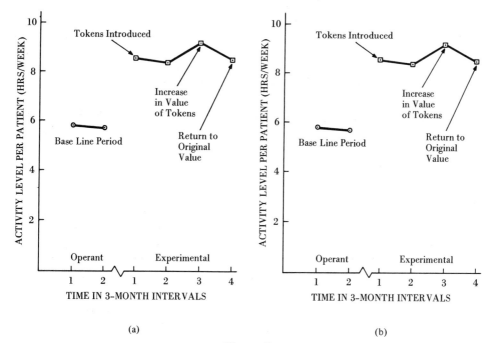

(a)   (b)

Figure 1

changed to the more token-producing and more responsible individual assignments within four months of the onset of the token economy.

A widening of interest and a lessening of apathy was shown by a marked increase in the number of patients going on passes, drawing weekly cash, and utilizing the ward canteen. Eighty per cent of the core sample of 60 patients had never been off the hospital grounds on their own for a period of eight hours since their hospitalization. During the experimental period, 19 per cent went on overnight or longer passes; 17 per cent went on day passes, and 12 per cent went out on accompanied passes for the first time. In other words, approximately one-half of those who had been too apathetic to leave the hospital grounds increased their interest and commitment in the world outside. Furthermore, 13 per cent of the core sample left on one or more trial visits of at least 30 days during the token program, although six out of every ten returned to the hospital.

For the entire ward, the lessening of apathy has been dramatic. The number of patients going on passes and drawing weekly cash have tripled. Twenty-four patients were discharged and eight were transferred to more active and discharge-oriented ward programs, as compared to 11 discharges and no such transfers in the preceding 11-month period. Of the 24 patients released, 11 returned to the hospital within 9 months.

Independence and greater self-sufficiency was shown by an increase in the number of patients receiving tokens for shaving and appearing neatly dressed. Fewer patients missed their showers, and bedwetting markedly diminished.

At the beginning of the study, we had 12 bedwetters, four of whom were classified as "frequent" wetters and two were classified as "infrequent." All bedwetters were awakened and taken to the bathroom at 11 P.M., 12:30 P.M., 2 A.M., and 4 A.M. regularly. As the program progressed, patients who did not wet during the night were paid tokens the following morning. In addition, they were only awakened at 11 P.M. the next night. After a week of no bedwetting, patients were taken off the schedule altogether. At the end of the experimental period no one was wetting regularly and, for all practical purposes, there were no bedwetters on the ward. The aversive schedule of being woken up during the night together with the receiving of tokens for a successful nonbedwetting night seemed to instigate getting up on one's own and going to the bathroom, even in markedly deteriorated patients.

Another ward problem which had required extra aide coverage in the mornings was the lack of "cooperativeness" in getting out of bed, making one's bed, and leaving the bed area by a specified time. Just before the system of specific contingency tokens was introduced, the number of infractions in each of these areas were recorded for three weeks. This three week baseline period yielded an average of 75 "infractions" per week for the entire ward, varying from 71 to 77. A token given daily was then made contingent upon not having a recorded infraction in any of the three areas above. This token was given as the patients lined up to go to breakfast each morning. In the week following the establishment of the contingency, the frequency of infractions dropped to 30 and then to 18. The next week the number of infractions rose to 39 but then declined steadily to five per week by the end of six weeks (see Figure 1b). During the last six months, the frequency of infractions varied between 6 and 13, averaging 9 per week.

A significant increase was shown in measures of social interaction and communication. A brief version of the Palo Alto Group Psypchotherapy scale (Finney, 1954) was used to measure social responsiveness in weekly group meetings. The change in ratings by one group of raters one month before the introduction of tokens compared with those of a second group of raters four months later was significant at the .001 level. A simple sign test based upon a two-tailed probability estimate was used. Neither set of raters knew which of their patients was included within the core sample. The rater reliability of the scale is .90 (Finney, 1954). Evidence of enhanced social interaction was dramatically shown by the appearance of card games using tokens as money among some of the more "disturbed" patients and an increased frequency in playing pool together.

Discussion and Conclusion

A detailed description of the entire procedures and results is in preparation. However, we wish to point out in this paper the usefulness of a systematic contingency program with chronic patients. The program has been quite successful in combating institutional behavior. Prior to the introduction of tokens most patients rarely left the ward. The ward and its surrounding grounds were dominated by sleeping patients. Little interest was shown in ward activities or parties. Before the tokens were introduced, the ward was cleaned and the clothing room operated by patients from "better" wards. During the experimental period the ward has been cleaned and the clothing room operated by the patients of this ward themselves. Now, no one stays on the ward without first earning tokens; and, in comparison to prior standards, the ward could be considered "jumping."

Over 90 per cent of the patients have meaningfully participated in the program. All patients do take tokens, a few only infrequently. However, for about 10 per cent, the tokens seem to be of little utility in effecting marked behavior change. With most patients, the changes in behavior have been quite dramatic; the changes in a few have been gradual and hardly noticeable. These instances of lack of responsiveness to the program seem to be evident in those patients who had previously been "catatonically" withdrawn and isolated. Although most of the patients in this category were favorably responsible to the program, what "failures" there were, did come from this type of patient. Our program has been directed toward all patients; consequently, individual shaping has been limited. We feel that the results would be more dramatic if we could have dealt individually with the specific behavior of every patient. On the other hand, a total ward token program is needed both to maintain any behavioral gains and to bring about greater generality and permanence. Although it was not our initial objective to discharge patients, we are pleased that the general lessening of apathy has brought about a greater discharge rate. But, even more important, the greater discharge rate would point to the generalized effects of a total token economy.

The greater demands on the patient necessitated by dealing with future events and delaying immediate gratifications which were built into the program have been of value in lessening the patient's isolation and withdrawal. The program's most notable contribution to patient life is the lessening of staff control and putting the burden of responsibility, and thus more self-respect, on the patient himself. In the administration of a ward, the program provides behavioral steps by which the staff can judge the patient's readiness to assume more responsibility and thus to leave on pass or be discharged.

The program thus far has demonstrated that a systematic procedure of applying contingent reinforcement via a token economy appears effective in modifying specific patient behaviors. However, the evidence in the literature based on research in mental hospitals indicates that many programs, different in theoretical orientation and design, appear to be successful for a period of time with hospitalized patients. The question which arises is whether the success in modifying behavior is a function of the specific procedures utilized in a given program or a function of the more general social influence process (Krasner, 1962). If it is the latter, whether it be termed "placebo effect" or "Hawthorne effect," then the specific procedures may be irrelevant. All that would matter is the interest, enthusiasm, attention, and hopeful expectancies of the staff. Advocates of behavior modification procedures (of which the token economy is illustrative) argue that change in behavior is a function of the specific reinforcement procedures used. The study which most nearly involves the approach described in this paper is that of Ayllon and Azrin (1965), whose procedures were basic to the development of our own program. Their study was designed to demonstrate the relationship between contingency reinforcement and change in patient behavior. To do this they withdrew the tokens on a systematic basis for specific behaviors, and, after a period of time, reinstated them. They concluded, based upon six specific experiments within the overall design, that "the reinforcement procedure was effective in maintaining desired performance. In each experiment, the performance fell to a near-zero level when the established response-reinforcement relation was discontinued. On the other hand, reintroduction of the reinforcement procedure restored performance almost immediately and maintained it at a high level for as long as the reinforcement procedure was in effect" (Ayllon and Azrin, 1965, p. 381). They found that performance of desirable behaviors decreased when the response-reinforcement relation was disrupted by: delivering tokens independently of the response while still allowing exchange of tokens for the reinforcers; or by discontinuing the token system by providing continuing access to the reinforcers; or by discontinuing the delivery of tokens for a previously reinforced response while simultaneously providing tokens for a different, alternative response.

In the first year of our program we did not test the specific effects of the tokens by withdrawing them. Rather we approached this problem in two ways. First, we incorporated within the baseline period of nine months a three-month period in which tokens were received on a noncontingent basis. During this period patients received tokens with concomitant attention, interest, and general social reinforcement. This resulted in slight but nonsignificant change in general ward behavior. The results of the experimental period were then compared with the baseline which included the nonspecific reinforcement. The results indicate that the more drastic changes in behavior were a function of the specific procedures involved. The other technique we used was to change the token value of certain specific activities. An increase in value (more tokens) was related to an increase in performance; return to the old value meant a decrement to the previous level of performance (see Figure 1a).

We should also point out that the situation in the hospital is such that the token economy did not mean that there were more of the "good things in life" available to these patients because they were in a special program. The patients in the program had had access to these items, e.g., extra food, beds, cigarettes, chairs, television, recreational activities, passes, before the program began, as had all patients in other wards, free of charge. Thus we cannot attribute change to the fact of more "good things" being available to these patients that are not available to other patients.

Thus far, a contingent reinforcement program represented by a token economy has been successful in combating institutionalism, increasing initiative, responsibility, and social interaction, and in putting the control of patient behavior in the hands of the patient. The behavioral changes have generalized to other areas of performance. A token economy can be an important adjunct to any rehabilitation program for chronic or apathetic patients.

33 / Hospital and Community Adjustment as Perceived by Psychiatric Patients, Their Families, and Staff

Robert B. Ellsworth / Leslie Foster / Barry Childers
Gilbert Arthur / Duane Kroeker

For those experiencing major personal adjustment problems, the potential variety of treatment alternatives has never been greater. For one living in Snohomish County, Washington, for example, hospitalization would most likely occur in a 21-day program designed to rapidly reduce symptoms and prepare for release (Dexter *et al.*, 1965). If one lives in Los Angeles, California, he might be assigned to a seven-day treatment ward with a 76 per cent chance of release at the end of that time (Mendel, 1966). If one lives around Portland, Maine, a six-session crisis intervention approach would be available to him, an approach that prevents immediate psychiatric hospitalization 97 per cent of the time (Levy, 1965). If one lives in Louisville, Kentucky, he may be treated at home primarily with public health nursing care and medication (Pasamanick, Scarpetti, and Dinitz, 1967). And finally, if one lives in an area served by a comprehensive mental health center, he could be treated as an outpatient by one of growing numbers of mental health professionals who are now beginning to gain confidence and skill in working with those labelled as mentally ill. Most people with major mental illness are, of course, still referred to the nearest hospital, but alternative patterns of care and treatment are rapidly developing and increasingly available.

As the potential variety of treatment approaches expands, so, too, the need for

Abridged from the *Journal of Consulting Psychology*, 1968, **32**, 1–41. Copyright © 1968. Reprinted by permission of the authors and the American Psychological Association.

careful program assessment increases. Answers are urgently needed to questions about the comparative effectiveness of one approach over another. No longer adequate as sole measures of treatment effectiveness are such traditionally collected data as time-in-treatment, and incidence of rehospitalization or resumption of treatment. Time in treatment is an important measure of a program's efficiency, but not a measure of its effectiveness. Rehospitalization, or returning for further treatment, often indicates more about the variety of outpatient or referral services available to or used by the treatment agency, than about treatment failure. In a cooperative study of 21-day hospitalization for schizophrenic patients, Burton (1967) reported that readmission rates revealed more about staff attitudes toward the experimental treatment approach than about patients' community adjustment failure. A staff interested in seeing the 21-day treatment program succeed often attempted to keep patients out of the hospital using whatever resources they could. A project-critical staff, on the other hand, often made it easy for the 21-day treated patient to return to the hospital (Burton, 1967, p. 46). Readmission rates also vary in terms of the type of community placement used. Rates of return-to-hospital from foster home placement, for example, are found to be very low even though the adjustment level of patients in this type of setting has often deteriorated (Ellsworth, 1968, p. 145). The setting may be highly tolerant of marginal adjustment. Also the family's expectations regarding the patient's posthospital adjustment plays an important role in determining his return to the hospital (Freeman and Simmons, 1963). At best, then, resumption of treatment or rehospitalization represent only crude indices of treatment effectiveness.

In judging a program's relative effectiveness, most mental health professionals want to know whether or not clients treated with one approach actually function more adequately or comfortably than those treated by another approach. The initial rationale for many new programs, however, seems to be little more than one of "let's try it and see how it works." If a new approach appears to work, then the investigators have little more to fall back on in reporting its effectiveness than numbers of clients judged improved, case history reports of successful outcome, and percentages of patients returned to community living. While such data are acceptable as initial clinical trial reports, they rarely satisfy mental health professionals who want to know something about measurable changes in clients' functioning.

While everyone seems to agree that careful evaluation of various mental health programs is urgently needed, careful evaluation is often prohibitively expensive, particularly if one chooses to use professionally trained observers. Moreover, careful evaluation raises complex problems for which there are few answers. How does one decide, for example, which is the best data source (i.e., the patient, his relatives, or professionally trained observers) to use in collecting information about client functioning? How reliable and valid are reports or ratings from various data sources? Should one evaluate clients' functioning before as well as following treatment? What kinds of adjustment and functioning should one measure? Are observations and interviews in the treatment setting (clinic or hospital) related to functioning and adjustment at home or on the job?

That these questions have not always been resolved satisfactorily is suggested by inconsistencies among findings about the effects of psychiatric hospitalization. Lewinsohn and Nichols (1964), for example, reported highly significant improvement in areas of symptom, social, and work adjustment following psychiatric hospitalization. Freeman and Simmons (1963) and McPartland and Richart (1966) suggested that many areas of psychopathology are significantly improved following hospitalization, but that role skills (employment, social involvement, and the like) are not. And finally, Berger, Rice, Sewell, and Lemkau (1963) found no measurable pre-posthospital changes in 13 out of 16 measured areas of adjustment (4 groups × 4 adjustment areas). Thus findings vary from study to study depending on the data source used, time and method of collection (pre-post versus recall ratings), types of adjustment measured, and patient groups included.

In measuring the outcomes of psychiatric hospital treatment, two basic approaches have been employed. The first strategy is that of identifying a group of patients at release, and interviewing them (and/or their significant relatives) several weeks or months after their return to the community. The investigator obtains information about their posthospital community adjustment, and attempts to answer such questions as whether or not ex-patients function adequately, or how their adjustment compares with that of nonpatients.

The second strategy is that of obtaining measures of patients' adjustment both before and after hospitalization. By identifying the population at the beginning of hospitalization, rather than at the time of release, one can measure and contrast the pre- and posttreatment levels of functioning and adjustment. By making pre- and posttreatment comparisons, the investigator attempts to learn whether or not hospitalization had a measurable impact on patients' adjustment, and if so, which areas of functioning are affected most and least.

Strategies Used for Evaluating Treatment Outcome

Followup Studies

Employing the followup strategy to assess the outcome of hospital treatment, most studies indicate that expatients function differently than individuals who have never been hospitalized. The proportions of expatients estimated to function "normally" or as well as the average person vary widely from study to study. Expatients, for example, adjust comparatively well on some criteria but poorly on others. Some investigators seem overly critical in judging "normal" functioning. Schooler et al. (1967), for example, estimated that only 11 per cent of released schizophrenics function as well as the "average" person. Gurel (1965) found that only 12 to 15 per cent of their released schizophrenic population were making a "good" community adjustment two to four years after release. While other studies are more optimistic, all seem to indicate that most expatients adjust less well than most nonpatients.

One of the most extensive followup studies undertaken is that reported by Freeman and Simmons '(1963). If one uses the criterion of full time employment, only 23 to 31 per cent of male expatients functioned adequately after release (p. 49). For females, from half to two-thirds assumed responsibility for household chores (meals, laundry, and cleaning) (p. 54), a finding similar to that reported by Angrist et al. (1968). These data suggest that male expatients

have more difficulty in assuming a productive role (work) than female expatients (housekeeping), perhaps because housekeeping is an easier activity to
handle satisfactorily than is full time work.

Turning next to the area of posthospital symptom adjustment, Leyberg (1965)
found only 26 per cent of expatients symptom free one year after release.
Freeman and Simmons (1963, p. 66) reported that only 33 per cent of the
male and 24 per cent of the female expatients were in the "normal" range of
symptom adjustment at the time of their one year followup. Schooler *et al.*
(1967), however, reported that 68 per cent of their patients showed almost no
symptomatology on followup. While Angrist *et al.* (1968) found the female
expatient more poorly adjusted than her female neighbor, the differences were
small enough to also suggest that some neighbors were more poorly adjusted
psychologically than some expatients.

How well do nonpatients function in the area of symptom adjustment? Langner (1960) found that 46 per cent of a random sample of urban adults reported
sufficient psychopathology to warrant classification as moderately (22 per cent)
to seriously (24 per cent) impaired. In a nationwide survey, Gurin, Veroff, and
Feld (1960) found that 32 per cent of all people worry "a lot" or "all the
time" and had sufficient problems with sleeping, nervousness, and appetite loss
to be classified as highly anxious (pp. 42, 198). Srole, Langner, and Rennie
(1962), in their survey of an urban population, reported 24 per cent as showing clear signs of serious or marked psychopathology.

The percentage of expatients judged to be relatively symptom free, then,
fluctuates widely (26 to 68 per cent). The symptom adjustment of expatients
seems poorer than that of people in general, for at least 54 to 76 per cent of
randomly sampled nonpatient populations appear relatively symptom free.

The followup strategy, although providing fascinating data about expatients
in the community, does have some major disadvantages as an assessment technique. It cannot, for example, ordinarily be employed to evaluate the effectiveness of one program or hospital against that of another program or hospital.
Followup information can be used for program evaluation only when one knows
that the patient groups were similar in their initial or pretreatment adjustment.
This initial information, however, is precisely the kind of information an investigator ordinarily cannot obtain when he identifies and selects his patient population at the time of release. And yet attempts have been made to contrast the
outcome of hospital programs using followup information alone (Freeman and
Simmons, 1963, p. 79).

Also unwarranted, but sometimes practiced by those who rely on followup
information, is the categorizing of patients as successful and unsuccessful treatment cases, or as having good and poor outcomes. If, for example, a patient is
employed following hospitalization, he may be designated as a "treatment success" in the area of productivity. Hospital treatment, however, can be credited
for his success only if that patient was typically unemployed prior to hospitalization. Similarly, hospital treatment would be regarded as unsuccessful only
when the formerly employed patient was unable to return to work following
release. Once again, one must know something about patients' pretreatment
functioning and adjustment before he can draw any conclusions about treatment
outcome from the followup information.

Summarizing at this point, followup studies provide important information about how expatients function in the community following release, especially when their performance has been systematically contrasted with that of nonpatients (Angrist et al., 1968). Followup data can be used to compare the effectiveness of different hospitals or treatment programs only when patients have been matched either on their pretreatment adjustment (Ellsworth, 1968; Fairweather et al., 1960; Fairweather, 1964) or assigned randomly to treatment conditions (Gove, 1965; Mendel, 1966). Many who employ the followup approach, however, also attempt to judge patients as having good or poor treatment outcomes, or to judge programs as successful or unsuccessful without knowing about, or controlling for, the pretreatment adjustment of their population. Such practices are not justifiable.

Pre-post Outcome Studies

By contrasting patients' pre- and posttreatment adjustment, one can handle most of the problems in treatment evaluation. The pre-post study design allows one to explore such problems as: (a) examining the kinds of adjustment areas affected most and least by various treatment approaches; (b) determining good and poor treatment outcomes for each patient individually; and (c) evaluating the comparative effectiveness of different programs by controlling for differences in patients' initial adjustment. The primary limitation of such a design, however, is that one cannot determine the comparative effects of "treatment versus no-treatment" unless he utilizes an untreated control group. People who applied for treatment but received none, however, often improved as much as those seen in psychotherapy (Bergin, 1966). Often, the so-called control group obtained help from friends, employers, ministers, teachers, and the like. In this sense, one studies not the outcome of "treatment versus no-treatment," but the relative effects of alternative approaches to treatment.

Studies utilizing the pre- and posttreatment design have revealed information about hospital treatment outcome from two perspectives: first, the changes in patients' adjustment as viewed from the treatment setting itself; and secondly, the patients' adjustment as observed in his behavior outside the treatment setting. Also of interest has been the kinds of adjustment and behavior identified as most and least affected by treatment.

Symptom ratings at the time of a psychiatric patient's release from the hospital generally reveal a significant reduction in psychopathology from that seen at the time of his admission. This reduction in symptomatology between admission and release has been reported in studies of both staff ratings (Cohen, J. et al., 1966; Lewinsohn and Nichols, 1964) and patient ratings (Johnston and McNeal, 1965). Staff ratings of expatients' adjustment in the community have also revealed a significant improvement, as compared with staff ratings of patients' pretreatment symptom adjustment (Lewinsohn and Nichols, 1964; McPartland and Richart, 1966). Staff and patient posttreatment ratings of hospital and community adjustment, then, typically reveal significant improvement in symptomatology over that rated initially.

The purposes of the present study are to help resolve some of the complexities and cost problems of adequate psychiatric program evaluation. The data reported herein are part of a large scale three-year study in which the functioning and adjustment of 178 male veterans, diagnosed as schizophrenic, was evaluated by multiple scales and raters in both hospital and community settings. The design and comprehensiveness of this study allows one to obtain some answers to at least four basic questions. Section I presents the comparative reliability and validity of various sources of information about patients' functioning and adjustment. Although tradition compels us to place more confidence in the assessment of patient adjustment by trained staff, the data in this study do not support that tradition. For example, the reliability and validity estimates of relatives' ratings of patient adjustment are as high as those for trained staff. Having established the comparative reliability and validity estimates of different data sources and scales, one can next ask whether or not hospitalization results in any symptom and social-behavioral changes (Section II). While hospitalization results in marked reduction in observed levels of psychopathology, we find that instrumental or role performance show less change.

The third major issue discussed in this report asks whether or not there is any congruence between hospital behavior and community adjustment. For example, does a well adjusted hospital patient become a well adjusted community citizen? The data in Section III of this report suggest that behavior and adjustment are, to a large extent, situationally related phenomena, and that staff probably err when they attempt to judge the effectiveness of their treatment programs from a hospital-based appraisal. Finally, Section IV outlines a reasonable and an economically feasible approach to the measurement of patient improvement and program effectiveness. For this version of the article, Sections I, II, and IV have been condensed.

Study Setting and Background

During 1963, plans were made to evaluate the possibility of predicting, for male veterans with a diagnosis of schizophrenia, which of three treatment programs results in the best treatment outcome. The three treatment programs differed in terms of staff endorsement of attitudes toward mental illness. Assigned to one ward were professional and nursing staff who endorsed the attitude of Conventionality-authoritarianism. Protective-benevolent staff were assigned to a second ward. The third ward was staffed by Non-traditional personnel, or those rejecting the other two attitudes. Previous research had shown that these attitude groups differed in terms of their styles of interaction with patients (Ellsworth, 1965).

Each of the three treatment wards served about 110 patients, with a team of psychiatrist, psychologist, social worker, two or three nurses, and about 18 nursing assistants per 24-hour coverage. Each ward treated the complete range of acute and chronically hospitalized, young and old patients with a variety of diagnoses. All newly admitted patients remained on a small admission ward for a few days. Assignment to one of the three treatment wards was by strict rotation, each ward taking every third admission. The staff on each ward was free to develop its own treatment philosophy and method of operation. They differed primarily in the degree of treatment responsibility assumed by staff versus patients, ranging from a doctor centered ward (Conventional-authoritarian), to a levels system program in which patients themselves assumed many of the traditional staff functions (Non-traditional ward; see Childers, 1967). The Protective-benevolent staff developed a program including aspects of both doctor centered and patient centered concepts.

In order to enhance the possibility of predicting treatment outcome by patient by ward, careful attention was paid to the criterion or outcome problem. First, we selected a variety of symptom and adjustment scales, and a variety of observers (i.e., staff, patients, and patients' relatives). Secondly, we collected ratings of prehospital, inhospital, and posthospital adjustment. Thirdly, a project social worker spent much of his time in the community interviewing the family at the time of the patient's admission to the hospital, and interviewing both the patient and his family (twice) following the patient's release. In addition, inhospital behavior and symptom rating scales were completed twice by nursing and professional staff respectively.

This report is not intended to present data regarding the prediction of patients' response to treatment. What is presented are those data on treatment outcomes collected by a variety of rating scales and data sources across hospital and community settings.

Procedure

Patient Sample

The subjects included in this study were male veterans with a diagnosis of schizophrenia. Upon admission to the hospital, those who became project patients were those who: (a) had been in the community at least 100 days prior to admission, (b) were under 60 years of age, (c) had observable symptoms of psychopathology at the time of admission, (d) remained hospitalized for at least four weeks, and (e) had an identifiable informant (typically a relative) who knew the patient well, and who lived within a radius of about 200 miles of the hospital.

Between March 28, 1964, and June 30, 1966, 178 patients met the above criteria and were included in the study. The first 90 patients constituted the first half of the study sample, interviewed by one psychologist-social worker team (R.E. and D.K.). A second interview team (B.C. and G.A.) admitted to the project patients 91 through 178. Of these 178 patients, 163 or 92 per cent achieved a community stay of at least 90 days that began within one year after their admission.

Rating Scales Used in the Study

Five rating scales were used, and 20 dimensions of adjustment scored from them. Two scales had been standardized elsewhere, the other three were developed for this project. The first standardized scale was the MACC Behavioral Adjustment Scale (Ellsworth, 1962) yielding scores in four areas: (1) Mood, (2) Cooperation, (3) Communication, and (4) Social Contact. The second standardized scale was a factor analyzed Symptom Rating Scale (Cohen, Gurel, and Stumpf, 1966) yielding five scores (variables 5 through 9): (5) Uncooperative, (6) Depression Anxiety, (7) Paranoid Hostility, (8) Deteriorated Thought, and (9) Unmotivated.

COMMUNITY ADJUSTMENT SCALE (VARIABLES 10-15)   Not available or known to us was a satisfactory scale for measuring a wide range of symptom and social community adjustment as rated by patients' relatives. One scale, developed by Berger *et al.* (1964), measured primarily social and self-care behavior. Another scale was too short and its items too general (Fairweather *et al.*, 1960). The Freeman and Simmons questionnaire (1963) obtained information from relatives about many aspects of patients' adjustment, but the items were designed to be completed by a professionally trained person after interviewing the informant. A very long but more adequate scale by Katz and Lyerly (1963) was not known to us at the time. We needed, then, a scale to be filled out by the relative himself covering both social and symptom areas since, in our opinion, neither area alone would have constituted an adequate measure of community adjustment.

A 39-item four-point rating scale describing patients' community behavior was developed for use by relatives. Some of these items were adopted from the work of Freeman and Simmons (1963) and Berger *et al.* (1963), while other items were developed from interviews in which relatives described the kinds of behaviors they had typically observed during the month preceding admission. The rating items were designed so that abstract clinical concepts were translated into concrete behavior. A time interval of one month was chosen since ratings covering a longer recall period of time have been found to result in lowered item reliabilities (Berger *et al.*, 1964, p. 14). Our Community Adjustment Scale was factor analyzed after the first 60 patients had completed the study, and six factors were identified. The factor model used was a principal components analysis (unities in the diagonal), followed by a varimax rotation. The factors, their items, and factor loadings (in parenthesis) are listed below:

Variable 10, Dependent Confusion (Factor I, 16% of the variance)

    (a) Has helped with regular household chores. (−.76)
    (b) Has forgotten to do important things. (.74)
    (c) Appears to be in a daze recently. (.72)
    (d) Talk makes sense. (−.67)
    (e) Loses track of time. (.67)
    (f) Seems more like a 10-year-old child than a responsible adult. (.66)
    (g) Needed supervision and guidance from the family. (.64)
    (h) Gets into debt by foolish buying. (.63)
    (i) Finds it difficult to make everyday decisions. (.60)
    (j) Has trouble recognizing people. (.56)
    (k) Appears to be nervous. (.55)
    (l) Because the veteran lives at home, it has been necessary to neglect other family members in order to spend the necessary time with him. (.51)

Variable 11, Agitation Depression (Factor II, 15% of the variance)

    (a) Seemed unhappy and feels that things look hopeless. (−.74)
    (b) Argued with family members recently. (−.72)
    (c) Said that life doesn't seem worth living. (−.70)

(d) Has made other family members nervous. (−.65)
(e) Worried or complained about his problems. (−.65)
(f) Wanted to talk to and be with people. (.57)
(g) Having him home has affected the family's normal routine (−.56)
(h) Sitting around the house all day. (−.56)
(i) Tried to hit or hurt somebody recently. (−.51)
(j) Stays by himself recently. (−.49)
(k) Thinks people talk about him. (−.48)

Variable 12, Unacceptable Behavior (Factor IV, 7% of the variance)

(a) Drinking too much alcoholic beverages recently. (.71)
(b) Damaged or wrecked things. (.64)
(c) Talks or mutters to himself. (.58)
(d) Said that he hears voices. (.40)

Variable 13, Friendship Skills (Factor III, 10% of the variance)

(a) Spends time with his own friends. (.90)
(b) Has outside friends of his own. (.89)
(c) Is a person of little or few outside interests versus has a wide variety of outside interests. (.78)
(d) Socializes and talks with people who visit the house. (.71)
(e) Has a drinking problem which interferes with family, job, or community adjustment. (−.53)

Variable 14, Organization Participation (Factor V, 7% of the variance)

(a) Participates in the activities of social organizations. (−.84)
(b) Attends social organizations. (−.84)
(c) Attends church. (−.70)
(d) Is neat and clean (−.41)

Variable 15, Employment (Factor VI, 7% of the variance)

(a) Held a full-time job. (−.79)
(b) Amount of earnings from his work or job. (−.78)

SOCIAL WORK SCALE (VARIABLES 16-19)   Of great interest to us was a measure of patients' adjustment which would include an estimate of whether or not that adjustment met, fell short of, or exceeded the family's expectations (Freeman and Simmons, 1963). A scale was designed to enable the social worker to rate the relative's expectation and degree of satisfaction, and the patient's level of performance, in four areas: Personal Comfort, Employment, Family Interpersonal Relations, and Socialization. Two additional scores were derived for each of these areas, the congruence between expectation and performance, and the congruence between satisfaction and performance. These 20 scores were cluster analyzed using a method proposed by Frochter (1954). A cluster is defined as a group of items having high intercorrelations with each other, but low correlations with items outside the cluster. Three of the five scores in each of the four areas were highly interrelated and seemed to express the overall adjustment level for each of these areas.

Variable 16, Personal Comfort. A high score indicates a patient whose relative is rated as highly satisfied, whose performance level is judged by the social worker as high, and whose rated performance meets or exceeds the judged expectation (these three scores have an average intercorrelation of .55, and an average correlation of .19 with all other items outside this cluster).

Variable 17, Productivity. A high score indicates a social worker rating of high adjustment for the patient, a judged high expectation on the part of the relative, and a patient whose adjustment is congruent with the degree of judged relative satisfaction (these three item scores correlate .71, and correlate .16 with items outside the cluster).

Variable 18, Family Interpersonal. A high score reflects a high social worker rating of patient's adjustment, a high rating of family satisfaction, and a score that reflects a patient whose adjustment meets or exceeds family expectation (the scores of these three items intercorrelate .68, and correlate .24 with items outside the cluster).

Variable 19, Socialization. A high score reflects a high social worker rating of patient's adjustment, a high rating of family satisfaction, and a patient who meets or exceeds expectation (item intercorrelation within cluster .51; correlations outside cluster, .23).

PATIENT SELF-RATING SCALE (VARIABLE 20)   The patient was asked to rate his own symptom adjustment at the time of admission, and again at the time of community followup. Seventeen items were taken from the 39-item Community Adjustment Scale developed for use by patients' relatives. These seventeen items were reworded for use by the veteran himself. Seven items were taken from the Dependent Confusion factor (Variable 10, items a, b, e, g, h, i, and j). Eight items were taken from the Agitation Depression factor (Variable 11, items a, b, c, e, f, h, j, and k); and two items were taken from the Unacceptable Behavior factor (Variable 12, items a and b. In general, the score derived from these items portrays the extent to which the veteran himself perceives and reports an absence or presence of psychopathological symptoms.

Scoring the 20 Variables

Using the scores for the first 60 patients who completed the study, raw scores were converted into standard scores. For each patient, the admission and first posthospital ratings were pooled, and converted to standard scores with a mean of 50 and a standard deviation of 10. All scales are scored so that a *high score* (above 50) means *good adjustment* in that area. A patient who obtains a score of 60 on Variable 5 (Uncooperative), for example, is realtively well adjusted or cooperative in that area. In order to avoid confusion, all negative scales are relabelled as positive scales. Uncooperative becomes Cooperative, for example, so that a high score on Variable 5 indicates cooperation, while a low score indicates an uncooperative or poorly adjusted person in that area. This relabelling of negative dimensions is done only to facilitate and simplify the presentation of data in this report.

TABLE I

DATA COLLECTION SCHEDULE AND RATER USED

Data Collected	Time 1 Admission	Time 2 Two Month Post Admission	Time 3 Three Weeks After Release	Time 4 Three Months After Release
MACC Scale (variables 1–4)	Admission ward aides	Treatment ward aides	Social worker	Social worker
Symptom Ratings (variables 5–9)	Psychologist, social worker	Psychologist, social worker	Social worker	Social worker
Community Adjust- ment Scale (variables 10– 15)	Patient's rela- tives	Not obtained	Patient's rela- tives	Patient's rela- tives
Social Work Scale (variables 16– 19)	Social worker	Not obtained	Social worker	Social worker
Patient Self Rating Scale (variable 20)	Patient	Not obtained	Patient	Patient

Data Collection Schedule

Four data collection points were scheduled, as shown in Table I. At the time of admission (Time 1) the MACC Scale was completed by one evening shift and (at least) one day shift aide within three days after the patient's admission, and scores from all aide raters were averaged. A psychologist-social worker team interviewed the patient shortly after admission and independently rated the Symptom Rating Scale. Their scores were later corrected for constant rater bias, combined, and averaged. And finally, the patient completed the 17-item Symptom Adjustment Scale at this time.

Within a few days after admission, the social worker visited the patient's relatives in their home. After identifying the relative most involved with the patient, he asked him (or her) to rate the patient on the Community Adjust- ment Scale so as to describe the patient's preadmission behavior. After inter- viewing the relatives, the social worker completed the Social Work Scale de- scribing the patient's behavior, and relative's expectation and satisfaction for four areas of patient adjustment.

TIME 2 In order to assess initial response to treatment, each patient was again evaluated two months after admission. If the patient was scheduled for release between the fourth and eighth week, he was interviewed and rated a day or two before his actual release. As seen in Table I, the treatment ward aides (day and evening shift) completed the MACC Scale and the psychologist-social worker team completed the Symptom Rating Scale at Time 2. Since the patient was not in the community at this time, the Community Adjustment, the Patient Self-Rating, and the Social Work Scales were not completed.

TIMES 3 and 4. Three weeks and again three months after release, the pa- tient's family was contacted and visited in their home by the social worker.

The patient was interviewed and the Symptom Rating Scale was completed by the social worker. After interviewing the family, the social worker completed the MACC and Social Work Scales. During this time, the patient completed the Self-Rating Scale, and the significant relative completed the Community Adjustment Scale.

Section I of this article deals with the comparative reliability and validity of the five instruments (20 scales) and three sources of information (patients, their relatives, and staff). Once the validity and reliability estimates are presented, one then considers in Section II the symptom and social-behavioral adjustment areas that change most and least as a result of hospitalization. For the purpose of this book the major findings of Sections I and II are summarized below.

Section I. Reliability and Validity
of Staff, Patient, and Family Ratings

(a) Various estimates of scale reliability indicated that adjustment rating data from all three sources were acceptably reliable.

(b) Initial family and staff ratings predicted equally well the length of hospitalization. Patients' self-ratings had no predictive validity.

(c) Followup family and staff ratings were equally predictive of patients' self-ratings of adjustment, the second estimate of scale validity.

(d) And finally, family ratings were correlated with staff ratings in order to estimate concurrent validity. When the patients' posthospital community adjustment was rated by both family and staff, significant correlations occurred in those areas measuring similar behavior.

It is important to note that the validity estimates of relatives' ratings were equal to those for staff ratings. It may be that relatives have better data on which to base their ratings than staff. Relatives have the advantage of observing the patient in the living situation over a long period of time. Staff ratings are based primarily on what a patient says, rather than on observations of his behavior (Auerbach and Ewing, 1964).

Section II. Adjustment
Changes Following Hospitalization

Consider the three questions asked earlier in this paper. First, "Do staff ratings of patient adjustment reveal greater improvement than family ratings?" The results indicate that both family and staff ratings reveal significant improvement in patients' pre- and posthospital adjustment, but that greater pre-post changes often occur in those symptom adjustment areas rated by patients' families. These findings are limited to the particular patient population and hospital setting (i.e., males diagnosed as schizophrenic treated in a Veterans Administration hospital). Nevertheless, our data support the conclusion by Lewinsohn and Nichols (1964) that significant changes in symptom adjustment are reported by patients' relatives. The Berger et al. (1963) population was drawn from state hospitals, and the infrequent gains in adjustment reported by their patients' families may have been peculiar to those treatment settings.

Secondly, "What is the relationship between symptom adjustment and instrumental functioning?" This depends on what areas of functioning and adjustment one is considering. We found that an expatient's participation in social organizations was largely unrelated to his symptom adjustment. Other instrumental areas, such as work and interpersonal social skills, are sometimes mildly or moderately related to various areas of symptom and behavioral adjustment. Symptom and instrumental performance, then, are not clearly independent phenomena. The 20 areas of functioning, on the other hand, do appear to fall into categories (primary factor dimensions) readily identifiable as symptom and instrumental adjustment.

And thirdly, "Does psychiatric hospitalization result in significant symptom reduction, but little if any improvement in social and instrumental functioning?" In general, yes. Our data do not support the findings by Lewinsohn and Nichols (1964, p. 277) that all areas of social and economic community adjustment were improved following hospitalization. Instead, our data agree with those reported by Berger *et al.* (1963) and McPartland and Richart (1966), who suggest that psychiatric treatment often results in significant symptom reduction, but not instrumental performance changes.

One rather clear inference can be drawn from these results regarding the relevance of hospitalization for various areas of adjustment difficulty. If a patient's primary problem is an area of role functioning (i.e., work and/or social involvement), then psychiatric hospital programs are not now relevant. Either hospital programs need to be modified, or persons with role functioning difficulties sent elsewhere (Gurel, 1967). As things stand now, however, psychiatric hospital staff should concentrate on doing well the things they do best, that is, reducing symptoms such as anxiety, depression, confusion, and so forth. It appears unjustified to expend staff resources or keep patients hospitalized in hopes of altering those instrumental performance areas that cannot now be modified through hospital treatment.

Section III. Congruence Between Community and Hospital Adjustment and Behavior

Certain hospital practices have been established over the years, practices obviously arising from a set of basic assumptions regarding the nature of patient behavior and adjustment. Upon admission the patient is interviewed and a diagnosis made. Whether or not relatives are also interviewed does not deter the experienced clinician from making a diagnosis, for he has come to believe that he is observing a relatively stable and readily identifiable condition. At the time of discharge, the decision to release is based on some estimate of the patient's improvement as seen in the hospital setting. Having come to believe that improvement is primarily person-related (and therefore stable across situations), staff assume that the patient who improved most in the hospital will typically function better in the community than his less improved counterpart. The clinical investigator who concludes that treatment A is more effective than treatment B sees no need to specify that it is hospital behavior that treatment A affects, for he too has come to believe that adjustment and improvement are primarily intrapersonal phenomena.

How important are situational components in accounting for people's behavior? As far back as 1928, Hartshorne and May demonstrated that the characteristics of honesty and deceit were not stable phenomena, for children who stole or lied in one situation would not necessarily do so in another. Recent studies have also shown that situations are powerful determinants of behavior. The amount a man talks, for example, varies markedly depending on whether he is alone with his wife, or taking a golf lesson (Soskin and John, 1963). A boy may characteristically behave aggressively at camp, but not at home (Gump, Schoggen, and Redl, 1957). The data in this study indicate that patients are seen as much more cooperative in the hospital than after release. With its premium on compliance, the institutional setting is apparently more effective in "pulling" conforming behavior from its clients than is the community setting. And finally, staff are often quite surprised to observe a group of chronically hospitalized patients behaving quite appropriately in a downtown restaurant, but acting "crazy" in their own hospital dining room. For a long time it has been known that situations are powerful determinants of people's behavior, and yet many clinicians have continued to disregard the situation as an important component of behavior.

Some clinicians acknowledge the effects of situations on some behaviors, but argue that such characteristics as anxiety, hostility, and submissiveness remain fairly stable across situations. The relative contribution of situation versus person, as determinants of anxious behavior, has been explored in a study by Endler, Hunt, and Rosenstein (1962). Examining the proportion of response variance attributable to subjects and situations, these investigators found that more of the variance was attributable to situational than to personal effects. They concluded (p. 29): "The predominance of situational variance over subject variance clearly supports the contention of social psychologists that knowing the situation is more important for predicting behavior than knowing personal idiosyncrasies."

The interaction effects of person and situation have also been explored by Raush, Dittman, and Taylor (1959). In observing the friendly-hostile, and dominant-submissive behavior of institutionalized disturbed children, they found that situational and personal determinants of behavior were about equal in importance. More important than either, however, was the amount of variance accounted for by the effects of person-in-situation. Some children consistently acted aggressively at lunch but not during recreation. Others behaved themselves at lunch, but consistently acted out during recreation. Situational effects may also be greater for "normals" than for disturbed people (Raush et al., 1960). In other words, a disturbed person may not be able to tailor his actions entirely to fit the particular situation, whereas a "normal" person can act "student" in school, "parent" with child, "employee" at work, "buyer" in a store, and the like. To some degree, at least, shy people probably behave shyly across different situations, but not necessarily in all situations. Some situations pull certain classes of behavior but not others. The greatest amount of variance, however, may be accounted for by interactional or person-in-situation effects. Some people consistently behave aggressively in some situations but not others, while the opposite is true for other people.

Relationship between Hospital and Community Behavior and Adjustment

Since the reported relationships between hospital and community adjustment vary widely, further clarification is needed regarding the degree of congruence between patients' hospital and community behavior. This problem will now be examined, holding to a minimum the time interval between community and hospital adjustment ratings. These data will help clarify the extent to which behavior is stable across settings and therefore presumably person-determined. If patient behavior is primarily a function of intrapersonal determinants, such as the organism's physiological state (illness or disease concept) or of personality dimensions (trait psychology) then: (a) patients' preadmission behavior in the community should be similar to their behavior on the admission ward a few days later; and (b) patients who are well adjusted in certain areas at release should be well adjusted in these same areas three weeks later in the community. Data from the present study will next be examined in order to confirm or reject these hypotheses.

In this study, patients' preadmission community adjustment was rated by their relatives, while adjustment shortly after admission was rated by both staff and patients. Of the 178 patients in the study, 146 were admitted to Roseburg directly

TABLE II

RELATIONSHIP BETWEEN RELATIVE RATED PREADMISSION COMMUNITY ADJUSTMENT, AND STAFF AND PATIENT RATED ADMISSION WARD ADJUSTMENT ($N = 146$ DIRECT ADMISSIONS)

Initial Staff and Patient Ratings	Initial Relative Ratings of Community Adjustment					
	Good Contact* (10)	Calm Friendly* (11)	Acceptable Behavior* (12)	Friendship Skills (13)	Soc. Org. Partic. (14)	Employment (15)
MACC						
1. Mood	.03	.00	.03	−.21‡	−.01	.05
2. Cooperation	.04	−.12	−.02	−.16†	.05	.03
3. Communication	.06	−.17†	−.09	−.12	.05	−.01
4. Social contact	.14	.01	.00	.07	.12	.10
Symptom Rating						
5. Cooperative*	.15	−.05	.01	.04	.10	.10
6. Nonanxious*	−.24‡	−.01	−.22‡	−.20†	−.11	−.10
7. Trusting-friendly*	−.10	.00	.09	−.17†	.02	−.03
8. Clear thinking*	.03	−.13	−.09	−.13	.12	−.11
9. Motivated*	.12	.06	−.01	.16†	−.01	.33‡
Patient Self-Rating						
20. Symptom adjustment	.08	.10	.06	−.08	.15	−.28‡

* Reflected or reversed labels.
† $p < .05$
‡ $< .01$ for N of 146

from the community, while 32 others were hospitalized elsewhere more than five days before transfer. For these 146 direct admissions, then, the congruence between preadmission community and initial hospital behavior can be examined. Also, 52 patients were released within a few days after their Time 2 (two month) interview and ward behavior ratings. Three weeks later, the adjustment of these 52 men was rated in the community by the social worker, the patient, and his family. These subsamples of 146 direct-admission and 52 early-release patients were selected in order to keep the interval between community and hospital ratings to an absolute minimum while assessing the congruence between hospital and community behavior.

CONGRUENCE BETWEEN INITIAL COMMUNITY AND ADMISSION WARD ADJUSTMENT As seen in Table II, 8 of the 54 intercorrelations between initial staff ratings of hospital adjustment and relative ratings of community behavior are statistically significant. Six of these correlations, however, indicate a small (but definite) negative relationship between community and hospital behavior. For example, the patient who is rated by the staff as anxious (6) on the admission ward tends to be rated in the community by his family as in Good Contact ($r = -.24$), showing Acceptable Behavior ($r = -.22$) and having Friendship Skills ($r = -.20$). The largest of the two positive correlations was .33 between Variables 9 and 15, which means that the man who receives a high score on Employed from his family is rated by staff as Motivated. Of interest, also, is that the patient who rates himself as experiencing symptoms tends to receive a high score on Employed ($r = -.28$). Despite these few statistically significant correlations, however, the most obvious conclusion from the data in Table II is that there is no consistent congruence between initial community adjustment as rated by family, and admission ward behavior as rated by staff.

CONGRUENCE BETWEEN HOSPITAL EXIT RATINGS AND COMMUNITY ADJUSTMENT THREE WEEKS LATER This data analysis again indicates very little relationship between staff rated adjustment at the time of hospital release, and family rated community adjustment three weeks later. The patient who is rated by his family as having his own friends and spending time with them (13) had been rated at exit as Unpleasant ($r -.34$ with Mood) and Hostile ($r -.42$ with Trusting-Friendly). In many ways, the interpretation of the negative relationships between hospital and community behavior is reminiscent of the conclusion reached by Vernier et al. (1961): namely, that the independent and socially assertive community patient tends to have made a poor hospital adjustment.

Summarizing the statistically significant findings from Tables II and III, the relatively well adjusted community patient sometimes makes, or has made, a poor adjustment in the hospital. The anxious hospital admission ward patient tends to have been rated by his relatives as being in good contact, showing acceptable behavior, and having friends in the community before admission. The released patient who has friends in the community tends to have been rated by staff as unpleasant and hostile in the hospital at the time of release. In general, however, one can predict little about admission ward behavior from relatives' ratings, or about relative rated posthospital community adjustment from exit staff ratings. Since relative and staff ratings of adjustment are found to be equally reliable and valid (Section I), one cannot dismiss the lack of congruence between hospital and community behavior as a function of invalid relative (or staff) ratings. What

TABLE III

RELATIONSHIP BETWEEN STAFF RATED ADJUSTMENT AT RELEASE, AND
RELATIVE AND PATIENT RATED COMMUNITY ADJUSTMENT THREE WEEKS
LATER ($N = 52$ PATIENTS INTERVIEWED AT EXIT)

Staff Ratings at Release	*Relative and Patient Ratings Three Weeks After Release*						
	Good Contact* (10)	Calm Friendly* (11)	Acceptable Behavior* (12)	Friendship Skills (13)	Soc. Org. Partic. (14)	Employ- ment (15)	Patient Ratings (20)
MACC							
1. Mood	−.24	−.11	−.19	−.34†	−.01	−.02	.00
2. Cooperation	−.06	.07	.04	−.16	.18	−.05	−.04
3. Communication	.06	.07	.06	−.09	.19	.15	−.08
4. Social contact	−.08	−.05	−.03	−.08	.17	.13	−.20
Symptom Rating							
5. Cooperative	−.15	−.23	−.03	−.11	.17	.11	−.16
6. Nonanxious*	−.01	.15	−.15	−.09	.05	.08	.09
7. Trusting- friendly*	−.22	−.05	−.02	−.42‡	.05	.08	.16
8. Clear thinking*	.02	−.12	−.24	−.05	−.09	.20	−.15
9. Motivated*	.26	.11	.11	.22	.12	.52‡	−.25

* Reflected or reversed scale labels.
† $p < .05$
‡ $< .01$ for N of 52

the data do suggest is that symptoms and social adjustment, as viewed by patients'
relatives in the community, have little relationship to symptoms and adjustment
as viewed by staff in the hospital setting.

Behavioral Consistency Across Time
as a Function of Scale, Rater, and Setting

The data presented in Tables II and III indicate that patients' behavior changes
between hospital and community settings. The possibility of finding behavioral
stability across settings and time is reduced because different raters (staff versus
relatives) and different scales have been used to assess hospital and community
behavior. One might ask whether there is any measurable behavioral consistency
across settings when the patient is rated on the same scale in both settings. Also,
how much consistency is there in a patient's behavior in different settings when
the same scale *and* rater are used? And finally, what is the consistency in patients' behavior over time when scale, rater, *and* setting are held constant?
Answers to these three questions should also help clarify the general problem of
whether patients' behavior is primarily a function of personal characteristics or
setting conditions.

The design of the present study provides data that help clarify these questions
and issues. Recall that each patient was rated on the MACC Scale two months
after admission by the treatment ward aides. Each patient was also interviewed
and rated at that time by the psychologist-social worker team. Fifty-two of these
patients exited from the hospital at that time, and were rated three weeks and

three months later by the social worker on the MACC and Symptom Rating Scales. Comparing Time 2 and Time 3 MACC scores, one can determine the congruence between hospital and community behavior when identical scales are completed by different raters. Comparing the Time 2 and 3 staff rated SRS scores, one can determine the congruence that occurs in ratings of patients' behavior when both scales and raters remain constant. And finally, by comparing Time 3 and Time 4 community followup ratings, one can estimate the amount of behavioral consistency when scale, rater, and setting are held constant. These data are presented in Table IV.

TABLE IV

BEHAVIORAL CONSISTENCY ACROSS TIME AS AFFECTED BY RATER AND SETTING CHANGES

| | Correlations Across Time | | t Value of |
Scales	Setting Shifts Time 2 and 3 N = 52 (1)	Setting Stable Time 3 and 4 N = 163 (2)	Correlation (z) Increase When Setting Is Stable (3)
MACC			
1. Mood	.13	.74#	5.13#
2. Cooperation	.17	.71#	4.50#
3. Communication	.26	.65#	3.19#
4. Social contact	.14	.72#	4.81#
Average of correlations	(.18)	(.71)	—
Variance accounted for (r^2)	(3%)†	(50%)§	—
Symptom Rating			
5. Cooperative*	.32‖	.59#	2.25‖
6. Nonanxious*	.32‖	.60#	2.25‖
7. Trusting-friendly*	.63#	.74#	1.31
8. Clear thinking*	.14	.57#	3.19#
9. Motivated*	.42#	.64#	1.94
Average of correlations	(.37)	(.63)	—
Variance accounted for (r^2)	(14%)‡	(39%)§	—

* Reversed or reflected labels.
† Per cent of variance accounted for when rater and setting not held constant.
‡ Per cent of variance accounted for when rater constant but setting shifts.
§ Per cent of variance accounted for when rater and setting held constant.
‖ $p < .05$
$< .01$

The correlations across time for Variables 1 to 4 (Column 1 of Table IV) indicate that little or no behavioral consistency is found when different raters (treatment ward aides versus social worker) rate the patient on the same scale in the hospital and community settings (Time 2 versus Time 3). When different raters use the same scale, then, the correlations range between .13 and .26, and only 3 per cent of the variance is accounted for by behavioral consistency across situations. When the same rater is used for both Time 2 and Time 3 (SRS Variables 5 to 9, Column 1), the correlations range between .14 and .63. Thus, when rater and scale are held constant, but the setting changes, the consistency in rated behavior across settings accounts for about 14 per cent of the variance.

Explanation is needed for the .14 to .63 range in correlations between Time 2 and 3 SRS scores (Variables 5 to 9, Column 1). Why, for example, is Trusting-Friendly behavior so consistent across situations when rated by the social worker? As already seen in the research by Buss *et al.* (1962), friendliness and hostility were not invariant personality characteristics, for the patient who reacted in a hostile way toward hospital staff was not necessarily hostile toward his family in the community (p. 85). Data already reported in Table III of this study confirm that finding, for patients rated by the staff as hostile at exit are often rated by their families as friendly and sociable in the community three weeks later ($r = -.42$). If friendliness is a phenomenon specifically related to persons, the correlation of .63 between Time 2 and Time 3 in Table IV (Column 1) simply means that the patient who is friendly to the social worker in the hospital is also friendly to him in the community three weeks later. In other words, Trusting-Friendly behavior appears consistent across settings when limited to a specific relationship but not consistent across settings when relationships vary.

Motivation, on the other hand, appears to tap an adjustment dimension that remains generally consistent across settings ($r = .42$, Table IV). Already noted in Tables II and III is the consistency between family rated Employment and hospital staff rated Motivated. Not only is the person who is rated by staff as Motivated likely to be rated by his family as Employed in the community, but he is likely also to be rated by the social worker as Motivated three weeks later ($r = .42$). In general, then, the dimension of Motivation appears fairly stable across situations whether rated by the same or different raters.

That the Time 2 and 3 correlations for SRS rated Cooperative, Nonanxious, and Clear Thinking are so low (range .14 to .32) seems strange, since scales and raters remained constant across both hospital and community settings. The field social worker, for example, usually remembered with ease what the patient was like at exit, and therefore was likely to anticipate, and find, similar behavior three weeks later. Apparently, however, Cooperative, Nonanxious, and Clear Thinking behaviors change markedly between hospital and community settings, even when the probability of finding congruence is maximized (i.e., same rater using identical scale in hospital Time 2, and community Time 3 settings).

Summarizing at this point, Column 1 of Table IV reveals small but nonsignificant relationships between hospital and community behavior when the same scales are used by different raters in the two settings (Variables 1 to 4). When the same scale *and* raters are used, the consistency in rated behavior accounts for about 14 per cent of the variance. Most of this accounted for variance, however, is attributable to the stability of Trusting-Friendly behavior between social worker and patient, rather than an indication of any great amount of consistency in patient behavior across situations.

Now consider the consistency in rated behavior over time when scale, rater, and setting are held constant (i.e., at Time 3 and 4 when the social worker rated the patients' community behavior on both the MACC and Symptom Rating Scales). Seen in Column 2 of Table IV is that, under these conditions, the consistency of rated behavior over time accounts for about 45 per cent of the variance (range 39 per cent to 50 per cent). Also seen in Column 3 of Table IV is that seven of the nine correlations reflecting behavioral stability increase significantly when situation, scale, and rater are held constant, as compared with those correlations found when only rater and/or scale are held constant.

In general, then, one can conclude that consistency in behavior is seriously disrupted when situations change. When scale, rater, and situation are held constant, behavioral consistency accounts for 45 per cent of the variance. When, however, the patient moves between settings, but is rated on the same scale by the same rater, only 14 per cent of the variance can be accounted for. This 31 per cent drop in the accounted for variance is clearly a function of situational change. As suggested earlier, even this 14 per cent of accounted for variance is inflated since stability of patients' friendliness toward the social worker is apparently a person-specific phenomenon. Under those conditions most favorable to finding behavioral consistency across situations (i.e., same rater using the same scale), only little behavioral consistency across settings can be demonstrated.

Comments on Incongruity
Between Hospital and Community Behavior

Clearly suggested by the data in Section III is that behavioral consistency is primarily a function of the situation the patient finds himself in, and secondarily a function of personal characteristics (such as "symptoms," "traits," "mental illness," and "diagnosis"). How professionally trained staff have come to ignore the situational components of behavior, and focus instead on behavior as intrapersonally determined, is not entirely clear. Older trait psychology and the traditional disease or illness model have both undoubtedly had a marked impact on many mental health clinicians. More than this, however, behavior appears consistent over time simply because situations remain stable for most people. The fact that John seems to remain about the same over time is not an illusion, but one does commit an error in logic when he assumes that behavioral consistency is primarily a product of John, and is unrelated to his situation.

Some of the data suggest that some behavior, at least, is primarily a function of person-centered variables, for ratings of motivation did remain fairly stable across different settings and observer-raters. We suggest, however, that situation effects are far more important than most clinicians believe them to be. But how does one account for the finding that patients often behave differently on the admission ward than they did in the community a few days earlier? To some patients, hospitalization may offer a refuge from a stressful community setting. For these patients, hospitalization may be perceived as an opportunity for reintegration and stabilization. For others, hospitalization apparently enhances the image of oneself as "sick." Thus, for these patients, it becomes less important to control one's impulses in the hospital than in the community. A patient's behavior, then, may change as a function of what that situation means to him. In other words, an interaction effect between personal variables and situational dimensions probably occurs, as suggested by Raush et al. (1959, 1960) and Vernier et al. (1961). Some socially outgoing, independent community citizens may well become hostile in the hospital if they view hospitalization as an unnecessary restriction, while the opposite may be true for patients who view the hospital as a refuge.

Data presented in Section III lead to questions about the relevance of certain standard procedures as currently practiced by hospital staff. They probably err, for example, when they attempt to identify patients' relevant problems on the basis of psychiatric interviews at the time of admission. Patients who appear upset and anxious on the admission ward may have been functioning comparatively well in the community a few days earlier. The data in this section suggest that for some patients at least, such problems as anxiety, confusion, and hostility may be, to a large extent, hospital-induced phenomena. Although disrupting anxiety becomes a relevant problem to be solved in the hospital setting, this does not necessarily mean that its resolution is relevant for later community adjustment. Since a patient's adjustment and functioning in the hospital does not predict his functioning in the community, it also becomes difficult to see how hospital staff can make adequate decisions about readiness for release on the basis of patients' hospital behavior.

Some have recently questioned the relevance of institutional treatment programs by suggesting that the patients' problems are community based (i.e., problems with job, wife, and the like) and can best be treated in a community setting. Whether or not a patient develops a good relationship with his therapist or other hospital staff may indicate nothing about his relationship with his wife or employer. Also, as noted earlier, if a patient's primary deficit lies in an area of instrumental performance, hospitalization will most likely be an irrelevant experience in so far as modifying this deficit.

Whether or not community based programs are more effective than hospital programs is yet to be demonstrated. What is suggested is that hospital staff might well improve the effectiveness of their own programs if they identified clearly patients' relevant problems from the standpoint of their behavior in the community. If staff not only had better data on patients' preadmission behavior, as well as feedback from the community on the outcome of their treatment efforts, the effectiveness of hospital based programs might well be improved significantly. The community informant system is such a system for routinely collecting initial community adjustment and followup data on treatment outcome.

Section IV. A Proposed Community Informant
Procedure for Measuring Treatment Effectiveness

Many of the advantages and problems of the community informant system approach have been outlined by Berger et al. (1964) and will not be repeated here. One of the undiscussed but compelling reasons for using this approach to evaluating treatment or program effectiveness is that, in the final analysis, the consumers of our hospital and clinic services are the patient and his family. A successful treatment program, then, is one that satisfies these consumers, and not necessarily one that fulfills the expectations of professional staff. Viewed in these terms, the families' assessment of patients' response to treatment is highly relevant. Since their assessment also appears to be as valid and reliable as staff evaluations, and since staff assessed hospital adjustment is unrelated to family rated community adjustment, a meaningful study of treatment program effectiveness can indeed be undertaken by using community informants. Such an appraisal system, in fact, may well offer more relevant data than most other evaluation systems that depend on the availability of professional trained staff.

Using an improved scale, the Roseburg VA Hospital has been routinely collecting pre- and posthospital community adjustment ratings for the past 15 months (since June, 1966). The patient is asked, at the time of admission, for the name of the person who knows most about his recent community adjustment, and is also asked for permission to contact this informant for further information (only about 1 per cent refuse to grant this permission). To be eligible for the community informant evaluation procedure, a patient must (*a*) have been in the community at least 30 days before admission, (*b*) have an identifiable community informant, and (*c*) remain in treatment at least two weeks. A questionnaire is then mailed to the informant. If no answer is received, a second questionnaire is sent again two weeks later. If still no answer is received, the informant is contacted by telephone. This procedure has resulted in a 92 per cent return rate. Of these, an additional 8 per cent are unusable because the returned questionnaire is either incomplete (i.e., didn't know veteran well enough) or obviously invalid. Thus, adequate initial information is obtained on 84 per cent of eligible patients.

When an initial questionnaire is received, a community diagnostic profile is prepared for the treatment staff. This profile enables the staff to identify, more precisely, those areas of adjustment that represent problems in community functioning for this particular patient. Hopefully, then, the staff can better help the patient with his community relevant problems.

At the time of release, the patient is asked for his permission to contact the community informant again. Three weeks after release, the same community informant is contacted and again asked to complete the 41-item scale. About 65 per cent of informants return an adequately completed questionnaire, with most who are unable reporting that they have seen little if anything of the patient since his release. When a followup questionnaire is returned, the residual scores are given to the treatment team so that they can evaluate the outcome of their efforts.

It is this last issue, feedback of results, that represents perhaps the greatest potential contribution of the community informant system. Typically, most staff rarely receive feedback on the effectiveness of their efforts. They know whether their patients adjust well in the hospital environment, and they sometimes know something about the average length of stay, and release and return rates for their patients. These data, however, provide inadequate and incomplete feedback since treatment teams know almost nothing about the level of patients' posthospital functioning. When hospital staff learn almost immediately which patients made a better-than-predicted posthospital community adjustment (positive residual) and whose outcome fell short of predicted, they are then in a position to begin to identify the things they did with successful-outcome patients that they failed to do with unsuccessful patients. The impact of feedback on staff treatment effectiveness is now being examined systematically. The hypothesis being tested is that feedback will significantly increase the treatment effectiveness of the hospital staff.

One final but very important use of the community informant method is that it permits treatment teams or clinicians to explore tentatively the potential effectiveness of new treatment methods. This requires that base rates of expected change (residual scores) be established for traditional treatment approaches. Having these base rates, the clinician can then ask, "I wonder what would happen if this approach was tried with the next 20 patients?" If the majority of these patients improved more than expected, the approach would then warrant a more carefully controlled evaluation. New approaches to treatment, then, could be given a systematic clinical trial, using the community informant procedure.

Once freed from the routine of devoting great amounts of their own time to assessing treatment outcomes, professionally trained staff should be increasingly able to undertake meaningful treatment and program evaluation. Not only can different treatment approaches be assessed without great expenditures of professional staff time, but the potential effectiveness of new approaches can be estimated from previously established baserate data. The often heard complaint that "we just don't have the time to both treat and evaluate," may well prove to have been less a rationalization for resistance to evaluation, and more an expression of a real and, until now, unresolved problem.

34 / The Day Hospital:
Partial Hospitalization in Psychiatry

Bernard M. Kramer

All disease runs an uneven course—and mental disease is no exception. I base my remarks about psychiatric day care on the assumption that in the course of mental illness there are varying manifestations that call for differing approaches to care and treatment. The circumstances and characteristics of each patient's state of illness or health change, and as they change our approach should be modified accordingly. Our approaches also should be governed by the fact that mental illness is not a unitary entity. On the contrary, it is made up of a wide variety of conditions.

It is clear today that not all of the conditions and stages collectively known as mental disease are suitably managed and treated by recourse to the traditional mental hospital. The long-term, full-time mental hospital, and the earlier practice of jailing the mentally ill, were based at bottom on the implicit notion that once a mental illness occurred in an individual it would last for a long time. Moreover, the dangers to self and others were thought to be enduring in this underlying conception of mental illness. It was implied that methods for handling the mentally ill should be essentially the same at the beginning of illness, during its midlife, and until the moment of discharge or death. But the natural history of mental disease leads us to an altogether different conclusion.

At one stage of psychosis there is florid, bizarre behavior; at other stages the picture is relatively calm. At one stage danger to self or society is minimal; at other stages aggressive or self-destructive trends are in the forefront. At certain times self-care is almost impossible for the patient; at other times it is quite feasible and desirable.

In the unfolding of most mental illness the period of boiling crisis is surprisingly short. And this presents us with a paradox in caring for psychotic individuals. The acute phase of stark, crazy behavior is terribly frightening to most people, particularly those close to the patient. This frightening quality is precisely what

From pp. 513–516 of *Third World Congress of Psychiatry. Proceedings. Volume I.* Revised. Copyright © 1961. (Montreal: University of Toronto Press, McGill University Press, 1961). Reprinted by permission of the author.

has driven society over the ages to expel the psychotic from the community. It has impelled us to establish the large full-time mental hospital and endow it with the qualities of a social institution.

Yet, paradoxically, the acute fulminating phase is least characteristic of all the years to come in the life of the disease. Most psychotics, most of the time, are relatively undisturbed and calm in surface manifestations. This leads us to the conclusion that most patients, most of the time, may be managed, cared for, and treated without recourse to full-time custody and protection. Bluntly stated, our proposition is that partial hospitalization is not only adequate but also appropriate for the largest portion of patient-days of severe mental illness with which society has to be concerned.

A wide variety of organizational forms, physical facilities, and treatment modalities is necessary for sensible management of mental illness as a societal problem. Moreover, we submit, this variety should be organized and integrated so as to constitute a program of comprehensive psychiatry for a defined population residing in a geographic district and exposed to the risk of becoming mentally ill. A benefit to be derived from such a comprehensive psychiatry would be that of forwarding continuity of care for individuals for as long a period of time and for as wide a set of circumstances as might be potentially necessary.

Day Hospital is one kind of facility which, when added to and integrated with all the other psychiatric facilities of the community, becomes an important element in the whole network of comprehensive psychiatry. Taken together, this network enables us to deal with each patient in accordance with the nature of his condition and to place him in that particular facility that is most suitable for the specific phase of illness or health in which we find him. On the whole, bedding down in a full-time hospital should rarely be needed for more than a very short time. Many, if not most, patients can, in fact, be directly admitted on a daytime basis without going through any initial period of 24-hour care. And when the patient's condition indicates a need for other facilities, such as halfway-house, sheltered workshop, or home visiting, the network of comprehensive psychiatry makes possible rapid mobilization of forces relevant to the patient's needs and potentialities.

When patients are fully hospitalized fluidity of motion is lacking and shifting of gears is made difficult and time-consuming. By contrast, the widespread use of day care or other types of partial hospitalization will tend to nourish flexibility and aid in the effective utilization of all elements of comprehensive community psychiatry.

Over the past several years I have had the opportunity of observing at close hand the Day Hospital at the Massachusetts Mental Health Center (formerly known as the Boston Psychopathic Hospital). I shall not go into the history and current status of day care at this setting inasmuch as these have been detailed elsewhere by Colman and Greenblatt (1961), Cohen (1960), Ewalt, Alexander, and Grinspoon (1960), Kramer (1960, 1962), Mack and Pandiscio (1958). I need only mention here that the Massachusetts Mental Health Center today offers day care both as an integrated feature of its in-service wards and as a separate facility of the hospital. The remainder of this paper, however, deals with the Day Hospital, which has existed since the early 1950's as a quasi-autonomous unit of the Mental Health Center and which I studied in 1958 and 1959. I take this opportunity to mention some of the motifs revealed by our investigation of the social and psychological atmosphere in this day hospital.

The unit's treatment philosophy has stressed psychotherapy and the milieu as key vehicles for achieving its primary goals, that is to say, resocialization of the patient and his earliest possible return to full community living. Yet putting this philosophy into practice brought with it for staff an interesting pattern of duality with respect to a number of issues.

Take, for example, the matter of length of stay. On the one hand, the dominant character of the hospital as a short-term intensive treatment center tends to favor the patient who displays active movement with therapeutic potential. Excessive concentration in the unit of chronic cases stabilized at static vegetative levels tends to be viewed as a threat to the therapeutic concept of the hospital. Yet, on the other hand, there is the recognition that many, many cases unavoidably call for "the long haul." Staff must be prepared to retain long-term interest in patients with little promise of visible results—results that tend to be so vital to the clinician and to an active facility. While there are no solid guidelines concerning length of stay, it is clear that this is an issue with which any day hospital must come to terms. How to keep a dynamic facility in motion and, at the same time, maintain responsibility for the ever-present and large group of chronic cases continues to be a delicate balancing problem.

Another issue that tends to evoke a dual pattern of attitudes is that of patient participation in activities of the unit. The prevailing psychodynamic and permissive orientation fosters a reluctance to push patients into activities for which they are not yet willing to take the initiative. Yet, there is an almost equally strong value that opposes inactivity, withdrawal, and passivity. Most commonly this conflict between opposing values is resolved by tailoring the approach to the patient's condition. Less frequently, however, alternation is observed as the response.

Dependency upon the hospital also emerges as a salient item of concern. There are those who view the hospital ideally as a refuge in moments of distress—a source of comfort to which the patient may always turn. They look with favor on the role of alumnus as a self-image for the patient. The opposing view sees danger in making the hospital so comforting as to reinforce sick behavior. Proponents of this view stress the need for stimulating the patient toward independence and responsibility and urge early efforts to prepare the patient for separation from the all-giving hospital. Here, again, the problem is one of balance, for, to quote a staff member, "This hospital is like one big breast: if you don't watch out, the patients would be here forever."

On a day-to-day basis the work of staff members such as nurses, social workers, occupational therapists, and others is of special importance. Though patients run the gamut of feelings in their views of these personnel it is crystal clear that each is vitally involved in the other. One patient, talking about his confidence in the nurse, said:

> She's not like the professionals around here. You talk with them and you never know if they're going to understand or if they're going to blab about it. She's a wonderful person to talk to.

Another patient sees her in an entirely different light and is vocal in her disaffection, saying:

> What's the use of talking to her. You can't get any place with her. She gives you the same old routine, just like the rest of them. I've had enough of this psychotherapy business. They won't give me any medicine for my pains and they won't let me leave. The only reason I go to sessions with the doctor is because they tell me I have to. But let me tell you I don't want to. It's no good.

In a word, staff is important not only insofar as its direct relation with patients is concerned but also in respect to its ability to foster those conditions in the unit that make it possible for patients to interact with each other in potentially therapeutic ways.

I return now to my earlier theme of the day hospital as part of the total psychiatric picture: What makes partial hospitalization possible today? What factors in society and in psychiatry give it support and foster its viability?

First, there are the psychotropic drugs. These have surely played a part in modifying the visible picture of psychosis. Additionally, new social expectations have emerged concerning the behavior of patients in mental hospitals. Under the impact of both these forces we have witnessed a striking change in the outward appearance of psychosis and today the mental hospital is no longer overwhelmed by the starkness of raving individuals. Bald management problems need no longer preoccupy personnel and energies are freed for more creative efforts. This fact has acted as one nutrient condition for the growth of day care.

A second factor that we believe to be important for the maintenance of a sound day care facility is that the unit should have control over admissions. Different day centers apply differing criteria for admission. Each seeks to limit its activities to those areas in respect to which it feels competent. Control over admission enables each setting to carve out an area of competence and to intensify its skills. At its present stage of development day hospital appears to gain support from control over admissions through its power to prevent units from being overwhelmed by problems beyond current capabilities.

Ready availability of inpatient services is a third ingredient for successful organization of a day center for severe mental illness. The value to the patient of such accessibility is self-evident; for the staff it is vitally comforting to know that if and when a patient needs full-time hospitalization it can be smoothly accomplished.

A fourth foundation is the existence of a supporting set of beliefs and values on the part of staff. In the day hospital to which I have referred staff held two supporting beliefs: (1) that disturbed individuals are not hopelessly deranged because of constitutional or other factors and therefore are manageable during the day if families are willing to provide care at home; (2) that psychotherapy and the therapeutic use of all kinds of personnel will help to create or restore a capacity for socialized living.

To my knowledge, no studies have definitively shown whether any of these approaches is superior to any other. Nor, in fact, have studies shown whether day care is more or less effective than traditional care, from a therapeutic or rehabilitative standpoint. A reasonable statement, nonetheless, would seem to be that day care is not grossly less effective than full-time care. Yet it has, at the same time, the advantage of preserving the patient's communal ties. Likewise, it would seem fair to say that the various approaches to day care are equally valid if adequate provision is made for efficient transfer of patients to other facilities when day care appears not to be in their best interest.

In the long run, the most distinctive and enduring feature of the day hospital is its intrinsic character as a link between the hospital world and that of the community. This linkage takes shape in several ways. First, and probably most telling, is the fact that day patients return home nightly to their families and neighborhoods. Patients are reminded each day of their continuity with their own setting. Local sights and sounds retain their familiarity. Expected behavior and activity hold their customary force. Social skills in moving back and forth between hospital and community do not become atrophied through disuse. The daily trips to and fro declare concretely that, despite illness, they are not irreparably cut off from their homes. To be sure, some patients would prefer to do just this and withdraw into the narrower and perhaps less trying world of the hospital. On the whole though, preservation of neighborhood ties is probably the most important single value of day care.

A second involvement of day care in the community is through patients' families. When a patient is admitted on a full-time basis, the hospital takes responsibility for his care and the family recedes into the background as an interested, but psychologically distant, party. Under day care, by contrast, the family is always in the foreground, in that it shares responsibility with the hospital.

Although the patient is away at the hospital during the day, the family has to help the patient muster ego-strength to execute the often taxing job of just getting to the hospital. The family must also often assist the patient to make it back home. Although coming and going is for many patients quite simple and smooth, the family is never really quite sure how well the process will work, and therefore tends to remain in a poised position, ready to step in when needed. Likewise, caring for the patient at home evenings and weekends carries with it special problems and difficulties which call for a relationship of mutuality between family and hospital. Episodes of turmoil will arise which call for special family reflexes and the day care unit must be ready to assist when needed. In brief, the hospital cannot execute a day program without the cooperation of the family, and the family cannot carry out its end without the assistance of the hospital. This interdependence between hospital and family operates as a continuing link between the institution and an important segment of the community.

A third nexus between day hospital and the community is represented by neighbors and other individuals in the patient's orbit. If the patient's activities proceed fairly smoothly, neighbors and significant others, seeing his daily movement between home and hospital, may undergo significant changes in attitudes toward the mentally ill. Indirectly this may heighten community receptivity for psychiatric rehabilitation. If, on the other hand, these individuals experience recurrent episodes of violent or other disturbing behavior by the patient, a boomerang effect may occur. People in the locality might call for greater strictness in the control of patients or for abolishing partial hospitalization. Under such a circumstance a strong relationship with the community stands the hospital in good stead. Expression of negative community attitudes provides an opportunity for the hospital to encounter directly the feelings of the community and, through the process of confrontation, assist the community to develop workable attitudes toward mental illness.

Although day hospitals today constitute a small part of the total psychiatric picture, the significance is much greater. The smallness of the part is witnessed, to be sure, by the fact that in 1961 in the United States there are no more than two or three thousand day patients while over half a million are confined in full-time mental hospitals. But the significance lies in the fact that the idea of day care is on a rising trend. In the United States about 25 day centers were in existence two years ago. Today we estimate that there are over 50 such units and new ones are steadily emerging. In Great Britain 65 day hospitals are in operation as revealed by Farndale's thorough study (1961) of the day hospital movement in that country. In the Soviet Union, where, so far as we know, the day hospital first came into being, the concept is written into the legal framework. In Canada, where day care in the context of the general hospital was pioneered, many varied centers are found. In Nigeria, Yugoslavia, Greece, Thailand, and other countries we find similar trends. Altogether then, day care in psychiatry is accelerating. Because it is accelerating, but more importantly because it is in tune with the essential nature of mental disease, we favor the conclusion that day hospital is potentially the major primary psychiatric facility of the future.

35 / The Self-Help Organization in the Mental Health Field: Recovery, Inc.: A Case Study

Henry Wechsler

The past decade has witnessed the growth of a relatively new form of activity in the mental health field: the self-help group of former mental patients. Forty-two such groups are currently in existence, the majority established in the past five years. The largest and perhaps the oldest of these groups is Recovery, Incorporated: The Association of Nervous and Former Mental Patients. Recovery reports over 1,800 dues-paying members, and a total regular attendance of over 4,000 individuals. It officially recognizes 250 local groups in 20 states, located mainly in Illinois and Michigan. Other self-help groups in the mental health field tend to be small and have relatively short life-spans, while Recovery has exhibited a significant growth. However, despite this growth, Recovery has as yet failed to make any perceivable impact upon professionals in the mental health field. Prior to this report, no extensive study of the structure, functioning, and therapeutic potential of this organization has been attempted.

For the purposes of this study, information about Recovery was obtained from a number of available sources:

1. The Recovery literature.
2. Visits to various groups by the author, and four consultants.

Abridged from the *Journal of Nervous and Mental Disease*, 1960, 130, 297–314. Copyright © 1960. Reprinted by permission of the author and The Williams and Wilkins Co.

3. A questionnaire study of the membership.
4. A questionnaire survey of psychiatrists' opinions about Recovery.

Historical Development

Recovery was founded in 1937 by the late Abraham A. Low, M.D., a neuro-psychiatrist on the faculty of the University of Illinois College of Medicine. Originally, the organization was limited to patients at the Psychiatric Institute of the University. In 1942, the organization and the Institute severed connections, and Recovery secured private offices in Chicago. Under Dr. Low's leadership, Recovery acquired a specific method of self-help and after-care aimed at the prevention of relapses and chronicity among the mentally ill. Group meetings were conducted as part of Low's treatment procedure, and Recovery members were drawn mainly from patients in his private practice.

During the early days of the organization, Low kept in close contact with the activities of the groups. He received regular reports from the leaders, and personally attended the larger discussions at which he presented the final interpretations of the subject matter. Gradually, as the organization grew in size, Low's direct control over group activities of necessity decreased. Finally, in 1952, he withdrew his objections to the expansion of Recovery on a national level, in effect placing the direct control of the widely scattered local groups in the hands of his former patients who had become group leaders. With Low's death in 1954, the transition of Recovery from a professionally supervised adjunct to psychotherapy to a lay-run form of self-help became complete.

Recovery is incorporated under the laws of Illinois as a non-profit organization, and is financed through annual membership dues, the sale of literature and records, and individual "good will" donations. The national headquarters of Recovery, Inc., is located in Chicago. The organization is run by a Board of Directors, a councilors committee, and organizational officers. The councilors and directors are elected annually by the dues-paying members, and the officers are appointed by the Board of Directors. There are no formal criteria for membership, other than that of being a former mental patient or "nervous person." Essentially then, any individual who perceives himself to be emotionally disturbed may join. Furthermore, an individual may start a new group if, in addition to qualifying for membership, he studies the Recovery method, receives at least one week's formal leadership training, and obtains authorization from the Board of Directors.

The Recovery Method

Recovery utilizes exclusively the techniques, principles, and terminology described in its official text, *Mental Health Through Will-Training* (Low, 1950). The member is expected to read this book, learn Dr. Low's system, utilize the system in his everyday life, and obtain practice in its application by attending weekly group meetings. The book does not present an over-all systematic formulation of a theory of mental health, but rather each chapter is intended to illustrate one or more principles through the use of examples.

In order to present most accurately the Recovery method, it was necessary to outline its major basic assumptions and concepts. In each case, the reader is referred to the page in the textbook where a more complete statement may be found. The method will be presented without any attempt to evaluate the validity of its assumptions or the effectiveness of its techniques. These points which follow will be discussed in a later section.

1. The returned mental patient and the psychoneurotic both suffer from similar symptoms (Low, 1950, p. 18).
2. The psychoneurotic or postpsychotic symptom is distressing but not dangerous (p. 112).
3. Tenseness intensifies and sustains the symptom, and thus should be avoided (p. 135).
4. The psychoneurotic and postpsychotic patients are particularly susceptible to the arousal of tenseness because of their excessive irritability (pp. 86, 88).
5. The use of free will is the basis of the Recovery method and the solution to the nervous patient's dilemma.
   a. The life of the individual is governed by free will (p. 185).
   b. The psychoneurotic or postpsychotic patient can attain mental health through the use of his will (pp. 19, 145, 209).
   c. The function of the will is to accept or reject thoughts or impulses (p. 132).
6. Mental health should be the supreme goal for the mental or nervous patient (p. 384).
7. The "physician" is the supreme authority on all matters pertaining to mental health (p. 24).

In summary, these assumptions state that when the physician diagnoses a condition of a psychoneurotic or postpsychotic patient as a nervous symptom, the patient should realize that, although the condition is distressing, it is not dangerous. The patient should accept the diagnosis of the physician, and should attempt to employ his will in order to eliminate the tenseness which sustains and intensifies the symptom.

The situation is to be restructured in terms of the following Recovery principles, and the individual is to act within this new cognitive framework:

SPOTTING   When a symptom, impulse, or thought appears, it must be "spotted" for what it is. The individual must see that there is no danger involved. Spotting is a form of introspective relabeling of various components of the situation.

THE RECOVERY LANGUAGE   When an individual restructures the situation, he must employ the basic tool of the method, the Recovery Language. The use of Recovery Language is intended to change a situation from one that is felt to be beyond the control of the individual to one that can be coped with.

DIFFERENTIATION BETWEEN EXTERNAL AND INTERNAL ENVIRONMENT   An individual's life space is composed of the external and internal environment. The external environment consists of the "realities" of the situation, and can seldom be changed. The internal environment consists of various "subjective" components, such as feelings, thoughts, impulses, and sensations. These can be controlled, restructured, or reappraised.

AVOIDANCE OF JUDGMENTS OF "RIGHT" OR "WRONG"   For any given life situation, an evaluation of "right" or "wrong" is merely an opinion, or a subjective judgment. The Recovery member should refrain from making such evaluations as they serve only to produce temper, which in turn increases tenseness and contributes to symptoms.

THE AVERAGE VERSUS THE EXCEPTIONAL The member should consider himself to be an average person, and should strive to be average. He should realize that his symptoms are no worse than anyone else's symptoms, that he is no sicker than anyone else. Each situation is average as it has been and will be encountered by numerous other individuals.

Once the situation has been restructured in accordance with these principles, it remains for the individual to act. Recovery guide lines for action can be characterized broadly by the term *control*. In essence, the individual is told to control those aspects of his internal environment which serve to propagate tenseness. The primary condition that is to be controlled is *temper*. Two types of temper exist: fear and anger. Temper is a combination of feelings with an evaluation that the self or the other person is "right" or "wrong." The individual is to control temper, to reject and suppress thoughts and impulses which result in tenseness. He is to force himself to bear the discomfort of doing that which he fears. In situations which are not dangerous, the individual must act despite the subjective anguish which his symptoms may be expressing.

The individual must constantly *endorse* himself for each effort at the practice of Recovery, no matter how minute. Self-endorsement is a basic principle of Recovery. It is a way in which the member can congratulate himself, not necessarily because he was successful, but because he tried to utilize the method. Low believed that, eventually, each effort will entail less work; each attempt will be more successful. The restructuring of the situation will become automatic and will require little or no conscious application. With each success, the individual's self-esteem will be increased, and he will eventually come to believe what he has been told: that he can, through the use of his will, achieve mental health.

The Recovery Group Meeting

At the present time, meetings of Recovery groups are intended to serve the purpose of providing members with the opportunity to practice the techniques of Recovery. Groups are usually composed of between 11 and 30 members. Meetings follow a rigid schedule in order to assure conformity with the methods and beliefs of Recovery. It is the leader's function to guide the meeting along the prearranged format. Each meeting is divided into four parts.

Reading from the Textbook

The first part of the meeting is usually devoted to the reading of a chapter from the textbook. The leader may call on members to read short paragraphs. A technique widely used in some groups is to call on members who are hesitant about reading in public. This may serve the function of encouraging newcomers to join in the activities of the group. At the conclusion of his paragraph, the reader is quite often asked whether he had any symptoms during the reading. He is then "endorsed" for having the "will to bear discomfort," the "courage to make mistakes," and for being "group minded" by doing what he "feared to do." Thus at the same time that the newcomer is encouraged to participate in the meeting, he is also given a practical demonstration of the Recovery method at work in reference to his own reading. This is frequently an important first step in motivating the curious newcomer to become a Recovery member.

The Presentation of Examples

RULES FOR PRESENTATION   The leader introduces this portion of the meeting by stating that only members who have read Dr. Low's book may participate. Newer members who as yet have not read the book are asked to listen quietly, and to save their questions and remarks for the question period. The participants form the "panel" and are usually seated face-to-face around a table.

The leader informs the group that all examples have to be taken from "trivial" everyday occurrences, and, since Recovery is a lay-run non-medical organization, it cannot help individuals with major problems. This is often qualified by stating Dr. Low's belief that such "trivial" incidents comprise the bulk of a nervous patient's problems. The leader then asks one of the members to read a portion of the official outline (Low, 1956) for the presentation of an example. The outline divides each example into four parts:

      a. A detailed description of an event.
      b. Description of the symptoms and discomfort that the event aroused.
      c. Description of the utilization of Recovery principles to cope with the event.
      d. Description of the reaction which the member would have experienced before joining Recovery.

THE NATURE OF THE EXAMPLES   As a result of the rigorous regulations for the presentation of panel examples, there is very little variation as to the type of examples given at the meetings. In addition to the actual rules, the "model" examples included in Low's book also serve to set the tone for the members' examples. In general, the examples presented at Recovery meetings may be characterized by:

a. *Familiarity.* Only commonplace everyday events are usually discussed. The events have usually taken place in the very recent past.

b. *Concreteness.* Very literal, extensive descriptions of these events are given. Specific times, places, and individuals are usually mentioned.

c. *Uniformity of Symptoms.* The same symptoms are usually mentioned by most of the panel participants. These symptoms are almost always identical to the symptoms cited in the textbook. It is as if the textbook is used as a basic symptom list, from which members may choose the symptoms most appropriate for them.

d. *Somatization of Symptoms.* In addition to the uniformity in the symptoms, there is a tendency to present symptoms in somatic terms. This, too, is probably influenced by the type of examples discussed in the textbook. The most frequent types of symptoms discussed are: air hunger, heart palpitations, perspiration, and tremors.

e. *Exclusive Use of Recovery Concepts.* In nearly all cases, examples are presented in terms of Recovery language. If an occasional term such as "projection" or "identification" is introduced, it is soon withdrawn by the speaker.

f. *The Testimonial.* The majority of examples serve as testimonials, since they refer to the success obtained through the use of the Recovery method as compared to the failures encountered previously. . . .

Group Participation

After the speaker has finished giving an example, the meeting is thrown open for comments from the panel. This is called "group spotting" and involves an analysis of the example through the use of Recovery concepts. The leader usually starts the discussion and calls upon volunteers. Comments must be phrased in Recovery language, and must pertain to the example under consideration. . . . The individual who has given the example is free to accept or reject the comments and criticisms of the panel. The tendency is for him to accept all comments, and to agree with the group. In cases when negative comments are made, the group congratulates the individual for the Recovery methods utilized, and for being able to present an example not fully successful in nature. In addition, the individual is told not to attempt to be too perfectionistic by always expecting total success. Thus, both successful and unsuccessful examples are praised. The tendency is not to permit any example to pass, regardless of how successful the narrator may have thought it was, without adding additional Recovery concepts that may be applied to it. . . .

The Question and Answer Period

At the conclusion of the panel presentations, there is a brief question and answer period, which usually lasts no longer than 15 minutes. . . . Comments must be limited to the examples, and at no time may one question the Recovery method itself, except to obtain clarification of a term or concept. No discussion of other psychological theories or systems is permitted. . . .

The "Mutual Aid" Social Meeting

Nearly all the members remain after the formal part of the meeting has been concluded. Refreshments are usually served, and individual members may talk to each other and to the leader. The designation of this period as "mutual aid" refers to the fact that this is an opportunity to discuss problems and to obtain advice from others. There is an attempt to keep this informal discussion within the bounds of the Recovery method, and to utilize only the techniques and concepts of Recovery, Inc. A rule of thumb is that all discussions of problems should be limited to five minutes, so as not to leave time for self-pity and complaining. During this part of the meeting the leader and the veteran members usually speak to newcomers in order to interest them in Recovery.

Recovery provides an additional mechanism through which a member may obtain help from other members during a time when no meetings are being held. A member who is experiencing difficulties may telephone a veteran member or leader. The problem must be presented and discussed in the same way as any panel example.

The Recovery Membership

In order to obtain information about the personal characteristics of the Recovery members, questionnaires were sent to the Chicago headquarters and to the state leader in Michigan, to be distributed to the members. Of the 1,875 questionnaires that were distributed, 779 were completed and returned. The answers seemed to present a rather clear picture of the typical Recovery respondent, although general interpretations should be made with some caution. Since there was no control over the distribution of the questionnaires, and since it cannot be assumed that the non-responders would have answered in the same way as the respondents, the characterization which follows may not apply to the entire Recovery membership. It does, however, describe in general at least 779 members.

BACKGROUND FACTORS   The modal Recovery respondent appears to be a middle-class, middle-aged, married woman. She has had at least some high school education, and may have attended college. Her husband is employed in a nonmanual occupation and the yearly family income is approximately $6,000.

The typical Recovery respondent has one or more dependent children. She is active in community and church affairs, belongs to one or more voluntary community associations, and attends church services weekly. She takes part in various leisure time activities, *e.g.*, hobbies, and visits or entertains her family, friends, and neighbors. Thus she is an individual who appears to be integrated into her community and who, at least on the basis of certain socio-economic criteria, appears to hold an average or perhaps better-than-average status.

REASONS FOR JOINING RECOVERY   Most of the respondents had originally learned about Recovery in the lay press, and had joined at the suggestion of a relative or friend. Only about a tenth of the respondents stated that they had joined on the advice of a physician.

The respondents reported that they entered this activity because they believed that they had one or more symptoms usually associated with a nervous or mental disorder. The major reasons for joining were given as follows:

  a. psychological symptoms, such as fears, delusions, and "nerves";
  b. psychosomatic symptoms, such as tremors and heart palpitations;
  c. curiosity about whether the organization could help.

HISTORY OF HOSPITALIZATION AND TREATMENT   The respondents reported relatively few extensive histories of treatment for nervous or mental disorders prior to joining Recovery. Half of the respondents reported no hospitalization, and about one-fifth reported no professional treatment of any kind before joining Recovery. Among the respondents who reported hospitalization, there was little indication of chronicity, since the majority indicated very few hospitalizations, and of very short duration.

EXTENT OF PARTICIPATION IN RECOVERY   For most of the respondents, Recovery appears to be a regular and long-term activity. Such obligations of membership as regular attendance and participation in the panels are conscientiously fulfilled. It is apparent from statements made by these individuals that membership in Recovery is treated as a vital, significant activity.

Approximately one-third of the respondents had been in Recovery for less than one year, one-third for one to two years, and one-third for three years or more. Almost all of the respondents reported that they attended meetings weekly. The length of membership, high frequency of attendance, and high level of participation are of interest in view of the observation that over a third of those answering the questionnaire stated that they no longer need to attend meetings in order to function adequately.

THE SPECIAL CASE OF THE LEADER   Of the 779 questionnaires, 112 were returned by leaders or assistant leaders of local Recovery groups. In general, the leaders displayed the same characteristics as regular members, with only a few minor exceptions. Leaders tended to be of a slightly higher socio-economic level. They reported more activity in church and community groups, and they displayed slightly more extensive histories of previous treatment for nervous or mental disorders.

The Role of the Member

The distinctive philosophy and method of Recovery facilitates establishing a particular type of role for the member. . . . Each member has certain obligations toward his fellow members. . . . He is expected to show concern about the condition and progress of other members, to provide them with support, . . . and to help them in the "correct" application of the Recovery method. He has expectations that others will act toward him in a similar manner. Because of the mutual aid quality of Recovery, the group feels helped by any individual's successes or harmed by any individual's failures.

By joining Recovery, the participant formally admits to himself and to others that he is "a nervous patient," and that he is formally associating himself with a group of nervous and former mental patients. . . .

The term "nervous patient" may be a strange one to apply to the members of an organization completely lay-run and directed, since "patient" usually implies treatment by a physician or other professional. However, the Recovery members do refer to themselves at meetings as "patients," and can be said to assume the nervous patient role. Of itself this role has a number of implications.

THE RECOVERY NERVOUS PATIENT ROLE IS VOLUNTARY   Adopting the nervous patient role is completely voluntary: the individual has the choice of joining or not joining. For some people this may be merely a formalization of a role status which has already been in existence. Such individuals may have formerly been hospitalized, or may have previously been under treatment for a nervous or mental disorder. Through the utilization of various mental health facilities, they may have already identified themselves as nervous patients. However, according to data obtained with the questionnaire survey, a sizable segment of the Recovery membership has had no contact with such mental health facilities. For these individuals, the act of joining Recovery seems to imply a voluntary acceptance of a role that may be highly devalued in contemporary American society, and a consequent exposure to the stigma that is often associated with this role.

THE RECOVERY NERVOUS PATIENT ROLE IS AN ACCEPTANCE OF "DIFFERENCE"   Membership in any specialized group may result in the perception of the self as different from individuals who do not belong to the group. In certain groups, the feeling of difference may be extremely vague and unstructured, but in Recovery the theoretical framework is seen specifically to outline the nature of the difference. The member is told that he is different from the average person in that he is more prone to the development of tenseness, and that he cannot tolerate as much tenseness as the average person. Thus, the Recovery member is cautioned to control and avoid actions which may be completely permissible to the average person. . . .

The Special Role of The Leader

Like the member, the group leader assumes the role of a nervous patient through the act of belonging to Recovery and through the utilization of its method. In order to participate in panel meetings an individual must give examples concerning his own problems and symptoms. Leaders are not exempt from this, and in fact usually present numerous examples in order to keep the meeting active. The role of the leader, however, has certain additional features which deserve comment.

THE LEADER AS AN EXPERT   Perhaps the major function of the leader is to serve as an expert in the utilization of the Recovery method. Leaders are perceived by the group to be sophisticated in the use of Recovery terminology and concepts. Because of their position, they are able to control the agenda and content of the meeting, and serve as the major interpreters of the method. Most leaders stress that the Recovery method is not open to interpretation, and must be employed as it is written. However, a leader's comments at the panel meeting are usually more highly valued by the group than those of any other individual. . . .

Basic Functions of Recovery

Undoubtedly Recovery helps to satisfy some of the needs of its members; otherwise it would cease to exist. In response to the questionnaire survey, almost all of the members indicated satisfaction with the organization. They reported that they had been helped, and were particularly enthusiastic about the group aspects of Recovery.

The functions the organization may serve for its members may be separated into two major categories: the functions of the Recovery method, and the group functions of Recovery.

Basic Functions of the Recovery Method

ORDERING THE PSYCHOLOGICAL FIELD AS A MEANS OF REDUCING ANXIETY   The Recovery method is characterized by a search for order amidst a labyrinth of complex psychological problems and processes. Personal experiences are restructured within the cognitive framework provided by Recovery so that events which may be anxiety-promoting and unfamiliar may be translated into a more familiar and understandable form. Examples are presented in such a way that complex psychological problems tend to be treated as tangible symptoms of a somatic nature. Since examples must be about trivial incidents, they tend in the main to entail familiar everyday experiences. Symptoms appear to become standardized, and somaticized, almost exclusively adhering to the type cited in the textbook. In this manner a degree of certainty is introduced into the psychological realm, since even the most threatening emotions may be viewed as conforming to a set of universal regulations.

In addition members are given a simple routine to counteract the anxiety-producing uncertainty associated with their problems. This is done by imposing a rigidly standardized procedure characterized by repetitiveness. The meetings assume the characteristics of ritual and may serve to reduce anxiety in the same manner as the ritualistic ceremonies described by Malinowski (1948) in his study of primitive religions. Each member is provided with a set of simple semantic labels to be used as tools for restructuring subjective experiences. The tools are available to all and may be manipulated with relative ease, once the Recovery method has been learned.

INTRODUCTION OF CONTROLS TO STRENGTHEN DEFENSES AGAINST ANXIETY The basic component of the Recovery method is the belief that an individual can and must exercise control and self-discipline in all matters that affect his mental health. The will is to be trained to achieve this desired end through the continuous application of Recovery techniques. It is as if an attempt is made to strengthen the defense mechanisms of the Recovery member and to provide him with new controls and defenses against anxiety. Control is to be first introduced at the simplest and most basic level. The individual must learn to walk when he is tempted to run, to lie down when he is agitated, to make decisions in the simplest situations. Eventually, control is to be extended to the more complex processes, such as the suppression of temper and the rejection of anxiety-producing impulses. Self-discipline is to be gradually generalized to all spheres and levels of activity. The Recovery meetings themselves assume the characteristics of exercises in self-control. Impulses to speak must be checked. The individual must first raise his hand, and must make his comments in accordance with the strict procedural regulations.

INSPIRATION AND THE POWER OF POSITIVE THINKING The continuous reporting of successful examples at Recovery meetings may provide inspiration for the members. If one hears that other members are successfully coping with their problems, he may begin to believe that he too can do the same. In line with the inspirational aspects of Recovery meetings is the stress upon what may be designated as "the power of positive thinking." The member is constantly told to employ positive thoughts and to reject negative ones. The Recovery theory is presented in such a way that all psychological difficulties appear to be manageable. It is almost as if the nurturing of positive thought is believed to lead to positive results.

This aspect of Recovery resembles a once-popular form of psychotherapy based on auto-suggestion, devised by Emile Coué. In effect, the members are to tell themselves that "every day I get better and better." It is hoped that such auto-suggestion will lead to actual success in the elimination and suppression of symptoms. However, there appears to be a basic contradiction which may affect the operation of this form of positive thinking. The Recovery member is not only told to have positive thoughts, but he is also told that he *must* have them because he is a nervous patient and can only afford to have positive thoughts. All positive thoughts, therefore, are based on the assumption that the person is a nervous patient. The acceptance and maintenance of this basic assumption may keep the self-fulfilling prophecy from operating.

MAINTENANCE OF ACTIVITY AND SATISFACTION OF DEPENDENCY NEEDS Recovery on the one hand implies a passive acceptance of the authority of the founder of the method and, on the other hand, the belief that mental health can only be attained through active effort. Recovery requires that the members accept the authority of Dr. Low, as embodied in his writings and their presentation by the leader of the group. The new member passively puts himself in the hands of

Recovery, forming a dependent type of relationship with the leaders, the members, and the basic authority of Dr. Low's text. In return, he is given a method and told what to do. Through the acceptance of the group's authority, the newcomer may obtain gratification of his basic dependency needs. He may feel that if he obeys the rules and regulations of Recovery, he will be taken care of.

However, counteracting this trend toward dependency and passivity is the stress in Recovery upon self-help. The Recovery method must be actively practiced. The member is told that progress can only come through continual effort and work. The individual can receive help from others, but in the long run it is his own effort which will produce progress. The combination of the passive dependency and active self-help elements in Recovery may serve to fulfill the individual's dependency needs without lulling him into passive inactivity. Salvation in Recovery may be obtained only through work, but the work must be done along the lines prescribed by the organization and by Dr. Low.

CATHARTIC VALUE OF THE RECOVERY CONFESSIONAL The group confessional aspects of the meetings may aid the individual in removing some of the anxiety associated with his symptoms. The mere act of publicly admitting the symptom may serve to disassociate some of the affect with which the symptom is labeled. Guilt and stigma associated with the attempt to hide the presence of symptomatology may be eliminated. Getting the symptom "off one's chest" may provide at least temporary relief. In addition, when one individual confesses his symptoms, others may learn that the symptoms which they have are similar.

The Semi-Religious Nature of Recovery

The Recovery method and its practice at panel meetings is clearly reminiscent of various elements characteristic of certain organized religions. The method involves faith and acceptance of regulations handed down by a higher authority. The method stresses self-discipline and the volitional aspects of human nature. This type of approach is more amenable to certain religious beliefs than is the Freudian and Darwinian notion of man as an instinct-driven animal. The emphasis on the power of positive thinking and on inspiration is also clearly analogous to some religious tenets.

The analogy between Recovery and religion may be extended further. Recovery has a bible, the textbook of Dr. Low. Hero worship of Low sometimes assumes the proportions of making him almost appear a god-figure. The leaders assume the role of disciples. In certain Recovery groups, the desire for expansion and for national recognition is analogous to the missionary zeal in religious groups. In addition, the repetitive ritual-like panel meetings resemble certain forms of religious ceremonies.

The Group Functions of Recovery

Current organizational policy is to de-emphasize the social nature of the organization and to concentrate on the method. However, the importance of the group atmosphere is not neglected. Members take part in extracurricular social activities such as outings and parties. A social period of "mutual-aid" has become institutionalized as part of every meeting. Individuals come to meetings early and remain until the late hours of the evening to spend additional time with their fellow members.

Membership in Recovery involves more than the practice of a particular method of self-help and aftercare. It also entails membership within a community of individuals who have joined together because of perceived mutual problems and goals. Members form interpersonal relationships with one another, are affected by and in turn affect each other. The Recovery method serves to increase the solidarity of the group. The uniqueness of the Recovery language allows it to serve as a badge of membership which can be used to distinguish the in-group member from the outsider. The agreement upon basic goals also serves to strengthen group feeling.

The Recovery group provides the individual with significant others with whom he may interact. For the social isolate this, in itself, would constitute an important motive for membership. For the members who have other opportunities to interact in the community, certain special aspects of the Recovery group setting may be particularly attractive.

RECOVERY AS A SHELTERED SOCIAL ENVIRONMENT   Recovery differs from other types of organizations because of its distinctive composition and general goals. All members are perceived to be in need of help, and are encouraged to discuss their symptoms freely. No one is stigmatized for having psychological problems. The members need not conceal the nature of their difficulties in order to obtain group acceptance. It is almost as if Recovery provides its members with a sheltered social environment in which everyone is treated as being equal, despite the level of his mental health or the nature of his symptomatology.

The Recovery group exhibits a greater tolerance for deviant behavior than other organizations. Individuals are generally accepted by their peers despite behavior that might be considered abnormal in other groups, as long as these persons adhere to the basic regulations of Recovery. The over-all atmosphere is supportive, since members have joined together to help each other. Within such a group environment, the person whose concern over his symptoms might have previously interfered with his social interaction may find it easier to relate to other group members. He may also be able to test various patterns of behavior, and to abandon those which are inappropriate.

The individual may learn that other people are confronted with similar difficulties and problems. In this way, he may change his previous perceptions of his particular situation as unique. He may identify with other members of the group, and lose the feeling of isolation and sense of stigma imposed upon him by his symptomatology.

THE GROUP AS A SOURCE OF SECONDARY REWARDS   Inherent within the Recovery framework is a formal reward system designed to motivate participation at the meetings. Individuals are to be endorsed for reading from the textbook, for presenting examples, and for appropriate comments and questions. The reward system covers almost all behavior that goes on during the meeting. If an individual is not as yet able to present an example, he may be endorsed for not feeling forced to give one, or for just listening. As a consequence, the mere presence of an individual at a meeting warrants some form of endorsement. Continuous endorsement is intended to raise the level of self-esteem of the members. Besides the formal reward system, the individual obtains other rewards in exchange for his membership. He is provided with a social group which will accept him, and give him support and recognition. These social rewards are not contingent upon the degree of success or improvement that may be obtained through the method. To be sure, apparent successful utilization of the method may result in a higher level of social reward, but a certain amount accrues to all members.

It may be that the social rewards which had previously served as a means to an end have become functionally autonomous, and may serve as ends themselves. A member may join to receive help for his particular difficulties, but because of the social rewards may remain in the organization even if he has not obtained sufficient help to alleviate his symptoms, or if he has obtained enough help to be able to function adequately without further attendance at meetings.

THE GROUP AS A CONTROLLER OF BEHAVIOR   The group may serve to control behavior through the manipulation of rewards and sanctions. Control is applied primarily to assuring conformity to the doctrines of Recovery. Thus, the individual must use the accepted vocabulary, must provide appropriate examples, and must conform to the various regulations. The group socializes each member. He must learn to control his impulses by speaking only after raising his hand. He must refrain from autistic verbalization which could prevent him from utilizing the method appropriately. He must sit still when not participating, so that he does not disrupt the meeting. If his behavior is anti-social he is a threat to the group and must be controlled. Very few sanctions are applied by the group, but perhaps the simplest and most effective one is to ignore completely the non-conformer. If he does not adhere to the method, his comments are cut off by the leader and his remarks are ignored by the group.

RECOVERY AS A CAUSE   In many local groups there is the tendency for Recovery to be a cause in itself. The member may not only identify with his fellow group members, but also with all Recovery members. This act of identification may extend the person's ego boundaries in such a way that the success or failure of the organization is perceived as the success or failure of the self. The member becomes totally involved in the organization, and serves as a missionary whose desire it is to convert the non-believing world to Recovery's cause. Identification with Recovery may enable the individual to transcend his immediate problems and difficulties. Recovery becomes a cause to be preached to all who will listen. In this way, the individual may remove a great quantity of libidinal energy from his symptoms and utilize it in missionary activities. This zeal can take many directions. It may be used to build up Recovery membership and to gain national recognition for the organization. It may also be employed to foster anti-professional attitudes, and to foster the belief that it is "Recovery against the world." The exact nature that this may take depends upon the individual and the climate of opinion in his group.

Potential Problems Arising from Membership in Recovery

Although Recovery is the largest self-help group in the mental health field, its membership comprises only a small segment of the potential number of former mental patients and emotionally disturbed individulas. Alcoholics Anonymous, founded at the same time as Recovery, reports that in 1956 it had 5,000 groups in 60 countries with a total membership of 150,000 (Alcoholics Anonymous, 1956). In addition, while A.A. has received widespread professional and lay recognition for its efforts, Recovery has yet failed to do so. Although the problems of alcoholism and mental illness may not be similar, the differences between the two self-help organizations may be indicative of certain limitations of the Recovery approach.

When a survey of opinions about Recovery was made among members of the American Psychiatric Association in Detroit and Chicago, certain important qualifications concerning the effectiveness of the organization became apparent.

In general, the psychiatrists felt that Recovery is a helpful and valuable tool because of its group aspects. They felt that the group meetings satisfy the needs of some ex-patients for various forms of group support. However, they were concerned that the organization is not under medical or professional supervision, and that there is no systematic screening of members and no thorough selection and training of leaders. Some psychiatrists were particularly wary of the particular method that Recovery utilizes. Criticisms of the method included statements like the following:

1. It offers magical-omnipotent-authoritarian-unrealistic solutions.
2. It is superficial, limited, and prevents or hinders insight.
3. It is regressive, fixes defenses, forces adjustment at a low level of maturity.
4. It creates complacency about the problem of mental illness.

These criticisms illuminate two major potential problem areas in the functioning of Recovery: problems relating to the absence of professional supervision, and problems arising from the Recovery method itself.

Problems Relating to the Absence of a Professional

The transition of Recovery from an adjunct to the treatment regimen of Dr. Low to a lay-run self-help organization has left a number of unresolved problems. The Recovery method specifies that the physician is the primary authority in all matters pertaining to mental health. Only he is qualified to make a diagnosis, and the patient must follow his directions if he is to get well. At present, there is no physician associated with Recovery. As a consequence, certain functions that may have previously been fulfilled by Dr. Low now are either relegated to the lay leaders or no longer performed.

SELECTION OF MEMBERS At present, the Recovery method is to be used by all the members, regardless of the specific nature of their disorders. Originally, members were mainly patients of Dr. Low. It may safely be assumed that he had some control over their selection. Current Recovery membership, of course, includes many people who were never treated by Dr. Low, and some who have never received any professional treatment for psychiatric disorders. There is real doubt as to whether the method is appropriate for all of these individuals.

Recovery, it should be remembered, is a voluntary organization, and participants are free to leave at any time. An individual who feels that he is not receiving adequate help, or that he is being harmed, will probably drop out. However, it is possible that secondary social rewards stemming from membership in the group may motivate some persons to continue as members even if the Recovery method is inappropriate for them.

SELECTION OF LEADERS Recovery also has no formal criteria for the selection of leaders. In view of the crucial position of the leader within the organization, this may constitute one of the organization's greatest weaknesses. When the founder was guiding the activities of the Recovery groups, he was in the position to exercise a strong influence in leader selection. At present anyone may become a leader if he takes the short-term training course and gains the approval of the Board of Directors. Thus, there is the real possibility that mentally ill persons may become leaders and may manipulate the group in accordance with their own needs. This is a high order of potential danger since the leader may serve as a role model for the behavior of others.

Leaders, however, must present examples about their own personal problems and difficulties. They must be able to operate in a group, and must be sufficiently fluent verbally to utilize the method. These requirements may eliminate certain types of mentally ill individuals from leadership roles. In addition, since Recovery is a voluntary organization, the leader must be able to motivate the members to remain in the group. Although these factors may serve as partial safeguards against poor and unhealthy leadership, they by no means eliminate the danger completely.

"Graduation" policy   Recovery does not have any specific policy for the "graduation" of its members. When Dr. Low was present, he may well have advised certain members that they no longer needed to attend meetings. Without this type of advice, members may remain in the organization after they no longer need to, or when they are not receiving sufficient help from it. Many individuals who have been in the organization for three years or more still attend meetings frequently. Others still attend meetings regularly despite feeling that they no longer need to. Because Recovery is in a state of expansion and desires to build up its membership, it is highly unlikely that any member will be asked to leave, even when such a course would be beneficial to him. Of course, for certain individuals, continued membership, perhaps even on a lifetime basis, may be instrumental in the obtainment of necessary support.

Control over the contents of the meeting   Dr. Low was in the habit of making the final summaries and interpretations after all examples had been presented at the panel meetings. He reserved the right to modify or to correct any statement he considered to be inappropriate. At present, there is no qualified professional who fulfills this function. The group may misinterpret the method or may provide inappropriate advice in areas where lay persons are not competent. It is equally possible, under improper leadership, for discussion at meetings to range beyond the limits of the Recovery method. Surely all of these potential difficulties are possible, and others as well, but the method is so structured as to tend to minimize these dangers. All discussion at the meetings must be presented within the framework of the Recovery concepts and must deal only with trivial examples. The member can also always disregard inappropriate advice.

Relation to the network of traditional aftercare services   Recovery has no formal connection with any facilities, agencies, or professionals in the mental field. Because of its relative isolation from other potential sources of help, Recovery is in the position of providing a limited range of services to its members. It may not be able to refer a member to other sources of help which may be necessary. A potential consequence of such isolation may be the development of anti-professional attitudes, and reluctance on the part of the members to obtain professional help when it is necessary. Anti-professionalism need not always be a characteristic of a lay-run self-help organization. Alcoholics Anonymous, which is completely lay run, appears to have good relations with professionals and in many instances has cooperated with professionals in order to provide maximum help for the alcoholic.

CONTROL OF DEVIANCY   An important problem arising from the utilization of lay-run groups for emotionally disturbed individuals involves the possibility of their becoming channels for deviant behavior. Groups like Recovery, because of their unique composition, may foster bizarre and maladaptive behavior on the part of the members. Such groups may be tolerant of behavior which elsewhere would be considered deviant, and may produce deviant group norms. In this sense, such groups may become "fringe" or "crackpot" types of organizations.

The possibility of this kind of development, however, appears to be minimal. The survey of membership has strongly suggested that the organization is not composed of marginal individuals, but rather is made up of persons of solid middle-class status. Observation of group meetings has not uncovered unusually predominant manifestations of abnormal or unacceptable behavior. The philosophy of Recovery, rather than being deviant, resembles in certain respects the general ethos of middle-class American society. The value placed on salvation through work and effort is strongly reminiscent of the Protestant Ethic. The focusing of the Recovery method on concrete symptoms can be compared to current pragmatic and behavioristic ideologies. Finally, the inspirational nature of Recovery is in line with the current fashionableness of "positive thinking." If Recovery is a deviant organization, it is not deviant because of its philosophy or because of the type of members that it attracts; it may be deviant, however, in the sense that it stands outside of the network of traditional rehabilitation and aftercare services.

Problems Related to the Recovery Method

THE RIGIDITY OF THE RECOVERY METHOD   The Recovery method is to be literally applied to all examples presented at the panel meetings. The method is viewed as a perfected, finished system of self-help and aftercare. No provision is made for any changes in the Recovery concepts and techniques, nor is such change viewed as desirable. Questioning of the basic assumptions of the method is not permitted.

The great concern displayed by Recovery leaders and members over the faithful application of the method prevents individualized consideration of each member's problems. The tendency is to change each panel example so that it fits the method, rather than to modify the method so that it applies to the example. As a consequence, appropriate consideration of an individual's problems may have to be rejected in order to maintain the Recovery method intact.

The Recovery outlook contrasts sharply with the position of Alcoholics Anonymous. Although A.A. has a basic set of "Traditions" and "Steps" which in certain respects are similar to the Recovery method, they are not so literally and rigidly employed in all instances as is the Recovery method. A.A.'s position, briefly stated, is as follows (Bill, 1955): "Nobody invented Alcoholics Anonymous. It grew. Trial and error has produced a rich experience. Little by little we have been adopting the lessons of that experience, first as policy and then as tradition.

That process still goes on and we hope it never stops. Should we ever harden too much, the letter might crush the spirit. We could victimize ourselves by petty rules and prohibitions; we could imagine that we had said the last word. We might even be asking alcoholics to accept our rigid ideas or stay away. May we never stifle progress like that!"

Of course, the rigid application of the Recovery method may also have certain advantages. The schedule of the meeting may prevent discussion from extending into areas in which the members may not be qualified. The method prevents the giving of advice to members outside of the context of Recovery terminology, and serves to control the content of discussion. In addition, the feeling that the method is perfect and can help all members is in line with the inspirational aspects of the organization.

THE STRESS UPON CONTROL   Recovery emphasis upon control may provide members with defenses against anxiety, and may help them to cope with their symptoms. However, the basic concern over emotional control may serve to neglect the provision of adequate mechanisms for the release of affect.

Some release of emotion may be a by-product of the catharsis ensuing from the public presentation of a behavioral example, but this kind of release is not a major concern of Recovery. Recovery appears to stress a denial or affect, rather than a release aimed at the establishment of new insights. For the individual whose basic problem is the expression of feeling rather than its control, such a method may be unsuitable. Individuals with over-rigid systems of defenses against anxiety may be harmed by increments arising from the Recovery method. Despite the problems which may arise from the lack of inclusion of a "release" mechanism in the Recovery method, the omission may also serve as a potential safeguard. If emotional content was released at the meetings, it is doubtful whether lay persons would have sufficient skill to cope with such material.

THE SUPERFICIALITY OF THE METHOD   The Recovery method does not attempt to probe for the etiology of symptoms. The major concern is the treatment of an individual's problems as they exist at the present. Problems are viewed in the form of symptoms, usually presented in a highly concrete, somaticized form. Dynamic interpretations are not permitted, as they are outside the realm of the method. The total effect may be the temporary suppression of the symptom rather than recognition and management of underlying cause. This suggests that any help that the Recovery method provides for a person may be temporary. Symptoms which are suppressed in one form may reappear in altered context. Observation of panel meetings has indicated that although members tend to report successful coping with symptoms, such symptoms persist from meeting to meeting, changing only slightly in form.

THE REGRESSIVE-INFANTILIZING ASPECTS OF THE METHOD   Although the Recovery method places much emphasis on self-help and individual initiative, it nevertheless encourages the member to submit to a higher form of authority. The member must unquestioningly accept the Recovery method in its entirety, with the image of Dr. Low as the supreme authority. The method leads the individual to reduce complex psychological problems to concretized somatic symptoms. The participant is given certain basic tools of a highly ritualized nature, which are to be used in warding off anxiety-producing situations. The new Recovery language which is supplied to the individual creates the appearance of verbal labels which are to be manipulated. For certain people, the employment of these aspects of the Recovery method may tend to force adjustment at low levels of psychological maturity. The individual is placed in the situation of a child who must obey a father figure and use certain semi-magical rituals. He is to gain salvation through complete obedience. Individuals capable of deeper insights into the meaning of their problems may be forced to regress to obtain psychic equilibrium.

DEALING ONLY WITH SYMPTOMATOLOGY Recovery provides help for an individual only in reference to his symptomatology. It does not deal with such areas as his potential for growth and development. Its focus is limited to maladaption in effect to the "unhealthy" facets of the participant. There is no clear conceptualization in the Recovery method of what the healthy person is like. All members must constantly present examples of their problems and difficulties. The leaders, who serve as role models for the newer members, present these types of examples most frequently. The majority of Recovery group meetings are concerned with the various symptoms individuals in the group may experience. As a consequence, the group appears to be at all times concerned with illness. For the individual with a potential for growth beyond his immediate symptoms, the great concern in Recovery over symptomatology and illness may well be over-restrictive. As a consequence, for some persons psychological growth may be impeded.

There are certain safeguards within the Recovery method which to some extent serve to counteract this preoccupation. All examples and problems must be discussed within Recovery terminology. A time limit is placed on all discussion, and descriptions must be of an objective, concrete nature. These features of the method may prevent the degeneration of the panel examples into "gripe sessions." However, they may not eliminate completely the basic preoccupation with illness which is shared by the members.

EMPHASIS ON INSPIRATION The focus upon inspirational aspects in Recovery may prevent individuals from obtaining a realistic appraisal of the severity of their illness. Certain members may be given a false sense of complacency as to the actual nature of their problems. Because of Recovery's emphasis on inspiration and the belief that the problems of all members can be successfully coped with through this simple method, persons on the verge of acute episodes may be prevented from obtaining necessary professional help.

COST OF THE NERVOUS PATIENT ROLE An earlier section of this report has discussed the type of nervous patient role which membership in Recovery may imply. This role may lead to certain basic problems. It may stigmatize the member by formally defining him as different from other persons who are not emotionally disturbed. It may force him to view all of his behavior from within the cognitive framework provided by the role of a patient. As a result, he may have difficulty in perceiving himself in any other way. This may tend to reinforce his feelings about his illness. The role may be a permanent one: there are no mechanisms for a formal termination of it. The individual's integration into community life may be significantly impeded. If maintenance of the role permits the individual to remain outside of the hospital, and to be reasonably productive, it may serve a positive function despite its limitations and relative permanence. And the group to which he is attached by the role of patient may provide him with a certain amount of support that could not be found elsewhere.

36 / The Social Context of Treatment: Unresolved Issues

Leonard Solomon

Psychiatric treatment and hospitalization represent the end state of an interpersonal process which begins outside the hospital. When a person exhibits deviant and disordered behavior, such as confusion and disorientation, inappropriate emotional reactions, severe depressions, phobias, or "florid symptoms" (delusions and hallucinations), the nature of his social ecology will determine whether or not he receives psychiatric attention. Such social conditions as the person's degree of "social visibility," the likelihood that relevant audiences will identify his behavior as "symptomatic" of mental illness, his potential for harming others, the emotional and material support he receives from his family, and the available psychiatric resources in the community, all interact to determine whether and for how long he can remain part of a residue of untreated persons with psychological disorders. An appreciation of the prepatient's primary groups and the mutually influencing parts of his social ecology (family, work, school, and so on) will enhance our understanding of the pathways to psychiatric treatment and their personal meaning for the patient in treatment.

Most clinical research which seeks to assess differences in behavior and psychological functioning between groups of patients and nonpatients confounds or ignores the effects of the prepatient (and inpatient) career. In part, some social and cognitive deficits may be outcomes of the social experiences associated with the prepatient phase. As Sarbin (1968a) observes:

> The pre-patient sequence has this special characteristic—members of a person's significant audience have begun to look upon him and act toward him as if he were a person who could only enact roles with minimal obligations. The upshot of reducing the number of roles that a person may play is to reduce the size and complexity of his social ecology, thereby forcing him to depend more and more on inputs from his private world. He is subjected to subtle degradation rituals, the effect of which is to reduce his claims to being a person (p. 11).

In effect, during the phase of prepatienthood, the person who enacted inappropriate behavior has been prediagnosed and informally treated by family, friends, and neighbors. "Treatment" takes the form of changes in role relationships and changes in the pattern of positive and negative social reinforcement. In a sense, the deviant person helps to create a new social ecology which, in turn, generates a new set of experiences for him. Whether and to what extent this change in the social ecology is disturbing to the deviant person and contributes to such behaviors as social withdrawal and a preoccupation with personal fantasy is an open research question. Similar questions can be raised with respect to the social ecology of the inpatient and expatient career phases.

The entrenched medical model of disease tends to assume that the internal bio-psychic system of the deviant person can be diagnosed independently of his social ecology. Wing *et al.* (1967), for example, make this bias explicit when they state:

> A psychiatric bias, on the other hand, is based, at least in theory, on the same concept of illness as is used in the rest of medicine. That is, the clinician selects elements from the history and examination which seem to suggest that the patient is suffering from a certain disease and, on the basis of this hypothesis, makes statements about etiology, pathology or "natural history" (p. 499).

The implicit assumption is that an "underlying disease process" gives rise to the characteristic "symptoms" or behavior disorders of, for instance, schizophrenia. This "underlying disease" may be viewed as organic, psychic, or both, in origin. An alternative formulation of the question might be: What are the antecedent and concurrent conditions responsible for a particular enactment or pattern of deviant behavior? A social psychological analysis would identify some of the antecedent stressor conditions for the prepatient, such as the stigma of being labeled "mentally ill," the breakdown of intimate socioemotional relationships in the family, the stripping of social identity and role responsibilities, social isolation, and the impact of unemployment. It would seek to specify the social influence of the family and other salient reference groups and to assess their effects upon the overt behavior and self-assessment of the prepatient or inpatient (Mishler and Waxler, 1968).

During the early part of this century, most mental hospitals were primarily concerned with the safe custody of the inmates at a low cost to public funds. Belknap (1956) and Dunham and Weinberg (1960) have described some typical custodial institutions of that era. Their major function was surveillance, preventing escape or violence. Rigid routines of control, geared to treating batches of patients economically, were devised. Locked doors, windows that would only open two inches, fixed time off the ward, and warning whistles carried by every attendant characterized the custodial institution. In this way, a small, poorly paid, and untrained staff managed a large patient population and spawned the worst effects of institutionalization. Ironically, the "moral treatment" practiced in many asylums 100 years ago was based upon the generally accepted philosophy of treatment today; namely, treating the patient with dignity and respect, individualizing the treatment approach, and seeking early discharge. Gerald Grob, using the tools of a historian, provides a clinical case history of one state mental hospital. He documents the stages of development of the mental hospital over a span of 100 years from "moral" to "custodial" treatment orientations. In 1830, Worcester State Hospital had 120 patients, most of whom were middle- and upper-class Protestants. They were all on an intimate basis with the Superintendent. The moral therapy included individualized care and open wards. By 1850, the hospital housed up to 500 patients, a large portion of whom were working class immigrants. The doctor-patient ratio rose from 1:58 to 1:140. Therapy was transformed into custodial care—control by restraints and neglect under an impersonal system. Grob's thesis is that the internal transformation of the identity of this hospital was not determined by scientific or medical criteria. He traces the influence of such forces as industrialization, new immigrant population, ethnic conflict, and a new intellectual climate upon the transformation of the mental hospital from moral treatment to custodialism.

Grob's study has some important implications for those who seek to change the structure and functions of mental hospitals.

1. In the absence of a historical perspective as well as a social system analysis, there is a tendency to blur the distinction between the goals of the community (and its political system) and the therapeutic goals of the hospital.
2. Mental hospitals are not functionally autonomous institutions. The hospital must secure patients, staff, facilities, and financial support from the outside community. Professional staff members within the hospital are identified with the values of their professional organizations outside the hospital, and these values may conflict with their goals inside the hospital.

The research by Strauss *et al.* (1964) provides a useful counterbalance to Grob's approach, since the authors examine the relationship between the current social system of the psychiatric hospital and its treatment ideology. Employing an "arena-negotiation model," these authors propose that the most striking feature of psychiatric hospitals today is their proliferating division of expert labor. The various professional groups brought together in the psychiatric institution stake their claims to share in the treatment process and define their identities in relation to the treatment operations that occur. The superordinate position of the medical profession in the handling of the sick is by no means absolute. Strauss *et al.* found that social workers and psychologists laid claim to direct therapeutic roles. They did not automatically grant leadership to a psychiatrist; he had to earn it. A great deal of informal negotiation and bargaining occurs between professional and semiprofessional groups concerning types of treatment and roles of individual team members. Strauss *et al.* (1964) cite some ideological conflicts between differing professional groups.

> Psychotherapeutically oriented people take a jaundiced view of shock therapy, regarding it as at worst barbarous or medieval and at best crudely expedient. Professional courtesy generally stood between physicians, preventing direct confrontation over specific practices. But nurses were not always so reticent and occasionally displayed moral indignation and even took steps to block shock treatment. . . . In turn, somaticists were critical of psychotherapists. For them, moral considerations revolved around the time, money, and anguish of parents or families. . . .
>
> Contention over drug usage most often involved the same arguments but with some differences. Psychotherapists would accept minimal amounts of drug usage but often criticized somaticists for turning patients into "zombies," contending that heavily drugged patients could not be helped with basic problems. The somaticists, on the other hand, believed that psychotherapists were unnecessarily cruel in not diminishing patients' suffering. Said one somaticist, "Patients have a right to be comfortable, and doctors an obligation to make them so" (pp. 365–366).

The selection by Hollingshead and Redlich indicates that there are latent social factors, besides medical criteria, which determine who is treated where, how, and for how long. They demonstrate the existence of a relationship among social class status, prevalence, and mode of treatment received. They also examine the way in which the social class of the prepatient, in a sense, predetermines the possible pathways and treatment resources available to him. Their findings reveal that there is a greater proportion of diagnosed schizophrenics found in the lower social classes (Classes IV and V), and a lower proportion of schizo-phrenics in the upper classes, particularly Class III. Their data with respect to incidence parallels that of prevalence—the lower social classes also seemed to be producing a greater number of new cases of schizophrenia. The lower class schizophrenic patient is more likely to be found in state mental hospitals, receiv-ing organic treatment (such as electric shock) or custodial care rather than psychotherapy, and his hospital stay is likely to be more prolonged. Bean *et al.* (1964), in a ten year follow-up study of the schizophrenic patients in the Hol-lingshead and Redlich sample, report that fewer lower class patients were dis-charged from the hospital. In addition, the higher class patient showed more severe symptoms than the lower class patient at the time of release. Goldberg and Katz (1967) provide a summary of some current findings with respect to the schizophrenic poor. They state:

1. First, in comparison with the prevalence in other social classes, diagnosed schizophrenia exists to a proportionately greater extent among the poor.
2. As a group they are becoming poorer.
3. The schizophrenic poor are disproportionately reproducing schizophrenics, who in turn are becoming poorer. (Schizophrenia runs in families even though different explanations are offered for this fact.)
4. Eliminating the patients' psychopathology in itself will not necessarily in-sure against the dismal outlook just painted (p. 17).

Hollingshead and Redlich's measure of social class is based upon the dimension of educational attainment and occupational prestige. A detailed version of the method of measurement, with exemplifications of the five social class levels, is pro-vided in Levinson and Gallagher's paper. This operational definition, however, tells us little about the subjective meaning of class status or differential social behavioral systems of different classes. Dohrenwend and Dohrenwend (Part II) have emphasized the difficulty in identifying symptoms of psychological dysfunc-tion without a thorough knowledge of the base rates for a particular population. Knowledge of the social context is necessary to distinguish situational and transient dysfunction from pathological disorders. What are the cultural patterns (gestalts) in terms of model family systems, core values, cultural traditions, and housing conditions? What are the psychological perspectives of different class cultures, e.g., in terms of achievement motivation, sense of inferiority and stigma, sense of continuous identity, and cultural roots?[1] Fried's research (Part V) on re-location of families in Boston and Sollenberger's (1968) study of Chinese-American families in New York City serve to remind us that there is no one-to-one relationship among economic, social, or psychological deprivation. Different "cul-tures of poverty" are characterized by different syndromes of psychological dis-order. Lewis (1966) suggests that in the United States "the elimination of

---

[1] Silone (1968) gives an incisive description of the new attitudes toward the poor in some parts of Italy: "Their chief concern, be they Catholic or Communists, is that other people should not think them poor . . . nowadays the most frightful insult conceivable, second only to disrespectful insinuations about the ancestors of one's adversary—the insult that leaves one no choice but to resort to violence—is the epithet *Morto di fame!*: 'starved to death' (in English it might be rendered as 'You penniless wretch!'). . . . In the minds of the common people of Italy poverty has become a disgrace, even when, as is mostly the case, the poor are poor through no fault of their own" (p. 30).

physical poverty *per se* may not be enough to eliminate the culture of poverty which is a whole way of life" (p. lii). Systematic, long-term research is certainly needed in this area.

Levinson and Gallagher's contribution provides a more provocative view of social class as reflected in the personality functioning of the patient. They indicate the process by which the patient's class-conditioned attitudes and the staff treatment orientations are mutually selective and reinforcing. For example, patients who are high on authoritarianism (which is class-related) are more resistant to psychotherapy. On the other hand, psychotherapists are more willing to work with patients who are intraceptive and low on authoritarianism. It is worth noting that, even in the heyday of individualized moral therapy at Worcester State Hospital, treatment differed for the lower class patient. Individual distinctions existed; lower class patients were not accorded the same privileges as middle or upper class patients and were housed in separate wards. Levinson and Gallagher also introduce the valuable social psychological concept of the "modal patient status." Hospital rules and practices tend to be geared to the behavior disorder, social class, and age of the "modal patient." A patient's career in the psychiatric hospital is shaped by his degree of discrepancy from the modal patient status as well as his objective social status.

Both Goffman and Caudill *et al.* give us a close view of what it feels and looks like to be a mental patient. They open a window into the experience of the patient and provide colorful images of the patient's engagement in the psychiatric hospital. Their method is that of participant observation. Goffman assumed the role of an assistant athletic director in a large federal hospital where the modal patient was diagnosed as psychotic. Caudill, on the other hand, assumed the role of an actual patient. He lived in a ward with patients diagnosed as "severe psychoneurotics" in a private psychiatric hospital. In both studies, top hospital management knew what the aims of the research were and provided administrative support. Each author's personal reminiscences and feelings about his particular research role have been appended to their selections. They are revealing, not only for the insights into the character of the researcher, but also for the way in which they enhance our understanding of how the social values of the participant cannot be divorced from the methods and concepts which guide systematic observation.

Goffman traces the developmental stages of the modal patient's moral career from the decision to commit the person to his inpatient experience. His incisive description of how the self is transformed in the process of becoming a stabilized mental patient prompts one to question what effect this career would have upon a "normal person." How would such a person react to the experience of family betrayal, loss of social identity, self-degradation, and the various forms of mortification?

The major thrust of Goffman's polemic is that the "total institution" (1958) of the mental hospital, by its very structural design and application of the medical model, degrades the patient and discredits his claims to being treated with personal dignity. The arbitrary power of all staff over patients breeds a coercive and corrupting political system which leaves the institution virtually immune to feedback from the inmate perspective. Moreover, the institution comes to rely on the defining characteristic of its patients' "mental illness" to legitimatize all forms of bureaucratic depersonalization and irrationality. The structural design of the "total institution" is such that each phase of the inmate's daily activity is carried out in the company of a large number of other patients. All of the patients are treated alike and are required to do the same thing at the same time. Routines are tightly scheduled and imposed through an all-inclusive system of rules. Relationships with the outside are kept to a minimum. In this way, a small number of untrained supervisory personnel can control a large population of patients. The system insures predictability and economy of effort. It would, for example, save time and trouble if everyone's soiled clothing could be indiscriminantly placed in one bundle, and laundered clothing redistributed, not according to membership, but according to rough size. Custodial mental hospitals share this characterization with other "total institutions," such as prisons, TB sanitoria, and refugee camps.

Goffman's analysis, however, tends to obscure important differences between institutions which promote qualitatively different social environments. Brown and Wing's (1962) comparative study of three mental hospitals revealed hospital differences in matters of central importance to the life of the patients. For example, three times as many long-stay patients left the ward some time during the day at Hospital A as at Hospital C, and there was a similar difference in the number of patients possessing a toothbrush or some personal ornament such as a ring, brooch, or watch. Hospitals also differ with respect to the positive resources and pressures they provide (work and training opportunities), the degree of staff control, and their "openness" and relatedness to the community.

Wing (1968) has conceptualized the relationship between "institutionalism" and schizophrenia in the following manner: "The end state shown by schizophrenic patients in mental hospitals as a primary component due to the disease, and a secondary component due partly to *specific* schizophrenic vulnerability to an understimulating environment and partly to institutionalism; that is to a gradual acquiescence in the institutional mode of life" (p. 2). It is the secondary components that are most influenced by variations in the social environment. For example, delusions and hallucinations do not seem to get worse over a long period in the hospital. On the other hand, Wing reports a correlation between the degree of institutional restrictiveness and understimulation and the likelihood that the patient will be socially withdrawn, underactive, silent, and affectively blunted. Improvement in the social environment was related to changes in these behaviors. "Time doing nothing" seemed the most sensitive index of the effects of social change. These findings are consistent with those reported by Hunter *et al.* (1962) and Klein and Spohn (1962, 1964).

Goffman's analysis also does not indicate the contribution made by the patient's behavior disorder. In what way do the psychological deficits of the patient generate and reinforce the pessimism and neglect which characterize the custodial hospital? Different types of patients show different patterns of resistance and vulnerability to certain institutional climates. Thus, the patient diagnosed as an "aggressive psychopath," the "withdrawn paranoid schizophrenic," or the "severe psychoneurotic" react quite differently to institutional pressures, and are likely to generate different relationships and patterns of staff interaction. It is necessary to carry Goffman's pioneering contribution from the level of analysis of a generic institution and a generic patient to a level which encompasses individual differences and the processes of social change.

Caudill's classic study of the informal social structure of a ward group highlights some of the positive functions such a group may provide for the patient. This group of psychoneurotic patients evolved its own norms, informal leaders, and forms of mutual support which may have had as much significance in their treatment as the formal types of interpersonal therapy. Certainly the norms of the patient group were consistent with the basic tenets of psychotherapy—the value of exploring life history, relinquishing "defenses," permissive attitudes toward deviation in other patients, and mutual support. A potential therapeutic resource is the ward society itself. How can we create the social conditions which would facilitate the growth of therapeutic ward groups?

The problem of how to deal with staff-patient differences in perspective and goals needs clarification. Who speaks for the patients? What social inventions can be devised to provide legitimate opportunities for (open) communication and the resolution of differences? Patient self-government may be one such solution (Ellsworth, 1956; Stubbins and Solomon, 1959). Caudill also emphasizes the notion that patient behavior cannot be understood in the restrictive terms of the individual's case history alone, but reflects his role and emotional relationships within the ward society. Caudill's study serves to clarify the manner in which the ward group can serve such functions as "reality testing," exchange of information, emotional support, and development of interpersonal skills. The potentialities for developing therapeutic ward societies, however, may be limited by the type and severity of the behavior disorder (Murray and Cohen, 1959). Sociometric research indicates that "sicker" patients are characterized by "simpler" and more poorly integrated (anomic) forms of ward social organization.

Kelman focuses upon the process of personal change in a therapy group. He advances the notion that social influence operates via such mechanisms as modeling, the use of sanctions, and new shared information to induce change. Furthermore, he differentiates among change at the level of compliance, identification, and internalization. His theoretical scheme seeks to relate antecedent patterns of social influence to consequent levels of personal change. He also attempts to conceptualize a "corrective emotional experience" in group therapy, and examines the probability that such learnings are transferable to different settings, such as family or work situations. What is needed is systematic research to evaluate the utility of Kelman's theory as well as the relative efficiency of group therapy.

The short excerpt by Redl provides a further elaboration of the challenge group therapy holds for traditional clinical or social psychological concepts. The four phenomena which Redl describes are "contagion," "group role suction," the "tax powers" of group structure and group code, and the "action threshold impact of spatial designs." Redl and his coworkers (Polansky et al., 1950; Lippitt et al., 1952) have done a considerable amount of systematic observational research on the conditions under which the contagion effect occurs. The other phenomena need to be validated by measurement techniques that include interobserver reliability and construct validity. This, in turn, requires an extension of our present conceptual system for analyzing group processes. The systematic study of delinquent and other deviant groups may promote the development of a more comprehensive clinical, social psychological theory of small group processes.

The paper by Raush et al. demonstrates how research evaluating clinical outcomes of residential treatment can be effectively studied by the direct observation of interpersonal behavior in a natural group setting. The authors focus on therapeutic change from the viewpoint of "relationship changes" in the inter-action of the boys and their staff. This concentration on behavioral observation is a healthy corrective to excessive reliance upon measures of attitude change as indicative of behavioral change. Ellsworth's study (1965) of the behavioral correlates of staff attitudes indicates: "One cannot assume that a basic or under-lying attitude change has indeed taken place unless one also knows the extent to which there has been a parallel change in the relationship behavior between the student nurse and the hospitalized patient" (pp. 199–200).

Residential treatment emphasizes the notion that therapy can take place in real-life situations and that the important persons in the process are those who have daily contact with the children. Schedules, routines, and time arrangements are aimed at inducing change in the children; they are elastic to fit the require-ments of different groups. On the basis of his own work in this area, Redl (1966) emphasizes "the great opportunities that the closeness to daily life, daily conflicts, and mistakes offers the clinician, in contrast to the traditional seclusion of the action-remote interview technique" (p. 144).

The personnel of a typical hospital ward use a variety of rewards and punish-ments to control and shape the behavior of patients. These often take the form of loss of privileges, transfer to different wards, or social isolation from the staff. Maher (1966) points out that this system of behavior control is primarily oriented toward manageability rather than mental health. For example, there is no reward system for independence or creativity. An interesting aspect of the system is that reinforcement for improved behavior is delayed, whereas punishment for un-desirable behavior is likely to be immediate. Moreover, "improvement" is more difficult to define and requires more repetition before it is viewed as "reliable" by the staff. The system, when viewed in this way, readily discrminates and pun-ishes unacceptable behavior but is less able to identify "improvement" and, by comparison, has an ineffective system for reinforcing it. The ward attendant him-self is also responding to a system of reinforcements. He, too, can be transferred to a back ward with incontinent patients. The nursing system operates so that an attendant is more likely to be reinforced for the fulfillment (or nonfulfillment) of visible housekeeping duties than for the quality of his participation with the patient. One approach toward an understanding of the way in which patient and staff behavior are shaped is to study the influence of the continuous social en-vironment in terms of the pattern and intensity of the reinforcement system as well as the motives of the participants.

Atthowe and Krasner describe the design of an experimental ward based upon a token economy. A system of contingent reinforcement was applied to all phases of the patient's life. Once put into effect, the system can be varied to fit the individual level of functioning of different patients (e.g., the "carte blanche"). The researcher is able to make direct tests of the type and degree of reinforce-ment necessary to modify specific behaviors. The behavior therapy approach specifies an assembly of techniques and a target effect. By identifying the be-havior of patients which will be reinforced, these techniques provide discrimina-ble criteria of desired or nondesired behavioral change. This reward structure compels the professional staff to make explicit definitions regarding which classes of behavior on the ward are "healthy" (positively reinforced), which are "patho-logical" (negatively reinforced), and which are irrelevant to the contingent reinforcement system. Moreover, it would be possible to individualize the reinforced behaviors as well as the schedule and value of the reinforcer. Ullmann (1967) proposes that the professional staff may do a disservice when it emphasizes "insight" rather than behavioral change. The goal of insight may be appropriate for a patient from a "professional" subgroup, but it may be irrelevant for working class patients. There is also some evidence to suggest that changed behavior precedes rather than is the outcome of changes in intrapsychic feelings.

Unfortunately, Atthowe and Krasner do not indicate how many patients actually achieved independence of the token reward system ("carte blanche") and how this affected their cognitive and interpersonal behavior. What are the characteristics of those patients who respond to the token economy and those who do not? Can the modified behavior be maintained after the token economy is withdrawn? What effect is there on the social structure and patterns of interaction on the ward? Are there changes in the attitudes and behavior of the attendants? What are the "secondary effects" of the attendant who now conducts his role with the expectation that the patient is not a passive object without control over his choices, but is able to change, and that the attendant can shape such changes with tangible payoffs?

It should be noted that the token economy was developed on a ward of "hard core," older, chronic patients (median age, 57; median length of hospitalization, 22 years). In most mental hospitals, this group represents the "graveyard of therapists' hopes" (Spohn, 1958). The physical setting of the ward is likely to be impoverished. The patients themselves are characterized by passivity, apathy, and neglect. These studies serve to demonstrate that the possibilities for therapeutic change by restructuring the social environment do exist; this is one of a variety of imaginative alternatives to the medical model.

The concept of a therapeutic milieu (total treatment environment) originally spurred by Maxwell Jones has also served to generate a number of innovative treatment approaches (Raush with Raush, 1968; Spohn, 1958; Ellsworth, 1968). The key features of a therapeutic milieu program are high levels of social interaction (with minimal status differentials), a democratic ward structure (patient government or collaboration in rule setting), and the blurring of patient-staff distinctions so that they are likely to form a solidarity of ingroup with respect to certain issues. There is a greater reliance on informal group pressure and positive rewards which are particularized for the individual patient.

The "therapeutic community" (Wax, 1963) is characterized by the following treatment dimensions:

1. Emphasis is placed on the current social behavior of the patient.
2. Treatment responsibility is distributed among patients and staff; the patient is expected to participate actively in his own treatment as well as that of fellow patients.
3. Social distance between patients and staff and between echelons of staff is reduced to facilitate authentic communication of feelings and information.
4. Psychopathology of the patient and the attainment of psychodynamic insight is deemphasized.

With any new treatment program, we need to ask whether it works, with which patients it works (and which are set back), and what are the effective ingredients of that program. The paper by Ellsworth *et al.* provides a research strategy which evaluates the relative effectiveness of hospital treatment programs for the patient in the hospital, with the family, and in the community. The data suggest that patient "improvement" is "situation specific." An improved hospital patient is not necessarily able to transfer his adjustment to the outside social context of his community or family. Ellsworth *et al.* pose a fundamental question; namely, what is the relationship between symptom reduction and improvement in social (family) and instrumental (job) functioning? Preparing the patient for return to the community implies a thorough understanding of the *patient's* community and its behavioral expectations. What is his family's level of aspiration with regard to the patient's social and work performance? What do his employer and coworker expect? The answers to these questions have important implications for realistic programs of treatment in the hospital (Gurel, 1966). Such information would also contribute to more adequate prognostic studies (Nuttall and Solomon, 1965, 1970).

The posthospitalization phase of the patient's career often represents a kind of probationary "twilight period" for the patient and the family. After-care treatment, where it exists, generally takes the form of supervision at a distance rather than treatment or rehabilitation. Rehabilitation efforts tend to cease at discharge. "Time out of the hospital," as Ellsworth demonstrates, may not be an adequate criterion of adjustment. Families may accept an overwhelming burden of care and management of the patient without complaint. The fact that they do not complain does not mean the patient has made an adequate adjustment. Many families, rehabilitation workshops, and halfway houses may foster a different brand of "institutionalism."

Kramer provides a convincing rationale for the use of the Day Hospital as a form of partial hospitalization. This treatment design serves the twin purpose of avoiding the effects of long-stay "institutionalism" and, at the same time, providing a pathway for the extension of treatment into the patient's early phase of posthospitalization. Kramer focuses on the need to coordinate the design of a treatment facility with the "natural course" of the disorder and the characteristics of the community which the facility must serve.

Wechsler's paper presents a systematic description of the philosophy and group processes of Recovery, Inc., a mutual aid organization. The avowed purpose of the organization is to prevent relapses and chronicity among the mentally ill. Wechsler's data, however, indicate that one-half of the responding sample of members reported that they had had no prior hospitalizations, and one-fifth had received no professional treatment of any kind. Recovery, Inc., is therefore likely to serve a number of preventive and "informal treatment" functions as well as providing support for the ex-mental patient. Recovery members receive "treatment" under conditions of minimal community exposure. It would be valuable to learn what proportion of "untreated members" of Recovery, Inc., subsequently choose to receive professional attention. If so, to what extent is this a function of the group experience?

More research is needed to assess the operation of informal social treatment networks both for rehabilitation and prevention of mental disorder. The work of Landy (1965), Raush with Raush (1968), and Ellsworth (1968) indicate that much can be done for people in trouble, outside as well as inside mental hospitals, by nonprofessionals. Is it possible to design social environments which enhance the opportunities for informal "treatment relationships" to develop? In a fundamental conceptual sense, the design of social environments for the prevention and treatment of mental disorder is inseparable from the task of designing social environments which promote positive mental health among "normals."

Part IV

MENTAL HEALTH ATTITUDES

A principle of social psychology holds that attitude and action go hand in hand. Some have argued that attitude precedes action. Others, encouraged by recent experimental evidence, have advocated the reverse sequence. Whatever the sequence, it is clear that attitude continues to be a major concern of social psychologists. Nothing illustrates this better than the history of research by social psychologists in the field of race relations. Accompanying the effort to achieve national unity in the 1940's was an outpouring of race relations research with a major emphasis on prejudiced attitudes.

In the 1950's and 1960's mental health research occupied the attention of growing numbers of social psychologists. Though frequent reference to the importance of attitudes may be found in the mental health literature, the volume of empirical research on mental health attitudes is microscopic when compared to the quantity generated by the earlier surge of race relations research. Surveys, laboratory experiments, field experiments, and case studies aimed at elucidating mental health attitudes were carried out in rather modest proportions.

Our decision to allocate an entire Part of this volume to the topic of mental health attitudes is not based on the quantity of available research, but rather on our conception of its importance for a complete social psychology of mental health. With this in mind, our selections tap major approaches to the study of mental health attitudes, with the hope that this might stimulate further research.

485

We particularly hope that the burgeoning experimentalism of present-day social psychology will be brought to bear on the study of mental health attitudes in more forceful ways than we have seen till now.

The first group of selections have in common a reliance on the attitude survey as a means of gaining knowledge. Halpert's paper offers a summary of public opinion surveys about mental health, ranging from the Trenton, N.J., survey of 1948, through the NORC national survey of 1950, to the Joint Commission survey conducted in the late 1950's.

Dohrenwend and Chin-Shong's paper is the result of a thoughtful use of survey methodology to analyze the mental health attitudes of community leaders and residents of Washington Heights in New York City. It links social status and attitudes toward psychological disorder in an effort to clarify the relation between social class and tolerance of deviance.

Schmuck and Chesler interviewed a series of individuals opposed to the current mental health movement. Focusing on one sector of the anti-mental health movement, their paper offers a revealing counterpoint to the cross-sectional surveys summarized by Halpert. The dimensions of the anti-mental health movement, hinted at in this paper, should give the reader pause concerning the politics of mental health today.

Of all the research in mental health attitudes, the most intensive and most steadily focused upon is that of Nunnally and his associates. His book, *Popular Conceptions of Mental Health*, is a landmark in its field. Unable to reprint the entire book and not wishing merely to summarize it, we decided to present three chapters reflecting its essential character. The first selection by Nunnally, "Public Attitudes Toward the Mentally Ill," presents measuring instruments, population samples, and results of research influenced by the semantic differential and its underlying theory of meaning.

The next piece by Nunnally, "Other Variables of Effective Communication," involves the realm of experimental social psychology. He reports on three experiments in mental health attitudes: one on the effect of "contact" with a former mental patient on attitude change; one designed to test the effect of personal versus impersonal styling; and one dealing with information change and attitude change. This selection should give the reader a concrete feeling for Nunnally's research style. Finally, to provide an overview of Nunnally's approach to mental health communication, we reprint the chapter entitled, "An Interpretive Overview," which contains his analysis of attitudes, mass media, and communication strategies. He lists a series of requirements for effective communication and concludes that, without these, "no amount of sermonizing, haranguing, or factual presentation will work; and it would be better not to communicate at all."

The next paper, that of McGinnies, Lana, and Smith, is an earlier experiment on mental health communication. Dealing with the effects of films on opinions about mental illness, it concludes that "films shown in a coherent series can significantly modify opinions and beliefs."

Farina and Ring used the experimental method to study the influence of perceived mental illness. Their work makes a strong argument for the importance of attitudes in the field of mental health. "The most important conclusion of this study," they say, "is that believing an individual to be mentally ill strongly influences the perception of that individual; this is true in spite of the fact that his behavior in no way justifies these perceptions. When a co-worker is viewed as mentally ill, subjects prefer to work alone rather than with him on a task and also blame him for inadequacies in performance. Since objective measures of performance do not warrant such responses, these findings attest to the importance of believing another to be mentally ill as a factor in interpersonal relationships."

The next group of papers in this section represents work that centers on attitudes as they occur in the mental hospital context. The paper by Gilbert and Levinson on custodialism and humanism was inspired by the famous authoritarian personality research in which Levinson collaborated in the late 1940's. They constructed the custodial mental illness ideology scale and proceed in this paper to establish a connection among ideology, personality, and hospital policy. In the hospitals under study, they found "relatively great congruence between prevailing policy, modal ideology, and modal personality."

Cohen and Struening use a factor-analytically derived set of scales called OMI (Opinions about Mental Illness) to study the relation between aspects of hospital performance and the attitudes of personnel. From their data, they crystallize out "an association between an authoritarian-restrictive attitude climate among the employees and a relative delay in releasing patients. . . . We interpret the main lines of causal influence as emanating from the policy-setting professionals, who influence employee attitude on the one hand, and determine the duration of patients' hospital stay on the other."

Rosenberg and Pearlin turn their sociological eye to the question of how attitudes relate to hospital life. Focusing on power-orientations, they analyze data obtained from over 1,000 nursing personnel in a large public mental hospital. Their work yields a helpful insight into the workings of power-attitudes in the mental hospital context.

To conclude this section we offer a case study of community attitudes and responses to a mental health research program. Eron and Walder's paper, "Test Burning: II," documents a complex, real-life interplay of attitudinal forces in the mental health arena. It should remind the reader once again of the importance of attitudes in the social psychology of mental health.

37 / Public Opinions and Attitudes about Mental Health

Harold P. Halpert

During the past 15 years several surveys have been made of public opinions and attitudes about mental illness. A review of the findings of these surveys indicates that public attitudes toward the mentally ill are no longer wholly negative.

Trenton, N.J., Survey

One of the earliest of these surveys reported by Ramsey and Seipp in 1948 was designed to obtain research data on opinions and information of a representative urban group regarding causative factors associated with mental disease. An interview questionnaire containing six basic questions was administered by the two authors and five trained graduate assistants to a representative sample of 345 persons, 18 years of age and older, in Trenton, N.J., a typical middle-sized city (125,000 population). Data were correlated according to age, sex, race, religious affiliation, educational level, and occupational class.

The six questions were:

1. Have you any ideas why people go insane (crazy)?
2. (a) If someone you knew began to show signs of very strange or odd behavior, do you believe anything could be done to help him or her?
   (b) What do you feel should be done?
3. Do you believe that insanity is God's punishment for some sin or wrongdoing?
4. Do you or do you not think that insanity is inherited?
5. Do you or do you not believe that people who are around those who are insane tend to become odd or strange themselves?
6. Some people believe that poor living conditions are a cause of insanity. Others disagree. What is your opinion?

This survey revealed what has been confirmed by several surveys since then; namely, that the higher the educational and occupational level, the more "enlightened" the opinions about mental illness. Although the majority of respondents cited emotional difficulties as causes of "insanity," the higher the educational level, the more often emotional and physical difficulties were cited; the lower the educational level, the more often environmental and behavioral causes, such as alcoholism, overeating, and overwork were cited. More of the women ascribed mental illness to emotional problems; more of the men mentioned environmental and behavioral factors. The overwhelming majority (92 per cent) felt that treatment would be of help to a mentally ill person. Most of the re-

From U.S. Public Health Service Publication No. 1045 (Washington, D.C.: U.S. Department of Health, Education, and Welfare, 1963). Reprinted by permission of the author.

spondents were clear about not associating sin with insanity. The respondents were less sure of themselves in answering the question about whether insanity is inherited; a large number of the responses were qualified answers.

The higher the educational and occupational level, the more optimistic the respondent was about likelihood of recovery, the greater his tendency to recommend professional treatment rather than home care, the more frequently he qualified his response about the possibility of hereditary factors being involved in mental illness, the less often he associated sin and "insanity," the less he believed it is harmful to associated with the "insane," and the less frequently he cited poor living conditions as a cause of mental disease. The older age groups in the survey associated poor living conditions with mental illness more often than did the younger groups. In general, however, Ramsey and Seipp found that the factors which determine a person's educational and occupational level also determined the extent of his enlightenment about mental illness.

Washington Survey

Community mental health education programs often have been based on a premise congruent with these findings. Assuming that attitudes about mental health are linked to level of education and knowledge of psychiatric concepts, those who have planned such programs have stressed providing the public with the facts about mental illness. However, a recent report (Freeman and Kassebaum, 1960) based on data from a 1950 survey, raises serious question about the validity of this assumption. The survey, conducted by the Washington Public Opinion Laboratory, was designed to answer two questions: (1) Are the opinions that people have about the etiology and prevention of mental illness related to the level of their formal education? (2) Are these opinions related to their familiarity with the technical vocabulary of psychiatry? Findings from 438 interviews of a sample population in the State of Washington revealed that ". . . opinions regarding the etiology and prevention of mental illness are only slightly, if at all, related to the level of formal education and . . . only weakly correlated with knowledge of the technical vocabulary of psychiatry" (p. 47). The only strong correlation was between level of formal education and knowledge of the technical vocabulary of psychiatry.

Freeman and Kassebaum caution that it is rash to conclude from this one study that knowledge has little influence on opinions and attitudes toward mental illness. The study does indicate that we cannot assume that giving people "the facts" will necessarily alter their opinions. The authors conclude their report by suggesting the need for basic research on "frames of reference by which persons integrate factual information and personal opinion. Such research would [provide guides for] . . . more realistic community mental health programs" (p. 47). The desirability of such research is underscored by two more recent surveys, which will be described later in this article. One of these surveys (Lemkau and Crocetti, 1962) revealed a relatively high level of sophistication about mental illness in a poorly educated, low socioeconomic urban population. The other (Dohrenwend, Bernard, and Kolb, 1962) showed a relatively low mental health orientation in civic leaders who had had much contact with the mentally ill.

The Louisville Survey

During the summer of 1950 a study was made of the attitudes of the citizens of Louisville, Ky., on the general subject of mental health. The study, financed by the city of Louisville and *Collier's* magazine, was one of a series conducted by the firm of Elmo Roper, at the request of Mayor Farnsley, in order to determine what local citizens thought about problems of city administration. In Louisville, 3,971 residents (1 in every 90 people in the city), aged 18 and over, were interviewed in their homes by trained interviewers equipped with carefully prepared questionnaires. Each interview lasted 45 minutes. Representative samplings were made of various age groups, income and educational levels, races, and both sexes. A special survey was also made of four additional groups: doctors, lawyers, clergymen, and teachers (Woodward, 1951; Maisel, 1951).

Most of the respondents regarded mental illness as a sickness, requiring sympathy and treatment, rather than as a condition warranting punishment or ridicule. The younger age groups and the better educated revealed a more humanitarian and scientific outlook than the older and less well educated, but an overall majority expressed relatively enlightened views about the need for medical treatment of mental illness, and an awareness of the lack of sufficient doctors and hospitals in Louisville to provide that treatment. Although the respondents supported psychiatry and medicine in general, the survey revealed a lack of recognition of psychiatric problems as such. Most people favored trying the family doctor, the clergyman, members of the family, or friends before "resorting" to psychiatry for help with emotional disorders.

The Louisville interviewers described four "cases," without identifying them as examples of mental illness, as a way of probing people's knowledge and attitudes. One of these was a description of a paranoid woman. A large proportion of the respondents failed to recognize the seriousness of this illness, recommending "commonsense" measures. Less than 7 per cent favored sending this woman to a mental hospital, and slightly more than 20 per cent suggested that the family doctor give her something to calm her nerves (an interesting indication of the public's prior readiness for the tranquilizers, which did not make their appearance until about 5 years later). Twenty-six per cent favored consulting a minister or priest; 21 per cent recommended that this woman's husband give her a "good talking-to"; and 13 per cent that he stay home with her and prove that he loves her. Only 1 per cent favored a punitive approach.

In the next case, that of a suicidally depressed man, there was an even greater tendency to rely on kindliness and "commonsense." Only 2 per cent recommended the mental hospital, 11 per cent favored consulting a psychiatrist, and 16 per cent suggested the family doctor.

Only 2 per cent recognized the case of a schizophrenic girl as mental illness; 4 per cent recommended seeing a psychiatrist, 2 per cent a doctor. Most respondents urged increased social contacts as a means of solving her problems.

The majority of interviewees responded to the fourth case, that of a 15-year-old truant and automobile stealer, with suggestions favoring more modern techniques of treatment—but only *after* such alternatives had been presented to them.

When asked the open question of what ought to be done . . . the most frequent responses are of the repressive type (punish him, send him to a reform school). But the minute the boys' club is suggested to them as one of six possible courses of action, it commands clear majority support. The reformatory and the "old-fashioned whipping" retreat almost to the bottom of the list, behind juvenile probation and referral to a psychiatrist (Woodward, 1951, p. 448).

Eighty-one per cent of the Louisville sample agreed in theory that "It's always worthwhile to get a psychiatrist's help when someone begins to act queerly or get strange ideas." The 19 per cent who disagreed with this statement did so because they thought it too drastic a first step, though they said they were not "against" psychiatrists. Seventy-five per cent of the general public felt that there were not enough doctors or hospitals in Louisville to take care of the mentally ill. Of the professional groups who were "oversampled," only the clergy and teachers agreed with the general public on this. One-third of the lawyers and 48 per cent of the doctors did not think there were insufficient psychiatric resources in Louisville.

The importance of the individual's frame of reference seems apparent in the responses to the statement that "Experts themselves often can't agree on whether a man is mentally ill enough to be put in an insane asylum or not." The general public, teachers, and clergy voted this true by 5 to 3. Doctors voted it true by 5 to 4. Lawyers, perhaps thinking of conflicting court testimony, voted it true by 4 to 1. Frame of reference also appears to have affected responses of the four professional groups to the question of who should be on an "expert committee" to decide how a city or state government should spend its money to prevent mental illness.[1]

Teachers

1. Psychiatrists
2. Clergymen
3. Social workers
4. Family doctors
5. Mental hygienists
6. Juvenile court judges

Clergymen

1. Clergymen
2. Family doctors
3. Psychiatrists
4. Juvenile court judges
5. Social workers
6. Mental hygienists
7. Businessmen

Doctors

1. Psychiatrists
2. Family doctors
3. Businessmen
4. Social workers
5. Juvenile court judges
6. Clergymen

Lawyers

1. Businessmen
2. Psychiatrists
3. Family doctors
4. Clergymen
5. Juvenile court judges
6. Bankers

The Louisville survey revealed that the attitudes of lawyers differ from those of the other professional groups surveyed. Approximately 25 per cent of the

[1] The general public voted for the inclusion of a priest, minister, or rabbi (62 per cent); family doctor (60 per cent); psychiatrist (42 per cent); social worker (39 per cent); mother (35 per cent); juvenile court judge (33 per cent); mental hygienist (24 per cent); businessman (21 per cent); school principal (16 per cent); banker (11 per cent); psychologist (8 per cent); psychoanalyst (8 per cent); sociologist (5 per cent). The college educated, as did teachers, listed the psychiatrist first and the clergyman second.

lawyers favored punitive measures for dealing with the juvenile delinquent, more than 40 per cent were opposed to seeking the help of a psychiatrist when someone acts strangely, and more than two-thirds endorsed secrecy about mental illness in the family. Teachers, doctors, and clergymen did not differ so much among themselves as they differed from lawyers. Since lawyers often are consulted by people at critical junctures in their lives and when they are emotionally upset, a vigorous program of mental health orientation for the legal profession may seem indicated.

As for the general public, perhaps the most significant finding of the Louisville survey is that, although they had largely given up old ideas and superstitions about mental illness, people still were unable to recognize serious mental symptoms as bona fide illness. Another major problem was the public's reluctance to seek psychiatric help except as a desperate "last resort." Perhaps the newer community-based treatment facilities may eventually "educate" the public to seek counseling and other mental health services before their problems overwhelm them. The presence of mentally ill persons treated in the community may also help inform people about how the mentally ill look and act.

The NORC Survey

One of the most revealing indications of the complexities involved in attempting to influence public attitudes toward the mentally ill is contained in the analysis of the nature of popular thinking about mental illness made by the National Opinion Research Center of the University of Chicago in 1950. Although the full report has not been published, the senior study director has reported on various of the findings (Star, 1955, 1956, 1957) and has made certain unpublished materials (NORC, 1952) available. The study involved 3,500 intensive interviews, each lasting 1½ hours, with a representative cross section of the American public. Its goals were to describe the characteristic ideas about mental illness current in our society, and to explain why popular conceptions about mental illness assume the form that they do.

The survey results indicate that the average American knows that mental illness can be treated, and that this entails special facilities, institutions, and the services of psychiatrists. The public is aware (and this was also demonstrated in the Louisville survey) that there are insufficient facilities and medical personnel to provide the needed treatment. However, although over 70 per cent of the respondents indicated that they believed a psychotic *can* recover, only about a fifth believed that most psychotics actually do get better. The reasons given were that there are not enough treatment facilities and that people do not seek help early enough.

When interviewees were asked to describe the meaning of mental illness, many contradictions appeared. At first questioning, a majority differentiated between "insanity" and "nervous conditions" (the former comprising violent and unpredictable behavior, and the latter a whole range of personality disorders), and included both under the heading of mental illness. Under further explicit questioning, however, they seldom maintained this inclusive definition, tending to equate mental illness only with severe psychosis and eliminating "nervous breakdowns" from this definition because people recover from them.

Brief descriptions of the personality and behavior of six mentally ill persons were presented, and interviewees were asked, in each case, to tell whether they thought anything was wrong with the person, what was wrong, what could have caused the condition, and whether the person should be regarded as mentally ill. The six cases, and the percentages of respondents who regarded them as mentally ill, were:

Paranoid	75%
Simple schizophrenic	34%
Alcoholic	29%
Anxiety neurotic	18%
Childhood conduct disturbance	14%
Compulsive-phobic	7%

One-sixth of the interviewees did not categorize any of the cases as mental illness. One-third saw mental illness only in the paranoid case. Of the 43 per cent who recognized mental illness in the other cases, only half—or about one-fifth of the total group—recognized neurotic symptoms as a manifestation of illness. The other half of this 43 per cent saw mental illness in the case of the alcoholic and the juvenile delinquent, but not in the case of the anxiety neurotic or the compulsive-phobic.

In general, people who had included neurotic as well as psychotic symptoms in their definition of mental illness tended to perceive mental illness in more of the cases than those who did not. There was a great disparity between intellectual appreciation and concrete recognition. Of the people who had included the anxiety syndrome in their abstract definition of mental illness, only 20 per cent recognized the specific case of the anxiety neurotic as an example of such illness. Thus, although many people started their discussion by saying that there are all kinds and degrees of mental illness, they ended by admitting only extreme psychosis into their actual working definition.

The director of the NORC survey states that people do not generally regard behavior as proof of mental illness unless three conditions prevail: (1) loss of cognitive functioning; (2) loss of self-control, usually to the point of violence; and (3) inappropriate behavior beyond what can be explained on a rationalistic basis (Star, 1955). The popular approach sets out to explain only *normal* behavior, not all behavior. Its premise is that rationality and the ability to exercise self-control are the distinctively human qualities; mental illness, which implies loss of rationality and self-control, is therefore perceived as an extremely threatening phenomenon. One can speculate about the reinforcement of this pragmatic approach to human behavior in much of the popular mental health literature dealing with "commonsense" ways of handling everyday emotional problems. Telling people that mental illness is nothing to be afraid of also will not help, since people reserve the term "mental illness" for behavior which frightens or antagonizes them. Sixty per cent of the respondents stated that they would not act or feel normally toward a former mental patient, even though they did not learn of his illness until they had known him for some time without noticing anything wrong about him.

Interesting differences in attitudes traceable to social and other factors were revealed by the NORC survey. The views of people who reported that they had a great amount of exposure to information about mental illness (from newspapers, books, lectures, articles, radio programs, etc.) were more likely to approach professional views. There was a direct correlation between the amount of education the respondent had and his concern with social problems, his knowledge about mental illness, and the number of information sources from which he derived that knowledge. (People with the most education mentioned professional training, formal education, lectures, and books as their principal sources of information.) At every educational level, people who derived their information about mental illness from a greater number and variety of information sources were more knowledgeable than their educational peers. High school graduates with high exposure to information sources perceived each of the six cases as mentally ill more often than college graduates with low exposure to information sources. One may speculate whether the great amount of mental health information poured into the mass communications channels during the 1950's did have a significant effect. Surveys conducted by Nunnally in 1955 and Lemkau in 1960 (described later in this article) revealed a greater public sophistication about mental illness than was evident from the NORC survey in 1950.

NORC respondents who knew individuals receiving psychiatric treatment tended to be more knowledgeable about mental illness. People who knew non-institutionalized psychiatric patients read and listened to more information about mental illness than people who knew patients in mental hospitals. General educational level may have been a factor here, since findings from another study (Hollingshead and Redlich, 1958) indicate that private psychiatric care is associated with higher socioeconomic class status. Less than 25 per cent of the population surveyed knew anyone who had consulted a psychiatrist privately or had visited a public clinic. People in or near large metropolitan centers were most likely to have contact with people receiving psychotherapy. If contact with people receiving noninstitutional psychiatric care is correlated with greater knowledge about mental illness, one may expect changes in public attitudes during the next 10 or 20 years with the increase in the number of community-based psychiatric treatment centers.

The New Jersey Surveys

Two mental health surveys, much more limited than the NORC survey, were conducted in the fall of 1954, under the auspices of the Division of Mental Hygiene and Hospitals, New Jersey Department of Institutions and Agencies, in an attempt to obtain a better understanding of knowledge and attitudes toward mental illness in that State. One of these was a survey of the general public, the other of physicians (*New Jersey Mental Health Surveys*, 1954). Both studies were designed by the chief of the department's Community Mental Health Services and both were carried out by Audience Research, Inc., of Princeton, N.J.

In the first study, replies were received from 1,209 respondents, age 21 and over. Of these, only 1 per cent listed mental disorder as the most serious disease today. Although 65 per cent knew of hospitals and clinics which treat the mentally ill, and 56 per cent were able to identify at least one public mental hospital in the State of New Jersey, only 3 per cent were able to identify at least one mental health clinic. Sixty-three per cent said there were not enough doctors or hospitals to treat the mentally ill in New Jersey. Eighty-five per cent agreed that it is worth while to get the help of a psychiatrist when someone begins to act strangely, but 59 per cent said that the trouble with most of the mentally ill is that they don't want to face their everyday problems. Some of the same dichotomies in thinking about behavior that appeared in the NORC survey also appeared here. Thus when people were asked to choose factors that might cause a person to have "a nervous breakdown without actually losing his mind or having to be put in a mental hospital," many answers were selected from the list. Too much "brainwork," too much drink, money trouble, trouble with spouse, menopause, and rundown physical condition were each selected by more than half the respondents. Far fewer factors were selected as reasons for causing a person "to actually lose his mind and have to be put in a mental hospital." Those mentioned most often were too much drink, menopause, money trouble, and too much "brainwork." Twenty-six per cent mentioned no causative factor for mental illness, as compared to only 5 per cent who mentioned no factor for "nervous breakdown."

Seventy-four per cent said that most mental illness is not inherited. Forty per cent believed that most people who "lose their minds" get well again, 26 per cent thought most "stayed that way," and 16 per cent thought about half get better and half do not. Fifty-one per cent said that "a person who goes out of his mind can get completely well again," and 33 per cent said he "would always show some signs of having once been mentally ill." Sixty-one per cent said they would tell their friends if a member of their family were mentally ill.

In the second New Jersey survey, replies were received from 405 physicians, only 6 per cent of whom were connected with a public or private mental hospital or sanitarium. Sixteen per cent said they found it useful to refer patients to a psychiatrist often, 67 per cent occasionally. Fifty-eight per cent said that from 1 to less than 10 per cent of their patients benefited from psychiatry. Thirty-eight per cent thought psychiatry is of some help, 39 per cent that it is a great deal of help. Eighty-six per cent said there was a local psychiatrist to whom to refer patients, 94 per cent knew psychiatrists personally, and 77 per cent unqualifiedly affirmed that they are pretty able men. Forty-four per cent always use a psychiatrist in committing patients to the mental hospital, 12 per cent normally do, 11 per cent occasionally, 12 per cent never use a psychiatrist for this purpose, and 21 per cent said they do not commit patients.

Most of the doctors were unfamiliar with the State's operations in handling the mentally ill: 52 per cent did not know how many patients were in the State mental hospitals, 63 per cent did not know how much tax money the State spends on mental illness, and 41 per cent did not know which State department runs the hospitals. Fifty-eight per cent, however, thought the State mental hospitals were unable to handle the job; 44 per cent advocated more hospitals, beds, and other facilities; and 21 per cent recommended more staff.

With regard to mental health clinics, 69 per cent of the New Jersey physicians said there is a local clinic to which to refer patients, but many did not know the details of its services. This may account for the fact that only 32 per cent gave an unqualifiedly favorable opinion of clinic services. Forty-one per cent favored increasing the amount of mental health clinic services. In response to another question, 42 per cent said they would like to have more psychiatric services, including clinics, at less cost to patients. Asked whether they would like to see more psychiatric facilities or clinics in their own community, 71 per cent of the physicians said yes, 22 per cent said no.

In naming the three most common causes of mental disorders, 54 per cent of the physicians mentioned stress of modern life; 30 per cent, anxiety and emotional maladjustment; 30 per cent, inherited predisposition; 20 per cent, family tensions; 19 per cent, marital and sexual tensions; 18 per cent, emotional deprivation; 14 per cent, physical illness and injury; 13 per cent, toxic substances, including bacteria; and 12 per cent, anxiety about health, including menopausal anxiety. Shock therapy was listed most often (38 per cent) as the best specific method to treat mental disorder. The other most frequently preferred therapies were: psychotherapy, 28 per cent; psychoanalysis, 26 per cent; and hospitalization, 20 per cent. Thirty-four per cent saw good results from psychiatric treatment for psychosis, 39 per cent fair, and 15 per cent poor. The percentages for neurosis were not too different: 41 per cent saw good results from psychiatric treatment, 41 per cent fair, and 8 per cent poor.

These physicians expressed considerable personal interest in psychiatry. Sixty-eight per cent said they would like a "down-to-earth popular pamphlet" on psychiatry for their own information, 40 per cent would definitely attend an extension course in psychiatry if it were offered nearby, and 41 per cent said they would like to see more psychiatrists on county medical society programs. Most do little reading about psychiatry—30 per cent almost none or none at all, 52 per cent a little, and only 18 per cent quite a bit.

Eighty-eight per cent of the New Jersey physicians believed they could distinguish between psychosis and neurosis, and, of these, 57 per cent thought they were able to treat neurosis. The number of patients for whose complaints the doctors were unable to find adequate cause was relatively small: 60 per cent of the doctors said that 70 per cent or more of their patients have definite organic or physiological pathology, and 47 per cent said that less than 30 per cent of their patients suffer from a neurosis of any kind. Forty-five per cent said they see a good deal of psychosomatic disease in their practice, and 53 per cent said they were comfortable treating psychosomatic complaints.

An analysis of the responses of the New Jersey physicians under 50 years of age as compared with those 50 years and over revealed significant differences (Myers, 1955). The younger physicians thought more of their patients could benefit from psychiatry. They did more reading in the field, showed more interest in seminars and speakers on psychiatry, and more of them advocated increased psychiatric facilities. Younger physicians also thought more of their patients have mental disorders, and they see more psychosomatic illness. Another important difference is that fewer younger than older physicians include, under mental illness, such conditions as feeblemindedness, epilepsy, multiple sclerosis, and cerebral palsy. This may be important in determining which kinds of patients older and younger physicians will commit to the mental hospital.

The Illinois Survey

One of the most ambitious studies of public attitudes toward mental illness was conducted over a six-year period (1954–59) by a team of research investigators at the Institute of Communications Research, University of Illinois. In an attempt to develop improved guidelines for mental health information programs, these investigators measured opinions and attitudes of the public and of specialists in the mental health field, analyzed the mental health content of the mass media, and studied methods of effecting changes in public attitudes and opinions. Starting from the premise that ". . . the effective prevention and treatment of mental illness depends in large measure on knowing how to communicate the information (Nunnally, 1961, p. 2), the investigators sought to determine existing conceptions about mental illness, and how they might be improved.

The surveys of popular information and attitude were based on samples of from 100 to 700 people. Extensive use was made of an "opinion panel" of some 400 people, most of them from central Illinois, but representative of the United States as a whole with regard to education, sex, income, religion, and race. A measuring instrument was devised by collecting more than 3,000 statements about mental health problems—causes, symptoms, prognosis, treatment, incidence, and social significance—from expert sources (books, pamphlets, and professional publications), from public opinions expressed in detailed personal interviews, and from samples of the mental health content in the mass media. These were then consolidated into a list of 50 items, grouped about 10 basic "information factors": (1) The mentally ill look and act different; (2) willpower is the basis of personal adjustment; (3) women are more prone to mental disorder than men; (4) avoiding morbid thoughts promotes mental health; (5) mental health can be maintained by guidance and support from strong persons in the environment; (6) mental illness is hopeless; (7) mental disorders are caused by immediate environmental pressures; (8) emotional difficulties are not serious; (9) people are more susceptible to mental illness as they grow older; and (10) mental illness is caused by organic factors such as poor diet and disease. The same basic questionnaire was used to ask the public what they believed, and the experts what they thought the public should be told. Samples from the mass media were coded according to the same 10 information factors.

Measured on the basis of the 50-item questionnaire, the public's information about mental illness was found to be neither highly structured nor highly crystallized. Respondents in the Illinois study did not have logically grouped patterns of opinions, and they were unsure of them, being willing to change them fairly readily. They differed most from the experts in believing that a person can read or control himself into, or be taught good mental health. People with less than a high school education and people over 50 years of age tended to be misinformed.

The Illinois group devised a set of measuring instruments to study public attitudes toward the mentally ill. These attitudes were found to be largely negative. The mentally ill are regarded with fear, distrust, and dislike, and are thought to be unpredictable. Psychotics are held in lower esteem than neurotics; neurotics are considered to be weaker, and psychotics less predictable. The word "neurotic" is associated with women and intelligent people, the word "psychotic" with the older and more ignorant person. There were only slightly different attitudes toward the mentally ill among respondents in different age and educational subgroups. The investigators feel it is possible to overcome the public's extreme devaluation of the mentally ill if their behavior can be made more understandable and predictable.

The interviewees had moderately high positive attitudes toward mental health professionals, although they valued professional workers who treat physical disorders more than those who treat mental disorders. Mental treatment methods and institutions were held in relatively low esteem. The respondents did not trust them as much as physical treatment methods and institutions, and mistrusted them more than they mistrusted mental health professionals. The investigators feel that the public already believes psychiatrists are intelligent, friendly, and sincere, but needs to be convinced that their methods are safe and effective.

Nunnally and his associates sampled the mental health content of the mass media. The sample included (1) the total output (about 111 hours of transmission time) of a VHF–TV station in Champaign, Ill., for one week in 1955; (2) one week's total broadcasting by four radio stations, affiliated with four different networks, in four widely separated areas; (3) one issue of 91 different magazines on display on newsstands at about the same time in March, 1955; and (4) one week's "home" editions of 49 daily newspapers. It was found that information about mental illness appears relatively infrequently, and that the mass media generally present a distorted picture of mental health problems. The investigators mention two mitigating circumstances: (1) The public probably is able to discriminate between valid and unrealistic presentations and no doubt learns something from the better media presentations, however rare they are. (2) The content analysis of the mass media was made in 1954 and 1955, and presentations about mental health and mental illness may have improved since then.

The Illinois survey reports that the general practitioner has a "good" opinion about psychiatry. The physicians interviewed stated that 54 per cent of the cases referred to a psychiatrist are helped considerably, 30 per cent little or not at all. In general, they regard the results of psychiatric treatment as only moderately good. They recognize the role of mental problems in their patients' complaints, and 77 per cent report they treat some kinds of mental illness themselves. They rate shock therapy as the most effective psychiatric procedure, with psychoanalysis, occupational therapy, drug therapy, and group therapy given moderately high ratings. The general practitioner reported high regard for the psychiatrist, but tended to have the same negative attitudes toward the mentally ill as does the lay public. Younger and better informed doctors had more enlightened attitudes toward mental illness and were more apt to treat mental patients. In general, these findings are in accord with those from the survey of New Jersey physicians described above.

In summary, the Illinois group concludes that the public is uninformed rather than misinformed about mental illness, they are unsure of their opinions, and look to the experts for assurance. Negative attitudes toward the mentally ill are based on the unpredictability of sick behavior. The public places value on the mental therapist, but not his methods. They want information to help relieve the personal threat that mental illness poses for them. They want solutions, not anxiety. Destruction of preexisting information without providing new information results in negative attitudes. Nunnally suggests that even if the information conveyed should prove to be incorrect and need to be negated, public attitudes toward mental illness are improved by the transmission of this tentative information.

One of the problems in communicating information is the lack of clear and concise terms about mental health phenomena. Terms currently in use tend to be misleading, people are not sure what they mean, and some have strong negative connotations. Nunnally recommends the construction of a new set of terms which will translate mental health phenomena into terms the public already understands. He also believes that the experts need to compile a list of *new* things to tell the public about mental illness and suggests the possibility of a series of "good" soap operas to be presented via the mass media. Nunnally states that whatever messages about mental illness are transmitted must be clear, interesting, and authoritative, and must sound certain, provide solutions, and reduce anxiety.

The Baltimore Survey

A more recent survey (Lemkau and Crocetti, 1962) of popular opinions and knowledge about mental illness has produced findings considerably different from most of the preceding surveys. Before establishing a plan to provide emergency and home care services for psychiatric patients, the success of which would depend to a large extent on community acceptance, the health authorities in Baltimore decided to secure information about public attitudes toward mental illness and the mentally ill. Previous studies had characterized these attitudes as "denial, isolation, and rejection," but the Baltimore survey, conducted in 1960, failed to support this point of view. Opinions and beliefs of a sample population were surveyed, using the interview and a standard questionnaire to secure data. The population sampled was from a relatively low socioeconomic group with a median family income of $4,730. The median age of respondents was in the low 30's and median education was 9.7 years of formal schooling. Forty per cent were Negroes, the majority of whom had migrated to Baltimore from the South. Respondents in this survey reported about the same degree of acquaintance with people who had been in a mental hospital as did the respondents in the Louisville and the National Opinion Research Center studies.

The most striking contrast between the responses of this sample population and those in previous studies was in their ability to identify descriptions of behavior as indicative of mental illness. Three of the case stories from the NORC survey were used: the paranoid, the simple schizophrenic, and the alcoholic. In all three cases, the overwhelming majority identified the person as mentally ill. Fifty per cent identified all three as mentally ill; only 4 per cent identified none. The percentages identifying the cases as mentally ill, compared with the percentages in the NORC survey, were:

	NORC Survey	Baltimore Survey
Paranoid	75	91
Simple schizophrenic	34	78
Alcoholic	29	62

Age, race, marital status, and urban or rural birth were not significantly correlated with the tendency to identify the case as mental illness. As in most other studies, however, education and income did make a difference; the greater the amount of education and the higher the income, the greater the likelihood that the person would recognize mental illness. The big difference between this and most other studies was the high proportion of the least educated who identified all three cases—46 per cent of those with an elementary school education or less, as compared to 63 per cent of those with a college education. Fifty per cent of the respondents with less than 5 years of formal education identified all three cases. Forty-nine per cent of those in the lowest education-occupation status group (class V according to the Hollingshead Two-Factor Index of Social Position) identified all three cases. Only 5 per cent of the respondents in this status group confined the identification of mental illness to the case of paranoia.

When an individual identified a case as mental illness, he was asked if he thought the person could recover. Seventy-nine per cent thought the paranoid individual could recover; 72 per cent, the schizophrenic; and 56 per cent, the alcoholic. There was no strong evidence of rejection of the mentally ill. Fifty per cent said they could imagine themselves falling in love with someone who had been mentally ill; 50 per cent were willing to room with someone who had been a mental patient; 81 per cent would not hesitate to work with a person who had been mentally ill; 62 per cent disagreed that "almost all who have a mental illness are dangerous"; 85 per cent agreed that people with certain kinds of mental illness can be cared for at home; and 60 per cent agreed that people who have been in a state mental hospital are no more likely to commit crimes than those who have not been in such a hospital. In all, only about 15 per cent of the responses could be categorized as rejecting or wanting to isolate the mental patient.

Lemkau and Crocetti ask whether there is something different and special about the Baltimore population which accounts for the results of their survey. They entertain the more hopeful possibility that popular attitudes toward mental illness are indeed changing. If this is so, what, they ask, is the role of mental health education in this process? If people are viewing the mentally ill as sick rather than as transgressors, if they are beginning to distinguish between social deviation and mental illness, then perhaps they will look increasingly to the physician for cues on how to react to the mentally ill.

The Urban Leader Survey

Representatives of the opposite end of the socioeconomic status scale were surveyed in another recent study (Dohrenwend, Bernard, and Kolb, 1962). Conducted in 1960 in a "bedroom community" for New York City's commercial and industrial center, a densely populated lower middle-class and working-class district, the survey concentrated on the orientation of the civic leaders in this urban area toward problems of mental illness. Questionnaire-interviews, each lasting 1¾ hours, were held with leaders from each of the four main ethnic groups (Jewish, Irish, Negro, and Puerto Rican) and from the politicolegal, economic, religious, and educational institutional orders. The respondents were presented with the six case descriptions of mental disorders used in the NORC survey. They were asked to express their judgments about the presence of mental stress in these cases, the seriousness of the illness, and whether they would recommend help from the mental health professions. The central purpose of the survey was to determine whether the orientation of the leaders varied with their institutional order.[2]

The following percentages of respondents identified each case as mental illness, felt that it was serious, and recommended help from mental health professionals.

	Presence of Mental Illness	Seriousness	Help from Mental Health Professionals
Paranoid schizophrenia	100	93	87
Simple schizophrenia	72	62	74
Alcoholism	63	78	49
Anxiety neurosis	50	27	58
Juvenile character disorder	50	63	70
Compulsive-phobic behavior	40	6	46

Recognition of the presence of mental illness was much greater than in the NORC survey and more on a par with the experience of Lemkau and Crocetti in the Baltimore survey. Ethnic background did not seem to account for differences among the leaders. Neither did contact with mental illness. Education had some effect, but did not alter the basic differences among the different institutional orders. These basic differences were as follows:

	Tendency to See the Case as Mental Illness	Tendency to Regard It as Serious	Tendency to Recommend Help from Mental Health Professionals
High	Educational leaders	Educational leaders	Educational leaders
Relatively high	Politicolegal leaders	Religious leaders	Politicolegal leaders
Relatively low	Religious leaders	Politicolegal leaders	Religious leaders
Low	Economic leaders	Economic leaders	Economic leaders

The high tendencies of the educational leaders and the low tendencies of the economic leaders were in accord with expectations. Educational leaders have a strong psychiatric orientation, but their reputation for influence in the community (as reflected by the opinions of the other leaders) is relatively weak. Economic leaders, who have the greatest reputation for influence in the community, are the least psychiatrically oriented of the institutional orders. The politicolegal

[2] The politicolegal order contained 31 per cent of the leaders, including state senators, district leaders, state assemblymen, city councilmen, heads of organizations like the League of Women Voters, municipal court justices, and police captains. The economic order (16 per cent of the leaders) consisted mainly of high banking officials and heads of large businesses. The educational order, with 29 per cent of the leaders, included a university president, an assistant superintendent of schools, public school principals, and the chairmen of local boards of education. The religious order (16 per cent) included Catholic, Jewish, and Protestant clergymen. The remaining 8 per cent of leaders were heads of Puerto Rican social-recreational clubs.

leaders, who have almost as much reputation for influence as the economic leaders and who, along with them, are most able to influence policy and win support for community programs, are closest to the educational leaders in psychiatric orientation. However, like the economic leaders, the politicolegal leaders are low on the "seriousness" quotient. The investigators theorize that perhaps their legal background leads them to think of behavior disorder as serious in terms of whether it is likely to harm others rather than the individual himself. The strong tendency of the politicolegal leaders to recommend help from mental health professionals contrasts rather sharply with the findings of the 1950 survey conducted in Louisville. In that earlier survey, lawyers showed a strong tendency to resort to repressive measures in dealing with juvenile delinquency and mental illness, and demonstrated less faith in psychiatry than doctors, teachers, and clergymen.

The orientation of the religious leaders in the New York City study was unexpected, and the investigators feel that this orientation appears to be competitive with psychiatry. They point out that though 70 to 80 per cent of the religious leaders have had contact with the mentally ill, as compared with only 30 to 50 per cent of the educational leaders, their mental health orientation is relatively low. The investigators theorize that the differences are traceable to varying frames of reference which govern activities in the different professional and occupational groups, and which serve as the basis for their appraisal of deviant behavior. The theory that professional and occupational frames of reference determine people's attitudes toward mental illness suggests that there really is no common cultural approach to the subject, and that no simple strategy of mental health education will suffice to alter public attitudes for the better.

The Joint Commission Reports

The final report (*Action for Mental Health*, 1961) of the Joint Commission on Mental Illness and Health contains much material commenting on the public's interest in and knowledge of mental health and mental illness. The survey conducted for the Joint Commission by Gurin and his associates (1960) indicated that one in every four Americans has felt the need for help with emotional problems, and one in every seven has sought that help. Of those who have sought help, 42 per cent have consulted clergymen, 29 per cent physicians, 18 per cent psychiatrists and psychologists, and 10 per cent social agencies or marriage clinics. Forty-two per cent had marriage problems, 18 per cent personal adjustment problems, and 12 per cent problems with their children. People with personal problems and problems with their children tended to seek help from a psychiatrist, as did the better educated. Most people sought advice and support, rather than personal change. Fifty-eight per cent said that they had been helped with their problems, 14 per cent reported some help, and 20 per cent said they had not been helped. Sixty-five per cent of those who consulted clergymen or physicians reported they had been helped, whereas only 46 per cent of those who consulted psychiatrists said so. It must be remembered, though, that psychiatrists see the more difficult cases and attempt to do therapy. The Joint Commission concludes that public information has increased the general understanding about human behavior, that mental health information has helped the public recognize and seek help for their psychological problems, and that there is now a great demand for mental health services which is not being met.

The Commission squarely faces the problem of the stigma against mental illness. Its stand is that there must be a change in public attitudes and concepts of responsibility, and that we must overcome rejection of the mentally ill which interferes with the treatment process. According to the Commission, this is the primary responsibility of public education in the field of mental health. Simply telling the public the facts about the mental illness problem will not neecssarily bring the desired reforms; the public is already acquainted with the extent of the problem. The basic difficulties in changing public attitudes are that people find it hard to see illness as having psychological forms, and also that the mentally ill lack appeal and are too uncomfortable to have around. The Commission recommends that we try to help people recognize mental illness and how to deal with it as one way of overcoming the rejection and defeatism which make the mental hospital an "endpoint" rather than a way station in treatment.

Summary

The surveys summarized in this report have only occasional areas of congruency which permit meaningful comparisons. This is natural, since each is more or less unique in terms of methodology and target audience. The samplings have, in effect, drawn different quantities of water, in different pails, from different streams, at different times. Yet the over-all impression one unmistakably gets from a review of these surveys is that there has been forward motion during the past decade in terms of better public understanding of mental illness and greater tolerance or acceptance of the mentally ill. It appears to be reasonably clear that the American public does not universally reject the mentally ill, nor is it thoroughly defeatist about the prospects of treating mental illness. Certainly, any program of public education must seriously take into account the strong likelihood that there are many varieties of public opinions and attitudes about mental illness in the total population, and that these are far from static.

38 / Social Status and Attitudes toward Psychological Disorder: The Problem of Tolerance of Deviance

Bruce P. Dohrenwend / Edwin Chin-Shong

Of the attitudes of members of different social classes toward problems of mental illness, Hollingshead and Redlich (1958) write:

> Perception of the psychological nature of personal problems is a rare trait in any person and in any class, but it is found more frequently in the refined atmosphere of Classes I and II than in the raw setting of Class V. As a consequence, we believe that far more abnormal behavior is tolerated by the two lower classes, particularly Class V, without any awareness that the motivations behind the behavior are pathological, even though the behavior may be disapproved by the class norms (pp. 172–173).

The most systematic evidence Hollingshead and Redlich present in support of this view is not on class attitudes towards deviance but rather on the consequences of such attitudes for referral processes. As they show, lower-class patients are far more likely to have come into treatment via the police and the courts than higher-class patients of similar diagnostic types. In contrast, higher-class patients are far more likely to be referred by family and friends. It seems possible, therefore, that the lower classes tolerate deviant behavior up to the point where outside intervention brings it to treatment agencies. On the other hand, the fact that lower-class patients are more likely to be referred by the police and courts may indicate a lack of positive orientation toward the mental health services. It does not necessarily imply tolerance of deviance—especially if it were to be found that calls to the police often come from the families and neighbors of lower-class patients.

Another possible indication that there is greater tolerance in lower-class groups for the kinds of deviance involved in mental disorder is contained in a study by Freeman and Simmons (1963). They found that the instrumental performance of higher-class patients was better than that of lower-class patients following discharge from mental hospitals. They speculate that this may be due to higher expectations for good performance and stronger sanctions against poor performance from the upper-class families of such patients. As Freeman and Simmons point out, however, a plausible alternative interpretation is that the upper-class patients were capable of, or could develop, superior instrumental performances to begin with.

The most direct data on class differences in attitudes towards mental disorder comes from studies such as those of Star (1955) and the Cummings (1957).

From the *American Sociological Review*, 1967, 32, 417–433. Copyright © 1967. Reprinted by permission of the authors and the American Sociological Association.

Most of them center on differences in the reactions of people with different amounts of education, an indicator of social class, to fictitious descriptions of different types of mental disorder. Meant to illustrate paranoid schizophrenia, simple schizophrenia, anxiety neurosis, alcoholism, compulsive-phobic behavior, and juvenile character disorder, the six descriptions were developed by Star with psychiatric consultation and are stated as follows to respondents:

1. I'm thinking of a man—let's call him Frank Jones—who is very suspicious; he doesn't trust anybody, and he's sure that everybody is against him. Sometimes he thinks that people he sees on the street are talking about him or following him around. A couple of times, now, he has beaten up men who didn't even know him. The other night, he began to curse his wife terribly; then he hit her and threatened to kill her because, he said, she was working against him, too, just like everyone else.

2. Now here's a young woman in her twenties, let's call her Betty Smith . . . she has never had a job, and she doesn't seem to want to go out and look for one. She is a very quiet girl, she doesn't talk much to anyone—even her own family, and she acts like she is afraid of people, especially young men her own age. She won't go out with anyone, and whenever someone comes to visit her family, she stays in her own room until they leave. She just stays by herself and daydreams all the time, and shows no interest in anything or anybody.

3. Here's another kind of man; we can call him George Brown. He has a good job and is doing pretty well at it. Most of the time he gets along all right with people, but he is always very touchy and he always loses his temper quickly, if things aren't going his way, or if people find fault with him. He worries a lot about little things, and he seems to be moody and unhappy all the time. Everything is going along all right for him, but he can't sleep nights, brooding about the past, and worrying about things that *might* go wrong.

4. How about Bill Williams? He never seems to be able to hold a job very long, because he drinks so much. Whenever he has money in his pocket, he goes on a spree; he stays out till all hours drinking, and never seems to care what happens to his wife and children. Sometimes he feels very bad about the way he treats his family; he begs his wife to forgive him and promises to stop drinking, but he always goes off again.

5. Here's a different sort of girl—let's call her Mary White. She seems happy and cheerful; she's pretty, has a good job, and is engaged to marry a nice young man. She has loads of friends; everybody likes her, and she's always busy and active. However, she just can't leave the house without going back to see whether she left the gas stove lit or not. And she always goes back again just to make sure she locked the door. And one other thing about her: she's afraid to ride up and down in elevators; she just won't go any place where she'd have to ride in an elevator to get there.

6. Now, I'd like to describe a twelve year old boy—Bobby Grey. He's bright enough and in good health, and he comes from a comfortable home. But his father and mother have found out that he's been telling lies for a long time now. He's been stealing things from stores, and taking money from his mother's purse, and he has been playing truant, staying away from school whenever he can. His parents are very upset about the way he acts, but he pays no attention to them.

The Cummings, describing their own results in using these cases write:

> One overall impression emerges from the responses to these cases. The definition of mental illness is much narrower in the minds of the lay public than in the minds of psychiatrists and the professional mental health workers . . . . Our interviewers were shocked at the respondents' denial of pathological conditions in the case histories, because they assumed that lay people could accept *less* behavior as normal. But a very wide spectrum of behavior appears to be tolerated by the laity—at least verbally—as reasonably close to normal . . . (Cumming and Cumming, 1957, pp. 100–101).

Since the usual finding is that the tendency to deny pathological conditions in these case descriptions varies inversely with education (Lemkau and Crocetti, 1962), the inference is that tolerance of such behavior is greatest in the low status groups.

However, the Cummings also found that the less-educated expressed greater social distance from "former mental hospital patients" and from "a person who had been mentally ill." Here, the respondent was not being asked to say whether different kinds of behavior indicated mental illness but to react to hypothetical situations in which he was asked to include in or exclude from certain activities and relationships persons officially defined as once having been mentally ill. By extension of this reasoning we would say that the lower-status respondents showed less tolerance.

When we consider attitudes towards types of deviant behavior other than those included under mental disorder, the picture is further complicated. Stouffer (1955) showed in a nationwide study that in attitudes toward political nonconformity, it is the high-status leaders and the well-educated who are most tolerant of deviance. In contrast, it is the lower-educated, lower-status groups who are least tolerant of politically deviant behavior. Lipset, in reviewing the evidence, finds it "clear and consistent—the lower strata are the least tolerant" (Lipset, 1963, p. 103). He cites, for example, a study by Eysenck which shows that working-class members, in contrast to middle-class members, in the Conservative, Liberal, Socialist, and even the Communist Party in England tended to be less tolerant of deviations from standard moral or religious codes, as well as more anti-Negro, anti-Semitic, and xenophobic (Eysenck, 1954).

The work of Kohn strongly suggests that more than in the middle class, working-class parents appear concerned with conformity and the consequent display of "respectable" behavior (Kohn, 1963). Middle-class parents, in contrast, seem to value self-direction rather than conformity to external proscriptions. The difference appears to be more in what is valued than in tolerance of departures from what is valued.

The Problem

We must ask ourselves why the notion that there is greater tolerance in the lower classes of the kinds of deviance involved in mental disorder seems so compelling in the face of inconclusive and even conflicting evidence. Is it possible that the idea of greater tolerance of deviance is appealing because it is somehow in accord with prevailing stereotypes of lower-class life (see Bronfenbrenner, 1958)? If so, the stereotypes themselves require re-examination.

Recall that Hollingshead and Redlich specify the lowest status groups as most likely to show greater tolerance of deviance. Should we look, then, for tolerance of mental disorder mainly in slum environments characterized by high rates of delinquency and crime? Again there are problems. The fact that there are high rates of deviant behavior in a group need not imply that it is tolerated by the group—if, by tolerance, we mean "sympathy or indulgence for beliefs or practices differing from or conflicting with one's own" (Webster, 1963). There are at least two other possibilities. One is that the slum dwellers do not share the norms of the wider society, in which case they are not reacting to deviance at all, as *they* define it. Second, the behavior may be seen as deviant, but the reaction is one of fearful immobility or apathy rather than sympathy. Here, "to tolerate" would have to have the connotation not of indulgence but rather that of "to suffer to be or to be done without prohibition, hindrance or contradiction" (Webster, 1963). Clearly, there can be different kinds of "tolerance" for different kinds of "deviant" behavior. We shall have to specify what we mean by "tolerance" and "deviance" in relation to social status and mental disorder.

Our aim is to investigate the proposition that there is greater tolerance of deviance in lower- than in higher-status groups. Let us first be clear about the kinds of deviance with which we will be concerned and with what can reasonably be meant by tolerance of these kinds of deviance.

The Behavior Which Is Seen as Deviant

We are concerned with the kinds of deviance involved in what the 1952 *Diagnostic and Statistical Manual* of the American Psychiatric Association defines as mental disorders, especially those that may be of psychogenic origin. Although these include a tremendous range and variety of behaviors, our problem is narrowed somewhat. We exclude, for example, political nonconformity and the unusually high performance that stems from genius. In short, we are concerned with certain *kinds of behavior which depart from psychiatric norms in such a way as to be clinically judged harmful to the individual displaying it or to others in social relationships.* Descriptively, these behaviors are consonant with illustrations in the APA manual. Thus the behaviors with which we are concerned are those officially defined by the mental health professions as deviant and within their jurisdiction.

Earlier we described the six fictitious case descriptions developed by Star with psychiatric consultation to illustrate mental disorder. We asked 34 psychiatrists to make judgments similar to those made about the cases in studies of public attitudes.[1] Almost unanimously, the psychiatrists have seen all six as illustrations of different types of mental disorder. Thus the descriptions do indeed provide an illustrative, though not completely representative, sample of the kinds of behavior with which we are concerned.

Still another index of such behavior is the label "patient" in a mental hospital or outpatient facility. The assumption here is that the behavior over which the

---

[1] Of the 34 psychiatrists, 24 were trainees in the Division of Community Psychiatry at Columbia and 10 were students at the William Alanson White Institute. All but eight of the 34 had completed residency training or, in the case of three foreign trained psychiatrists, the equivalent. The majority of the remainder were in the third year of residency training. There were no noticeable differences between the Columbia as against the William Alanson White psychiatrists in any of the judgments we asked them to make.

agency has jurisdiction must have occurred in order for the admission to have taken place. Here, of course, it is the jurisdictional fact that is clearly represented by the index rather than the specific behavior involved.

The Question of Whether Such Behavior Is Seen as Deviant by Other than Members of the Mental Health Professions

There is no question that behaviors such as those portrayed in the six fictitious case descriptions are seen as deviant, that is, as harmful departures from their norms, by psychiatrists. There is a question, however, as to how widely their views are shared. Star found in 1950 that, of the six case descriptions, only the paranoid was seen as mentally ill by the majority of a nationwide sample of adults in the United States. The Cummings obtained similar results in their study of a Canadian town a year later. Three studies 10 to 15 years later got rather different results. The first of these was conducted by Lemkau and Crocetti in Baltimore (1962) and the second by Meyer in Easton, Maryland (1964). The third consists of our research with community leaders[2] and with a probability sample of Jewish, Irish, Negro and Puerto Rican adult residents of Washington Heights in New York City.[3] As Table I shows, respondents in the three studies done in the 1960's were far more likely to see the cases as mentally ill than respondents in the two studies done around 1950.

[2] These leaders include state senators, assemblymen, municipal court justices, police captains, businessmen, school principals, clergymen, and heads of such organizations as the local Chamber of Commerce, League of Women Voters, and Puerto Rican hometown clubs. In all, 91 persons were designated on the basis of position and/or reputation for inclusion in the study. Interviews were obtained with 87 of these, all but eight of whom come from one of the four main ethnic groups in Washington Heights: Jewish, Negro, Irish, and Puerto Rican. Almost three-fourths are college graduates and, as a rule, have gone on to graduate training as well. (For a more detailed description of these leaders and how they were selected, see, for example, Dohrenwend, Bernard, and Kolb, 1962.)

[3] This small sample of adults under 65 years of age was selected from a larger probability sample drawn in Washington Heights by the Community Population Laboratory of the Columbia University School of Public Health and Administrative Medicine. The larger sample is described in Elinson and Loewenstein (1963). The present probability subsample was selected on the basis of the ethnicity of the male head of the household. An equal number of households was designated from each of the four main ethnic groups in Washington Heights: Jewish, Negro, Irish, and Puerto Rican, in that order of size. Within each ethnic group, proportional allocation according to educational level was employed. Negro and Puerto Rican respondents were interviewed by Negro and Puerto Rican interviewers. Husbands and wives were interviewed separately but simultaneously in different parts of their apartments by male and female interviewers respectively. In all, 94 married couples and 26 single male household heads (214 individuals in all) were to be interviewed. Interviews were completed with the designated respondents in 69 per cent of the households. An additional 12 per cent had to be removed from the sample because we could not locate them or because of verified moves out of the state, death, etc. Respondents in 19 per cent of the households, disproportionately first-generation Irish, refused to be interviewed after repeated call-backs. In all, 71 per cent of the designated respondents were interviewed. This gives us a rather good representation of married couples in all groups other than the Irish who were born in Ireland. We fared less well with the 26 single male household heads designated for interview. Of these, 14 were Negro and we succeeded in obtaining interviews with only 8. Single female household heads were excluded altogether by our design for selecting the subsample. Further description and analysis of the subsample in relation to the larger sample from which it was drawn are contained in Dohrenwend (1966) and Dohrenwend and Dohrenwend (1968).

TABLE I

PERCENTAGE OF RESPONDENTS IDENTIFYING MENTAL ILLNESS IN FICTITIOUS CASE DESCRIPTIONS: SIX SAMPLE SURVEYS

Case Description	U.S., 1950 (N = 3,500)	Small Canadian Town, 1951 (N = 178)	Baltimore, 1960 (N = 1,736)	Easton, Md., 1962 (N = 139)	Washington Hts., 1963–64 (Cross Section) (N = 151)	Washington Hts., 1960–61 (Community Leaders) (N = 87)
Paranoid	75	69	91	89	90	100
Simple schizophrenia	34	36	78	77	67	72
Alcoholic	29	25	62	63	41	63
Anxiety neurotic	18	20	*	*	31	49
Juvenile character disorder	16	4	*	*	41	51
Compulsive-phobic behavior	7	4	*	*	24	40
Median years of formal education	9.3†	9.9‡	9.7	*	11.7	16+

* Not available.
† U.S. Bureau of the Census, *U.S. Census of Population: 1950, Vol. II, Part I.*
‡ Calculated from Cumming and Cumming (1957).

While it is true that the five populations sampled differ in size and other characteristics, there is no ready explanation for the marked contrast between results of the later studies and results of the earlier. Star's 1950 nationwide sample is demographically different, to be sure, from respondents in metropolitan Baltimore or New York during the 1960's. However, the nationwide sample is also different demographically from that of the Canadian town whose population was about 1,500. Yet the Canadian town was studied, with similar results, at about the same time Star did her research. Moreover, among the three later studies, Easton, with a population of 6,337, contrasts greatly with the two metropolitan areas in demographic character though not in judgments about the case descriptions.

Lemkau and Crocetti, aware of the usual finding of a strong positive relation between educational level and tendency to see the cases as mentally ill, point out that the median of 9.7 years of school in Baltimore is hardly high enough to explain the difference between their own results and those obtained in the earlier studies. Nor, as Table I shows, is Baltimore an exception in this regard. The educational levels of the populations studied show far less relation to tendency to see mental illness in the cases than to the dates the studies were done. In the absence of a follow-up study of a nationwide sample which would settle the issue, it seems plausible to interpret these results as indicating an increase over the last 10 to 15 years in the public's readiness to see such behavior as mentally ill.[4] Why

---

[4] We at first thought that the difference in results obtained by Star in 1950 and those obtained by Lemkau and Crocetti in 1960 might have been due to the fact that Lemkau and Crocetti changed the order in which the three case descrptions they used were presented to the respondents. They presented the simple schizophrenic first, the alcoholic second, and the paranoid third. In contrast, Star presented the paranoid first, the simple schizophrenic second,

TABLE II

PERCENTAGE OF FICTITIOUS CASE DESCRIPTIONS BY DEGREE OF SERIOUSNESS:
THIRTY-FOUR PSYCHIATRISTS

Degree of Seriousness	Case Description					
	Paranoid	Simple Schizophrenic	Alcoholic	Juvenile Character Disorder	Compulsive-Phobic	Anxiety Neurotic
1 (most serious)	64.7	32.4	2.9	0.0	0.0	0.0
2	29.4	52.9	11.8	2.9	0.0	2.9
3	5.9	11.8	61.8	17.6	2.9	0.0
4	0.0	2.9	17.6	44.1	20.6	14.7
5	0.0	0.0	2.9	14.7	41.2	41.2
6 (least serious)	0.0	0.0	2.9	20.6	25.3	41.2
Total	100.0	100.0	99.9	99.9	100.0	100.0

such a shift may have taken place and what it may mean are quite other matters.

Lemkau and Crocetti interpreted their Baltimore results as possible evidence of a triumph for efforts at mental health education.[5] It may be, however, that the apparent historical shift is more one of superficial labeling than of conviction, for there are still some important differences in the way psychiatrists and the public view these cases.

the anxiety neurotic third, and the alcoholic fourth. We tested the effect of this change on our Washington Heights cross section respondents by systematically alternating the Star and the Lemkau and Crocetti order in which the cases were presented. Analyses of variance showed, however, that there is no main effect of order, nor are there interactions between order and education, ethnicity, or sex. We also thought that the high tendency of low-educated respondents in Baltimore to recognize mental illness in the cases might be due to acquiescence on the part of low-educated Negroes (see, e.g., Couch and Kenniston, 1960; Dohrenwend, 1966).

We could find no evidence that a curvilinear relationship in Lemkau and Crocetti's data between tendency to see mental illness in the cases and educational level is due to an acquiescence response on the part of Negroes with less than five years of education. However, a separate study Dohrenwend did on this problem, a study of a small sample of low-educated Negroes, may have failed to provide an adequate test of acquiescence. The experimental manipulation consisted of alternating a question sequence asking about whether the cases were "mentally ill" with a question sequence asking whether they were "mentally healthy." Unfortunately, the latter is probably not the only alternative to mental illness in the minds of our respondents.

[5] Whether increased use of the label "mentally ill" helps or hinders the aims of mental health education is another matter. We do find that the higher the tendency to recognize mental illness in these cases, the higher the tendency to recommend help from the mental health professions. Indeed, judgments that the behavior is mentally ill are better predictors of whether referral to the mental health professions will be advocated than judgments that the behavior represents a serious problem. Nevertheless, Phillips found that with hypothetical cases like Star's, fictitious persons showing identical behavior were more likely to be rejected on a social distance scale if they were said to be receiving help from a psychiatrist than if they were said to be receiving help from physician or clergyman, or were not getting professional help (see Phillips, 1963). Thus, the increased use of the label "mentally ill" for various kinds of behavior may be helpful or not, depending on the aim. If the aim is to have more of the individuals who show such behavior referred to the mental health professions, increased use of the label may do so. If, however, the end is to reduce social distance between disturbed persons and the community, then use of the label "mentally ill" would be a hindrance.

When asked to rank order the six cases from most to least serious, our groups of psychiatrists expectably saw the paranoid schizophrenic and the simple schizophrenic as most serious, as Table II shows. In contrast, our community respondents in Washington Heights appear to have given higher priority to other factors than the seriousness of psychopathology from a clinical point of view.

In the Washington Heights studies of both leaders and ethnic cross sections from the community, we asked each respondent first whether he thought there was anything wrong with a case or not. If he said yes, he was then asked whether he thought the fictitious person described had some kind of mental illness or not. Then, *regardless of whether or not* he thought that the fictitious person was mentally ill, he was asked whether what was wrong was serious. This procedure, in which the judgment about mental illness preceded the judgment about seriousness, might have been expected to produce judgments of seriousness contingent on judgments about the presence of mental illness. As Table III shows, however, there is by no means a one-to-one relationship between the two sets of judgments. The combined leader and cross section respondents from Washington Heights were most likely to see as serious those cases that threaten others: the paranoid, the alcoholic, and the juvenile character disorder.[6] The resulting rank ordering of

TABLE III

PERCENTAGE DISTRIBUTION OF FICTITIOUS CASE DESCRIPTIONS BY DEGREE OF SERIOUSNESS AND WHETHER MENTALLY ILL: WASHINGTON HEIGHTS SAMPLE

Degree of Seriousness and Whether Mentally Ill	Case Description					
	Paranoid	Alcoholic	Juvenile Character Disorder	Simple Schizophrenic	Anxiety Neurotic	Compulsive-Phobic
Nothing wrong	2.5	8.8	15.6	6.7	29.2	42.9
Something wrong but not mental illness and not serious	1.3	16.4	16.0	15.1	25.0	23.5
Mental illness but not serious	6.7	10.5	14.3	28.6	25.4	27.7
Not mental illness but serious	2.5	25.2	21.5	9.7	6.4	1.3
Serious mental illness	87.0	39.1	32.5	39.9	14.0	4.6
Total	100.0	100.0	99.9	100.0	100.0	100.0
Number of respondents*	238	238	237	238	236	238
Per cent judging case mentally ill	93.7	49.6	46.8	68.5	39.4	32.3
Per cent judging case serious	89.5	64.3	54.0	49.6	20.4	5.9

* Leaders and cross section combined. Respondents who did not answer the question are excluded from the base.

[6] Leaders and cross section respondents are combined in Table 3 because the relationships between judgments that each case is serious and judgments that the case represents mental illness do not differ in the two groups.

the cases on seriousness thus differs sharply from that of the psychiatrists.[7] For example, the simple schizophrenic, which was second only to the paranoid in the psychiatrists' rankings of seriousness, is fourth in likelihood of being judged serious by the community respondents.

Although the definition by these respondents of the seriousness of the problems differs from that of the psychiatrists, the likelihood of their seeing the cases as mentally ill directly parallels the psychiatrists' rankings of the relative seriousness of the six cases.[8] Note that there are distinctive minority tendencies for the alcoholic and juvenile character disorder to be judged serious problems but not mentally ill, while the simple schizophrenic, anxiety neurotic, and compulsive-phobic tended to be judged mentally ill but not serious. The net result was that more community people saw the alcoholic and juvenile character disorder as serious problems than saw them as mentally ill. Just the opposite was the case with the simple schizophrenic, anxiety neurotic, and compulsive-phobic. Only in the case of the paranoid did the two judgments coincide so that a majority of the community respondents thought of it as serious mental illness.[9]

In a preceeding study, we found that there were sharp contrasts within the leader group in the degree to which their responses to these case descriptions

TABLE IV

PERCENTAGE JUDGING FICTITIOUS CASE DESCRIPTIONS AS SOMETHING WRONG, MENTALLY ILL, A SERIOUS PROBLEM, OR REQUIRING PROFESSIONAL HELP: LEADERS AND CROSS SECTION SAMPLES

Judgments	Leaders ($N = 87$)	Cross Section ($N = 151$)	χ^2 ($df = 1$)	P
Sees something wrong in all six cases	70.1	33.8	29.3	$< .01$
Definition of mental illness includes more than the two cases of psychosis	64.4	45.7	7.7	$< .01$
Definition of serious problem includes more than the three cases which threaten others	54.0	29.1	14.5	$< .01$
Recommends help from members of the mental health professions for more than half of the cases	64.4	28.5	29.3	$< .01$

[7] It should be noted that the ranking procedures differed for the psychiatrists and the community respondents. The psychiatrists ranked each case from most to least serious whereas the community respondents were asked to make an either/or judgment as to whether each case was or was not serious. The resulting rank ordering for the community respondents is thus in terms of the relative likelihood that a given case will be judged serious rather than the relative likelihood of its being placed by judges in one or another rank on seriousness. However, since these judgments in the community form a Guttman scale we can assume that the resulting rank ordering is unidimensional in the case of the community procedure as well as in the case of the procedure used by the psychiatrists.

[8] As Table I showed, almost identical proportions (50 per cent) of leaders see the anxiety neurotic and the juvenile character disorder as mentally ill. In contrast, the cross section respondents are more likely to see the juvenile character disorder as mentally ill (41 per cent) than the anxiety neurotic (31 per cent). Otherwise the rank ordering of the cases on likelihood of being seen as mentally ill is the same for leaders and cross section respondents.

[9] The range who see the paranoid case as both mentally ill and a serious problem is from about 95 per cent of the leaders to about two thirds of the Puerto Rican cross section respondents.

were consistent with a psychiatric frame of reference (Dohrenwend, Bernard, and Kolb, 1962). Table IV shows that, using the measures and cutting points developed in the study of leaders, there are also sharp contrasts between the leader group as a whole and the combined ethnic cross sections from Washington Heights.[10]

At first glance, the differences appear to stem from a lesser tendency on the part of the cross section respondents to see something wrong in the cases, since all other judgments were contingent on this one. Note, however, that the difference is between per cents of those who saw something wrong in all six cases. This cutting point, which describes the standard set by the large majority of the leaders, obscures a rather high degree of consensus between the leaders and the cross section respondents on most of the cases. Thus, like the leaders, large majorities of the cross section respondents, ranging from 97 per cent to 80 per cent, saw something wrong in the cases describing paranoid schizophrenia, simple schizophrenia, alcoholism, and juvenile character disorder. Only in the case of the compulsive-phobic behavior did less than a majority (46 per cent) of the cross section respondents say that something was wrong. This is in contrast to slightly over 80 per cent of the leaders. Here, and to a lesser extent in the case of the anxiety neurotic where 87 per cent of the leaders as opposed to 62 per cent of the cross section respondents said there was something wrong, is where the main difference lies. Overall, the cross section respondents saw something wrong in an average of 4.6 of the cases compared to a leader average of 5.5—a difference, to be sure, but also a consensus that there was something wrong in the large majority of the cases. Whether these cases were mentally ill or not, the seriousness of the problems involved, and what should be done about them, are the questions on which there were large differences between the leaders and the cross section respondents. Table IV shows that the Washington Heights cross section respondents departed much more from a psychiatric view in that they tended to restrict their definition of what was mentally ill to the two psychotic cases, regarded only the cases that threaten others as serious, and were less likely to advocate help from the mental health professions for the problems described.

The ethnic cross sections are composed of Jewish, Irish, Negro, and Puerto Rican residents of Washington Heights. From the social history of Washington Heights, we know that both Jews and Irish have been assimilated to more advantageous positions in the area in contrast to Negroes and Puerto Ricans, who, as more recent arrivals, inhabit the poorer sections (Lendt, n.d.). The Puerto Ricans especially, as newest arrivals, would be expected to depart furthest from the leader group in orientation toward the case descriptions.

Table V shows that both the Irish and the Puerto Ricans were less likely than the Jews and Negroes to see something wrong in all six cases. The difference is due largely to the fact that only slightly more than a quarter of the respondents in the Irish and in the Puerto Rican cross sections judged that there was something wrong in the case of the compulsive-phobic, in contrast to about three-fifths of the Jews and slightly over half the Negroes. Only a small majority of the Irish and 40 per cent of the Puerto Ricans saw something wrong in the case of

[10] In the leader group, judgments about mental illness in the cases and about whether the problems were serious or not formed Guttman scales. The same judgments also scale in the cross section sample, with reproducibilities of .907 (mental illness) and .926 (serious) and scalabilities of .656 (mental illness) and .738 (serious).

TABLE V

PERCENTAGE JUDGING FICTITIOUS CASE DESCRIPTIONS AS SOMETHING
WRONG, MENTALLY ILL, A SERIOUS PROBLEM, OR REQUIRING PROFESSIONAL
HELP, BY ETHNIC BACKGROUND: CROSS SECTION SAMPLE

Judgments	Jewish (N = 49)	Irish (N = 30)	Negro (N = 32)	Puerto Rican (N = 40)	χ^2 (df = 3)	P
Sees something wrong in all six cases	51.0	16.7	37.5	22.5	12.9	< .01
Definition of mental illness includes more than the two cases of psychosis	53.1	53.3	50.0	27.5	7.35	NS
Definition of serious problems includes more than the three cases which threaten others	38.8	43.3	21.9	12.5	11.31	< .05
Recommends help from members of the mental health professions for more than half of the cases	44.9	23.3	25.0	15.0	10.63	< .05

the anxiety neurotic. In the cases of the paranoid, simple schizophrenic, alcoholic, and juvenile character disorder, at least two-thirds of the cross section respondents in all four ethnic groups saw something wrong. Thus, as was the case in the comparison of leaders vs. cross section respondents, there was substantial consensus on this count for the majority of the six cases. Again, the important contrasts, this time among the ethnic cross sections, are in what was wrong with the cases, the seriousness of the problems involved, and what should be done about them. Table V shows that the sharpest differences are indeed between Puerto Ricans, who appear to depart furthest from a psychiatric frame of reference, and the other three groups. Also, however, the Negroes, like the Puerto Ricans, have low tendencies to regard the disorders as serious. And of the four ethnic groups, only the Jews even approached a majority that would recommend help from the mental health professions.

One of the most consistent findings in studies of attitudes toward mental illness, however, is that it is the more educated who come closest to a psychiatric point of view (cf. Freeman, 1961). Table VI shows that this is the case in Washington Heights: the lower the educational level, the further the departure from a psychiatric frame of reference.

The question arises whether or not the ethnic differences shown in Table V above are a function of lower educational levels in the Negro and Puerto Rican groups. Almost a fifth of the Negroes and slightly over 30 per cent of the Puerto Ricans did not graduate from grammar school. In contrast, only about 3 per cent of the Irish and none of the Jews are in this category. Moreover, slightly over a quarter of the Jews are college graduates, which gives them almost a monopoly on higher education. Our ability to control educational level while examining ethnic differences is, therefore, limited to respondents with 8–11 and 12–15 years of education. Even here, the number of respondents in some cells is very small. Nevertheless, when this control is introduced, it appears that differences in the tendency to see mental illness in the cases and the tendency to advocate help

TABLE VI

PERCENTAGE JUDGING FICTITIOUS CASE DESCRIPTIONS AS SOMETHING
WRONG, MENTALLY ILL, A SERIOUS PROBLEM, OR REQUIRING PROFESSIONAL
HELP, BY EDUCATION: CROSS SECTION SAMPLE

| | Years of Formal Education | | | | | |
| | 0–7 | 8–11 | 12–15 | 16 or More | χ^2 | |
Judgments	($N = 19$)	($N = 47$)	($N = 65$)	($N = 15$)	($df = 3$)	P
Sees something wrong in all six cases	31.6	25.5	33.8	60.0	6.10	NS
Definition of mental illness includes more than the two cases of psychosis	31.6	29.8	58.5	60.0	11.81	< .01
Definition of serious problems includes more than the three cases which threaten others	10.6	27.7	29.2	60.0	10.09	< .05
Recommends help from members of the mental health professions for more than half of of the cases	10.6	19.2	35.4	53.3	11.01	< .05

from members of the mental health professions are largely a function of education: the higher the educational level, the stronger these tendencies, regardless of ethnic background. In contrast, the tendencies to see something wrong and to regard the problems as serious appear to be related to a complex interaction of ethnicity and education.

Let us look further into the relationship between regarding the disorders as serious and the ethnic and educational backgrounds of the cross section respondents. We had found in the earlier study that the cutting point on the "serious" scale used above obscured an important difference between the leaders from the more-advantaged Jewish and Irish groups and those from the less-advantaged Negro and Puerto Rican groups (Dohrenwend, 1963). Unlike those from the more-advantaged groups, the Negro and Puerto Rican leaders tended to focus their definition of what was serious on all three cases that threatened others—the paranoid, the alcoholic, and the juvenile character disorder—and not on any of the cases of harm primarily to the problem individual—the simple schizophrenic, the anxiety neurotic, and the compulsive phobic. Our present results indicate that there was a distinct likelihood for the cross section Negroes to show a similar modal focus on the three cases which threaten others. Thus 41 per cent of the Negroes, in contrast to only 16 per cent in the other three groups combined, are classified in this scale type. Moreover, a modal 44 per cent of the Puerto Ricans who did not graduate from high school, as compared to 16 per cent in all other groups combined, judged only the paranoid as serious.[11]

There is, then, considerable difference in the way the cases were viewed by

[11] Chi-square tests indicate probabilities of less than .01 that these differences could have occurred by chance. Note that these results are based on the Guttman scale of tendency to regard the cases as serious, and the scale ranks include a certain amount of error. When only respondents who were in the two scale types described above before error was assigned are used, the relationships are even stronger.

psychiatrists and the way they were viewed by groups in the wider community. The psychiatrists judged the cases largely by the seriousness of the intrapsychic pathology. The community respondents appear to have judged the seriousness of each in terms of whether or not it threatens others rather than on the nature of the intrapsychic pathology. This tendency to assess seriousness in terms of the possible threat to others was especially strong in members of the two disadvantaged ethnic groups, the Negroes and Puerto Ricans. Among the lower-educated Puerto Ricans, in fact, it seems to have focused almost exclusively on the most extreme example of threat, the paranoid case. Only when the individual was a highly-educated member of a relatively advantaged group did his view of these problems appear similar to that of psychiatrists.

The Question of Whether
Behavior Seen as Deviant Is Tolerated

The dictionary indicates a number of senses in which the words "tolerance" and "to tolerate" are used, some of them technical. Two of the nontechnical definitions have been mentioned. There is a third, more useful than these because it is the simplest, most neutral, and most inclusive: "the act of allowing something" (Webster, 1963).

If tolerance takes place according to this definition, we can then specify it further with regard to its source in "sympathy," "sufferance," or whatever (Webster, 1963). As we have shown, much of the behavior viewed by members of the mental health professions as serious departures from norms is not seen this way by large segments of the community—especially the lower-class members of the most disadvantaged ethnic groups. Our question now becomes, *for behavior that is judged to involve serious problems of deviance,* is there a greater or lesser tendency toward tolerance on the part of the low-status groups?

The greatest convergence between the psychiatric viewpoint and the community frame of reference for defining seriously deviant behavior was with regard to the paranoid. Here, majorities of all ethnic groups and at all educational levels

TABLE VII

PERCENTAGE DISTRIBUTION BY TYPE OF ACTION RECOMMENDED FOR LEADERS AND CROSS SECTION RESPONDENTS JUDGING PARANOID CASE AS MENTALLY ILL AND A SERIOUS PROBLEM

Type of Action Recommended*	Leaders	Cross Section
Mental hospitalization	46.9	60.6
Outpatient help from one or more members of the mental health professions	48.1	33.9
Other professional help	1.2	3.1
Help from family and friends or other similar recommendation	2.5	0.0
Other, e.g., vacation	1.2	0.8
None, believes individual can get over it himself	0.0	1.6
Total	99.9	100.0
Number of respondents	81	127

* A recommendation in one category precludes classification in categories below it.

Note: Contrasting "Mental hospitalization" with all other recommendations combined, the chi-square test indicates that these results could have occurred by chance (P < .10).

TABLE VIII

PERCENTAGE DISTRIBUTION BY TYPE OF ACTION RECOMMENDED, FOR CROSS SECTION RESPONDENTS CLASSIFIED BY EDUCATION JUDGING PARANOID CASE AS MENTALLY ILL AND A SERIOUS PROBLEM

Type of Action Recommended*	Years of Formal Education			
	0–7	8–11	12–15	16+
Mental hospitalization	84.6	61.0	60.0	46.7
Outpatient help from one or more members of the mental health professions	0.0	31.7	36.4	53.3
Other professional help	7.7	2.4	3.6	0.0
Help from family and friends or other similar recommendation	0.0	0.0	0.0	0.0
Other, e.g., vacation	0.0	2.4	0.0	0.0
None, believes individual can get over it himself	7.7	2.4	0.0	0.0
Total	100.0	99.9	100.0	100.0
Number of respondents	13	41	55	15

* A recommendation in one category precludes classification in categories below it.

Note: Contrasting "Mental hospitalization" with all other recommendations combined, the chi-square test indicates that these results could have occurred by chance (P > .10). Given its consistency with our other results, however, the difference of almost 40 percentage points between college graduates and respondents with 0–7 years of education is regarded as important.

believed that this was both a serious problem and an example of mental illness. Considering just those respondents, both leader and cross section, who agreed that the paranoid case describes serious mental illness, let us test their tolerance in terms of the action they recommend. As Table VII shows, the only difference between the leaders and the cross section respondents as a whole seems to have been a somewhat stronger inclination for the leaders to recommend outpatient help rather than hospitalization. This difference becomes part of a startling set of results, however, when we look at educational contrasts within the cross section sample. As Table VIII shows, the lower his educational level, the more likely the respondent was to recommend hospitalization. In general, moreover, the relationship with educational level appears to hold within ethnic groups.

Consider what such a relationship means in terms of tolerance of deviance. Hospitalization is the one alternative that implies isolation of the person from family and community, and hence an extreme of intolerance of deviance.[12] What is the basis of this apparently strong tolerance on the part of the lower-educated?

Paradoxically, in this one instance, the least educated respondents came nearest to the recommendation most likely to be made by psychiatrists in the paranoid case.[13] It is hardly plausible, however, to believe that the basis for their assess-

[12] We mean, of course, from the point of view of groups to which the individuals belonged, or, under ordinary circumstances, would belong. See, for example, LaPiere (1954, p. 328), who describes extreme deviation as ". . . conduct which so violates the norms of a group to which the individual would normally belong that he is excluded from membership."

[13] We asked a small class including seven psychiatrists to write out what treatment they would recommend for each of the case descriptions. Six out of the seven psychiatrists recommended commitment of the paranoid to a mental hospital. In contrast, none of the psychiatrists recommended hospitalization for the juvenile character disorder, compulsive-phobic, or anxiety neurotic. And only one of the seven recommended hospitalization for the simple schizophrenic, as did one of the seven for the alcoholic. As a brief further check, we also asked for an open vote in a subsequent class. This time, two out of seven psychiatrists in the class equivocated, but the other five recommended hospitalization for the paranoid case.

TABLE IX

PERCENTAGE ACQUAINTED WITH MENTAL PATIENTS: LEADERS AND CROSS
SECTION SAMPLES

| | | Cross Section | | | |
| | Leaders (N = 87) | 0–7 Years of School (N = 19) | 8–11 Years of School (N = 47) | 12–15 Years of School (N = 65) | 16+ Years of School (N = 15) |
Acquaintance with Mental Patients					
Know one or more mental hospital patients	96.6	78.9	68.1	63.1	66.7
Know one or more psychiatric outpatients	86.2	26.3	23.4	60.0	86.7

ment is a sudden highly specific psychiatric sophistication. A more likely possibility is that coincidence was born of their lack of awareness of the alternatives
available for the treatment of mental illness.

To get some idea of their knowledge of these matters, we asked both the leader
and cross section respondents if they had ever known anyone who was in a
hospital because of mental illness and whether or not they had ever known anyone who was going to a private psychiatrist, a private psychologist, a guidance
clinic, or a mental hygiene clinic. Table IX shows that very large majorities of the
leaders and somewhat smaller, but substantial majorities of the cross section respondents who had graduated from college knew one or more persons in each of
the two broad categories. In sharp contrast are the cross section respondents who
did not graduate from high school. Although these lower-educated respondents
were more acquainted with persons in mental hospitals, only about a quarter of
them knew one or more outpatients.

On their face, the results shown in Table IX seem consistent with the hypothesis
that the stronger tendency of the lower-educated to recommend hospitalization is
due to ignorance of available alternatives. This implication is, however, more
apparent than real. For, if recommendation of hospitalization by cross section
respondents who viewed the paranoid case as serious mental illness resulted
mainly from ignorance of outpatient alternatives, we would expect such recommendations to decrease as acquaintance with outpatients increased. Table X

TABLE X

PERCENTAGE RECOMMENDING MENTAL HOSPITALIZATION, BY NUMBER OF
OUTPATIENTS KNOWN, FOR CROSS SECTION RESPONDENTS JUDGING THE
PARANOID CASE AS MENTALLY ILL AND A SERIOUS PROBLEM

| | Number of Outpatients Known | | | |
Recommendation	0 (N = 65)	1 (N = 32)	2 (N = 17)	3 or More (N = 13)
Mental hospitalization	63.1	62.5	58.8	46.1

shows that there is little or no relationship between the number of ouptatients a
cross section respondent knew and his recommendation of hospitalization for the
paranoid case. Moreover, given the very few respondents with less than eight
years of school who knew one or more outpatients and the very few college

graduates who knew none, there appears to be no effect at all within educational levels. Thus even the slight difference shown in Table X by those who knew three or more outpatients can be accounted for by the fact that 8 of these 13 respondents were college graduates.[14] Is there, then, an alternative explanation which is less seemingly obvious, more theoretically interesting, and empirically more persuasive?

We have data on another set of circumstances in which both high- and low-status respondents are likely to see evidence of serious mental illness—circumstances involving patients from mental hospitals. Let us again test the tolerance of the community respondents, this time by examining the social distance they say they would place between themselves and a hypothetical ex-mental hospital patient. Our measure of social distance consists of responses to the items described in Table XI. These form a Guttman scale in both the leader and cross section samples, in the orders of rejection shown.[15] Since these orders differ slightly for leaders and cross section, we can compare the two types of respondents in terms

TABLE XI

PERCENTAGE WILLING TO ACCEPT AN EX-MENTAL HOSPITAL PATIENT ON SEVEN SOCIAL DISTANCE ITEMS: LEADERS AND CROSS SECTION SAMPLES

Social Distance Item	Response	Leaders (N = 87)	Cross Section (N = 150)
It would be wise to discourage former patients of a mental hospital from entering your neighborhood.	Disagree	94.3	82.0
It would be unwise to encourage the close friendship of someone who had been in a mental hospital.	Disagree	89.7	72.0
You would be willing to sponsor a former patient of a mental hospital for membership in your favorite club or society.	Agree	86.2	67.3
If you were a personnel manager, you would be willing to hire a former patient of a mental hospital.	Agree	85.1	62.0
If you were responsible for renting apartments in your building, you would hesitate to rent living quarters to someone who had been in a mental hospital.	Disagree	86.2	54.0
You should strongly discourage your children from marrying someone who was formerly in a mental hospital.	Disagree	39.1	37.3
It would be unwise to trust a former mental hospital patient with your children.	Disagree	55.2	26.7

[14] Among the 8 out of 15 college graduates in Table X who knew three or more outpatients, half recommended hospitalization for the paranoid case; of the remaining seven college graduates with fewer outpatient acquaintances, three made the same recommendation. In contrast, of the 13 respondents who did not graduate from grammar school, all three who knew one or more outpatients recommended hospitalization while of the remaining ten respondents from the lowest educational level, eight made the same recommendation.

[15] The scale order of the social distance items, from most to least likely to elicit acceptance, is that of their listing in Table XI, except for the "child-care" and "child-marry" items. These two items scale differently in the cross section and leader groups, as is indicated by the reversal of the "popularities" of these items in the two groups. For the leaders, reproducibility of this scale is .957 and scalability is .752. For the cross section respondents, reproducibility is .909 and scalability is .602. It is interesting to speculate on why the leaders show more rejection in the "child-marry" situation than in the "child-care" situation while the opposite is true for the

TABLE XII

PERCENTAGE DISTRIBUTION BY SOCIAL DISTANCE FROM HYPOTHETICAL
EX-MENTAL HOSPITAL PATIENT: LEADERS AND CROSS SECTION RESPONDENTS
CLASSIFIED BY EDUCATION

		Cross Section			
Social Distance	Leaders	0–7 Years of School	8–11 Years of School	12–15 Years of School	16+ Years of School
Would accept in all situations	34.5	15.8	14.9	16.9	20.0
Would accept in all situations except *either* child-marry *or* child-care	24.1	21.1	21.3	12.3	33.3
Would accept in all situations except *both* child-marry *and* child-care	25.3	10.5	14.9	23.1	13.3
Would accept in community and one or more of the following: friendship, club, hire, tenant	11.4	21.1	29.7	32.3	26.7
Would accept only in the community	1.1	21.1	6.4	9.2	6.7
Would not accept in any of these situations	3.4	10.5	12.8	6.2	0.0
Total	99.8	100.0	100.0	100.0	100.0
Number of respondents	87	19	47	65	15

Note: With the two top, the two intermediate, and the two bottom social distance categories collapsed, the chi-square test indicates that the difference between the leaders and the combined cross section respondents could not have occurred by chance ($P < .01$). Within the cross section, the educational differences could have occurred by chance ($P > .10$). Given its consistency with our other results, however, the difference on the last two social distance categories between the college graduates among the cross section respondents and those with 0–7 years of education is regarded as important.

of the cutting points portrayed in Table XII. Table XII shows that the leaders expressed less social distance from ex-mental patients than cross section respondents at all educational levels. This result is consistent with findings, mentioned earlier, that indicate greater tolerance by leaders of other types of nonconformity such as political deviance (Stouffer, 1955).

Moreover, there are educational differences within the cross section. Only the college graduates have a majority who said, like the leaders, that they would extend their acceptance of ex-mental hospital patients to the "child-marry" and/or "child-care" situations. In contrast, the lower the educational level, the larger the proportions who showed unwillingness to extend their acceptance to activities closer than bare admission to the community, if that.

When we investigate the impact of educational level within each ethnic cross section, a further difference becomes apparent. Negroes and Puerto Ricans with 12–15 years of formal education expressed less social distance from ex-mental hospital patients than Jews and Irish of similar educational level.[16] In fact, the Negro and Puerto Rican high school graduates, the educational elites in these

---

cross section respondents. Possibly this is because the leaders are in general an older group and hence more likely to be concerned with their child's marriage partner than their child's nurse. It is also possible, however, that the higher-educated leaders are more likely to worry about a possible genetic component of mental illness.

[16] Chi-square test indicates that the probability is less than .01 that the difference could have occurred by chance.

disadvantaged groups, resemble the predominantly Jewish college graduates shown in Table XII. Why should this be so?

It seems possible that the harsher discrimination experienced by Negroes and Puerto Ricans, coupled with awareness of the growing impetus of the civil rights movement, has enabled the higher-educated among them to identify with the hypothetical ex-mental hospital patients in the situations described. However, the large majority of respondents who did not graduate from grammar school are also Negroes and Puerto Ricans. Why should they, experiencing the same prejudice and living through the same civil rights movement, have expressed the greatest social distance from ex-mental hospital patients? A strong clue to the answer may lie in the consistency of these results with Robin Williams' (1964) findings on attitudes toward outgroups. His results show that lower-educated Negroes as well as lower-educated whites tended to be more prejudiced toward the opposite group than higher-educated Negroes and whites. His main measure of prejudice was attitudinal social distance. It seems plausible, then, that our findings on tendency to recommend hospitalization and on tendency to express greater social distance from ex-mental hospital patients, like Williams' findings, are all largely functions of the same important phenomenon: a strong, generalized disposition by the low-status members of most groups to reject what they define as deviant.

Conclusion

We interpret our results as supporting Hollingshead and Redlich's observation (1958, p. 172) that "perception of the psychological nature of personal problems is a rare trait in any person and in any class." If the norms of the classes themselves are used to define deviant behavior, however, our results contradict the belief that "more abnormal behavior is tolerated by the . . . lower classes . . . even though the behavior may be disapproved by the class norms" (Hollingshead and Redlich, 1958, pp. 172–173).

Star noted from her 1950 nationwide study that the general population has encountered in the mass media a widely disseminated point of view about mental illness, expounded by the mental health professions in their attempts at mental health education:

> According to this doctrine, and it is usually presented as a fact rather than a point of view, all manner of emotional disturbances belong within the general category of mental illness. So, when we ask people to consider abstractly and intellectually the question of just what mental illness is supposed to cover, it is this modern definition that they give us. We are, in other words, in a period of transition in which the modern definition of mental illness has been rather widely disseminated without anything like equal acceptance of the point of view about the nature of mental illness and about the roots of human personality and behavior which lies back of this usage of the term. It is a definition which people simply cannot work with in practice within the context of their fundamental beliefs about human behavior (Star, 1955).

Our comparison of results from more recent studies with those of Star and the Cummings strongly indicate that there has been an increase in the tendency to describe as mentally ill the six fictitious descriptions she developed. It seems likely that this is due to the tendency of the mental health professions themselves to widen the variety of behaviors labeled as mental illness. Since Star's research in 1950, mental health education efforts may well have led the public to extend this label to wider varieties of behavior. Why is this likely to have happened and what does it imply?

The public's judgments of who is mentally ill do not show a one-to-one correspondence with their judgments about what constitutes a serious problem. Seriousness is judged not by the severity of psychopathology evidenced by the behavior but rather by the amount of threat to others the behavior embodies. These latter judgments as measured by our scale of tendency to regard the problems as serious, we believe, come nearer to what Star described as the public's fundamental beliefs about human behavior and its deviations from social norms.

How can the public adopt the label "mental illness" for increasingly wider varieties of behavior, without fully incorporating the underlying psychiatric points of view about the nature of psychopathology? The leaders and the more highly educated of the cross section respondents showed attitudes toward mental illness that appeared to be the most congruent with those of psychiatry—but with one important exception: the paranoid case was considered serious mental illness by all groups. The higher-status groups showed a relatively tolerant attitude by recommending outpatient treatment for the paranoid case; this recommendation contrasted with the more drastic recommendation of hospitalization—which was made not only by the lower-status groups, but also by psychiatrists! It is possible that while theories of psychopathology are less than clear, the humanistic message of the mental health professions has resonated with liberal political and social views (Joint Commission, 1961). Such views are especially dominant among the highly educated in our society. Though compatible with aspects of the message of the mental health professions, however, these liberal attitudes confer no special psychiatric understanding of psychopathology (cf. Davis, 1938). It may well be that not only our lower-status respondents, but most of our higher-status ones as well, do not view the cases from a psychiatric frame of reference.

Conditions of living in lower-status groups are less conducive to a liberal social orientation, and produce less receptiveness to the humanistic aspects of mental health education. Definitions of deviant behavior in the lower-status groups appear to be narrower, more restricted to aggressive, anti-social behavior—the sorts of problems that are more prevalent in what Hollingshead and Redlich described as the "raw" environments of low-status groups than in the "more refined" environments of high-status groups. And "raw" environments apparently breed disposition to harsh remedies.

Thus we are suggesting that lower-status groups are predisposed to greater intolerance of the kinds of deviance that *both* they and higher-status groups define as serious mental illness. Their definition of serious mental illness is narrower than that of higher-status groups, giving the appearance of greater tolerance of deviance as seen *from the vantage point of higher-status groups, including the mental health professions.* In short, lower-status groups may appear to higher-status observers to "tolerate" what such observers define as seriously deviant behavior, but the word "tolerant" has no meaning as a description of these attitudes. Rather, the attitudes of lower-status groups towards what they themselves define as serious mental disorder are in keeping with what most studies have shown about their attitudes towards civil rights, political nonconformity, and toward outgroups —intolerance of behavior, customs, or appearances that deviate from their norms.

39 / Superpatriot Opposition
to Community Mental Health Programs

Richard Schmuck / Mark Chesler

While most Americans support the growing national concern for mental health and the application of the behavioral sciences to community problems, some people are opposed to these developments. A wide variety of people object to mental health programs for many different reasons. One particular group of "opposers" is superpatriots. For them, anti-mental health attitudes are part of an embracing ideology and activism directed toward many contemporary trends. Not all superpatriots are opposed to mental health programs, however. It is the content and tenor of some typical superpatriot concerns about mental health programs that are explored in this report. Other data or insights into the psychology of superpatriotism as it relates to mental health may be found in Marmor, Bernard, and Ottenberg (1960), Auerback (1963), and Schiff (1964).

A Definition of Superpatriotism

Several major dimensions of belief and activity define superpatriotism. One dimension is a *patriotic or nationalistic conservatism*. The investigators measured this dimension by asking respondents about their political affiliation, their identification with liberal or conservative elements of each major party, and their reaction to the statement "Whereas some people feel they are citizens of the world, that they belong to mankind and not to any one nation, I, for my part, feel that I am first, last, and always an American."

A second major dimension is a vigorous *anticommunism*, not only with regard to international affairs, but especially to the internal danger of subversion. Many superpatriots attribute great power to the communists, who are seen as the "agent provocateur" of most of the world's and nation's ills. This dimension was measured by asking respondents how many communists there were and how much danger they represented in the American government and in both major political parties. A third defining dimension of superpatriots is their clear *commitment to action*. Lecture audiences, magazine or newspaper subscribers, and group members are urged "to do something" about their nation's condition. Action may involve becoming educated, educating others, protesting, or politicizing, but the commitment to some action is a critical part of superpatriotism. This dimension was measured by asking respondents how many partisan, sociopolitical organizations they belonged to that had regular meetings, and what they did to act upon their attitudes and values. Individuals who share the first two characteristics of the superpatriot ideology but do not act upon it are an important segment of the

From the *Community Mental Health Journal*, 1967, 3, 382–388. Copyright © 1967. Reprinted by permission of the authors and *Community Mental Health Journal*.

American population, perhaps even greater in number than the superpatriots. But precisely because they are not active opposers or resisters to change and are more passive, they are not the concern of this study.

In studying superpatriots' views, the authors first performed a content analysis of the literature published by extremist individuals and groups regarding mental health programs. Further, in order to ascertain whether such ideas were reflected in the beliefs of persons participating in superpatriot groups, 62 superpatriots were interviewed and their views compared with those of 38 conservatives and 34 moderates. These three groups were defined by their positions on an index composed of the three dimensions described above. Conservatives were defined as politically conservative and fairly nationalistic, but not particularly active, certainly not active in extremist organizations, and not believing that communists have a strong influence in government and in both political parties. Moderates ranged from traditionally moderate Republicans to moderate Democrats; they saw little communist influence in government, none in the political parties, and were not active in political organizations.

Superpatriots' Concerns
Regarding Mental Health Programs

Mental health programs have been scrutinized and criticized by many people for many different reasons. The reactions range from scientific studies through literary critiques to ideological and political attacks. Much of this opposition does not come from superpatriot organizations and individuals. However, some virulent opposition is presented in the writings and activities of superpatriots that can be summarized into five issues.

Psychological Testing Often Constitutes
an Invasion of Privacy and "Brainpicking"

Superpatriots are especially concerned with the use of psychological tests that assess personality characteristics. The concern for the use of such tests in the schools has been widely debated and some extreme criticisms have been entered into The Congressional Record (Ashbrook, 1962):

> A school would be in serious trouble if it would undress students for examination or inoculate them with some serum without parental permission. Yet virtually the same thing is being done all the time through these brain picking tests which literally undress young people and interfere in private areas which would be better left alone.

Psychological testing and invasions of private beliefs are seen sometimes as dangerous extensions of "adjustment theories of education." In a special issue of The National Health Federation Bulletin devoted to "Counselors and the Schools" (1962), it was argued that the purpose of the Minnesota Multiphasic Personality Inventory, the Blacky Test, and other psychological inventories was to destroy the child's moral and spiritual foundations. The resultant moral vacuum was seen as the ideal condition for the further promulgation and acceptance of the doctrine of the "welfare-police-slave state." It was also seen as providing:

. . . an opportunity for a vicious attack upon the children of the nation. Parents should not rest easy until they know exactly what is being done with their children and with others in the guidance counseling program in the school attended by their own children. Only united public action can stop this program of harm to children and of government control reaching into private thoughts and feelings.

In the interviews respondents were asked how they felt about psychological counseling in the public schools. Responses indicated that the superpatriots were much more opposed to psychological services in the school than were the conservatives and moderates. The results are presented in Table I.

TABLE I

REACTIONS OF SUPERPATRIOTS AND OTHERS TO PSYCHOLOGICAL COUNSELING SERVICES IN THE SCHOOLS*

	% Yes	% Ambivalent	% No
Superpatriots	37	15	48
Conservatives	63	8	29
Moderates	80	7	13

* Problems of adjustment and emotional problems have become an increasing concern of public schools in recent years. Many schools have hired professional psychologists and social workers to deal with these problems. Some people feel that such persons are beneficial in schools; others feel that they are more harmful to the children than good. Do you think that there should be such services in the elementary and high schools?

Community Mental Health Programs Are Extensions of the Federal Bureaucracy

In general, the superpatriots are concerned with increasing federal control of health and welfare programs. Further, they are generally opposed to further federal expansion, aid to education, or urban renewal programs and fear the end of local and private initiative in the face of a vast federal bureaucracy. Some critics have interpreted federal mental health efforts as attempts to secure "dictatorial powers" (Brengel, 1963). In addition to a concern about centralized power, others feared that many state and community mental health programs provide for aliens and intellectuals to take charge of individual citizens in every phase of their lives. To be taken charge of, to lose personal and local independence, seems to be a major theme in superpatriot opposition to most federally financed programs.

The answers to one question in the interview also suggested that superpatriots would resist greater federal funds for mental health. The investigators asked for agreement or disagreement with the statement "Local medical facilities are inadequate." Table II suggests that whereas most citizens agree with this statement, superpatriots were more satisfied with current facilities.

Mental Health Practitioners Encourage Immorality, Sin, and Social Disorganization

One aspect of this view is that psychodynamic analysis de-emphasizes personal responsibility and encourages free expression and moral license. An example of

TABLE II

REACTIONS OF SUPERPATRIOTS, OTHERS, AND THE GENERAL PUBLIC TO THE
INADEQUACY OF CURRENT MENTAL HEALTH FACILITIES

	% Inadequate	% Adequate
General public		
Roper, 1950	73	27
Jaco, 1955	79	21
Crawford,* 1959	85	15
Current study, 1964		
Conservatives		
and moderates	79	21
Superpatriots	50	50

* See Crawford, Rollins, and Sutherland, 1960, 1961.

these views of mental health was presented by Stormer in a widely distributed
book, *None Dare Call It Treason* (1964). In discussing the psychiatric theories of
Chisholm, Overstreet, and others, Stormer stated that:

> The Chisholms faced by a patient overcome with guilt because of extra-
> marital relations, homosexual practices, or other antisocial tendencies will devote
> their efforts to convincing the patient that such actions are perfectly normal,
> that no guilt should be experienced. This is an outgrowth of the materialistic,
> psychodynamic approach to understanding human behavior. This school holds
> that when an individual feels a drive that the drive must be satisfied or result-
> ing tensions will produce insanity. . . . Not relying on free will, morals or
> conscience for guidance, such amoral criminal minds are typical of the man
> Marx envisioned (pp. 162–163).

In addition, such a psychodynamic position has been seen as helping to identify
"society" as the culprit when man errs. By finding root causes for deviant behavior
in the character of the social system, mental health workers are seen as absolving
man of moral culpability. Attempts to change or reorganize aspects of the society
are seen as threatening personal adherence to established norms.

Perhaps one reason superpatriots are concerned about the assumptions and
implications of mental health programs is their general emphasis on morality and
moral principles. In discussing the things about modern America that most disturb
or worry them, the superpatriots who were interviewed concentrated upon "moral
decay," "a loss of morality," or "not sticking up for American principles." The
investigators also asked the respondents: "What are some of the names of the three
greatest contemporary Americans? What is it about him or her that is great?"
The most frequent person named by the superpatriots was General Douglas Mac-
Arthur. Superpatriots differed from conservatives and moderates in that they more
often attributed greatness to him on the basis of "his strong moral character," or
"fighting for his principles." Conservatives and moderates who suggested Mac-
Arthur most often did so on the basis of his "service to his country," "great intel-
lect," or "brilliant generalship." This perspective on traditional moral values is also
evident in the finding that superpatriots were more strongly antihedonistic as

compared to others. The investigators asked for agreement or disagreement with the statement: "Since life is so short, we might as well eat, drink, and be merry and not worry too much about what happens to the world." Most interviewees disagreed with that statement, but 72 per cent of the superpatriots, compared with 31 per cent of the conservatives and 26 per cent of the moderates, strongly disagreed with the statement.

Mental Health Programs Are
Politically and Ideologically Biased

Often, mental health programs are seen as masking political policies of internationalism and racial integration. Brengel (1963) and McClay (1964) expressed this concern in interpretations of materials of the World Federation of Mental Health. The WFMH discusses some of the psychological and social problems created by prejudice, hostility, and excessive nationalism and was seen by these commentators as being committed to political positions rather than to health concerns. Another writer (Matthews, 1958) has criticized the World Health Organization, which is seen as an attempt to "internationalize" and "one-world-ize" the American citizenry. WHO's concern for worldwide mental health has been interpreted as a plan to change the political, social, and economic institutions of society as well as to cure individual health problems.

One of the John Birch Society's directors expressed a similar fear about the partisanship inherent in current mental health policies. He noted that General Walker was forced to undergo a psychiatric examination but that the Freedom Riders were not (Anderson, 1962). Recently, news reports indicated that a southern mental health society was picketed by the Ku Klux Klan. The Klan distributed literature claiming that the purpose of the society was to brainwash Southerners into accepting integration and that lobotomies would be performed, making them submissive to communism and integration (Robinson, 1965).

Mental health program directors are sometimes seen as ideologically committed to liberal political ends. They are also seen as having power to refer or confine people to mental institutions. Consequently, mental health practitioners may be viewed as using their power for insidious purposes of controlling the thoughts and actions of the citizenry. In one view, people have been put into mental institutions because they are opposed to the "established liberal order."

One of the most dramatic case studies of this concern about mental health programs and political thought control revolved around a federal bill originally intended to finance a mental hospital in Alaska. Superpatriots interpreted this as the beginning of "Siberia, USA." A concise summary of this superpatriot concern was presented in Stormer's book:

> For the rare citizen who escapes indoctrination in the new social order in progressive schools, for the Bible believing Christian who rejects theologians who teach that socialism is the new kingdom of God on earth, for all the sturdy souls who hold to age-old concepts of right and wrong and are vocal about it; the collectivists have one final, ultimate weapon. Declare them insane! . . . The new leaders in the psychiatric field . . . hold the weapon of commitment to a mental institution over the heads of those reactionaries who rebel at accepting the new social order (Stormer, 1964, p. 155).

Mental Health and Mental Health Practitioners
Are Part of the Communist Plot to Destroy America

Several superpatriot attacks in this vein were documented in the article "Is Mental Health a Communist Plot?" in the *S.K. and F. Psychiatric Reporter* (1962). One description of the psychiatrist Chisholm that subtly presented this theme was delivered in a speech by a prominent superpatriot:

> While I do not contend he is a member of the Communist party, his philosophy calls for, freely and in sophisticated terms, the main key points of Communism, namely: an amoral society, ridicule of the family, of religion, and of patriotism, ruthless world-wide police force, and redistribution of wealth. Mental health enthusiasts decry as preposterous the many documented charges of Communists being active in the movement; in fact, they don't want to discuss such irresponsible criticisms. But there are plenty such connections.

The Russian leader, Beria, is said to have extolled the virtue of psychopolitics, skilled psychological manipulations for political ends. He is reported to have set out to train American psychopoliticians to take over our nation. Many American psychiatrists are viewed as foreigners who were educated in Russia. A spokesman for the Public Relations Forum also elaborated upon the perceived extent of such communist infiltration:

> If you are an officer in any club that wields some power, you doubtless have your psychopolitician. . . . If he or she is not a real psychopolitician and is really working in your best interests, then there are others who will eventually turn you against her and have her fired so that a psychopolitician can replace her. Now more than ever before, it is necessary to keep your wits about you. When confusion reigns supreme, the Communists make their greatest inroads.

Personal Characteristics and
Recruitment Patterns of Some Superpatriots

Although some of these views of mental health programs may seem extreme, the interviews suggested that superpatriots opposed to mental health programs were not typically psychotic, irrational, or disturbed; rather, they appeared to be socially effective and hospitable. For the most part, they seemed to be pleasant, considerate, and law abiding. Generally, they appeared to be comfortable and happy with their familial relations. Furthermore, they were not particularly dissatisfied or frustrated with their jobs or bureaucratic roles. In fact, within the present sample of superpatriots, little sense of personal anomie or demoralization was found. They were very much in touch with the world and were quite well informed and active in public affairs. The sample included people of all ages and social statuses. There were college students, young adults, middle-aged and older persons. They held all kinds of jobs and ranged from lower or lower-middle class to upper-middle or upper class.

Superpatriots were originally defined in part by the active involvement in public affairs. However, they also indicated more optimistic feelings of political effectiveness compared with the conservatives and moderates. Over 90 per cent of the superpatriots either agreed or strongly agreed with the statement that "Working in groups is one way people like me can influence the government." Compared with others, these people did not feel politically alienated or helpless. They felt involved in, although in disagreement with, the processes of local and federal government.

Another pervasive characteristic of superpatriots was their religious fundamentalism. Respondents were asked about their beliefs in God, in an afterlife, in punishment and rewards in the afterlife, and in the literal interpretation of the Bible. Those people who agreed strongly with all of these items were identified as religious fundamentalists. So-called religious modernists were those who had a belief in God and immortality but who minimized the idea of punishment in the afterlife and who disagreed that the entire Bible should be taken as literal truth. Nonbelievers were those who disagreed with all of the questions. Seventy-two per cent of the superpatriots, compared with 49 per cent of the conservatives and 32 per cent of the moderates, were classified as fundamentalists.

In addition to this religious perspective, the superpatriots, in contrast to conservatives and moderates, scored higher on items to measure dogmatism (Rokeach, 1960). It appeared that they tended to reduce differences in the environment, especially when they viewed the objects of consideration to be evil. Other results of the interviews that showed the superpatriots reducing differences were that they engaged in stereotypic thinking about Jews. However, they showed little emotional fervor and hatred of Jews. Oversimplification of thought, involving reduction of information rather than hatred, characterized these superpatriots' views.

Many people with similar characteristics never express them through political means and never endorse superpatriot views. Moreover, such personal characteristics alone would not lead one to become an active member in superpatriot organizations. Some organizational means and supports must exist to channel and recruit these persons into existing groups and activities. In building local chapters, superpatriots often rely on neighborhood contacts and friendships. Members usually probe one another about their interested friends and are encouraged to invite newcomers. The approach is one of inclusion rather than exclusion: so long as a person shares an ideology and attitudes close to that of the superpatriot, he is recruited and readily accepted. Membership in religious or ethnic minorities does not typically disqualify or discourage a person from active membership. In this open search for new recruits, members are trained to inform others about the work of the organization and are taught that all good Americans, whoever they are, are likely to agree with the patriots once they are informed.

In some places, organizations such as the John Birch Society execute a subtle and well-planned introduction into the society. Typically, induction first involves convincing a new participant of the expertise of the chapter leader and other members, then interesting him in reading some of the society's literature, and finally getting him to recruit other members. In one of the interviews this story about Mr. X (superpatriot) and Mr. Y (John Birch Chapter leader) was told to the interviewer.

> X told me he has been feeling quite helpless about the world situation and had little information about it until he ran into the Birch Society. His first contact was going with neighborhood friends to Mr. Y's house in another town for a meeting. He had little to say about the meeting but was very impressed

with the Birch library which he claimed had books and information you couldn't get anywhere else. The library is a lending library. He showed me a book, *Nine Men Against America*, which he had borrowed. He told me that the Birch Society teaches people that things don't have to keep going this way and that they can influence events as individuals. They must start work in the community—in the PTA—the local political parties and local government, then work up to the state and finally the national level. He started talking to the other employees where he works. At first, he claimed, they didn't know much about what was going on. But he told them things gradually, and now they can talk about a lot of things together. He has given them some pamphlets and lent them some books, but hasn't identified these as from the Birch Society. "Eventually, I will," he says, and hopes at least one or two will join.

In addition to neighborhood contacts and friendships, many superpatriot groups use the technique known as "popular fronting," i.e., identifying one's cause with a popular public issue while at the same time working out a more broadly based ideology. For instance, superpatriot-sponsored antifloridation programs may sometimes have the effect of bringing Christian Scientists into a multifaceted group. Right wing campaigns against urban renewal attract some urban landowners, while anti-Negro organizations in the cities, such as the National Association for the Advancement of White People, may attract urban whites. Protests at PTA meetings over curriculum materials or the recommendations of counselors may recruit some disgruntled parents into an anti-school or anti-mental health campaign. Once in any of these specific-type campaigns, the new participants receive literature, make new friends, gain new satisfactions, and may gradually be brought into broader activities. Sometimes they may be persuaded to form new opinions against community mental health programs.

One particularly salient topic for recruitment recently involved the Supreme Court's decision regarding praying in the schools. The investigators asked the interviewees: "How do you feel about the Supreme Court decision against praying in the school?" Most of them, including a large number of moderates, were opposed to the decision. Ninety-two per cent of the superpatriots, 73 per cent of the conservatives, and 60 per cent of moderates disagreed with the ruling.

Since a large number of people opposed the Supreme Court decision, many of them were probably receptive to attempts to protest that decision. One can understand the broad public appeal of Project America, a product of the "20th Century Reformation Hour." This project organized mass rallies and petitions that asked for a constitutional amendment to overturn the Supreme Court's decision. Many conservatives and moderates were active in this superpatriot-organized protest. Under such circumstances, persons with a generally conservative to moderate outlook, or dogmatic fundamentalists who have been apolitical, may be recruited into other superpatriot activities, such as anti-mental health campaigns.

In all of these activities, involvement and commitment in superpatriot organizations have the effect of raising participants' feelings of esteem, status, and political effectiveness. This cycle of gratification serves to encourage members to be active and to seek continually new recruits to their organizations and ideology.

40 / Public Attitudes
Toward the Mentally Ill

Jum C. Nunnally, Jr.

People in the mental-health-education field commonly say that one of the most difficult problems to overcome is the *stigma* attached to the mentally ill. This assumes that the public holds negative attitudes toward the mentally ill. We performed a series of studies to determine (1) to what extent the mentally ill are held in low esteem, (2) whether the public holds different kinds of attitudes toward different kinds of mental illness, and (3) whether attitudes toward the mentally ill correlate with demographic characteristics such as education, age, and the like.

Measuring Instruments

To measure public attitudes toward mental-health phenomena, we relied heavily on an instrument called the Semantic Differential (see Osgood, Suci, and Tannenbaum, 1957, for a detailed description of the measurement method). In essence, the Semantic Differential requires a subject to rate a concept on sets of bipolar adjectives. An illustration follows:

Psychiatrist

Ignorant	___:___:___:___:___:___	Intelligent
Effective	___:___:___:___:___:___	Ineffective
Weak	___:___:___:___:___:___	Strong
Anxious	___:___:___:___:___:___	Calm
Ugly	___:___:___:___:___:___	Handsome
Simple	___:___:___:___:___:___	Complicated
Strange	___:___:___:___:___:___	Familiar

The concept in the example above is *psychiatrist*. Almost anything can be used as a concept, for example, peach ice cream, Marilyn Monroe, United Nations, Communist, shock treatment, or Cadillac. In our studies we were interested in ratings of concepts related to mental health, such as a mentally ill person, insane man, nervous breakdown, neurotic woman, mental hospital, psychologist, nurse, psychotherapy, and related role concepts such as my father, my mother, me (the self-concept), marriage, old man, and child. . . .

The seven-point rating continuum used for each pair of bipolar adjectives is called a *scale*. Scales were chosen to incorporate the factors which have been found in previous studies. There are three well-known factors: (1) *evaluation*, defined by scales like good-bad, valuable-worthless, and kind-cruel; (2) *potency*, defined by scales like strong-weak, large-small, and rugged-delicate; and (3) *activity,* defined by scales like active-passive, fast-slow, and sharp-dull. A fourth factor, *understandability,* occurs prominently in our studies of mental-health concepts. It is defined by scales like understandable-mysterious, familiar-strange, simple-complicated, and predictable-unpredictable.

One of the advantages of the Semantic Differential is that it provides not only an over-all index of attitude but different facets of meaning as well. The *evaluative* factor appears to measure *attitude* as it is conventionally thought of, and high correlations have been found between the factor and conventional attitude-measuring instruments (see Osgood, Suci, and Tannenbaum, 1957). Two concepts that have the same *evaluative* meaning may be given different *potency* and *activity* ratings, and these differences help explain the differential meanings of concepts to the public. The finding of *understandability* as a factor in ratings of mental-health concepts was an important development in our studies. *Understandability,* or rather the lack of it, is a very important component of public reaction to the mentally ill.

In addition to the Semantic Differential, a number of other instruments were used to study public attitudes and meanings. One of these was a "free-association" test in which subjects were asked to provide associations to terms like psychiatrist, emotion, mental hospital, neurotic mother, and mental patient. (This instrument was applied only to college students.) Another instrument which we used was a multiple-choice association form. A sample item follows:

> When I think of a neurotic person, I also think of
> > a. Selfishness   ———
> > b. Physical weakness   ———
> > c. Fear of something   ———
> > d. Wild sex life   ———
> > e. Being lonesome
> >   and unloved   ———
> > f. Paying for misdeeds ———

A fourth instrument which we used was a "pair-comparison" technique in which, for example, subjects were asked whether they would seek help for a mentally ill family member from a psychiatrist or a psychologist, a psychiatrist or a minister, a psychiatrist or a family doctor, and so on for all possible comparisons. The pair-comparison technique was used mainly to study public attitudes toward treatment sources. In addition to the four types of instruments described above, on occasion we employed ranking methods and conventional rating scales.

The Population Samples

Our attitude-measuring instruments were administered to several broad segments of the general population as well as to numerous special groups. In the early studies we were primarily concerned with measuring typical public feelings (attitudes) about mental illness, the mentally ill, and the persons who treat the mentally ill. We speak of these as our survey studies. Attitudes were also measured incidentally in a number of our experimental studies. Since the experimental studies were primarily concerned with changing attitudes toward concepts like *psychiatrist* and *mental patient,* attitudes had to be measured. In sum, we administered a variety of measuring instruments, concerning a variety of concepts, to a variety of groups. The data that will be cited in this chapter illustrate the general attitude trends found in all of our studies. Confirming evidence and supplementary findings are scattered throughout the book.

The first major study of public attitudes was performed on our opinion panel. The panel is a group of about 400 persons, most of whom live in central Illinois. Except for its geographic bias, the panel approximates the country as a whole in terms of sex ratio, age, education, income, and other demographic characteristics. A Semantic Differential form was applied to 270 panel members who had not been contacted for any of our studies during the prior ten months (a precaution against "panel effect"). A self-explanatory Semantic Differential form was mailed to each subject with an addressed return envelope. Subjects were routinely mailed one-dollar checks for their participation in each study. A follow-up "prod" was mailed two weeks after the form was sent to obtain a maximum of returns. Of the 270 forms mailed out, 257 were returned. Seven of the 257 returns had errors of one kind or another, leaving 250 to be analyzed.

Results

The 250 Semantic Differential replies from the opinion panel were analyzed in various ways. First, we computed mean responses for all subjects on all concepts and on all scales (see Table I). Next, the total sample was broken into a "high-education" and a "low-education" group (see Table II). Subsequently, breakdowns were made for other demographic characteristics, such as sex and age. Because these comparisons produced no striking findings, the results will not be given in this chapter. In addition to the results from the 250 panel members, the results from some of our other studies will be cited at points to help complete the picture of public attitudes toward the mentally ill.

PROPOSITION 1: PUBLIC ATTITUDES ARE RELATIVELY NEGATIVE TOWARD PERSONS WITH MENTAL-HEALTH PROBLEMS   As is commonly suspected, the mentally ill are regarded with fear, distrust, and dislike by the general public (see Table I). Comparing public attitudes toward the mentally ill (concepts like mental patient, insane woman, neurotic woman, and neurotic man) with public attitudes toward "normal" persons (concepts like average man, me, my father), the mentally ill are regarded as relatively worthless, dirty, dangerous, cold, unpredictable, insincere, and so on. This proposition is supported by a number of other Semantic Differential studies reported in following chapters.

The two scales which most clearly distinguish the "normal" concepts from the mental disorders are predictable-unpredictable and tense-relaxed. Evidently, erratic behavior and anxiety were regarded by the public as the key signs of mental disorder.

PROPOSITION 2: PUBLIC ATTITUDES ARE DIFFERENT TOWARD NEUROTIC AND PSY-CHOTIC DISORDERS   Although neurotic concepts (neurotic man, neurotic woman, person with a nervous breakdown, and so forth) and psychotic concepts (insane man, insane woman, mental patient, and so forth) are both regarded with fear and distrust, some distinctions are made between the two (see Tables I and II). Psychotics are generally held in lower esteem than neurotics, being rated as more bad, worthless, dirty, and so on. Neurotics are viewed as being less potent than psychotics, being rated as more weak and delicate. The scale that best differenti-

TABLE I

MEAN SCALE POSITIONS* ON THE SEVEN-STEP SEMANTIC DIFFERENTIAL SCALES
(RESPONSES BY 250 MEMBERS OF THE ILLINOIS OPINION PANEL)

Scales	Neurotic Man	Average Man	Insane Woman	Average Woman	Old Man	Psychiatrist	Neurotic Woman	Insane Man	Child	Me	Mother	Father	
Foolish	3.00	5.19	2.64	5.00	5.11	5.98	2.75	2.79	4.77	4.94	5.93	5.71	Wise
Ignorant	4.10	5.48	3.45	5.44	5.31	6.42	3.98	3.43	5.38	5.52	5.98	5.80	Intelligent
Sad	2.61	5.76	1.77	5.65	4.94	5.16	2.64	2.96	6.35	6.00	5.67	5.69	Happy
Passive	3.92	5.93	3.40	5.80	3.70	5.80	3.92	3.55	6.56	6.12	6.04	5.91	Active
Insincere	3.80	5.77	3.17	5.78	5.60	6.08	3.66	3.16	5.86	6.26	6.41	6.21	Sincere
Poor	3.83	4.03	3.70	4.04	4.06	5.05	3.94	3.75	4.04	3.78	4.08	4.02	Rich
Unpredictable	3.64	5.24	1.69	5.45	4.20	5.27	2.54	1.73	3.02	5.24	5.72	5.46	Predictable
Weak	2.82	5.37	3.22	4.79	3.40	5.45	2.75	3.27	5.01	5.26	5.44	5.62	Strong
Slow	3.75	5.01	3.80	4.84	2.53	4.80	3.90	3.77	5.60	5.09	5.05	5.04	Fast
Delicate	3.60	5.46	3.72	4.20	3.67	4.82	3.20	4.04	4.74	5.02	4.38	5.45	Rugged
Cold	3.60	5.42	3.69	5.41	4.87	5.08	3.38	3.48	6.08	5.68	5.92	5.74	Warm
Dirty	4.63	5.84	3.96	6.13	4.83	6.20	4.80	3.74	5.10	6.35	6.42	6.19	Clean
Dangerous	3.43	5.99	2.78	6.08	5.46	6.04	3.46	1.94	5.60	6.34	6.46	6.33	Safe
Tense	1.98	5.26	1.96	4.80	5.20	5.41	1.98	1.96	5.22	4.76	4.69	5.18	Relaxed
Worthless	4.03	5.94	3.32	5.90	5.38	6.28	4.03	3.18	6.37	5.64	6.47	6.31	Valuable
Sick	2.32	5.56	1.77	5.35	3.90	5.70	2.32	1.66	5.84	5.91	5.24	5.33	Healthy
Bad	4.21	5.81	3.85	5.93	5.65	5.94	4.25	3.55	5.96	5.88	6.42	6.30	Good

* The means are restricted to the range of 1 to 7. A mean of 1.00 indicates an average scale position at the extreme left of the bipolar continuum. For example, a mean of 1.00 on the foolish-wise scale would indicate an average rating of completely "foolish." A mean of 7.00 indicates an average reaction at the extreme right, in the example above, extremely "wise." The middle of the continuum, 4.00, can be regarded either as "don't now" or "neutral"—using the above example again, "neither foolish nor wise."

535

TABLE II

MEAN SCALE POSITIONS* ON THE SEMANTIC DIFFERENTIAL FOR A HIGH-EDUCATION GROUP (UPPER FIGURE) AND A LOW-EDUCATION GROUP (LOWER FIGURE)

Scales	Neurotic Man	Average Man	Insane Woman	Average Woman	Old Man	Psychiatrist	Neurotic Woman	Insane Man	Child	Me	Mother	Father	
Foolish	3.22 / 2.81	4.56 / 5.39	2.69 / 2.54	4.49 / 5.20	4.96 / 5.29	5.82 / 5.94	2.75 / 2.78	2.87 / 2.62	3.91 / 5.09	5.22 / 4.94	5.69 / 6.26	5.62 / 5.78	Wise
Ignorant	4.47 / 3.93	4.65 / 5.64	3.85 / 3.07	4.76 / 5.78	4.78 / 5.35	6.44 / 6.35	4.34 / 3.94	3.84 / 3.07	4.76 / 5.52	5.78 / 5.54	5.56 / 6.30	5.64 / 5.78	Intelligent
Sad	2.64 / 2.88	5.18 / 5.93	2.80 / 2.93	5.04 / 5.83	4.14 / 5.16	4.75 / 5.20	2.66 / 2.90	2.81 / 2.90	5.82 / 6.51	5.67 / 6.14	5.16 / 6.01	5.29 / 5.90	Happy
Passive	4.46 / 3.75	5.13 / 6.13	3.82 / 3.29	5.22 / 5.84	3.73 / 3.78	5.38 / 6.17	4.22 / 3.95	4.00 / 3.42	6.27 / 6.67	5.80 / 6.32	5.71 / 6.33	5.58 / 6.25	Active
Insincere	3.85 / 3.78	5.02 / 5.83	3.82 / 2.64	5.11 / 5.93	5.16 / 5.45	5.71 / 6.10	3.73 / 3.93	3.03 / 2.64	5.62 / 5.68	6.31 / 6.29	6.16 / 6.42	5.95 / 6.23	Sincere
Poor	4.07 / 3.59	4.00 / 3.81	3.84 / 3.72	3.96 / 3.88	3.89 / 4.15	5.33 / 4.84	4.07 / 3.78	4.02 / 3.81	4.00 / 3.90	3.82 / 3.30	4.18 / 3.84	4.25 / 3.65	Rich
Unpredictable	4.64 / 2.87	4.93 / 5.42	1.80 / 1.84	4.11 / 4.78	4.16 / 4.10	5.09 / 5.33	2.58 / 2.78	1.89 / 1.68	2.87 / 3.12	5.31 / 5.36	5.44 / 5.88	5.18 / 5.43	Predictable
Weak	3.33 / 3.04	4.73 / 5.52	3.33 / 3.00	4.40 / 4.94	3.36 / 3.51	5.25 / 5.57	2.95 / 2.86	3.82 / 3.35	4.45 / 4.96	5.04 / 5.23	5.46 / 5.67	5.40 / 5.90	Strong

The following table is printed sideways on the page. Each cell contains two stacked means: the upper value is for the high-education group and the lower value is for the low-education group.

Scale (–)													Scale (+)
Slow	4.20 / 3.54	4.67 / 5.25	4.15 / 3.54	4.47 / 4.97	2.84 / 2.54	4.64 / 4.77	4.33 / 3.86	5.53 / 3.78	4.33 / 5.28	5.06 / 5.00	5.27 / 4.91	4.96 / 5.20	Fast
Delicate	3.65 / 3.87	4.84 / 5.48	3.71 / 3.88	4.00 / 4.52	3.45 / 3.62	4.49 / 5.00	3.29 / 3.26	4.25 / 4.33	4.69 / 4.67	4.91 / 5.00	4.56 / 4.33	5.00 / 5.67	Rugged
Cold	3.40 / 3.62	4.85 / 5.70	3.64 / 3.71	5.05 / 5.61	4.44 / 4.90	4.80 / 5.22	3.45 / 3.45	3.56 / 3.45	5.82 / 6.13	5.45 / 5.71	5.78 / 6.00	5.40 / 5.93	Warm
Dirty	4.34 / 4.54	5.31 / 6.04	3.87 / 4.01	5.60 / 6.33	4.40 / 5.01	5.93 / 6.28	4.67 / 4.72	3.73 / 3.61	4.24 / 5.38	6.11 / 6.54	6.09 / 6.59	5.82 / 6.36	Clean
Dangerous	3.11 / 3.74	5.45 / 6.13	2.33 / 2.32	5.45 / 6.27	5.31 / 5.55	5.75 / 6.01	3.33 / 3.65	2.16 / 1.90	5.29 / 5.72	6.13 / 6.49	5.18 / 6.67	5.98 / 6.46	Safe
Tense	2.04 / 2.23	4.65 / 5.45	2.05 / 1.99	4.31 / 5.26	5.00 / 5.07	5.02 / 5.17	2.18 / 2.30	2.25 / 1.77	4.89 / 5.00	4.67 / 5.10	4.36 / 4.96	4.73 / 5.35	Relaxed
Worthless	4.25 / 3.94	5.54 / 5.93	3.53 / 3.06	5.51 / 6.00	5.33 / 5.46	6.27 / 6.19	4.27 / 3.91	3.64 / 1.90	6.16 / 6.39	5.69 / 5.71	6.29 / 6.61	6.18 / 6.30	Valuable
Sick	2.38 / 2.55	4.87 / 5.83	1.84 / 1.81	4.87 / 5.51	3.85 / 4.06	5.42 / 5.74	2.24 / 2.62	1.82 / 1.64	5.42 / 5.81	5.71 / 5.71	5.05 / 5.45	4.89 / 5.74	Healthy
Bad	4.00 / 4.19	3.88 / 5.90	5.53 / 3.78	5.45 / 6.07	5.73 / 5.65	4.20 / 5.96	3.80 / 4.16	5.53 / 3.25	5.73 / 5.94	5.62 / 6.00	6.13 / 6.57	4.89 / 6.39	Good

* The means are calibrated on the seven-point scale which was described in the footnote to Table 1. The high-education group consists of 55 persons who had at least some college training. The low-education group consists of persons who did not complete high school. The two groups were equated for the demographic variables of age and sex. To illustrate how the table is read, look at the foolish-wise scale for the concept *neurotic man*. On that scale the high-education group has a mean of 3.22 and the low-education group has a mean of 2.81. This indicates that the low-education group regards *neurotic man* as more foolish (less wise) than the high-education group does.

ates the two kinds of disorders is "predictable," the psychotics being rated as much more unpredictable. In subsequent studies it was found that the scale predictable-unpredictable is one of the primary elements of a new factor called *understandability*. In addition to predictable-unpredictable, it contains scales like understandable-mysterious, simple-complicated, and familiar-strange.

Lack of predictability seems to be a cornerstone of public attitudes toward psychotics. Because unpredictable behavior is frightening and disruptive, much societal machinery is devoted to making the behavior of individuals predictable to others. For example, if you are being introduced to someone and you say, "I am pleased to meet you," you can usually predict that the other individual will respond in kind. If he replies with "Fish for sale" or "I hate you," it is, to say the least, disturbing. Much of the dread of the mentally ill might be removed if the public could learn some meaningful patterns and consistencies in psychotic behavior so that it is more understandable and more predictable.

A study employing a multiple-choice association test (of the kind illustrated previously) supports the results described above and adds some more information about the difference in public attitudes toward psychotic and neurotic disorders. The term "neurotic" is associated with women rather than men (the Semantic Differential studies also show that the characteristics attributed to the neurotic are generally feminine) and intelligent rather than ignorant persons. The term "insane person" is associated with an older and more ignorant individual.

PROPOSITION 3: SUBGROUPS IN THE POPULATION HAVE SLIGHTLY DIFFERENT ATTITUDES TOWARD THE MENTALLY ILL   Whereas there are marked differences in the kinds of *information* held by old as compared with young people and by more educated as compared with less educated people, differences in *attitudes* of these and other subgroups are relatively small. There is a small, but statistically significant, tendency for more-educated people to hold less derogatory attitudes toward the mentally ill (see Table II). Even in the better educated group, however, there is a marked tendency to isolate the mentally ill as relatively bad, dirty, dangerous, and so on.

None of the other demographic breakdowns produced more than a few clear-cut differences. For example, we found some significant differences (by *t*-test) between the mean responses of women and men. The differences formed no clearly interpretable pattern, however, and differences in one study sometimes were not found in other studies. The nature and size of our samples prevented us from interpreting small differences.

The finding that subgroups in the population do not differ substantially in their attitudes toward the mentally ill relates to a point which I made (1961, Chapter 1). There it was said that our moderately representative, moderately sized population samples were more than adequate to document some of the findings. Most of the conclusions about public attitudes in this chapter would have been the same if we had dealt only with male high-school students in a middle-class neighborhood.

Incidental Findings

The major aim of our studies of attitudes was to learn the public feeling toward different kinds of mental disturbances. In order to do this, it was necessary to compare the meaning of mental disorders with the meanings of concepts encountered in everyday life such as father, me, and child. Some results reported in this chapter (see Tables I and II) show some interesting things about the meanings of everyday concepts. In order not to distract from the central theme of the book, no effort will be made to give a detailed account of the "incidental" findings. Two of the findings, however, are of particular interest.

The low-education group as compared to the high-education group gives more favorable ratings on most scales to the concept child, rating it, for example, as much more wise, intelligent, healthy, clean, and safe. Perhaps child-rearing is a problem only for the *middle class* in our society.

Another interesting finding is that the public at large expresses relatively unfavorable attitudes toward the concept old man. In comparison to concepts like me and average man, old man is rated as relatively unpredictable, cold, dirty, dangerous, worthless, and so on. Insofar as the results here are indicative of popular attitudes in general toward the aged, they exemplify a serious problem.

Altering Public Attitudes

Now that we know how the public *does* feel about the mentally ill, it is important to discuss the question, "How *should* the public feel?" What kinds of changes in public attitudes can realistically be expected?

In terms of the *evaluation* factor, it is probably unreasonable to expect that the public will ever react to the mentally ill as they do to "normal" people. Psychotics, neurotics, and emotionally disturbed people are often unpleasant to have around. They sometimes do dangerous things, they are often undependable or inefficient, and they often embarrass and provoke. The only realistic hope is that the public will come to devalue the mentally ill *less*. Both practical experience and our results indicate that the public's devaluation of the mentally ill (the stigma and the feeling of danger) is unreasonably extreme.

In terms of the *understandability* factor, the goals are quite clear. Hopefully the mentally ill will become as understandable and predictable as possible to the general public. Not only is this a laudable and reasonable goal in and of itself, but, as was hypothesized earlier in this chapter, the more understandable the mentally ill are to the general public, the more the public will react to them as sincere, clean, valuable, and safe.

Summary

A careful distinction should be made between *information* held by the public and *attitudes* held by the public. A comparison of the results discussed in this chapter (relating to attitudes) with those earlier (1961, Chapter 2) (relating to information) shows why the distinction is crucial. Whereas the *information* held by the public is not really "bad" in the sense that the public is not grossly misinformed, the *attitudes* held by the public are as "bad" as is generally suspected. Whereas correctness of information correlates with demographic variables such as age and education, correlations between attitudes and such demographic variables are very small. Old people and young people, highly educated people and people with little formal schooling—all tend to regard the mentally ill as relatively dangerous, dirty, unpredictable, and worthless.

One of the most important findings is that there is a strong "negative halo" associated with the mentally ill; they are regarded as all things bad. Such unselectively negative attitudes may, in part, be due to a failure to observe and learn about mental-illness phenomena in daily life.

41 / Other Variables of Effective Communication

Jum C. Nunnally, Jr.

This chapter will be used as a catch-all for three experiments dealing with communication variables not discussed in other chapters. The first experiment is concerned with the effects on information and attitudes of "contact" with the mentally ill; the second, with the differential effect of "personal" versus "impersonal" messages; and the third, with relationships between changes in information and changes in attitudes. Some other communication variables were considered in each of the three studies. Also, some of the findings from the three studies help confirm and clarify results reported in previous and subsequent chapters of the book.

Study 1: Contact

It is often supposed that if people had more face to face contact with the mentally ill and with those who have recovered from mental illness, much of the stigma associated with mental illness would be removed. For this reason, some people have proposed that the general public be encouraged to visit mental hospitals and meet the patients at first hand. Does contact actually have the desired effect?

The first experiment[1] described here concerns one aspect of the "contact" issue: the differential effectiveness of messages when the sources are identified as former mental patients and when the sources are identified as "normal" persons. A standard talk was delivered to different groups of subjects; in some groups the speaker was identified as a "former mental patient"; in other groups the speaker was not so identified. In addition, some of the messages were keyed to a personal approach and others were keyed to an impersonal approach. Tests were then made to determine the differential effectiveness of the various presentations.

[1] The study was conducted by Dr. T. R. Husek.

Experimental Procedure

The subjects' view of the study was rather simple. One day, a Friday, a young woman came into their class in high school and gave a 20-minute talk on mental health. On the following Monday, someone else came into class and gave tests.

The experimental design was more complicated. Two different women were used as communicators. The speaker may or may not have said that she was a former mental patient, and if she did claim to be one, she may have said it at the beginning of the talk or at the end of the talk. In addition, the talk may have been presented in a personal or an impersonal manner.

Classes in two high schools were used (480 students). They were tested one week apart. The communicators told the subjects that they were from a "state organization" and were visiting some high schools giving talks on mental health. They made the presentations during regular class sessions. Then, on the following Monday a different person came to the class and said he was making a survey for the "university." He passed out the testing materials during the regular class meetings. In this way it was hoped that the test materials would be dissociated from the talks given earlier.

On both occasions the teachers of the classes participated only by introducing the experimenters; during the session they sat in the back of the room and merely watched. The experimenters answered questions about the instructions for the test materials but not about the content and purpose of the tests.

On the day after the testing (Tuesday), the experimenter returned to the classes, explained the nature of the experiment, and answered frankly any questions the subjects had, both about the experiment and the talk.

THE TALK A 20-minute talk was composed which attempted to promote favorable attitudes toward some mental-illness concepts and to correct some common misconceptions about mental illness. The content of the talk ranged widely over topics concerning mental illness, mentioning such items as the shortage of hospital beds, the fact that a vacation is not a cure for mental illness, and the fact that mental patients are not just pretending to be sick. Here is a short section of the presentation which was intended to promote favorable attitudes:

> Patients in a mental hospital seem to behave in a confused manner. But when you get to know the patients in the hospital and understand what's wrong with them, you find that their behavior is not so strange after all. The doctors in the hospitals have to understand why the patients behave the way they do in order to cure them. The way a person develops an emotional disturbance is closely related to his personality, history, and environment. And when you understand more about him, his behavior doesn't seem so strange any more; for the way that a patient acts follows from the kind of a person he is and the problem he has. Most of you in this room, given enough time to study the problem, could understand why mentally ill people act the way they do.

Here is a part of the talk which attempted to impart some information about mental illness:

> Let's discuss the idea that a mental illness will clear up if a person is helped with his financial and social problems, or can just "get away from it all." If

things get bad, avoid them, and they'll go away. Well, sometimes if a person is overworked and overtired, he will show symptoms of mental illness. In these few cases a trip or a rest may help. But in most cases it will just not work. A trip or help with financial problems will lessen some of the pressures on a disturbed person. It may keep him busy and get his mind off the problems for a while. But the problems of an emotionally disturbed person are not so trivial that they'll blow away with the wind if you ignore them. No one would ever suggest that somebody with cancer or appendicitis should go on a trip if he wants to feel better. In the same way, a trip or some help with financial and social problems is not a cure for mental illness.

COMMUNICATORS   The talk was presented orally. Because the communicator is usually an important factor in oral communications, two female speakers were used in the study. They were about the same age and their backgrounds were similar.

Although the speakers did not memorize the talk, they were able to present the material only occasionally glancing at their notes. They practiced for several weeks and watched each other's presentation with a view to standardizing the talk as much as possible.

THE CONTACT VARIABLE   For one third of the presentations, the speaker mentioned at the beginning of the speech that she was a "former mental patient." For another third of the presentations, the point was made at the end of the talk. For the last third no mention was made about the background of the speaker. (Neither speaker had actually been a "mental patient.")

At each of the two high schools, the role of each of the two speakers was held constant. That is, for all of the classes tested in one high school, one of the speakers played the role of the former mental patient (sometimes announcing the fact at the beginning of the talk and at other times announcing the fact at the end of the talk). In that high school, the second speaker consistently made no mention of being a former mental patient. Roles were reversed in the other high school.

The Personal versus Impersonal Variable

Half of the talks were presented in an impersonal manner; the other half were made as personal as possible. Here is a section from the personal-treatment version:

> Right now 9,000,000 people in this country are suffering from mental illness or a personality disturbance. What does this mean to you? It means that on the average two people in this class here today would be expected to have some kind of mental illness or personality disturbance. It means that on the average, every one of you might have one close relative suffering from a mental illness or a personality disturbance right now.

Here is the impersonal treatment for the same section:

> It is estimated that right now there are about 9,000,000 people in the United States suffering from mental illness and personality disturbances. This counts only the people who have trouble right now. One out of every 12 people in the United States will spend some time in his life in a mental institution.

The Experimental Design

There were two communicators, three variations of contact, and personal and impersonal treatments. The complete design is outlined in Table I.

TABLE I

EXPERIMENTAL DESIGN FOR STUDY 1

Variable		Treatment	
Communicator	Miss X	Miss Y	
Contact	Early contact	Late contact	No contact
Personal versus impersonal styling	Personal	Impersonal	

Attitude and Information Measures

A form of the Semantic Differential was used to measure attitudes, and 20 items from the information questionnaire were used to measure information. A list of the Semantic Differential concepts and scales used in the experiment is found in Table II.

The information questionnaire contained items such as "The best way to mental health is by avoiding morbid thoughts" and "Nervous breakdowns seldom have a physical origin." The subjects marked the amount of their agreement or disagreement with the items on a seven–point scale.

Results

Semantic Differential results were obtained for the concepts *me, psychotherapy, neurotic people, mental hospital,* and *ex-mental patient.* Scores were obtained for the *evaluation* factor and for the scales predictable-unpredictable (which related prominently to *understandability*), sick-healthy, and dangerous-safe.

Means were obtained for each of the four scale groups for each of the five concepts for the three contact treatments. These results are presented in Table II. The following results are found when the 20 variables for the early-contact, late-contact, and no-contact groups are compared. By signed-rank test, late contact results in more favorable attitudes than early contact beyond the .01 level of confidence. Late contact is better than early contact for all of the 20 possible comparisons. If a communications program on mental health requires that a former mental patient be the communicator, the results indicate that the announcement of the past treatment is better made after the communication than before.

The no-contact treatment is also better than the early-contact treatment, beyond the .01 level of confidence by signed-rank test. In addition, the late-contact treatment is slightly better than the no-contact treatment; the difference between the two treatments is significant by the signed-rank test at about the .05 level of confidence.

The results should be a warning to anyone who supposes that contact with the mentally ill necessarily promotes favorable attitudes. Of course, we investigated only one way in which contact might be employed. If contact is to be employed by the communicator, then it is important how that contact is handled. Our

TABLE II

MEAN SCORES ON THE SEMANTIC DIFFERENTIAL FOR THE "CONTACT" TREATMENTS*

Scales	Early Contact	Late Contact	No Contact
Evaluation (worthless-valuable, dirty-clean, insincere-sincere, foolish-wise)			
Me	5.83	5.97	5.93
Psychotherapy	5.72	5.81	5.71
Neurotic people	3.64	3.67	3.77
Mental hospital	5.72	6.04	6.03
Ex-mental patient	5.35	5.55	5.53
Grand means	5.26	5.41	5.40
Unpredictable-predictable			
Me	4.42	4.79	4.61
Psychotherapy	4.03	4.46	4.00
Neurotic people	2.07	2.28	2.37
Mental hospital	4.02	4.23	4.15
Ex-mental patient	4.30	4.54	4.46
Grand means	3.77	4.06	3.92
Sick-healthy			
Me	6.18	6.33	6.26
Psychotherapy	4.00	4.34	4.22
Neurotic people	1.79	2.11	2.02
Mental hospital	2.82	3.50	2.64
Ex-mental patient	5.01	5.50	5.16
Grand means	3.96	4.36	4.06
Dangerous-safe			
Me	5.95	6.17	6.19
Psychotherapy	5.57	5.78	5.63
Neurotic people	3.20	3.45	3.47
Mental hospital	5.14	5.34	5.37
Ex-mental patient	5.32	5.43	5.37
Grand means	5.04	5.23	5.21

* The means are restricted to the range of 1.00 to 7.00. The higher the mean, the more "positive" the attitude—that is, higher means are associated with ratings of higher *evaluation,* more predictability, more health, or more safety.

results indicate that if the speaker is to identify himself as being or having been mentally ill, it is better for him to do so after he has delivered the substance of his message. If the identification is made at the start of the talk, it may have a harmful effect on attitudes toward the mentally ill. Our hypothesis is that early identification allowed the subjects to discount the speaker and, hence, to offset the influence of the talk on their attitudes toward the mentally ill.

On the basis of these results, we offer the following proposition: PROPOSITION 1: IF THE SOURCE OF A MESSAGE IS TO BE IDENTIFIED AS BEING, OR HAVING BEEN, MEN- TALLY ILL, IT IS BETTER FOR THE IDENTIFICATION TO BE MADE AFTER THE SUBSTANCE OF THE MESSAGE HAS BEEN IMPARTED.   The above findings, however, must be quali- fied. The speaker himself is a very important element if contact is to be employed in a communication. We performed analyses of variance on the 20 variables listed in Table II. For eight of the analyses, the interaction between the speaker variable and the contact variable was significant at or beyond the .05 level of confidence. The variables which show significant interaction are listed in Table III. The statistical significance of the interaction terms indicates that the contact variable does not have the same effect for one speaker as it does for the other. Even though, overall, late contact is better than no contact and both are better than early contact, the person of the speaker is very important.

TABLE III

VARIABLES WHICH DISPLAYED A SIGNIFICANT INTERACTION BETWEEN THE "CONTACT" VARIABLE AND THE COMMUNICATOR VARIABLE

Concept	Semantic Differential Scales
Mental hospital	health
Neurotic people	evaluation; predictableness; health
Ex-mental patient	evaluation; safety
Psychotherapy	evaluation; predictableness

Personal versus impersonal treatments apparently had little, if any, effect on attitudes. The means for the two treatments for the Semantic Differential scales and concepts are presented in Table IV. An examination of the table indicates that the two treatments did not produce different attitudes. More findings about the personal versus impersonal variable will be presented in the next section of this chapter.

The results in general for the information questionnaire were not as clear as those for the attitude measures. There were nine items which were directly mentioned in the talk. There were no consistent differences between the various "contact" groups in terms of the information they acquired from the talks. There was a slight difference between the personal and impersonal treatments. There was an impersonal and personal treatment for the early-contact groups, for the late-contact groups, and for the no-contact groups. Considering nine items for each pair of groups, this allows us to make 27 comparisons between the personal and impersonal treatments. In only seven of these comparisons was the impersonal treatment more successful than the personal treatment in terms of moving the groups in the direction advocated by the message. This difference between treatment groups is significant by sign-test at the .05 level of confidence.

Study 2: Personal versus Impersonal Treatments

In numerous places so far in this book we have mentioned the message variable which concerns the personal versus impersonal treatment of topics. Topics can be discussed in such a way as to enlist the active identification of the audience, or they can be discussed in such a way as to let the audience feel remote from the events. We had thought that the variable would play an important part in the communicative effectiveness of messages designed to promote favorable attitudes toward mental-health concepts. In comparing personal and impersonal treatments, however, we have consistently found negative results. An experiment will be described which principally concerned the differential effectiveness of personal and

TABLE IV

MEAN SCORES ON THE SEMANTIC DIFFERENTIAL FOR THE PERSONAL AND THE IMPERSONAL TREATMENTS*

Scales	Personal	Impersonal
Evaluation		
Me	5.95	5.88
Psychotherapy	5.74	5.76
Neurotic people	3.67	3.72
Mental hospital	6.02	5.84
Ex-mental patient	5.58	5.38
Unpredictable-predictable		
Me	4.60	4.62
Psychotherapy	4.04	4.29
Neurotic people	2.13	2.34
Mental hospital	4.01	4.25
Ex-mental patient	4.54	4.33
Sick-healthy		
Me	6.30	6.22
Psychotherapy	4.33	4.04
Neurotic people	1.89	2.06
Mental hospital	3.08	2.90
Ex-mental patient	5.29	5.15
Dangerous-safe		
Me	6.18	6.03
Psychotherapy	5.57	5.75
Neurotic people	3.26	3.48
Mental hospital	5.47	5.11
Ex-mental patient	5.55	5.20

* The means are restricted to the range of 1.00 to 7.00. The higher the mean, the more "positive" the attitude—that is, higher means are associated with ratings of higher *evaluation*, more predictability, more health, or more safety.

impersonal messages.[2] Because the experiment serves only to add further negative evidence regarding the variable, it will be summarized briefly.

Design

Two versions of the same message were composed. One version was made as personal as possible; the other was made as impersonal as possible. One month before the messages were given to the subjects, the subjects were tested on a Semantic Differential form measuring attitudes toward various mental-illness concepts (mental patient, cured mental patient, and others) and toward various "normal" concepts. After the subjects read the messages, the Semantic Differential measures were administered again. Analyses were made of the amounts of attitude change produced by the messages and of the different amounts of change induced by the two versions of the message.

Messages

The personal version of the message described how the reader would react and how he would be treated if he were mentally ill. The impersonal version de-

[2] The study was designed and conducted by Dr. Edward E. Ware.

scribed how other people behave and how they are treated when they become mentally ill. The differences are illustrated by the following paragraph as it appeared in the personal and impersonal versions.

> PERSONAL VERSION   Have you ever thought how it would be if you were mentally ill? How would you behave? Two of the major types of mental illness that you might have are neuroses and psychoses. A neurosis is a type of emotional illness which interferes with your happiness and efficiency. The psychoses are more severe mental illnesses. As a neurotic person you might feel that you are not loved; you might feel guilty, inferior, and inadequate without reason; you might have an almost constant sense of dread and fear. Some of the symptoms you might show are: extreme fears, like fear of high places or closed-in places; tiredness or nervous tension; excessive shyness; sleeplessness; constant fear of physical illness; inability to get along with people. Let us suppose you become psychotic instead of neurotic. In this case you might lose touch with reality and go back to childish behavior. As a psychotic you would generally be placed in a mental hospital for treatment, whereas as a neurotic you would probably be able to continue your daily business while receiving treatment.

> IMPERSONAL VERSION   What is mental illness like and how do mentally-ill people behave? Two of the major types of mental illness are neuroses and psychoses. A neurosis is a type of emotional illness which interferes with a person's happiness and efficiency. The psychoses are more severe mental illnesses. Neurotic people feel that they are not loved; they feel guilty, inferior, and inadequate without reason; they have an almost constant sense of dread and fear. Some of the symptoms shown by neurotics are: extreme fears, like fear of high places or closed-in places; tiredness or nervous tension; excessive shyness; sleeplessness; constant fear of physical illness; inability to get along with people. How does the psychotic differ from the neurotic? The psychotic has lost touch with reality and goes back to childish behavior. The psychotic is generally placed in a mental hospital for treatment, whereas the neurotic generally is able to continue his daily business while receiving treatment.

Subjects and Procedures

High school students were randomly divided into two groups corresponding to the two treatment conditions. The Semantic Differential measure was first applied alone. One month later, the experimenter returned, presented the messages, and re-administered the Semantic Differential form. For the impersonal version of the messages, 37 subjects participated in both the first and second testings. For the personal version, 34 subjects participated in both testings.

Analysis and Results

The Semantic Differential contained scales to measure *evaluation* and *understandability*. In addition, clusters of scales were used to measure "anxiety" and "safety." Means were obtained for each treatment group and for each scale applied to each concept, separately for the two testing occasions. Before-after differences were computed in order to determine the amounts of attitude change. Finally, tests of statistical significance were made on the observed differences.

Both versions of the message produced "favorable" attitude changes which were statistically significant. This was no surprise—most of our experimental messages produced favorable changes.

The important point of the experiment was to determine whether the personal and impersonal treatments produced different amounts of attitude change. The answer is clearly "no." In order to make a thorough test, we applied Hotelling's T statistic, a simultaneous test over all scales and concepts relating to mental illness. The result was not significant. The same statistic was applied to the "normal" concepts employed in the Semantic Differential form: *me, my parents,* and *most people.* Again the statistic was not significant.

On the basis of these results we offer the following proposition: PROPOSITION 2: PERSONAL VERSUS IMPERSONAL TREATMENTS ARE NOT IMPORTANTLY RELATED TO THE EFFECTIVENESS OF COMMUNICATIONS THAT ARE DESIGNED TO PROMOTE FAVORABLE ATTITUDES TOWARD MENTAL-HEALTH CONCEPTS. Ordinarily we do not reach major conclusions on the basis of negative results. In testing personal and impersonal treatments, however, we found negative results in a number of experiments. In the first experiment reported in this chapter personal and impersonal treatments made no significant difference in the amounts of attitude change. Moreover, this variable has little, if any, effect on the public's interest in mental-health topics. If personal and impersonal treatments have an important influence on communicative effectiveness, it is certainly difficult to demonstrate in controlled experiments. It may be that, as was suggested by the results of the "contact" study, the variable influences *information transmission* (amount of learning); but when the major experimental concern is with the variables that influence *attitudes,* as ours is here, it apparently makes little or no difference whether personal or impersonal styles are used.

Study 3: Information and Attitude Change

The primary method of changing attitudes is to supply people with information. For example, you tell people, as we have done in some of our experiments, that schizophrenia is caused by X and is cured by Y. Then you sit back to see whether the new information has a good or a bad effect on attitudes toward the mentally ill and related concepts. Of course the problem is more complicated than that: it is necessary to determine which kinds of facts, presented in which ways, produce which kinds of attitude changes.

In this experiment,[3] an effort was made to learn some of the relations between kinds of information changes and kinds of attitude changes. Four short written messages, each supplying some correct information about one of the ten information factors discussed earlier (1961, Chapter 2) [factors are identified in following section] were distributed to our subjects. After reading one of the messages, each subject completed questionnaires measuring (1) information about mental illness and (2) attitudes toward mental-illness concepts. Analyses were made of the amounts and kinds of information and attitude changes, and comparisons were made between attitude changes and information changes.

Messages

The four messages concerned the factors *look and act different* (I), *will power* (II), *avoidance of morbid thoughts* (IV), and *hopelessness* (VI). These four factors were chosen because they are ones on which experts (psychologists and psychiatrists) are in good agreement. Predominant expert opinion disagrees with the factors. (The "incorrect" pole of each factor was purposely made the high

---

[3] The study was designed and conducted by Dr. Edward E. Ware.

end of the item score. Most of the factors could have easily been reversed, for example, "hopefulness" instead of hopelessness.) Two of the four messages are as follows:

> HOPELESSNESS (FACTOR VI) Mental illness has become an important health problem. Mental illness is a name covering several sicknesses of the mind which affect the way a person thinks, feels, and behaves. There are several misconceptions or mistaken beliefs about mental illness and the mentally ill. Some misinformed people still believe that mental illness is a hopeless condition. The experts, psychiatrists and psychologists, agree that this is not true. Mental illness is not a hopeless condition. Today tens of thousands of patients are being treated successfully. In those hospitals with good facilities where patients are given the best and latest treatments, as many as seven to eight out of ten leave the hospital recovered or definitely improved. With less severe mental disturbances not requiring admission to a mental hospital, the recovery rates are, of course, much higher.

> WILL POWER (FACTOR II) Mental illness has become an important health problem. Mental illness is a name covering several sicknesses of the mind which affect the way a person thinks, feels, and behaves. There are several misconceptions or mistaken beliefs about mental illness and the mentally ill. Some misinformed people still believe that mental illness is caused largely by lack of will power. The experts, psychiatrists and psychologists, agree that this is not true. People do not become mentally ill because they have little will power. Some of the strongest-willed people become mentally ill. Telling a mentally ill person to use his will power to cure himself is like telling a person with a fever to use his will power without giving him medical help. Will power alone will not cure mental illness. Most mentally ill people are incapable of controlling their thoughts and feelings. They need scientific treatment in order to get well.

Measures

The amount of information the subjects obtained from the messages was measured by our revised information questionnaire. (The revised questionnaire grew out of our standard 50-item information questionnaire.) Two of the questionnaire items were used to measure each of the four factors. For example, to measure the *hopelessness* factor, the following two items were used: "There is not much that can be done for a person who develops mental disorder" and "Mental disorder is not a hopeless condition." Questionnaire items that were not related to any of the four factors were used to test for generalization of information.

To measure attitudes, a Semantic Differential form was used. Scales were employed to measure the factors of *evaluation* and *understandability*, and groups of scales were combined to measure "anxiety" and "dangerousness." Six concepts relating to mental illness were used: mental patient, mental hospital, cured mental patient, insane person, psychiatrist, and methods for the treatment of mental patients.

Subjects and Procedures

The subjects were 330 high school students, randomly divided into five groups. Four groups read one of the four messages; the fifth, a control group, received no message. The numbers of subjects in a group ranged from 63 to 71.

Our routine experimental procedure was applied. Students were supplied with self-explanatory test booklets. For four of the five groups, the first section of the test booklet contained one of the four messages about mental illness. For the control group, the test booklet introduced the student directly to the information questionnaire and the Semantic Differential form.

Analysis and Results

INFORMATION   As we were sure they would, the messages affected information as evidenced on the information questionnaire. Differences between the four experimental groups and the control group were all in the predicted direction. Three of these were statistically significant either at or beyond the .05 level by t-test. The difference for the message pertaining to the *hopelessness* factor was not significant. (In the analysis of results we discovered an "end effect" for the *hopelessness* factor: the students as a whole disagreed so strongly with the factor that there was little room for improvement.)

Information pertaining to any one factor did not generalize to information pertaining to other factors. For example, the students who read the message pertaining to the *look and act different* factor did perform differently from the control group on items pertaining to that factor; but they did not perform differently from the control group on items pertaining to other factors represented in the information questionnaire. The failure for any generalization to occur is what we expected. The items principally concerned knowledge about mental illness, and consequently, generalization is not expected. (In contrast we expect and usually find generalization of changes in attitudes. For example, in one study we found that a message about the treatment of schizophrenia generalized to the improvement of attitudes toward psychiatrists, who were not mentioned in the message.)

ATTITUDES   Mean Semantic Differential ratings were obtained for each group of scales for each concept. As we expected, the messages about mental illness resulted in different attitude ratings than those found in the control group. Some of the statistically significant differences are shown in Table V.

TABLE V

ATTITUDE CHANGES OCCURRING IN RESPONSE TO MESSAGES CONCERNING INFORMATION ABOUT MENTAL ILLNESS*

Message Concerning Factor	Attitude Changes Induced by Message
I. Look and act different	*Psychiatrist* rated more anxious.
II. Will power	*Mental patient* rated lower on *evaluation* and predictability and higher on anxiety.
	Mental hospital rated more predictable and less dangerous.
	Insane person rated more anxious.
	Methods for the treatment of mental patients rated less dangerous.
III. Avoidance of morbid thoughts	*Mental patient* rated less predictable.
	Mental hospital rated less dangerous.
IV. Hopelessness	*Mental hospital* rated more predictable and less dangerous.
	Cured mental patient rated more predictable and less anxious.

* Attitude changes are defined as differences from a control group which were statistically significant beyond the .05 level.

Table V contains an interesting finding: the messages did not always have "good" effects on attitudes. For example, the message pertaining to the *will power* factor had an over-all "bad" effect on attitudes toward the concept mental patient. This demonstrates that correct information can sometimes defeat the purpose of the communication by bringing about unfavorable changes in attitudes.

We think we know why the messages about mental illness had some "bad" effects on attitudes. The messages were not well controlled for content variables such as anxiety, solution, certainty, and destruction of information. Our principal oversight in this study (we think) was to "destroy" information, which promotes unfavorable attitudes toward mental-illness concepts. For example, in the message concerning the *will power* factor (quoted previously) we told students that "will power" was not the answer but we supplied them with no positive information to replace what was "destroyed." Consequently, although the information in the four messages was correct, the failure to control for important content variables led to some unfavorable changes in attitudes. The notable exception is the message relating to the *hopelessness* factor, where we did supply positive information. For that message, the attitude changes are predominantly favorable.

Although more clear-cut results in other respects might have been obtained from this study had we more carefully controlled some of the important content variables, the results here serve to illustrate a common mistake in applied programs of communication. It is commonly assumed that as long as the communication is about an important issue and as long as the audience "learns" something from the communication, favorable attitudes develop toward related concepts. As the results here illustrate, however, this is not always an effective communication strategy. Even if the information in the communication is correct and even if the audience actually learns the information, the failure to control for important content variables may induce unfavorable attitudes. Thus we are able to come to the following conclusion: PROPOSITION 3: IF IMPORTANT CONTENT VARIABLES ARE NOT CONTROLLED, CORRECT INFORMATION SOMETIMES PRODUCES UNFAVORABLE CHANGES IN ATTITUDES. . . . [T]he converse also holds: false information can be very effective in promoting favorable attitudes if content variables are properly manipulated.

Summary

This chapter reported experimental studies which tested for the importance of three variables in communicative effectiveness: "contact" with an identified source, personal versus impersonal styling of messages, and the relationship between changes in information and changes in attitudes.

The first experiment tested for the effect of "contact" with a former mental patient on attitude change. When we compared the effectiveness of three different approaches—no contact, early contact, and late contact—we found that, if used at all, contact (in this case, identifying the source of a message as a former mental patient) is better made *after* the body of the message has been delivered.

A number of studies reported in this book dealt with a potentially important message-treatment variable: personal versus impersonal styling. In none of the studies did this variable produce differences in amount and kinds of attitude change. Differences in attitudes attributable to the personal versus impersonal styling of verbal communications were examined as an incidental aspect of the first experiment discussed in this chapter, and no significant differences were found. The second experiment discussed here was specifically designed to test the effect of personal versus impersonal styling. The results were uniformly negative and support our earlier results. Although personal and impersonal styling may influence the acquisition of *information*, or retention, and some results from our experiments suggest that this is so, such differences in treatment apparently have very little effect on *attitude* change.

The third experiment reported here explored the correlations between changes in information and changes in attitudes. Our major finding sustained our hypothesis: changes in information do not generalize beyond the information factor relating to the message. This is in contrast to changes in attitudes, where generalization usually occurs.

This experiment yielded a surprising discovery. Some of the "correct" information contained in the messages led to some *unfavorable* changes in attitudes toward mental-health concepts. We attributed this to our failure to control for several important content variables. This finding illustrates a common fallacy about the effectiveness of communications: even correct information may not effect the desired change in attitudes.

42 / An Interpretive Overview

Jum C. Nunnally, Jr.

The reader who has faithfully followed our research to this point is probably asking himself, "What does it all mean?" We will try to give at least a partial answer to that question. Because of the number, diversity, and bulk of the studies, a complete summary of the results would consume too much space. Instead, this chapter will present what we believe to be some of the most important implications of the total research.

It is hoped that in previous chapters we stuck fairly close to the actual research results and did not overly interpret the meaning of particular findings. Here we will let our hair down and make some broad interpretations; such interpretations should be considered mainly as food for future studies.

The Public

Information

In studying what the public knows and thinks about mental-health problems, we could foresee only two possible results: (1) the public is *misinformed*, in the sense that the "average man" holds numerous misconceptions about mental illness, or (2) the public is *uninformed,* in the sense that the average man has little information, correct or incorrect, about many of the problems. It was, and is, inconceivable to us that the average man could be *well informed.* If he were, it would present a curious paradox: because so much is yet to be discovered, even psychologists and psychiatrists are not well informed in the absolute sense.

Our results show clearly that the average man is not grossly misinformed. That is, it is difficult to document specific misconceptions which are widely held by the public. Consequently, the major job in future communication programs will be to fill in the voids where people are uninformed.

Partially because of the anxiety associated with mental-health topics and partially because of the lack of semantic referents for his terms (for example, "neurotic"), the average man does not systematically learn about mental-health phenomena from daily experience. What information he has exists largely as an abstract system. Although the average man swims in a sea of mental-health phenomena, he usually does not catalogue them as such. Consequently, the abstract system is neither confirmed nor denied.

The average man is relatively unsure of his opinions about mental-health phenomena. Consequently, he eagerly looks to experts for "the answers." We found that people do not resist new information, even when that information is plainly incorrect. In general, we found that people will accept almost any seemingly factual and authoritative-sounding information on mental health.

Attitudes

It is commonly asserted that people attach a stigma to the mentally ill. Our research results leave little doubt that the stigma exists. The most important finding from our studies of public attitudes is that the stigma is very general, both across social groups and across attitude indicators. There is a strong "negative halo" associated with the mentally ill. They are considered, unselectively, as being all things "bad." Some of the "bad" attitudes that people have toward the mentally ill are partially supported by the facts—for example, the mentally ill sometimes *are* unpredictable and dangerous. However, the average man generalizes to the point of considering the mentally ill as dirty, unintelligent, insincere, and worthless. Such unselectively negative attitudes are probably due in part to a lack of information about mental illness and a failure to observe and learn about mental-illness phenomena in daily life.

Our research suggests some of the dynamics of public attitudes toward the mentally ill. One of the cornerstones of public attitudes is the feeling that the mentally ill are highly unpredictable. The mentally ill are thought to be people who do not go by the "rules" and who, because of their erratic behavior, may suddenly embarrass or endanger others. The feeling is like that of sitting next to a temperamental explosive which may detonate without warning. Consequently, most people are very uncomfortable in the presence of someone who is, or is purported to be, mentally ill.

Public attitudes toward psychologists, psychiatrists, and other mental-treatment specialists are evidently not as "bad" as is commonly suspected. The public holds moderately high, favorable attitudes toward mental specialists *as individuals.* What is "wrong" with public attitudes is a moderate distrust and devaluing of mental-treatment methods and institutions. Consequently, the emphasis in information programs should be on improving attitudes toward the tools and methods used by mental specialists.

Interests

Public interest in mental-health topics varies considerably with the topic and with the way in which the topic is treated in communications. Most of the interest is not due to intellectual curiosity, as it is, for example, with information about space flight. Instead, the interest is motivated by a somewhat panicky "need to know." The public is mainly interested in information about mental health of a kind that will relieve immediate personal threats. The public will reject (e.g., not continue to read) messages that raise anxiety and do not supply "solutions." One of the difficulties in preparing a program of public information is designing messages that contain reasonably simple facts about mental-health phenomena and how-to-do-it rules for handling problems; but this is what the public wants.

The Experts

If experts had a more definitive body of knowledge about mental-health problems, and if they could agree on particular points, the job of communicating with the public would be immensely simplified. We found reasonably good agreement among experts about some things that should be said in a program of public information about mental-health problems. In our studies, however, we dealt only with the relatively narrow range of ideas with which the public is presently familiar. What is needed now is to determine what *new* things can be told to the public. One approach to this problem would be to ask psychiatrists and psychologists to compile a list of facts, or near-facts, that can be communicated to the public about the causes, symptoms, treatment, and social effects of mental-health problems. Such a list might provide many new things to tell the public, or it might prove to be embarrassingly short.

General practitioners of medicine play an important role in the treatment of mental-health problems. They act as "gatekeepers" between the public and the mental specialists. It is often the general practitioner who determines whether or not a patient sees a mental specialist, and if so, what type of specialist he consults. Equally important as the number of referrals that they make are the number of mental cases that general practitioners treat themselves. It remains to be determined what kinds of cases general practitioners treat and what kinds of treatment they give. One of our most important findings was that the younger, better-informed physicians tend to have "better" attitudes toward mental patients; and it is this type of general practitioner who is more likely to treat mental problems instead of referring them to mental specialists.

The Mass Media

If the average man uncritically accepted the information contained and implied in mass-media presentations, he would indeed be misinformed. In those cases where media presentations are specifically designed to enlighten the public and where expert advice and cooperation are available, the results are often quite good. Such presentations, however, comprise only a minute proportion of the total "information" relating to mental-health phenomena carried by the media. Most of the information is obliquely woven into dramatic presentations, for example, the suggestion that a healthy person can be driven insane after a rather short exposure to a frustrating or frightening situation.

Evidently, presentations of mental-health problems in the mass media have been stylized to fit the requirements of fiction and drama. The symptoms of mental illness are exaggerated, the causes and treatment are greatly oversimplified and often erroneous, and mental illness usually appears in a context of "horror," sin, and violence. The "cognitive," or informational, implications of such presentations are either so amorphous and contradictory, or so obviously incorrect, that the average man is not particularly affected—he knows better. The affective, or attitudinal, implications may be strong, however, because they closely match the attitudes that the public holds toward the mentally ill.

Mass-media personnel are not to be "blamed" for the nature of presentations relating to mental-health problems. Their primary business is not to educate the public but to entertain, in the broad sense of the word, and that must be done at a profit. Because of the subtle way in which mental-health "information" is woven into programs, and because of the many hands that shape such presentations, even if the media tried to "control" they would find it very difficult. When media personnel try to promote "better" presentations, they often obtain confusing and contradictory advice from mental experts, and the experts are often loathe to cooperate.

We are not sure what should, or could, be done to utilize more effectively the mass media in programs of mental-health information. Because of the faddism that dominates the media, it is doubtful that any sustained drive will be exerted by the media personnel unless they are encouraged and helped by professional societies and other organizations concerned with mental-health problems. We did come up with one solution, though half in jest: Some organization might finance a "good" soap opera, to be produced cooperatively by experts and media personnel and specifically intended to enlighten the public about mental-health problems as well as to be entertaining. Many such programs, in forms suitable to the different media, might go a long way toward providing the public with better information and developing better attitudes toward mental-health phenomena.

Communication Strategies

The Topic

The topic itself constitutes an important variable in selecting communication strategies. Thus, very different strategies might be needed in order to communicate about labor-management relations than about mental illness. This does not mean that no general science of communication is possible and that communication strategy is chaotically dependent on particular topics. Communication strategy in general consists of promoting interest, satisfying human needs, providing desired information, verbal conditioning, and so on. Before strategies for communicating about a particular topic can be established, it is necessary to determine where that topic presently resides in a nexus of psychological variables. For example, does information about the particular topic supply a pertinent human need? In this section will be summarized some research results which serve to index mental-health information in terms of its communicative properties.

Some of the points relating to this section were mentioned in earlier sections of this chapter. To reiterate: (1) People know very little, and are unsure of what they think; (2) people want to obtain more information about mental health, but their interest is largely restricted to learning ways to meet or avoid threatening situations; (3) people do not systematically gather information from their daily experiences or do not catalogue their experiences as pertaining to mental health, and (4) people want authoritative answers but seldom get them from mass-media presentations, nor do they obtain "closure" from what the experts say.

Another important feature of mental-health topics is that they tend to generate anxiety. People are uneasy when they hear or read about emotional disturbance, neurosis, mental hospitals, hallucinations, psychotherapy, and many other related matters. The reduction of that anxiety is a primary route to increasing public interest and promoting favorable attitudes.

Mental-health topics are beset by a "language" problem. A number of things are wrong with the available terminology: (1) there is a shortage of terms, (2) the terms bear strong negative connotations, and (3) the terms suggest misleading explanations of mental-health phenomena. These "language" problems limit the effectiveness of some communication strategies. For example, in our experiments we found it nearly impossible to promote more favorable attitudes toward the concept *insane man*. When we translated the term to *mental-hospital patient*, however, we obtained favorable changes in attitudes. Until more is done to develop a suitable terminology, it will be very difficult to undertake effective large-scale programs of public information. We need a lexicon for communicating about mental-health problems, one that is based on agreement among experts and on research evidence concerning the suitability of particular terms.

Information Transmission

Apparently it is very easy to get people to accept new facts about mental-health problems. People will gobble up any seemingly factual and authoritative-sounding information. Indeed, we were surprised to learn the extent to which explanations could be oversimplified and distorted, and still accepted as true. Among high school students in psychology courses, we were surprised to find huge changes in information (expressed opinions) during the semester. Consequently, for the purpose of transmitting new information, strategy is not an important consideration. In that case, strategy largely concerns rhetorical skill, journalistic niceties, and the maintenance of interest. However, the type of information given to people will very much affect the *attitudes* that they hold, and, consequently, the choice of information to communicate becomes an important aspect of attitude-change strategy.

Attitude Change

In many communication experiments, the effort is to *convince* people to hold opinions (information) that are different from those which they held initially. As was said above, there is little difficulty in convincing people to hold new ideas in the mental-health domain. The widespread "bad" attitudes are not held *because* of existing information, but rather because of the *lack* of it. Early in our research, we hypothesized that to relieve the threat associated with mental-health problems the important ingredient is for people to *think* that they have a valid system of information regardless of its real validity. Our research results tended to bear out this hypothesis. We found that the mere act of *changing* from one set of opinions to another (scrambling information) promoted favorable attitudes toward the mentally ill and toward treatment specialists and methods. This was so even though the new "information" was in many cases less correct than what had been believed initially. Although we do not know how long people can be "fooled" in this way, the results illustrate the comfort that people obtain from having, or thinking they have, mental armament against anxiety-provoking problems.

It should not be implied that *any* communication will have the desired effect. Messages must actually contain information—understandable statements about factual or potentially factual matters. According to this definition, many messages contain little or no information. Instead, they (1) say little that people can understand, (2) ask questions rather than give answers, (3) "destroy" what information people have rather than provide new information, or (4) make exhortative appeals for people to develop better attitudes. Even if messages actually do contain information, that information must have certain optimum properties before it will produce the desired effect. It should usually be related to some problem-solving aspect of mental health. That is, it should help people in some way to cope with mental-health problems. Much of the information currently given to the public does not serve that function; for example, telling people that half the hospital beds in this country are filled with mental patients raises anxiety but does not help them to deal with the problem.

In toto our studies show that the factual content of messages is important largely to the extent that it induces a proper *emotional state*. A message will promote favorable attitudes toward mental-health concepts if (1) the concepts are visible in the message (directly mentioned) or associated with visible concepts (generalization), (2) the message has a high interest-value, (3) the message is thought to come from an authoritative source (e.g., a university or a psychiatrist), and (4) the message makes the reader feel *secure* by sounding certain, by providing solutions, by presenting an understandable explanation, and by reducing anxiety in other ways. If these content characteristics are present, people will develop more favorable attitudes and will be more open to continued learning about mental-health phenomena. If these characteristics are not present, no amount of sermonizing, haranguing, or factual presentation will work, and it would be better not to communicate at all.

43 / The Effects of Sound Films on Opinions about Mental Illness in Community Discussion Groups

Elliott McGinnies / Robert Lana / Clagett Smith

Research concerning the effects of mass communications on attitudes and opinions has generated a rather perplexing set of results. Despite common belief that the mass media exert a profound influence upon the manners and morals of recipients, evidence to this effect is still fragmentary and controversial. Early investigators in the area of motion picture films, for example, have reported not only immediate but persisting attitude changes following exposure to a single film. The findings of Peterson and Thurstone (1933), who used films to induce changes in the attitudes of children on such topics as nationality, crime, and war, are typical of results reported in this area. These investigators further reported that a series of films was sometimes successful in inducing attitude change where a single film had failed. Hoban and van Ormer (n.d.), on the other hand, have examined studies done with Army training films and educational films and have concluded that a single communication produces only a temporary effect upon attitudes, if any. Fearing (n.d.), who expresses scepticism with respect to the usefulness of films for this purpose, states that ". . . research, conducted as carefully as we know how to conduct it, reveals that the effects of these media—films and radio, especially films—on human attitudes and behavior is unexpectedly slight." Factual knowledge, however, as many studies have shown, can effectively be imparted by the use of instructional films (Hoban and van Ormer (n.d.).

Evidence has also been presented to show that group discussion facilitates learning, attitude change, and readiness to make a decision with respect to communicated material. Hovland, Janis, and Kelley (1953) suggest the possibility that acceptance as well as learning may be affected by eliciting overt verbalizations about a persuasive communication. They state, "When an individual verbalizes an idea to others he becomes more inclined to accept it himself." Bennett (1953) has concluded that the function of a group discussion is to "facilitate decision and/or the perception of consensus. . . ." Somewhat more tangential evidence for the efficacy of group discussion under these conditions comes from a study by Timmons (1939), who found that individuals allowed to discuss a problem in a small group obtained solutions superior to those of persons who did not discuss the material.

In light of the possibility that motion picture films may under some circumstances be effective persuasive devices, the present study was undertaken for

From the *Journal of Applied Psychology*, 1958, **42**, 40–46. Copyright © 1958. Reprinted by permission of the authors and the American Psychological Association.

the purpose of evaluating the effects of one or more mental health films in adult community groups. A questionnaire covering opinions and beliefs with respect to mental illness was given to groups before and after exposure to a single film or to a series of films. In order to determine whether active participation would facilitate any effects of the films, discussions were held in half of the groups following film presentations and prior to the second administration of the opinion inventory.

The hypotheses examined in these experiments were as follows:

1. A single mental health film presented to an audience without discussion will significantly influence opinions about mental illness.
2. Group discussion of a single film will facilitate opinion change as compared with the nondiscussion situation.
3. A series of three mental health films presented without discussion will result in greater opinion change than that generated by a single film under the same conditions.
4. Group discussion following each of a series of three films will bring about greater opinion change than under nondiscussion conditions.

Experiment One

Method

SUBJECTS   Six small groups totaling 76 individuals were formed from larger P.T.A. and child-study groups in Prince Georges County, Maryland. Four of these groups, varying in size from 11 to 18 members, were shown a series of mental health films. Two additional groups containing nine members each served as controls. In general, the group members were drawn from the upper middle class segment of the population and were fairly homogeneous with respect to age and education. Several of the groups contained both men and women, while the remainder were composed entirely of women. Since there is no evidence to indicate that sex is systematically related to susceptibility to a persuasive communication, no attempt was made to balance this factor over all of the groups. The mean age of the Ss was 38.8 years, they enjoyed on the average 2.8 years of college education, their mean family income was $7,800, and 63 per cent identified their occupation as "housewife." On a nine-point self-rating scale of "familiarity with mental health problems and concepts" they assigned themselves a mean scale value of 4.5.

MATERIALS   The films selected for study were *The Feeling of Rejection, The Feeling of Hostility,* and *Breakdown.* The first two deal with etiology of personality disturbance, while the third is concerned with institutional treatment of psychotic disorders. All three films were produced by the National Film Board of Canada and are widely used in mental health education programs.

In order to construct an instrument that would enable us to assess the opinions and beliefs of the Ss with respect to various aspects of mental illness, we first assembled a pool of 112 relevant statements derived from several sources (National Opinion Research Center, 1950; Nunnally, 1954; Ramsey and Seipp, 1948a; Woodward, 1951). The statements dealt in general with the etiology, perception and prognosis, treatment, and posttreatment perception of mental illness.

A questionnaire consisting of these items was initially administered to 157 students in psychology and sociology at the University of Maryland. Item analysis employing Flanagan's approximation method (Flanagan, 1939) justified reduction of the questionnaire to 72 statements. Repetition of this procedure with adult groups yielded a final list of 47 items. Test-retest reliability of this form on samples of university students and adult P.T.A. groups was about .86. A split-half reliability coefficient of .33 was obtained from an independent sample using the Spearman-Brown formula. Responses to the statements were made on a five-point rating scale ranging from "strongly agree" to "strongly disagree," and the method of summated ratings was used to obtain individual scores. Following are examples of the types of items included on the form:

1. It is better not to discuss a mental illness as one would a physical illness.
2. Few of the people who seek psychiatric help need the treatment.
3. An employer should avoid hiring someone who has been in a mental hospital.
4. Nervous breakdowns are due to overwork.

Scoring of the items are based upon the responses of 12 staff members and graduate trainees at the University of Maryland Counseling Center. A high score was obtained by S if his responses were in the same direction as those expressed by these "experts." A low score indicated disagreement with this professional opinion. As nearly as could be determined, the opinions and beliefs of our panel of professionals coincided with the general points made in the films. It should be noted that we do not refer to the measuring instrument as an "attitude scale," since we have little evidence that the assumptions underlying a true scale have been met. Experience with the questionnaire, however, has indicated that it does measure reliably certain beliefs and opinions that people hold with respect to various aspects of mental illness. We shall refer to the questionnaire as the "Mental Health Opinion Inventory."

The range of possible scores on the inventory was 47–235. If S checked the middle, or indeterminate, position for each statement he would achieve a total score of 141, indicating neither agreement nor disagreement with professional opinion. A total score on all items of 188 would indicate *agreement* but not *strong agreement* with expert opinion. Since the group mean pretest scores ranged from 163.5 to 184.9, it is apparent that our Ss were initially somewhat predisposed toward professional judgment on the scale items. Our experience, however, has been that in groups of the types studied it is exceedingly difficult to discover opinions about mental health issues that are markedly naive or inaccurate. The individuals who would be most likely to score low on questionnaires of this type are precisely those persons who do not participate in community activities designed for educational purposes. In the present instance, the goal of the communicator is limited to overcoming certain misconceptions that exist among groups of interested persons who otherwise are fairly well-informed about mental health problems.

A biographical questionnaire was also given to all Ss in the experiments so that we could determine whether the groups were comparable with respect to a number of socioeconomic criteria. As indicated earlier, no serious discrepancies appeared among the several groups in this respect.

PROCEDURE Two of the groups viewed the three films at bi-weekly intervals. Each film presentation was followed by a half-hour discussion of the film or of related topics. The same discussion leader, a professional psychologist, met all of the groups in order to control any effects that the leader's personality might have upon the discussion process. In order to permit the fullest expression of individual opinion by the group members, a permissive or nondirective approach was taken by the discussion leader. At the outset of the meetings, the groups were informed that the discussions would be recorded. No further mention was made of this, and most of the Ss later appeared oblivious to the fact that a tape-recording was being made. The recording apparatus was always operated from the rear of the room, and the microphones were strategically located before the Ss assembled. A fuller description of this procedure is reported elsewhere (McGinnies, 1956). The Mental Health Opinion Inventory was administered before the first film was shown and at the conclusion of the third discussion.

The same procedure was followed for two additional groups except that discussion of the films was omitted from the meetings. In order to control for expectancy of discussion and the possible effects of this upon perception of the films, these groups were told that they would discuss all three films at the conclusion of the final screening. They were allowed to do this only after they had completed the inventory for the second time, so that the discussion could have no effect upon the measurement of opinion change.

Two control groups simply responded twice to the inventory, with a four-week interval between administrations.

Results

It had been predicted that opinions and beliefs about mental illness, as reflected in responses to the Mental Health Opinion Inventory, would be altered as a result of exposure to the film series. It was also hypothesized that opinion change would be greater in those groups that had discussed the films as com-

TABLE I

PRETEST, POSTTEST, AND DIFFERENCE SCORES FOR ALL GROUPS

Group	Pretest		Posttest		Group Mean Difference	Treatment Mean Difference
	M	SD	M	SD		
Film-discussion I N = 16	163.5	18.6	183.1	16.0	19.6	
Film-discussion II N = 18	184.9	17.8	198.0	14.2	13.1	16.4
Film-alone I N = 13	174.6	26.4	186.5	23.7	11.9	
Film-alone II N = 11	173.1	19.5	191.9	10.7	18.8	15.4
Control I N = 9	174.7	15.6	171.7	17.8	−3.0	
Control II N = 9	169.8	17.8	173.7	19.1	3.9	.5

pared with the groups that were given no opportunity for discussion. Discrepancies between scores on the pre- and posttreatment administrations of the inventory were taken as measures of opinion change. Table I shows the mean scores for all of the groups before and after experimental treatment. Positive difference scores indicate movement in the direction of professional opinion on the questionnaire.

Before testing for the effects of treatment upon opinions and beliefs about mental illness, the difference scores for the two groups within each treatment were examined for heterogeneity of variance and for differences between means. In all cases, the two groups representing each treatment did not differ significantly in either of these respects. The within-treatment groups, therefore, were combined in assessing over-all effects of experimental procedure upon opinion change. These treatment means are shown in Table I. It is apparent that both the film-alone and film-discussion groups were influenced by the experimental conditions, while the control groups made approximately the same scores on both administrations of the inventory.

TABLE II

ANALYSIS OF VARIANCE ON ADJUSTED POSTTEST SCORES
(COVARIANCE METHOD)

Source	df	Sum of Squares	Mean Square	F	P
Between	2	3,562.4	1781.2	17.10	< .001
Within	73	7,604.0	104.2		
Total	75	11,166.4			

In order to control for differences among the groups in initial opinion, analysis of covariance of the mean opinion change scores was employed. The results of this analysis are summarized in Table II. Treatment effects, as indicated in the table, were significant beyond the .001 level. To determine the specific sources of this between-treatment variance, three analysis of covariance t tests were performed. This test involves weighting the denominators of the conventional t ratios by the coefficient of alienation of the entire sample. Of the three possible comparisons, two were significant. Both the film-discussion and the film-alone groups differed significantly at the .001 level from the control groups. The third comparison, that between the film-discussion and the film-alone conditions, was not significant at the .05 level. Participation through group discussion of the films did not enhance the effects of the films so far as changes in opinion scores were concerned.

In order to examine the possibility that a "consensus" effect might have been generated in the discussion groups, even though this was not reflected in greater opinion change, the variances of pre- and posttreatment inventory scores were compared for the various experimental conditions. In no instances did the variances differ between groups, either before or after treatment, indicating that convergence of opinions following exposure to the film series was no greater under discussion than under nondiscussion conditions.

The possibility now remained that one of the films was responsible for the obtained opinion changes. It had been determined, for example, that the groups tended to prefer the film *Breakdown* the most and *The Feeling of Rejection* the least. It was also conceivable that discussion had failed to summate with the effects of the films because the accumulated impact of the film series produced a maximum effect by itself. A further study, therefore, was designed to determine (*a*) whether one of the three films was responsible for most of the measured effects upon opinion, and (*b*) whether group discussion would generate greater opinion change as compared with nondiscussion conditions when a single film rather than a series of films was used.

Experiment Two

Method

SUBJECTS   A total of 64 individuals forming six groups participated in this study. The groups varied in size from 8 to 13 members. Since they were recruited from the same types of P.T.A. and child-study groups as the Ss in Experiment One, they were similar in all important respects to the participants in that study. The mean age of the Ss was 38.3, they had attained an average of 2.5 years of college education, their mean family income was $7,280, and 76 per cent identified themselves as "housewives." On the nine-point self-rating scale of familiarity with mental health problems they achieved a mean scale value of 4.1.

MATERIALS   The films, biographical questionnaire, and Mental Health Opinion Inventory were the same as those used in the first experiment. In this first instance, however, the films were shown singly rather than as a series.

PROCEDURE   In order to make the interval between administrations of the opinion inventory comparable to that of the previous investigation, the first testing was done at a regularly scheduled meeting of each group. The experimental sessions were held one month later, at the conclusion of which the post-treatment measures were taken. Each of the three films previously described was shown to a different group, the members of which engaged in discussion of the film with the same leader who had served in Experiment One. At the conclusion of the discussions they filled out the opinion inventory to which they had first responded four weeks earlier.

The remaining three groups each viewed one of the films and were posttested on the questionnaire without discussion. Since the previous study had shown that no opinion changes could be expected in groups which were not experimentally treated, it was considered unnecessary to include this type of control in the design. The principal concern of this study was to determine the effectiveness of a single film with and without discussion upon changes in opinions and beliefs about mental illness. Since the same three films were used as in the first experiment and were randomly assigned to the participating groups, it was expected that any differences in their relative effectiveness would appear in the pre- and posttreatment opinion measures. Any interaction between number of films shown and opportunity for discussion by the audience members would be revealed in differences between the film-alone and film-discussion groups, no such differences having been obtained with a three-film series.

TABLE III

PRETEST, POSTTEST, AND DIFFERENCE SCORES FOR ALL GROUPS

	Pretest		Posttest		Mean
	M	SD	M	SD	Difference
Film A*-discussion N = 13	165.3	23.9	171.4	18.9	6.1
Film A-alone N = 8	158.1	21.5	158.5	22.2	.4
Film B†-discussion N = 13	169.9	19.8	171.8	17.4	1.9
Film B-alone N = 8	155.0	15.6	169.5	17.2	14.5
Film C‡-discussion N = 11	168.5	18.7	167.4	19.5	−1.2
Film C-alone N = 11	171.3	18.4	175.9	16.4	4.6

* Film A = *The Feeling of Hostility.*
† Film B = *Breakdown.*
‡ Film C = *The Feeling of Rejection.*

Results

The initial and posttreatment scores of the various groups, together with the mean difference scores, are shown in Table III. It will be noted from the table that the range of mean group pretest scores is somewhat less than in Experiment One, ranging in this instance from 155.0 to 169.9. The mean score for these Ss is also somewhat lower than for those participating in the first study. Since these individuals were further from the ceiling of the measuring instrument than the Ss in the prior experiment, they might have been expected to change more readily under persuasive influence, which in this case consisted of a single film rather than a series of three films.

In order to discover whether any over-all differences existed among the various groups, an analysis of covariance was done on the opinion-change scores. The F test, as indicated in Table IV, was not significant at the .05 level, and the null hypothesis of no differences among the six groups is accepted.

To determine whether any of the mean difference scores from pre- to post-treatment were significantly greater than zero, six analysis of covariance t tests

TABLE IV

ANALYSIS OF VARIANCE ON ADJUSTED POSTTEST SCORES
(COVARIANCE METHOD)

Source	df	Sum of Squares	Mean Square	F	P
Between	5	992.4	198.5	1.05	> .05
Within	57	10,774.3	189.0		
Total	62	11,766.7			

were performed. Only one of the groups, the film-alone group viewing *Breakdown*, showed a significant change in mean opinion score following treatment. It would be unjustified on the basis of this one significant finding to conclude that a single mental health film, with or without discussion, is capable of influencing opinions about mental illness. Noteworthy, however, is the fact that five of the six groups showed opinion-change scores in the direction supported by the films, even though just one of these changes is significant. The insignificant *F* test for between-group treatments indicates that the discussions added nothing to the measured effectiveness of the films in the present study.

Discussion

Considering the results of both experiments, it is apparent that only one of our original hypotheses has been confirmed, namely, that a series of three mental health films presented without discussion will result in greater opinion change than that generated by a single film under the same conditions. In fact, only one of three films shown singly was effective in modifying scores on a questionnaire dealing with opinions about mental illness, and this was under nondiscussion conditions. While a series of three films proved useful in bringing opinions about mental illness more in line with professional thinking, discussions following each film in the series failed to augment this effect.

What do these findings imply for the use of mental health films in educational programs as well as for questions concerning the susceptibility of opinions and attitudes in general to influence through motion pictures? For one thing, the findings in these two studies suggest strongly that a series of films dealing with a common topic may be effective modifiers of opinions where a single film is likely to produce no measurable result. It should be noted, of course, that none of the films used here had a running time of more than 40 minutes. The rather dramatic results in attitude change obtained by Peterson and Thurstone (1933) may be attributable in part to the fact that they employed full-length Hollywood productions with considerable emotional impact. Educational-indoctrination films, such as those used by the armed forces and those in the present study, are generally limited in both scope and dramatic appeal. It is not surprising, then, that the effects of these more conservative productions upon attitudes and beliefs are often difficult to detect, and that a single presentation is apt to produce no measurable changes.

The failure of active participation to facilitate opinion change in the two investigations reported here may be due to several factors. First, the discussions were permitted to develop along any lines suggested by the group members. In general, the discussions centered about the characters and plots of the film rather than about mental health problems in general, so that generalization from the films to the more discursive items on the questionnaire was probably minimized. A second and more probable explanation for the failure of the discussions to implement the impact of the films is that the films by themselves induced as much opinion change as might reasonably be expected in audiences of this type. The participants in these studies were all of superior educational and economic status, as are most active members of community groups formed voluntarily for self-education. Consequently, their initial reactions to the questionnaire items were oriented in the direction of those expressed by our panel of professionals who provided us with anchoring points for the scoring system. That the group members moved further in this direction following treatment is a tribute to the effectiveness of the films; to expect even greater change as a result of group discussion is perhaps unreal.

It should not be concluded from these findings that group discussion has no salutary effects in conjunction with film presentations. There was noticeable discontent among some members of the film-alone groups, who mildly resented being dismissed without an opportunity to talk about the film that they had just seen. Even the promise of an organized discussion at the conclusion of the film series did not completely allay these complaints. It has been our experience that community groups welcome a chance for discussion of films of this type, but it also is important to note that the instructional value of the film does not seem to rest upon a related discussion. Whether discussions of a different type, for example, those held under a directive leader, would be more effective in influencing attitude change remains a subject for experimental determination.

A final comment with respect to certain methodological problems encountered in research of this sort may be useful. Sampling is necessarily subject to some serious limitations. It is virtually impossible to assign individuals randomly to treatments when dealing with adults who are under no compulsion to appear at scheduled times or to meet in inconvenient places. Groups must be located and persuaded to participate in the research project, and it is frequently difficult to schedule a series of meetings with the same individuals in attendance. While it would have been highly desirable to include more groups under the several conditions of these experiments, these practical considerations militated against such a procedure. Statistical controls, therefore, must frequently be exerted where experimental controls are lacking.

Despite these limitations, we feel reasonably confident in concluding: (a) that motion picture films shown in a coherent series can significantly modify opinions and beliefs, and (b) that a series of mental health films shown with or without audience participation through organized discussion are effective in changing opinions and beliefs about mental illness.

Summary

Two experiments were designed to evaluate the hypotheses that one or more sound motion picture films would modify the opinions and beliefs of audience members, and that group discussion of the films would augment this effect. Participants in the studies were members of adult community groups. Opinions were measured before and after experimental treatment by means of a 47-item questionnaire containing statements about mental illness and scored by the method of summated ratings.

Results of the two investigations indicated that a single mental health film did not produce significant changes in opinions toward mental illness in groups, regardless of whether or not the groups engaged in discussion of the films. A series of three films, however, induced significant shifts of opinion in the directions intended by the film content. Degree of opinion change was no greater in groups which had discussed the films than in groups which had not held discussions.

The findings have been discussed in terms of the types of films employed as well as the characteristics of typical audiences for which these films are intended.

44 / The Influence of Perceived Mental Illness on Interpersonal Relations

Amerigo Farina / Kenneth Ring

It seems clear that, in America at least, there is a generalized highly unfavorable attitude toward the mentally ill (Nunnally, 1961; Nunnally and Kittross, 1958). Evidence suggests that such a pandemic attitude can color the perception of a person believed to be mentally ill even when his behavior is, by all objective standards, "normal." For example, it has been found (Jones *et al.*, 1959) that subjects listening to standardized taped "interviews" dislike the speaker more when they are told (by the experimenter) that she is maladjusted than when they believe she is well adjusted.

Interesting as such studies are, in general they provide no more than a glimpse into prevalent American attitudes and stereotypes about the mentally ill. Conceivably, such attitudes are maintained through what Newcomb (1947) has called "autistic hostility." That is, these attitudes resist change because an individual holding them ceases to communicate with the class of persons unfavorably evaluated. Certainly, most Americans have very limited face-to-face contact with the mentally ill. The situation is reminiscent of the early studies on stereotypes (e.g., Katz and Braly, 1933) where it was shown that, in the main, Turks were strongly disliked in spite of the fact that few of the respondents had ever known one.

In the present study we are concerned with the modifiability of such stereotypes as a function of face-to-face interaction with a "mentally ill" person whose behavior in no way supports the common attitude toward him. We are asking, in effect, if the mentally ill person is a prisoner of his own reputation. In this, the present research is relevant to certain hypotheses recently suggested by Goffman (1963) regarding the stigma attached to the ex-mental patient.

In addition to studying the effect of direct interaction (something that earlier studies lacked) on the perception of a person believed to be mentally ill, the effects of such a belief on the performance of a dyadic cooperative task is also of interest. If, as the previously cited research would suggest, unfavorable attitudes toward the mentally ill are highly generalized, one would expect them to influence behaviors over a wide variety of interpersonal contexts. For this reason, in the interaction studied, a motor task which seems completely unrelated to mental illness was deliberately chosen.

The question now arises: what is likely to be the effect of believing a co-worker to be mentally ill on the performance of a cooperative task? There seem to be several possibilities. First of all, on the basis of an anxiety-performance decrement hypothesis, it might be expected that perceiving the co-worker as emotionally disturbed would lead to decreased adequacy of performance. This

From the *Journal of Abnormal Psychology*, 1965, **70**, 47–51. Copyright © 1965. Reprinted by permission of the authors and the American Psychological Association.

would occur if the perceiver's level of anxiety were raised by the belief that the co-worker was, because mentally ill, unpredictable, tense, and dangerous. This increased anxiety should interfere with the performance on the very difficult task used.

On the other hand, two other possibilities suggest that seeing the co-worker as mentally ill would increase performance adequacy. It might be *less* threatening to work with someone who is seriously maladjusted and consequently in a poor position to evaluate others than to work with a normal person who might be more justifiably critical and judgmental. In this case, anxiety should be higher and, therefore, the performance lower when the co-worker is perceived as normal than when he is perceived as mentally ill. The same relationship is suggested by the very different possibility that when the co-worker is perceived as mentally ill, he is thought to be less competent to perform the task. The subject may compensate for the imagined inadequacy of his co-worker by trying harder. Therefore, better performance would be associated with the perception of the partner as mentally ill. In view of the seeming reasonableness of these contradictory alternatives and the absence of any guiding data, no predictions were made. It was thought, however, that if differences in adequacy of performance in fact emerged, their meaning would be clear when examined in the light of measures of perception of the co-worker.[1]

Method

Subjects

The subjects of this study were 60 male undergraduate students enrolled in psychology classes at the University of Connecticut. They were all volunteers and were given no pay for participating in the experiment. The subjects participated in pairs composed in all cases of two students who were unacquainted with each other.

Procedure

After the subjects were introduced, they were asked to sit at two desks facing each other. However, a partition was placed between the desks in such a way that the students could not see each other but could at all times be seen by the experimenter. They were then told that this study sought to determine how much a person could tell about another from certain standard cues and were instructed to refrain from talking to each other. It was explained that the experimenter wanted them to know some specific things about each other and that they were to write that information on blank sheets of paper which would subsequently be exchanged. They were asked to list three kinds of information: (*a*) the sort of person they were, (*b*) anything unusual about themselves, and (*c*) something about their plans for the future. They were urged to be as candid as possible inasmuch as it would be very important to the study.

When a student indicated he was finished (generally 5 to 15 minutes) his background information sheet was picked up by the experimenter and the subject was

---

[1] It is of course conceivable that two of these processes might counterbalance each other, in which case no differences would emerge in spite of the presence of these processes.

given a brief one-page questionnaire about his school and family. The sole purpose of this questionnaire was to facilitate the substitution of faked background information sheets for the real ones. These fake sheets, which described the writer either as normal or maladjusted, were placed on the students' desks while they were engaged in completing the questionnaire. They were then told that, as soon as they had completed the questionnaire, they were to read their co-worker's information sheet very carefully.

The normal information sheet was as follows:

> I tend to think of myself as a relatively normal person; at least I don't have what you could call any "problems." I enjoy going to college, but like to have my fun, too. I think I'm pretty popular with my group, am engaged, and am doing pretty well (29 QPR)[2] in school.
>
> Frankly, I can't think of anything that's "unusual" about myself.
>
> As for my goals for the future, after graduating from college, I plan to get married and hope to go to graduate school.

The "sick" one on the other hand read:

> You asked us to be candid, so here goes: I have certain problems in adjustment which I first noticed in high school and which still bother me quite a bit. I guess I am somewhat different from most people. I tend to keep pretty much to myself and, frankly, I don't really have any close friends. At school I am doing pretty well (29 QPR).
>
> I suppose what's most unusual about me is that twice (once in my senior year in high school and once in college), I have been placed in a mental institution when I had a kind of nervous breakdown.
>
> As for my goals for the future, after graduating from college, I hope to go to graduate school.

When both subjects had finished, they were taken to another section of the room where a toy manufactured in Sweden and sold under the brand name *Labyrintspel* (Labyrinth Game) was on top of a table. Subjects were asked to sit on chairs in front of the *Labyrintspel*, their chairs were drawn up against each other, and they were asked to examine the toy. It resembles a box, measuring 13 × 11 inches, it is approximately 4¾ inches high, and there is a knob at each of two sides. Each knob controls an angle of the plane at the top of the box so that a small steel ball on it can be made to follow any path desired by appropriate and simultaneous manipulation of the two knobs. The movable plane is a maze formed by raised wooden partitions and a series of 40 holes. There is only one possible path from the starting point to the goal and that is indicated by a black line. There are 59 points at which the ball can fall into a hole and these are numbered from 1, which is the first pitfall, to 59, which is the last, before the goal.

The subjects were each assigned a knob and they were told to make the ball go as far as possible on each trial and when the ball fell in a hole they were to pick it up as it emerged, place it in the starting box, and begin another trial.[3] They were given three practice trials and told that they were free to talk about the task at any time. The performance consisted of 50 consecutive trials with a

---

[2] About a B average.

[3] A small percentage of subjects (15 per cent overall) had had some prior experience with the toy but the percentage did not differ across groups.

one-minute rest period after Trial 25. For each trial the hole in which the ball fell was noted and the time required was also recorded. The latter variable was not analyzed and served primarily to reduce the time the experiment required by causing the subjects to work more rapidly.

At the termination of the maze performance subjects returned to their desks and were given a final questionnaire to complete. They were told that the questionnaire was strictly confidential and would not be seen by their co-worker. It consisted of 14 statements which subjects could answer by placing a check mark at the appropriate place and a fifteenth statement which called for a free description of the co-worker. After the questionnaire, a discussion was held with the subjects in order to determine if any were suspicious and, subsequently, to reveal the true nature of the study to them. Two subjects guessed the real intent of the study and were discarded.

Experimental Design

The subjects were randomly assigned to one of three groups, each group being composed of 10 pairs of subjects for a total of 30 pairs. The groups differed only with respect to the information sheet received. In the normal-normal (N-N) group, both subjects received a normal information sheet. For the normal-sick (N-S) group one student received the normal information sheet but the other received the sick one. The last group was the sick-sick (S-S) group and each student in the group received the sick background information sheet. For the analysis of the performance measures, these three groups are compared. However, for the measures of perception only two groups of 30 subjects each were compared. Those who received the sick background information sheet comprised one while those receiving the normal sheet formed the other group. The three groups were combined into two after it was determined that the perception of the co-worker was not influenced by the background information sheet the co-worker received.

Results

An important fact to determine at the outset is how successful the manipulation was in inducing the subjects to perceive their co-worker in line with experimental intentions. On the final questionnaire there were four items which are relevant to this question. Those who received the sick sheet, in comparison to those who received the normal one, described their co-worker as: less able to get along with others, less able to understand others, less able to understand himself, and more unpredictable. For these four items the differences reached significance levels ranging from $p < .01$ to $p < .0001$. These results indicate that the manipulation was completely successful and, in addition, confirm Nunnally's (1961) findings that mentally ill persons are perceived as unpredictable.

The results of the performance on the *Labyrintspel* are presented in Table I. The numbers in this table represent sums of scores obtained for the 50 trials. The N-N group was least adequate while the S-S group performed best, suggesting that perceiving the co-worker as mentally ill enhances performance. These results were analyzed by means of a trend analysis (Edwards, 1960) which showed that only the trials main effect reached a statistically significant level. Neither the

TABLE I

MEANS AND STANDARD DEVIATIONS OF TOTAL SCORE OBTAINED FOR 50
TRIALS ON THE LABYRINTSPEL

Group	M	SD
N-N	252.3	71.8
N-S	275.5	101.8
S-S	334.8	94.6

groups main effect nor the Groups × Trials interaction was found to be statistically significant. Since it had been expected that the N-N and S-S group scores
would be most disparate (whatever the effect of perceived mental illness), an
additional analysis was carried out. Here the performance of the N-N and S-S
groups was compared by means of a t test. The results indicate that the S-S group
performance was reliably better than that of the N-N group ($t = 2.2$, $df = 18$,
$p < .05$) and suggest that perceiving the co-worker as mentally ill facilitates
performance.

Analysis of questionnaire items concerned with social perception (other than
those mentioned at the beginning of this section) revealed that the background
information sheet had a significant influence on the perception of the co-worker
in spite of the opportunity the students had of interacting with him. The results
from one item which required the subjects to state whether they thought their
co-worker helped or hindered in the performance of the task are presented in
Table II. Subjects who received the sick information sheet, more often than those

TABLE II

NUMBERS OF SUBJECTS DESCRIBED AS HELPING OR HINDERING PERFORMANCE
AS A FUNCTION OF BACKGROUND INFORMATION SHEET RECEIVED

| | | Co-worker Described as: | | | | |
		Helping	Hindering	χ^2	df	p
Background information	Normal	27	3	5.7	1	.02
sheet received	Sick	18	12			

receiving the normal sheet, reported their co-worker hindered the joint performance. This occurred *in spite of the fact* that the former group did objectively
better on the task than the latter. Subjects were also asked to indicate whether
they preferred working on the task by themselves (controlling both knobs) or
with their partner. The relevant data are presented in Table III. They clearly sup-

TABLE III

NUMBERS OF SUBJECTS CHOOSING TO WORK WITH PARTNER OR ALONE AS A
FUNCTION OF BACKGROUND INFORMATION SHEET RECEIVED

| | | Choice to Work With: | | | | |
		Partner	Alone	χ^2	df	p
Background information	Normal	17	13	7.1	1	.01
sheet received	Sick	6	24			

port the idea that believing an individual to be mentally ill reduces the perceiver's willingness to work with him. A third item of this kind was in the same direction as the preceding two in that the sick co-worker tended to be held more responsible for causing the ball to drop into a hole. However, the difference between the groups did not reach statistical significance.

Of the remaining items on the questionnaire, those concerned with estimates of the co-worker's intelligence and his ability to perform well on similar motor tasks showed no difference between groups. While sick co-workers were judged to be less liked by *others* than normals ($p < .01$), subjects themselves did not rate a sick co-worker any less likeable than a normal one. Neither did subjects feel any less "comfortable" working with a sick co-worker compared to a normal one. These two findings seem to be at variance with the data already presented which would lead one plausibly, if not logically, to expect differences on these items. Also somewhat surprising is the absence of any difference between groups on questions dealing with how much attention the co-worker gave to the task and how willing the subject would be to work with his partner on a future, similar task.

Discussion

The most important conclusion of this study is that believing an individual to be mentally ill strongly influences the perception of that individual; this is true in spite of the fact that his behavior in no way justifies these perceptions. When a co-worker is viewed as mentally ill, subjects prefer to work alone rather than with him on a task and also blame him for inadequacies in performance. Since objective measures of performance do not warrant such responses, these findings attest to the importance of believing another to be mentally ill as a factor in interpersonal relationships.

The significance of this variable is further emphasized by several considerations. The subjects of this study were young and well educated, characteristics shown to be associated with relatively favorable attitudes toward the mentally ill (Nunnally, 1961). Also, it seems very likely from the data referred to at the end of the Results section that the sick sheet either created a rather strong sympathy reaction in the subjects or made them less willing to say anything unfavorable about the co-worker. In spite of these counteracting factors it was still found that the generalized negative attitude had a strong effect on interpersonal relationships.

The finding of a difference in performance on the *Labyrintspel* suggests that perceiving someone as mentally ill affects a very broad spectrum of interpersonal behaviors. That is, while it might be expected that such a perception would influence a person's decision to hire someone as a baby sitter, the behavior measured in this study seems quite peripheral to mental illness. What factors may account for this finding?

It will be remembered that two possibilities were suggested for anticipating the finding obtained: (*a*) one was based on the hypothesis that a normal and successful peer would be threatening, and (*b*) another assumed that compensation for perceived inadequacy would occur. If the first hypothesis were true, it would imply a decrement in performance in the N-N group, while the second would suggest a facilitation of performance in the S-S group. Obviously these two hypotheses are not mutually exclusive.

It was decided to test the second of these hypotheses by running an additional group of ten pairs of students. In this group, the clumsy-clumsy (Cl-Cl) group, each student received a background information sheet which was identical to the normal one except for the addition of one phrase: "About the only thing I can think of is that I'm 'all thumbs'; I don't learn to do things with my hands very well." The success of the manipulation was checked by comparing the N-N to the Cl-Cl group on the item which asked for an estimation of the co-worker's dexterity at motor tasks such as the one they had just completed. The z score yielded by the Mann-Whitney U test was 4.1, which is highly significant and in the expected direction. However, the task performance of the group was not different from that of the N-N group nor were the groups different with respect to their perception of the co-worker. These results are inconsistent with the compensation hypothesis, leaving the threat hypothesis as a possibility.

Of course, it could well be that the list of alternative hypotheses which could explain the original S-S—N-N difference has not been exhausted. For example, Ghiselli and Brown (1955, pp. 293–294) cite evidence indicating that performance on certain tasks is improved by distracting influences such as noise. Perceiving the co-worker as mentally ill may constitute a distracting influence and may have enhanced performance. Such hypotheses, clearly, may be subjected to direct test.

It has been demonstrated that, under certain circumstances, what a person reportedly says about himself significantly influences the interpretation of his behavior by another even though the behavior does not justify that interpretation. But, it might be argued, the type of encounter studied here was brief and superficial. If contact had been prolonged and intimate, isn't it reasonable to suppose that one's interpretation of another's behavior would be based less on stereotypes and more on the behavior itself? This is possible. Insofar as stereotypes about mental illness are concerned, however, this objection can be answered by submitting that it is precisely because of these stereotypes that distortions in perception are likely to occur in the *initial* phases of interaction and thus reduce the likelihood of further interaction of the kind necessary to eradicate such stereotypes.

45 / "Custodialism" and "Humanism" in Mental Hospital Structure and in Staff Ideology

Doris C. Gilbert / Daniel J. Levinson

This inquiry concerns the ideologies of mental hospital members regarding the nature and causes of mental illness and regarding hospital aims and policies in treating the mentally ill. We are interested in the nature of these ideologies as well as their institutional and intrapersonal roots. The research was carried out chiefly at three Massachusetts hospitals: A large (1,800 bed) state hospital dealing largely with "chronically ill" patients; a Veterans Administration hospital of about the same size; and a small (120 bed) state hospital providing short-term active treatment. Early in our explorations we realized that these hospitals, like many others in this country and abroad, are going through a period of ideological ferment and organizational change. Policies and viewpoints that have prevailed for many years are being challenged by various new approaches intended to broaden the hospital's aims, to increase its therapeutic effectiveness, and to provide a greater measure of participation, satisfaction, and support for its members. Clearly, the newly emerging viewpoints involve much more than the application of new treatment techniques. What gives them their fundamental—one might say, revolutionary—quality is their conception of the hospital as a community of citizens rather than a rigidly codified institutional mold, and their conception of the hospital members as persons rather than as mere objects and agents of treatment (cf. Bettelheim, 1950; Greenblatt *et al.*, 1955; Jones, 1953; Stanton and Schwartz, 1954). In this respect as in many others, the ongoing developments in the mental hospital parallel those in other "correctional" institutions such as schools and prisons, and in larger bureaucratic structures such as industry and government (cf. Leighton, 1944; Mayo, 1933; Tannenbaum, 1951). Because of this wider relevance, research in the mental hospital can make use of, and can contribute materially to, the main body of sociopsychological theory and knowledge.

Although there is much ideological controversy in the hospital, there appear to be no commonly accepted names for the major competing viewpoints. We were therefore required to adopt our own nomenclature. The term *custodialism* serves reasonably well, we believe, to denote the traditional viewpoints and policies. It indicates the hospital's main functions in patient care. Terms such as "rehabilitative" or "therapeutic" were considered as possible names for the more modern approaches, emphasizing as they do active treatment rather than merely passive

From Chapter 3 by Doris C. Gilbert and Daniel J. Levinson in Milton Greenblatt, Daniel J. Levinson and Richard H. Williams (eds.), *The Patient and the Mental Hospital.* Copyright © 1957. (New York: The Free Press, 1957). Reprinted by permission of the authors and the Macmillan Company.

containment of the patient. We have finally chosen, however, to refer to these as *humanistic* orientations, despite the several meanings now attributed to this term in religion, literature, and intellectual history. We use the term in the socio-psychological sense suggested by Fromm (1947). It indicates what seems to us the most fundamental feature of these orientations: Their attempt to recognize the individuality of each patient and to create a setting meeting a wide range of human needs in both patients and personnel. The terms "custodialism" and "humanism" refer to contrasting types of individual ideology and to the corresponding types of hospital organization that they seek to rationalize and justify.

There are many variations on the custodial theme and perhaps a greater number of humanistic viewpoints. Nevertheless, it seemed theoretically and strategically most sound to begin with an analysis of the two major themes, and this is the focus of the present paper. Further studies dealing with variants of humanism will be described elsewhere.

The primary aims of this study are the following:

1. To formulate the main characteristics of the custodial and the humanistic ideologies, and to construct an ideology scale that will provide a crude measure of the degree of an individual's preference for one or the other viewpoint.
2. To investigate the personality contexts within which these orientations most readily develop.
3. To investigate the relationships of individual ideology and personality to membership in particular types of hospital system and occupational status.
4. To investigate the ways in which the hospital's over-all policy is related to the modal (most common) ideology and modal personality of its members.

Custodialism and Humanism as Ideological Orientations in the Mental Hospital

We have found it most fruitful, in our attempts at ideological analysis, to begin by asking: "What are the major "problems" or issues of institutional life for which some kind of adaptive rationale is needed? The mental hospital presents at least the following issues with which every individual member must deal. The *patient:* what is he like, how did he get that way, how much can he be helped and in what ways? *Patient-staff relations:* what should be the role of hospital personnel vis-à-vis the patient; how much interaction should there be, with what emotional qualities and therapeutic aims? *Staff-staff relations:* how should specific functions and responsibilities be distributed; how much communication and status distinction should there be? *General hospital practices:* what formal treatment methods are best; how should ward life be organized; in what ways should patients be encouraged, left alone, controlled, punished?

Custodialism and humanism offer two contrasting sets of answers to these questions, that is, two modes of thought that may be used to guide institutional policy and individual adaptation. A brief, schematic formulation of each ideology is presented below. It is to be emphasized that these are prototypes—"ideal types" in Weber's sense—or analytically derived constructions. There are probably few individuals or hospitals that represent either type in its pure form. The two types may be thought of as polar extremes of a continuum containing various intermediate positions. Our chief assumptions, to be validated empirically, are that this continuum is *realistic,* in the sense that viewpoints and policies approximating the prototypes will commonly be found, and that the continuum is *significant,* in the sense that adherence to one rather than the other viewpoint will seriously affect the individual's or the hospital's mode of functioning.

The model of the custodial orientations is the traditional prison and the "chronic" mental hospital which provide a highly controlled setting concerned mainly with the detention and safekeeping of its inmates. Patients are conceived of in stereotyped terms as categorically different from "normal" people, as totally irrational, insensitive to others, unpredictable, and dangerous. Mental illness is attributed primarily to poor heredity, organic lesion, and the like. In consequence, the staff cannot expect to understand the patients, to engage in meaningful relationships with them, nor in most cases to do them much good. Custodialism is saturated with pessimism, impersonalness, and watchful mistrust. The custodial conception of the hospital is autocratic, involving as it does a rigid status hierarchy, a unilateral downward flow of power, and a minimizing of communication within and across status lines. A genotypically similar formulation of the custodial orientation in the prison setting, as well as similar hypotheses concerning its psychological basis, are given by Powelson and Bendix (1951).

The humanistic orientations, on the other hand, conceive of the hospital as a therapeutic community rather than a custodial institution. They emphasize interpersonal and intrapsychic sources of mental illness, often to the neglect of possible hereditary and somatic sources. They view patients in more psychological and less moralistic terms. They are optimistic, sometimes to an unrealistic degree, about the possibilities of patient recovery in a maximally therapeutic environment. They attempt in varying degrees to democratize the hospital, to maximize the therapeutic functions of nonmedical personnel, to increase patient self-determination (individually and, through patient government, collectively), and to open up communication wherever possible.

While the humanistic orientations have in common the broad tenets outlined above, and even more an opposition to custodialism, they still differ among themselves in important respects. These differences result in part from differing ecological bases and organizational requirements of the particular hospitals involved. For example, the concrete manifestations of humanism will differ, though the guiding spirit may be the same, in a large, architecturally horrendous, financially limited state hospital, as contrasted with a small, well-subsidized, private hospital that accepts only patients whom it regards as good therapeutic risks. There are important variations in theoretical position, e.g., in relative emphasis on intensive psychotherapy or on the emotional climate and social organization of the hospital. There are related differences in treatment aims, in conceptions of the needs of patients (as ill persons and as members of the hospital community), in sensitivity to existing status differentials, and in readiness to undertake the diffusion of therapeutic functions among the total hospital staff. . . .

It is difficult to conduct a dispassionate inquiry into custodialism and humanism without idealizing the latter through contrast with the former. There is, of course, much evidence showing the therapeutic ineffectiveness, not to speak of the inhumanity and decadence, of the custodial system. Nevertheless, it is clear that the proponents of humanistic change are still groping their way in semi-darkness.

"Modern" viewpoints tend to crystalize prematurely and then to resist further change. And, like all ideologies, these human productions reflect the illusions and self-deceptions as well as the rationality of their producers and consumers. In each instance, the ideological aims will likely be more noble than the actions and effects generated, particularly in the short run. This inquiry makes no assumptions about the actual therapeutic effectiveness of the various approaches. Our primary concern at this point is with the nature and the determinants of custodialism and humanism.

The "Custodial Mental Illness Ideology" (CMI) Scale

The initial, exploratory study led to the formulation of the "custodialism-humanism" continuum, the polar extremes of which have been described above. We believed that the concepts of custodialism and humanism could meaningfully be applied not merely to hospital policies and to formal administrative philosophies, but as well to the orientations of *individual* hospital members toward mental illness and its treatment.

The next step was to construct the "Custodial Mental Illness Ideology" (CMI) Scale, an admittedly crude instrument that had two chief functions in the research: (a) To test the hypothesis that a set of seemingly disparate ideas do in fact "go together" to form a relatively coherent orientation in the individual. A derivative function is to determine whether viewpoints approximating our posited prototypes exist with some frequency within various hospital settings. (b) To provide a quantitative and at the same time meaningful measure that facilitates additional study of the nature of these ideas and their relation to other aspects of the individual and his milieu.

The CMI Scale consists of 20 statements, broadly diversified to cover numerous facets of the ideological domain: the nature and causes of mental illness, conditions in the hospital, patient-staff relations, and the like. The items were derived from interviews, conversations, and observations of conferences and everyday hospital life. The scale is presented in Table I. A more extensive description of the field work and derivation of the CMI Scale can be found in Gilbert (1954).

Scoring Procedure

The subjects were instructed to indicate the degree of their agreement or disagreement with each item on a scale ranging from +3 (strong agreement) to −3 (strong disagreement). The responses were converted into scores by means of an a priori, seven-point scoring scheme. It was intended that a high score represent strong adherence to "custodial" ideology as here conceived, and that a low score represent opposition to this viewpoint. Of the 20 scale items, 17 were regarded as custodial, 3 as humanistic. For the "custodial" items, seven points were given for the +3 response, one point for −3.

For the "humanistic" items the scoring was reversed. When the total score is divided by the number of items we obtain the mean score per item on a 1–7 scale. For convenience in comparing scores from scales differing in length, we shall use the mean per item, multiplied by 10. The possible range is thus 10–70 points.

The CMI Scale was initially developed on a sample of 335 staff members

TABLE I

THE CUSTODIAL MENTAL ILLNESS IDEOLOGY (CMI) SCALE

Item	Mean	DP
1. Only persons with considerable psychiatric training should be allowed to form close relationship with patients.	3.5	2.4
3. It is best to prevent the more disturbed patients from mixing with those who are less sick.	5.0	1.8
5. As soon as a person shows signs of mental disturbance he should be hospitalized.	3.3	4.2
°7. Mental illness is an illness like any other.	2.7	2.7
9. Close association with mentally ill people is liable to make even a normal person break down.	2.0	1.4
11. We can make some improvements, but by and large the conditions of mental hospital wards are about as good as they can be considering the type of disturbed patient living there.	3.0	3.6
15. We should be sympathetic with mental patients, but we cannot expect to understand their odd behavior.	3.2	3.8
17. One of the main causes in mental illness is lack of moral strength.	2.8	3.2
°18. When a patient is discharged from a hospital, he can be expected to carry out his responsibilities as a citizen.	3.0	0.5
19. Abnormal people are ruled by their emotions; normal people by their reason.	3.8	4.4
21. A mental patient is in no position to make decisions about even everyday living problems.	3.0	3.1
°23. Patients are often kept in the hospital long after they are well enough to get along in the community.	4.2	−0.2
25. There is something about mentally ill people that makes it easy to tell them from normal people.	3.0	2.9
27. Few, if any, patients are capable of real friendliness.	2.2	1.7
31. There is hardly a mental patient who isn't liable to attack you unless you take extreme precautions.	2.5	3.0
33. Patients who fail to recover have only themselves to blame; in most cases they have just not tried hard enough.	1.8	1.5
37. "Once a schizophrenic, always a schizophrenic."	2.3	1.3
38. Patients need the same kind of control and discipline as an untrained child.	3.3	2.4
39. With few exceptions most patients haven't the ability to tell right from wrong.	2.4	2.3
40. In experimenting with new methods of ward treatment, hospitals must consider, first and foremost, the safety of patients and personnel.	5.3	2.3

Notes:

1. The item means and DP's are those obtained by a sample of 196 mental hospital personnel in hospitals C, T, and H. Similar DP's have been obtained in other samples of personnel, patients, and visitors.

2. Items are numbered as they appear in the questionnaire, which contained other scales and questions.

3. Items marked with an asterisk take a "humanistic" position; all others are "custodial."

4. Items 15 and 23 have inadequate DP's and have been omitted from the scale in subsequent research.

(aides, student nurses, nurses, and psychiatrists) in three Massachusetts mental hospitals: Hospital C, a large (1,800 bed) institution dealing largely with "chronic" patients; Hospital T, a Veterans Administration hospital of about the same size; and Hospital H, a small (120 bed) state institution providing short-term active treatment. The range for this sample was 15–52, the Mean being 31.3 and the Standard Deviations, 9.5. Comparative data for various subgroupings will be presented below (Table II). The reliability (split-half correlation, corrected by Spearman-Brown formula) was .85, and test-retest correlations on several small groups were of similar magnitude. Table I represents the Means and Discriminatory Powers (DP) of the individual items.[1] The DP's of all items except number 18 and 23 reach the (minimally accepted) 5 per cent level of statistical significance, and most of them are beyond the 1 per cent level.

The following three items are among the most discriminating statistically and indicate the wide range of content comprising the custodialism syndrome. Item 11: "We can make some improvements, but by and large the conditions of mental hospital wards are about as good as they can be considering the type of disturbed patient living there." Item 15: "We should be sympathetic with mental patients, but we cannot expect to understand their odd behavior." Item 17: "One of the main causes in mental illness is lack of moral strength."

The above data indicate that the initial form of the CMI Scale has adequate reliability and internal consistency, and they provide a basis for further improvement. They suggest, moreover, that a person's stand on any single issue represented in the scale is part of a broader, fairly coherent (though seldom fully integrated) ideology that embraces numerous issues of hospital life.

Data were obtained on two "validation groups" to determine whether the CMI score adequately gauges an enduring ideological conviction. One group, containing 10 administrators at Hospital H who are known for their advocacy of humanistic policies, earned a CMI mean of 18.8, with an SD of 6.1. The second group comprised the professional staff at the Social Rehabilitation Unit, Belmont Hospital, England (Jones, 1953) and would also be expected to have a low CMI mean. The obtained mean was 22.9, the SD, 6.7. These findings offer additional evidence of scale validity.

The relation of CMI scores to the actual role of performance of hospital personnel is not, strictly speaking, a matter of scale validity. The CMI Scale is intended to be a measure of ideology, and the relation of ideology to action is a further, substantive problem that raises many new issues. However, since at least a moderate relation between ideology and action would be expected on theoretical grounds, evidence of such a relation has indirect validation relevance (Cronbach and Meehl, 1955). . . .

Psychological Bases of Custodialism and Humanism

This aspect of the research was based on the hypothesis that *the custodial orientation is one facet of an authoritarian personality, the humanistic orientation a facet of an equalitarian personality.* Several lines of theory and observation led to this expectation. Custodialism is strongly autocratic in its conception of the hospital and ethnocentric in its conception of patients as an inferior and threatening outgroup entitled to few if any of the rights of "normal" people. Humanism, on the other hand, seeks a more democratic hospital structure and regards patients

---

[1] DP of an item reflects its ability to differentiate between high scorers and extreme low scorers (the upper and lower 25 per cent) on the total scale. Mathematically, an item's DP is the difference between the means of the high-scoring and the low-scoring groups. The more significant the DP, the more likely it is that a given item is part of the total ideational complex tapped by the scale.

as individuals to be understood and treated rather than as an outgroup to be pitied or condemned. There is considerable evidence that autocratic viewpoints tend to exist within authoritarian personality structures (Adorno et al., 1950; Dicks, 1950; Fromm, 1947).

We accordingly predicted that the CMI Scale would correlate significantly with the F Scale (Adorno et al., 1950), a relatively nonideological measure of authoritarianism, and with the Traditional Family Ideology (TFI) Scale, a measure of autocratic ideology regarding issues such as husband-wife and parent-child relations[2] (Levinson and Huffman, 1955).

The obtained interscale correlations are as follows: CMI and F correlate .67, .69, and .76 in hospitals C, T, and H, respectively. The comparable correlations between CMI and TFI are .60, .56, and .77. The respective N's in the three hospitals were 115, 111, and 109. The scale means and SD's are presented in Table II below. The findings lend support to the hypothesis that an individual's views regarding mental illness and the hospital are imbedded within a broader ideological and psychodynamic matrix.

It may be argued that the F Scale is made of the same stuff as CMI, that it taps relatively superficial ideas or values rather than more central aspects of personality. If this be true, then the foregoing inferences concerning the psychodynamic bases of ideology are unjustified. It is certainly possible that a person may accept many of the ideas represented in the F Scale without being an "authoritarian personality." However, we propose on both theoretical and empirical grounds that such persons are rather the exception than the rule. The F items taken as a whole do not comprise an organized body of doctrine. The obtained consistency of response to these items is, we believe, determined for the most part by an enduring pattern of intrapersonal dispositions. Empirical support for this view is given by Adorno et al., (1950) and others; for a critical summary, see Christie (1954). Significant relationships between CMI scores and nonscale measures of authoritarianism have been obtained by Gilbert (1954) and by Pine (1955); see also Pine and Levinson (1957). These studies utilized content analysis of interviews, TAT's, open-ended questions, and the like, in assessing authoritarianism. The F Scale would seem to provide a relatively valid though by no means infallible estimate of personal authoritarianism.

Custodial ideology has important psychic functions for authoritarian hospital members. The idea that patient behavior is simply irrational and not understandable, has great value in reducing inner strain and maintaining self-esteem for personnel who have difficulty at the outset in taking an intraceptive, psychological approach. Again, for the person who has a great defensive need to displace and project aggressive wishes from authority figures onto those who can be regarded as immoral, custodial ideology has special equilibrium-maintaining value through its justification of punitive, suppressive measures.

Humanistic ideology has corresponding functions for its adherents. By supporting a critical attitude toward the established order, it permits many equalitarian individuals to express generalized anti-authority hostilities in an ego-syntonic

---

[2] An abbreviated F scale of eight items was used; it contained items 9, 13, 18, 25, 26, 37, and 42 from Form 45, and item 32 from Form 78 of the original F Scale (Adorno et al.). The TFI measure contained items 2, 3, 5, 6, 7, 9, 11, 12 of the short form presented by Levinson and Huffman.

form. The principle of "self-control through self-understanding," applied in the treatment of patients, often serves to maintain and consolidate the intellectualizing defenses of equalitarian personnel. In our view, then, both custodialism and humanism have important nonrational functions for their proponents. The problem of their relative rationality and effectiveness in an "objective" sense is not in the direct focus of this research.

Relationships Among Ideology, Personality, and Hospital Policy

Our inquiry will now be extended in two directions. First, we shall consider ways in which *individual* ideology and individual personality are related to membership in particular hospital systems and occupational statuses. Second, we shall shift our theoretical focus from the individual staff member to the hospital and occupational grouping. With this focus we are concerned with *modal ideology* and *modal personality* as characteristics of a collective unit. The modal ideology is the most common or typical ideology in each grouping. Modal personality refers to those ideology-relevant personality trends that are most common in each grouping. In particular we wish to understand how these characteristics are related to each other and to the dominant policies of the collectivity. For instance, to what degree does the modal ideology support prevailing policy? To what extent is modal personality congruent with policy requirements? To what extent does modal ideology have its roots in modal personality?

Our theoretical approach to the study of relationships among ideology, personality, and social structure may be briefly summarized as follows: One requirement for the stability and effectiveness of a mental hospital (or other) social structure is that most of its members have an ideology about the hospital that supports hospital policies. The hospital attempts to meet this requirement through various organized means: (a) the evaluations inherent in its system of role norms; (b) its various forms of indoctrination; (c) its social sanctions; (d) the restricted types of experience it offers; and (e) the recruitment of individuals whose ideas from the start are at least minimally compatible with its structurally-required ideology. These factors presumably operate to induce some degree of ideological uniformity among members of a given occupational status, as well as among members of the over-all hospital system.

Many social scientists, including psychologists, argue or implicitly assume that ideological conformity is ordinarily achieved and that some sort of J-curve or concentration of viewpoints approximating the institutional requirements will be found among members of a given institution. In other words, they assume that the modal ideology of the members is appropriate to the prevailing policies, and that individual differences (variability) are limited. Proponents of this view tend to regard contemporary social system pressures as the prime determinants of individual ideology.

One serious limitation of this approach, in our view, is its neglect of the part played by personality. We would expect that the achievement of a policy-congruent modal ideology depends in part on the presence of a corresponding modal personality. To the extent that there is variability in ideology-relevant personality characteristics, there is the likelihood of ideological variability among members of any system. These expectations are based on our assumption that ideology is in part a function of personality. Since a variety of personalities can fulfill the minimum requirements of any particular occupation, it can happen that a system recruits a large number of individuals whose personalities are initially incongruent with the structurally required ideology. We are interested in the consequences for these "unreceptive" persons. We want to know how often, and under what conditions, does the system induce in them a policy-congruent ideology; and conversely, when do they develop a deviant or variant ideology which represents a potential for change in the system.

Our empirical study of relationships among ideology, personality, and policy requirements has been carried out at two analytic levels.

1. Where the focus of analysis is on a *collective unit*, such as a hospital or an occupational status, we have asked the following questions. How congruent are the policy requirements and the modal ideology of a system? How much ideological variability exists among members of a hospital-occupational group? How congruent are the policy requirements and the modal personality of a social unit? How much dispersion of ideologically-relevant personalities is there among system members? Finally, how congruent are modal ideology and modal personality?

2. Where the focus of analysis is on the *individual member*, we are concerned with parallel questions: How closely is individual ideology related to membership in a given hospital or occupational group? How closely is personality related to group (system) membership? Finally, how congruent are ideology and personality within members of a single system? The empirical studies that follow are preliminary attempts to deal with these questions.

Our three domains of inquiry are *ideology, personality*, and *system requirements*. Within each domain we shall be concerned with variability along a continuum. (a) Variations in individual ideology were measured by the CMI Scale which indicates how relatively custodial or humanistic each subject is in his view of the mental hospital. (b) The corresponding continuum of personality is that of authoritarianism-equalitarianism as measured by the F Scale. (c) The third continuum is custodialism-humanism in system requirements. Custodialism and humanism, in this institutional sense, refer to differing forms of hospital organization and patient care. We proposed that a dominantly custodial system "demands" (though it may not achieve) a custodial ideology and is most congenial to an authoritarian personality; and similarly, that a humanistic system requires a humanistic ideology and best fits an equalitarian personality. The assessment of it leaves much to be desired. We proceeded as follows.

The sample contained 12 subsystems: Four occupational statuses (aide, student nurse, nurse, and psychiatrist) in each of three hospitals. The empirical task was to rank the 12 hospital-status units in order from relatively most custodial to relatively most humanistic with regard to the demands and pressures each system placed on its members. We ranked the hospitals first, then the statuses, and then combined the two into one series of 12 ranks.

In an absolute sense, few hospitals are prototypically custodial or humanistic. All three of the hospitals studied are changing to some degree. Our rankings are based on the hospital's rate of change away from a predominant emphasis on protection and bodily care of patients. The large state hospital, C, was assessed as the most custodial in view of its structural emphasis on detention, protection, and custodial care of patients in a highly controlled setting. The pressures it exerted on personnel, and the kinds of experiences it offered them, seemed most conducive to a custodial orientation. The large VA hospital, T, was considered intermediate or transitional in that it was in process of fairly rapid change away from custodialism. The third hospital, H, was the most humanistic of the three in its program of ward care, patient government, and general staff-patient relationships

Next the four statuses were ranked in degree of custodialism on the basis of educational level and job requirements vis-à-vis the patient. In order from high to low in degree of custodialism, they fall as follows: aide, student nurse, nurse, and psychiatrist. It is to be emphasized that this order refers *to the hospitals studied;* it may well not hold in other settings. The aide status in these hospitals is more custodial than the doctor's in several respects. The functions of the aide are primarily protection and custodial care of patients. His contact with modern humanistic concepts of mental illness is minimal; little in-service training is provided and educational requirements are few. On the other hand, the position of the physician in these hospitals carries with it the sole prerogative of therapy. The psychiatrist's main concern is to increase his capacity for psychological understanding of patients. Also, psychiatrists can be expected to have had the greatest contact with humanistic concepts of mental illness and its treatment. In predicting that most of these psychiatrists will take a humanistic position on the issues represented in the CMI Scale, we do *not* assume that they are in agreement on other matters of hospital ideology. . . .

The next step was to combine these two sets of rankings into a series of 12 status units ranked according to the degree of pressure toward custodialism. Since occupational status pressures operate over a longer period of time, and more selectively, than do hospital pressures, we made status a primary basis of stratification, and hospital secondary. That is, we assumed that statuses are relatively nonoverlapping in degree of custodialism in their policy requirements and that hospitals make a difference only within a single status grouping. Accordingly the rank 12 was given to the most custodial status in the most custodial hospital, namely, the aide status at hospital C; this is followed by the aide status at hospital T, and at H; then come the student nurse statuses at C, T, and H; and lastly the doctor statuses at hospitals C, T, and H with ranks of 3, 2, and 1 respectively (see Table II). Ideally a more intensive sociological analysis of the structure and policies of each status in each hospital should be carried out. However, the rankings used here seem adequate for our present purposes.

Having roughly assessed the degree of custodialism in the policy requirements of each hospital-status system, we can now investigate the degree to which these requirements are supported by the ideologies, and are congruent with the personalities, of the system members.

Relations between Policy Requirements and Ideology

What is the relationship between the degree of custodialism in the policy requirements of a hospital-status system and the degree of custodialism in the modal ideology of its members? The relevant data are given in Table II. We use the CMI Mean as a measure of modal ideology, for in the distribution of CMI scores the Mean, by and large, corresponds closely to the Mode. The obtained

TABLE II

CMI AND F SCALE DATA FOR 12 HOSPITAL-STATUS UNITS: MEANS, STANDARD DEVIATIONS, AND CORRELATIONS

Hospital-Status Unit		N	Index Policy Custod.	CMI Scale			F Scale			CMI-F
				Mean	Rank	S.D.	Mean	Rank	S.D.	
Attendants at										
hospitals:	C	29	12	38.0	12	10.2	46.1	12	13.0	.91
	T	51	11	37.3	11	10.3	41.4	11	11.7	.82
	H	48	10	32.1	8	9.7	32.5	9	13.0	.77
Student nurses at										
hospitals:	C	66	9	33.4	10	7.7	29.0	8	10.9	.44
	T	38	8	33.3	9	6.8	28.9	7	8.9	.25
	H	16	7	31.3	6	5.7	28.8	6	9.2	.59
Nurses at										
hospitals:	C	14	6	31.3	7	9.9	37.3	10	14.5	.90
	T	18	5	22.4	2	5.2	26.7	5	8.7	.53
	H	21	4	26.9	5	7.7	25.8	3	14.5	.73
Doctors at										
hospitals:	C	6	3	25.8	4	7.0	18.1	1	6.2	.75
	T	4	2	21.6	1	4.8	26.6	4	12.8	.80
	H	24	1	22.7	2	4.5	19.1	2	8.5	.50
Total Status										
Attendants		128	4	35.3	4	10.4	39.1	4	13.7	.82
Student nurses		120	3	33.1	3	7.3	28.9	3	10.2	.41
Nurses		53	2	26.5	2	8.3	27.9	2	12.8	.76
Doctors		34	1	23.1	1	5.3	19.7	1	9.1	.46
Total hospital										
	C	115	3	33.7	3	8.9	33.8	2	14.5	.67
	T	111	2	32.9	2	10.2	34.2	3	12.4	.69
	H	109	1	29.0	1	8.7	27.7	1	13.1	.76
Total sample		335		31.3		9.5	31.9		13.7	.71

rank-order correlation between degree of custodialism in policy requirements (status ranks) and in modal ideology (CMI Mean) is .92. Thus, the hospital-status units that are most custodial in their present modes of patient care tend also to have the most custodially oriented members, on the average. There is, in other words, relatively great congruence between policy demands and modal ideology. At the same time, the CMI Means of the 12 status units do not correspond fully in absolute degree to the estimated degree of custodialism in their structural pressures. For example, the aide status at hospital C was ranked most custodial both in policy requirements and in CMI Mean; however, in an absolute sense, the policy requirements are highly custodial, whereas the CMI Mean is only moderate.

The foregoing findings indicate that the 12 systems differ with regard to modal ideology and that these differences correspond to differences in policy require-ments. However, they do not tell us how much ideological variability exists within each system. Data on variability are given in Table II. It will be noted that the Standard Deviations of most of the 12 units approximate that for the total sample. Only in the doctor statuses is there anything approaching uniformity of opinion. Thus although *modal* ideology is fairly closely related to policy requirements, the findings on intrasystem variability suggest that an individual's ideology does not reflect in a simple way the demands of his occupational milieu.

In investigating the relationship between *individual* ideology and policy requirements, we consider system pressures as characteristics of the individual. Every individual in the sample of 335 was assigned an index figure representing the relative degree of custodialism in the policy requirements of his particular hospital-status unit. This index figure is simply the rank of the individual's status within the series of 12. For instance, each doctor at H, the least custodial status, is assigned an index figure of 1, and each aide at C is assigned an index of 12.

The obtained product-moment correlation[3] between CMI score and Index of Status-Custodialism is .47. This finding is evidence of a significant but moderate relationship between individual ideology and system pressures. If one assumed that system pressures were the most weighty determinants of individual ideology, he would then expect relative ideological homogeneity within statuses and thus a high correlation (of the order, .7 to .8) between an individual's CMI score and the degree of policy-custodialism of his work unit. We conclude that system membership is one determinant of individual ideology but not the only or the most crucial one.

To sum up: On the basis of policy requirements, we can predict in a general way where the nurse or aide *group* will stand (i.e., the modal ideology) on CMI relative to other status groups. At the same time, the degree of uniformity within any system is not as great as a system-centered mode of thinking would require. An individual's ideology can be predicted with only fair accuracy on the basis of his occupational-hospital membership.

Relations between Policy Requirements and Personality

If the individual's ideological orientation is thought to be simply and directly a result of pressures from his work milieu, relatively independent of his personality, one would not expect the degree of custodialism in system policy to be significantly related to the degree of authoritarianism in modal personality. Rather, the 12 units might be expected to show degrees of authoritarianism, as measured by the F Scale Means.

In our view, however, some congruence is to be expected between the policy requirements of a system and the modal personality of its members. Such congruence would be facilitated through recruitment, selective turnover, and possible personality changes in the direction of congruence. We are supported in this hypothesis by the finding of congruence (the correlation of .92) between policy requirements and modal ideology in the 12 status units. We would expect a parallel correspondence between policy requirements and modal personality.

For the 12 status units, the obtained rank-order correlation between Index of Status-Custodialism and F Mean is .90 (see Table II). Thus, there is relatively great congruence between policy demands and modal personality. This congruence is as great as that between policy demands and modal ideology.

The obtained correspondence between modal personality (F) and system requirements is accompanied by appreciable variability on the F Scale within most

---

[3] The use of indices based on rank in a product-moment correlation involves the assumption of equal intervals between ranks. This constitutes a possible source of error, but probably not a great one.

of the statuses (Table II). The size of the variance on F tends to covary with that on CMI (x = .61). This leads us to consider the degree to which system membership and personality are related in the individual. We would expect that the correlation found above between status membership and individual CMI score (.47) will hold as well for index of status membership and F score. The findings bear out this prediction. The correlation between the individual's F score and the Index of Custodialism for his status membership is .46.

Relations between Ideology and Personality

One of our fundamental postulates is that an individual's ideological orientation is intimately bound up with his deeper-lying personality characteristics. We therefore hypothesize, at the collective level, relative congruence between modal ideology and modal personality. The obtained rank-order correlation between CMI Mean (our measure of modal ideology) and F Mean (our measure of modal personality) for the 12 units is .81. Thus, the congruence between modal personality and modal ideology in a system is relatively great. As noted earlier, the size of the variance on CMI is also associated with that on F.

With the individual hospital member as the focus of analysis, the CMI-F correlation for the total sample of 335 (regardless of specific status membership) is .71. We can now consider the relationship between ideology and personality when system membership is held constant. The F-CMI correlations for the single status grouping are presented in Table II. They average .71, a value identical to the CMI-F correlations for the sample as a whole, and 11 of the 12 correlations are significant at the .05 level or better.

We thus have evidence that the differences in modal ideology among our 12 status units are closely related to differences in modal personality. When we find individual differences in ideology within a single status unit, these differences are closely related to differences in personality characteristics.

Summary and Conclusions

This inquiry has taken as its starting point the distinction between "custodialism" and "humanism" in the mental hospital. These terms refer to two contrasting ideological orientations and to the corresponding forms of hospital policy. We have investigated ideology both as an individual and a collective phenomenon— or, more accurately, we have used both individual and collective modes of analysis in the study of ideology. With regard to the individual, we have tried to assess ideology by means of a specially devised CMI (custodialism-humanism) Scale, and to determine the relationships between ideology and other individual characteristics such as psychodynamics and membership in various groups. With regard to the collective unit (e.g., hospital or occupational status), we have tried to assess the degree of custodialism in its policy requirements and in the modal ideology of its personnel, as well as the degree of authoritarianism in the modal personality of its personnel, and to determine the relationships among these.

In the individual, preference for a custodialistic orientation is part of a broader pattern of personal authoritarianism. Correlations averaging about .70 were found between the Custodialism (CMI) Scale and the scales measuring autocratic family ideology (TFI) and general authoritarianism (F). Although various hospital groupings differ significantly in Mean CMI score, there are appreciable individual differences within single hospitals and occupations are quite closely related to differences in personality.

In the collective unit, we found relatively great congruence among prevailing policy, modal ideology, and modal personality. The hospital-status units having the most custodial policy requirements had as well the most custodial modal ideologies and the most authoritarian personalities. At the same time, it should be noted that the correspondence among policy, ideology, and personality is far from complete. Each of these aspects of collective life can vary to some extent independently of the others, and the phenomenon of incongruence is as important as that of congruence.

Although none of our groups can be regarded as ideologically homogeneous, some of them showed relatively small dispersion in CMI scores. These groups had a similar dispersion in F Scores, and had low CMI and F Means. Our data do not tell how the low diversity and the high ideology-personality congruence came about, but they point up the need for answers to at least the following questions. To what extent do relatively homogeneous systems maintain themselves by recruitment and selective maintenance of individuals whose personalities are receptive to the structurally required ideology? To what extent do systems change the personalities which initially are unreceptive to the prevailing policy? Under what conditions can a system induce most of its members to support the required ideology even when this ideology is personality-incongruent? Under what conditions can the "incongruent" members change the system to a personally more congenial form?

Systems characterized by relatively great ideological diversity were very common in our sample. Moreover, the ideological diversity went hand-in-hand with diversity in personality, the standard deviations on CMI correlating .61 with those on F. We incline to the belief that significant heterogeneity of opinion and of personality obtains in the majority of institutional settings within modern societies undergoing rapid technological and educational change.

The above theoretical formulations concerning the mental hospital have their parallels in other settings such as the school, the prison, and the family. In all these institutions a small "administrative" elite has the power and responsibility to set goals and to control the destiny of a massive "membership." This larger population, whether children, patients, or prisoners, is a potential threat to society's values; various measures of education and social control are necessary. One of the major forms of conflict in these institutions is that between autocratic and democratic orientations. There is considerable evidence that the autocratic-democratic continuum of ideology is one aspect of a broader authoritarian-equalitarian continuum of personality. In other words, social ideologies have a psychological basis in the personalities of their adherents. A sociopsychological approach is, we believe, an important adjunct to historic-sociological approaches in the study of individual ideology.

46 / Opinions About Mental Illness: Hospital Social Atmosphere Profiles and Their Relevance to Effectiveness

Jacob Cohen / *Elmer L. Struening*

Until the post-World War II period mental hospitals were generally viewed as repositories for hopeless cases. For many reasons, sociological, psychological, and even pharmacological, this view has come to be challenged from many different quarters, and new roles are being assigned to mental hospitals. Thus, we have advocates of "small," "open," "general hospital," "day," "night," "week-day," and "week-end" facilities, and yet others.

Part of this ferment has had as an assumptive base the idea that the well-being of mental patients is materially influenced by their social context. The concept of "sick-role" self-perception and the more extreme view that chronic schizophrenia is an iatrogenic illness consequent upon the dehumanization of patients in large public hospitals both draw upon the idea that the attitudes of members of the larger society generally, and those of hospital personnel specifically, bear on the course and outcome of a mental illness. This report offers evidence on differences in hospital attitudinal atmospheres and investigates their relationship with an important aspect of hospital effectiveness.

In previously published research, we have described the attitude dimensions implicit in the opinions of mental hospital personnel about the mentally ill and techniques for their measurement (Cohen and Struening, 1962); the standardization, factorial invariance across hospitals, and psychometric properties of the resulting "Opinions about Mental Illness" (OMI) questionnaire (Struening and Cohen, 1963); and the results of an analysis of the data from 8,248 subjects into factor score profiles and profile clusters for mental hospital occupational groups (Cohen and Struening, 1963).

The tooling-up phase of our work behind us, in the present report we relate our material to the larger purposes of the VA's Psychiatric Evaluation Project (PEP), a centrally directed, cooperative research project involving 12 VA neuropsychiatric hospitals. The major purpose of PEP's Phase I was to investigate the relationship between hospital effectiveness and various large-scale characteristics of these hospitals, primarily staff-patient ratio, with its implications for patient per diem cost, patient capacity, and architectural design as it bears on size of nursing unit. The development of the OMI was undertaken with the ultimate purpose of providing a means for studying yet another large-scale characteristic of these hospitals, their attitudinal atmospheres.

The OMI[1] is a factor analytically derived set of scales made up of 51 Likert-

From the *Journal of Consulting Psychology*, 1964, **28**, 291–298. Copyright © 1964. Reprinted by permission of the authors and the American Psychological Association.

[1] Printed test forms and materials for scoring and interpretation of the OMI are available from Abacus Associates, Inc., 443 Park Avenue South, New York, N.Y., 10016.

type items which yield factorially stable scores on five dimensions of attitude toward the mentally ill: A—*Authoritarianism,* with its characteristic submission, anti-intraception, and view of patients as an inferior, threatening outgroup; B— *Benevolence,* based on humanistic or religious grounds; C—*Mental Hygiene Ideology,* the tenets of mental health professionals; D—*Social Restrictiveness* of patients and expatients, who are viewed as a threat to family and society; and E—*Interpersonal Etiology* of mental illness, particularly parental love deprivation in childhood. There is some tendency for A and D to form one cluster, B and C to form another, and for the two clusters to be negatively related. E is negligibly related to the other scales (Cohen and Struening, 1962; Struening and Cohen, 1963).

Method

"Subjects" and Prior Data Analysis

Despite the use of OMI scale scores from a total of 3,148 employees to characterize the social atmospheres of mental hospitals and of 1,304 patients to characterize their effectiveness, the *n* of this study is 12, the number of hospitals involved.

HOSPITALS. Although the 12 PEP hospitals are all part of the VA system, they show, because of deliberate selection, considerable heterogeneity with regard to the factors of primary interest in Phase I. Table I describes the hospitals' geographic location, average daily patient load (ADPL), cost in dollars per patient per day (Per Diem Cost) and the number of employees per patient (Staff-Patient Ratio). The data are averages taken over the period during which the OMI was administered to the employees. As can be seen from the table, the hospitals are not only widely dispersed over the country, but differ considerably among themselves on the other bases for comparison: The extremes differ by a factor of four in size, of two in per patient daily cost, and of three in staff-patient ratio. The latter may be surprising, for it means that two patients are cared for by anywhere between one and three employees in a sample of hospitals all of which are

TABLE I

SIZE, COST, AND STAFFING CHARACTERISTICS OF THE 12 PEP PHASE I HOSPITALS

Hospital	Geographic Location	ADPL	Per Diem Cost	Staff/Patient Ratio
A	Central	650	$16.80	1.13
B	Northeast	1,959	10.72	.70
C	East central	1,594	9.86	.66
D	Northeast	1,690	10.25	.67
E	South	1,867	10.09	.65
F	South	831	13.93	1.04
G	North central	1,336	8.70	.57
H	Northeast	936	16.18	1.20
I	West	496	19.56	1.64
J	Central	1,030	18.06	1.22
K	West	651	11.27	.72
L	West	1,334	10.40	.70
Range		496–1,959	$8.70–19.56	.57–1.64

in the same national system. Associated with the variety of geographic locale are subcultural differences, as evidenced by large differences in the distribution of religious affiliation of employees among three of these hospitals (Struening and Cohen, 1963, p. 291).

EMPLOYEES In all, the 12 hospitals yielded OMI scales from 7,701 employees in 16 occupational groups (Cohen and Struening, 1963). The strategy of the present study was to define the social atmosphere of each hospital as the profile of OMI's ten standard score means (Struening and Cohen, 1963) of "atmosphere samples" drawn from the available data. For each hospital there were available OMI scales for 60 per cent to 95 per cent of all employees. An atmosphere sample was constructed for each hospital by determining the number of people employed in each of eight key occupation groups and services, and drawing from the available data for each group a random sample of OMI records equalling one-half of that number. The result is that the atmosphere sample of each hospital parallels the parent population's occupation distribution. The groups chosen were those with maximum patient contact: aides (nursing assistants), nurses, Physical Medicine and Rehabilitation Service, Special Services, nonpsychiatric physicians and dentists, psychiatrists, social workers, and psychologists. Note that the effect of this procedure is that each employee, be he aide or psychiatrist, equally influences the scale for his hospital. Further, there are typically some 20 aides and 4 nurses for each physician in a hospital. The "one man one vote" principle was nevertheless used with the rationale that (a) patients have much more day-to-day social experience with the more numerous personnel classes (aides and nurses) and (b) the not inconsiderable influence of the mental hospital professionals in the determination of the hospital's atmosphere is reflected in these more numerous lower echelon personnel. Although it is unlikely, a priori, that equal weighting of individuals is optimal, no alternative which would command agreement suggests itself. In any case, the ultimate validity of this procedure would be reflected in the present study in the existence of correlates with hospital effectiveness. The resulting OMI scale means and employee sample sizes (n_E) are given in Table II.

PATIENTS Our "validity criterion" is a function of the outcome of the hospitalization of a sample of patients admitted (or more frequently readmitted) to each of the 12 hospitals. This is the core sample of PEP Phase I which was preliminarily described by Jenkins and Gurel (1959), and is to be much more extensively described elsewhere. In general, for a period of a year in each of the 12 hospitals, functionally psychotic males who on admission were under 60, without serious physical impairment, and who had spent no more than three of the six months preceding admission in a psychiatric facility, became part of the PEP sample. The patient sample sizes are given in Table II (n_p). These patients were thoroughly studied upon admission and at regular intervals both in and outside the hospital for a period of four years. The fate of these patients, then, constitutes the body of criterion data for comparing the effectiveness of these hospitals.

The basis for evaluating a hospital's effectiveness in this study is the mean cumulative number of days its patients spend in the community during the 6-month and 12-month periods beginning with their admission, thus the converse of length of stay in the hospital. We do not assume that community stay is the sole basis for evaluating hospitals, but maintain that it is the most important one. For the mean number of in-community days (ICD) to be a meaningful way to index a hospital's effectiveness, however, another problem must be solved.

TABLE II

OMI PROFILES AND ADJUSTED ICD MEANS FOR THE 12 PEP HOSPITALS

Hospitals	n_E	n_P	A	B	C	D	E	ICD_6	ICD_{12}
Cluster I									
A	214	78	4.8	4.7	4.6	4.7	4.0	50	146
B	340	111	4.8	4.3	4.6	4.9	4.2	28	121
C	306	110	4.7	4.3	4.3	4.9	4.9	40	142
D	300	107	4.7	4.4	4.5	4.8	4.7	31	112
E	331	112	5.0	4.6	4.5	5.0	4.5	36	147
F	271	112	4.7	5.0	4.3	4.7	4.3	72	190
G	246	116	4.6	4.4	4.4	4.6	4.5	41	137
	2,007								
m_I			4.8	4.5	4.5	4.8	4.4	43	142
Cluster II									
H	279	113	3.9	4.8	4.7	3.6	4.3	43	152
I	178	100	3.8	4.6	4.4	3.7	4.7	57	151
J	325	113	3.9	4.8	4.2	4.0	4.7	61	183
	782								
m_{II}			3.9	4.7	4.4	3.8	4.6	54	162
Unclustered									
K	127	117	4.7	4.6	5.0	4.2	4.4	51	173
L	232	115	4.2	3.8	4.8	4.4	4.7	63	178
$\sigma_M{}^2$			.158	.090	.049	.211	.062	$\Sigma \sigma_M{}^2 = .570$	
Percentage			28	16	9	37	11		
ϵ_H			.20	.14	.08	.23	.10	101%	
ϵ_C			.96	.66	.53	.91	.00		

As noted, our n is 12 hospitals. We can "score" each hospital's social atmosphere by a constant instrument which yields a vector of five scale means, as described. However, to "score" their effectiveness using mean ICD, we are faced with the difficulty that the "items" for such a score are the patients in each hospital's PEP sample, a necessarily varying "test" from hospital to hospital. The validity of our procedure in assessing hospital effectiveness would be destroyed if some hospitals were to have a harder "test" (patients of poorer average prognosis) than others. To adjust for this, a factor-analytic study of patient behavior and historical admission characteristics was undertaken (but not reported in detail here). This yielded seven common and four specific factors which were then used as predictors of the ICD criteria in multiple regression analyses for the pooled sample of 1,304 patients on the two criteria. Entering each patient's predictor scores into the multiple regression equation yielded the optimally predicted number of in-community days, given his admission characteristics. When this value was subtracted from his actual ICD, the resulting residual scores were linearly freed of the influence of individual differences in prognosis. When these residuals were added to the grand mean of ICD, gathered by hospital, and averaged, the result was the *adjusted* ICD. The procedure is essentially equivalent to an analysis of covariance with 11 adjusting covariates. By this procedure, we equated the patient items by which we tested the hospitals. (The complete procedure and its results will be described in detail elsewhere.) The resulting mean adjusted in-community days for 6 months following admission (ICD_6) and for 12 months following admission (ICD_{12}) are given in Table II.

DATA ANALYSIS   The preliminary analyses described above resulted in the data given in Table II. For the present study, the first (and minor) step was to subject the hospital means on each of the OMI scales to a simple analysis of variance, supplemented by the computation of correlation ratios.

Second, the variance of the means of the hospitals for each scale was determined, these five values summed, and the percentage of this total contributed by each scale was found. The latter serves as an indication of the extent to which each contributes to the total differentiation of the hospital atmosphere profiles.

Next, following the same procedure used in the clustering of occupation groups (Cohen and Struening, 1963), the profiles over the five OMI scales which represented the social atmospheres were clustered using the method of Sawrey, Keller, and Conger (1960). Each hospital's set of five means was treated as coordinates determining its position as a point in a five space. The squared distance between any two hospitals i and j in such a space is simply $\sum_{k=1}^{5} (\bar{S}_{ik} - \bar{S}_{jk})^2 = D^2_{ij}$, i.e., the sum of the squared differences between the hospitals' means on the five OMI scales. When all D^2 were determined, they were organized into a 12×12 matrix. This is analogous to a correlation matrix, except that the entry represents squared distances and is therefore conversely related to similarity. For example, the smallest of the 66 D^2 values was .10 (between Hospitals C and D, and between D and G), and the largest was 3.29 (between E and H). The procedure then provides objective criteria and procedures for determining sets of two or more points which are close to each other and distant from other sets, i.e., clusters of hospitals having similar profiles of attitudes toward the mentally ill. The final and crucial step involved comparisons between hospital clusters so derived with regard to their adjusted ICD_6 and ICD_{12} values by t and U tests.

Results

Table II gives for each hospital the employee sample sizes (n_E), the patient sample sizes (n_p), the OMI Scale means and the two adjusted mean ICD criteria, as well as other data to be discussed below.

When simple analyses of variance are run on hospital differences for each OMI scale, the resulting F ratios, each based on 11 and 3,136 df, are all significant at $p < .005$. This finding by itself is trivial in that the statistical test is so powerful that even inconsequentially small differences among the population means would almost certainly be detected as significant (Cohen, 1965). A more meaningful way to index the degree of association between a scale score and hospital group membership is by means of ϵ (epsilon), an unbiased correlation ratio (Cohen, 1965; Peters and Van Voorhis, 1940, pp. 319–324, 353–357). These values are given as ϵ_H in Table II. They are seen to be quite modest (although significant), much lower, for example, than comparable values obtained within hospitals when either occupation or education level is used as a grouping variable; these run as high as .6 (Cohen and Struening, 1962, p. 357). It would be surprising if hospital affiliation accounted for a large portion of the variance of attitudes toward the mentally ill. Within this range, we note that the 12 hospitals differ more sharply on Authoritarianism (A) and Social Restrictiveness (D) than they do on Benevolence (B), Mental Hygiene Ideology (C), and belief in Interpersonal Etiology (E).

The same relative differentiation is shown by the $\sigma_M{}^2$ row of the table. Since all scales are standardized to the same variance between individuals, the variance of the hospital means gives directly the relative amount of hospital differentiation yielded by each scale separately. To facilitate comparisons between scales, these values are also expressed as percentages of their total. They are necessarily perfectly monotonically related to the ϵ_H values, since they are alternative indexes of degree of differentiation. The percentages of total variance of means are included because of their significance to the clustering procedure. A scale's percentage value gives its relative contribution to the total of the squared distances between hospital points in the five space, and therefore the extent to which it determines cluster formation.

The outcome of the clustering procedure is given by the organization of Table II. Two clusters resulted, and, since the procedure is not procrustean, two hospitals (K and L) had sufficiently unique profiles to remain unclustered. Thus, in effect, the procedure has yielded four types, two common and two unique. As a check on the efficacy of the procedure, simple analyses of variance were performed on the 12 *means*, organized into these four types, with *n*'s of 7, 3, 1, and 1, respectively, and the resulting ϵ_c values in Table II index the extent to which typal membership accounts for the differences among hospital means on the scales. The pre-eminence of Authoritarianism (.96) and Social Restrictiveness (.91) in determining cluster formation is again seen, with Benevolence (.66) and Mental Hygiene Ideology (.53) somewhat involved, and belief in Interpersonal Etiology noncontributory (.00).

Each of the two clusters' atmospheres is best described by the mean of its constituent hospitals' means on each scale. These values are given in rows m_I and m_{II} of Table II, and can be directly compared with each other and with those of the unclustered hospitals.

The essential distinction between the two clusters is that the Cluster I social atmosphere is high in Authoritarianism (4.8) and Social Restrictiveness (4.8) relative to that of Cluster II (3.9 and 3.8, respectively). The difference is quite large, being of the order of a half standard deviation. The other scales hardly differ between the clusters. We thus have a major authoritarian-restrictive axis polarizing the social atmospheres of the hospitals.

The type represented by Hospital K is as high on Authoritarianism as that of Cluster I, but is clearly lower on Social Restrictiveness and very high on Mental Hygiene Ideology (5.0). It is a relatively authoritarian atmosphere mitigated by the tenets of the mental hygiene movement and a relatively low level of restrictiveness.

The Hospital L type is unique in its lowest by far Benevolence (3.8) with high Mental Hygiene Ideology (4.8). Authoritarianism and Social Restrictiveness are relatively low. This profile is similar in form (but of course not in degree) to that given by mental health professionals, Benevolence being low presumably because of its "unsophisticated" quality (Cohen and Struening, 1962, 1963). Means on the Benevolence scale this low are, however, unusual, except in hospital "blue-collar" workers.

The final and "pay-off" step related the results of clustering the 12 hospital atmosphere profiles to the prognosis-adjusted "in-community days" in the 6 and 12 months following admission (ICD_6 and ICD_{12}). It is here that we face up to a total sample of 12 and the sharply reduced power of statistical tests based on such small samples (Cohen, 1962, 1965). In addition to comparing Cluster I ($n = 7$) with Cluster II ($n = 3$), we also contrasted Cluster I with the remaining five hospitals (Noncluster I), i.e., Cluster II plus Hospitals K and L. The first comparison is between seven high and three low authoritarian-restrictive hospitals. The second contrasts the seven high authoritarian-restrictive hospitals with the remaining five hospitals. The latter as a set are not of homogeneous atmosphere profiles, yet share the characteristic of *not* being authoritarian-restrictive. Table III gives the results of these two comparisons for both ICD_6 and ICD_{12}. Because of the possible effects of parametric assumption failure with such small samples (Cohen, 1965), the usual t tests were supplemented by Mann-Whitney U tests.

When one considers the low power of these tests due to small n, the two-tailed p values in the table are impressive, even reaching the conventional .05 level in both tests of one comparison. Another issue that bears on the appraisal of the p values is the consideration that if we limit our generalizations to the population of 40 VA mental hospitals, the application of the "finite-population correction" would increase the significance materially. Further, the significance tests (particularly t) are seriously affected by the discrepantly high ICD values of Hospital F (72 and 190), which are not only much higher than those of the other Cluster I hospitals, but are in fact the highest values among all 12 hospitals (see Table II). The eight significance tests in the table are, of course, not independent, both because of the pairing of t and U tests, but also because Noncluster I includes Cluster II and because ICD_{12} includes ICD_6. The eight tests constitute as many slightly different perspectives on the single question "Is hospital social atmosphere associated with length of patient stay in the community?" In the light of the foregoing statistical considerations, an appraisal of Table III leads us to respond

TABLE III

PROGNOSIS-ADJUSTED NUMBER OF IN-COMMUNITY DAYS AND HOSPITAL SOCIAL ATMOSPHERE TYPE

		Social Atmosphere Type		
		Cluster II (N = 3)	Cluster I (N = 7)	Noncluster I (N = 5)
ICD_6				
Mean		54	43	55
I versus II:	t	1.18, $p > .25$, $r_{pb} = .38$		
	U	4, $p = .18$		
I versus non-I:	t			1.68, $p = .14$, $r_{pb} = .47$.
	U			6, $p = .07$
ICD_{12}				
Mean		162	142	167
I versus II:	t	1.23, $p = .25$, $r_{pb} = .47$		
	U	3, $p = .12$		
I versus non-I:	t			2.23, $p = .05$, $r_{pb} = 5.8$.
	U			5, $p = .05$

with little hesitation in the affirmative. Specifically, these data show that the high authoritarian-restrictive atmosphere is associated with fewer days spent by the patient in the community.

To provide a descriptive index of *degree* of relationship between atmosphere group membership and ICD, the *t* ratios in Table III were converted into point-biserial *r*'s (r_{pb}) (Cohen, 1965). This also avoids the fallacious comparison of *t*'s based on differing *df*. The four r_{pb} values suggest that the association is of the same order of magnitude for ICD_6 and ICD_{12}, but that the contrast of the high authoritarian-restrictive hospitals (I) is less sharp when compared with only those of mirror-image profile (II) than when compared with hospitals of both mirror-image and other *non*authoritarian-*non*restrictive profiles (Non-I).

Since our unit of comparison is quite concrete, namely a day spent by a patient outside the hospital, there is an eminently practical way of describing our results. Depending on the basis of comparison (Cluster II or Noncluster I), a mean net addition of 11–12 days in the hospital during the half year following admission, and 20–25 days in the year following admission, is seen to be associated with the high authoritarian-restrictive atmosphere (after adjustment for differences in prognosis).

Discussion

In our work thus far, we have cautioned repeatedly against a too ready assumption that psychologists know what kind of hospital atmosphere is good for mental patients prior to an objective empirical assessment (Cohen and Struening, 1962, 1963). For our scientific pains, we are now open to the scornful charge of having worked several years to discover what everyone knew, namely that authoritarian-restrictive hospital atmospheres are bad for patients. Before we draw this "obvious" conclusion even now, some issues still merit attention.

The Criterion

It might be argued, for example, by the directors of such hospitals as B or D, that a mental hospital's function far transcends getting its patients out quickly and keeping them out. Indeed, being physicians they might point out that no one would dream of using such a criterion in general hospitals—why use it in psychiatric hospitals? There are several reasons.

1. The patient population under study is almost entirely made up of chronic schizophrenics who, although recently in the community, were first hospitalized 10–15 years before, i.e., during or shortly after World War II. These are now predominantly "way of life" schizophrenics, in and out of mental hospitals for periods of varying length. For such patients, cure is not a realistic goal. One seeks instead to achieve "social recovery" or at least an avoidance of deterioration, for the first of which being out of the hospital is a minimum condition, and possibly for the latter as well (cf. Goffman, 1962). We assume that over a period of time, on the average, the more time spent in the community by a group of such patients, the greater their degree of social recovery. We also assume that, when readmissions occur, the effective hospital keeps them brief.

2. We subscribe to the view that the mental hospital is a necessary evil, and that, with some exceptions, patients tend to be dehumanized or at least de-

personalized by large doses of the total institution. Although much can be done and is being done to mitigate these effects, we believe that the typical patient, when no longer acutely psychotic, is better off in his typical home and community than he is in the typical mental hospital. On humanitarian grounds, then, we believe that the best possible amount of hospitalization is the least possible amount.

3. One might prefer to define a hospital's effectiveness in terms of the symptomatic improvement of its patients. We accept this criterion in principle, and a later PEP report will be devoted to its application in detail. However, we have preliminary evidence which suggests that this criterion is lacking in between hospital variance, i.e., the hospitals do not seem to be strongly differentiated in their ability to reduce psychopathological symptoms.

4. Finally, there are the obvious financial considerations: The less time spent in the hospital and the more time spent in the community, the less the net cost to society.

Causality

The proposition "The authoritarian-restrictive hospital atmosphere is bad for patients" requires specification and causal analysis. We do not claim, because we have not shown, that such atmospheres delay symptomatic improvement, or hasten deterioration, or foster dependency, although these are possible concomitants. What we claim to have shown is that this type of atmosphere is associated with fewer days spent in the community in the year following admission. Although all community days were cumulated, overwhelmingly, community days are lost due to delayed release and not to a pattern of release and return to the hospital during this period. What crystallizes out, then, is an association between an authoritarian-restrictive attitude climate among the employees and a relative delay in releasing patients. The relationship is not directly causal, since the makers of general hospital policy and decisions about release constitute so small a portion of the employee sample that their *direct* effect on the OMI scale means is small. However, as the experts and opinion leaders of the hospital community, through precept, example, and policy, their indirect effect on employee attitude is probably large. Thus, we interpret the main lines of causal influence as emanating from the policy-setting professionals, who influence employee attitude on the one hand, and determine the duration of patients' hospital stay on the other. We thus revise our proposition to read,

> The professional leadership which fosters (without necessarily professing) authoritarian-restrictive attitudes among its employees also sets policies which delay the release of their patients, and that (for the reasons given above) is bad.

This statement, in turn, requires some qualification. The relationship is a moderate and not a strong one. We have traced out a skein from a tangled causal network, and no more. Clearly, there are other factors involved. Witness Hospital F, a relatively small, relatively high-staff Southern hospital (see Table I). Although a Cluster I hospital, it has the highest values for ICD_6 and ICD_{12} in the entire sample. Is this perhaps partially accounted for by its size and/or staff? Or are its relatively high Authoritarian and Social Restrictiveness scale means an artifact of its Southern locale? Or, continuing in this vein, and despite the evidence of the clustering procedure, is it really not properly classed with the other Cluster I hospitals, since it has the highest Benevolence mean among the twelve hospitals which is particularly discrepant among Cluster I hospitals (Table II)? Later work may make possible some tentative answers to these conundrums. Suffice it here to say that the relationships are complex.

Hospital Atmosphere Types and Effectiveness

Finally, we need to consider the meaning of the contrasts in atmosphere types. We have seen that the profile of high authoritarian-restrictiveness (Cluster I) was poorer on the criterion than that of low (Cluster II), but that the other profiles (Hospitals K and L) were at least as good as the latter (Table III). Thus, we can at least say that effectiveness as we have defined it is not solely a matter of standing on the authoritarian-restrictive axis. For example, Hospital K, which is relatively high in effectiveness, has an Authoritarianism scale mean typical of Cluster I hospitals, but is relatively low on Social Restrictiveness. But one cannot conclude that it is the latter which counts, since the unique profile of this hospital features the highest Mental Hygiene Ideology (C) mean in the sample (Table II). Hospital L, which is low on both Authoritarianism and Social Restrictiveness, has the second highest Mental Hygiene Ideology mean and the lowest Benevolence mean. With two unique profiles occurring in 12 hospitals, both associated with relatively high criterion values, there must certainly be yet other "good" profiles in the population of hospitals awaiting discovery. The only generalizations that we can hazard here are that (*a*) the high authoritarian-restrictive *combination* (with other scales at the mean) is "bad," (*b*) its mirror-image is "good," (*c*) there are at least two other "good" profiles (possibly characterized by high Mental Hygiene Ideology) and (*d*) further generalizations are dangerous until many more hospitals are studied.

We have resisted the temptation of relating the characteristics of the hospitals of Table I to the atmosphere profile and ICD data, and warn the reader that he does so at his own risk. In all, there are some 11 variables involved for the 12 hospitals, and the number of degrees of freedom dwindles rapidly toward zero. The PEP staff plans later presentations along these lines, including some based on the total population of VA hospitals.

47 / Power-Orientations
in the Mental Hospital

Morris Rosenberg / Leonard I. Pearlin

Among the various interpersonal processes in which sociologists have legitimate interest, power must stand among those in the front rank. Power has been defined, probably most appropriately, as the ability to influence the behavior of others in accord with one's intentions (Goldhamer and Shils, 1939, p. 171). The requirements of social function and social control in the mental hospital make it imperative that nurses direct the behavior of patients in certain ways, i.e., that they exercise power. This is unavoidable and indispensable. It is not a question of *whether* nursing personnel will exercise power, then, but what *means* they will employ.

In the present report we do not have information regarding actual power exercise, but we do have data dealing with the methods different nurses *say* that they actually would use in a particular situation. For this reason we shall not be concerned with actual power exercise, which connotes an act involving the behavioral compliance of one person with the intention of another, but with *power-orientations*.

Sample and Method

The subjects of the study are members of the nursing service below the level of supervisor in a large public mental hospital in the Middle Atlantic region. There are approximately 7,500 inpatients on the hospital's rolls; approximately half are white and half are Negro. The questionnaires were self-administered and anonymous; of the 1,315 nursing personnel who received questionnaires, 1,138, or 86 per cent, returned completed and usable questionnaires. In addition, selected questionnaire topics were examined by means of intensive interviews.

Three ranks are represented among the personnel included in the study, each differing in responsibilities, authority, and rewards. The lowest rank is called nursing assistants; next to them are charge attendants who have been given the charge of wards on the basis of experience and demonstrated ability. The third group, smallest in number, is composed of registered nurses. This group has authority over the preceding ranks and is usually responsible for running the wards. These three groups are collectively referred to as nursing personnel. Forty per cent of them are males and 60 per cent are females.

One of the topics covered in these questionnaires was the power-orientations of nursing personnel toward patients. The respondents were presented with a hypothetical situation and were asked to rank each of five power methods from the one

From *Human Relations*, 1962, **15**, 335–349. Copyright © 1962. Reprinted by permission of the authors and *Human Relations*.

they would be most likely to employ to that which they would be least likely to employ. The hypothetical situation was the following:

> *What would you do in this situation?* Patient J. R. is a male schizophrenic, 25 years of age. He has been in the hospital seven months. Recently he has gotten into the habit of sleeping much of the day and is up during the night walking around and disturbing the other patients. You feel that the patient is not especially nervous or depressed and he can understand perfectly anything you tell him. However, in the past he has shown an unwillingness to go along with ward routine and you expect him to be stubborn about changing his sleeping habits. Nevertheless, you feel that the patient *should* change his sleeping habits —that it would be best for him and the other patients. Let's say that you could not ask for advice or help from the doctors or anyone else, but that you had to decide for yourself how you would get this stubborn patient to change his sleeping habits.
>
>   Which of these things would you *actually* do?

The alternatives presented were:

1. I would force him to go to bed when everybody else does. (This statement was intended to serve as an index of *coercive power,* i.e., power based on compulsion, sanctions, or the threat of sanctions.)
2. Since a nurse or nursing assistant has the right to tell a patient what to do, I would simply tell him to change his sleeping habits. (This was the index of *legitimate authority,* i.e., the individual's right to control the behavior of another by virtue of his objectively defined status in a formal organization.)
3. I would offer him certain privileges or grant him certain benefits if he changes his sleeping habits. (This was the index of *contractual power,* i.e., power based upon a system of reciprocal obligations.)
4. I would try to explain to him the reasons for changing his sleeping habits and try to convince him that it is for his own good or the good of other patients. (This was the index of *persuasion,* i.e., power based upon the ability to convince another to behave in the desired way.)
5. I would try to figure out some ways to keep him busy during the day so he would *want* to sleep at night. (This was the index of manipulation,[1] i.e., a method of getting someone to behave in the desired way without this person being aware that this is the power-wielder's intention.)

Respondents were asked to indicate which of these methods they would actually use first in this situation, which they would actually use second, and so on up to the fifth method. Since various considerations or criteria inevitably enter into a power decision of this sort, they were also asked to rank these methods in terms of which method had the "best chances of working" (the criterion of *effectiveness*), which method involved the "most work and trouble" (the criterion of *effort*), and which method they personally "like best" (the criterion of *values*). (This differentiation among modes of power and criteria for power decisions is drawn from Rosenberg, 1956.)

It should be emphasized that we are dealing with a single hypothetical situation which, though quite realistic, cannot be taken to represent all possible situations requiring the exercise of power in the mental hospital. Our aim, then, is to learn

---

[1] Though the term "manipulation" has, in common parlance, pejorative connotations, we shall indicate later that this is actually a form of "benevolent manipulation."

something about how nursing personnel tend to *think* about power—what criteria are likely to be brought to bear or what factors taken into account when a power decision is required. While the responses are necessarily influenced by the nature of the situation presented, they may still serve the central purpose of this paper, *viz.*, to illustrate and elaborate some of the mental operations used by nurses when confronted with situations requiring the exercise of power.

Preferences for Power Modes

Table I indicates the proportions selecting the various power modes as their first choices in terms of their predicted actual behavior and in terms of the criteria of effectiveness, effort, and values. Nursing personnel, we find, are most

TABLE I

MODES OF POWER SELECTED AS "FIRST CHOICE" IN TERMS OF PREDICTED BEHAVIOR AND ACCORDING TO POWER CRITERIA

	Method Would Actually Use	Method Considered Most Effective	Method Considered Most Work and Trouble	Method Would Like to Use
Persuasion	54	37	13	54
Benevolent manipulation	38	47	27	32
Legitimate authority	5	4	3	12
Contractual power	1	7	3	1
Coercion	2	4	55	2
Total per cent	100	100	100	100
Number	(1,033)	(1,037)	(1,035)	(1,040)

likely to say that they would actually use persuasion; the second most frequently chosen alternative is manipulation. With regard to the criterion of effectiveness, manipulation is most often chosen, followed by persuasion. With regard to the method considered the most work and trouble, coercion is most frequently chosen; manipulation is next most likely to be selected. With regard to the method the respondents would most like to use, persuasion is most frequently chosen, followed by manipulation.

In general, then, nursing personnel are most likely to say that they would use persuasion; this method is most highly valued and is second most likely to be considered effective. Manipulation is the method second most likely to be used and second most likely to be valued; although manipulation is considered the most effective of all methods, it is, next to coercion, viewed as involving the most work and trouble. Few nurses say that they would actually use coercion, contractual power, or legitimate authority as their first choice; only about a sixth value any of these methods most highly and an equally small proportion consider them most effective. Authority and contractual power are rarely considered the most work and trouble, but coercion stands first in this regard.

The question we now wish to raise is: Why are some modes of power so frequently selected and, equally important, why are others so consistently avoided?

In order to obtain a clearer understanding of the bases of these various selections and rejections, let us consider these various power modes in greater detail.

Coercion

One of the most striking findings in the study of power-orientations in the mental hospital is the general repugnance felt about the use of coercion. This is not to say, of course, that coercion is not used. In dealing with psychotics there is often no alternative. A patient in an uncontrollable destructive rage must often be constrained by sheer physical force. In addition, of course, sadistic nursing personnel who obtain pathological satisfaction from the use of coercion are not unknown. But it is impressive how strongly the hospital norms are opposed to the use of force. In our hypothetical example, fully 68 per cent said they would use force only as a last resort. However much nursing personnel may actually employ force, they do not freely admit to its use; overwhelmingly, they express repugnance at the exercise of brute power.

One might be inclined to suspect that this apparent distaste for the use of coercion is less a reflection of the nurses' actual attitudes than of their belief that this is the "right" thing to say. We found, however, that our respondents very rarely rejected the use of coercion with pious proclamations of lofty and ethical motives. On the contrary, pragmatic and self-interested considerations assumed first priority. For example, we asked our respondents which of the five power modes they would consider the "most work and trouble." For more than any other single method—indeed, *more than all four other methods combined*—the coercive solution is viewed as producing the maximum difficulty *for the nurse*.

One obvious reason for avoiding force is that it is likely to elicit physical resistance. In the ensuing struggle, both sides may often end up spent, exhausted, injured, and resentful. A male nursing assistant said:

> Well, forcing the patient, in my opinion, I don't like to force nobody to do nothin'. Sometimes the situation arises, you have to force the patient to do certain things. . . . But sometimes you start to force the patient, that's when the patient starts swinging on you. Then he may hurt you, or you get tangled up together, you may hurt him. . . . One of these times you can be on the ward by yourself and . . . he'll clobber the devil out of you. I always find it best to try to talk to him.

A second objection to coercion appears to lie in the *impermanence* of its consequences. In other words, while coercion may accomplish the nurse's immediate purposes, it is often viewed as having deleterious effects in the long run. A male head nurse said:

> If a nursing assistant ordered him to go to bed, and he didn't, he tried to take him by the hand and lead him to bed and he didn't, he'd call for some help. If he called me, chances are I'd be back up four or five times during the night. And the next night. . . . Some patients will get up just to be doing the opposite of what he told them to do.

A third consideration in the use of coercion is that it is believed to generate resentment, which, by reducing voluntary cooperation, compounds the difficulty it was designed to alleviate.

> Yes, the problem, I think, once you force the patient, if you ever ask (him) to do something else, he'll say: "No, I'm not going to do it" or "I don't want to do it"—especially if they have the choice—because "You made me go to bed when I didn't want to go to bed." If he has the choice, he won't do it.

A fourth objection mentioned by the nursing staff is that coercion not only bears upon the resistant patient but may have consequences for the entire ward; these consequences, in turn, react back to plague and afflict the nursing staff.

> When force was used to put the patient to bed, the patient became loud, combative, disturbing the other patients, and naturally the other patients got upset and, as a result, the whole ward was upset, causing the other patients to remain up all night.

Nursing personnel pointed out another consequence of the involuntary compliance which attends the use of coercion. The patient may indeed yield, but it is the nature of his compliance which is affected, *viz.*, if the patient reluctantly yields to the threat, he may tend to sabotage or undermine its purpose. He may in fact do what is desired, but do it in such a half-hearted, inefficient, reluctant manner that the purpose of the coercion is often defeated. Thus, one male nurse reported that many patients were compelled to seek work outside the hospital. They immediately told their prospective employers, who were initially disposed to hire them, that they were mental patients; they were almost certain to be refused employment. They could then return to the hospital and report that they had been unable to obtain employment.

Finally, one broad, long-range consequence considered by the nursing staff is that the use of coercion may tend to poison the atmosphere on the ward. Although compliance might be achieved in the immediate situation, coercion may render the ward an unpleasant place *for the nurse* to work in. A female nurse said:

> Certainly if you try to force him to do something without any explanation, you just generate extreme hostility and resentment, and this can lead to all sorts of repercussions. I certainly don't like to handle a ward that has discontented, sullen, irritable people. Your ward atmosphere is one thing that can be poisoned by a small group of malcontents.

Nursing personnel thus do not reject coercion with pious proclamations of horror; their emphasis rather is on the fact that it has definite *practical* disadvantages. There is, first of all, the danger of immediate resistance, with possible injury to the nurse or patient. Second, there is the generation of resentment, which may call forth future violent reprisal, lack of cooperation in situations in which the patient has an option, or half-hearted compliance. Third, although coercion may achieve its immediate purpose, it may be necessary to repeat it time after time, at great cost to the nursing staff. Fourth, the use of force may produce general confusion and consternation on the ward, thus expanding the nurse's problem from the resistant patient to the entire ward. Finally, coercion may generate a sullen resentment which makes work unpleasant for the nurse. Over the long haul, then, it is easier and more effective to get someone to *want* to do as you like, or to be willing to do as you like, than to force him to do as you like. It is no wonder that nurses are inclined to employ force only when all else fails, when no other recourse remains. In the mental hospital, coercion is not only impolite; it is downright dangerous and difficult.

Contractual Power

In advanced societies, one of the most common methods of affecting the behavior of others is by means of contractual power. Specifically, contractual power involves gaining compliance with one's will by providing rewards or advantages in return. In the present context, it was expressed in the phrase: "I would offer him certain privileges or grant him certain benefits if he changes his sleeping habits." Despite its general popularity, however, this mode of control is firmly opposed by the nursing personnel of the mental hospital. Only 5 per cent said that they would actually use this method as one of their first two choices and only 10 per cent said that this was either their first or second value preference.

Why, then, are nurses so reluctant to use this method? It is certainly not considered much work and trouble—indeed, it ranks with legitimate authority as the easiest method of all. The simplicity and parsimony of using contractual power are indicated by the male nurse who said:

> I know a lot of nursing assistants do (use this method). . . . I do too. If I ask a patient would he mind helping me, he'll say no. Well, I'll just automatically say: "Well, I'll give you a cigarette if you do," and he'll help, because most of the people here will respond to tobacco.

Nothing could be simpler. Nor is contractual power considered particularly ineffective—indeed, more nurses feel that it works well than consider authority or coercion effective.

The main opposition to contractual power stems from a quality it possesses which is not characteristic of other power modes, *viz.*, that each party influences the behavior of the other to some degree. If, in order to get someone to do what we want, we agree to do what he wants, then we are subject to his control and thereby sacrifice some of our own freedom. This is obviously a desirable form of power from the viewpoint of the power-subject, but not from the viewpoint of the power-wielder.

One male nursing assistant stated:

> Oh yeah, that works well. If you say, "I'll give you parole" or "You can have cigarettes" or whatever he wants—something like that, you know—it'll work, but you always got a kickback. When you don't have no cigarettes or some candy, the patient won't do what you ask him. So when you come to a problem like that, you're leaving yourself open for the kickback. If you don't start it, you won't have the problem to confront with.

With reference to this mode of power, an assistant said:

> If you start a patient—go and give him cigarettes and candy or buy him a Coca-Cola—he start lookin' for that. And when you stop doin' that for him, he's going to be demandin' that he wants it. And it cause bad friendship between you and patients.

Another limitation to the use of contractual power stems from the requirement of objective treatment in a formal organization. If this form of power, so desirable from the viewpoint of the patient, is applied to one patient, then other patients, occupying the same status, may claim the same privilege for themselves. A male nursing assistant reported:

> It has a tendency to change the whole morale on the ward, too. If one patient can get privileges and candy and stuff for doing something, the rest of them, they want the same thing. When they don't get it, then they resent you too. So it pays—no favors. . . . Once you start giving them candy, this one will get candy, that one will get candy, they going to tell you about it.

A third reason for the reluctance to employ contractual power in the mental hospital is that it is seen as an ethically dubious method. In this context it smacks of bribery, a method which to many nurses is morally repugnant.

The rejection of the use of contractual power is thus based upon both ethical and pragmatic grounds. To yield to the use of this method places the nurse under an obligation to the patient; a new set of expectations are established based on the fact that the nurse, in exercising power over the patient, at the same time places himself in the power of the patient. And since large organizations tend to develop impersonal and abstract rules, the advantages of contract to one patient are liable to be claimed by all. Contractual power, if it is to be exercised, must either be employed generally or not at all. Hence the nurse's resistance to the use of contract is based emphatically on his *self-interest* as well as on moral opposition to the method.

Legitimate Authority

Legitimate authority refers to the *right* of an individual to direct the actions of another by virtue of his objective, impersonal position in a social system. The essential underpinning of most formal organizations is legitimate authority, usually supported by implicit coercion. We may say that most formal organizations tend in the direction of the increasing use of legitimate authority for both ethical and pragmatic reasons. In the present study, it was indexed by the statement: "Since a nurse or nursing assistant has the right to tell a patient what to do, I would simply tell him to change his sleeping habits."

It is thus interesting to note that only 13 per cent of the respondents said that legitimate authority would be either the first or second means of power they would employ. Is this attributable to an ethical repugnance about the use of this method? The answer is no; for we find that twice as many respondents (28 per cent) say they would *like* to use this method as their first or second choices as claim they would *actually* do so. Nor is it due to the difficulty of employing authority; authority shares almost equal rank with contractual power as the *easiest* method to apply. The main reason why so many people who would like to use legitimate authority do not do so is that they feel it *will not work*.

It should be pointed out that this relationship between values and effectiveness is not generally true of other methods of exercising power. We find, for example, that only 17 per cent of those who valued authority most highly also thought it was most likely to work. This contrasts with 79 per cent of those who most valued manipulation, 56 per cent of those who most valued persuasion, and 53 per cent of those who most valued coercion. The only comparable alternative is the contractual method, which was considered most effective by only 15 per cent of those who valued it most highly.

Why is legitimate authority considered so ineffective by members of the nursing staff? One reason is that legitimate authority is always based upon a system of mutual expectations and the acceptance of rights. When nurses therefore say that they consider legitimate power relatively ineffective, they are essentially saying that patients do not accept the *right* of the nurse to tell them what to do. This is illustrated in the response of a male nurse:

> I think that many of the patients feel that hospital employees are nothing but bosses and such, and that they don't want to be told what to do by hospital employees. I hear it once in a while: "Well, who does he think he is, just because he happens to be a hospital employee or an attendant or a nurse—tell me what to do." And it comes from the whole group, not just one type of patient. "You better not boss me around."

Not only are nurses inclined to doubt that patients will acknowledge their right to direct their actions, but there are many nurses who do not *claim* this right; they, too, deny that their position entitles them to use this mode of power.

> Well, I'm not so sure that we really do have a right. Sometimes I don't sleep all night and I wouldn't want someone to force me to go to bed if I wanted to stay up. If someone gave me a logical reason for going to bed, then, if it was necessary for someone's convenience, that I could help them—then I would go. But if someone said: "All right, let's get to bed," then I [would start] swinging.

It should be recognized that the relatively small number saying that they would use legitimate power is probably more a function of the difficulty of the hypothetical situation posed than the actual frequency with which it is employed. In the routine day-to-day and moment-to-moment situations on the ward, legitimate authority is almost always the most common mode of power-exercise, but this does not mean that it is most likely to be employed when a difficult situation arises. It is under these conditions—special, extraordinary, non-routine situations—that nursing personnel are likely to doubt that their claims for legitimacy will be honored or should even appropriately be invoked.

Why, under such conditions, do nursing personnel so often expect legitimate authority to fail in its purpose? For one thing, most mental patients do not enter the hospital voluntarily and therefore do not accept its authority structure. They may yield to coercion or persuasion, but they may refuse to acknowledge rights. If a patient rejects the institution and his position in it, then the entire basis of legitimacy is undermined.

An additional factor is that the scope of one's life which comes under the authority system in a "total institution" (Goffman, 1957) tends to be vaguely defined. In a university, for example, a professor has the right to tell a student to read a certain book but he has no right to tell him to date a certain girl or to eat a certain food. In the mental hospital, on the other hand, the limits as to what a nurse can or cannot control are more vaguely defined. The nurse may feel he has certain rights of control which the patient denies are legitimate. In these circumstances quite different forms of power must be invoked.

Benevolent Manipulation

The least overt form of power, the one least violating the individual's sense of freedom, is manipulation. The essence of the manipulative mode of power lies in the fact that A gets B to do what he wants without B being aware of the fact that this is A's intention; in this situation, B cannot feel that his freedom is abridged or violated. This mode of power exercise, we find, is one of the most frequently selected; it ranks second only to persuasion among the five power alternatives presented. Fully 38 per cent of our sample said that this was the means they would be most likely to employ, and an additional 50 per cent ranked it second. In other words, seven out of every eight respondents indicated that this was one of the two methods they would be most disposed to use.

The term "manipulation," of course, was not used in the questionnaire, since it tends to smack of trickery, indirection, and below-board maneuvers. In the situation under consideration, the alternative did involve manipulation, but it might more appropriately be called "benevolent manipulation." The distinctive characteristic of benevolent manipulation is that the power-wielder exercises power over the power-subject for the benefit of the subject or of the institution, not for his own benefit, and the manipulation does the power-subject no harm. It is this sort of manipulation which achieves such popularity in the mental hospital.

On what basis do we conclude that the manipulation under consideration actually has this benevolent property? (1) Next to coercion, manipulation was said to involve the *greatest* effort and difficulty. Twenty-seven per cent considered it the *most* work and trouble and an additional 29 per cent said it was the second most difficult. If the nurses were selfishly motivated in their selection of this means, they would hardly choose a method which they personally considered more time-consuming and energy-consuming than almost any other. (2) Next to persuasion, manipulation is characterized as the most *desirable* form of power exercise. This mode of power is thus hailed by nurses as corresponding to their highest ideals. (3) There is some indication that this mode of power is selected by those nurses who are most kindly disposed toward patients. Those who completely *denied* that "patients don't have the same feelings as others" (p<.10) and that "patients are on the lookout to get around the ward rules" (p<.10) were more likely to choose manipulation than those who agreed with these statements. It is further relevant to note that those who had high faith in people were more likely to select manipulation than those with low faith in people (p<.01). The manipulation suggested here, then, is not a self-interested manipulation based on contempt for, and hostility toward, patients; on the contrary, it is one motivated by kindness, respect, and a desire to help.

It is interesting to note that the method of benevolent manipulation is selected not because it is thought to be easy but in spite of the fact that it is considered difficult. A male nurse explains this fact in the following way:

> Well, if you have 45 or 50 patients and are trying to figure out something for one patient when you're worried about the others and you have medicines . . . you find that these people can (wander) off awfully easy and you're spending your time looking for them and finally find them in a corner somewhere sleeping. . . . Then, too, to keep them busy, actually busy, once you do find them is about as bad as getting them to go to bed—forcing them to go to bed.

The complexity of the problem is amplified by the fact that it is so often necessary to take account of the unique, idiosyncratic qualities of each patient.

> Well, I wouldn't try to follow courses of action which are truly make-do methods—work for work's sake sort of thing. I think I would try to find courses of action which would concern his interest, his previous background which

would include such things as his hobbies, and his work background, what sort of tasks were assigned to him. I certainly wouldn't expect a man who was interested in botany to be interested in cleaning out latrines. Nor would I expect a man only capable of cleaning out latrines to do statistical work.

Given the idiosyncrasies of each patient, the large number of patients requiring care, and the variety of institutional regulations limiting the range of solutions potentially available, benevolent manipulation is understandably difficult to use. What, therefore, may account for the popularity of benevolent manipulation as a mode of power in the mental hospital?

One factor is probably the general suspicion of power which tends to characterize a democratic society. Where power must be exercised, the value system prescribes that it be made as palatable and inoffensive as possible. When manipulative power is employed, the power-subject's sense of abridgement of freedom is at a minimum.

The second reason has to do with the image of the relationship of the nurse to the patient. In a sense, it is seen as similar to the relationship of the parent to the child or the doctor to the patient, i.e., power is exercised for the benefit of the power-subject rather than for that of the power-wielder. In order to avoid the less desirable techniques of force or bribery, and recognizing the ineffectiveness of rational persuasion, a mother may often resort to indirect means, such as distraction, to keep her child from harm or otherwise to advance his interests. The nurse may tend to see her relationship to the patient in a similar way. Benevolent manipulation achieves the desired end with no harm to the patient or anyone else and with the minimum of patient resistance and resentment. Despite the difficulty in its use, then, benevolent manipulation is considered a happy solution to the problem of power in the mental hospital, for it is the least overt, least conspicuous, least evident form of power.

Persuasion

The most favored method of exercising power in the mental hospital is persuasion. Fifty-four per cent of our respondents said this would be the first method they would actually employ and an additional 39 per cent ranked it second. Persuasion appeals particularly to the *value* system of the nursing staff— 54 per cent saying it was the method they most like to use and 39 per cent ranking it second. It is also deemed relatively effective; three-quarters of the respondents considered it one of the two surest ways of inducing the patient to comply with their wishes. Nor is it deemed unusually time- or energy-consuming; it is not thought to take as much work and trouble as coercion or manipulation, although it is seen as more work and trouble than contractual or authoritative power. Among the five modes of power, then, persuasion ranks first by the value criterion, second by the effectiveness criterion, and third by the effort criterion. We can thus see why nursing personnel are so likely to say that they will employ it.

The strong value emphasis placed upon persuasion reflects a system of ideals springing from manifold sources. First, the nursing ideology of "tender loving care" is sharply opposed to blatant or coercive modes of power exercise. Kindness and respect for the individual are watchwords of this creed. "Angels of mercy" are not expected to bludgeon, command, or bribe people to do their bidding; but they have their ways.

Second, the value of democracy, fundamentally resting on assumptions concerning the rationality and perfectibility of men, also favors persuasion. Democracy is founded on the assumption that men are and should be moved by reason, not by force or authority; hence, the negative valuation of coercion and the positive ideal of persuasion.

One surprising finding is the very widespread belief among nursing personnel that persuasion is effective with mental patients. This finding is especially impressive because it is precisely the irrationality of mental patients which has induced society to expel and segregate them. Despite this, nursing personnel tend to feel that patients are fundamentally rational. A male nursing assistant averred:

> He [the mental patient] may be sick, but he's still got plenty sense. And he's still got feelings. . . . Many times the patient may be so sick, but you sit down and talk to him—he understand what you say.

A female nurse expressed it as follows:

> Well, I think that you get much more cooperation from the patient. No matter how ill the patient is I do think that you get through to him. Not in total maybe, but at least in part.

Mental patients thus tend to be seen as amenable to persuasion, responsive to reason. Such persuasion, of course, is not always "rational" persuasion; patients do not yield only to the power of strict logic. On the contrary, as in all communications, a wide variety of "appeals" are utilized: (1) Appeals based upon positive feelings for the nurse, e.g., the patient should comply because this will help the nurse. (2) Appeals emphasizing the benefits accruing to the patient himself, e.g., the argument that sleeping at night will make the patient feel better. (3) Appeals emphasizing the consequences for other patients, e.g., the argument that it is not fair to other patients for the individual not to shower daily. (4) Appeals referring to the necessity for compliance with institutional rules, e.g., that patients must dress, remain tidy, trim their beards, wear shoes, etc. In addition to such appeals, it was noted that simply talking to the patient could so modify the emotional state of the patient, calm him down, that he would then be willing to comply. Finally, the desirability of persuasion often appears to be based upon emphatic identification with the patient. The nurse states that if he were a patient, he would like to have the reasons for action explained to him; the same courtesy should be accorded the patient.

Why is persuasion considered to be relatively little work and trouble? It is, after all, easier to tell a patient what to do or give him something than to go into a long explanation. The advantage, it appears, lies in its *long-term* benefits. A male nurse expressed it as follows:

> How much work is involved in each of these? Well, I think that in the final analysis, explaining things to them, although it may seem time-consuming initially, is not really time-consuming. Because working on the assumption that most patients are reasonable, once things are explained to them, I feel that the very next time the problem comes up I will spend far less time in securing his cooperation.

The Repercussions of Power Acts

In presenting our respondents with a specific hypothetical situation, the following point captured our attention: that nursing personnel do not tend to react to the situation solely as an immediate and specific problem to be dealt with entirely on its own terms—an event isolated from all others, with a specific end point—but rather are very alert to the possible repercussions of the act.

Thus, the *present* act was consistently interpreted in the light of *future* consequences. For example, one might coerce a patient now, but this might make the patient more hostile, violent, or uncooperative in the future; the simplicity of the immediate solution had to be weighed against the anticipated increased difficulty in time to come. Or one might offer a patient candy or certain privileges (contractual power) in order to gain immediate compliance, but the danger was foreseen that the patient would continue to demand these as a condition for compliance in the future. Conversely, persuasion might be more difficult in the immediate situation, but it was seen as producing increased cooperation in the future. In responding to the criteria of power, then, nursing personnel characteristically adopted the "long view;" it was recognized that a direct and simple solution might solve the current problem but compound the nurse's difficulties in the future.

A second consideration in the selection of criteria was the concern with the "spreading effect" of the act, i.e., its consequences for other patients. Thus, a nurse might be reluctant to use coercion because this would upset the other patients, thereby vastly multiplying the nurse's problems. Similarly, many nurses shied away from offering patients benefits as a price for compliance because they anticipated that all patients would then demand the same advantages.

We thus see that the power act is not based upon a decision divorced from time and society but is, on the contrary, consistently evaluated in terms of potential repercussions. While this is true of most situations involving interpersonal interaction, it is probably accentuated in the present situation because nurse-patient interaction on the mental hospital ward is of such extended duration. Just as G. H. Mead (1934) has shown that the later stages of a social act are implicit in, and influence, the earlier stages, so it would appear that future possible acts are given serious consideration, and influence the immediate power decision.

Hospital Status and Preference for Power Modes

Which people are disposed to use which power methods in the mental hospital? Registered nurses, it appears, are most likely to favor benevolent manipulation, whereas nursing assistants are least likely to do so (Table II). On the other hand, legitimate authority, while not highly favored by any group, is more likely to be selected by nursing assistants than by any other group (Table III).

The higher status nurses, we see, prefer to proceed by indirection, by applying their interpersonal skills, by foreseeing possible difficulties and evading them in advance. The lower status people, on the other hand, show a greater tendency to rely on formal roles in dealing with patients.

The use of legitimate authority is apparently also related to the amount of time one has worked in the mental hospital. Generally speaking, those who have worked longer in this environment (4 to 20 years) tend to show a greater preference for this effortless and impersonal mode of power than those who are relative newcomers to the job (under four years). Among the small number who have worked in the hospitals for over 20 years, however, the number selecting this method again goes down (Table IV).

TABLE II

POSITION IN HOSPITAL AND PREFERENCE FOR BENEVOLENT MANIPULATION

	Position		
Would Actually Use Benevolent Manipulation	*Nursing Assistants*	*Charge Attendants*	*Head Nurses*
First choice	35	40	51
Second choice	50	53	47
Third, fourth, fifth choice	15	7	3
Total per cent	$\overline{100}$	$\overline{100}$	$\overline{100}$
Number	(694)	(168)	(156)

$$\chi^2 = 30.9; df = 4; p < .001$$

TABLE III

POSITION IN HOSPITAL AND PREFERENCE FOR LEGITIMATE AUTHORITY

	Position		
Would Actually Use Authority	*Nursing Assistants*	*Charge Attendants*	*Head Nurses*
First or second choice	16	9	3
Third choice	47	44	45
Fourth or fifth choice	37	47	52
Total per cent	$\overline{100}$	$\overline{100}$	$\overline{100}$
Number	(640)	(156)	(150)

$$\chi^2 = 30.4; df = 4; p < .001$$

TABLE IV

LENGTH OF SERVICE AND PREFERENCE FOR LEGITIMATE AUTHORITY

	Length of Service		
Would Actually Use Legitimate Authority	*a* *1–4 Years*	*b* *4–20 Years*	*c* *Over 20 Years*
First or second choice	4	17	3
Third choice	53	44	43
Fourth or fifth choice	44	39	53
Total per cent	$\overline{100}$	$\overline{100}$	$\overline{100}$
Number	(262)	(615)	(58)

a vs. b: $\chi^2 = 27.8$; df = 2; $p < .001$
b vs. c: $\chi^2 = 8.6$; df = 2; $p < .02$

Those who have served in the mental hospital a shorter period of time, on the other hand, tend to show some preference for the method of benevolent manipulation. This is the "preferred," the "idealistic" approach, and it is not too surprising to find it embraced more by those who have not been jaded by experience (Table V).

TABLE V

LENGTH OF SERVICE AND PREFERENCE FOR BENEVOLENT MANIPULATION

Would Actually Use Benevolent Manipulation	Length of Service		
	a Up to 4 Years	b 4–20 Years	c Over 20 Years
First choice	45	36	41
Second choice	51	49	54
Third, fourth, or fifth choice	4	15	5
Total per cent	100	100	100
Number	(271)	(672)	(63)

a vs. b: $\chi^2 = 25.0$; df $= 2$; $p < .001$
b vs. c: $\chi^2 = 5.3$; df $= 2$; $p < .10$

In the course of time, it would appear, the more imaginative and idealistic approach of benevolent manipulation appears to give way to the more bureaucratic and standardized approach of legitimate authority. The exception, once again, is among those who have worked in the hospital over 20 years.

The preference for a particular mode of power is, as one might anticipate, also related to a broader orientation toward one's work and what one hopes to get out of it. Those who are interested in the extrinsic rewards of their job— its economic or prestige aspects—are more likely to say they would employ the method of legitimate authority than those who are concerned with its service aspects. For example, we asked our respondents what they liked best about their jobs. Those who selected as their first choice the fact that it represented "clean, dignified work" or "steady, secure pay" were characterized as concerned with the "extrinsic rewards" of the job; those who said that it gave them a chance to "do something for others" or "help people in trouble" were considered to show special concern for "service." We find that those emphasizing the extrinsic rewards of work are significantly more likely than those concerned with service to say they would use legitimate authority ($p<.02$).

Legitimate authority is an objective, impersonal method of influence, based on formal rank and position, and operating independently of those who occupy the position. We would thus expect that those people who do not wish to get close to patients, who do not wish to be intimate with them, to give of themselves in the relationship, would be relatively inclined to favor this power mode. Our data suggest that the less the nurse's feelings of intimacy for patients and the greater his status distance from them, the more likely is he to favor the use of authority ($p<.10$). (See Pearlin and Rosenberg, 1962, for a more complete description of this "status distance" scale.)

Lower formal position in the hospital structure, greater length of experience (with the exception of the over 20 years group), concern with the extrinsic rewards of work, and attitudes of status distance toward patients are thus all associated with a tendency to favor the use of legitimate authority. Authority thus appears to appeal more to those who are themselves more powerless in the hospital, who are more alienated from its purposes, or, with some exceptions, who have more experience in learning to use this method effectively.

Conclusion

In the mental hospital, as in any area of life involving human interaction, power must be exercised. The question thus becomes: What *means* do people use to influence the behavior of others in accord with their intentions and what considerations or criteria enter into their selection of various means? The present study has been confined to the examination of *power-attitudes*. In order to obtain a more complete understanding of power in the mental hospital, further studies based on observations of actual power-exercise, joined with motivational investigations of nurses at the time of power-exercise and with analyses of patient compliance, would be required.

48 / Test Burning: II

Leonard D. Eron / Leopold O. Walder

This is a report on public reaction to a community-wide psychological research program which in many ways is similar to the situation in Houston, Texas, reported by Gwynn Nettler (1959). The present situation has had a more favorable resolution, however, and it would be beneficial perhaps to document the attendant circumstances which have affected the final results.

The setting is Columbia County, a semirural area of 43,000 population, 22 miles long and 27 miles wide, in the Hudson valley of New York State. There is one small city of 12,000, Hudson, and six or seven villages ranging in population from 100 to 1,000. The rest of the population is scattered through the open country. There is a wide range of social class, income, and ethnic group. The chief occupations are dairy and fruit farming but there is also some light industry and two cement plants. Only a small part of this industry is locally owned. There is one newspaper printed in Hudson five days a week, one weekly paper printed in Chatham, and a local radio station in Hudson. In addition, the two Albany papers, morning and afternoon, each has a special section in which they carry news items about this area.

The research has been conducted by staff members in the research department of the Rip Van Winkle Foundation, an organization which sponsors a group practice of medicine providing comprehensive medical care on both a

From the *American Psychologist*, 1961, **16**, 237–244. Copyright © 1961. Reprinted by permission of the authors and the American Psychological Association.

prepaid and fee-for-service basis. There is a central clinic in Hudson which offers services in all the specialties and five area clinics in outlying districts, each of which is staffed by one or two internists, a pediatrician, and a dentist, with the other specialties provided on a rotating basis. This organization, now 15 years old, was founded in an attempt to provide the population of a relatively poor rural community with high quality medical care at a cost that at least 90 per cent of the people could afford. Since 1954 there has been a continuous mental health unit including psychologists, psychiatrists, and psychiatric social workers integrated into the comprehensive medical program. Demand for mental health services which are provided to both children and adults has steadily increased since inception of the service. This unit has had contracts providing for such services to children in school districts covering two-thirds of the county. Another indication of the acceptance of psychiatry in this rural area is that the 140-bed community general hospital now receives psychiatric patients for short-term care.

The research program sponsored by the foundation started in 1955 and has been concerned with mental health in rural areas. The content selected for one study was the development of aggression in children. For purposes of this research it was decided to study all third grade children in their classrooms and to interview the parents of each child. Between 1955 and 1959, when the first complete county-wide study of both parents and children was launched, much thought and work was devoted to preparing the community for this program and gaining acceptance of it. Preliminary meetings were held in 1956, first with the superintendent of each supervisory district, then with administrative heads of the individual school districts, who in turn presented the plan to their own school boards. Each of the boards approved the program and granted permission to this outside organization to conduct the testing of the students which entailed four to five hours of class time over a period of three months. The Catholic priest who heads the parish was consulted and his permission obtained. Subsequently, the Mother Superior of the school was also informed of our plans, as were any school principals not included in the previous meetings. One month before the initial testing session, the director of the research program visited each classroom teacher, 40 in all, and explained the project in some detail. A large cocktail party was held at the home of the research director to which all third grade teachers, school nurses, guidance teachers, principals, and superintendents were invited so that all researchers involved in the study would get to meet all the school personnel before the program started. A party for researchers and school personnel has now become an annual event.

A week before the children were seen initially in February, 1957, notices were sent home with each of them advising the parents that their children would be seen in class for games and tests by a group of psychologists from the Rip Van Winkle Clinic who were doing a study in child behavior. A number of news items were inserted in the papers about the program and the program was mentioned in talks that members of the research team gave at various civic meetings. We saw every third grader in the county including those in one-room schools as well as the large centralized schools, 974 children in all; there was no objection noted on the part of any parent at this time. In the fall of that year, 1957, the members of the research team began receiving invitations from more local service organizations (PTAs, church groups, etc.) to discuss the research program. All invitations were accepted. It was a predetermined policy that in all contacts with the public we would be quite candid in our description of the research and take the subjects, i.e., the parents themselves, into our confidence. We never disguised the fact that we were interested in aggressive behavior and its parental antecedents and we discussed what evidence there was in the scientific literature about the relationship of these two areas. After one talk to the Lions Club about the research and its importance that club voted a $500 contribution to the research program and the speaker was asked to become a member. The Columbia County Tuberculosis and Health Association, which previously had contributed $1,000 a year from the sale of Christmas Seals to the mental health services program, voted to direct this money to the research program and has made an annual contribution ever since. In the fall of 1957 we also started to interview parents of randomly selected children in an attempt to work out an interview schedule. By the spring of 1958 we had interviewed 200 parents. In contacting parents for interviews up until that time very little resistance was found, but it should be mentioned that as soon as a respondent showed reluctance the matter was dropped. That year we also tested all the children in six classes from divergent socioeconomic areas. Of the group of 158 children, we decided to interview the mothers and fathers of 60, selected on the basis of their aggression scores, and made a concerted effort to enlist their cooperation. Only three families ultimately refused to participate and they were replaced with other families with children who had comparable scores. The fathers of two of the refusing families were doctors not connected with the clinic. One of these doctors said he refused because the whole scheme was just advertising for the Rip Van Winkle Clinic. This degree of cooperation on the part of parents was gratifyingly surprising and no doubt lulled us into a false sense of security concerning the acceptance of the research program by the entire community.

The following year we saw 600 children in 25 classes for one or two sessions, and 200 more parents, this time again not pressuring when there was the slightest sign of reluctance. At this time plans were completed for our final data collection year in which we were to see all third grade children and parents in the county. A meeting was held with the county school administrators and our plans completely outlined to them. Because of the good response we had been getting up until then, the school personnel suggested that it was not necessary to send home notices with the children. They considered our testing program like any other routine school procedure.

We accepted this decision. However, in retrospect, it is seen that this decision made us vulnerable because just at this time a campaign was being launched by a few members of the Hudson Post of the American Legion opposing the organized "mental health movement." A series of articles was published in the Hudson newspaper linking mental health with "world citizenship, one worldism, internationalism, communism, and socialism." They included wholesale quotations from such publications as the *American Mercury,* the *Economic Council Letter,* the *Dan Smoot Report,* and the *Newsletter of the American Flag Committee.* One quotation from an article is representative: "Mental health is a misnomer for what is really a weapon being skillfully used by communist propagandists to bring about conformity to the Marxist ideology." An "exposé" of the Lansdale affair[1] was included. Finally, a resolution was adopted by the post objecting to community mental health boards,[2] the employment of school psychologists, and expenditures by boards of education for mental health programs; and a congressional investigation of the "mental health movement" was demanded. This resolution was then proposed to the county organization made up of nine local posts. Only the Hudson post voted in favor of the resolution; there were four noes and four abstentions. The matter then apparently was dropped. However, at a meeting of the Lions Club, when a proposal for renewing their contribution was brought up, there was a lot of opposition on the basis of communist infiltration of the "mental health movement" and the motion was voted down after much heated discussion, accusations, and recriminations. The man who spearheaded this opposition was also a member of the American Legion and active in supporting its anti-mental health resolution. This same individual later read a statement along the same lines at a PTA panel on which members of the research team appeared. He accused us of implanting "Red" ideas in children's minds and said our "Guess-Who" technique was a way of "fingering" certain children (designating them at an early age so they would be marked for life for our own ulterior motives).

This was the background against which our major interview study was launched. Mental health had become a dirty word in some segments of this community. The testing of the children was completed without incident. Simultaneously and subsequently parents were contacted for interviews. A day after letters were sent out to the Chatham area, the supervising principal of that district phoned the director of the research and said she received a number of calls from irate parents concerning the letter from the Mental Health Research Center about their child in school. The parents reported that they had engaged a lawyer to see what action could be taken to prevent this study from going any further. The principal felt that the words "Mental Health" in our letterhead had scared them and that we had made a tactical error in not sending the initial contact letters out on school letterheads over the signature of the individual principals.[3] Thus to the parents in the succeeding four school districts, letters went out on school letterheads over the supervising principal's signature. The letter remained the same with some minor changes in pronouns. After that there were only two direct complaints made to a supervising principal.

In the meantime, however, the situation in the Chatham district had blown up. The parents demanded a public meeting with the school authorities and the research team. At the meeting, held on a snowy evening, only 18 parents

[1] This concerned an application to NIMH for support of research on which drugs were to be administered to underachievers and a control group. Although the application had been denied this was never mentioned in the release and it was cited as evidence that mental health professionals were dangerous, wanting to try out unproved drugs on the guinea pigs conveniently assembled in schools with the ultimate motivation of "brainwashing" the children.

[2] Under the New York State Community Mental Health Services Act of 1954 (Forstenzer and Hunt, 1958) a local community may sponsor an outpatient mental health facility for which half of the total operating expenses is reimbursed by the State.

[3] This had been discussed with the school personnel at a prior meeting and at that time they felt they would rather not be associated with the parent contact because parents might conceive of it as coercive if the letter came from the school authorities.

showed up. Questions were asked primarily by two mothers, one of whom was secretary to the aforementioned lawyer. The questions which were raised by the questioners had obviously been prepared by someone else since the questioners stumbled and mispronounced the words as they read them. The questions had to do primarily with what authority the school could allow an outside agency to come in and test their children, who was behind the study, who financed it, who was making money out of it. There were vague references to personal questions being asked of the children and parents but the wording of these purported questions could not be ascertained at the meeting by either the school authorities or the researchers. We were frank and candid in our replies and offered to show the procedures which we had with us to the parents who were present. After describing each of the children's tests and giving sample items, one of the speakers then started to read the parents' questionnaire, item by item; after three pages, the audience lost interest. No one asked to look at the materials afterwards. Many of the parents did come up to us and say that the fuss was all much ado about nothing.

A reporter from one of the Albany newspapers (the only reporter present) wrote a humorous article in the next issue of the paper attributing the whole thing to a misunderstanding about alleged sex questions and making the objectors seem foolish. During the following week we were fortunate in getting the TV station in Schenectady which beams programs to this area to give us 20 minutes on a program devoted to interesting things going on in the area covered by the TV station. This spot included introductory comments by the research director, a sequence of actual testing in the classroom, and a segment of a real interview between parent and researcher in the parent's home. To stress the impersonality and confidentiality of the procedures, shots of the staff at work in their offices, scoring tests and using IBM equipment, were included. Later in that week there was a panel discussion on the local radio station among the researchers and the station's moderator. These all seemed to be well received and it was felt thus that all the parents had by now been reassured.

However, a week later during a routine meeting of the Chatham Board of Education, without warning the opposition appeared in force (30 persons including only 12 families from the district of whom a handful were parents of third graders). They brought with them the reporter of the paper other than the one which had spoofed them in their misgivings about the research. (Consistently thereafter they refused to give any news to the "unsympathetic" reporter.) The board was unprepared for the uninterrupted barrage of questions. The report of the meeting which made the front pages the next day made the school board look foolish and the researchers sinister. We were accused of asking the third graders such questions as "How often do you have sexual relations?" "Do you get suicidal thoughts?" "Do you prefer your mother to your father?" "Is your father a tyrant?" etc. Needless to say, none of these questions had been ever asked in our survey procedures, either with the children or the parents. The matter of confidentiality, invasion of privacy, lack of parental permission, etc., were all brought up. The penny candy which we gave the children as prizes after each session was alleged to be a bribe. One mother said: "I give my children strict training never to take candy from strange men." The President of the board asked for and received a motion to suspend any further testing until a subcommittee of the board could investigate the whole matter and make a recommendation.

The "unsympathetic" reporter who had not been told in advance of the fireworks and thus did not attend the meeting or get the story called us the following day saying he had been called down by his editor who had accused him of favoring our side over the other and also of being a communist for his pro mental health stand. He insisted that we "had to get him off the hook" by giving him an interview and the opportunity to see all our materials. Prior to this we had had an order from the Executive Director of the foundation not to say anything to any reporter, but because of the urgency of this and with the approval of the Administrative Assistant (since the Director was out of town) we did grant the reporter a detailed interview in which he was allowed to look at all our materials with the stipulation that he take no notes and repeat none of the questions in the paper. He did not abide by this requirement completely and did reveal a number of questions asked of children along with a general description of the children's procedures. He also included a number of questions which were paraphrases of the ones that we had in the parent interview, including some peculiar (to the layman) F scale items (Christie, Havel, and Seidenberg, 1958). In addition, he printed a statement, which we had approved, that any parent who wanted to see any of the procedures used with the children could come to our offices or to the office of any one of the principals where we had deposited copies and they could look at them either in our presence or in the presence of the principal. The parent interview we would only show as the parent took the interview. If there were any questions the parent did not wish to answer, he did not have to do so.[4]

The principal then announced that anyone who wanted his child's records destroyed could have this done. To date, only three parents, the ones who started the fuss in Chatham, have made such a request and their children's protocols were burned in the presence of the principal and two school officers.

In the meantime the lawyer's secretary (who, as mentioned above, was a third grade mother) had written to the New York State Department of Education asking for a legal opinion and to the Department of Health, Education, and Welfare, asking about our NIMH grant.[5] The response from the latter organization was extremely supportive of the research effort and was most beneficial to the morale of the researchers whose spirits were at a low ebb as the daily onslaught of rumor and innuendo was repeated in the press. It also marked a turning point in our public relations. When the lawyer's secretary received the letter, she called in the newspaper reporter who had been printing reports favorable to her point of view and read him excerpts from that letter but refused to let him see the whole letter. At this point he became suspicious and called the research director. The whole letter, of which we had been sent a copy, was then read to him. The reporter realized at that point that perhaps he had been "taken in." The excerpts from the letter were thus not printed; and the reporter set out to do a series of

[4] To date only two parents have asked to see those procedures. However, members of The Taxpayers Coalition from a neighboring county demanded to see them and were refused because the committee they sent included no parents of third graders in the study.

[5] Since that time we have learned that the Congressman from this district was also contacted. He referred the inquiry to NIMH.

articles on social science in general and this project in particular, basing much of the report on the contents of the letter from NIMH. It was a factual and reasonable report stating both sides of the issue in what seemed to us an unbiased manner.

From that point on, publicity became more favorable. The subcommittee of the Chatham Board of Education drew up a recommendation to continue whole-hearted support of the research effort with the proviso that, in the future, permission from the parents should be obtained before testing the children in school. This recommendation was then presented at a well-advertised board meeting at which no one of the objectors appeared and it was unanimously approved by the board after no opposition from the floor. A petition against continuation of the research purportedly signed by many parents was not presented. A very fine statement was made at this meeting by the Executive Director of the foundation, supporting the research and its place in a community oriented organization. The statement was taped by the radio station and rebroadcast a number of times the following day.

In regard to the matter of consent, the legal opinion of the counsel for the Education Department which influenced the subcommittee report, and subsequent developments on a state-wide level which may or may not have been instigated by this fracas, should be noted. The counsel rendered an opinion after hearing only one side of the controversy. This opinion, which was given full coverage in the press, was to the effect that no outside agency had the permission to enter the school for the purpose of testing students without the permission of the parents. It is of interest that before this opinion was rendered, counsel did not try to contact the school authorities for their side of the case. His position was that as a state employee he renders opinions on any "facts" presented him by a citizen. Whether or not they are really facts is of no concern to him. What was of concern to us, however, was that this opinion, based on inaccurate evidence, was given wide publicity in the newspapers and on the radio. Furthermore, the various boards of education are still uncertain whether or not parental consent was indicated by the fact that each board approved the project, that notes were sent to the parents during the first year of the study, and that there was much advance publicity in the newspaper and radio and in discussions at civic and church organizations, PTAs, etc., with not a single objection voiced to them until this year. Also, since two psychologists who did the testing had certificates from the State Education Department and performed a service for the schools by supplying IQ scores on each child in the survey and since each board felt the program was a way of furthering education objectives, they were uncertain that the characterization of the researchers as an outside organization was indeed accurate. The counsel advised also that since the data on the children were already collected no legal action could now be taken. However, there would be a basis for action perhaps if we were to see the children again as planned in the sixth grade.[6]

What has been the effect of this entire controversy on the data gathering? Actually, the ruckus did not blow up until the period of data collection from the

[6] A final opinion rendered by counsel since this article was prepared states that indeed parent consent was not necessary. However, from a public relations standpoint it might have been wise to notify the parents before the testing started.

children was in its last week. Data from only three children were destroyed in compliance with the wishes of their parents. The effect on interview acceptance by the parents is really unassessable. The controversy exploded midway in our six-month field period and extended until the end. However, there did not seem to be a lessening of cooperation on the part of parents; in fact, the publicity may have helped. For the total sample of 875 third graders, we successfully interviewed at least one parent in 83 per cent of the cases and both parents in 75 per cent. Thus we feel confident we had the support of the majority of parents.

An examination of the forces operating in this community and how they were utilized, often inadvertently to be sure, should be interesting for other persons starting community-wide research in mental health.

The primary factor we feel is that the researchers themselves were highly visible, established members of the rather small community. They were not part of a team that comes into a community from some outside university or research organization for the purpose of collecting data, who then pull out, publishing findings sometimes putting the community in an unfavorable light. The members of this team have a stake in the community; they are homeowners and taxpayers, sending their children to the local schools, and are active in community organizations and social affairs.

Allied to this factor of permanence and visibility of the researchers is the sponsorship of the research team by an established, highly respected local organization which has been providing quality medical care in this semirural area. The Executive Director of this foundation is a surgeon of considerable parts who derives from one of the old families in the area. He is held in high esteem by a large segment of the community. On the other hand, he and the foundation and what they are doing to traditional patterns of medical practice in the area have some strong antagonists. This will be discussed below.

Another important aspect of our ultimate acceptance was the careful preparation and slow pace at which we went. While the research program was still an idea, we consulted with all the top level school people who did a good job of interpretation to their respective boards; after the ideas had culminated in a plan, we consulted with each of the 40 teachers individually. In addition, it has always been our policy to accept every invitation to speak before PTAs, church groups, service organizations, etc. In four years more than 50 such engagements have been kept. The only PTA that had not been covered before the final survey had been started was the Chatham chapter. Ironically, there had been a long-standing engagement for a joint discussion by two of the members of the team to the Chatham Women's Club a week after this situation broke. These talks, in addition to the radio, TV, and newspaper publicity, showed that we were not anonymous and served to clear up some apprehensions and misunderstandings; unfortunately they also tended to create others.

Our interviewers were carefully selected, well trained, and mature; they created a good impression in the field. Six full-time members of the research staff, aided by five professionals from the clinic staff and ten special interviewers hired for this purpose, carried out the interviewing program. Each interviewer knew the purposes of the study, was sensitive to community reactions, and was able to handle most recalcitrant interviewees. All except four of the special interviewers were also residents of the county. It was a policy, however, for no one to interview in the specific community in which he lived or to interview anyone he knew. Confidentiality was always stressed. Since it was a precoded, objective inventory it was possible to impress this on most respondents.

The support (in the form of the letter mentioned above) from NIMH was also profoundly important, assuring us, when our spirits were low, that we were doing a meaningful job that could be properly interpreted and that we would continue to receive not only financial but moral support from the federal agency which had granted us funds in support of this study.

A matter of practical importance was that the data were stored in our own offices and not in the schools, as was the case in Texas, and thus they were never threatened by capricious action on the part of intimidated public servants. It would have taken a court order or larceny to pry them loose. Fortunately we were protected from both eventualities.

There were a number of counterforces operating in the community which mitigated against successful completion of this research. A discussion of these, perhaps, is more interesting in terms of what other researchers conducting community-wide investigations might be aware of.

One of these is faulty communication with the public. Despite our careful preparations and groundwork and our indefatigable efforts in public relations and our striving to be candid at all times, there was a lot of misunderstanding about just what we were doing. This is perhaps inevitable when psychological concepts which have restricted meanings to psychologists have to be communicated to the lay public in an open meeting. The words are in English and carry the extra freight of both conventional and personal meaning to each individual. For example, at one open discussion meeting, one of our staff members, in explaining a measure of identification which had to do with preference for sex-typed activities, used the term "proper sex role" without any further explanation. Sometime later someone in the audience got up and stated it was indeed true that we were asking intimate questions about sexual activities as witness what was said about "sex role." Fortunately, since this was brought out in the open at this time, the term could be better explained and the rumor scotched. How many other times such terms were used blithely by us and misinterpreted by our audiences is uncertain. This is illustrated by the following quotation from a newspaper account of one board meeting:

> Some parents want another meeting with the research director. Others charge that this would do no good. "All he would do," one said, "would be to stand up there and turn on the charm and give us a bunch of vague and meaningless terms about norms and statistics and such, and none of us would find out anything" (*Register-Star*, 1960, p. 1).

Closely allied to the problem of communication in public meetings and uncertainty about what is getting across is the accounting of events in the mass communication media. The two local newspapers, the two Albany papers, and the local radio station are all in serious competition with each other. Each one tries to outdo the other in sensationalism in order to sell papers and obtain listeners. For example, when the reporter of one paper called about the letter from NIMH to a complainant (mentioned above) and we released our copy of the letter to him, we felt we had to do the same for the other paper. However, it was too late to go to press for the second paper, so this reporter informed the radio station reporter who read the letter over the air and thus "scooped" the first paper. Once this competitiveness worked to our advantage in that the weekly paper published in Chatham which originally had played up the affair backed off when the competing Hudson daily manufactured it into a "cause celebre," and in an editorial the former paper castigated the latter for its sensational reporting (*Chatham Courier*, 1960, p. 4).

Representatives of the press attended most of the meetings we addressed and, on the whole, the reports were not unfactual. However, when the radio station received an item it tended to repeat it every hour on the hour; thus even if the item were favorable, people may have tended to get annoyed. One difficulty was statements released to the press. The "opposition" was continuously doing this. We were reluctant to issue statements in response because there was no guarantee that they would be printed the way they were given; but more important, it was felt that such statements would fan the fires. If our opponents planted items in the newspapers and they got no response from us, eventually they would lose interest, but if we were to issue a counterstatement to each of their statements this would give them publicity on which they seemed to thrive and also more ammunition with which to keep the issue alive indefinitely. The only beneficiaries would be the newspapers who would be able to sell more copies. Our strategy thus was "no statements to the press." However, it was impossible to implement this. Reporters could not be barred from the meetings we addressed. Also it was very difficult to dodge the constant barrage of phone calls, telegrams, chance meetings on the street, etc. The whole situation was even further complicated by personal and professional relationships between members of this research staff and various members of the press, a condition more likely in a small community.

Another current running against us was the suspicions about mental health which no doubt were present on a latent level all the time but received expression in the series of articles by the local American Legion. Although it is safe to say that most parents were not convinced that all members of the research were partaking in a communist plot to implant alien, subversive ideas in the minds of innocent children, many thought that we were indeed invading their privacy. There was some opposition to the hiring of a school psychologist which had been discussed at school budget meetings but had not yet been filled. Some persons expressed the belief that the research program was a wedge for getting a psychologist into this school system. The amount of personal threat that the individuals most vociferous in their opposition to the program felt could not, of course, be assessed.[7] There were some who felt that we, as experts, were trying to tell them how to raise their children and were sincere in their opposition to us despite the fact that we continually stated that we were not "experts" and the reason we were asking the questions was because neither we nor anyone else knew the right answers. Our assurances of anonymity, confidentiality, and lack of interest in any particular set of parents and child, and our interest only in the general observations that could be obtained from the group as a whole, convinced some, but there are obviously others who still thought we were prying into what

---

[7] Recently it has been learned that one of the local leaders of the anti-mental health movement who had demanded release of our procedures and data has been indicted by the Grand Jury for sodomy.

is none of our business. And they may well be right even though our curiosity appeared to us without doubt to spring from a pure well of scientific motivation.

Other counterforces had to do with primarily local situations which do not perhaps have general applicability but are instances of incidental matters which must be taken into account when laying plans for gaining total community acceptance of a social psychological investigation. As mentioned above, the Rip Van Winkle Foundation is well accepted by a majority of the people in the county. However, there is a large segment of the community which is opposed to the organization and its objectives. Some persons said that the project was just a publicity gimmick for the clinic, a way of attracting new patients and of infiltrating public institutions like the schools. They were opposed to it on these grounds and joined forces with those who were opposed on economic, philosophical, and theoretical bases. At the same time there was a small element of the population which was opposed to the school administration (especially in the specific district in which the trouble originated). The same persons who took up the hue and cry against the research program had been opposed to centralization of the school district, new bond issues, building programs, etc. It is significant that they were even quoted in the newspapers as saying: "Our quarrel is not with the Rip Van Winkle Foundation or the research, but with the school board." The same sentiment was repeated when we asked them to meet with us alone to see if we could settle our misunderstanding. Awareness of this sentiment had been responsible for the original decision to send out the personal contact letters on Rip Van Winkle stationery so as not to involve the schools in the requests for interviews. It was a calculation that misfired with some people, although another solution might well have misfired with more persons.

Another happenstance was that just prior to the launching of our survey, many of the inhabitants of the community had been circularized by the American Cancer Society to fill out questionnaires which actually had to do with reporting many of the personal habits we were accused of inquiring about. Also at this time the failure of juvenile delinquency prevention studies in New York City and Massachusetts based on questions about family life was given much publicity nationally. These were undoubtedly confused in the minds of many individuals with our own less personal questionnaire.

This account is being reported in detail in the hope that it will instigate others doing psychosocial research in the community to share their experiences. Eventually, it may be possible to draw up a handbook detailing likely pitfalls, sensitive spots, etc., as well as some general rules to ameliorate community pressures.

Part V

MENTAL HEALTH ASPECTS OF SOCIAL PROBLEMS

Since its inception, the Society for the Psychological Study of Social Issues has had a strong commitment to engage in research on the psychological aspects of important social issues. In so doing, it has been guided by Lewin's dictum that "there is nothing so practical as good theory."

In this Part, we have sought to bring together a set of papers which serve to exemplify psychosocial analyses of social problems, with special reference to mental health. These selections do not constitute a representative sample of the research and action research with a social psychological orientation, nor are they intended to do so. They do, however, indicate the range of theory and research method that can be applied in an effort to illuminate the personal and social adjustment aspects of these social problems.

Social events now move at breakneck speed. America has entered a "technetronic age " (Brzezinski, 1968). The problems of international violence, population explosion, and automation are now flanked by racial strife and the student rebellion. And on the horizon there are others: the "genetic tinkering" with man, new and deadlier means of chemical and biological destruction, the capacity to exert constant surveillance over members of a society, and the loss of privacy. Seemingly unpredictable changes occur. The tacit assumptions we have about our social structure appear to collapse under the force of new historical winds. Technological progress has not automatically brought with it progress in culture, nor has it promoted the freedom and responsibility of man either individually or collectively. Social scientists are increasingly viewed as oracles who can read omens and augur the future in the entrails of a massive amount of research data. Their clinics, laboratories, and field settings enable them to cultivate the "gift of foresight."

Yet the contribution of the social sciences to the formation of public policy has been fraught with difficulty. Moynihan (1967) identifies two major problems which need to be resolved if the findings of social scientists are to be effectively translated and implemented in the form of public policy. The first concerns the fact that the methodology and language of social research has become extremely complex, and research results are no longer directly accessible to the policy-maker. He cannot judge the validity of results, nor does he feel that he can make an independent interpretation of the scientific data. We need persons who can speak the language of both worlds—social science and public policy.

A second and more value-laden problem pertains to what Moynihan refers to as "the differences between the politics of social scientists and the social science of politics." Social scientists (as well as their natural scientist brethren) have in more recent years been playing an active role in seeking to shape public policy.

> They have been deeply committed to the need for and possibility of social change. They have been often as not at odds with the forces of personal wealth and political power. . . . As a result, many minority groups, of which school teachers and Negro Americans are prominent examples of the moment (trade unions would be a good example from the preceding generation), have come to assume that social scientists will always be on their side, and this in turn has led to the assumption that social *science* will be as well. This is not necessarily so, the more so if being on the "side" of a given group involves attesting to the efficacy of whatever social program that group is favoring at the moment. Social scientists worthy of the name will call 'em as they see 'em, and this can produce no end of outrage at the plate, or in the stands.
>
> There is no cure for this. . . . What we can hope for, however, is a larger sensitivity to this matter from the information media and within the social sciences themselves. This form of rejection will never become a pleasant experience for anyone, but to understand, even to anticipate, it is hopefully to be better able to ride out the storm (Moynihan, 1967, pp. 11–12).

In the first selection, Marc Fried attempts to integrate the intrapsychic model of psychoanalysis with the sociological model of social structure. Fried's paper serves to illuminate the nature of the complementarity between ego functioning and social organization, and as such provides a theoretical umbrella for the other selections in this section.

Rainwater provides a vivid and pungent description of slum Negro family patterns of living and their adaptive functions to the caste aspects of the socio-economic system. But the culture of poverty is not only an adaptation to a set of objective conditions. Oscar Lewis (1966) has pointed out that once the culture comes into existence it tends to perpetuate itself from generation to generation We know very little about the effects of differing aspects of the culture of poverty because of its effect upon the children. The cycle begins and ends with children. upon the emotional and intellectual development of the young child. For example, what is the impact of father absence, maternal deprivation, multiple mothering, homelessness, and/or disorganized and unpredictable environments upon the young child (Minuchin *et al.*, 1967)? Are there "critical periods" in the development of the child which require adequate environmental conditions? Are certain impairments less readily and less completely reversible than others—e.g., impairments in language, in abstraction, and capacity for relationships (Bernstein, 1964)?

The selection by Lesser and Stodolsky presents theoretical and experimental findings dealing with the problem of culturally disadvantaged children. The authors generate proposals for social action which they believe to be consistent with their research findings. Pasamanick and Knobloch (1966) have suggested the notion of a "minimal social environmental threshold" necessary for the normal development of intellectual potential in the child. Bowlby (1952) and Ainsworth (1952) have stated analogous hypotheses with respect to the relationship among minimal social contact, critical periods, and the normal affectional (and motivational) development of the infant. In spite of some important leads, we are still a long way from identifying or measuring the pattern of dimensions which represent minimal environmental thresholds (Jensen, 1967; Knobloch and Pasamanick, 1966). One possible way out of the cycle of poverty and cultural deprivation would be to have the public school assume for the culturally disadvantaged child more of the responsibilities of child-rearing. Lesser and Stodolsky help to distinguish intelligence testing which is culturally biased—"culture-free" and "culture-fair." Their study of Chinese, Jewish, Negro, and Puerto Rican children reveal that "ethnicity fosters the development of a different *pattern* of abilities," while social class affects the level but not the profile of abilities associated with ethnicity. On the basis of these findings, the authors search for a more pragmatic definition of the term "disadvantaged." They also challenge Coleman's (1966) concept of "equal educational opportunity" and propose an alternative solution.

The selection by Short describes the structure, function, and values of delinquent gangs studied by the author. Short's hypotheses seek to link "social disabilities" to status threats, social structure, and gang behavior. His concepts serve to bridge the relationship between ego and social structure.

In presenting a social psychological profile of the Detroit factory worker in the 1950's, Kornhauser's findings are based upon extensive interviews with a sample of 407 automobile blue collar workers supplemented by a smaller sampling of white collar and nonurban workers. While he collected data on a variety of worker attitudes and life experiences, the vast majority of his questions dealt with present life adjustment and mental health. The major finding is that mental health varies consistently with the occupational level and associated life conditions of the jobs men hold. Kornhauser (1966) rejects the notion that these differences are due to differential selection of the kinds of persons who enter and remain in certain occupational positions. Kornhauser's conclusions regarding the worker's authoritarian sociopolitical orientation are prophetic in the light of presidential candidate George Wallace's popularity in 1968 with a segment of blue collar factory workers. Kornhauser states: "We find enough evidence of authoritarian attitudes and alienation from social norms and democratic principles (including substantial opposition to racial equality and free speech) to present seriously disturbing problems."

Lifton, in the final selection, examines some of the psychological effects of the Hiroshima disaster upon the survivors. He advances the notion that we are caught in a psychological and historical circle in which the potential for nuclear holocaust impairs our symbolic relationship to death and immortality.

49 / Social Problems and Psychopathology

Marc Fried

The Principle of Psychosocial Complementarity

Conceptual advances in the behavioral sciences have led to wide appreciation of the fact that all forms of human behavior involve both intrapsychic and environmental determinants. But this formulation is of little help in understanding any single instance or form of behavior as a manifestation of the interaction between individual and social variables. The problem requires explicit and detailed conceptual models and propositions that can clarify the patterns of interplay among a range of individual and social resources and conflicts, and their consequences for ordered and disordered functioning. Yet, there remains an apparently insuperable gulf in models, concepts, and methods between those fields that stress the primacy of individual variables and those that emphasize the primacy of culture and social structure.

The conceptual dilemma becomes particularly pointed, and our failures to resolve it become particularly unfortunate, when we consider the mutual influences that affect the development and persistence of social pathology and psychopathology. This polarity of views is apparent in comparing those two major figures who provided the most basic general models for contemporary investigations of disordered functioning, Freud and Durkheim. Both Freud and Durkheim were concerned with the relationship between stimulation and motivation, between individual and group, between personal and social variables. Yet, despite many similarities in interest, each of them selected a path that led to diametrically opposed conceptualizations.

Freud's Model for Psychopathology

In his earliest effort at elaborating a fairly comprehensive theory of psychopathology, "The Neuro-Psychoses of Defence," Freud (1894) delineated his focus on the internal mechanisms involved in the transposition of a previous social experience into a current symptom or syndrome. Despite his awareness that factors apart from these internal mechanisms might affect the course of subsequent events, his attention remained in the realm of these internal mechanisms themselves.[1] Moreover, Freud repeatedly faced the question of the distinction between those individuals who succumbed to neurosis and those who did not, despite

From pp. 403–446 by Marc Fried in Leonard J. Duhl (Ed.), *Urban America and the Planning of Mental Health Services*. (Revised.) Copyright © 1964. (New York: Group for the Advancement of Psychiatry, 1964). Reprinted by permission of the author and GAP.

[1] In referring to his formulation of the primary defensive act, Freud stated: "I cannot, of course, maintain that an effort of will to thrust things of this kind out of one's thoughts is a pathological act; nor do I know whether and in what way intentional forgetting succeeds in those people who, under the same psychical influences, remain healthy. I only know that this kind of 'forgetting' did not succeed with the patients I analyzed, but led to various pathological actions . . ." (Freud, 1895).

similar prior histories. He employed a number of types of explanation but, as Hartmann and Kris (1945) have pointed out, he often resorted to ad hoc support from constitutional factors even when developmental psychoanalytic concepts were at hand to clarify the issue.[2] At no point, however, did he consider the possibility that differences in *external* resources of either a situational or structural nature might account for the differences in subsequent "internal" fate of an event or experience.

In spite of his several great studies of social psychological phenomena, Freud's model (1913, 1921, 1927, 1930) implies a number of propositions that are antithetical to Durkheim's views. Briefly, we may summarize several central components of Freud's model. (1) All behavior is motivated and any act can be fully (or almost fully) accounted for by the motives involved in the action and their sources in personal history. (2) The psychological significance of external events can be viewed wholly from the vantage point of the reality principle as one of the guiding forces in the development and functioning of the ego. And (3) the personal history of the individual and the unresolved conflicts that are maintained provide the necessary and sufficient conditions for neurosis or, at the very least, create a predisposition that may readily be precipitated by unfavorable environmental circumstances. Thus, the model of psychopathology can be stated in these terms: *Unresolved conflicts determine both the impulses and the defenses against impulse that result in psychopathology when the ego is incapable of adapting the behavior to the demands of reality.*

Freud was certainly aware that social relationships and social resources could facilitate (or impede) the adaptation of the ego to the demands of reality, but he did not formulate any systematic propositions that took account of this fact.[3] As a consequence, the psychoanalytic model could only treat the external world and its effects on motivation, conflict resolution, and ego structure as an array of random and discrete events and situations. In these terms, individual differences are due primarily to differences in *selection* on the part of the individual rather than to *systematic* differences in social roles, positions, and cultural patterns. Social relationships might influence the development of the individual in critical ways, but differences in socially structured resources and controls could have no consistent and widely observable effects on current behavior or psychopathology.[4]

---

[2] This is particularly striking in view of his own earlier efforts to stress "acquired" factors in neurosis in contrast to the predominant view. In fact, he was highly critical of the fact that "others may declare the case to be determined by heredity even when there is no heredity, so that they overlook the whole category of acquired neuroses" (Freud, 1895).

[3] It is worth noting that Freud, like other great thinkers, was aware of many more issues and complexities than he was ever able to formulate systematically in the framework of his model. In this sense, Freud left a heritage that goes beyond the model or the theory he formulated or even implied. Unfortunately, the very force of the model and of the theory makes it that much more difficult to utilize these profoundly insightful but passing observations more systematically than he did since, almost inevitably, it would mean altering the model and the theory. Even in those instances in which he went further and delineated the fundamental components of a new model and a new theory, as with ego psychology, there appears to be considerable reluctance to carry its implications to their logical conclusions.

[4] Freud realized the potential influence of differences in social organization (social class, religious affiliation) on adult personality and behavior (Dayton, 1940; Freud, 1930). However, this did not alter his basic model. This is particularly evident in *Civilization and Its Discontents* (1930), in which he discusses social cohesiveness. Clearly, he regards the pressures for stable

Contrasting Views of Durkheim

Durkheim presents several striking contrasts to Freud. He was, perhaps, even more aware of the operation of psychological forces than Freud was of social forces and never rejected their empirical importance. However, Durkheim self-consciously set himself the task of developing a field of sociology and rejected the fundamental *theoretical* importance of psychological factors as basic, explanatory variables. The work in which he most explicitly addressed himself to the clarification of this problem was *Suicide* (1951). In his analysis of suicide, Durkheim recognized that particular psychological states are frequently associated with suicide but maintained that these are sufficiently diverse and result from a wide enough variety of actual experiences that they cannot provide a general explanation for suicide. Durkheim realized that consciousness did not represent the most critical aspect of human motivation. But he did not explore the underlying commonalities among apparently diverse psychological states. For Durkheim, psychological events were, thus, random and discrete factors determined by highly idiosyncratic personal histories. Despite the fact that individual psychological experiences might account for individual instances of suicide, they could provide no basis for generalizations regarding the common factors that caused suicidal behavior.

> Sometimes men who kill themselves have had family sorrows or disappointments to their pride, sometimes they have had to suffer poverty or sickness, at others they have had some moral fault with which to reproach themselves. But . . . these individual peculiarities could not explain the social suicide-rate; for the latter varies in considerable proportions, whereas the different combinations of circumstances which constitute the immediate antecedents of individual cases of suicide retain approximately the same relative frequency. They are therefore not the determining cause of the act which they precede. Their occasionally important role in the premeditation of suicide is no proof of being a causal one (Durkheim, 1951).

In effect, Durkheim points out that individual behavior is the individualized expression of socially determined tendencies. Certainly he admits that selective

---

social organization as impediments to the free expression of impulses and therefore as limitations on happiness. He never conceives of social relationships as intrinsically rewarding but conceptualizes only the limitations they impose on impulse gratification. This is partly due to his equating impulse gratification and happiness, a formulation that is untenable in the light of psychoanalytic ego psychology. In effect, the developmental primacy and partial persistence into adulthood of primitive sexual and aggressive wishes played an inordinate part in his formulation of their *theoretical* primacy. The issue is, in part, taken into account in Hartmann's formulation of the primary and secondary autonomy of the ego (1956, 1958). As in Allport's statement of the principle of functional autonomy (1960, 1964), developmental changes in the vicissitudes of drives and of their objects lead to a total change in the structure of the ego and, therefore, of the relative significance one may attribute to any single motivating factor. This conceptualization is, in a sense, already implicit in Freud's distinctions between primary and secondary processes or of pleasure and reality principles. But Freud did not carry to its logical conclusions his own dictum that the reality principle involved the postponement of immediate pleasure for the sake of greater future rewards since he was, generally speaking, more strongly influenced by problems of pain and their diminution than of rewards and their maximization.

factors operate to produce individual instances of suicide. But he rejects the idea that these selective factors can be formulated as the causal factors. The differences in suicide rate are associated with differences in social organization and, thus, an "individual yields to the slightest shock of circumstances because the state of society has made him a ready prey to suicide."

Durkheim developed neither a model nor a theory as fully as did Freud. However, certain fundamental propositions stand out as components of a model and of a theory. In contrast to Freud's emphasis on individual motivation to action, Durkheim stressed the social regulation of behavior inherent in the cohesiveness and stability of the society and in the individual's commitment to social relationships. His analysis of suicide distinguishes several types of suicide: those which are due to decreased social organization and heightened individualism (egoistic suicide); those in which suicide represents a societal ideal or expectation (altruistic suicide); and those in which the disruption of familiar patterns of social organization and of the bases for social behavior lead to suicide (anomic suicide). Although Durkheim did not examine motivation closely, he clearly conceived of the motivation itself as social in origin. The social origin of suicidal motivation might be of three different types, related to the three forms of suicide. (1) It might involve a sense of *emptiness* (as in egoistic suicide) resulting from the absence of that social cohesiveness which alone makes living meaningful and worthwhile. (2) It might be a sense of *courageous self-sacrifice* or social fulfillment (as in altruistic suicide) because the individual participates in the social good through suicide. Or (3) it would be a gesture of *anger and bitterness* (as in anomic suicide) when social instability and crisis disrupt the patterns of experience that are the foundation for the individual's entire set of expectations. In this formulation, Durkheim comes close, indeed, to a statement of mutual influences but maintains that the individual state is largely a reflection of the social condition which produces the particular type and rate of suicide.

These conceptualizations of Durkheim imply a more general conception of man and society than do Freud's views. For Freud, the individual can achieve gratification only *despite* society; the reality principle determines the price he must pay in the reorganization and delay of impulse expression. Neurosis, in fact, can be conceived as the result of excessive conformity in which the more personal aspects of impulse life can be given only symptomatic expression. For Durkheim, on the other hand, the individual can achieve gratification and meaning only *through* social commitment. Complex and highly differentiated modern societies involve a high degree of individuation and individualism that place an enormous burden on the individual. If there is a lack of cohesiveness within smaller segments of the individual's systems of social relationship due to marital disruption, to economic crises, or to the absence of a religious community, there is ready and widespread disenchantment with life.

In stating the formulations of Freud and of Durkheim in this way, it is apparent that although there is a sharp contrast in the models, they are not truly disjunctive. Freud (1930) was well aware of the importance of social cohesiveness and saw clearly that social commitment was the central feature guiding the fate of libidinal and aggressive drives. Similarly, Durkheim was well aware of the importance of individualism and the meaning inherent in fulfillment of individual desires and goals. His analysis of the development of industrial societies in *On the Division of Labor in Society* (Durkheim, 1933) introduces a distinction between two modes of social organization that lead to differences in the tolerance for individualism in personality. The first of these bases for social organization is *mechanical* solidarity. It presupposes a relatively simple society in which commitments are to the larger group with a common set of values and sentiments; there is little opportunity for the development of individuality since cohesiveness depends upon the fact that each person is an embodiment of the collectivity. The second basis for social organization he calls *organic* solidarity. It is characteristic of industrial societies with a highly developed division of labor; there is a high degree of social differentiation, and the primary foci of social commitment are in the reciprocities among individuals in small groups (family, neighborhood, friendships, work groups). Opportunities for individuality and for the development and expression of individual personality are at a maximum in societies with organic solidarity.

When Freud and Durkheim address a common problem, such as the increased complexity and potential for disorder in highly civilized societies, they appear to be speaking in opposite terms. Freud stresses the greater need for self-denial and repression of impulses; Durkheim talks of the narrower framework for social solidarity and the conditions of social disorganization in which individuality becomes a burden. Yet both of these views are tenable, and it requires only a slight shift in perspective to see them as formulations of a *complementary relationship between the individual and his society.*

The greater the difficulty of establishing social solidarity, the more the individual must rely upon himself and his own resources and regulatory mechanisms. The more he must rely upon himself, the less can he develop facility in anticipating common desires and sentiments or the degree of self-subordination necessary for maintaining reciprocity in the regulation of impulse and desire. To this extent in the absence of social resources for regulation and fulfillment, the burden of repression is in greater degree an individual expectation and a personal necessity. We come, thus, to the apparent paradox that the most civilized populations are those in which individual freedom and personality regulation replace communal resources and social control to a considerable extent; and social solidarity involves a greater degree of independently achieved and developed reciprocity, commitment, and social affiliation. But while there is heightened emphasis on individuality and increased opportunity for the personal fulfillment of sublimated goals in highly differentiated, industrial societies, the individual pays a price in decreased security, in an increased need for the inhibition of impulses, and in greater danger of isolation and estrangement under conditions of social disruption.

Psychosocial Relationships: The Congruence Model

The opposition between individual and social regulatory mechanisms, the fact that extensive development of internal and, thus, individual regulatory mechanisms precludes a high degree of responsiveness to external and, thus, social regulatory mechanisms and, conversely, that extensive organization of external and, thus social regulatory mechanisms precludes a high degree of internal regulation, provides the basis for one form of interactional model of behavior. This model implies that social and psychological mechanisms of regulation, which we shall categorize as resources and controls, are virtually interchangeable phenomena in establishing and insuring ordered, adaptive, goal-oriented behavior. However, there are many aspects of development and functioning for which this is not the case, which require concurrence or compliance between social stimuli and psychological motives. Social development rests upon the socialization of a biological organism dependent on the environment for growth and development to different degrees.

Effective socialization involves learning to modify and channelize impulses, desires, affects, and actions to accord more closely with the individual's actual or anticipated statuses and roles or, under certain conditions, to modify these statuses and roles to accord more closely with impulses, desires, and goals. Integrated development and effective performance require considerable congruence among psychological dispositions, among social roles, and between psychological dispositions and social roles. The content of social expectations must be sufficiently similar to individual desires, strivings, and plans to allow at least a moderate degree of personal meaning or fulfillment in social commitments and in social action. We may speak of these social expectations and norms, in a highly condensed way, as the content of roles; the individual, inner (conscious or unconscious) desires and strivings may be referred to, in equally condensed fashion, as the content of *goals*. Thus, effective functioning necessitates a moderately high degree of congruence between the content of roles and the content of goals, sufficient so that some degree of pleasure in goal-achievement is commensurate with socially acceptable role performance and so that the pursuit of individual goals is compatible with the limits of actual or potential role performance.[5]

To the extent that theories of behavior have made any attempt to explain the interaction of psychological and social processes, they have almost invariably devoted primary attention to the similarity between individual strivings and sociocultural expectations. This emphasis on the parallelism between the individual and his society we may say is based upon an implicit or explicit *congruence* model.[6] It is clear that the existence of such congruence between psychological motives and social expectations is quite fundamental. However, the congruence model has serious limitations in accounting for specific behaviors, in permitting us to distinguish deviance from conformity, and in separating pathological from normal functioning except under highly restricted conditions. There are several reasons for these difficulties in modelling all relationships between the individual and his society on the basis of congruence, and their explication helps to point up

[5] Erikson (1950) and Parsons (1951) have contributed particularly to our understanding of the mechanisms involved in developing this form of congruence. In a recent essay, Inkeles (1963) has generalized and further clarified an integrated approach to this problem for the study of adult behavior. Hartmann's (1958) concept of social compliance refers to a related phenomenon.

[6] A number of studies fall outside this predominant trend and try to link significant propositions concerning individual impulse and social regulation or control in empirical analysis. These, in addition to the work of Freud and, especially, of Durkheim, form the literature for the complementarity model. One of the most systematic and successful of these studies is in Henry and Short's analysis of *Suicide and Homicide* (1954). A number of other fine examples are Riesman's *The Lonely Crowd* (1960), Aronfreed's study of morality in children (1961), Miller and Swanson's analysis of entrepreneurial and bureaucratic systems (1958), Gouldner and Peterson's provocative study of preliterate social organization (1962), and Fromm's earlier but still important and stimulating work (1941).

some of the central problems that have characterized psychosocial explanations of behavior.

The transformation of drives and impulses in the course of social development and their effects on the structure of a relatively autonomous ego-organization never dispose wholly of the potential conflict between personal wishes and social expectations. There can be little doubt that relatively primitive and undifferentiated impulses persist in adulthood and are accessible to consciousness (or even direct action) under conditions which are only moderately disruptive of familiar, socialized ego patterns. Thus, despite the enormous impact of socialization, congruence can be maintained only with persisting environmental regulation (stimulation and control) and with constant adjudication between roles and goals.

Certainly this is a dimension of individual variability, and the more effective the ego resources and controls, the more extreme must the disruptive factors be to facilitate the primitivization of goals. It is also, however, a dimension of societal variability: the more varied the roles an individual fulfills, the more complex the roles and role relationships involved, the less can any simple set of principles guarantee congruence between motives and expectations. In a highly differentiated "open" society such as those in urban, industrial countries, it is manifestly impossible for socialization to guarantee a high degree of congruence, and it becomes essential that the demands and expectations most fundamental for the integration of the society be represented *internally* in the goals and organizational principles of the ego.

The social environment is not only a source of demands and constraints. It also provides rewards, gratifications in role performance (role satisfaction) that do not depend entirely upon the satisfaction of impulses, and pleasures in social relationship and social experience that only secondarily become associated with personal motives. The fact of environmental reward implies that it is possible for individuals to develop patterns of social conformity without an initial investment in and desire for the particular behaviors and roles required by such conformity. The extent to which "reinforced" behaviors are dependent on environmental stimuli and can occur or develop only under conditions that forcibly restrict individuality and freedom accounts for the regularities obtained by reinforcement in the laboratory. Moreover, conformity that derives from social rewards need not be as constricted or narrowly defined as conformity that operates primarily under threat of punishment. Conformity based on efforts to obtain better pay, to receive group support and even group control, or to establish reciprocal and meaningful obligations may become quite generalized in behavior and in social orientations. Asch's study (1956) of the effects of "rigged" group unanimity on individual judgments of a stimulus reveals that, even under the limited conditions of a laboratory experiment, it is possible to obtain great variability in the extent to which individuals make quite "unrealistic" judgments in order to maintain conformity with the group.[7] Prior congruence between roles and goals is, clearly, not a necessary condition for social conformity.

Beyond constraints and rewards, the social environment is a source of opportunities, stimulation, and challenge, which can lead to changes in behavior and to

---

[7] In Merton's typology (1959) we may refer to the alteration in perception as attitudinal conformity and the alteration in response only as behavioral conformity. It is particularly striking that *attitudinal* conformity could be attained simply through persistent group pressure.

changes in ego structure that alter the balance of intraphysic forces. In conditions of social change, a most pervasive characteristic of industrial societies, opportunity and challenge are multiplied. Even in relatively restricted situations, as for the more deprived groups in industrial societies or for the tradition-bound peasant, the roles for which an individual was prepared during growth have generally altered sufficiently to require new adjustments and adaptations for which no socialization experience could have prepared him. As a consequence, any equilibrium between role expectations and goal aspirations toward which socialization is directed is likely to be constantly disrupted by changes from both societal and individual forces. The very concept of adaptation implies the readiness to alter familiar modes of orientation in the face of internal or external changes; in the extreme, it implies the ability to alter or modify internal goals in the presence of changing environmental potentials and to redefine external roles under the direction of changing personality potentials. Thus, congruence between roles and goals can only represent a rudimentary base that delimits the range of behavior and serves as a gross orientation for anticipation and planning.

We have already indicated that there is both individual and societal variability in the socialization of primitive impulses and desires; in the variety and complexity of roles that allow more differentiated motivational fulfillment; in the degree to which immediate social (group) rewards are meaningful and can generate attitudinal conformity; and in abilities to utilize environmental opportunities and challenges for realizing personal goals in adaptive achievements. We are familiar with all of these patterns as important differences between people (e.g., Riesman's "inner-directed" and "other-directed" patterns), as differences which can only synoptically be described as the primacy of personal goal aspirations as determinants of behavior. The actual ways in which different people equilibrate roles and goals to avoid disruptive conflict are infinitely varied and idiosyncratic. But the fact of the dominance of commitments to roles or to goals, and, by extension, the primacy of group-oriented or of ego-oriented behavior, is neither so varied, so flexible, nor so completely individual. It is, rather, a dimension of variability from one society to another and from one subgroup in society to other subgroups.

Some societies allow little room for independent goal-definition and individuality and, through tradition and group observability, maintain relatively clear and specific role definitions and minimal-maximal performance expectations.[8] Socialization is directed to conformity, to compliance with group expectations, to the rewards of consensus, to the comforts of being like others. As a consequence, there is little opportunity for the development of independence and initiative and little encouragement to the differentiation of ego resources and ego controls. Under these conditions, a highly developed ego organization is maladaptive, except in circumstances that provide extensive opportunities for mobility out of the group or which require leadership roles.

Those societies or societal subgroups that emphasize the importance of autono-

---

[8] The post-Feudal European peasantry of the eighteenth and nineteenth centuries are among the best examples of this type, although the contemporary urban, industrial working class approximates it in many ways. The alternative "ideal type" is particularly evident among the elites of expanding empires and in the large middle- and upper middle-class groups of highly developed industrial societies.

mous behavior, of independent choices among alternative courses of action, and of initiative in changing external circumstances to meet inner desires, must allow wide latitude for the exercise of personal goals and of internal controls. All efforts of socialization are directed to the development of the ego even if, in immediate behavior, it involves nonconformity and strain. The expression of personal goals and the manifestation of inner resources for goal-achievement, anticipation, planning, mastery, and ambition are necessarily rewarded and often can justify a wide range of otherwise deviant behaviors. The proliferation of external restrictions or rewards is viewed as potentially dangerous for, in fact, they tend to undermine the functional significance of internal mechanisms as sources of constraint or esteem.

Psychosocial Relationships: The Complementarity Model

We arrive by this route at a principle of psychosocial complementarity: *adaptive behavior is based on the central regulative function of internal resources and controls when mechanisms of social regulation are relatively undifferentiated and role definitions are diffuse and flexible; it is based on the central regulative function of external resources and controls when mechanisms of ego regulation are relatively undifferentiated and goal directions are ambiguous and limited.* The distinction between these types can be made at the level of personality (e.g., ego-differentiation and ego-diffusion) or at the level of the social system (e.g., organic or contractual solidarity). The principal of complementarity implies that the modal pattern will always involve the predominance of *either* personal *or* societal regulation. At the extremes, of course, all societies must have institutionalized mechanisms for insuring a modicum of conformity and for minimizing severely disruptive forms of deviance. Similarly, human behavior requires some minimal commitment to societal expectations and some minimal demand for personal satisfaction. Within these extremes, however, an emphasis on the priority of role expectations and social conformity virtually precludes the extensive development or functioning of an ego-organization capable of supplying internal resources or maintaining internal controls. The widespread development of individuality, of personal strivings for mastery, of personal desires for achievement can only arise in a relatively "open" society and, in turn, is likely to encourage the attrition of laws, regulations, ascribed statuses, and rigidly defined roles that too drastically limit the exercise of independence and intiative. Even the bureaucratization of industrial societies only modifies the degree to which and the roles within which such independence and initiative are desirable and is incomparably more flexible than the monolithic organization of preindustrial communities.

Although we may describe the modal patterns of effective adaptation in terms of the complementary relationship between individual and group mechanisms of regulation, it is evident that such complementarity does not obtain for all individuals in a society. Complementary patterns have considerable stability, but they are by no means static. An individual may move out of these relatively stable situations for many reasons of internal or external change. Under ordinary circumstances, individuals move into and out of complementary arrangements throughout the course of growth. In fact, the major transitions of human development may be seen as the disruption of temporarily stable and complementary states, disruption due to changes in internal desire or social demand, and their transformation into noncomplementary patterns. In turn, the noncomplementary patterns lead to subsequent efforts and expectations to achieve new forms of complementarity.

These movements away from the "ideal type" of complementary relationship between ego structure and social organization can be designated as noncomplementary patterns because they represent either the *simultaneous* force of individual goals and social expectation or the *simultaneous* absence of individual goals and of social resources. Thus, the noncomplementary situation of a struggle for freedom from the family on the basis of intensified individuality during adolescence is often associated with the development of increased complementarity in the somewhat less binding expectations of peers; phases of apathy or indifference toward goal-achievement coupled with the lack of adequate supportive or interactive social relationships is a typically unstable noncomplementary pattern in adolescence. Noncomplementary patterns are as varied in type and in consequence as are complementary patterns. They differ, however, from complementary patterns by virtue of their intrinsic instability. Noncomplementary patterns in which *both* social and psychological regulatory mechanisms are powerful or in which *neither* type of regulation is notably available are the primary sources of change either in the direction of more satisfying and socially effective arrangements or of dysfunction and pathology. The dynamic forces involved in developing noncomplementary relationships and in reestablishing complementarity are complex, and it is possible only to delineate several major sources and directions of these patterns.[9]

In modern industrial societies, it is primarily in working-class communities that one finds the basic conditions for that complementary pattern which involves the subordination of personal goals to social roles and the modest development of ego resources and controls in the presence of highly cohesive and omnipresent group relationships. This pattern is relatively stable despite the manifest pressures toward and opportunities for social and residential mobility into higher status positions (Fried, 1965). Data from a working-class community in the West End of Boston reveal how frequently individuals are reluctant to relinquish their close-knit network ties despite the development of ego resources and of competence for independent activity. At the same time, such noncomplementary patterns are unstable, and those individuals with high ego resources *and* available social resources most frequently plan to move out of the area.

Although we cannot trace the full early history of these people, they tend to be distinguished from those in the same community who show a complementary pattern in a number of ways: (1) they often maintain close contact with parents but are not as often embedded in highly obligatory local kinship or network ties; (2) they are relatively content with the dependability and "encapsulating" presence of long-term ties to others but show an ability to establish new ties *de novo* outside the framework of the residential community; (3) they are frequently "central persons" in neighborhood groups and manifest many forms of initiative in small ways that do not obtrude themselves in their social role behavior; (4) clearly they show more highly developed ego functions and superego orientations

[9] These refer only to the forms of complementarity involving individual stability and change. The same principle is applicable at a societal level but requires a different level of analysis in dealing in the large-scale evolutionary or revolutionary social change.

that tend, however, to be inhibited by a "common man" ideology; and (5) there is a relatively high degree of "role articulation" in the marital relationship, indicating the greater capacity of the nuclear family to serve as a residual resource in the absence of the neighborhood peer group. All of these attributes define them as "transitional types" between the characteristics typical of the working class and those of the middle class.

This noncomplementary pattern is, par excellence, the basis for social mobility. With social mobility, implying mobility out of the socially cohesive group, a new pattern of complementarity is established, one which involves increased opportunity for goal-directed behavior without a constant requirement to fit these goals to already defined roles and social expectations. The transition is not an easy one, and undoubtedly many people experience it as a severe deprivation (Fried, 1963). In fact, if ego resources are not commensurate with the task of freeing oneself from the constant availability of group resources and controls, familiar patterns of psychopathology may develop. An even more frequent source of psychopathological development would appear to arise from another direction of movement out of the working-class pattern of complementarity. This is the pattern that results from movement out of communally-oriented group resources under the impact of psychological or social deprivation and results in the absence of *either* effective ego organization *or* effective social organization.

The principle of psychosocial complementarity implies that group resources provide alternative bases to ego resources in encouraging effective adaptation. Under conditions of intensified social deprivation, whether due to loss of employment, marital disruption, lack of familiarity with the group, ill health, or any other of the many potential factors, there is simultaneously an intensified need for group resources and a more perceptible inability of the group to meet these needs. In working-class communities there are many mechanisms of mutual assistance in emergency, but these are insufficiently based in a stable collectivity to maintain unrelated individuals through long-term deprivations.

On the basis of the data from the West End before and after relocation (Fried, 1963, 1964), several factors stand out as common characteristics of this particularly problem-prone group: (1) quite frequently, they are discrepant in cultural background from the major population groups in the community; (2) they tend either to have fewer group contacts or do not utilize the group as compensation for deficits in other relationships (e.g., distance from the husband); (3) far more often do they have significant reservations about various "slummy" features of the environment (rats, buildings, space, amenities); (4) despite frequent complaints about the West End they often show an *increase* in positive feelings and longing after leaving; (5) both in the past and the present, they more frequently seem beset with deprivations and disruptions, with past neglect, loss, and trauma, and with current unemployment, alcoholic spouses, illnesses, and problems with children.

For those with few ego resources and few group resources, it is evident that difficulties in establishing close-knit relationships have generally been quite extensive over long periods of time, and that with the move from the West End and its ever-present "friendliness," the precarious balance that many of these people maintained was totally disrupted. Although the crisis of transition was quite global and affected a majority of this working-class population, those who were least integrated into the socially cohesive patterns and who suffered less pure "grief" also could least cope with the added (and not wholly expected) deprivation. Thus, this noncomplementary pattern involved a set of circular reinforcements in which social resources and controls do not as readily become available and, when present, cannot as easily be utilized to supplement the lack or inadequacy of psychological resources and controls.

From a psychological viewpoint, we often conceive only of the presence or absence of differentiated ego-regulation (in the form of "ego-strength") as a source of pathological behavior. From a sociological viewpoint, deviance is often attributed only to the absence of differentiated mechanisms of social regulation and of social integration. Despite their larger understanding of many concrete situations, Freud and Durkheim represent these opposing viewpoints. In the light of a principle of psychosocial complementarity, it is apparent that the analysis of both ego organization and of social organization is essential for an adequate explanation of normal or pathological functioning. The absence of a differentiated ego structure with effective regulatory mechanisms is not, in itself, an indication of adaptive failure or of psychopathology. In the presence of meaningful social networks that define role expectations and demand little in self-definition of goals, it may result in a most effective pattern of stable adaptation. Only when this organization of ego functions is coupled with ineffective mechanisms of social regulation or in crises that cause the loss or disruption of familiar patterns of group organization (Lindemann, 1960) do problems arise that lead to increasing maladaptation and the development of social pathology and psychopathology.

The many forms of social deprivation that occur in our society result in an intensified need for these external social resources. In the extreme, they involve a need that goes beyond the resources of any available natural group structure. The failure of community groups to meet these needs is likely to increase the degree of social isolation. Here we can visualize one primary function of professional health and welfare services, including psychiatric hospitalization, as virtually the only forms of organization that can supply external resources and controls adequate for establishing a more stable and complementary base for the emergence of more effective patterns of individual adaptation. With an understanding of the fundamental nature of complementary relationships, it may be possible to delineate these functions more precisely or to appreciate the potentials of alternative social resources in meeting the need for social regulatory mechanisms under conditions of psychological disorganization.

Psychiatric Epidemiology of Social Problems

Epidemiological Studies and Psychosocial Analysis

Ideally, a rigorous test of the hypotheses and derivations from the principle of psychosocial complementarity requires some form of highly controlled experimental or quasi-experimental design. In the absence of more adequate materials, however, it is useful to examine a readily available source of data in order to consider the more general implications of the principle of psychosocial complementarity. Such a source of data lies in the epidemiological literature on psychiatric hospitalization and the different conditions which reveal increases or decreases in rates of psychiatric hospitalization for an entire segment of the population or for some subgroup. The use of epidemiological data for such analytic purposes has not become widespread but offers considerable possibility for the examination of theoretical questions that require large population studies. For present purposes, however, these data can only be used to exemplify two components of the complementarity theses: (1) the rather general proposition that there is a close link (and, often, an arbitrary distinction) between psychological and social determinants, and (2) the more specific proposition that crises and transitions are particularly disruptive for lower status people. It does not, clearly, permit us to test the feature of the complementarity thesis that is more specific to this principle, that these disruptive effects are selectively important among those people with relatively few internal resources who are thereby more vulnerable to changes in the availability of situational resources.

In considering the theoretical issue of the interaction between psychological and social processes through the relationship between social problems and psychopathology, we have an opportunity to study relatively extreme instances. The most evident bases of social problems lie in that realm which we may describe as deprivation. In its simplest and starkest forms, it may include deprivation of material resources for daily living, such as food, shelter, and clothing. In more elaborate or subtle ways, it can involve deprivation of security or freedom, of opportunities and access, of social relationships and social esteem, or of skills, abilities, and privileges.

The use of epidemiological data for purposes of psychosocial analysis presents a number of problems and, in attempting to organize these data according to their implications for the effects of social deprivation, we shall rely more heavily on epidemiological findings than the solidity of the data warrants. Thus, it is essential to note certain important limitations. There is an excellent discussion of the utility of data on the first admissions to psychiatric hospitals as evidence for the incidence of psychiatric disorders by Kramer and his co-workers (Kramer *et al.*, 1961). This provides sufficient caution against any interpretation of these data that does not, at the very least, understand these findings as indices of complex social phenomena. There is no path to treatment, no diagnostic procedure, and, consequently, no rate of psychiatric disorder that is not influenced, at every point in the process of being counted, by various social phenomena which literally create the rates of observed illness. In principle, this is neither more nor less true for psychiatric disorders than for any form of behavior or performance that must be evaluated by various human beings in different social contexts, by individuals who have specific value-orientations and stable commitments to a relatively narrow range of functioning.

On the other hand, the development of institutionalized facilities for dealing with specific types of disturbed behavior and the education of communities to the use of these facilities necessarily results in some degree of uniformity. In most communities this means that those individuals who are least able to deal with the normal range of roles and role expectations, and whose failure appears to be associated with marked affective or cognitive deviation from community norms, will be defined as mentally ill. When there are similarities in the social structure of communities, common expectations for role performance within these communities, and common criteria among a body of professional "experts," we can anticipate some minimal common core of psychological and social malfunctioning among people who are classified as psychiatrically ill. These facts preclude a meaningful comparison of rates in different societies unless the comparison takes such variability into account. However, given such general similarity in "mental health" values, the analysis of internal relationships between rates of hospitalized or treated disorders and other variables is a legitimate basis for the interpretation of results.[10]

In comparing the effects of different conditions of social deprivation on rates of psychiatric hospitalization, we shall use data based on first hospitalization or those that approximate first hospitalizations almost exclusively. Technically, these are closest to the epidemiological category of "incidence" studies in which the first occurrence of a particular symptom or disease is the datum to be aggregated. The reason for this limitation is that, whatever the variations in designating a person as mentally ill or in hospitalizing people for psychiatric disorders, it is almost certain that there is even greater variability in the conditions and evaluations that determine whether or not a person remains in the hospital, having been once hospitalized, or returns to the psychiatric hospital after prior discharge.

Social Class Status

Numerous studies suggest that the form of adult deprivation implied by lower social class position is a significant determinant of severely disordered psychological functioning. This issue has received widespread attention in recent years as a result of the work of Hollingshead and Redlich (1958), although the relationship between social class and psychiatric hospitalization has been observed and reported over many years. In a recent and extensive review, Mishler and Scotch (1963) have carefully considered the most substantial studies of social class and hospitalization for schizophrenia and other psychoses. They point out that eight of the nine studies reviewed show that the highest incidence of psychiatric hospitalization occurs in the lowest social class groupings used in each study. Similarly, and almost as consistently, the lowest rates occur among the managerial group. Between these extremes of social class position, however, relationships are less clear and consistent.

[10] This is one way of stating a more general principle in the analysis of data based on surveys of populations in which the sources of error and bias are unknown. The raw data are subject to greater error than are the interrelationships between variables, with the exception of those instances in which the error (or bias) happens to be systematically selective with respect to the variables being analyzed. One relevant assumption about the discrepancy between psychiatric hospitalization and the incidence of psychosis which is often made is logically unwarranted. This assumption is that the errors are all or mainly in the direction of false negatives resulting from the failure to count all "true" cases of psychosis in the community. In fact, false positives may be the result of numerous factors: transitory behavior which appears initially more ominous than it proves to be, low tolerance thresholds in certain families or communities, errors of judgment and evaluation. Moreover, it seems likely that the advance of a field tends to reduce both false negatives and false positives. If this is, in fact, the case, two conclusions follow: (1) Discrepancies between observed and "true" rates of psychosis are, from the point of view of the accounting system, truly random errors and are not likely to be the source of consistent associations. (2) In the language of information theory, this increases the signal to noise ratio, and in the presence of considerable random error (noise), relatively minor signals that are consistently produced may signify greater underlying uniformities than are clearly revealed in the data.

If we consider the entire range of social class statuses, there is no warrant for the proposition that a simple, inverse relationship obtains between social class position and the incidence of psychiatric hospitalization. However, the lowest status groups do show the highest rates of hospitalized (or treated) psychiatric disorders. In addition to those studies selected for review by Mishler and Scotch, numerous other findings provide further evidence for this conclusion with few contrary results.[11]

Although the data appear relatively clear and consistent, the meaning of this association is more ambiguous. Many hypotheses have been suggested to account for the relationship: differences in community tolerance, class influences on psychiatric diagnosis, downward social mobility as an expression of early psychiatric disorder, and the cumulative stress most readily engendered among lower status groups.[12] The influence of differences in community tolerance for psychiatric disturbance is difficult to assess. The one study specifically directed to this problem (Kaplan, Ree, and Richardson, 1956) indicates fewer instances of non-hospitalized psychosis in a lower middle-class area. Freeman and Simmons (1961) show that the lower the social class, the less the feeling of stigma concerning patients who had been hospitalized. Jaco's data (1960) indicate that if we consider only public treatment for psychosis, the incidence rates more nearly approximate a linear distribution of greater frequency with decreasing social class position (with the exception of the professional and semiprofessional group). Although these results suggest higher extrusion rates among lower status people, they do not offer much promise of explaining the larger findings so simply.

There can be little doubt that the cultural patterns associated with social class status influence diagnostic judgments, and the lower the status, the more severe the diagnoses are likely to be (Blane, Overton, and Chafetz, 1963; Miller and Mishler, 1959). But if this factor were to account for the relationship between social class position and psychiatric hospitalization, we would expect consistently linear associations for all status levels, and least of all would we anticipate high rates among professional groups. Thus, although the influence of diagnostic bias leading to higher rates of psychiatric hospitalization for low status groups cannot be dismissed, it would not appear to be sufficiently powerful or consistent to provide the single most general explanation.

The effect of predispositions to psychosis on downward social mobility has frequently been hypothesized as an explanation for the relationship between social class and psychiatric hospitalization. On logical grounds, the effect of predispositional factors on downward mobility should produce roughly equivalent effects at all status levels and lead to a linear association between social class status and psychiatric disorder. We have already indicated that such linearity does not obtain. Moreover, although the various efforts to examine the relationship between downward mobility and psychiatric hospitalization do not adequately dispose of

---

[11] See Hyde and Kingsley (1944); Johanson (1958); Kaplan, Ree, and Richardson (1956); Kleiner and Tuckman (1961); Langner and Michael (1963); Lee (1963); Locke, Kramer, and Pasamanick (1960); Rowntree, McGill, and Hellman (1945); Srole et al. (1962); Stein (1957); Thomas and Locke (1963); and Tietze, Lemkau, and Cooper (1942).

[12] I shall not consider any of the genetic hypotheses here since they represent one type of specification of predispositional factors and, without far more adequate data, are indistinguishable from other formulations which rest on the significance of selective factors in accounting for rate differentials.

this hypothesis, they lend little substantial support to this proposition as a general explanation (Mishler and Scotch, 1963). We may also note that higher rates of psychiatric disorder are observed at the lowest educational levels as well as at the lowest occupational levels.[13] Since the finding is most notable for extreme educational deprivation, one could account for the casual influence of predispositions to psychosis only by maintaining that there is a widespread effect of such predispositions on educational attainment prior to adolescence. This proposition cannot be documented, nor can it explain the high rates among people with high educational achievements. Thus, it must remain an hypothesis that requires more systematic study and, in any case, is unlikely to be the predominent source of the social class relationship.[14]

The final hypothesis to be considered is that higher rates of psychiatric disorder appear among the lowest status groups because low status is itself stressful or because the limited resources available to people of low status result in greater impact and/or cumulation of other stresses and crises. One of the findings in Jaco's study (1960) of psychiatric disorders in Texas offers some suggestions. In contrast to most other studies on social class and psychiatric disorder, Jaco distinguishes the unemployed from all other occupational categories and finds that the rates of treated psychiatric disorder are disproportionately high in this group. Among the employed manual laborers and service workers, the rates are high, but this is not so marked as in other studies. To what extent, one may legitimately wonder, are the very high rates of psychiatric disorder found in the lowest status groups a function of an association between *unemployment* and psychiatric hospitalization? The lowest status groups, by occupational or educational criteria, have by far the highest rates of unemployment (U.S. Dept. of Labor, 1963). Thus, the strong association of low socioeconomic status and treated psychiatric disorders could result largely from the fact that unemployment is higher in the lowest status levels and is also markedly associated with psychiatric hospitalization or treatment.

Such a relationship in which the higher rates of psychiatric hospitalization among lower status people are largely accounted for by the higher rates of unemployment might provide a basis for a more dynamic explanation of the perplexing social class finding but, for the time being, must remain a promising conjecture. In any case, it would hardly soften the conclusion that extreme, overt deprivation is a prominent source of manifest psychiatric disorder.[15] However,

[13] See Jaco, 1960; Kleiner and Tuckman, 1961; Lee, 1963; Locke, Kramer, and Pasamanick, 1960; Thomas and Locke, 1963.

[14] It is, of course, possible that downward mobility in occupation or minimal educational attainment is more readily produced by psychotic predispositions at lower than at higher status levels. This is not an unreasonable hypothesis in view of the fact that socialization to higher levels of performance may facilitate modest effectiveness in occupational and educational activity in spite of relatively severe psychological or even organic impairments. Some support for this view is provided by the observation that, following psychiatric hospitalization, the lower the initial occupational level, the greater the relative frequency of downward occupational mobility (Durkheim, 1933). However, if this proved to be an important factor explaining the social class relationship to psychiatric disorder, it would transpose the sphere in which deprivation functioned to produce impairment and to limit adaptive potentials, without necessarily vitiating the significance of deprivation phenomena.

[15] In this connection we may note that Sainsbury (1955) found a significant correlation between unemployment and suicide in a case by case analysis, although there was no "ecologi-

it would tend to contradict the proposition that low social class status per se is a form of deprivation leading to increased psychiatric impairment. It would suggest rather some more complex hypotheses: either (1) a greater variety of deprivations and/or stresses occur at lower status levels, leading to a cumulative effect on impairment; or (2) there is greater likelihood that the characteristic deprivations among lower status groups will be more severe and incapacitating crises; or (3) because of less adequate internal resources among lower status people, the same frequency and same severity of deprivation and/or stress will produce more severe impairments.[16]

Up to this point we have considered each possible explanation of the relationship between extreme status deprivation and psychiatric hospitalization as if it were a unitary factor that had to account for all or most of the association. Such singular explanations, whether directly revealed by the data or based on a more comprehensive conceptual formulation, are particularly satisfying to the aesthetic of science. Clearly, however, it is possible that all of the factors considered (and others as well) might account for these findings. Certainly it is possible that higher rates of hospitalization among the lowest socioeconomic status groups could result from a conjunction of: (1) differences in the frequency or severity of, or the resources for handling, deprivation in different social class groups; (2) the downward mobility potential of psychologically disturbed, relatively low status people; and (3) their frequent "extrusion" from the community and readier diagnosis of psychosis. Even if we assume that for any moderate proportion of the cases the disturbed psychological state is antecedent to the situation of social deprivation, it is evident that the greater frequency of, greater severity of, or less effective mechanisms for dealing with deprivation engendered by very low status necessarily means a far greater likelihood that disturbing and disruptive situations will occur. The larger number of factors that, alone or in concert, might produce disproportionate rates of psychiatric hospitalization among the lowest status group tends, thus, to highlight the ways in which the simple form of deprivation indicated by lower social class position may have complex and varied ramifications. We shall turn, therefore, to further areas in which social deprivation or social disruption may play significant parts in the observed rate differentials for severe psychiatric disorders.

---

cal correlation" between rates of unemployment in different areas and suicide rates. In spite of the fact that we cannot automatically classify suicides among severe psychiatric disorders, the many parallel conditions associated with suicide rates and with rates of psychiatric hospitalization lend some further support for the view that crises such as unemployment cause a marked increase in severe psychological disruption. One further piece of evidence supporting this view comes from a study of selective service registrants (Rowntree, McGill, and Hellman, 1945) in which a mixed category, which included primarily the unemployed and emergency workers, showed a much higher rate of rejection for "mental and personality disorders excluding psychoneurosis" than did any of the occupational categories.

[16] The recently published study by Langner and Michael (1963) arrived too late to be given adequate consideration in this analysis. It is important, however, to note their finding that the number of stress factors was not significantly greater for lower than for higher status people. Their data indicate that for every unit of stress, there was greater impairment among the lower than among the higher status groups. This led to their explanation of the inverse relationship between social class position and psychiatric impairment on the basis of differences in types of adaptation to stress at different social class levels.

Negro-White Differences

Although it is possible to regard Negro-white differences as one aspect of social stratification, the situation of the Negro is sufficiently different from that of the white at equivalent educational or occupational levels to warrant special consideration. At every level of social class status, the Negro suffers a greater range and more intense forms of overt deprivation (and implicit threat) than do whites. If extreme deprivation is a causal factor in hospitalization for psychiatric disorder, then Negro rates of psychiatric hospitalization lend considerable support to its importance. *At the present time, Negro rates of first admission to psychiatric hospitalization are consistently and overwhelmingly higher than white rates for both sexes and for virtually every age group.*

The full extent of this finding has only emerged in data for relatively recent periods. Pugh and MacMahon (1962) point out that by 1922 the rates for Negroes had risen to parity with white rates and by 1933 "the non-white population was entering mental hospitals at higher rates than the native white in all except nine of the states. . . ." However, as Malzberg (1940) had previously shown, even in the 1922 statistics the rates for the white population exceeded that for the Negroes only in several of the southern regions of the United States in which there were inadequate psychiatric hospital facilities for Negroes. Most studies show that current rates are at least twice as high for Negroes as for whites with the greatest differentials in the younger age groups and greater for males than for females.[17] Moreover, the same indices of deprivation or disruption that lead to increased rates for whites also cause increments to the Negro rates: low education, low occupation, migration, divorce, and separation.[18]

Unfortunately, the available data do not allow us to go much beyond this descriptive statement about the extremely high rates of first admission to psychiatric hospitals among Negroes. Nonetheless, more clearly than in any other situation, it is essential to conclude from these data that being Negro is of basic causal significance in producing higher rates of severe psychiatric disorder. The extreme versions of a selection hypothesis are rather evidently ruled out. There can be no question that being a Negro is *not* the result of predispositions to psychosis. Moreover, although psychological deprivation and disorganizing experiences of personal history may occur more frequently among Negroes than among whites, social deprivation and disruption, systematically related to many features of social structure that affect the Negro at all phases of development and functioning, are considerably more frequent and more severe among Negroes than among whites. If we consider the numerous other spheres in which malfunctioning is manifest, in unemployment and underemployment, in delinquency and crime, in poor health and high mortality rates, in dependence on social agency assistance, it is evident that overall rates of deviance and disorder are so great among Negroes that few alternative hypotheses are reasonable. We are bound to conclude that *severe social deprivation of the type so widely experienced among Negroes is of fundamental causal significance for psychological impairment.*

[17] See Kleiner and Tuckman, 1961; Lee, 1963; Malzberg, 1940; Pugh and MacMahon, 1962; Thomas and Locke, 1963.

[18] See Jaco, 1960; Lazarus, Locke, and Thomas, 1963; Lee, 1963; Locke *et al.*, 1958; Malzberg and Lee, 1956.

We have pointed to evidence that extremes of status deprivation, manifest among the lowest socioeconomic groups and among Negroes, are rather powerful components of the causal network leading to increased rates of first admission to psychiatric hospitals. In the absence of contrary data, the evidence is quite convincing that the extreme social deprivation implicit in these status positions, either directly or in conjunction with the frequent and relatively severe associated threats, disruptions, and crises, must be placed at a relatively early point in the causal chain that accounts for psychiatric disorder and hospitalization. At the same time, it becomes increasingly apparent that social deprivation is hardly ever *simply* deprivation. Extreme deprivation, at the least, implies frequent threat, likely frustration of many desires and impulses, widespread experiences of helplessness and futility, and the lack of inner or outer resources to serve as equilibrating mechanisms in a crisis, thereby intensifying the disruptive significance of modest frustrations and stresses. At an unconscious level, it is likely that more primitive impulses and fantasies are engendered by the same "objective" threat, deprivation, stress, or crisis and thus make the adaptive task more difficult. *Deprivation is the focal point in extremes of low status, but it is most often associated with a manifold of other social and psychological sources of disruption.*

Schematically, we can diagram the immediate sequences leading to psychiatric hospitalization as in Figure 1. The scheme is not meant as an inclusive substantive statement; it attempts only to diagram major points in the sequences and in the

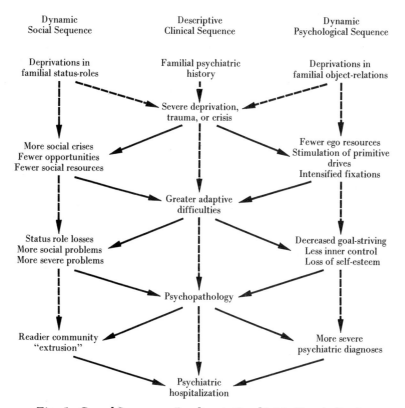

Fig. 1. Causal Sequences Leading to Psychiatric Hospitalization

interactions. The middle column is labelled *Descriptive Clinical Sequence* because, without implying any specific causal theory, it takes account of precipitating circumstances and the downhill course that so often appear to characterize the emergence of psychopathology prior to hospitalization. The first column, labelled *Dynamic Social Sequence*, indicates that with deprivations at the level of familial status and familial roles, two major directions may be traced: (1) a series of further deprivations, disruptions, crises, lacks, and losses are more likely to arise given the initial deprivations; and (2) at any point in the sequence those social deprivations may lead to intermediate "clinical" manifestations and, more significantly, can result in psychological changes that may be traced through the levels of "inner" psychological malfunctioning. Similarly, the *Dynamic Psychological Sequence* implies that deprivation at the level of familial object-relations, on the one hand, leads to increased likelihood of additional forms of psychological deficit and, on the other, can result in both "clinical" manifestations and in social deprivations and disruptions at any point in the sequence.

This chart is, thus, a synopsis of many possible paths to psychiatric hospitalization. For any given individual, the primary direction of "regressive" movement may be seen as a series of shifts along the vertical axis of the Dynamic Psychological Sequence with occasional, diagonal forays into the Descriptive Clinical Sequence. For another person, the most appropriate characterization may be through the increasing difficulties of the Dynamic Social Sequence, occasionally showing up as one of the clinical manifestations in the Descriptive Clinical Sequence. We may suspect that, for most people, a very careful psychological and social assessment would reveal frequent movements from Dynamic Psychological Sequence to Dynamic Social Sequence and the reverse. The diagonal arrows, which stress these shifts in the sphere of manifest difficulty, point up the interaction of forces that are easily overlooked if we follow any singular psychodynamic or sociodynamic formulation of the causes of psychiatric hospitalization.

The chart, thus, is drawn in this particular way, with multidirectional sequences, to emphasize this one point: *it is possible to treat one of these sequences as systematic and everything else as random, idiosyncratic, or situational, but this is only a function of a particular perspective which understands psychological or social phenomena systematically, but not both.* In fact, both represent distinguishable systems that bear upon one another at select points and with respect to specific problems of human action. But problems of pathological behavior are precisely issues that are psychological *and* social in origin, in intervening processes, in definition, and in consequences. The more clearly we can understand the independent functioning of each sequence *and* its interactions with other factors that form partial systems and sequences in their own right, the more effectively may we be able to explain the complexity of observed patterns of psychopathology.

Social Deprivation and Situational Crises

We have pointed to the fact that at the lowest levels of status, socioeconomic deprivation is accompanied by many other problems of living and that for any given level of "objective" stress the absence of inner or outer resources to facilitate adaptation means a greater degree of *relative* deprivation or experienced stress. Although there is little evidence concerning the effects of cumulative difficulties on psychiatric disorder, there is some suggestion in the data that an increase in overt psychiatric pathology occurs with an increased number of deprivations and stresses.[19] Moreover, as we have suggested, even if there is no greater likelihood that a particular form of deprivation or disruption will occur among the lowest status groups, it is likely that when these do occur in any form they will be more seriously incapacitating. There are no available data that allow us to assess this problem directly. However, a number of situational crises for which data exist do permit us to evaluate more fully the effects of social problems more generally on psychiatric hospitalizations. We shall turn to a brief consideration of some of these data on economic disruption, marital disruption, and residential disruption before evaluating the larger problem posed.

ECONOMIC DISRUPTION   We have already indicated that unemployment may well be a particularly significant intervening variable accounting for high rates of psychiatric disorder. There is also evidence, although not unambiguous, that serious economic depressions, which produce high rates of unemployment and drastic alterations in economic and social status, produce high rates of disordered functioning. The data are most clear for suicide and appear to be consistently confirmed. There is a direct statistical relationship between indices of economic depression and rates of suicide.[20]

For psychiatric hospitalization, the data are more difficult to evaluate. If we consider all first admissions to psychiatric hospitals, there is evidence for a relationship between the economic depression of the 1930's and psychiatric disorders (Dayton, 1940; Dunham, 1959; Pugh and MacMahon, 1962). The issue, however, is complicated by two factors. (1) From Dayton's data (Dayton, 1940) it would appear that the critical period of rising rates for psychiatric hospitalization occurred during the onset of unemployment before the depression was in full evidence, and a similar pattern holds for suicide (Dublin and Bunzel, 1933). But there are few series of data available for the relevant periods which permit replicating Dayton's findings. (2) The increase in psychiatric hospitalization during the depression period was considerably greater for persons without mental disorder than for those with mental disorder. It is unclear whether the criteria for hospitalization or those for diagnosing mental disorder were more drastically affected by the widespread evidence of realistic deprivation during this crisis. In any case, Dayton does show that the effect holds for cases with mental disorder, albeit less strongly, and there is also a subsequent rise during the onset phase of the recession which occurred in 1937 (Pugh and MacMahon, 1962). Thus, we are led to conclude, tentatively, that the type of crisis manifested in an economic depression increases the likelihood of psychiatric disorders.

MARITAL DISRUPTION   The data on marital status and psychiatric hospitalization are virtually as clear and unambiguous as one could desire. Despite minor variations within subcategories, *first admission rates for psychiatric hospitaliza-*

---

[19] Apart from Langner and Michael's data (1963) the evidence is indirect, and shows that when different forms of deprivation (education, occupation, racial) or disruption (migration, divorce) are superimposed on one another, in the form of controls or statistical adjustments, rates of first admission to psychiatric hospitals are highest for the group representing multiple deprivations or disruptions. See Kleiner and Tuckman, 1961; Lazarus, Locke, and Thomas, 1963; Lee, 1963; Locke *et al.*, 1958; Malzberg and Lee, 1956; Thomas and Locke, 1963.

[20] See Dublin and Bunzel, 1933; Freud, 1930; Henry and Short, 1954; Sainsbury, 1955; Swinscow, 1951.

tion are consistently higher for the divorced than for any other group.[21] Moreover, the rank position of first admission rates is generally the same for different marital status groups. The divorced, single, widowed, and married represent a decreasing order of rates. A similar pattern exists for suicides and lends further support to the general significance for malfunctioning of these different marital situations (Dublin and Bunzel, 1933; Durkheim, 1951; Sainsbury, 1955).

More clearly than any other set of findings, the data on marital status and psychiatric hospitalization necessitate a model of multiple causation. In the higher rates for the widowed than for the married there is evidence for the importance of deprivation or disruption rather than selective factors. Selection might account for some unknown proportion of the high rates among both the single and the divorced, although the components of deprivation among the single and of disruption among the divorced are too apparent to require comment. However, since there is every reason to believe that selective factors should affect rates among the single to a considerably greater extent than among those who did marry but were later divorced, and yet the rates for the latter are the highest of all, we must grant a good deal of importance to the crisis of divorce or separation as one determinant of subsequent psychiatric hospitalization. Finally, the differential between the married, at one extreme, and the divorced, at the other, tends to be dramatic; first admission ratios of psychiatric hospitalization are of the order of three to five times higher for the divorced than for the married. The rate differences according to marital status are strong, and the factors involved do not lend themselves readily to any simple explanation. Rather the combinations of predispositional selective factors and of the stabilizing effects of cohesive marital relationships stand out as forces that reinforce one another in producing the observed effects on rates of psychiatric hospitalization.

RESIDENTIAL DISRUPTION   Differences in rates of psychiatric hospitalization for mental disorder between the native-born and foreign-born had become a public issue of considerable importance in the United States after World War I, when legislation was pending for more restricted immigration (Malzberg, 1940; Thomas, 1956). A frequent thesis in this argument was that these higher rates were due to the inherent inferiority of the immigrant nationalities. Ødegaard's (1932) famous study of Norwegians showed that the immigrants to the United States from Norway had higher rates than did those Norwegians who remained in Norway. These data could be interpreted in several ways—but Ødegaard chose to make a case for the selection hypothesis. Subsequent work clarified the fact that it was migration (whether due to selection or to the process of migrating) rather than nativity which bore the responsibility for these higher rates.[22]

Increasing evidence has given greater credence to the central importance of the disruptive experience of migration, although the selection hypothesis has not been ruled out as a general explanation or as a way of accounting for some proportion of cases.[23] Several recent studies introduce either new ways of ordering the data

[21] See Dayton, 1940; Locke *et al.*, 1958; Malzberg, 1940; Pugh and MacMahon, 1962; Srole *et al.*, 1962; Thomas and Locke, 1963.

[22] See Locke, Kramer, and Pasamanick, 1960; Malzberg, 1940; Malzberg and Lee, 1956; Thomas, 1956.

[23] Only a few points may indicate the basis for giving relatively little weight to the selection hypothesis. (1) Most of the historical materials suggest that the large migratory movements to the United States selected the best fit and most able among the peasantry and workers. Al-

or new ways of accounting for them. Recent rates of psychiatric hospitalization for mental disorder show the persistence of a relatively small difference between the foreign-born and native white rates (Fromm, 1941; Lee, 1963; Malzberg and Lee, 1956), with several negative findings (Jaco, 1960; Pugh and MacMahon, 1962). Of striking interest in these studies is the new evidence that *migrants from one state to another have even higher rates than do the foreign-born, and that this differential holds for both Negroes and whites.*

An important hypothesis to account for migration ratio differentials in psychiatric disorder has been suggested by Murphy (1961, 1964). He points out that there are differences in migrant rates that correspond to differences in the situation of the migrant in the specific host society. A wide range of migration situations require that the immigrant adapt to a wholly unfamiliar situation without adequate support or resources for making the transition, and it is in these societies that high migrant rates of psychiatric hospitalization appear. Migration from rural to urban areas and from preindustrial to industrial societies produces a crisis of transition in which, for a relatively long time, the migrant is deprived of the educational and cultural background necessary for effective functioning, of the occupational and prestige opportunities fundamental in urban life, and of the social resources of familiar and dependable ties and relationships to other people (Cassell, Patrick, and Jenkins, 1960; Fried, 1964, 1965). Crises have an inherent potential for creating disorder although they may also lead to higher levels of functioning (Caplan, 1963; Duhl, 1964; Lindemann, 1952). But the potential for change intrinsic to such crises of transition requires meaningful resources to maximize the opportunities and to minimize the dangers. Since the rural or peasant migrant rarely has commensurate internal resources for dealing independently with these unfamiliar challenges at the outset, he must find equivalent external resources. For many former peasants, these were available in the urban, ethnic, working-class slums (Fried, 1963, 1965). For the migrant who moves from one state to another, few such communities exist, and under these circumstances, without adequate internal or external resources, psychiatric disorder and hospitalization appear to be one of a number of manifestations of a high frequency of failures in adaptation.

Social Problems and Psychopathology: A Causal Matrix

In reviewing data on the relationships among social deprivation, social disruption, and differential rates of psychiatric hospitalization, we have come to several conclusions. Some of these are quite unambiguous, others less clear, and some remain as tentative hypotheses. In summarizing these results, it is possible to see the main lines of interpretation and their implications.

---

though the vast majority came to this country during conditions of adversity, those who came tended to be drawn from the group who had been less severely affected, those who could still pay for the voyage, those who could tolerate the extreme hardships (Handlin, 1952, 1959; Hansen, 1961). (2) Malzberg (1940) pointed out that the rapid decrease in rates for the second generation did not support any available genetic hypotheses. (3) Rates for the foreign-born are particularly high for the very youngest age groups, who had little part in electing migration and, therefore, could not have best represented the relevant selective factors. Regardless of the form of selection hypothesis, their rates should certainly be no greater than rates for their parents.

1. Extreme overt deprivation of economic and social resources and opportunities associated with the lowest status positions in our society is a serious impediment to effective functioning and is statistically asociated with higher rates of first admission to psychiatric hospitalization. Although no simple causal explanation accounts either for all the cases or for the fact that other persons in similar status positions show less marked (if any) evidence of psychological disorder, severe deprivation appears to have a very significant determining influence at numerous points in the complex sequences that result in psychopathology.

2. Overt social and economic deprivation, both in its most extreme form and in more modest degree, is very often related to various types of psychological disruption and deprivation. There are undoubtedly conditions in which *psychological* deprivation is a primary causal factor leading to *psychological* disorganization and resulting in *social* deprivation. With equal certainty, however, *social* deprivation may lead to *social* disruption and, in turn, may result in *psychological* disorganization.

3. There is no adequate evidence that overt social deprivation and rates of observed psychiatric disorder are related in a simple, linear pattern. In trying to account for the distinctiveness of the pattern among the most severely deprived groups, we suggested that available social resources can often counteract the more severe consequences of social or psychological deprivation. By implication, it is the effect of social deprivation on social disruption that potentiates the relationship between social deprivation and severe psychopathology. Their cumulative impact and consequences for psychological disorganization give dynamic meaning to the sequences that start with social deprivation and end with psychiatric hospitalization.

4. Crises of transition, manifest in such disruptions as economic depression, divorce, and migration, also produce marked increases in rates of psychiatric hospitalization. There is presumptive evidence that a social principle equivalent to Freud's concept of "over-determination," elaborated in Waelder's principle of multiple function (1936), holds for multiple external deprivations and disruptions. Moreover, any single deprivation or disruption increases the likelihood that other deprivations and disruptions will occur. It is also possible that when disruptions are experienced as severe deprivations and losses, their consequences for psychopathology are most serious (Fried, 1964).[24]

[24] Differentials between Negro and white rates of first admissions by differences in marital status provide some data suggesting the importance of the meaning of the particular form of disruption. Negro rates of psychiatric hospitalization are considerably higher than white rates; Negro rates of divorce and separation are also considerably higher than white rates. And the effect of divorce and separation on first admissions to psychiatric hospitals is less marked for Negroes than for whites. The data presented here are from Lee (1963) and are based on the detailed breakdown by marital status for all New York hospitals for mental disorder during 1950 in age standardized rates per 100,000 population. The non-white rates in these data are predominantly Negro. The relative differences according to marital status can be regarded from either extreme. Marital relationships may be less cohesive among Negroes, and a larger proportion may be listed as married although not living with their spouses. There is much data to suggest this is the case. Alternatively, because divorce, separation, and de facto separation are so widespread among Negroes, they may represent less serious disruptions and may involve less serious deprivation. There is also a good deal to suggest this is so. In either event (and certainly if both are correct explanations), we would expect a less marked difference in first admission rates for married and divorced/separated status among Negroes than among whites.

5. If we try to understand the great importance of extreme deprivation for psychopathology in relation to the disproportionate reduction of potentials for psychiatric disorder with less severe conditions of social deprivation, we come upon the considerable importance of the resources, social *or* psychological, that seem to modify the impact of deprivation or disruption. There are several factors that appear to be involved in this relationship: (1) the sense of security in the availability of resources during crises of transition; (2) actual assistance (economic aid, advice, homemaker service) of various types to compensate for deficits in temporary crises of deprivation or disruption; (3) implicit and explicit encouragement to reorganize psychological resources either through group denial of hopelessness or through ego support by clarifying alternatives. These appear only to be effective in relatively close-knit community relationships in which there is a sense of common "cultural identity" with widespread knowledge of deprivation.[25]

6. Finally, these results provide provisional support for the general view that numerous transitional states and situations are the most specific proximal causes of high rates of psychopathology. It is not so much the prior status of deprived groups (e.g., as lower class of Negro) but rather the particular vulnerability of these populations to conditions of internal or external change which appear to be associated with the incidence of psychiatric hospitalization. On theoretical grounds, we would anticipate that these transitions would represent noncomplementary conditions in which there is a simultaneous deprivation of internal and external regulatory mechanisms or a simultaneous convergence of internal and external regulatory mechanisms. While it is not altogether possible to draw from these findings a more precise conclusion than that these are, in fact and most fundamentally, noncomplementary conditions, the data indicate that this is one of the more plausible explanations for differences in rates of psychiatric hospitalization.

Thus, the difference in *meaning* of the marital state and of its disruption would seem to be a useful hypothetical approach in understanding these and other rate differentials.

Marital Status	White	Non-White	Ratio
Married	62	154	2.48
Widowed	227	472	2.08
Single	266	508	1.91
Divorced	461	419	.91
Separated	482	555	1.15

[25] It is hardly necessary to add that just as social deprivation has conscious and unconscious psychological meaning in addition to its "objective" significance as a realistic lack and potential hazard, so do social resources serve as a realistic bulwark against the more primitive interpretation of lacks and losses; even projected blame is less disorganizing psychologically when supported (and modified) by group consensus.

50 / Crucible of Identity:
The Negro Lower-Class Family

Lee Rainwater

> *But can a people . . . live and develop for over three hundred years by simply reacting? Are American Negroes simply the creation of white men, or have they at least helped create themselves out of what they found around them? Men have made a way of life in caves and upon cliffs, why can not Negroes have made a life upon the horns of the white man's dilemma? . . . American Negro life is, for the Negro who must live it, not only a burden (and not always that) but also a discipline just as any human life which has endured so long is a discipline teaching its own insights into the human conditions, its own strategies of survival. . . .*
>
> *For even as his life toughens the Negro, even as it brutalizes him, sensitizes him, dulls him, goads him to anger, moves him to irony, sometimes fracturing and sometimes affirming his hopes; even as it shapes his attitude towards family, sex, love, religion; even as it modulates his humor, tempers his joy—it conditions him to deal with his life and with himself. Because it is his life and no mere abstraction in someone's head. He must live it and try consciously to grasp its complexity until he can change it; must live it as he changes it. He is no mere product of his socio-political predicament. He is a product of interaction between his racial predicament, his individual will and the broader American cultural freedom in which he finds his ambiguous existence. Thus he, too, in a limited way, is his own creation.*
>
> —*Ralph Ellison*

As long as Negroes have been in America, their marital and family patterns have been subjects of curiosity and amusement, moral indignation and self-congratulation, puzzlement and frustration, concern and guilt, on the part of white Americans.[1] As some Negroes have moved into middle-class status, or acquired

Abridged from pp. 172–216 by Lee Rainwater in Talcott Parsons and Kenneth B. Clark (Eds.), *The Negro American*. Copyright © 1966. (Boston: Houghton Mifflin Company, 1966). Reprinted by permission of the author and Houghton Mifflin Company.

[1] Many of the ideas presented in this paper stem from discussion with the senior members of the Pruitt-Igoe research staff. Although this paper is not a formal report of the Pruitt-Igoe research, all of the illustrations of family behavior given in the text are drawn from interviews and observations that are part of that study. The study deals with the residents of the Pruitt-Igoe housing projects in St. Louis. Some 10,000 people live in these projects, which comprise 43 11-story buildings near the downtown area of St. Louis. Over half of the households have female heads, and for over half of the households the principal income comes from public assistance of one kind or another. The research has been in the field for a little over two years. It is a broad community study which thus far has relied principally on methods of participant observation and open-ended interviewing. Data on families come from repeated interviews and observations with a small group of families. The field workers are identified as graduate students at Washington University who have no connection with the housing authority or other officials, but are simply interested in learning about how families in the project live. This very intensive study of families yields a wealth of information (over 10,000 pages of interview and observa-

standards of American common-man respectability, they too have shared these attitudes toward the private behavior of their fellows, sometimes with a moral punitiveness to rival that of whites, but at other times with a hard-headed interest in causes and remedies rather than moral evaluation. Moralism permeated the subject of Negro sexual, marital, and family behavior in the polemics of slavery apologists and abolitionists as much as in the Northern and Southern civil rights controversies of today. Yet, as long as the dialectic of good or bad, guilty or innocent, overshadows a concern with who, why, and what can be, it is unlikely that realistic and effective social planning to correct the clearly desperate situation of poor Negro families can begin.

This paper is concerned with a description and analysis of slum Negro family patterns as these reflect and sustain Negroes' adaptations to the economic, social, and personal situation into which they are born and in which they must live. As such it deals with facts of lower-class life that are usually forgotten or ignored in polite discussion. We have chosen not to ignore these facts in the belief that to do so can lead only to assumptions which would frustrate efforts at social reconstruction, to strategies that are unrealistic in the light of the actual day-to-day reality of slum Negro life. Further, this analysis will deal with family patterns which interfere with the efforts slum Negroes make to attain a stable way of life as working- or middle-class individuals and with the effects such failure in turn has on family life. To be sure, many Negro families live *in* the slum ghetto, but are not *of* its culture (though even they, and particularly their children, can be deeply affected by what happens there). However, it is the individuals who succumb to the distinctive family life style of the slum who experience the greatest weight of deprivation and who have the greatest difficulty responding to the few self-improvement resources that make their way into the ghetto. In short, we propose to explore in depth the family's role in the "tangle of pathology" which characterizes the ghetto.

The social reality in which Negroes have had to make their lives during the 450 years of their existence in the western hemisphere has been one of victimization "in the sense that a system of social relations operates in such a way as to deprive them of a chance to share in the more desirable material and nonmaterial products of a society which is dependent, in part, upon their labor and loyalty." In making this observation, St. Clair Drake (1965) goes on to note that Negroes are victimized also because "they do not have the same degree of access which others have to the attributes needed for rising in the general class system —money, education, 'contacts,' and 'know-how.'" The victimization process started with slavery; for 350 years thereafter Negroes worked out as best they could adaptations to the slave status. After emancipation, the cultural mechanisms which Negroes had developed for living the life of victim continued to be serviceable as the victimization process was maintained first under the myths of white supremacy and black inferiority, later by the doctrines of gradualism

---

tion reports) which obviously cannot be analyzed within the limits of one article. In this article I have limited myself to outlining a typical family stage sequence and discussing some of the psychosocial implications of growing up in families characterized by this sequence. In addition, I have tried to limit myself to findings which other literature on Negro family life suggests are not limited to the residents of the housing projects we are studying.

which covered the fact of no improvement in position, and finally by the modern Northern system of ghettoization and indifference.

When lower-class Negroes use the expression, "Tell it like it is," they signal their intention to strip away pretense, to describe a situation or its participants as they really are, rather than in a polite or euphemistic way. "Telling it like it is" can be used as a harsh, aggressive device, or it can be a healthy attempt to face reality rather than retreat into fantasy. In any case, as he goes about his field work, the participant observer studying a ghetto community learns to listen carefully to any exchange preceded by such an announcement because he knows the speaker is about to express his understanding of how his world operates, of what motivates its members, of how they actually behave.

The first responsibility of the social scientist can be phrased in much the same way: "Tell it like it is." His second responsibility is to try to understand why "it" is that way, and to explore the implications of what and why for more constructive solutions to human problems. Social research on the situation of the Negro American has been informed by four main goals: (1) to describe the disadvantaged position of Negroes, (2) to disprove the racist ideology which sustains the caste system, (3) to demonstrate that responsibility for the disadvantages Negroes suffer lies squarely upon the white caste which derives economic, prestige, and psychic benefits from the operation of the system, and (4) to suggest that in reality whites would be better rather than worse off if the whole jerry-built caste structure were to be dismantled. The successful accomplishment of these *intellectual* goals has been a towering achievement, in which the social scientists of the 1920's, '30's, and '40's can take great pride; that white society has proved so recalcitrant to utilizing this intellectual accomplishment is one of the great tragedies of our time, and provides the stimulus for further social research on "the white problem."

Yet the implicit paradigm of much of the research on Negro Americans has been an overly simplistic one concentrating on two terms of an argument:

White cupidity⟶Negro suffering.

As an intellectual shorthand, and even more as a civil rights slogan, this simple model is both justified and essential. But, as a guide to greater understanding of the Negro situation as human adaptation to human situations, the paradigm is totally inadequate because it fails to specify fully enough the *process* by which Negroes adapt to their situations as they do, and the limitations one kind of adaptation places on possibilities for subsequent adaptations. A reassessment of previous social research, combined with examination of current social research on Negro ghetto communities, suggests a more complex, but hopefully more vertical, model:

White cupidity
creates
Structural Conditions Highly Inimical to Basic Social Adaptation (low-income availability, poor education, poor services, stigmatization)
to which Negroes adapt
by
Social and Personal Responses which serve to sustain the individual in his punishing world but also generate aggressiveness toward the self and others
which results in
Suffering directly inflicted by Negroes on themselves and on others.

In short, whites, by their greater power, create situations in which Negroes do the dirty work of caste victimization for them.

The white caste maintains a cadre of whites whose special responsibility is to enforce the system in brutal or refined ways (the Klan, the rural sheriff, the metropolitan police, the businessman who specializes in a Negro clientele, the Board of Education). Increasingly, whites recruit to this cadre middle-class Negroes who can soften awareness of victimization by their protective coloration. These special cadres, white and/or Negro, serve the very important function of enforcing caste standards by whatever means seems required, while at the same time concealing from an increasingly "unprejudiced" public the unpleasant facts they would prefer to ignore. The system is quite homologous to the Gestapo and concentration camps of Nazi Germany, though less fatal to its victims.

For their part, Negroes creatively adapt to the system in ways that keep them alive and extract what gratification they can find, but in the process of adaptation they are constrained to behave in ways that inflict a great deal of suffering on those with whom they make their lives, and on themselves. The ghetto Negro is constantly confronted by the immediate necessity to suffer in order to get what he wants of those few things he can have, or to make others suffer, or both—for example, he suffers as exploited student and employee, as drug user, as loser in the competitive game of his peer-group society; he inflicts suffering as disloyal spouse, petty thief, knife- or gun-wielder, petty con man.

It is the central thesis of this paper that the caste-facilitated infliction of suffering by Negroes on other Negroes and on themselves appears most poignantly within the confines of the family, and that the victimization process as it operates in families prepares and toughens its members to function in the ghetto world, at the same time that it seriously interferes with their ability to operate in any other world. This, however, is very different from arguing that "the family is to blame" for the deprived situation ghetto Negroes suffer; rather we are looking at the logical outcome of the operation of the widely ramified and interconnecting caste system. In the end we will argue that only palliative results can be expected from attempts to treat directly the disordered family patterns to be described. Only a change in the original "inputs" of the caste system, the structural conditions inimical to basic social adaptation, can change family forms.

Almost 30 years ago, E. Franklin Frazier (1939) foresaw that the fate of the Negro family in the city would be a highly destructive one. His readers would have little reason to be surprised at observations of slum ghetto life today:

> . . . As long as the bankrupt system of southern agriculture exists, Negro families will continue to seek a living in the towns and cities. . . . They will crowd the slum areas of southern cities or make their way to northern cities where their families will become disrupted and their poverty will force them to depend upon charity (p. 487).

The Autonomy of the Slum Ghetto

Just as the deprivations and depredations practiced by white society have had their effect on the personalities and social life of Negroes, so also has the separation from the ongoing social life of the white community had its effect. In a curious way, Negroes have had considerable freedom to fashion their own adaptations within their separate world. The larger society provides them with few resources but also with minimal interference in the Negro community on matters which did not seem to affect white interests. Because Negroes learned early that there were a great many things they could not depend upon whites to provide they developed their own solutions to recurrent human issues. These solutions can often be seen to combine, along with the predominance of elements from white culture, elements that are distinctive to the Negro group. Even more distinctive is the *configuration* which emerges from those elements Negroes share with whites and those which are different.

It is in this sense that we may speak of a Negro subculture, a distinctive *patterning* of existential perspectives, techniques for coping with the problems of social life, views about what is desirable and undesirable in particular situations. This subculture, and particularly that of the lower-class, slum Negro, can be seen as his own creation out of the elements available to him in response to (1) the conditions of life set by white society and (2) the selective freedom which that society allows (or must put up with given the pattern of separateness on which it insists).

Out of this kind of "freedom" slum Negroes have built a culture which has some elements of intrinsic value and many more elements that are highly destructive to the people who must live in it. The elements that whites can value they constantly borrow. Negro arts and language have proved so popular that such commentators on American culture as Norman Mailer (1957) and Leslie Fiedler (1964) have noted processes of Negro-ization of white Americans as a minor theme of the past 30 years. A fairly large proportion of Negroes with national reputations are engaged in the occupation of diffusing to the larger culture these elements of intrinsic value.

On the negative side, this freedom has meant, as social scientists who have studied Negro communities have long commented, that many of the protections offered by white institutions stop at the edge of the Negro ghetto: there are poor police protection and enforcement of civil equities, inadequate schooling and medical service, and more informal indulgences which whites allow Negroes as a small price for feeling superior.

For our purposes, however, the most important thing about the freedom which whites have allowed Negroes within their own world is that it has required them to work out their own ways of making it from day to day, from birth to death. The subculture that Negroes have created may be imperfect but it has been viable for centuries; it behooves both white and Negro leaders and intellectuals to seek to understand it even as they hope to change it.[2]

Negroes have created, again particularly within the lower-class slum group, a range of institutions to structure the tasks of living a victimized life and to minimize the pain it inevitably produces. In the slum ghetto these institutions include prominently those of the social network—the extended kinship system

[2] See Gouldner (1959) for a discussion of functional autonomy and dependence of structural elements in social systems. We are suggesting here that lower-class groups have a relatively high degree of functional autonomy *vis-à-vis* the total social system because that system does little to meet their needs. In general the fewer the rewards a society offers members of a particular group in the society, the more autonomous will that group prove to be with reference to the norms of the society. Only by constructing an elaborate repressive machinery, as in concentration camps, can the effect be otherwise.

and the "street system" of buddies and broads which tie (although tenuously and unpredictably) the "members" to each other—and the institutions of entertainment (music, dance, folk tales) by which they instruct, explain, and accept themselves. Other institutions function to provide escape from the society of the victimized: the church (Hereafter!) and the civil rights movement (Now!).

The Functional Autonomy of the Negro Family

At the center of the matrix of Negro institutional life lies the family. It is in the family that individuals are trained for participation in the culture and find personal and group identity and continuity. The "freedom" allowed by white society is greatest here, and this freedom has been used to create an institutional variant more distinctive perhaps to the Negro subculture than any other. (Much of the content of Negro art and entertainment derives exactly from the distinctive characteristics of Negro family life.) At each stage in the Negro's experience of American life—slavery, segregation, *de facto* ghettoization—whites have found it less necessary to interfere in the relations between the sexes and between parents and children than in other areas of the Negro's existence. His adaptations in this area, therefore, have been less constrained by whites than in many other areas.

Now that the larger society is becoming increasingly committed to integrating Negroes into the main stream of American life, however, we can expect increasing constraint (benevolent as it may be) to be placed on the autonomy of the Negro family system.[3] These constraints will be designed to pull Negroes into meaningful integration with the larger society, to give up ways which are inimical to successful performance in the larger society, and to adopt new ways that are functional in that society. The strategic questions of the civil rights movement and of the war on poverty are ones that have to do with how one provides functional equivalents for the existing subculture before the capacity to make a life within its confines is destroyed.

The history of the Negro family has been ably documented by historians and sociologists (see Stampp, 1961; Franklin, 1952; Tannenbaum, 1947; Frazier, 1939; Herskovits, 1941). In slavery, conjugal and family ties were reluctantly and ambivalently recognized by the slave holders, were often violated by them, but proved necessary to the slave system. This necessity stemmed both from the profitable offspring of slave sexual unions and the necessity for their nurture, and from the fact that the slaves' efforts to sustain patterns of sexual and parental relations mollified the men and women whose labor could not simply be commanded. From nature's promptings, the thinning memories of African heritage, and the example and guilt-ridden permission of the slave holders, slaves constructed a partial family system and sets of relations that generated conjugal and familial sentiments. The slave holder's recognition in advertisements for runaway slaves of marital and family sentiments as motivations for absconding provides one indication that strong family ties were possible, though perhaps not common, in the slave quarter. The mother-centered family with its emphasis on the primacy

[3] For example, the lead sentence in a *St. Louis Post Dispatch* article of July 20, 1965, begins, "A White House study group is laying the ground work for an attempt to better the structure of the Negro family."

of the mother-child relation and only tenuous ties to a man, then, is the legacy of adaptations worked out by Negroes during slavery.

After emancipation this family design often also served well to cope with the social disorganization of Negro life in the late nineteenth century. Matrifocal families, ambivalence about the desirability of marriage, ready acceptance of illegitimacy, all sustained some kind of family life in situations which often made it difficult to maintain a full nuclear family. Yet in the hundred years since emancipation, Negroes in rural areas have been able to maintain full nuclear families almost as well as similarly situated whites. As we will see, it is the move to the city that results in the very high proportion of mother-headed households. In the rural system the man continues to have important functions; it is difficult for a woman to make a crop by herself, or even with the help of other women. In the city, however, the woman can earn wages just as a man can, and she can receive welfare payments more easily than he can. In rural areas, although there may be high illegitimacy rates and high rates of marital disruption, men and women have an interest in getting together; families are headed by a husband-wife pair much more often than in the city. That pair may be much less stable than in the more prosperous segments of Negro and white communities but it is more likely to exist among rural Negroes than among urban ones.

The matrifocal character of the Negro lower-class family in the United States has much in common with Caribbean Negro family patterns; research in both areas has done a great deal to increase our understanding of the Negro situation. However, there are important differences in the family forms of the two areas (see Smith, 1956, 1963; Stycos and Back, 1964; Henriques, 1953; Blake, 1961; Kunstadter, 1963; Boyer, 1964). The impact of white European family models has been much greater in the United States than in the Caribbean both because of the relative population proportions of white and colored peoples and because equalitarian values in the United States have had a great impact on Negroes even when they have not on whites. The typical Caribbean mating pattern is that women go through several visiting and common-law unions but eventually marry; that is, they marry legally only relatively late in their sexual lives. The Caribbean marriage is the crowning of a sexual and procreative career; it is considered a serious and difficult step.

In the United States, in contrast, Negroes marry at only a slightly lower rate and slightly higher age than whites (Glick, 1957). Most Negro women marry relatively early in their careers; marriage is not regarded as the same kind of crowning choice and achievement that it is in the Caribbean. For lower-class Negroes in the United States marriage ceremonies are rather informal affairs. In the Caribbean, marriage is regarded as quite costly because of the feasting which goes along with it; ideally it is performed in church.

In the United States, unlike the Caribbean, early marriage confers a kind of permanent respectable status upon a woman which she can use to deny any subsequent accusations of immorality or promiscuity once the marriage is broken and she becomes sexually involved in visiting or common-law relations. The relevant effective status for many Negro women is that of "having been married" rather than "being married;" having the right to be called "Mrs." rather than currently being Mrs. Someone-in-Particular.

For Negro lower-class women, then, first marriage has the same kind of im-

TABLE I

PROPORTION OF FEMALE HEADS FOR FAMILIES WITH CHILDREN BY RACE, INCOME, AND URBAN-RURAL CATEGORIES

Negroes	Rural	Urban	Total
Under $3000	18%	47%	36%
$3000 and over	5%	8%	7%
Total	14%	23%	21%
Whites			
Under $3000	12%	38%	22%
$3000 and over	2%	4%	3%
Total	4%	7%	6%

Source: U.S. Census: 1960, PC (1) D. U.S. Volume, Table 225; State Volume, Table 140.

portance as having a first child. Both indicate that the girl has become a woman but neither one that this is the last such activity in which she will engage. It seems very likely that only a minority of Negro women in the urban slum go through their child-rearing years with only one man around the house.

Among the Negro urban poor, then, a great many women have the experience of heading a family for part of their mature lives, and a great many children spend some part of their formative years in a household without a father-mother pair. From Table I we see that in 1960, 47 per cent of the Negro poor urban families with children had a female head. Unfortunately cumulative statistics are hard to come by; but, given this very high level for a cross-sectional sample (and taking into account the fact that the median age of the children in these families is about six years), it seems very likely that as many as two-thirds of Negro urban poor children will not live in families headed by a man and a woman throughout the first 18 years of their lives.

One of the other distinctive characteristics of Negro families, both poor and not so poor, is the fact that Negro households have a much higher proportion of relatives outside the mother-father-children triangle than is the case with whites. For example, in St. Louis Negro families average 0.8 other relatives per household compared to only 0.4 for white families. In the case of the more prosperous Negro families this is likely to mean that an older relative lives in the home providing baby-sitting services while both the husband and wife work and thus further their climb toward stable working- or middle-class status. In the poor Negro families it is much more likely that the household is headed by an older relative who brings under her wings a daughter and that daughter's children. It is important to note that the three-generation household with the grandmother at the head exists only when there is no husband present. Thus, despite the high proportion of female-headed households in this group and despite the high proportion of households that contain other relatives, we find that almost all married couples in the St. Louis Negro slum community have their own household. In other words, when a couple marries it establishes its own household; when that couple breaks up the mother either maintains that household or moves back to her parents or grandparents.

Finally we should note that Negro slum families have more children than do either white slum families or stable working- and middle-class Negro families.

Mobile Negro families limit their fertility sharply in the interest of bringing the advantages of mobility more fully to the few children that they do have. Since the Negro slum family is both more likely to have the father absent and more likely to have more children in the family, the mother has a more demanding task with fewer resources at her disposal. When we examine the patterns of life of the stem family we shall see that even the presence of several mothers does not necessarily lighten the work load for the principal mother in charge.

The Formation and Maintenance of Families

We will outline below the several stages and forms of Negro lower-class family life. At many points these family forms and the interpersonal relations that exist within them will be seen to have characteristics in common with the life styles of white lower-class families (see Rainwater, Coleman, and Handel, 1959; Rainwater, 1965; Gans, 1962; Cohen and Hodges, 1963; Miller, 1964; Komarovsky, 1962; Drake and Cayton, 1962; Clark, 1965; Davis, Gardner, and Gardner, 1941; Lewis, 1955). At other points there are differences, or the Negro pattern will be seen to be more sharply divergent from the family life of stable working- and middle-class couples.

It is important to recognize that lower-class Negroes know that their particular family forms are different from those of the rest of the society and that, though they often see these forms as representing the only ways of behaving given their circumstances, they also think of the more stable family forms of the working class as more desirable. That is, lower-class Negroes know what the "normal American family" is supposed to be like, and they consider a stable family-centered way of life superior to the conjugal and familial situations in which they often find themselves. Their conceptions of the good American life include the notion of a father-husband who functions as an adequate provider and interested member of the family, a hard-working home-bound mother who is concerned about her children's welfare and her husband's needs, and children who look up to their parents and perform well in school and other outside places to reflect credit on their families. This image of what family life can be like is very real from time to time as lower-class men and women grow up and move through adulthood. Many of them make efforts to establish such families but find it impossible to do so either because of the direct impact of economic disabilities or because they are not able to sustain in their day-to-day lives the ideals which they hold (see Cohen, 1955; Rodman, 1963; Yancey, n.d.). While these ideals do serve as a meaningful guide to lower-class couples who are mobile out of the group, for a great many others the existence of such ideas about normal family life represents a recurrent source of stress within families as individuals become aware that they are failing to measure up to the ideals, or as others within the family and outside it use the ideals as an aggressive weapon for criticizing each other's performance. It is not at all uncommon for husbands or wives or children to try to hold others in the family to the norms of stable family life while they themselves engage in behaviors which violate these norms. The effect of such criticism in the end is to deepen commitment to the deviant sexual and parental norms of a slum subculture. Unless they are careful, social workers and other professionals exacerbate the tendency to use the norms of "American family life" as weapons by supporting these norms in situations where they are in reality unsupportable, thus aggravating the sense of failing and being failed by others which is chronic for lower-class people.

Going Together

The initial steps toward mating and family formation in the Negro slum take place in a context of highly developed boys' and girls' peer groups. Adolescents tend to become deeply involved in their peer-group societies beginning as early as the age of 12 or 13 and continue to be involved after first pregnancies and first marriages. Boys and girls are heavily committed both to their same sex peer groups and to the activities that those groups carry out. While classical gang activity does not necessarily characterize Negro slum communities everywhere, loosely-knit peer groups do.

The world of the Negro slum is wide open to exploration by adolescent boys and girls: "Negro communities provide a flow of common experience in which young people and their elders share, and out of which delinquent behavior emerges almost imperceptibly (Short and Strodtbeck, 1965, p. 114). More than is possible in white slum communities, Negro adolescents have an opportunity to interact with adults in various "high life" activities; their behavior more often represents an identification with the behavior of adults than an attempt to set up group standards and activities that differ from those of adults.

Boys and young men participating in the street system of peer-group activity are much caught up in games of furthering and enhancing their status as significant persons. These games are played out in small and large gatherings through various kinds of verbal contests that go under the names of "sounding," "signifying," and "working game." Very much a part of a boy's or man's status in this group is his ability to win women. The man who has several women "up tight," who is successful in "pimping off" women for sexual favors and material benefits, is much admired. In sharp contrast to white lower-class groups, there is little tendency for males to separate girls into "good" and "bad" categories (Green, 1941; Whyte, 1943; Rainwater, 1964). Observations of groups of Negro youths suggest that girls and women are much more readily referred to as "that bitch" or "that whore" than they are by their names, and this seems to be a universal tendency carrying no connotation that "that bitch" is morally inferior to or different from other women. Thus, all women are essentially the same, all women are legitimate targets, and no girl or woman is expected to be virginal except for reason of lack of opportunity or immaturity. From their participation in the peer group and according to standards legitimated by the total Negro slum culture, Negro boys and young men are propelled in the direction of girls to test their "strength" as seducers. They are mercilessly rated by both their peers and the opposite sex in their ability to "talk" to girls; a young man will go to great lengths to avoid the reputation of having a "weak" line (see Hammond, 1965; Reiss, 1964).

The girls share these definitions of the nature of heterosexual relations; they take for granted that almost any male they deal with will try to seduce them and that given sufficient inducement (social, not monetary) they may wish to go along with his line. Although girls have a great deal of ambivalence about participating in sexual relations, this ambivalence is minimally moral and has much more to do with a desire not to be taken advantage of or get in trouble. Girls develop defenses against the exploitative orientations of men by devaluing the significance of sexual relations ("he really didn't do anything bad to me"), and as time goes on by developing their own appreciation of the intrinsic rewards of sexual intercourse.

The informal social relations of slum Negroes begin in adolescence to be highly sexualized. Although parents have many qualms about boys and, particularly, girls entering into this system, they seldom feel there is much they can do to prevent their children's sexual involvement. They usually confine themselves to counseling somewhat hopelessly against girls becoming pregnant or boys being forced into situations where they might have to marry a girl they do not want to marry.

Girls are propelled toward boys and men in order to demonstrate their maturity and attractiveness; in the process they are constantly exposed to pressures for seduction, to boys "rapping" to them. An active girl will "go with" quite a number of boys, but she will generally try to restrict the number with whom she has intercourse to the few to whom she is attracted or (as happens not infrequently) to those whose threats of physical violence she cannot avoid. For their part, the boys move rapidly from girl to girl seeking to have intercourse with as many as they can and thus build up their "reps." The activity of seduction is itself highly cathected; there is gratification in simply "talking to" a girl as long as the boy can feel that he has acquitted himself well.

> At sixteen Joan Bemias enjoys spending time with three or four very close girl friends. She tells us they follow this routine when the girls want to go out and none of the boys they have been seeing lately is available: "Every time we get ready to go someplace we look through all the telephone numbers of boys we'd have and we call them and talk so sweet to them that they'd come on around. All of them had cars you see. (I: What do you do to keep all these fellows interested?) Well nothing. We don't have to make love with all of them. Let's see, Joe, J.B., Albert, and Paul, out of all of them I've been going out with I've only had sex with four boys, that's all." She goes on to say that she and her girl friends resist boys by being unresponsive to their lines and by breaking off relations with them on the ground that they're going out with other girls. It is also clear from her comments that the girl friends support each other in resisting the boys when they are out together in groups.
>
> Joan has had a relationship with a boy which has lasted six months, but she has managed to hold the frequency of intercourse down to four times. Initially she managed to hold this particular boy off for a month but eventually gave in.

Becoming Pregnant

It is clear that the contest elements in relationships between men and women continue even in relationships that become quite steady. Despite the girls' ambivalence about sexual relations and their manifold efforts to reduce its frequency, the operation of chance often eventuates in their becoming pregnant (see Short and Strodtbeck, 1965). This was the case with Joan. With this we reach the second stage in the formation of families, that of premarital pregnancy. (We are outlining an ideal-typical sequence and not, of course, implying that all girls in the Negro slum culture become pregnant before they marry but only that a great many of them do.)

Joan was caught despite the fact that she was considerably more sophisticated about contraception than most girls or young women in the group (her mother had both instructed her in contraceptive techniques and constantly warned her to take precautions). No one was particularly surprised at her pregnancy although she, her boy friend, her mother, and others regarded it as unfortunate. For girls in the Negro slum, pregnancy before marriage is expected in much the same way that parents expect their children to catch mumps or chicken pox; if they are lucky it will not happen but if it happens people are not too surprised and everyone knows what to do about it. It was quickly decided that Joan and the baby would stay at home. It seems clear from the preparations that Joan's mother is making that she expects to have the main responsibility for caring for the infant. Joan seems quite indifferent to the baby; she shows little interest in mothering the child although she is not particularly adverse to the idea so long as the baby does not interfere too much with her continued participation in her peer group.

Establishing who the father is under these circumstances seems to be important and confers a kind of legitimacy on the birth; not to know who one's father is, on the other hand, seems the ultimate in illegitimacy. Actually Joan had a choice in the imputation of fatherhood; she chose J.B. because he is older than she, and because she may marry him if he can get a divorce from his wife. She could have chosen Paul (with whom she had also had intercourse at about the time she became pregnant), but she would have done this reluctantly since Paul is a year younger than she and somehow this does not seem fitting.

In general, when a girl becomes pregnant while still living at home it seems taken for granted that she will continue to live there and that her parents will take a major responsibility for rearing the children. Since there are usually siblings who can help out and even siblings who will be playmates for the child, the addition of a third generation to the household does not seem to place a great stress on relationships within the family. It seems common for the first pregnancy to have a liberating influence on the mother once the child is born in that she becomes socially and sexually more active than she was before. She no longer has to be concerned with preserving her status as a single girl. Since her mother is usually willing to take care of the child for a few years, the unwed mother has an opportunity to go out with girl friends and with men and thus become more deeply involved in the peer-group society of her culture. As she has more children and perhaps marries she will find it necessary to settle down and spend more time around the house fulfilling the functions of a mother herself.

It would seem that for girls pregnancy is the real measure of maturity, the dividing line between adolescence and womanhood. Perhaps because of this, as well as because of the ready resources for child care, girls in the Negro slum community show much less concern about pregnancy than do girls in the white lower-class community and are less motivated to marry the fathers of their children. When a girl becomes pregnant the question of marriage certainly arises and is considered, but the girl often decides that she would rather not marry the man either because she does not want to settle down yet or because she does not think he would make a good husband.

It is in the easy attitudes toward premarital pregnancy that the matrifocal character of the Negro lower-class family appears most clearly. In order to have and raise a family it is simply not necessary, though it may be desirable, to have a man around the house. While the AFDC program may make it easier to maintain such attitudes in the urban situation, this pattern existed long before the program was initiated and continues in families where support comes from other sources.

Finally it should be noted that fathering a child similarly confers maturity on boys and young men although perhaps it is less salient for them. If the boy has any interest in the girl he will tend to feel that the fact that he has impregnated her gives him an additional claim on her. He will be stricter in seeking to enforce his exclusive rights over her (though not exclusive loyalty to her). This exclusive right does not mean that he expects to marry her but only that there is a new and special bond between them. If the girl is not willing to accept such claims she may find it necessary to break off the relationship rather than tolerate the man's jealousy. Since others in the peer group have a vested interest in not allowing a couple to be too loyal to each other they go out of their way to question and challenge each partner about the loyalty of the other, thus contributing to the deterioration of the relationship. This same kind of questioning and challenging continues if the couple marries and represents one source of the instability of the marital relationship.

Getting Married

As noted earlier, despite the high degree of premarital sexual activity and the rather high proportion of premarital pregnancies, most lower-class Negro men and women eventually do marry and stay together for a shorter or longer period of time. Marriage is an intimidating prospect and is approached ambivalently by both parties. For the girl it means giving up a familiar and comfortable home that, unlike some other lower-class subcultures, places few real restrictions on her behavior. (While marriage can appear to be an escape from interpersonal difficulties at home, these difficulties seldom seem to revolve around effective restrictions placed on her behavior by her parents.) The girl also has good reason to be suspicious of the likelihood that men will be able to perform stably in the role of husband and provider; she is reluctant to be tied down by a man who will not prove to be worth it.

From the man's point of view the fickleness of women makes marriage problematic. It is one thing to have a girl friend step out on you, but it is quite another to have a wife do so. Whereas premarital sexual relations and fatherhood carry almost no connotation of responsibility for the welfare of the partner, marriage is supposed to mean that a man behaves more responsibly, becoming a provider for his wife and children even though he may not be expected to give up all the gratifications of participation in the street system.

For all of these reasons both boys and girls tend to have rather negative views of marriage as well as a low expectation that marriage will prove a stable and gratifying existence. When marriage does take place it tends to represent a tentative commitment on the part of both parties with a strong tendency to seek greater commitment on the part of the partner than on one's own part. Marriage is regarded as a fragile arrangement held together primarily by affectional ties rather than instrumental concerns.

In general, as in white lower-class groups, the decision to marry seems to be taken rather impulsively.[4] Since everyone knows that sooner or later he will get married, in spite of the fact that he may not be sanguine about the prospect, Negro lower-class men and women are alert for clues that the time has arrived. The time may arrive because of a pregnancy in a steady relationship that seems gratifying to both partners, or as a way of getting out of what seems to be an awkward situation, or as a self-indulgence during periods when a boy and a girl are feeling very sorry for themselves. Thus, one girl tells us that when she marries her husband will cook all of her meals for her and she will not have any housework; another girl says that when she marries it will be to a man who has plenty of money and will have to take her out often and really show her a good time.

Boys see in marriage the possibility of regular sexual intercourse without having to fight for it, or a girl safe from venereal disease, or a relationship to a nurturant figure who will fulfill the functions of a mother. For boys, marriage can also be a way of asserting their independence from the peer group if its demands become burdensome. In this case the young man seeks to have the best of both worlds (Miller, 1963).

Marriage as a way out of an unpleasant situation can be seen in the case of one of our informants, Janet Cowan:

> Janet has been going with two men, one of them married and the other single. The married man's wife took exception to their relationship and killed her husband. Within a week Janet and her single boy friend, Howard, were married. One way out of the turmoil the murder of her married boy friend stimulated (they lived in the same building) was to choose marriage as a way of "settling down." However, after marrying the new couple seemed to have little idea how to set themselves up as a family. Janet was reluctant to leave her parents' home because her parents cared for her two illegitimate children. Howard was unemployed and therefore unacceptable in his parent-in-law's home, nor were his own parents willing to have his wife move in with them. Howard was also reluctant to give up another girl friend in another part of town. Although both he and his wife maintained that it was all right for a couple to step out on each other so long as the other partner did not know about it, they were both jealous if they suspected anything of this kind. In the end they gave up on the idea of marriage and went their separate ways.

In general, then, the movement toward marriage is an uncertain and tentative one. Once the couple does settle down together in a household of their own, they have the problem of working out a mutually acceptable organization of rights and duties, expectations and performances, that will meet their needs.

Husband-Wife Relations

Characteristic of both the Negro and white lower class is a high degree of conjugal role segregation (Rainwater, 1964). That is, husbands and wives tend to think of themselves as having very separate kinds of functioning in the instrumental organization of family life, and also as pursuing recreational and outside interests separately. The husband is expected to be a provider; he resists assum-

[4] See Rainwater (1960); see also Broderick (1965). Broderick finds that although white boys and girls, and Negro girls become more interested in marriage as they get older, Negro boys become *less* interested in late adolescence than they were as preadolescents.

ing functions around the home so long as he feels he is doing his proper job of bringing home a pay check. He feels he has the right to indulge himself in little ways if he is successful at this task. The wife is expected to care for the home and children and make her husband feel welcome and comfortable. Much that is distinctive to Negro family life stems from the fact that husbands often are not stable providers. Even when a particular man is, his wife's conception of men in general is such that she is pessimistic about the likelihood that he will continue to do well in this area. A great many Negro wives work to supplement the family income. When this is so the separate incomes earned by husband and wife tend to be treated not as "family" income but as the individual property of the two persons involved. If their wives work, husbands are likely to feel that they are entitled to retain a larger share of the income they provide; the wives, in turn, feel that the husbands have no right to benefit from the purchases they make out of their own money. There is, then, "my money" and "your money." In this situation the husband may come to feel that the wife should support the children out of her income and that he can retain all of his income for himself.

While white lower-class wives often are very much intimidated by their husbands, Negro lower-class wives come to feel that they have a right to give as good as they get. If the husband indulges himself, they have the right to indulge themselves. If the husband steps out on his wife, she has the right to step out on him. The commitment of husbands and wives to each other seems often a highly instrumental one after the "honeymoon" period. Many wives feel they owe the husband nothing once he fails to perform his provider role. If the husband is unemployed the wife increasingly refuses to perform her usual duties for him. For example one woman, after mentioning that her husband had cooked four eggs for himself, commented, "I cook for him when he's working but right now he's unemployed; he can cook for himself." It is important, however, to understand that the man's status in the home depends not so much on whether he is working as on whether he brings money into the home. Thus, in several of the families we have studied in which the husband receives disability payments his status is as well-recognized as in families in which the husband is working.[5]

Because of the high degree of conjugal role segregation, both white and Negro lower-class families tend to be matrifocal in comparison to middle-class families. They are matrifocal in the sense that the wife makes most of the decisions that keep the family going and has the greatest sense of responsibility to the family. In white as well as in Negro lower-class families women tend to look to their female relatives for support and counsel, and to treat their husbands as essentially uninterested in the day-to-day problems of family living (Komarovsky, 1962). In the Negro lower-class family these tendencies are all considerably exaggerated so that the matrifocality is much clearer than in white lower-class families.

The fact that both sexes in the Negro slum culture have equal right to the

[5] See Yancey, n.d. The effects of unemployment on the family have been discussed by Bakke (1940); Komarovsky (1940); and Koos (1946). What seems distinctive to the Negro slum culture is the short time lapse between the husband's loss of a job and his wife's considering him superfluous.

various satisfactions of life (earning an income, sex, drinking, and peer-group activity which conflicts with family responsibilities) means that there is less pretense to patriarchal authority in the Negro than in the white lower class. Since men find the overt debasement of their status very threatening, the Negro family is much more vulnerable to disruption when men are temporarily unable to perform their provider roles. Also, when men are unemployed the temptations for them to engage in street adventures which repercuss on the marital relationship are much greater. This fact is well-recognized by Negro lower-class wives; they often seem as concerned about what their unemployed husbands will do instead of working as they are about the fact that the husband is no longer bringing money into the home.

It is tempting to cope with the likelihood of disloyalty by denying the usual norms of fidelity, by maintaining instead that extra-marital affairs are acceptable as long as they do not interfere with family functioning. Quite a few informants tell us this, but we have yet to observe a situation in which a couple maintains a stable relationship under these circumstances without a great deal of conflict. Thus one woman in her forties who has been married for many years and has four children first outlined this deviant norm and then illustrated how it did not work out:

> My husband and I, we go out alone and sometimes stay all night. But when I get back my husband doesn't ask me a thing and I don't ask him anything. . . . A couple of years ago I suspected he was going out on me. One day I came home and my daughter was here. I told her to tell me when he left the house. I went into the bedroom and got into bed and then I heard him come in. He left in about ten minutes and my daughter came in and told me he was gone. I got out of bed and put on my clothes and started following him. Soon I saw him walking with a young girl and I began walking after them. They were just laughing and joking right out loud right on the sidewalk. He was carrying a large package of hers. I walked up behind them until I was about a yard from them. I had a large dirk which I opened and had decided to take one long slash across the both of them. Just when I decided to swing at them I lost my balance—I have a bad hip. Anyway, I didn't cut them because I lost my balance. Then I called his name and he turned around and stared at me. He didn't move at all. He was shaking all over. That girl just ran away from us. He still had her package so the next day she called on the telephone and said she wanted to come pick it up. My husband washed his face, brushed his teeth, took out his false tooth and started scrubbing it and put on a clean shirt and everything, just for her. We went downstairs together and gave her the package and she left.
>
> So you see my husband does run around on me and it seems like he does it a lot. The thing about it is he's just getting too old to be pulling that kind of stuff. If a young man does it then that's not so bad—but an old man, he just looks foolish. One of these he'll catch me but I'll just tell him, "Buddy you owe me one," and that'll be all there is to it. He hasn't caught me yet though.

In this case, as in others, the wife is not able to leave well enough alone; her jealousy forces her to a confrontation. Actually seeing her husband with another woman stimulates her to violence.

With couples who have managed to stay married for a good many years, these peccadillos are tolerable although they generate a great deal of conflict in the marital relationship. At earlier ages the partners are likely to be both prouder and less inured to the hopelessness of maintaining stable relationships; outside involvements are therefore much more likely to be disruptive of the marriage.

Marital Breakup

The precipitating causes of marital disruption seem to fall mainly into economic or sexual categories. As noted, the husband has little credit with his wife to tide him over periods of unemployment. Wives seem very willing to withdraw commitment from husbands who are not bringing money into the house. They take the point of view that he has no right to take up space around the house, to use its facilities, or to demand loyalty from her. Even where the wife is not inclined to press these claims, the husband tends to be touchy because he knows that such definitions are usual in his group, and he may, therefore, prove difficult for even a well-meaning wife to deal with. As noted above, if husbands do not work they tend to play around. Since they continue to maintain some contact with their peer groups, whenever they have time on their hands they move back into the world of the street system and are likely to get involved in activities which pose a threat to their family relationships.

Drink is a great enemy of the lower-class housewife, both white and Negro. Lower-class wives fear their husband's drinking because it costs money, because the husband may become violent and take out his frustrations on his wife, and because drinking may lead to sexual involvements with other women (Rainwater, 1964).

> The combination of economic problems and sexual difficulties can be seen in the case of the following couple in their early twenties:
>
> When the field worker first came to know them, the Wilsons seemed to be working hard to establish a stable family life. The couple had been married about three years and had a two-year-old son. Their apartment was very sparsely furnished but also very clean. Within six weeks the couple had acquired several rooms of inexpensive furniture and obviously had gone to a great deal of effort to make a liveable home. Husband and wife worked on different shifts so that the husband could take care of the child while the wife worked. They looked forward to saving enough money to move out of the housing project into a more desirable neighborhood. Six weeks later, however, the husband had lost his job. He and his wife were in great conflict. She made him feel unwelcome at home and he strongly suspected her of going out with other men. A short time later they had separated. It is impossible to disentangle the various factors involved in this separation into a sequence of cause and effect, but we can see something of the impact of the total complex.
>
> First Mr. Wilson loses his job: "I went to work one day and the man told me that I would have to work until 1:00. I asked him if there would be any extra pay for working overtime and he said no. I asked him why and he said, 'If you don't like it you can kiss my ass.' He said that to me. I said, 'Why do I have to do all that?' He said, 'Because I said so.' I wanted to jam [fight] him but I said to myself I don't want to be that ignorant, I don't want to be as ignorant as he is, so I just cut out and left. Later his father called me [it was a family firm] and asked why I left and I told him. He said, 'If you don't want to go along with my son then you're fired.' I said O.K. They had another Negro man come in to help me part time before they fired me. I think they were trying to have him work full time because he worked for them before. He has seven kids and he takes their shit."

The field worker observed that things were not as hard as they could be because his wife had a job, to which he replied, "Yeah, I know, that's just where the trouble is. My wife has become independent since she began working. If I don't get a job pretty soon I'll go crazy. We have a lot of little arguments about nothing since she got so independent." He went on to say that his wife had become a completely different person recently; she was hard to talk to because she felt that now that she was working and he was not there was nothing that he could tell her. On her last pay day his wife did not return home for three days; when she did she had only seven cents left from her pay check. He said that he loved his wife very much and had begged her to quit fooling around. He is pretty sure that she is having an affair with the man with whom she rides to work. To make matters worse his wife's sister counsels her that she does not have to stay home with him as long as he is out of work. Finally the wife moved most of their furniture out of the apartment so that he came home to find an empty apartment. He moved back to his parents' home [also in the housing project].

One interesting effect of this experience was the radical change in the husband's attitudes toward race relations. When he and his wife were doing well together and had hopes of moving up in the world he was quite critical of Negroes; "Our people are not ready for integration in many cases because they really don't know how to act. You figure if our people don't want to be bothered with whites then why in hell should the white man want to be bothered with them. There are some of us who are ready; there are others who aren't quite ready yet so I don't see why they're doing all of this hollering." A scarce eight months later he addressed white people as he spoke for two hours into a tape recorder, "If we're willing to be with you, why aren't you willing to be with us? Does our color make us look dirty and low down and cheap? Or do you know the real meaning of 'nigger'? Anyone can be a nigger, white, colored, orange or any other color. It's something that you labeled us with. You put us away like you put a can away on the shelf with a label on it. The can is marked 'Poison: stay away from it.' You want us to help build your country but you don't want us to live in it. . . . You give me respect; I'll give you respect. If you threaten to take my life, I'll take yours and believe me I know how to take a life. We do believe that man was put here to live together as human beings; not one that's superior and the one that's a dog, but as human beings. And if you don't want to live this way then you become the dog and we'll become the human beings. There's too much corruption, too much hate, too much one individual trying to step on another. If we don't get together in a hurry we will destroy each other." It was clear from what the respondent said that he had been much influenced by Black Muslim philosophy, yet again and again in his comments one can see the displacement into a public, race relations dialogue of the sense of rage, frustration, and victimization that he had experienced in his ill-fated marriage (see Brotz, 1964; Essien-Udom, 1962).

Finally, it should be noted that migration plays a part in marital disruption. Sometimes marriages do not break up in the dramatic way described above but rather simply become increasingly unsatisfactory to one or both partners. In such a situation the temptation to move to another city, from South to North, or North to West, is great. Several wives told us that their first marriages were broken when they moved with their children to the North and their husbands stayed behind.

"After we couldn't get along I left the farm and came here and stayed away three or four days. I didn't come here to stay. I came to visit but I liked it and so I said, 'I'm gonna leave!' He said, 'I'll be glad if you do.' Well, maybe he didn't mean it but I thought he did. . . . I miss him sometimes, you know. I think about him I guess. But just in a small way. That's what I can't understand about life sometimes; you know—how people can go on like that and still break up and meet somebody else. Why couldn't—oh, I don't know!"

The gains and losses in marriage and in the post-marital state often seem quite comparable. Once they have had the experience of marriage, many women in the Negro slum culture see little to recommend it in the future, important as the first marriage may have been in establishing their maturity and respectability.

The House of Mothers

As we have seen, perhaps a majority of mothers in the Negro slum community spend at least part of their mature life as mothers heading a family. The Negro mother may be a working mother or she may be an AFDC mother, but in either case she has the problems of maintaining a household, socializing her children, and achieving for herself some sense of membership in relations with other women and with men. As is apparent from the earlier discussion, she often receives her training in how to run such a household by observing her own mother manage without a husband. Similarly she often learns how to run a three-generation household because she herself brought a third generation into her home with her first, premarital, pregnancy.

Because men are not expected to be much help around the house, having to be head of the household is not particularly intimidating to the Negro mother if she can feel some security about income. She knows it is a hard, hopeless, and often thankless task, but she also knows that it is possible. The maternal household in the slum is generally run with a minimum of organization. The children quickly learn to fend for themselves, to go to the store, to make small purchases, to bring change home, to watch after themselves when the mother has to be out of the home, to amuse themselves, to set their own schedules of sleeping, eating, and going to school. Housekeeping practices may be poor, furniture takes a terrific beating from the children, and emergencies constantly arise. The Negro mother in this situation copes by not setting too high standards for herself, by letting things take their course. Life is most difficult when there are babies and preschool children around because then the mother is confined to the home. If she is a grandmother and the children are her daughter's, she is often confined since it is taken as a matter of course that the mother has the right to continue her outside activities and that the grandmother has the duty to be responsible for the child.

In this culture there is little of the sense of the awesome responsibility of caring for children that is characteristic of the working and middle class. There is not the deep psychological involvement with babies which has been observed with the working-class mother (Rainwater, Coleman, and Handel, 1959). The baby's needs are cared for on a catch-as-catch-can basis. If there are other children around and they happen to like babies, the baby can be over-stimulated; if this is not the case, the baby is left alone a good deal of the time. As quickly as he can move around he learns to fend for himself.

The three-generation maternal household is a busy place. In contrast to working- and middle-class homes it tends to be open to the world, with many non-family members coming in and out at all times as the children are visited by friends, the teenagers by their boy friends and girl friends, the mother by her friends and perhaps an occasional boy friend, and the grandmother by fewer friends but still by an occasional boy friend.

The openness of the household is, among other things, a reflection of the mother's sense of impotence in the face of the street system. Negro lower-class mothers often indicate that they try very hard to keep their young children at home and away from the streets; they often seem to make the children virtual prisoners in the home. As the children grow and go to school they inevitably do become involved in peer-group activities. The mother gradually gives up, feeling that once the child is lost to this pernicious outside world there is little she can do to continue to control him and direct his development. She will try to limit the types of activities that go on in the home and to restrict the kinds of friends that her children can bring into the home, but even this she must give up as time goes on, as the children become older and less attentive to her direction.

The grandmothers in their late forties, fifties, and sixties tend increasingly to stay at home. The home becomes a kind of court at which other family members gather and to which they bring their friends for sociability, and as a by-product provide amusement and entertainment for the mother. A grandmother may provide a home for her daughters, their children, and sometimes their children's children, and yet receive very little in a material way from them; but one of the things she does receive is a sense of human involvement, a sense that although life may have passed her by she is not completely isolated from it.

The lack of control that mothers have over much that goes on in their households is most dramatically apparent in the fact that their older children seem to have the right to come home at any time once they have moved and to stay in the home without contributing to its maintenance. Though the mother may be resentful about being taken advantage of, she does not feel she can turn her children away. For example, 65-year-old Mrs. Washington plays hostess for weeks or months at a time to her 40-year-old daughter and her small children, and to her 23-year-old granddaughter and her children. When these daughters come home with their families the grandmother is expected to take care of the young children and must argue with her daughter and granddaughter to receive contributions to the daily household ration of food and liquor. Or, a 20-year-old son comes home from the Air Force and feels he has the right to live at home without working and to run up an 80-dollar long-distance telephone bill.

Even aged parents living alone in small apartments sometimes acknowledge such obligations to their children or grandchildren. Again, the only clear return they receive for their hospitality is the reduction of isolation that comes from having people around and interesting activity going on. When in the Washington home the daughter and granddaughter and their children move in with the grandmother, or when they come to visit for shorter periods of time, the occasion has a party atmosphere. The women sit around talking and reminiscing. Though boy friends may be present, they take little part; instead they sit passively, enjoying the stories and drinking along with the women. It would seem that in this kind of party activity the women are defined as the stars. Grandmother, daughter, and granddaughter in turn take the center of the stage telling a story from the family's past, talking about a particularly interesting night out on the town, or just making some general observation about life. In the course of these events a good deal of liquor is consumed. In such a household as this little attention is paid to the children since the competition by adults for attention is stiff.

Boy Friends, Not Husbands

It is with an understanding of the problems of isolation which older mothers have that we can obtain the best insight into the role and function of boy friends in the maternal household. The older mothers, surrounded by their own children and grandchildren, are not able to move freely in the outside world, to participate in the high life which they enjoyed when younger and more foot-loose. They are disillusioned with marriage as providing any more secure economic base than they can achieve on their own. They see marriage as involving just another responsibility without a concomitant reward—"It's the greatest thing in the world to come home in the afternoon and not have some curly headed twot in the house yellin' at me and askin' me where supper is, where I've been, what I've been doin', and who I've been seein'." In this situation the woman is tempted to form relationships with men that are not so demanding as marriage but still provide companionship and an opportunity for occasional sexual gratification.

There seem to be two kinds of boy friends. Some boy friends "pimp" off mothers; they extract payment in food or money for their companionship. This leads to the custom sometimes called "Mother's Day," the tenth of the month when the AFDC checks come (Schwartz and Henderson, 1964). On this day one can observe an influx of men into the neighborhood, and much partying. But there is another kind of boy friend, perhaps more numerous than the first, who instead of being paid for his services pays for the right to be a pseudo family member. He may be the father of one of the woman's children and for this reason makes a steady contribution to the family's support, or he may simply be a man whose company the mother enjoys and who makes reasonable gifts to the family for the time he spends with them (and perhaps implicitly for the sexual favors he receives). While the boy friend does not assume fatherly authority within the family, he often is known and liked by the children. The older children appreciate the meaningfulness of their mother's relationship with him— one girl said of her mother's boy friend:

> "We don't none of us [the children] want her to marry again. It's all right if she wants to live by herself and have a boy friend. It's not because we're afraid we're going to have some more sisters and brothers, which it wouldn't make us much difference, but I think she be too old."

Even when the boy friend contributes ten or twenty dollars a month to the family he is in a certain sense getting a bargain. If he is a well-accepted boy friend he spends considerable time around the house, has a chance to relax in an atmosphere less competitive than that of his peer group, is fed and cared for by the woman, yet has no responsibilities which he cannot renounce when he wishes. When women have stable relationships of this kind with boy friends they often consider marrying them but are reluctant to take such a step. Even the well-liked boy friend has some shortcomings—one woman said of her boy friend:

> "Well he works; I know that. He seems to be a nice person, kind hearted. He believes in survival for me and my family. He don't much mind sharing

with my youngsters. If I ask him for a helping hand he don't seem to mind that. The only part I dislike is his drinking."

The woman in this situation has worked out a reasonably stable adaptation to the problems of her life; she is fearful of upsetting this adaptation by marrying again. It seems easier to take the "sweet" part of the relationship with a man without the complexities that marriage might involve.

It is in the light of this pattern of women living in families and men living by themselves in rooming houses, odd rooms, here and there, that we can understand Daniel Patrick Moynihan's observation that during their mature years men simply disappear; that is, that census data show a very high sex ratio of women to men (Moynihan, 1965). In St. Louis, starting at the age range 20 to 24 there are only 72 men for every 100 women. This ratio does not climb to 90 until the age range 50 to 54. Men often do not have real homes; they move about from one household where they have kinship or sexual ties to another; they live in flop houses and rooming houses; they spend time in institutions. They are not household members in the only "homes" that they have—the homes of their mothers and of their girl friends.

It is in this kind of world that boys and girls in the Negro slum community learn their sex roles. It is not just, or even mainly, that fathers are often absent but that the male role models around boys are ones which emphasize expressive, affectional techniques for making one's way in the world. The female role models available to girls emphasize an exaggerated self-sufficiency (from the point of view of the middle class) and the danger of allowing oneself to be dependent on men for anything that is crucial. By the time she is mature, the woman learns that she is most secure when she herself manages the family affairs and when she dominates her men. The man learns that he exposes himself to the least risk of failure when he does not assume a husband's and father's responsibilities but instead counts on his ability to court women and to ingratiate himself with them.

Identity Processes in the Family

Up to this point we have been examining the sequential development of family stages in the Negro slum community, paying only incidental attention to the psychological responses family members make to these social forms and not concerning ourselves with the effect the family forms have on the psychosocial development of the children who grow up in them. Now we want to examine the effect that growing up in this kind of a system has in terms of socialization and personality development.

Household groups function for cultures in carrying out the initial phases of socialization and personality formation. It is in the family that the child learns the most primitive categories of existence and experience, and that he develops his most deeply held beliefs about the world and about himself.[6] From the child's

---

[6] Talcott Parsons concludes his discussion of child socialization, the development of an "internalized family system," and internalized role differentiation by observing, "The internalization of the family collectivity as an object and its values should not be lost sight of. This is crucial with respect to . . . the assumption of representative roles outside the family on behalf of it. Here it is the child's family membership which is decisive, and thus his acting in a role in terms of its values for 'such as he' " (Parsons and Bales, 1955, p. 113).

point of view, the household *is* the world; his experiences as he moves out of it into the larger world are always interpreted in terms of his particular experience within the home. The painful experiences which a child in the Negro slum culture has are, therefore, interpreted as in some sense a reflection of this family world. The impact of the system of victimization is transmitted through the family; the child cannot be expected to have the sophistication an outside observer has for seeing exactly where the villains are. From the child's point of view, if he is hungry it is his parents' fault; if he experiences frustrations in the streets or in the school it is his parents' fault; if that world seems incomprehensible to him it is his parents' fault; if people are aggressive or destructive toward each other it is his parents' fault, not that of a system of race relations. In another culture this might not be the case; if a subculture could exist which provided comfort and security within its limited world and the individual experienced frustration only when he moved out into the larger society, the family might not be thought so much to blame. The effect of the caste system, however, is to bring home through a chain of cause and effect all of the victimization processes, and to bring them home in such a way that it is often very difficult even for adults in the system to see the connection between the pain they feel at the moment and the structured patterns of the caste system.

Let us take as a central question that of identity formation within the Negro slum family. We are concerned with the question of who the individual believes himself to be and to be becoming. For Erikson (1959), identity means a sense of continuity and social sameness which bridges what the individual *"was as a child and what he is about to become* and also reconciles his *conception of himself* and his community's recognition of him." Thus identity is a "self-realization coupled with a mutual recognition." In the early childhood years identity is family-bound since the child's identity is his identity *vis-à-vis* other members of the family. Later he incorporates into his sense of who he is and is becoming his experiences outside the family, but always influenced by the interpretations and evaluations of those experiences that the family gives. As the child tries on identities, *announces* them, the family sits as judge of his pretensions. Family members are both the most important judges and the most critical ones, since who he is allowed to become affects them in their own identity strivings more crucially than it affects anyone else. The child seeks a sense of valid identity, a sense of being a particular person with a satisfactory degree of congruence between who he feels he is, who he announces himself to be, and where he feels his society places him (Stone, 1962). He is uncomfortable when he experiences disjunction between his own needs and the kinds of needs legitimated by those around him, or when he feels a disjunction between his sense of himself and the image of himself that others play back to him.[7]

"Tell It Like It Is"

When families become involved in important quarrels the psychosocial underpinnings of family life are laid bare. One such quarrel in a family we have been studying brings together in one place many of the themes that seem to dominate

[7] The importance of identity for social behavior is discussed in detail in Goodenough (1963) and in Rainwater (1966). The images of self and of other family members is a crucial variable in Hess and Handel's (1959) psychosocial analysis of family life.

identity problems in Negro slum culture. The incident illustrates in a particularly forceful and dramatic way family processes which our field work, and some other contemporary studies of slum family life, suggests unfold more subtly in a great many families at the lower-class level. The family involved, the Johnsons, is certainly not the most disorganized one we have studied; in some respects their way of life represents a realistic adaptation to the hard living of a family 19 years on AFDC with a monthly income of $202 for nine people. The two oldest daughters, Mary Jane (18 years old) and Esther (16) are pregnant; Mary Jane has one illegitimate child. The adolescent sons, Bob and Richard, are much involved in the social and sexual activities of their peer group. The three other children, ranging in age from 12 to 14, are apparently also moving into this kind of peer-group society.

When the argument started Bob and Esther were alone in the apartment with Mary Jane's baby. Esther took exception to Bob's playing with the baby because she had been left in charge; the argument quickly progressed to a fight in which Bob cuffed Esther around, and she tried to cut him with a knife. The police were called and subdued Bob with their nightsticks. At this point the rest of the family and the field worker arrived. As the argument continued, these themes relevant to the analysis which follows appeared:

1. The sisters said that Bob was not their brother (he is a half-brother to Esther, and Mary Jane's full brother). Indeed, they said their mother "didn't have no husband. These kids don't even know who their daddies are." The mother defended herself by saying that she had one legal husband, and one common-law husband, no more.

2. The sisters said that their fathers had never done anything for them, nor had their mother. She retorted that she had raised them "to the age of womanhood" and now would care for their babies.

3. Esther continued to threaten to cut Bob if she got a chance (a month later they fought again, and she did cut Bob, who required 21 stitches).

4. The sisters accused their mother of favoring their lazy brothers and asked her to put them out of the house. She retorted that the girls were as lazy, that they made no contribution to maintaining the household, could not get their boy friends to marry them or support their children, that all the support came from her AFDC check. Mary Jane retorted that "the baby has a check of her own."

5. The girls threatened to leave the house if their mother refused to put their brothers out. They said they could force their boy friends to support them by taking them to court, and Esther threatened to cut her boy friend's throat if he did not co-operate.

6. Mrs. Johnson said the girls could leave if they wished but that she would keep their babies; "I'll not have it, not knowing who's taking care of them."

7. When her 13-year-old sister laughed at all of this, Esther told her not to laugh because she, too, would be pregnant within a year.

8. When Bob laughed, Esther attacked him and his brother by saying that both were not man enough to make babies, as she and her sister had been able to do.

9. As the field worker left, Mrs. Johnson sought his sympathy. "You see, Joe, how hard it is for me to bring up a family. . . . They sit around and talk to me like I'm some kind of a dog and not their mother."

10. Finally, it is important to note for the analysis which follows that the

following labels—"black-assed," "black bastard," "bitch," and other profane terms—were liberally used by Esther and Mary Jane, and rather less liberally by their mother, to refer to each other, to the girls' boy friends, to Bob, and to the 13-year-old daughter.

Several of the themes outlined previously appear forcefully in the course of this argument. In the last year and a half the mother has become a grandmother and expects shortly to add two more grandchildren to her household. She takes it for granted that it is her responsibility to care for the grandchildren and that she has the right to decide what will be done with the children since her own daughters are not fully responsible. She makes this very clear to them when they threaten to move out, a threat which they do not really wish to make good nor could they if they wished to.

However, only as an act of will is Mrs. Johnson able to make this a family. She must constantly cope with the tendency of her adolescent children to disrupt the family group and to deny that they are in fact a family—"He ain't no brother of mine"; "The baby has a check of her own." Though we do not know exactly what processes communicate these facts to the children it is clear that in growing up they have learned to regard themselves as not fully part of a solidary collectivity. During the quarrel this message was reinforced for the 12-, 13-, and 14-year-old daughters by the four-way argument among their older sisters, older brother, and their mother.

The argument represents vicious unmasking of the individual members' pretenses to being competent individuals (Spiegel, 1960). The efforts of the two girls to present themselves as masters of their own fate are unmasked by the mother. The girls in turn unmask the pretensions of the mother and of their two brothers. When the 13-year-old daughter expresses some amusement they turn on her, telling her that it won't be long before she too becomes pregnant. Each member of the family in turn is told that he can expect to be no more than a victim of his world, but that this is somehow inevitably his own fault.

In this argument masculinity is consistently demeaned. Bob has no right to play with his niece, the boys are not really masculine because at 15 and 16 years they have yet to father children, their own fathers were no goods who failed to do anything for their family. These notions probably come originally from the mother, who enjoys recounting the story of having her common-law husband imprisoned for non-support, but this comes back to haunt her as her daughters accuse her of being no better than they in ability to force support and nurturance from a man. In contrast, the girls came off somewhat better than the boys, although they must accept the label of stupid girls because they have similarly failed and inconveniently become pregnant in the first place. At least they can and have had children and therefore have some meaningful connection with the ongoing substance of life. There is something important and dramatic in which they participate, while the boys, despite their sexual activity, "can't get no babies."

In most societies, as children grow and are formed by their elders into suitable members of the society they gain increasingly a sense of competence and ability to master the behavioral environment their particular world presents. But in Negro slum culture growing up involves an ever-increasing appreciation of one's shortcomings, of the impossibility of finding a self-sufficient and gratifying way of living (Pettigrew, 1964). It is in the family first and most devastatingly that one learns these lessons. As the child's sense of frustration builds he too can strike out and unmask the pretensions of others. The result is a peculiar strength and a pervasive weakness. The strength involves the ability to tolerate and defend against degrading verbal and physical aggressions from others and not to give up completely. The weakness involves the inability to embark hopefully on any course of action that might make things better, particularly action which involves cooperating and trusting attitudes toward others. Family members become potential enemies to each other, as the frequency of observing the police being called in to settle family quarrels brings home all too dramatically.

The conceptions parents have of their children are such that they are constantly alert as the child matures to evidence that he is as bad as everyone else. That is, in lower-class culture human nature is conceived of as essentially bad, destructive, immoral.[8] This is the nature of things. Therefore any one child must be inherently bad unless his parents are very lucky indeed. If the mother can keep the child insulated from the outside world, she feels she may be able to prevent his inherent badness from coming out. She feels that once he is let out into the larger world the badness will come to the fore since that is his nature. This means that in the identity development of the child he is constantly exposed to identity labeling by his parents as a bad person. Since as he grows up he does not experience his world as particularly gratifying, it is very easy for him to conclude that this lack of gratification is due to the fact that something is wrong with him. This, in turn, can readily be assimilated to the definitions of being a bad person offered him by those with whom he lives (see Silverberg, 1953). In this way the Negro slum child learns his culture's conception of being-in-the-world, a conception that emphasizes inherent evil in a chaotic, hostile, destructive world.

Blackness

To a certain extent these same processes operate in white lower-class groups, but added for the Negro is the reality of blackness. "Black-assed" is not an empty pejorative adjective. In the Negro slum culture several distinctive appellations are used to refer to oneself and others. One involves the terms, "black" or "nigger." Black is generally a negative way of naming, but nigger can be either negative or positive, depending upon the context. It is important to note that, at least in the urban North, the initial development of racial identity in these terms has very little directly to do with relations with whites. A child experiences these identity placements in the context of the family and in the neighborhood peer group; he probably very seldom hears the same terms used by whites (unlike the situation in the South). In this way, one of the effects of ghettoization is to mask the ultimate enemy so that the understanding of the fact of victimization by a caste system comes as a late acquisition laid over conceptions of self and of other Negroes derived from intimate, and to the child often traumatic, experience within the ghetto community. If, in addition, the child attends a ghetto school where his Negro teachers either overtly or by implication reinforce his community's negative conceptions of what it means to be black, then the child has little opportunity to develop a more realistic image of himself and other Negroes as being damaged by whites and not by themselves. In such a situation, an intelligent man like

---

[8] See Rainwater, Coleman, and Handel (1959). See also the discussion of the greater level of "anomie" and mistrust among lower-class people in Mizruchi (1954). Unpublished research by the author indicates that for one urban lower-class sample (Chicago) Negroes scored about 50 per cent higher on Srole's anomie scale than did comparable whites.

Mr. Wilson (quoted earlier) can say with all sincerity that he does not feel most Negroes are ready for integration—only under the experience of certain kinds of intense personal threat coupled with exposure to an ideology that places the responsibility on whites did he begin to see through the direct evidence of his daily experience.

To those living in the heart of a ghetto, black comes to mean not just "stay back," but also membership in a community of persons who think poorly of each other, who attack and manipulate each other, who give each other small comfort in a desperate world. Black comes to stand for a sense of identity as no better than these destructive others. The individual feels that he must embrace an unattractive self in order to function at all.

We can hypothesize that in those families that manage to avoid the destructive identity imputations of "black" and that manage to maintain solidarity against such assaults from the world around, it is possible for children to grow up with a sense of both Negro and personal identity that allows them to socialize themselves in an anticipatory way for participation in the larger society (Ellison, 1964). This broader sense of identity, however, will remain a brittle one as long as the individual is vulnerable to attack from within the Negro community as "nothing but a nigger like everybody else" or from the white community as "just a nigger." We can hypothesize further that the vicious unmasking of essential identity as black described above is least likely to occur within families where the parents have some stable sense of security, and where they therefore have less need to protect themselves by disavowing responsibility for their children's behavior and denying the children their patrimony as products of a particular family rather than of an immoral nature and an evil community.

In sum, we are suggesting that Negro slum children as they grow up in their families and in their neighborhoods are exposed to a set of experiences—and a rhetoric which conceptualizes them—that brings home to the child an understanding of his essence as a weak and debased person who can expect only partial gratification of his needs, and who must seek even this level of gratification by less than straight-forward means.

Strategies for Living

In every society complex processes of socialization inculcate in their members strategies for gratifying the needs with which they are born and those which the society itself generates. Inextricably linked to these strategies, both cause and effect of them, are the existential propositions which members of a culture entertain about the nature of their world and of effective action within the world as it is defined for them. In most of American society two grand strategies seem to attract the allegiance of its members and guide their day-to-day actions. I have called these strategies those of *the good life* and of *career success* (Rainwater, 1966b). A good life strategy involves efforts to get along with others and not to rock the boat, a comfortable familism grounded on a stable work career for husbands in which they perform adequately at the modest jobs that enable them to be good providers. The strategy of career success is the choice of ambitious men and women who see life as providing opportunities to move from a lower to a higher status, to "accomplish something," to achieve greater than ordinary material well-being, prestige, and social recognition. Both of these strategies are predicated on the assumption that the world is inherently rewarding if one behaves properly and does his part. The rewards of the world may come easily or only at the cost of great effort, but at least they are there.

In the white and particularly in the Negro slum worlds little in the experience that individuals have as they grow up sustains a belief in a rewarding world. The strategies that seem appropriate are not those of a good, family-based life or of a career, but rather *strategies for survival.*

Much of what has been said above can be summarized as encouraging three kinds of survival strategies. One is the strategy of the *expressive life style* which I have described elsewhere as an effort to make yourself interesting and attractive to others so that you are better able to manipulate their behavior along lines that will provide some immediate gratification (Rainwater, 1966b). Negro slum culture provides many examples of techniques for seduction, of persuading others to give you what you want in situations where you have very little that is tangible to offer in return. In order to get what you want you learn to "work game," a strategy which requires a high development of a certain kind of verbal facility, a sophisticated manipulation of promise and interim reward. When the expressive strategy fails or when it is unavailable there is, of course, the great temptation to adopt a *violent strategy* in which you force others to give you what you need once you fail to win it by verbal and other symbolic means.[9] Finally, and increasingly as members of the Negro slum culture grow older, there is the *depressive strategy* in which goals are increasingly constricted to the bare necessities for survival (not as a social being but simply as an organism).[10] This is the strategy of "I don't bother anybody and I hope nobody's gonna bother me; I'm simply going through the motions to keep body (but not soul) together." Most lower-class people follow mixed strategies, as Walter Miller has observed, alternating among the excitement of the expressive style, the desperation of the violent style, and the deadness of the depressed style (Miller, 1958). Some members of the Negro slum world experiment from time to time with mixed strategies that also incorporate the stable working-class model of the good American life, but this latter strategy is exceedingly vulnerable to the threats of unemployment or a less than adequate pay check, on the one hand, and the seduction and violence of the slum world around them, on the other.

Remedies

Finally, it is clear that we, no less than the inhabitants of the ghetto, are not masters of their fate because we are not masters of our own total society. Despite the battles with poverty on many fronts we can find little evidence to sustain our hope of winning the war given current programs and strategies.

The question of strategy is particularly crucial when one moves from an examination of destructive cultural and interaction patterns in Negro families to the question of how these families might achieve a more stable and gratifying life. It is tempting to see the family as the main villain of the piece, and to seek to develop programs which attack directly this family pathology. Should we not

[9] Short and Strodtbeck (1965) see violent behavior in juvenile gangs as a kind of last resort strategy in situations where the actor feels he has no other choice.

[10] Wiltse (1963) speaks of a "psuedo depression syndrome" as characteristic of many AFDC mothers.

have extensive programs of family therapy, family counseling, family-life education, and the like? Is this not the prerequisite to enabling slum Negro families to take advantage of other opportunities? Yet, how pale such efforts seem compared to the deep-seated problems of self-image and family process described above. Can an army of social workers undo the damage of 300 years by talking and listening without massive changes in the social and economic situations of the families with whom they are to deal? And, if such changes take place, will the social-worker army be needed?

If we are right that present Negro family patterns have been created as adaptations to a particular socioeconomic situation, it would make more sense to change that socioeconomic situation and then depend upon the people involved to make new adaptations as time goes on. If Negro providers have steady jobs and decent incomes, if Negro children have some realistic expectation of moving toward such a goal, if slum Negroes come to feel that they have the chance to affect their own futures and to receive respect from those around them, then (and only then) the destructive patterns described are likely to change. The change, though slow and uneven from individual to individual, will in a certain sense be automatic because it will represent an adaptation to changed socioeconomic circumstances which have direct and highly valued implications for the person.

It is possible to think of three kinds of extra-family change that are required if family patterns are to change; these are outlined below as pairs of current deprivations and needed remedies:

Deprivation Effect of Caste Victimization	Needed Remedy
I. Poverty	Employment income for men; income maintenance for mothers
II. Trained incapacity to function in a bureaucratized and industrialized world	Meaningful education of the next generation
III. Powerlessness and stigmatization	Organizational participation for aggressive pursuit of Negroes' self-interest
	Strong sanctions against callous or indifferent service to slum Negroes
	Pride in group identity, Negro and American

Unless the major effort is to provide these kinds of remedies, there is a very real danger that programs to "better the structure of the Negro family" by direct intervention will serve the unintended functions of distracting the country from the pressing needs for socioeconomic reform and providing an alibi for the failure to embark on the basic institutional changes that are needed to do anything about abolishing both white and Negro poverty. It would be sad, indeed, if, after the Negro revolt brought to national prominence the continuing problem of poverty, our expertise about Negro slum culture served to deflect the national impulse into symptom-treatment rather than basic reform. If that happens, social scientists will have served those they study poorly indeed.

Let us consider each of the needed remedies in terms of its probable impact on the family. First, the problem of poverty: employed men are less likely to leave their families than are unemployed men, and when they do stay they are more likely to have the respect of their wives and children. A program whose sole effect would be to employ at reasonable wages slum men for work using the skills they now have would do more than any other possible program to stabilize slum family life. But the wages must be high enough to enable the man to maintain his self-respect as a provider, and stable enough to make it worthwhile to change the nature of his adaptation to his world (no one-year emergency programs will do). Once men learn that work pays off it would be possible to recruit men for part-time retraining for more highly skilled jobs, but the initial emphasis must be on the provision of full-time, permanent unskilled jobs. Obviously it will be easier to do this in the context of full employment and a tight labor market.[11]

For at least a generation, however, there will continue to be a large number of female-headed households. Given the demands of socializing a new generation for non-slum living, it is probably uneconomical to encourage mothers to work. Rather, income maintenance programs must be increased to realistic levels, and mothers must be recognized as doing socially useful work for which they are paid rather than as "feeding at the public trough." The bureaucratic morass which currently hampers flexible strategies of combining employment income and welfare payments to make ends meet must also be modified if young workers are not to be pushed prematurely out of the home.

Education has the second priority. (It is second only because without stable family income arrangements the school system must work against the tremendous resistance of competing life-style adaptations to poverty and economic insecurity.) As Kenneth Clark has argued so effectively, slum schools now function more to stultify and discourage slum children than to stimulate and train them. The capacity of educators to alibi their lack of commitment to their charges is protean. The making of a different kind of generation must be taken by educators as a stimulating and worthwhile challenge. Once the goal has been accepted they must be given the resources with which to achieve it and the flexibility necessary to experiment with different approaches to accomplish the goal. Education must be broadly conceived to include much more than classroom work, and probably more than a nine-months schedule (Clark, 1965).

If slum children can come to see the schools as representing a really likely avenue of escape from their difficult situation (even before adolescence they know it is the only *possible* escape) then their commitment to school activities will feed back into their families in a positive way. The parents will feel proud rather than ashamed, and they will feel less need to damn the child as a way to avoid blaming themselves for his failure. The sense of positive family identity will be enriched as the child becomes an attractive object, an ego resource, to his parents. Because he himself feels more competent, he will see them as less depriving and weak. If children's greater commitment to school begins to reduce their involvement in destructive or aimless peer-group activities this too will repercuss positively on the family situation since parents will worry less about their children's involvement in an immoral outside world, and be less inclined to deal with them in harsh, rejecting, or indifferent ways.

Cross-cutting the deprivations of poverty and trained incapacity is the fact of

[11] This line of argument concerning the employment problems of Negroes, and poverty war strategy more generally, is developed with great cogency by Tobin (1965), and previously by Myrdal (1963) and Gursslin and Roach (1964).

powerlessness and stigmatization. Slum people know that they have little ability to protect themselves and to force recognition of their abstract rights. They know that they are looked down on and scape-goated. They are always vulnerable to the slights, insults, and indifference of the white and Negro functionaries with whom they deal—policemen, social workers, school teachers, landlords, employers, retailers, janitors. To come into contact with others carries the constant danger of moral attack and insult (Rainwater, 1966a). If processes of status degradation within families are to be interrupted, then they must be interrupted on the outside first.

One way out of the situation of impotence and dammed-up in-group aggression is the organization of meaningful protest against the larger society. Such protest can and will take many forms, not always so neat and rational as the outsider might hope. But, coupled with, and supporting, current programs of economic and educational change, involvement of slum Negroes in organizational activity can do a great deal to build a sense of pride and potency. While only a very small minority of slum Negroes can be expected to participate personally in such movements, the vicarious involvement of the majority can have important effects on their sense of self-respect and worth.

Some of the needed changes probably can be made from the top, by decision in Washington, with minimal effective organization within the slum; but others can come only in response to aggressive pressure on the part of the victims themselves. This is probably particularly true of the entrenched tendency of service personnel to enhance their own sense of self and to indulge their middle-class *ressentiment* by stigmatizing and exploiting those they serve. Only effective protest can change endemic patterns of police harassment and brutality, or teachers' indifference and insults, or butchers' heavy thumbs, or indifferent street cleaning and garbage disposal. And the goal of the protest must be to make this kind of insult to the humanity of the slum-dweller too expensive for the perpetrator to afford; it must cost him election defeats, suspensions without pay, job dismissals, license revocations, fines, and the like.

To the extent that the slum dweller avoids stigmatization in the outside world, he will feel more fully a person within the family and better able to function constructively within it since he will not be tempted to make up deficits in self-esteem in ways that are destructive of family solidarity. The "me" of personal identity and the multiple "we" of family, Negro, and American identity are all inextricably linked; a healthier experience of identity in any one sector will repercuss on all the others.

51 / Learning Patterns
in the Disadvantaged

Gerald Lesser / *Susan S. Stodolsky*

General Review of Research

In a review of learning patterns in the disadvantaged, it is necessary to delimit certain key concepts: (1) Which population groups shall be included in the "disadvantaged"? (2) Which constructs or variables shall we consider as relevant indicators of learning?

We shall return at several points in this paper to the problem of definition of the term "disadvantaged." Since each new issue raised forces revision and refinement of this definition, we shall offer successive approximations to a useful definition as we proceed. For the review of research with which we begin this paper, we will follow the usual conventions regarding delimitation of the disadvantaged or deprived population. Typically included under this rubric are children who come from families of low socio-economic status (as measured by occupation of the breadwinner, educational attainment of the parents, income, place of residence, etc.) and children from minority groups (as determined by recent immigration of families from countries outside the United States or notable lack of acculturation of groups that may have been residents for generations) and minority racial status (in particular, Negroes and Indians who have been in a caste-like status in this country for generations). Also included in this population are children from rural areas which have been isolated from the mainstream of American culture (see Havighurst, 1964). These definitions usually have in common the element of poverty or low income in relation to the median income of Americans.

General Intelligence

The performance of children from low socio-economic status and minority groups on intelligence tests has been quite well documented. Studies of intelligence test performance and social-class status have provided the broad outlines of a picture which generally fits a *deficit* or less-than model. Mean differences between children of high SES and low SES have been found consistently when measures of intelligence are administered. These differences are unequivocally present at age four and have occasionally been demonstrated at younger ages (Bereiter, 1965; Gray and Klaus, 1965; Pasamanick and Knobloch, 1955; Bloom, 1964).

With increases in children's age such intelligence test differences tend to increase. Thus, there are larger mean differences in intelligence between low

Abridged from *Harvard Educational Review*, 1967, **37**, 546–593. Reprinted by permission of the authors and *Harvard Educational Review*.

and high SES children in adolescence than in the early years of school. This fanning-out effect and the evidence to support it has been carefully reviewed by a number of workers (Bloom, 1964; Hunt, 1961; Silverman, 1965; Gordon, 1965; Davis, 1948; Karp and Sigel, 1965; Coleman et al., 1966).

The nature of the tests and conditions of administration have been an object of considerable study. The hallmark work of Eells and Davis (1951) on cultural biases in intelligence tests spurred a multitude of studies which demonstrated inadequacies in the tests themselves as good samples of general intelligence in diverse populations. Factors which might influence test performance such as rapport, speed, motivation, and reward conditions were also studied (e.g., see Haggard, 1954). It appears clear now that Davis and his colleagues in their attempt to develop a culture-free measure of intelligence were accepting the idea that it was in fact possible to measure innate ability independent of cultural and experiential factors. They were assuming that it would be possible to tap the genotype of intelligence, and that intelligence would in fact be a stable quantity, randomly distributed by social class. (See Charters, 1963.)

Partly through the failure of the *Davis-Eells Games* and through increasing evidence from other quarters, both the belief in fixed intelligence and the notion of ridding intelligence measurement of cultural contamination have been abandoned. Now, rather than rejecting cultural effects as contaminants, researchers study them and take them into account in test construction and prediction. However, the notion of "culture-fair" testing has been widely accepted in the interest of making comparative statements about groups. Thus, as exemplified in one study of mental abilities (Lesser, Fifer, and Clark, 1965), items are based on a pool of experiences common to the subject population to be studied. Conditions of administration are arranged to minimize differences in rapport, motivation, and prior experiences with testing when intergroup comparisons are being made. Further, validity and reliability must be established for the relevant population. An excellent review of factors to be considered in testing minority groups is available (Deutsch et al., 1964).

The most important outgrowth of the work in the 1950's is the changed conception of intelligence. Only a few hardy souls will now maintain that intelligence tests measure something innate, fixed, and predetermined. (Hunt, 1961, reviews these ideas.) The validity of intelligence tests for predicting school achievement cannot be doubted, but the ability (aptitude) *versus* achievement distinction has been attenuated. Intelligence tests must now be thought of as samples of learning based on general experiences. A child's score may be thought of as an indication of the richness of the milieu in which he functions and the extent to which he has been able to profit from that milieu. In contradistinction, school achievement tests assume deliberate instruction oriented to the outcomes measured in the tests.

It should be remembered that the studies we have reviewed deal only with group differences using social class, ethnicity, or both as classificatory variables. Although mean differences favor majority group and high SES children, the overlap in distributions is great. It is by now a truism that *all* disadvantaged children do not fall below their more advantaged peers on tested intelligence and mental abilities. The deficit model applies to groups only. Individual differences within groups must also be examined.

Diverse Mental Abilities

Early research in subcultural differences attempted to demonstrate that minority-majority group differences were attributable to the verbal nature of most general intelligence tests. The results of investigations which utilized tests of a less verbal character are equivocal (Higgins and Sivers, 1958; Fowler, 1957; Stablein et al., 1961; MacCarthur and Elley, 1963). The most adequate conclusion for the moment seems to be that although group differences may be reduced somewhat by eliminating verbal components from the tests, other factors (such as experiential differences, attitudes toward test-taking, and speed) still affect test performance. And for certain groups such as Negroes, eliminating verbal items results in lower performance levels.

Coleman et al. (1966), as a part of a massive survey on equality of educational opportunity in the United States, administered a verbal and nonverbal (reasoning) measure to first graders of various backgrounds at the beginning of the school year. He found that children of low social status and children from minority groups (Negroes, Mexican-Americans, Puerto Ricans, and American Indians) start school at grade one with mean scores on verbal and nonverbal tests of general ability that are below the national white average. The only exception to this general finding is that Oriental children score at the national average on the verbal measure at grade one and above the average on the nonverbal measure. In addition, the American Indian group that was sampled score at the national average on the nonverbal measure at grade one.

School Achievement

Massive amounts of data are now available on a national sample of children at grades one, three, six, nine, and twelve in regard to school achievement (Coleman et al., 1966). The Coleman study employed verbal and nonverbal measures and tests of reading and mathematics achievement. As indicated in the previous section, most groups of minority children and those of low SES scored below the national average on verbal and nonverbal tests at the beginning of their school careers. The findings from this study are consistent with earlier ones dealing with the school achievement of disadvantaged children. Indications of social-class and racial differences, in favor of majority and high SES groups, had been found earlier when reading and arithmetic readiness tests[1] were administered to children at the kindergarten level (Brazziel and Terrell, 1962; Montague, 1964).

As minority-group children (with the exception of Orientals at grade three) proceed through school, they continue to perform below the national average at all grade levels on all measures: the relative standing of these groups in relation to the white population remains essentially constant in terms of standard deviations, but the absolute differences in terms of grade-level discrepancies increase (Coleman et al., 1966). This increase in the number of grade levels behind the normative population is what is commonly referred to as the "cumulative deficit" (Deutsch, 1960).

The Coleman survey is cross-sectional. The few longitudinal studies of achieve-

---

[1] The readiness tests, as opposed to the general ability tests, are more specifically oriented to learning necessary for successful achievement of a school subject. In fact predictive validities of the two types of tests do not differ appreciably.

ment in the literature reflect essentially the same pattern: as disadvantaged children move through the current school system, their achievement in grade levels as compared to the normative population becomes increasingly discrepant and low (Osborne, 1960).

The picture of educational disadvantage which emerges with examination of achievement data is a clear indication of the failure of the school systems. When intelligence test data and early achievement data are combined, we have a predictor's paradise, but an abysmal prognosis for most children who enter the school system from disadvantaged backgrounds. At the very least, this ability to predict school failure should be better exploited by the schools in an effort to remedy the situation. Payne (1964) has demonstrated that by the end of grade one, over one-half of the children who will be failing in arithmetic in grade six can be identified on the basis of socio-economic data, intelligence test scores, and an arithmetic achievement test. By the end of grade two, two-thirds of the failing children can be identified. This provides the school not with group tendencies but with individual tagging of children for whom the usual curriculum will surely fail. It also provides five years of lead time to remedy the situation.

Taken together, the data on general intelligence, mental abilities, and school achievement all give indications that general learning, first in the home and community and later within the school as well, is clearly associated with socio-economic status: the level of such learning is generally lower for children of most minority groups and children in low socio-economic status. Important variations in patterning of such learnings have yet to be studied systematically, with a few notable exceptions. Even in the school achievement area, data regarding progress in school subjects other than reading and mathematics are not readily available. It can perhaps be safely assumed that achievement in social studies, science, and other academic areas will be highly correlated with achievement in reading and arithmetic. Nevertheless, studies of performance of disadvantaged children in these areas should be carried out.

Laboratory Learning

There are only a few studies which have used laboratory learning paradigms to compare performance of children from different social and cultural backgrounds. As Jensen (1967c) has pointed out, it is somewhat inconsistent with the traditions of the learning laboratory to introduce examinations of individual difference variables. Thus, Subjects × Independent Variables interactions are usually considered to contribute to error variance (Jensen, 1967c, p. 117).

Semler and Iscoe (1963) compared the performance of Negro and white children on four conditions of paired-associate learning tasks; they also obtained WISC data on the children who ranged in age from five to nine years. Although significant racial differences were present on the WISC, they were not found in the paired-associate learning. Correlations between IQ and learning-task scores were low for both groups (.09 for whites, .19 for Negroes).

Zigler and DeLabry (1962) compared groups of middle-class, lower-class, and retarded subjects on a concept-switching task, using different reward conditions. They found that when each group performed under the reward condition considered optimal, there were no group differences in performance. The intangible reward condition was considered optimal for the middle class; tangible reinforcement was optimal for the lower-class group and the retardates. A similar study using a discrimination task was carried out by Terrell, Durkin, and Wiesley (1959). They also found material reward produced better performance in lower-class children and nonmaterial reward proved more effective with middle-class children.

Rohwer (1966), Jensen (1961), and Rapier (1966) have found that performance of lower- and middle-class Negroes, Mexican-Americans, and Anglo-Americans, and lower- and middle-class Caucasians, respectively, does not differ markedly in laboratory-learning tasks such as selective trial-and-error learning and paired-associate learning. These workers find that the relation between tested intelligence and performance on the learning tasks is high for the upper-status groups but negligible for the lower-status groups. Jensen (1967b) suggests that the equivalence of performance of the lower-status children with middle-class children on these tasks which do not require transfer from previous learning suggests the learning ability of children from lower-status backgrounds is not adequately reflected in general intelligence tests. Taken together with the findings of high correlations on these learning tasks and intelligence tests for upper-status groups and low correlations for low-status groups, he argues that research is needed to clarify the reasons for these unique relationships which probably reflect that intelligence tests are "truer" estimates of ability for the middle-class groups than for the lower-class groups.

Whether or not one wishes to join Jensen in his search for more accurate measurements of ability in low-status populations—it is admittedly reminiscent of the quest for culture-free measurement—his findings and those of his colleagues suggest the relevance of combining differential psychology with the tools of the learning laboratory in studying the learning patterns of the disadvantaged.

Other studies have been undertaken which deal with cognitive functioning but come from traditions other than the psychometric or learning laboratory. Although child psychologists are showing increasing interest in the work of Piaget, few studies from a stage theoretic point of view have been undertaken with children from disadvantaged backgrounds.

From the limited evidence to date, it appears reasonable to expect that the stage theory of Piaget is generally applicable to all children regardless of social class background. Nevertheless, longitudinal studies and studies of older children are needed. The studies which have found developmental sequence to apply to diverse samples of children have been with young children. It is still not known how much of the developmental sequence is general. Thus, we might find a truncated developmental sequence if we tested children of disadvantaged background in adolescence. In other words, such children might display the sequence to a point, but the stage of development reached might be lower than that achieved by their more advantaged peers.

New Directions for Research

Developmental Origins `

The explanatory, developmental direction of research would be oriented to tracing the origins of the characteristics which have been observed in the disadvantaged, as well as to charting the etiology of characteristics not studied to date.

Beginning with a broad description of the relation between a characteristic such as general intelligence and social-class status, one might ask: How can we account for the observed differences in performance among groups? What does it mean in psychological-process terms to be a member of a given social class? In order to answer these questions one moves quickly to variables which are more detailed and which should explain within-class variations as well as between-class variations.

A start in this research direction has been made in a number of quarters. Milner (1951) assessed parent-child relations and certain attributes of the home environment in relation to reading readiness. She used interview procedures in her study of first-grade children and their parents. More recently, Davé (1963) and Wolf (1965) related indices of home environment to school achievement and intelligence test scores respectively, in a fifth-grade white population of varying social class. These workers began by conceptualizing the home in terms of environmental process variables believed to be salient for the development of the outcome measures in which they were interested. They also used interviews to assess these environmental characteristics. They rated such characteristics as press for achievement, language models in the home, academic guidance provided by the home, and provisions for general learning. The ratings which they derived on the environmental process variables were then correlated with children's performance. Davé found a multiple correlation of .80 between his environmental indices and overall achievement on a standard test battery. Wolf achieved a multiple correlation of .69 between his ratings and intelligence test performance.

From the point of view of prediction, these correlations represented a considerable advance over the usual relation found between social class and achievement or intelligence test performance. More important, however, is the direction in which they orient future research. It is clearly demonstrated that one can move beyond gross classificatory variables, such as social class, to much more detailed assessment of environments. Although these studies are correlational, they move us conceptually in the direction of experimental studies of development by viewing environmental variables in dynamic, process-oriented terms.

Another important step in this direction is the research of Hess and Shipman (1965). In an extensive project studying Negro pre-school children, they have assessed numerous maternal characteristics including language (Olim, Hess, and Shipman, 1965) and teaching style (Jackson, Hess, and Shipman, 1965). Maternal teaching style is assessed in an experimental interaction session in the laboratory in which the mother is instructed in a simple task and then instructs her child. All interactions, both verbal and physical, are recorded and later analyzed into a number of dimensions. Olim, Hess, and Shipman report that maternal language is a better predictor of child's abstraction score on a sorting task than either the mother's IQ or the child's IQ. Jackson, Hess, and Shipman found that certain teaching variables were highly related to the learning outcome of the child in the experimental teaching situation. In addition, Stodolsky (1965) has extended these findings to predict a child's vocabulary at age five using a combination of maternal language and teaching variables assessed when the child was four. The multiple correlation of these process variables and the child's language score was .63, very close to the theoretical limits imposed by the reliability of the vocabulary test. She found that the quality of the mother's own language, the mother's use of reinforcement in a teaching situation, and the extent to which the mother made task-relevant discriminations in teaching a task were highly related to the child's vocabulary level.

The Hess and Shipman work posits that the mother's behavior, especially her linguistic and teaching behavior, is a key to the child's learning in the home. By drawing on learning theory and theories of language learning, they are able to point to relations between developments in the child and the mother's behavior which are both theoretically reasonable and have great heuristic power. The Hess and Shipman study is clearly an advance in the direction of explaining the origins of cognitive abilities in young children. Their work is more embedded in natural observation than the interview studies previously cited, but still does not go the whole way in assessment of what actually takes place in the home.

It should be clear that it will eventually be necessary to execute detailed observational studies of children in home environments if one wants to arrive at valid hypotheses about the dynamics of development in interaction with environment. The dearth of naturalistic data about children's behavior and concomitant environmental circumstances is most regrettable.

In order to extend knowledge of the development of intellectual abilities and learning in children, more investment in longitudinal studies which chart the course of growth within individuals will be needed. Such studies should be accompanied by investigations of relevant environmental circumstances. The types of studies we are suggesting here clearly need not be restricted to disadvantaged populations. It is to be hoped that such research would include children of diverse backgrounds. From a methodological point of view, variations in environmental circumstances and variation in child characteristics would be less restricted by studying a wide range of children. On the other hand, it is altogether possible that circumstances which are relevant in one subcultural context would not generalize across subcultures.

Is such developmental research of highest priority for school people? In many ways, we think not. We think we should assume for the moment that the job of the schools is a limited one (however arduous and complex). Children are sent to schools for a limited part of their daily lives to acquire certain knowledge and skills and ways of thinking which are considered essential for functioning in the society—in the world of work, leisure, and citizenship.

Some compensatory programs have operated on the assumption that school programs should be oriented toward changing home conditions relevant to educability. If school people want to take on the job of changing home conditions, for example, changing parent-child interactions in the home, then the study of developmental origins becomes more relevant. But we should also like to suggest that such home-based interventions will probably not be sufficient. Let us remember that life styles are usually quite adaptive to life circumstances (Lewis, 1961). We are not suggesting that it is impossible to achieve some modification of parental behaviors to facilitate the educational progress of students, but we would probably be a lot more succesful if we were to modify the conditions which probably lead to many of these behaviors: namely, lack of money and of access to jobs.

Now perhaps we are talking about politically-based action research! But while we are keeping psychologists and anthropologists busy studying the characteristics of people who are poor, might it not also be advisable to assess the degree to which these characteristics are situation-dependent? We are suggesting here a rather simple experiment which seems very important. Would poor people, given jobs and money, change in their behaviors relevant to the child's educability? Would parental behaviors such as cognitive level, teaching style, values, and attitudes change with a change in economic conditions? We do not know; but we think the matter bears empirical investigation.

We are suggesting that heavy investment in investigations of children in conditions (low income, poor housing, etc.) which are modifiable through political and economic actions, should be accompanied by knowledge of the outcomes of changing these conditions. We must know to what extent poor children's characteristics are simply a function of their economic circumstances. Further, we suggest that the type of research which is both legitimate and important for developmental psychologists is not the most direct route to solving the educational problems which the schools have to tackle right now. It is our opinion that a more ostrich-like approach to the learning of disadvantaged students might have salutary effects.

A Specific Case of Research

The Original Study

AIMS   Our goal was to examine the patterns among various mental abilities in six- and seven-year-old children from different social-class and ethnic backgrounds. We accepted the definition of intelligence which postulates diverse mental abilities and proposes that intelligent behavior can be manifested in a wide variety of forms, with each individual displaying certain areas of intellectual strength and other forms of intellectual weakness. A basic premise of this study is that social-class and ethnic influences differ not only in degree but in kind, with the consequence that different kinds of intellectual skills are fostered or hindered in different environments.

DESIGN   Hypotheses were tested regarding the effects of social-class and ethnic-group affiliation (and their interactions) upon both the level of each mental ability considered singly and the pattern among mental abilities considered in combination. Four mental abilities (Verbal ability, Reasoning, Number facility, and Space Conceptualization) were studied in first-grade children from four ethnic groups (Chinese, Jewish, Negro, and Puerto Rican). Each ethnic group was divided into two social-class components (middle and lower), each in turn being divided into equal numbers of boys and girls (Fig. 1).

Thus, a $4 \times 2 \times 2$ analysis-of-covariance design included a total of 16 subgroups, each composed of 20 children. A total sample of 320 first-grade children was drawn from 45 different elementary schools in New York City and its environs. Three test influences were controlled statistically: effort, responsiveness to the tester, and age of the subject.

The selection of four mental abilities (Verbal ability, Reasoning, Number facility, and Space Conceptualization) is described in detail elsewhere (Lesser, Fifer, and Clark, 1965, pp. 32–43). To obtain a first approximation to the assessment of intra-individual profiles of scores for the various mental abilities of children, these skills were assessed:

Verbal—The skill is defined as memory for verbal labels in which reasoning elements, such as those required by verbal analogies, are reduced to a minimum. Verbal ability has long been regarded as the best single predictor of success in academic courses, especially in the language and social-science fields. It is involved to a marked degree in the work of all professions and in most semiprofessional areas.

Reasoning—Reasoning involves the ability to formulate concepts, to weave together ideas and concepts, and to draw conclusions and inferences from them. It is, almost by definition, the central element of aptitude for intellectual activities and, therefore, is of primary importance in all academic fields and in most vocations.

Number—The ability is defined as skill in enumeration and in memory and use of the fundamental combinations in addition, subtraction, multiplication, and division. It is of great importance in arithmetic in elementary schools and in mathematics in secondary schools.

Space Conceptualization—The ability refers to a cluster of skills related to spatial relations and sizes of objects and to visualizing their movements in space. It is involved in geometry, trigonometry, mechanics, and drafting; in elementary-school activities, such as practical arts and drawing; and in occupations such as mechanics, engineering, and architecture.

PROCEDURAL ISSUES   In this brief report, it is impossible to describe all the details of the procedures employed. Yet since research on the intellectual performance of "disadvantaged" children does impose some unique demands upon the investigator, at least the following procedural issues should be outlined.

Gaining Access to the Schools: Perhaps the most formidable problem was that of gaining the cooperation of school boards and school authorities for research on such a supposedly controversial issue. An honest approach by the researcher to the school authorities must contain the words "ethnic," "Negro," "Jewish," and "lower-class," and yet it is precisely these loaded words which arouse immediate anxiety and resistance in those who are authorized to permit or reject research in the schools. We believed that our objective of supplying information and understanding about the intellectual strengths and weaknesses of the children being taught in school would be a strong inducement to participation. Not so. Only

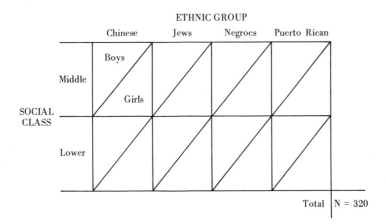

enormous persistence and lengthy negotiation—during which the researcher must agree to a succession of incapacitating constraints—permits such research at all.

Surely there are serious problems of ethics in educational research. Researchers should be (and most often are) as scrupulous as school authorities in maintaining the conditions of consent and confidentiality which protect subjects from unwarranted intrusions of privacy. But the legitimate ethical issues of privacy and free inquiry are not those that block access to the schools—the fear of controversy over racial issues seems to immobilize school authorities.

Beyond our own experiences in gaining acess to the schools, numerous examples exist of how research on the disadvantaged is prevented or distorted by the decisions of school authorities. For example, in Coleman's (Coleman *et al.*, 1966) study of *Equality of Educational Opportunity*, requested by the President and Congress of the United States, many major cities refused to participate, often because comparisons among racial groups were being made (although reasons for refusal were rarely stated).

Later in this paper, we shall discuss several new directions for future research comparing "disadvantaged" and "nondisadvantaged" children. These suggestions will remain the mental exercises of the academics unless some reasonable policies can be developed by researchers and school authorities to provide honest access to the school children, their parents, and their teachers.

Locating Social Class and Ethnic Group Samples: An associated problem was to achieve an unambiguous definition and assessment of social-class and ethnic-group placement. (The detailed procedures used for sample selection are described in Lesser, Fifer, and Clark, 1965, pp. 21–32.) Both variables are clearly multidimensional in character, and to define and measure the necessary components in each is a formidable task. Since members of each ethnic group were to be located in both lower- and middle-class categories, additional problems arose in attempting to maintain an equal degree of separation between the two social-class categories for each ethnic group.

In addition, obtaining the data necessary to identify the social-class and ethnic-group placement of each child presented many practical problems. There are strong legal restrictions in New York State upon collecting the data necessary for social-class and ethnic identification—and these restrictions are perhaps quite justified—but since we were not allowed to ask parents or school authorities directly about education, or religion, or even occupation, we were forced to use information gathered indirectly through 23 different community agencies and four sources of census and housing statistics. Among sources such as the New York City Regional Planning Association, the Commonwealth of Puerto Rico, the China Institute in America, the Demographic Study Committee of the Federation of Jewish Philanthropies, and the *New York Daily News* Advertising Department, our best single source of information was one of the largest advertising agencies in New York City, which has within its "Component Advertising Division" (which develops special marketing appeals for different ethnic groups) enormous deposits of information on the locations of the many cultural groups in New York City. There was little willingness, of course, to allow us to use these data. But after endless sitting-in and sheer pestering, we were given access to this information. We could not possibly have completed this study without it.

Developing "Culture-Fair" Test Materials: Perhaps the major technical problem was to insure the fact that observed differences among social-class and ethnic groups are in the children and not in the test materials themselves (or in the definitions upon which the tests are based). Therefore, tests were constructed which presuppose only experiences that are common and familiar within all of the different social-class and ethnic groups in an urban area. We had no intention to "free" the test materials from cultural influence, but rather to utilize elements which appear commonly in all cultural groups in New York City. If, for example, other Picture Vocabulary tests use pictures of xylophones or giraffes (which a middle-class child is more likely than a lower-class child to encounter in a picture book or in a zoo), we used pictures of buses, fire hydrants, lamp posts, garbage trucks, and police cars—objects to which all urban children are exposed.

Controlling "Examiner Bias": Each child was tested by an examiner who shared the child's ethnic identity in order to maintain chances of establishing good rapport and to permit test administration in the child's primary language, or in English, or, more often, in the most effective combination of languages for the particular child. Thus, we had a Negro tester, a Spanish-speaking Puerto Rican tester, a Yiddish-speaking Jewish tester, and three Chinese-speaking Chinese testers to accommodate the eight different Chinese dialects encountered among our Chinese children. Each tester had been trained beyond the Master's degree level, and each had extensive experience administering psychological tests; but the tendency of the testers to empathize with the children from their own cultural groups demanded careful control of the testing procedures to insure uniform test administration. This standardization was accomplished through extensive video-tape training in which each examiner observed other testers and himself administer the test materials.

SOME FINDINGS   Hypotheses were tested regarding the influence of social class and ethnicity (and their interactions) upon the levels of the four mental-ability scores and upon the patterns among them. The results are summarized in Table I.

TABLE I

SUMMARY OF RESULTS

Source of Influence	Level	Pattern
Ethnicity	Highly significant*	Highly significant*
Social class	Highly significant*	Nonsignificant
Social class x Ethnicity	Significant†	Nonsignificant

* $p < .001$
† $p < .05$

Distinctive Ethnic Group Differences: Ethnic groups are markedly different ($p<.001$) *both* in the absolute *level* of each mental ability and in the *pattern* among these abilities. For example, with regard to the effects of ethnicity upon the *level* of each ability, Figure 1 shows that:

1. On Verbal ability, Jewish children ranked first (being significantly better than all other ethnic groups), Negroes second, Chinese third (both being significantly better than Puerto Ricans), and Puerto Ricans fourth.

2. On Space Conceptualization, Chinese ranked first (being significantly better than Puerto Ricans and Negroes), Jews second, Puerto Ricans third, and Negroes fourth.

But the most striking results of this study concern the effects of ethnicity upon the *patterns* among the mental abilities. Figure 1 (and the associated analyses-of-variance for group patterns) shows that these *patterns* are different for each ethnic group. More important is the finding depicted in Figures 2–5. Ethnicity does affect the pattern of mental abilities *and, once the pattern specific to the ethnic group emerges, social-class variations within the ethnic group do not alter this basic organization.* For example, Figure 2 shows the mental-ability pattern peculiar to the Chinese children—with the pattern displayed by the middle-class Chinese children duplicated at a lower level of performance by the lower-class Chinese children. Figure 3 shows the mental-ability pattern specific to the Jewish children—with the pattern displayed by the middle-class Jewish children duplicated at a lower level of performance by the lower-class Jewish children. Parallel statements can be made for each ethnic group.

The failure of social-class conditions to transcend patterns of mental ability associated with ethnic influences was unexpected. Social-class influences have been described as superseding ethnic-group effects for such diverse phenomena as child-rearing practices, educational and occupational aspirations, achievement motivation, and anomie. The greater salience of social class over ethnic membership is reversed in the present findings on patterns of mental ability. Ethnicity has the primary effect upon the organization of mental abilities, and the organization is not modified further by social-class influences.

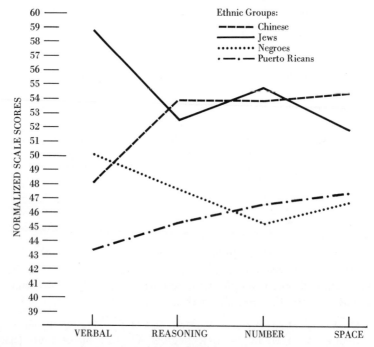

Fig. 1. *Pattern of Normalized Mental-Ability Scores for Each Ethnic Group*

Many other findings are described in our full report of this original study (Lesser, Fifer, and Clark, 1965). Only a few additional findings will be mentioned here, either because they are prominent in our recent replication study or in our plans for future research.

Interactions Between Social Class and Ethnicity: Table I, summarizing our earlier findings, indicates significant interactions (p < .05) between social class and ethnicity on the level of each mental ability. Table II shows the mean level of each mental ability for Chinese and Negro children from each social-class group; the same interaction effects appear when Jewish and Puerto Rican children are included, but the present table has been reduced to the Chinese and Negro children to simplify the present discussion. Two effects combine to produce the interaction effect between social class and ethnicity:

TABLE II

MEAN MENTAL-ABILITY SCORES FOR CHINESE AND NEGRO CHILDREN FOR EACH SOCIAL-CLASS GROUP

	Verbal				*Reasoning*		
	Chinese	*Negro*			*Chinese*	*Negro*	
Middle	76.8	85.7	81.3	Middle	27.7	26.0	26.9
Lower	65.3	62.9	64.1	Lower	24.2	14.8	19.5
	71.1	74.3	72.7		25.9	20.4	23.2
	Class ethnicity, $F = 7.69, p < .01$				Class ethnicity, $F = 11.32, p < .01$		
	Number				*Space*		
	Chinese	*Negro*			*Chinese*	*Negro*	
Middle	30.0	24.7	27.4	Middle	44.9	41.8	43.4
Lower	26.2	12.1	19.2	Lower	40.4	27.1	33.8
	28.1	18.4	23.3		42.7	34.4	38.6
	Class ethnicity, $F = 8.91, p < .01$				Class ethnicity, $F = 10.83, p < .01$		

1. On each mental-ability scale, social-class position produces more of a difference in the mental abilities of the Negro children than for the other groups. That is, the middle-class Negro children are more different in level of mental abilities from the lower-class Negroes than, for example, the middle-class Chinese are from the lower-class Chinese.

2. On each mental-ability scale, the scores of the middle-class children from the various ethnic groups resemble each other to a greater extent than do the scores of the lower-class children from the various ethnic groups. That is, the middle-class Chinese, Jewish, Negro, and Puerto Rican children are more alike in their mental ability scores than are the lower-class Chinese, Jewish, Negro, and Puerto Rican children.

Some earlier research (see Anastasi, 1958, Chap. 15) suggested that social-class influences upon intelligence are greater in white than in Negro groups. No distinct contrast with white children was available in our study, but the evidence indicates that social-class influences upon the mental abilities of Negro children are very great compared with the other ethnic groups represented. One explanation for the apparent contrast between the earlier and present findings is that the earlier research, perhaps, did not include middle- and lower-class Negro groups that

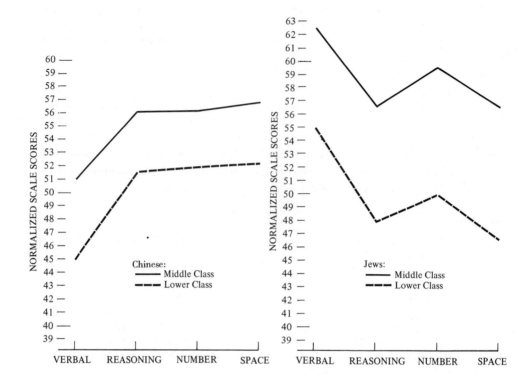

Fig. 2. Patterns of Normalized Mental-
Ability Scores for Middle- and Lower-
Class Chinese Children

Fig. 3. Patterns of Normalized Mental-
Ability Scores for Middle- and Lower-
Class Jewish Children

were distinctively different. In any event, our findings show that the influence of
social class on the level of abilities is more powerful for the Negro group than
for the other ethnic groups.

SOME CONCLUSIONS   The study demonstrated that several mental abilities are
organized in ways that are determined culturally. Referring to social-class and
ethnic groups, Anastasi (1958) proposed that "groups differ in their relative
standing on different functions. Each . . . fosters the development of a different
pattern of abilities." Our data lend selective support to this position. Both social-
class and ethnic groups do "differ in their relative standing on different functions";
i.e., both social class and ethnicity affect the *level* of intellectual performance.
However, only ethnicity "fosters the development of a different *pattern* of abilities," while social-class differences within the ethnic groups do not modify these
basic patterns associated with ethnicity.

To return to our continuing discussion of defining and delimiting the term
"disadvantaged": Defining the "disadvantaged" as belonging to a particular ethnic
group has one set of consequences for the development of intellectual skills—
ethnic groups differ in both level and pattern of mental abilities. Defining the
term using the social-class criteria of occupation, education, and neighborhood
leads to quite different consequences—social class affects level of ability, with
middle class being uniformly superior, but does not alter the basic patterns of

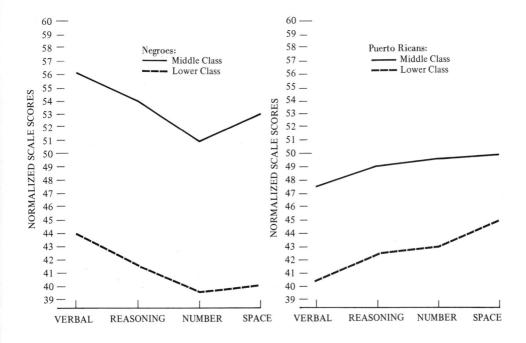

Fig. 4. Patterns of Normalized Mental-
Ability Scores for Middle- and Lower-
Class Negro Children

Fig. 5. Patterns of Normalized Mental-
Ability Scores for Middle- and Lower-
Class Puerto Rican Children

mental ability associated with ethnicity. Still other definitions—for example, un-
availability of English language models, presence of a threatening and chaotic
environment, matriarchal family structure, high family mobility, parental absence
or apathy, poor nutrition—probably generate still other consequences, although
we really know very little empirically about these relationships.

A Replication Study

Since our early results were both surprising and striking in magnitude, our next
step was to conduct a replication and extension with first-graders in Boston. The
replication was conducted with middle-class and lower-class Chinese and Negro
children (the samples of Jewish and Puerto Rican children who fit our social-
class criteria were not available); the extension included an additional ethnic
group—children from middle- and lower-class Irish-Catholic families.

Once again, the results were both striking and surprising. The replication data
on Chinese and Negro children in Boston duplicated almost exactly our earlier
data on similar samples in New York City.

We have some confidence, then, in our earlier findings on the effects of social-
class and ethnic-group influence on the development of patterns of mental abilities
in young children: at least several mental abilities are organized in ways that are
determined culturally, social-class producing differences in the *level* of mental
abilities (the middle-class being higher) and ethnic groups producing differences
in both *level* and *pattern* of mental abilities.

Future Research

To pursue the educational relevance of these findings, we are now studying the following questions:

1. What actual school behaviors are predicted by the patterns of mental ability?
2. Are the differential patterns related to ethnic-group differences stable over time or do intervening experiences modify them?
3. What are the specific origins or antecedents of differential patterns of mental ability?
4. How can our knowledge about patterns of mental ability be fitted to the content and timing of instruction?

Implications for Educational Policy

COLEMAN'S ARGUMENT IN "EQUALITY OF EDUCATIONAL OPPORTUNITY:" EQUAL OPPORTUNITY FOR EQUAL DEVELOPMENT   We mentioned earlier the recent study on *Equality of Educational Opportunity* directed by James S. Coleman. The results and particularly the interpretation of this study provide a useful point of departure for analyzing the implications for educational policy of the data described here on ethnic-group and social-class differences in mental-ability patterns.

Coleman failed to find what he expected to find, direct evidence of large inequalities in educational facilities in schools attended by children from different majority or minority groups. The study set out to document the fact that for children of minority groups school facilities are sharply unequal and that this inequality is related to student achievement. The data did not support either conclusion. What small differences in school facilities did exist had little or no discernible relationship to the level of student achievement.

Starting with these facts, Coleman develops an argument which we shall contrast with the implications of our mental-ability study. Inequality of educational opportunity still prevails, he says, because white and Negro (and other minority-group) students do not display equal levels of educational achievement when they complete high school. *Ipso facto*, the schools are unequal, despite the absence of direct evidence of such inequality.

Coleman's argument starts with the premise that the proper function of the schools in a democracy is to produce equal achievement levels among different groups in our society. Arguing from this premise, the demonstrated fact that Negroes and whites are unequal in level of educational attainment testifies to the inequality of educational opportunities provided by the schools. That is, by definition, schools are designed to make groups equal. They do not do so. Therefore, schools are unequal in the educational opportunities they provide. Indeed, following this argument, the single decisive criterion for judging equal educational opportunity is that mean school performance of all groups be equal.

Coleman makes his position clear by saying that the role of the schools is to "make achievement independent of background" and to "overcome the differences in starting point of children from different social groups" (Coleman, 1966, p. 72). This position is shared by much research on the "disadvantaged," where the

objective is to seek means to reduce the discrepancy in achievement levels between "deprived" and "nondeprived" children.[2]

THE "EQUAL-FOOTING" BASIS OF COLEMAN'S ARGUMENT At one level—the
"equal-footing" level—Coleman's line of reasoning seems to epitomize logic, common sense, and compassion. It seems to ask only that we give children from
"disadvantaged" backgrounds a fair shake—that through the educational system,
we educate all children to a point of equality in school achievement so that all
groups can compete on equal terms for jobs or future educational opportunities.

However, it is our contention that Coleman's analysis does not go far enough,
does not tell the whole story or consider all the evidence, and therefore is misleading and perhaps destructive. It fails to consider either the role of diversity
and pluralism in our society or several alternative definitions of the function of
schooling. Should schools provide equal opportunities to promote the *equal*
development of all groups and individuals or equal opportunities for the *maximum* development of each group or individual? Can schools aim to do both?

AN ALTERNATIVE ARGUMENT: EQUAL OPPORTUNITY FOR MAXIMUM DEVELOPMENT
We believe that our data on patterns of mental ability clarify these two alternative and perhaps complementary assumptions regarding the function of education:
(1) to provide equal opportunity for *equal* development, or (2) to provide equal
opportunity for *maximum* development of each group or individual, whether or
not group differences remain, enlarge, or disappear as a consequence. These
positions are apparently incompatible but need closer examination in the light of
empirical evidence.

Data on Social Class: From our mental-ability data, what would we predict
would happen if we modified the social-class characteristics of all our lower-class
families—elevating the jobs, educations, and housing of the lower-class families
in all ethnic groups? Within each ethnic group, we would expect to elevate the
mental abilities of the lower-class children to resemble those of the middle-class
children in that ethnic group, making them more similar to their middle-class
counterparts in that ethnic group in level of ability. In this sense, we would be
making groups of children more similar, removing the differences in mental
ability associated with differences in social-class position.[3]

If we elevated the social-class position of lower-class families, we might produce still another effect which increases the similarity among groups. The inter-

---

[2] The counterpart to Coleman's reasoning about equal educational opportunity exists in the
history of "culture-free" test construction, another topic of great relevance to the education of
the disadvantaged. Early developers of "culture-free" tests (e.g., Eells *et al.*, 1951) argued that
only tests which eliminated items distinguishing among groups were free of "bias." The parallel
to Coleman's argument is apparent: (1) the proper function of a "culture-free" test is to produce equal test scores for different social-class and ethnic groups; (2) if equal scores are not
obtained, the fault is that the test (or some kinds of test items) produce the difference. Difference in test scores, *ergo,* bias in test items. The logical fallacy of this argument is now well-
documented (e.g., Anastasi, 1958; Lorge, 1966), but the simple and surface persuasiveness
of the argument stalled progress for many years in the study of cultural influences upon
intelligence.

[3] We noted earlier that social-class position produces more of a difference in the mental
abilities of Negro children than for the other groups. From this finding, it is possible to speculate that elevating the social-class characteristics of lower-class Negro families would produce
a more dramatic increase in the level of the Negro children's abilities than would a comparable
change in social-class position affect the children from other ethnic groups.

action effect between social class and ethnicity showed that the mental-ability scores of middle-class children from various ethnic groups resembled each other more than the scores of the lower-class children from these ethnic groups. This interaction can be described as a convergence effect: the scores of the middle-class children across ethnic groups converge to a greater extent than the scores of lower-class children.

Thus, by elevating the occupations, educations, and neighborhoods of our lower-class families, our data would lead us to expect an increased resemblance of mental-ability levels for children within each ethnic group and, in addition, a convergence of scores of children across ethnic groups. To the extent that level of performance on mental abilities predicts school achievement, these convergences would narrow the range of differenes in school achievement among social-class and ethnic groups.

Data on Ethnic Groups: To this juncture, our analysis supports the argument for equal educational opportunities for *equal* development: our data on level of mental ability suggest that elevating social-class characteristics of lower-class families would contribute to a greater degree of equality of development in level of intellectual functioning. Now, what of the alternative conception that the proper function of education is to provide equal opportunity for *maximum* development no matter what the consequences for the absolute magnitude of group differences? Since the data on patterns of intellectual functioning indicates that once the mental-ability pattern specific to the ethnic group emerges, social-class variations within the ethnic group do not alter the basic organization associated with ethnicity, this finding suggests that lower-class children whose social-class position is elevated would still retain the distinctive mental-ability pattern associated with their ethnic group. The implication is that no matter what manipulations are undertaken to modify the social-class positions of children within an ethnic group, the distinctive ethnic-group pattern of abilities will remain.

From this set of observations, the question then arises: how can we make *maximum* educational use of the distinctive patterns of ability the child possesses? We do not have definitive answers to this question, which forces us to consider the line of future research discussed earlier on matching instructional strategies to the patterns of mental ability. In our discussion of school-based research, we called for a program to identify and explore mental attributes of children and the instructional methods which could be matched most effectively to these attributes to produce successful learning. In the simplest case, we can conceive of successful matching producing equal levels of achievement for children; such an outcome would be consistent with Coleman's argument. We think that at least for basic skills (e.g., literacy) the achievement of equal levels by all children is desirable.

Two possible contradictions to Coleman's argument remain, however. Beyond deploying all necessary resources to achieve minimal equality in essential goals, further development of students may well be diverse. A continuous utilization of student strengths and weaknesses may well lead to diverse development beyond a minimal set of achievements. To the extent that past experience, interests, and achievements of students are regularly related to subcultural membership, educational outcomes may differ. Second, we do not know what effects the matching procedure will have over time. We start, let us say, by using suitable alternative routes to identical educational objectives. Assuming we successfully achieve these outcomes, what else have we done? Have we, perhaps, reinforced and strengthened abilities, interests, or personality characteristics which are in fact associated with subcultural membership? In the long run, will we develop more diverse students than we started with?

Let us take a specific, if partially hypothetical, case. Our evidence indicates (see Figure 1) that young Chinese children have their strongest skill in Space Conceptualization and their weakest in Verbal ability. Conversely, young Jewish children are strongest in Verbal ability and weakest in Space Conceptualization. Following our principle of matching instruction and ability, we incidentally may enhance the initial strengths which each group possesses. For example, through the incidental enhancement of the space-conceptualization skills of the Chinese children, we may produce proportionally more Chinese than Jewish architects and engineers. Conversely, through incidental enhancement of verbal skills of the Jewish children, we may produce proportionally more Jewish than Chinese authors and lawyers. We will not have put members of these two ethnic groups on an "equal footing" for entering a particular occupation. But can we say that we have produced a socially-destructive outcome by starting with the knowledge of differences in ability patterns and adapting our instructional strategies to this knowledge to produce a maximum match for each child, even if this process results in inequality of certain educational and professional attainments? We are willing to accept, then, one possible consequence of arranging instruction to capitalize maximally on distinctive patterns of ability: that, in certain areas of intellectual accomplishment, rather than reducing or bringing toward equality the differences among various groups, we may actually magnify those differences.[4]

A SUMMARY We challenged Coleman's "equal-footing" argument on the grounds that it did not tell the whole story or use all known data. Some of these data, mainly the effects of social class upon level of mental ability, testify in favor of the argument for equal educational opportunity for *equal* development. Other data, namely the effects of ethnicity upon patterns of mental ability, testify to the importance of providing equal educational opportunities for the *maximum* development of groups and individuals, even if inequality of groups occurs as a consequence.

Are equalization and diversification necessarily incompatible goals? We do not believe so. If accelerating the feasible gains in jobs, education, and housing of lower-class families accelerates the gains in intellectual development of their children and reduces the difference in intellectual performance between social-class groups, we can all agree on the desirability of this outcome. On the other hand, if recognizing the particular patterns of intellectual strengths and weaknesses of various ethnic groups and maximizing the potential power of these patterns by matching instructional conditions to them makes the intellectual accomplishments of different ethnic groups more diverse, we can all accept this gain in pluralism within our society. Thus, if lower-class children now perform

---

[4] At this point in the argument, the counterpart topic is that of the difference between "compensatory" and "supportive" educational programs for "disadvantaged." "Compensatory" programs aim to compensate, to make amends, to eradicate symptoms and causes—to give "disadvantaged" children what they need to make them like everyone else. In contrast, the aim of what might be termed "supportive" education is to give disadvantaged children what they need and can use maximally in order to learn to cope with and change their particular environments, even if they are made more different from everyone else in the process.

intellectually more poorly than middle-class children—and it is clear that they do —and lower-class status can be diluted or removed by a society truly dedicated to doing so, this gain in equalization seems to be one legitimate aim of education. If the maximum educational promotion of particular patterns of ability accentuates the diverse contributions of different ethnic groups, this gain in pluralism seems another legitimate aim of education.

Our main point is that the study of mental abilities suggests that there may be patterns of attributes (cognitive, personality, motivational, and so forth) which are related in some regular way to ethnic-group membership. School-based research has not as yet identified the particular patterns of attributes which are educationally important and which (when matched with the appropriate instructional strategies) will maximize school achievement. Thus, we do not yet know if attribute patterns associated with ethnic-group membership will, in fact, be identified as educationally important. We believe, however, that data such as those derived from the current mental-abilities study must be considered since their implications may in fact require revisions of Coleman's position. We raise the issue because we are committed to our program of school-based research; whether ethnic-group differences are in fact minimized, held constant, or inflated by the programs which match individual differences to instructional strategies, we believe it important to pursue these programs nonetheless.

Perhaps this position asks no more than to change what is bad and changeable in education and society (resulting perhaps in greater equalization) and to use maximally what is good in education and society (resulting perhaps in increased diversity). Logic—and the empirical evidence—endorses both conclusions.

Toward a New Definition of the Disadvantaged

Let us start with the simplest possible definition of "disadvantaged," i.e., the "not advantaged." Given this definition, one might argue that the "advantaged" have something (or many things) that the "disadvantaged" do not have, that these "have not's" should be given what the "have's" already possess, and then we shall all be equal. Certainly, matters are not that simple.

Defining the "disadvantaged" in terms of differences in social-class position adds some precision to the definition of "not advantaged." It identifies more clearly some of the characteristics on which the "have's" and the "have not's" differ: jobs, education, housing. A social-class definition thus specifies three dimensions of the limited social boundaries within which the lower-class child may move. The empirical implications of the social-class definition are not very different in substance, however, from the definition of "not advantaged." We have argued from our data that providing a lower-class family with what a middle-class family has—better jobs, education, and housing—will produce levels of mental ability resembling those of middle-class children. We thus provide equal education and social opportunities for equal development.

What happens, however, when we introduce ethnicity into our definition of "disadvantaged"? The consequences now change. It is no longer possible to follow the strategy of giving the "have not's" what "have's" possess; changing ethnic membership cannot be accomplished through the social decree of federal action programs. We know ethnic groups differ in patterns of ability no matter what the social-class level within the ethnic group, and our educational problem now becomes that of providing equal educational opportunity to all ethnic groups to maximize their development, even at the expense of magnifying differences among the groups.

The point for defining the term "disadvantaged" is clear. The many different meanings assigned to this label may have accumulated arbitrarily according to the idiosyncratic choices of the various users of the term. But it is not merely a matter of whose definition sounds most convincing, or elegant, or compassionate. Each definition brings different empirical results and suggests different implications for educational policy and social action. We cannot afford this confusion; we are forced to be clearer about our definitions and their educational and social consequences.

We began this paper by accepting the common definition of disadvantaged status based on gross environmental characteristics: social class and ethnicity. This definition of disadvantage is strictly environmental and pre-assigned; it ignores the child's characteristics completely. It is a gross classification of children according to group membership only, and what we can learn about children by using this definition is usually expressed in terms of group tendencies (although we have suggested some techniques for moving from group data to individual analysis). Our suggestions for future research, both of developmental origins and school-based studies, direct us to some necessary refinements and extensions of these gross classifications.

Our recomendations for studies of developmental origins or environmental process analyses move us strongly in the direction of more precision and detail about environmental circumstances. Developmental research demands that a new definition of disadvantaged status be based on a much more refined assessment of environmental circumstances. Such an assessment would proceed far beyond the group characteristics we have dealt with in the past, specifying environmental circumstances which are closely articulated with developmental processes and which vary considerably within and across social-class and ethnic lines. Particular clusterings of environmental circumstances known to be related to developmental processes would lead to identification of disadvantaged status in more complex but precise terms.

Our discussions of school-based research suggest that disadvantaged status be expanded to include characteristics of the child. We refer now to assessments of children which are intimately connected with instructional objectives and procedures. From this point of view, a multiplicity of child attributes would have to be used to assess readiness for learning a variety of school tasks. Such measurements of readiness would give much power and operational substance to the concept of disadvantage.

We are therefore suggesting that an important advance in definition could be made by joining more precise descriptions of environments with instructionally-based assessments of child characteristics. Beginning with environmental characteristics and then assessing children's learning patterns would lead to one grouping of those we would class as disadvantaged; the other direction of attack, starting with child characteristics and then assessing environments, would lead to another grouping. The usefulness and desirability of each direction of approach must await both empirical and practical assessment. In either case, the lesson is clear: a new definition of "disadvantaged" should include psychologically mean-ingful statements about the environment and the child. The complexity of such statements will reflect a plethora of constructs and if-then statements about child-environment interactions but will be a realistic reflection of the diversity and individuality of children and the lives they lead.

52 / Social Structure and Group Processes in Explanation of Gang Delinquency

James F. Short, Jr.

Early in *Reference Groups,* the opinion is expressed that "the conception of gangs as unique formations in a class of their own makes advance in the analysis of their formation and the behavioral consequences of membership well-nigh im-possible" (Sherif and Sherif, 1964, p. 48). The misconception to which the Sherifs refer is, to some extent I suppose, a regrettable by-product of Thrasher's classic survey of gangs in Chicago, and of the enthusiasm of the old Chicago school for studying the phenomena of the inner city (Anderson, 1923; Thrasher, 1927; Shonle, 1928; Wirth, 1928; Landesco, 1929; Zorbaugh, 1929; Shaw, 1929, 1930; Shaw and McKay, 1931, 1942; Cressey, 1932; Frazier, 1932; Reckless, 1933; Hayner, 1936). So many interesting problems were found to be concentrated in the slum that the impression was perhaps inevitable that these problems were unique to the slum and causally related primarily to one another rather than to more general social processes. The fact that this was not the intention of the Chi-cago school was offset by the descriptive, as contrasted with theoretical, interests of most of its adherents, and by their failure to incorporate in study design the principles of comparative study. The confusion is compounded by the fact that persons whose primary interests are in amelioration of social ills find it easier to focus on the slum as a physical and social entity and to deal with its immediate problems rather than facing the conceptually more realistic, but operationally more difficult task of identifying and working with general social processes related to the behavior with which they are concerned, and with realities of social struc-ture which concentrate so many social problems in the slum.

   This chapter deals with the relation of different levels of behavior explanation to one another, and specifically to the manner in which they become "translated" into behavior. The levels of explanation to which I refer are *social structure, cul-ture* (or the currently more popular *subculture*), *group process,* and *individual personality.* I shall be concerned with the behavior of members of groups com-prised largely of adolescent boys and referred to commonly as "delinquent gangs," although, as we shall see, the groups to which I refer do not by and large conform to the popular stereotype of gangs. The term "gang" is unnecessary, and its popular connotation is inappropriate to the theoretical resolution I shall suggest.

To those who have followed the monumental work of the Sherifs and their associates over the past several years, it will be clear that in many respects we have been pursuing the same objectives—too much in isolation from one another, I regret to say. This very isolation makes similarities of findings more impressive, however, and differences provide grist for the theoretical mill and for more direct empirical tests in the future.

The chapter draws heavily on the work of others, both theoretical and empirical. I shall be most concerned, however, with data from an ongoing study of delinquent gangs in Chicago with which I have been associated since the fall of 1958 (Short and Strodtbeck, 1965). At that time, the YMCA of Metropolitan Chicago and the department of sociology at the University of Chicago brought together four academicians (Albert Cohen, Lloyd Ohlin, Walter Miller, and myself) whose substantive research interests in the phenomena of gang delinquency meshed well with Philip Hauser's interests in human ecology and social organization and Fred Strodtbeck's social-psychological interests. Lay and professional leaders of the YMCA met with us also and made important contributions and commitments to the action-research collaboration which emerged. At that meeting the academicians were encouraged to present and argue about alternative theoretical positions and their implications for research design and for possibilities of working with the new Y program. The others doubtless were curious to know what research and theory had to say about problems which they considered most pressing, and whether, after all, academicians might have some contribution to make to action problems. That conference was the springboard for an action-research program of considerable proportions, with very generous foundation, university, and YMCA support. En route to discussion of research strategies and findings from this program, I should like to discuss the notion of delinquent subcultures, their nature, and their generality. In the process, perhaps some notion can be gained as to whether the concept is helpful in the scientific enterprise, and how it relates to other levels of explanation.

Delinquent Subcultures

The sociology of subcultures is not well developed theoretically. A subculture generally is understood to be a "way of life" that has become traditional among members of a particular category or subgroup of individuals within a larger society which shares a common culture. Subcultures commonly are distinguished by specialized argots and behavior expectations of participants (oftentimes by others as well as by participants themselves), as well as by special training of those who are carriers of the culture (as in the case of members of professions and learned disciplines), or physical or social characteristics such as race, class, and ethnicity. These characteristics do not define subcultures, and their possession does not make one automatically a carrier of a particular subculture. A person may be, and quite likely is, a carrier of more than one subculture, with varying degrees of commitment to the values and the customs of each, depending upon such factors as amount and type of interaction with other carriers, personal experience with the problems to which subcultures are a collective solution, etc.

Though "hard data" on the matter are extremely rare, enough evidence and informed opinion exist to suggest that some type of delinquent subculture is to be found in communities that vary widely in size, population, composition, and regional location. Even in the metropolis, however, except in relatively rare instances, these do not appear to take the highly specialized forms described in the literature as *conflict, criminal,* or *retreatist* (Cohen and Short, 1958; Cloward and Ohlin, 1960; Yablonsky, 1962). The behavioral versatility of most "delinquent gangs" is attested to by virtually every empirical effort which has been directed to the problem, from Thrasher's classic survey to current studies (Thrasher, 1927; Bloch and Niederhoffer, 1958; Short, Tennyson, and Howard, 1963). It is against this background of versatility, I believe, that the emergence of more specialized varieties of delinquent subcultures must be understood. Let us look, therefore, at the characteristics of the more common and diffuse varieties which have been reported.

In describing the community setting of the Provo Experiment in Delinquency Rehabilitation, Empey and Rabow comment as follows concerning delinquents in the "string of small cities . . . ranging in size from four to forty thousand" from which the experiment was drawn:

> Despite the fact that Utah County is not a highly urbanized area, when compared to large metropolitan centers, the concept of a "parent" delinquent subculture has real meaning for it. While there are no clear-cut gangs, *per se,* it is surprising to observe the extent to which delinquent boys from the entire county, who have never met, know each other by reputation, go with the same girls, use the same language, or can seek each other out when they change high schools. About half of them are permanently out of school, do not participate in any regular institutional activities, and are reliant almost entirely upon the delinquent system for social acceptance and participation (Empey and Rabow, 1961).

Similar reports have been received from other western cities, with occasional and usually short-lived gangs being reported. More recently, the Lane County Youth Project, on the basis of early returns, appears to be discovering a similar phenomenon in rural Oregon, as well as in smaller towns and cities (Polk, 1963).

Across the continent, in Vermont's idyllic Green Mountain Town and in Mountain City, where delinquents are hard to come by, Himelhoch reports that "There is evidence in both communities that the delinquents share a subculture which distinguishes them from the conformists who participate in an opposite subculture. The delinquent subculture comprises . . . a cluster of anti-moralistic attitudes which support and encourage law violation, usually of a minor or moderate nature." He concludes further that "the typical rural and small city convicted youthful offender in Northeast State belongs to a loosely organized, non-exclusive, sporadically delinquent group. The shifting membership of this group draws upon a larger population of youth who are mostly, but not always, of lower class backgrounds" (Himelhoch, 1964).

From the midwest, Elmtown and John Clark's samples, and from Reiss and Rhodes in Nashville, come similar reports (Hollingshead, 1949; Reiss and Rhodes, 1961; Clark and Wenninger, 1962). I have emphasized these reports from rural and smaller urban areas because most of the literature has concentrated on the highly urban slum as the locus for gangs and for delinquent subcultures (Crawford, Malamud, and Dumpson, 1950; Glane, 1950; Bloch and Niederhoffer, 1958; Yablonsky, 1962). This was Thrasher's great emphasis, and it has tended to characterize virtually all the research and speculation since. Even in Thrasher's day, however, there was recognition of the generality of youth groups referred to as gangs beyond city boundaries. In his Editor's Preface to the first edition of *The Gang*, Robert E. Park remarked that "Village gangs, because they are less hemmed about by physical structures and social inhibitions of an urban environment, ordinarily do not become a social problem, certainly not a problem of the dimensions and significance of those which constitute so obvious and so obdurate a feature of city life" (p. ix in abridged edition).

Albert Cohen and I coined the phrase, "parent delinquent subculture," in the course of an investigation into varieties of subcultures which seemed to characterize delinquent groups in various cities (Cohen and Short, 1958). These groups —e.g., "bopping" gangs in New York City, drug-using "cats" in Chicago, and semiprofessional "hoods" engaged in theft for profit in several places, seemed not to fit *the* delinquent subculture described earlier by Cohen (1955). So, we set out, by literature search and by correspondence with police and others in dozens of places, to delineate variations on Cohen's earlier theme. Very early in the process we were impressed by the absence of reports of highly specialized gangs, even from large cities such as Detroit and San Francisco. This, plus such notions as the "natural history" of delinquent careers and "differential association," provided by our mentors, Clifford Shaw and Edwin Sutherland, and our own research, led us to the concept of a parent delinquent subculture from which variations were thought to emerge by processes we hoped to discover. Thus, drug users in both Chicago and New York emerged from the ubiquitous street corner groups found in those cities, only later forming or joining associations which were the carriers of distinct subcultures. The latter appeared to be characterized by very loose group ties, but strong attachment to subcultural norms and values. Youngsters who stole for profit came from similar initial groups, developing their theft patterns only after earlier and repeated delinquencies, including minor thefts not of a profit nature. Bopping gangs started out in similar fashion, adopting their bellicose posture, it appeared, in response to common cultural values such as "toughness" and local opportunities, not the least important of which were the availability of rival groups.

At the time of our initial speculations we had no very clear ideas as to just how varieties of delinquent subcultures emerged from what we were calling the parent delinquent subculture, but we were convinced of the relevance of Kobrin's notions concerning the relative integration of the carriers of criminal and conventional values in lower class communities. We did not know of Cloward's brilliant addition to the theory of "Social Structure and Anomie," having to do with the differential availability of illegitimate means to success goals; and only later (at the Chicago conference) did we learn that he and Ohlin were engaged in writing *Delinquency and Opportunity*. We were perhaps not sensitive enough to the characteristic gradual isolation of drug users from their more "conventionally delinquent" groups, described by Chein and his associates in New York (Kobrin, 1951; Chein and Rosenfeld, 1957; Cloward, 1959; Cloward and Ohlin,

1960); or of the extent to which these boys were therefore thrown on their own resources, and the implications this appears to have for formation of the "society of cats" described by Finestone (1957). In retrospect it seems also we did not fully appreciate the implications of our own data on semiprofessional stealing, which we described as appearing "to be more of a differentiation of emphasis within a more diversified climate of delinquency than an autonomous subculture independently organized." Certainly we were not aware of the extent to which even elaborately organized conflict gangs with cherished names and a strong sense of corporate identity were loosely organized and shifting in membership and "attendance" on the corner or at other hangouts. Nor were we aware of the forces motivating conflict among these gangs.

The notion of varieties of delinquent subcultures provided the basis for the design of the Chicago research concerning "street corner groups and patterns of delinquency" (Short, 1963). Theoretical focus was derived from Cohen's *Delinquent Boys*, from *Delinquency and Opportunity*, from Walter Miller's thesis (1958) of lower class culture as the "Generating Milieu of Gang Delinquency," and from our own determination, at first only vaguely formulated, to keep a window open on the gangs in order to bring to bear data on group processes and later to study both characteristics of individual gang members and the cultural and social structural data implied by the other theories. I will summarize our research procedures and findings rather than present detailed data on these myriad matters. The synthesis which I shall attempt must be seen as an approximation based on data at hand, from our own work and from the work of others; it is subject, of course, to revision in the process of coming closer to reality, which is the hallmark of the scientific endeavor.

I will bring to bear findings from a considerable variety of data generation procedures, including field observation by members of the research team and by detached workers, ratings on the basis of such observation, interviews with gang boys, workers, and local community adults, paper and pencil instruments, and carefully controlled laboratory assessments of gang boys. For comparative purposes, data (except for field observations) were gathered on non-gang boys from the gang neighborhoods and on middle class youngsters as well as gang boys. We have studied Negro and white boys in each of these categories. Our basic research design thus permits comparisons by race, social class, and gang status, as well as comparisons among the different groups under observation.

From Social Structure to
Gang Delinquency: An Interpretation

In the interest of clarity, I will first summarize some notions about the classes of variables and the nature of their relation to one another, which, on the basis of our research, appear to be involved in the "translation" of social structure into gang delinquency (and at least some other forms of "deviant" behavior).

Realities of social structure, such as class and ethnic differentiation and the operation of ecological processes, place severe limitations on the realization of certain cultural universals—for example, the high value placed on material wealth and status achievement in the contexts of important institutions such as school and the world of work. For many lower class and ethnically disadvantaged per-

sons, failure to achieve these goals begins early in life due to socialization practices which are defective in meeting the criteria for achievement of the larger
society. This process is complicated by the existence of subcultures with distinctive ethnic and lower class characteristics, and by youth subcultures, some of
which are delinquent in a variety of ways. These subcultures have both historical
and contemporary roots. They serve both to insulate their adherents from experiences which might make possible achievement of many "respectable" goals in
terms of "respectable" criteria, and to compensate in some measure for failure,
or the likelihood of failure, in these areas. Indeed, compensation appears to be
one of the chief functions of peer group participation in every strata of society
and at every age.

Important *goals* of the larger society are quite successfully communicated, as
Merton suggests (1957). So, also, are values concerning legitimate means for their
achievement. Evidence from a variety of sources, e.g., the Flint Youth Study and
our own, suggests that disadvantaged youngsters do not become alienated, that
even the gang ethic is not one of "reaction formation" *against* widely shared
values in society (Gold, 1963).

Peer groups in the lower class often come to serve important *status functions*
for youngsters who are disadvantaged according to the success criteria of the
larger society's institutions (schools, churches, places of business, etc.). Peer
groups become the most salient status universe of such youngsters. Group norms
and values come to stress means of achievement not prescribed by conventional
norms and values, which in effect provide alternative means of achievement for
group members. Delinquency arises sometimes as a by-product and sometimes as
a direct product of peer group activity.

The groups and institutions which are the primary carriers of lower class,
ethnic, and delinquent subcultures are marked in many cases by instability and
by a high incidence of physical objects and social situations which combine to
create a high risk of involvement in delinquency. One thinks of elements such as
the public nature of drinking and "party" behavior, shifting sexual and economic
liaisons, widespread possession of guns, and the acceptance of violence as a means
of settling disputes.

There is evidence that the gang offers less solidarity and less satisfaction to its
participants than nostalgic accounts of "that old gang of mine" would suggest.
There is evidence, too, that the "lack of social assurance" which Whyte attributed
to his corner boys is especially aggravated among these seriously delinquent
youngsters, and that they are characterized by other social disabilities which
contribute to delinquency-producing status threats within and outside the gang
(Whyte, 1955; Gordon and Short, 1962).

Though evidence from our own study is incompletely analyzed, such measures
as we have been able to obtain of social structural variables (such as race, class,
and gang status; some, but not all, measures of "position discontent"; and perceptions of opportunity structures) and of individual social disabilities (such as
negative self-concept and low intelligence) are found to *order* the groups by
race, by class, or by gang status in much the same way as their delinquency
rates. The same measures, however, are not highly correlated with individual behavior in the group context. That is, these variables generally are not predictive
of behavioral variations of individual gang members. In accounting for this find-

ing, it is insufficient simply to regard the group as a catalyst that releases potentials for delinquency not readily apparent in known characteristics of its individual members. To further specify the relation between the group and the behavior of its members, we have looked for specific group processes and mechanisms which are involved in delinquency episodes. Three of these have been suggested in our recent work.

Reactions to Status Threats

When gang boys perceive threats to some valued status, delinquency often follows (Short and Strodtbeck, 1963). This mechanism has been found to operate in response to perceived threats to status as a leader, as male, as a member of a particular gang, or as an aspiring adult. It may operate individually or collectively, though the delinquent solution characteristically involves other members of the group. Why status threats should produce delinquency episodes doubtless is a very complex matter, but we have observed several characteristics of gang boys and their social worlds that are apparently related to this mechanism.

There is, first of all, the lack among gangs of a formal structure supporting group continuity and stability. There is further the lack of institutionalized support in adversity, in contrast to more formal organizations such as voluntary associations, schools, churches, businesses, and governments. At a more individual level leaders can control few resources of crucial value to the group, so that their own ability to dominate the group by internally directed aggression is severely restricted. Gang members tend to lack social skills which might permit them to meet status threats in more creative, less delinquent ways. At the group level, delinquent actions often are acceptable, if not generally prescribed, by group norms. They constitute a sort of "least common denominator" around which members can rally. Finally, externally directed delinquency, particularly of an aggressive nature, serves to unify these loosely structured groups in common cause. Indeed, the latter appears to operate not only in conjunction with status threats, but independently, as a basic mechanism accounting for delinquency involvement by these youngsters (Gordon and Short, 1962). This point will be further developed later in the chapter.

The Gamble of Status Gain versus Punishment Risk

In the calculus of decision making, status *rewards* within the group often tip the scales toward "joining the action," and therefore becoming involved in delinquency. The chief *risk* in such behavior appears to be the probability of punishment at the hands of a society which seems disinterested in one's personal fate (Strodtbeck and Short, 1964). Episodes which on the surface seem to reflect simply a hedonistic orientation to life thus may actually involve a rational assessment of probabilities resulting in a decision to risk the consequences of joining the action, going along with the boys, etc. The decision is understandable in view of the low risk of serious consequences associated with most delinquency episodes, and the somewhat higher probability of associated group rewards consequent to joining the action—affirmation of friendship bonds, status accruals from performance in an episode, personal satisfaction derived from demonstration of toughness, masculinity, etc.

The Discharge of Group Role Obligations

As obvious examples, a leader may be *required* to "join the action," or even to precipitate it if the situation involves *group threat*. A "War Counselor" is required to perform when gang conflict appears imminent or is engaged. Centrality in the group, or striving toward this goal, exposes one to involvement in situations with a high "delinquency potential," by means of the previously discussed mechanisms, including those associated with specific roles in the group. Thus, an apparent paradox in our self-concept data may be resolved. As reported earlier, boys who describe themselves in "scoutlike" terms (loyal, polite, helpful, religious, obedient) are *more* involved in conflict behavior than are boys who describe themselves as "cool aggressives" (mean, tough, troublesome, and cool) (Short and Strodtbeck, 1965). Our interpretation rests upon the connotation of *responsibility* in personal relations and recognition of their implied obligations, which are characteristic of the "scout" terms. The "cool aggressive" terms, by contrast, carry overtones of disruption or disregard of obligations to associates or to convention, and of a type of detachment which is the antithesis of reciprocity in personal relations. The scouts, we believe, facilitate cohesive relations and reduce interpersonal tensions in these loosely structured groups, becoming more central in the group. They then find themselves in situations in which role expectations, status threats, and potential rewards associated with joining the action make their involvement in episodes of aggression more likely.

Social Structure:
Position Discontent and Perceived Opportunities

Having sketched major conclusions concerning the topic of this chapter, some of the evidence upon which they are based seems in order. I will begin, like most recent sociological treatises on the subject, with social structure. The "Social Structure and Anomie" paradigm and related theoretical efforts say, in effect, that pressures toward deviance are greatest among those persons who have accepted culturally defined success goals but who find culturally approved means to achieve them unavailable (Cohen, 1955; Merton, 1957; Cloward and Ohlin, 1960). The discrepancy between goals and means is commonly expressed as "position discontent," which in turn is hypothesized as a principal component of pressures toward deviant behavior. But, how are we to measure position discontent, and likewise, pressures toward deviance? We have tried several ways. For the moment we will ignore differences between gangs and concentrate on comparing our highly delinquent gang boys with their non-gang counterparts, both lower and middle class. Consistent with the stress that anomie theory puts on the "success theme" as a universal in our culture, we find that both gang and non-gang boys aspire to occupational levels considerably above their fathers. This finding was based on Duncan's modification of the NORC—North-Hatt scale of occupational prestige as shown in column 1 of Table I (Duncan and Reiss, 1961; Gold, 1963; Rivera, 1964; Sherif and Sherif, 1964; Short, 1964).

This criterion orders our six groups quite differently from the two measures of delinquency involvement—mean number of offenses known to the police per boy

TABLE I

INDEXES OF POSITION DISCONTENT AND DELINQUENCY INVOLVEMENT, RANKED FOR SIX POPULATION GROUPS*

1	2	3	4	5
Mean Discrepancy between Fathers' Occupational Levels and Boys' Aspirations*	Mean Discrepancy between Fathers' Occupational Levels and Boys' Expectations*	Mean Discrepancy between Boys' Occupational Aspirations and Expectations*	Mean Number of Offenses Known to the Police per Boy	Self-Reported Delinquency Factor (Corner Boy Delinquency)†
NLC 16.6	NMC 14.4	NG 7.1	NG 3.14	WG 15.8
NMC 15.2	NLC 12.1	NLC 5.8	WG 2.73	NG 17.3
NG 13.8	NG 7.3	WG 5.7	NLC .47	WLC 21.0
WLC 11.4	WLC 6.8	WLC 4.6	WLC .31	NLC 22.7
WG 9.2	WMC 4.9	WMC 1.2	NMC .06	NMC 23.8
WMC 6.1	WG 3.7	NMC .8	WMC .02	WMC 27.9

* N's for each column are as follows:	1	2	3	4	5
NG = Negro gang boys	204	205	194	350	153
WG = White gang boys	88	87	88	100	55
NLC = Negro lower class, non-gang boys	89	89	82	117	111
WLC = White lower class, non-gang boys	74	74	74	91	71
NMC = Negro middle class boys	26	26	26	34	29
WMC = White middle class boys	53	53	53	51	50

† *Lower scores indicate more delinquency*. Scores range from 7, representing "every day" involvement in seven activities, to 35, representing no involvement. The activities, extracted from factor analysis of 22 behaviors of 469 boys, are *gambling* (playing cards or pool for money, shooting dice, penny pitching); *signifying or playing the dozens; hanging* (being with the boys on the street); *drinking* beer, wine, whiskey; *riding in cars; fighting* (humbug or rumble); *making money* (bread) *illegally.*

(column 4) and a measure of self-reported delinquency (column 5). (Differences between gang and non-gang boys are highly statistically significant on both of these behavior measures.) Negro boys, especially the less delinquent non-gang boys, both aspire (column 1) and expect (column 2) to achieve far beyond their fathers' levels. White boys, whose fathers have achieved higher occupational levels, have less lofty ambitions than do any of the Negro boys. So, by the criterion of column 2, white gang (WG) boys should be least delinquent of the lot; and by those in columns 1 and 2, Negroes, both middle class (NMC) and lower class non-gang boys (NLC), should be most delinquent. Although these discrepancies probably reflect pressures to succeed, they do not generate pressures toward deviance in the manner that anomie theory predicts. This may be because they do not indicate the same type of position discontent that the theories discuss; one of the great difficulties with the theory is that it is not specific in this regard. Column 3 offers yet another index of position discontent; this time, within race, the groups rank in the same order as they do according to police contacts and self-reported "corner boy" delinquency. For both Negroes and whites, class differences in this index are greater than gang—non-gang differences.[1]

[1] The situation is more complex with respect to self-reported behavior, where class differences are slightly greater among whites, gang status among Negroes. In both instances, there is less "spread" among Negro populations than among whites. Analysis of the data and more extended discussion are presented in Short and Strodtbeck (1965).

To support the theory, it might be argued that the discrepancy between an individual's occupational aspirations and expectations is the index most directly relevant to his own feelings of disjuncture between goals and aspirations. On the other hand, discrepancy between class of origin (father's occupation) and class of orientation (one's own ambitions and/or expectations) seems likely to reflect a more objective disjuncture in terms of its consequences for the individual. Certainly we can assume that, viewed objectively, opportunities are more restricted for Negroes than for whites, and for lower class than for middle class boys. If it could be shown that *gang membership* itself restricts occupational achievement, and/or that gang members are less able to achieve than non-gang youngsters (from the same class of origin), an important advance would have been made; this effect would add factors to the subjective disjuncture shown in column 3.

Some leverage on this question is provided by the fact that school adjustment of the non-gang boys is more successful than that of the gang boys (Freedman and Rivera, 1962), and that their mean intelligence level is higher (Howard, Hendrickson, and Cartwright, 1962). Estimates of the latter were obtained with a "culture-free" test, as well as a standardized arithmetic test, and vocabulary, memory, and information tests designed especially to avoid "middle class" biases which would disadvantage lower class and gang subjects. Nearly one-half of the gang boys (46.8 per cent of the Negroes; 42.7 per cent of whites) were judged to be unsuccessful in school adjustment on the basis of a composite objective index derived from their interview responses; only about one-quarter of the lower class non-gang boys and virtually none of the middle class boys were judged unsuccessful. Among gang boys, those with poor school adjustment have, as expected, higher delinquency rates. But those who also have high educational aspirations are "protected" to an extent against delinquency involvement (in the sense that their delinquency rates are lower than those of boys with lower aspirations). I have suggested elsewhere that high educational aspirations indicate an identification with norms of the larger social order concerning legitimate means, and hence they operate to restrain involvement in delinquency, despite blocked opportunities in the form of poor educational adjustment (Short, 1964). This "protection," however, is too limited to explain a great deal of the variance in the behavior of the boys.

Another way of looking at social structural variables that possibly influence our youngsters concerns their own evaluation of their "areas" in terms of legitimate and illegitimate opportunities following Cloward and Ohlin (1960). Boys were asked whether or not a series of 26 statements applied to the area where their group hung out. The statements concerned educational and occupational opportunities, integration of the carriers of criminal and non-criminal values, opportunities for learning crime, the visibility of criminal careers and of criminal elites, and general perceptions of the power of adults and their helpfulness to teenagers. Mean summary scores of boys in each sample are presented in Table II (Short, Rivera, and Tennyson, 1965). Here the groups rank the same in both perception of legitimate opportunities (column 1) and perception of adult power and helpfulness (column 3) as they do in the official delinquency rate. This is consistent with Cloward and Ohlin's reference to illegitimate opportunities as intervening for lower class youngsters *following* assessment of legitimate opportunities. Our data support the notion that legitimate achievement tends to be the universal

TABLE II

PERCEPTION OF OPPORTUNITIES AND OFFENSES KNOWN TO THE POLICE, BY SIX POPULATIONS

Legitimate Educational and Occupational Opportunities (low to high) (0 to 22)	Perception of Illegitimate Opportunities (less inclusive) (high to low) (0 to 18)	Perception of Adult Power and Helpfulness (low to high) (0 to 8)	Total Opportunities Score* (low to high) (− 18 to 30)	Mean Number of Offenses Known to Police, Per Boy (high to low)
NG (9.0)	NG (11.4)	NG (4.5)	NG (2.1)	NG (3.14)
WG (9.3)	NLC (9.5)	WG (4.7)	WG (5.0)	WG (2.73)
NLC (11.0)	WG (9.0)	NLC (5.6)	NLC (7.1)	NLC (0.47)
WLC (13.7)	NMC (8.2)	WLC (5.6)	WLC (12.6)	WLC (0.31)
NMC (15.6)	WLC (6.7)	NMC (6.2)	NMC (13.6)	NMC (0.06)
WMC (20.2)	WMC (3.5)	WMC (7.4)	WMC (24.1)	WMC (0.02)

* Total Opportunities Score is designed to reflect both legitimate and illegitimate pressures toward delinquency, and is obtained by adding together legitimate educational and occupational opportunities and adult power and helpfulness scores, and from this sum subtracting illegitimate opportunity scores. Hence it is expected to be negatively correlated with delinquency.

standard against which alternatives are weighed. However, illegitimate opportunities do exist and provide an avenue to financial success; and, within race, perception of these illegitimate opportunities (column 2) places the boys in the same order as their official delinquency rates.

We may comment briefly on the relatively high "illegitimate opportunity" scores of the Negro boys. Despite white hoodlums' generally acknowledged domination of organized crime in Chicago (and, one suspects, in part because of it), much large-scale organized vice flourishes in Negro communities (e.g., prostitution, heroin, and "the numbers"). There is more independent entrepreneurship in the form of street-walking prostitutes, marijuana peddling, pool sharks, professional burglars and robbers, smaller policy wheels, etc., than in lower class white communities. Intercorrelations of illegitimate opportunities with the measure of adult "clout," furthermore, indicate that the white areas are more "integrated," in the Cloward and Ohlin sense, than are the Negro areas. Finally, perceptive analyses by Drake and Cayton, and Frazier, indicate the extent to which criminal and "shady" elements penetrate Negro social structure from bottom to top, providing a type of pervasive influence, but one less powerful than that found in some white communities (Drake and Cayton, 1962; Frazier, 1962).

Behavior Patterns: Subcultures?

Returning now to behavioral variation *among* gang boys, we may assess its patterning in terms of various suggested delinquent subcultures. From the beginning of the study we had been impressed by the lack of "purity" of the hypothesized types, even though our selection of gangs, with the full cooperation of the YMCA detached workers, was oriented toward obtaining the best possible representatives of the three most discussed types in the literature—conflict, crimi-

nal, and retreatist. Negro conflict gangs were plentiful, but they were also involved in a great deal of stealing; we were unable to locate a real criminal gang,
despite a determined and prolonged effort to do so. We did find occasional
cliques or other subunits within larger gangs, which engaged in special criminal
activities, e.g., systematic theft or strong-arming. In one group there was a clique
of "winos," and several had "singing" cliques. After a full year of investigation
we located what appeared to be a genuine retreatist group. Thus it became clear
that the subcultural emphases specified in the literature were not as exclusive as
their descriptions suggested. Our factor analysis of ratings by detached workers
isolated a conflict pattern; and a combination of drug use, homosexuality, common-law marriage, attempted suicide, and pimping which we could label as
retreatist, but not a criminal factor. Neither conflict nor retreatism characterized
exclusively any one gang under study. Other activities also emerged as factors
and blended into the behavior patterning of these boys; e.g., stable corner-boy
activities, heterosexual behavior, and an "authority protest" factor involving chiefly
auto theft, truancy, running away from home, vandalism, and creating public
disturbance (Short, Tennyson, and Howard, 1963). The described *simplicity* of
subcultural patterns clearly was challenged by these data, if not their hypothesized
etiology.

Field observation, coupled with systematic measures of the boys' values according to a semantic differential, indicated that gang boys' commitment to
delinquent norms was quite tenuous (Short, Strodtbeck, and Cartwright, 1962).
Indeed, commitment was virtually nonexistent except in specific types of situations involving the group, such as a threat from another gang, or, in some
instances, threats to the status of boys individually. Analysis of behavior patterns
and self-concept measures suggested that the gangs contained considerable numbers of "stable corner boys" and even a few "college boys"; there were "scouts" as
well as "cool aggressives" within the same gang. This led us to question both the
homogeneity of gangs and the degree of normative commitment which they place
on their members (Gordon *et al.*, 1963).

Yet there was, within each of these gangs, a shared perspective, which was
often shared with members of other groups as well. For some gangs, conflict with
other gangs was a major focus of group activity, and the source of considerable
status within the gang. These gangs more often than others engaged in a variety
of violent episodes in addiiton to gang conflict. These gangs were *invested* in
their reputation for fighting, though the "boundaries" of their concern for such
a "rep" are not clear. We know it includes other fighting gangs, but there is
evidence, also, that it includes a much broader public. Members of such gangs
often evidenced great pride when the mass media noticed their activities, even
though the notices often were derogatory. A prominent member of one such gang
compiled a scrapbook filled with newspaper articles featuring his gang. Newsmen
looking for a story found that gang boys would be suspicious and ambivalent at
first, but to the best of my knowledge reporters never experienced prolonged
difficulty, and always found willing informants.

Conflict gangs also created roles expressive of their conflict orientation, thus
differing in structure from other gangs. Such positions as "war counselor" and
"armorer" were jealously guarded, even though the duties and privileges of office
were rarely defined in a formal way. These roles served as a focus of ceremonial

deference within the group, and they provided still another basis for individual status and for group identity. The nature of typical "guerrilla warfare" and its function for the participants is dramatically portrayed by a detached worker's report of a minor skirmish between the Knights and the Vice Kings, two groups which had been feuding for some months:

> [I] was sitting there talking to the Knights . . . re-emphasizing my stand on guns, because they told me that they had collected quite a few and were waiting for the Vice Kings to come down and start some trouble. . . . I told them flatly that it was better that I got the gun rather than the police, and though they agreed with me, they repeated their stand that they were tired of running from the Vice Kings and that if they gave them trouble, from now on they were fighting back.
>
> . . . While I was sitting there in the car talking to William (the remaining guys have gotten out of the car in pursuit of some girls around the corner), William told me that a couple of Vice Kings were approaching. I looked out of the window and noticed two Vice Kings and two girls walking down the street by the car. . . . William then turned around and made the observation that there were about fifteen or twenty Vice Kings across the street in the alley and wandering up the street in ones and twos.
>
> At this point, I heard three shots go off. I don't know who fired these shots, and no one else seemed to know, because the Vice Kings at this point had encountered Commando, Jones, and a couple of other Knights who were coming from around the corner talking to the girls. The Vice Kings yelled across the street to Commando and his boys, and Commando yelled back. They traded insults and challenges, Commando being the leader of the Knights and a guy named Bear being the leader of the Vice Kings. . . . I got out of the car to try to cool Commando down, inasmuch as he was halfway across the street hurling insults across the street and daring them to do something about it, and they were doing the same thing to him. I grabbed Commando and began to pull him back across the street.
>
> By this time the Vice Kings had worked themselves into a rage, and three of them came across the street yelling that they were mighty Vice Kings and to attack Commando and the Knights. In trying to break this up, I was not too successful, I didn't know the Vice Kings involved, and they were really determined to swing on the Knights, so we had a little scuffle around there. . . . At this point, along the street comes Henry Brown, with a revolver, shooting at the Vice Kings. Everybody ducked and the Vice Kings ran, and Henry Brown ran around the corner. When he ran around the corner I began to throw Knights into my car because I knew that the area was "hot," and I was trying to get them out of there. Henry Brown came back around the corner and leaped into my car also. I asked him if he had the gun, and he told me that he did not, and since I was in a hurry, I pulled off in the car and took him and the rest of the boys with me.
>
> . . . In the car Commando and the other boys were extremely elated. There were expressions like: "Baby, did you see the way I swung on that kid"; "I really let that one kid have it"; "Did you see them take off when I leveled my gun on them"; "You were great, Baby. And did you see the way I . . . ," etc. It was just like we used to feel when we got back from a patrol where everything went just right [the worker had been a paratrooper in the Korean conflict]. The tension was relieved, we had performed well and could be proud (Short and Strodtbeck, 1965).

Our comment on this is in Chapter 9 of the *Group Process* book (Short and Strodtbeck, 1965):

> Here the status function of the conflict subculture is seen in bold relief. No doubt the Vice Kings, too, felt the thrill of the conflict. They had faced great danger and had a perfect alibi for not winning an unequivocal victory, viz., the fact that the opposition had a gun—and so, of course, did the Knights, for the worker intervened to prevent them from following up their advantage. Thus, participants on both sides of such a conflict can share the elation and the status-conferring glow of an encounter such as this. It is, in effect, *not* a "zero-sum game" in the sense that points won by a party to the conflict are not necessarily lost by his adversary. No one need necessarily be defeated; behavior in conformity with the norms of the subculture takes place and is rewarded, and law and order are restored. In this way society, too, shares in this non-zero-sum game. Lest we be accused of too sanguine a view of gang behavior, we note that boys may be defeated, individually and collectively, and much injury and property damage may and often does result from this "game."

We know from studying numerous incidents that not all members of conflict gangs participated in such skirmishes even though they may have been on the scene. We do not fully understand why this is the case. In part, it is because much of the analysis so far has not concerned intergang differences; and analyses which have studied these differences have focused on hypothesis formation rather than testing, and on illustration rather than demonstration. Our suspicion, however, is that boys who are involved at any one time are those who are most heavily committed to the gang at the moment, usually gang leaders or other boys who aspire to prominence in the gang. Outstanding performance on such occasions is one of the few available avenues to achieving real prominence in gangs such as these, for reasons which we shall note presently.

So much for conflict. What of retreatism? The contrast between our one group of retreatists and all other gangs under observation was striking. I quote from the same book's earlier description of these young men:

> The basis of camaraderie among the drug users was their common interest in kicks. Past and present exploits concerned experiences while high, and "crazy" behavior rather than bravery or toughness. Use of pills and other drugs seemed virtually a way of life with these boys, interspersed with other kicks such as sex, alcohol, and "way out" experiences which distinguished them, individually and collectively. After several observations of this group in their area, a member of the research team reported:
>
>> The guys make continual references to dope. They talk about it much as a group of drinkers might talk about liquor. It comes up freely, easily in the conversation, a couple of remarks are made about it, who's taken it recently, how it affected this or that person, etc., and then it is dropped only to come up again before long. Today the guys made comments about dope and baseball. (You get the feeling that whatever the activity of the moment, the guys will talk about it in relation to dope—how taking dope affects their participation in the activity.) A commonly expressed notion was that so and so played baseball better when he was "high" than at any other time. Whether they believed this was hard to tell. It sounded much like oft heard remarks that "I play poker better when I'm half drunk or high" (i.e., remarks made in the community at large). . . . The guys like

to talk about their "highs," how much they have taken, how high they were, what they did while high, etc. . . . Perhaps one attitude is implicitly expressed, though, in these remarks; the attitude of acceptance.

Five months later this same observer reported on a hanging session in which the group related "tales about some of the crazy and humorous things" in which various of the drug users had been involved.

The relating of these tales was greeted by laughter from all. Often the worker or observer would mention an incident and Butch would fill us in or correct us on details. Some of the incidents mentioned:

(1) The time Willie was so high he walked off a roof and fell a story or two and broke his nose . . . . Butch said it was over a week before he went to the doctor . . . . Harry said he walked around the hospital in a crazy looking green coat whenever the guys went to visit him.

(2) The time Snooks, Baby, and Jerry climbed on a roof to wake Elizabeth. One of the guys reached through the window and grabbed what he thought was Elizabeth's leg and shook it to wake her up. It turned out to be her old man's leg and it woke him up.

(3) The more recent incident in which Sonny leaped over the counter to rob a Chinaman who proceeded to beat him badly. When the police came, Sonny asked that they arrest this man for having beaten him so. He was doped out of his mind and didn't know what was happening.

(4) Walter got into an argument with a woman over whose car it was they were standing by. He insisted they call the police, and waited confidently until the police showed and took him away.

(5) Sonny tried to break into a building and was ripping off a door when the police found him.

(6) Some of the guys slept out in a car and woke the next morning to find the car was being pulled away. They asked the tower to stop just long enough so they could get out.

(7) One of the guys broke into a car and just about tore the door off doing so—this was a car with all the windows broken out—he was too high to notice.

(8) One of the boys tried to start a car but just could not manage it. The car had no motor.

All laughed at these true tales. Butch even noted that he had been with the guy who broke into the car with no windows.

[The observer then remarked] "These tales may be in the process of becoming legendary within the group. They are so characteristic of this group and describe it so well."

Though several of these boys had "grown up" together, they were not bound to each other by feelings of loyalty. Virtually their only common bond appeared to be use of drugs and the type of experiences which are recounted above. They did not really *share* drugs. Every boy was expected to "cop" (purchase drugs) on his own. In a peculiar way this was functional to the group, for although all the boys who were financially and otherwise able to do so would get high, seldom were more than a few heavily under the influence of drugs at any one time. They liked to get high together, but boys who were not high appeared to enjoy the antics of others who were. They were really quite individualistic in their pursuit of kicks. Often the worker would find a boy off by himself, or with a girl friend or perhaps one other member. But these were not stable friendships. The group served the function of a sounding board for their common but individualistic interests—of moral support for a way of life (Short and Strodtbeck, 1965).

Finally, we may describe briefly the most clearly criminal group of boys we were able to locate—a clique of eight boys from a number of loosely related "hanging groups," that coalesced sporadically and in widely varying numbers for activities such as drinking, athletic contests, occasional drug use, driving around in cars, general "roughnecking" and "hell raising," and once in a great while, a fight of major proportions. According to the leader of the criminal clique, these boys had joined together specifically and exclusively for the purpose of promoting theft activities.

> They were engaged in extensive auto stripping, burglary, and shoplifting— no "heavy stuff" such as strong-arming, robbery, or shakedown. The boys hung on the corner with the larger group, and when they did so were in no way distinguishable from this larger group. They were a clique only when they met away from the larger group, usually in each other's homes, to discuss and plan their theft activities. According to the worker assigned to these boys, "Bobby and his guys talk about what they are doing in one room, while Bobby's old man, who used to be some sort of wheel in the syndicate, talks to his friends about the 'old days' in the next room." The boys made it a point not to "clique-up" visibly on the street, and apparently their chief motivation for association with one another was the success of their predatory activities. In this way they were quite successful for a period of approximately two years. There is testimony that Bobby, in particular, enjoyed a considerable degree of police immunity.

In each of these instances, representing extremes of "specialization" in delinquency orientation, I believe the term "delinquent subculture" (or some variant) is appropriate, but not sufficient to explain the behavior of the members of the groups. Similarly, I believe the behavior of less specialized but highly involved groups is more easily understood in terms of subcultural participation. Norms are generated by the group; many shared activities and perspectives among participants are, so far as group members are concerned, unique to the carriers of a particular subculture, though the boundaries of participation often transcend a particular group. Characteristically, the group effectively constrains individual members from expressing conventional "middle class" values by deriding whatever attempts are made, and by espousing alternative (rather than "anti") values such as toughness, sexual prowess, being "sharp" or "cool," etc. Specific examples from our data include the merciless kidding of youngsters who attempt serious discussion of matters such as responsible family relations and future aspirations regarding the family (Short, Strodtbeck, and Cartwright, 1962), or occupational and educational hopes and problems (Short and Strodtbeck, 1965). Yet these boys remain troubled and ambivalent about many of these problems, and their mention does not always meet with derisive or invidious comment relative to other goals and activities. Even when serious comment is entertained, however, it is not likely to be helpful, because the boys' experiences, individually and in common, can rarely provide any basis for solutions or realistic hopes. Delinquent subcultures do not minister directly to these concerns, but deal with alternative means of finding gratification through association and status in many dimensions. In some measure, we believe, this compensates for rebuffs in more conventional institutional contexts and perhaps for relatively poor prospects of future achievement in the conventional world.

I do not believe these, and perhaps other, characteristics of gangs can be portrayed adequately without the subculture concept. Yet these characteristics are not adequate to explain the boys' behavior unless the notion of subcultures can include other processes, chief among them the characteristics of individual gang boys, group mechanisms such as are discussed above, and the nature of lower class "instituitons." The next section examines these "institutions" briefly.

Lower Class Institutions as a Generating Milieu of Gang Delinquency

In thus paraphrasing the title of Walter Miller's rich and provocative treatment (1958) of lower class culture in relation to delinquency, we intend to focus on organizational forms of association within lower class communities and how they are related to delinquency causation. The nature of this relation goes beyond, but is intimately related to, gang delinquency.

William Foote Whyte's brilliant depiction (first published in 1943) of significant features of *organization* in the slum he called Cornerville dispelled many false notions that blighted areas lacked organization. From Doc and the Nortons, through the police and the racket, politics, the church, and "old country" ties, Whyte demonstrated that Cornerville was organized into "a hierarchy of personal relations based upon a system of reciprocal obligations" (Whyte, 1955, p. 272).[2]

We will focus here on organizational forms that are even less formally structured and less "conventional" in orientation than those suggested by Whyte. Even in Cornerville it was clear that social organization was conducive to some types of behavior considered "deviant" by conventional standards—police and political corruption, gambling and exploitation of sexually available girls. The "institutions" to which I shall direct attention appear to lack the commitment to ethnic values and community welfare which characterized Cornerville, as well as the constraining features of such commitments. They appear to be motivated instead by more "elemental," personal, and immediate goals, perhaps in part because the future holds little more promise than the bleak present. The rewards they provide are in many cases short-lived but concrete, unstable but compelling and available. The contrast with Whyte's classic treatment is important, for I will be discussing institutions characteristic of a different ethnic subculture (I will focus on lower class Negro communities) and of persons deeper in poverty than the residents of Cornerville. As in Cornerville, however, these forms of association are recurrent, they have structure, and they function in a variety of ways to their clientele. The variety of their functions provides an added dimension to youth problems, inasmuch as both youth and adults often are involved. Although the literature contains no systematic treatment of lower class institutions, as such, some descriptions of various lower class ethnic communities are rich and suggestive in this regard (Drake and Cayton, 1962). Since our concern is with juvenile delinquency, we will not discuss institutions in which the clientele is primarily adult, such as store-front churches.

The type of institution with which we are primarily concerned is cogently revealed by the response of a detached worker to a question posed by the director of the YMCA program with which the Chicago study of "Street Corner Groups and Patterns of Delinquency" was associated. The director, R. W. Boone, posed

---

[2] Whyte was not the first to call attention to these forms of organization. See, for example, the volumes by McKay (1949) and Shaw and McKay (1942).

this question to the staff: "What are the most significant institutions for your boys?" (Meaning members of gangs with which the program was in contact.) He had explained briefly the concept of institutions as recurrent forms of association which satisfy important needs of participants and which have recognizable structure. The detached worker who first answered the question deliberated briefly, then said slowly:

"I guess I'd have to say the gang, the hangouts, drinking, parties in the area, and the police."

The other workers nodded assent, though a few thought they might want to add the boys' families. Certainly this list is not definitive, but it is instructive. The only reference to a conventional institution is the police, and this was clearly a negative association, an antagonistic link with the conventional world of social control associated with political and economic institutions. No reference was made to the school or the church, and the family received only half-hearted acknowledgment. The "institutions" listed, with the exception of the police, have much in common, for adults as well as adolescents. They call to mind Drake and Cayton's description (1962) of "The World of the Lower Class":

> Lower-class people will publicly drink and play cards in places where people of higher status would lose their "reputations"—in the rear of poolrooms, in the backrooms of taverns, in "buffet-flats," and sometimes on street corners and in alleys. They will "dance on the dime" and "grind" around the juke-box in taverns and joints, or "cut a rug" at the larger public dance halls. They will "clown" on a street corner or in public parks.

It is in such settings that much illicit behavior is encouraged:

> These centers of lower-class congregation and festivity often become points of contact between the purveyors of pleasure "on the illegit" and their clientele —casual prostitutes, bootleggers, reefer peddlers, "pimps," and "freaks." Some of these places are merely "fronts" and "blinds" for the organized underworld.

However, the relation between institutions of this sort and delinquent behavior goes much beyond the contact they afford between illegitimate "purveyors of pleasure" and their potential clientele. In such settings much behavior occurs that is disruptive to both the larger social order and the local community because of its threat to basic values of life and property. Of particular concern are episodes of violence which result in serious injury, death, or property destruction, and which are a constant threat in situations ranging from the shifting liaisons of common-law marriage to the more elaborate but even less formally structured quarter parties, pool halls, and street corners. Drake and Cayton provide an apt example of the former in their portrayal of the trials and tribulations of Baby Chile and Ben, which gave these authors an ideal vehicle for contrasting styles of life among lower and middle (professional) class Negroes in *Black Metropolis* (1962).

The more informally structured situations are the subject of more extended treatment in the *Group Process* book (Short and Strodtbeck, 1965). Here I will examine only the "quarter parties," as revealed by detached workers from the Chicago project. These case materials are particularly instructive about the structure and functions of such gatherings in a lower class Negro community, home of the King Rattlers, a tough Negro group known throughout the city for their prowess as gang fighters, strong-armers, and purse snatchers. "Quarter parties" are regular events in this and in many other such communities. Although they vary in format and participants, they all have common objectives. Typically, an adult will hold a party in his or her (usually her) home for adults and teens, usually some of both. The objective of the hostess is to make money. (In Seattle, I am told, such gatherings are called "rent parties.") Partygoers pay a quarter to get into the party, and a quarter per drink after they are in. The parties are boisterous, loud, and crowded. Fights are not unusual—often they involve members of rival gangs. Two examples, one of "body punching," which is common among these groups, and one of relations with girls, illustrate how these gatherings may precipitate serious gang conflict. In both instances, intervention by a detached worker appears to have averted serious consequences.

> A. This teenage party that was held at the girl's house on 10th and Harwood. Her mother and father were there, although they stayed out of the way. There was friction. The Rattlers were there, and there were some boys from the projects just west of the area [members of a rival gang known as Navahoes]. They weren't in the Rattlers. David and Donald, Duke's brother, took me down. It was a pay-at-the-door party. Pay a quarter at the door. Right away when I got in I knew there was friction because there was this one group of boys in one room and another group in another. I saw several bumpings as they came through the door and looks, "Stay out of my way." They were trying to see how much each group would take. They had three rooms occupied. Living room, dining room, and kitchen. I was in the dining room around 10:00, I guess. I heard this noise in the living room. Right away everyone started running for the living room. There's a fight out there. I started out and tried to get through the crowd to get into the living room, and just as I was fighting my way through the crowd I saw one of my boys, Bill, he's 16—very big though for his age. . . . He and this other fellow from the projects—it started out as these things usually do—they had started out boxing at a party. Bill had hit the other fellow a little too hard and he had hit back, and it led to that. This other fellow was much smaller than Bill but he was older, and he hit Bill and knocked him into this huge window, and *plang*, the window went out. By this time I saw my way through the crowd and I stopped them. . . . David helped me break it up. They respected him. . . . He grabbed the other fellow. Nobody bothers him. I just got between them and told Bill to stop. Bill said, okay. . . . He was coming back for the boy, though, after he broke the window, and he's a big boy. The other fellow stopped right away.
>
> Q. Party go on?
>
> A. No, the lady said this was it. But I thought there might be a little trouble 'cause some of the other boys from the projects were waiting outside, so I told Bill to stick close to me and we would leave together. Bill, myself, David, and Donald. This we did. The other boys were standing outside. They made a few remarks but they didn't do anything.

Two weeks later this same worker provided a more elaborate picture of a similar party in which adults played a major role. Here the objectives of various classes of partygoers is commented on:

> This woman who is called "Ma" was giving the party. . . . There was a lot of drinking—inside, outside, in the cars, in the alleys, everywhere. There were Rattlers and a bunch of boys from the [housing] projects. They had two rooms, neither of them very large. There was some friction going on when I got there —boys bumping each other, and stuff like this.

There were a lot of girls there. Must have been about 50 to 75 people in these two rooms, plus another 20 or 25 outside. There were some older fellows there, too—mainly to try and grab one of these younger girls. The girls were doing a lot of drinking—young girls, 12- and 13-year-olds. This one girl, shortly after I got there, had passed out. I took her home. Nobody there, but two of the other girls stayed with her.

The age group in this party amazed me—must have been from about 11 to the 30's. There were girls there as young as 11, but no boys younger than about 15. The girls are there as a sex attraction, and with the older boys and men around, you know the younger boys aren't going to do any good.

We had one real fight. One of David's sisters was talking to one of these boys from the projects—a good sized boy, bigger than me. I guess she promised to go out to the car with him. . . . To get outside you had to go out this door and down this hall, and then out on the porch and down the stairs. She went as far as the porch. As she got there, I guess she changed her mind. By this time the guy wasn't standing for any "changing the mind" business, and he started to pull on her—to try and get her in the car. She yelled for David, and he came running out. All he could see was his sister and a guy he didn't know was pulling on her. David plowed right into the guy. I guess he hit him about 15 times and knocked him down and across the street, and by the time I got there the guy was lying in the gutter. David was just about to level a foot at him. I yelled at David to stop and he did. I took him off to the side and told Gary to get the guy out of there.

The worker walked down the street with David, trying to cool him down. What happened next very nearly precipitated a major gang conflict:

Duke, Red, and Mac were standing eight or ten feet away, sort of watching these project boys. This one boy goes up the street on the other side and comes up *behind* David and me. We didn't see him. All of a sudden Duke runs right past me. I was wondering what's going on and he plows into this guy—crashed the side of his mouth and the guy fell flat. Duke was about to really work the guy over. . . .

Duke said, "Well look, man, the guy was sneaking up behind you and I wasn't gonna have him hit you from behind! I did it to protect you."

I got the guy up and he said, "I wasn't going to hit you—I just wanted to see what was going on," and this bit.

By now, Duke says, "Well, the heck with it. Let's run all these project guys out."

They banded together and were ready to move, but I talked them out of it. I said, "Look, don't you think you've done enough? The police aren't here yet, but if you start anything else they'll be here. Somebody is bound to call them. The party is still going on so why don't we all just go back inside. No sense in breaking up a good thing—you paid your quarter."

I finally got them all back inside, but Duke says, "We've been laying off fighting for the last year or so. Looks like we'll have to start again" (Dillard, 1961).

Other examples could be given explicitly involving many forms of behavior considered delinquent by the larger society, such as fighting, extensive property damage, excessive drinking, illicit sex (violent and non-violent), drug use, disturbing the peace, and at times various forms of theft. Other settings, such as pool halls and the street itself, could be similarly described, but perhaps the point is sufficiently made.

I must also comment briefly concerning community level differences between our Negro and white lower class youngsters. Conventional ecological data indicate clearly that the white areas were less disadvantaged economically than the Negro areas. Occupational prestige data indicate that the mean decile rank of the fathers' occupations was, for Negro gang boys, 3.6, or the level of a laborer in metals industry, cook, or waiter; for white gang boys this figure was 5.0, or, say, an auto mechanic or bartender. In the white areas our observers and workers reported the distinct impression that life tended to revolve around more conventional institutions such as the Catholic Church, local political and "improvement" associations, ethnic and extended kinship organizations, unions, and such formally organized recreational patterns as bowling leagues, and social and athletic clubs. The research of Kobrin and his associates in largely white communities in Chicago is particularly instructive in this regard (Kobrin, 1961; Kobrin, Puntil, and Peluso, 1963).

Finally, with regard to community-level problems, our data suggest that relations with adults differ for gang and for non-gang boys. Although gang boys gave various local adult incumbents more credit for having an interest in teenagers and being "right guys" than would be expected from "reaction formation" or "adolescent protest" theories, non-gang boys tend to rate these adults still higher (Short, Rivera, and Marshall, 1964). Non-gang boys also report more contact with these adults, and among Negroes, the non-gang youngsters report that the adults have more "clout." When the boys were asked to nominate adults with whom they have the most contact (they were probed for four names), gang boys gave fewer names than the other boys (Negro = 3.2; white = 2.5), and their nominees had significantly lower occupations than the nominees of the non-gang boys. In sample interviews with these "high contact" adults, far more of those named by non-gang boys reported that they had been consulted about school problems than did the gang nominees. In other respects, non-gang nominees appeared more "middle class" in their aspirations for their nominators, their attitudes toward juvenile misbehavior, and their conceptions of "a good life" for these youngsters (Short, Marshall, and Rivera, 1964). Contrary to expectations based on the Cloward and Ohlin position on the difference between adult-adolescent relations in "integrated" and "unintegrated" communities and its impact on adolescent behavior, nominees from a conflict gang area agreed as much about such behavior as did those from an area characterized by a high degree of "integration" of the carriers of criminal and non-criminal values (Marshall, 1964). Negro lower class boys, both gang and non-gang, had more multiple nominees than did their white counterparts. The conception that conflict gang boys' relations with adults are especially "weak" appears to call for some revision on the basis of findings such as these.

Social Disability and Gang Delinquency

We have seen, and inferred further, the nature of group influences on expression of individually held values consistent with "responsible" goals, and of efforts toward their realization. In this final section I should like to give some of the evidence concerning individual characteristics of the boys which appear to be related to the nature of their behavior in the group context. In so doing

I will draw heavily from earlier work with Gordon and with Strodtbeck (Gordon and Short, 1962; Short and Strodtbeck, 1965).

A "lack of social assurance" among the gang boys, more serious in its implications for their social adjustment than that seen by Whyte in his corner boys, was apparent almost from the beginning of our contact; and as with so many types of observations, it was especially aggravated among Negro gang boys. Workers reported frequently that their boys did not feel comfortable outside "the area" and that they were ill at ease in most social situations outside the gang context. However, some surprising semantic differential data from these boys directed our attention to their apparent lack of gratification even in gang membership and interaction. We moved then to a hypothesis about a fundamental lack of social skills which seems even more crucial in understanding gang boys' behavior than does lack of social assurance.

Gang boys were found to rate "someone who sticks with his buddies in a fight" less highly than "someone who stays cool and keeps to himself," while both lower class and middle class non-gang boys (Negro and white) reversed these ratings. Gang boys evaluated *themselves* higher than they did *fellow gang members,* while the other boys' evaluations were more nearly equal, and white middle class boys even rated their friends as "better" than themselves. Further evidence of ambivalence with respect to peer associations was found in a motivational opinionaire administered to the boys. Gang boys were more likely to endorse such statements as "Friends are generally more trouble than they are worth," and "Time spent with the guys is time wasted." And they agreed less often with the statement, "A guy should spend as much time with friends as he possibly can." Yet they also agreed *more often* than the other boys that "You can only be really alive when you are with friends," and *less often* that "People can have too many friends for their own good." We believe that there is an implication here of dissatisfaction with present associates and perhaps an expression of things as they might be more ideally.

The range of Negro gang boys' physical movements is especially restricted, only to a minor degree by fear of infringing on a rival gang's territory. More importantly, both Negro and white gang boys are reluctant to expose themselves to situations demanding skills which they lack and so their development of role-playing abilities and sensitivities, and their sensitivity to normative requirements of varying situations, is further retarded (Goffman, 1963).

There is evidence that even in activities which are inherently gratifying, and for which the gang provides the chance to achieve such gratifications, such as sexual intercourse, gang boys (and girls) come off with less than satisfying experiences, particularly in terms of interpersonal relations. It is true that our gang youngsters were a good deal more sexually active than their non-gang counterparts, either lower or middle class, but most of these boys and girls are neither knowledgeable nor skilled in sexual matters or in interpersonal relations (Salisbury, 1958; Rice, 1963, pp. 153 ff). Relations with persons of the opposite sex tend to be characterized by the same sorts of aggressive expression as are many other interpersonal relations. For males the norm is sexual exploitation of females, and for females the economic exploitation of males, which combine to produce a situation with a high potential for tension and frustration, and very little likelihood of mutual and lasting gratification.

The gangs we have studied lack stability in membership and in attendance; hence the rate of social interaction is lower than was the case with the Nortons (Whyte, 1955). Mutual obligations tend to be tenuous among most gang members and in many instances, as with the requirements of group norms, to be specific to the situation. Hence, according to the argument, group cohesion is low. It seems likely, however, that gang boys are dependent upon one another for a large measure of interpersonal gratification, so that the gang has a high relative value for the boys. According to this interpretation, the gang gives its members a reasonably realistic solution to their problems—problems which derive in part from the fact that these boys are adolescents, and in part from the peculiar situations in which they find themselves. Given the gratifications of gang membership and the lack of apparent available alternatives, it seems likely that the gang will be highly valued, especially by those boys who have experienced the most gratification and/or those whose interpersonal skills and perhaps other abilities are most impaired. When a boy is caught up in the group process, however, he may become involved in delinquency, regardless of his personal skills or even of the amount of gratification which he derives from gang membership.

Jansyn's research in Chicago is relevant at this point (Jansyn, 1960; see also Sherif and Sherif, 1964). He recorded daily the "attendance" and time spent with the group of members of a white gang with whom he was in contact for more than a year. A "solidarity index" constructed on the basis of these data was related to measures of individual and group behavior during this period. Delinquent acts, by individuals or by group members, and non-delinquent group activities, were found to occur most frequently following low points of the index of group solidarity. The index characteristically rose following these acts. Jansyn's interpretation was that the boys were responding to low solidarity by creating situations which would bring the gang together, thus raising group solidarity. This was done, he believes, because solidarity of the gang was a primary value for these youngsters.

Our interpretation is similar. Symbols such as group names and individual nicknames, styles of dress and other behavioral affectation provide a basis for group identity. But why delinquency? Aside from certain inherent gratifications, delinquent activities provide opportunities for the expression of dependency needs, and they create instrumental problems demanding cooperative enterprise (Homans, 1950; Allport, 1962). This, for youngsters lacking in basic social skills, can be very important. Expressing dependency needs is likely to be hard for lower class youngsters because of the persistent concern with toughness (Miller, 1958). The problem is aggravated for gang boys whose experiences in conventional institutional contexts are less than satisfactory in this respect, and whose gang norms interpret dependency, except under special circumstances, as weakness. (Among the excepted circumstances are protecting and caring for one another when under attack or taking care of a buddy who may be in danger from too much alcohol or drugs.) In effect, such delinquent activities represent contrived opportunities to realize important gang functions.

Our hypothesis, therefore, is that social disabilities contribute both to group norms and to group processes which involve these norms. The hypothesis is important, for by extension it provides a possible linkage between early family socialization, later experience, and gang behavior. Space does not permit this extension except to suggest that important elements involved are identity problems in early childhood, the inculcation of role-playing abilities, along with flexibility in this regard, and the cultivation of sensitivity to situational requirements for behavior. The aggressive posture and rigidity of response found among many gang youngsters cannot be explained by cultural themes alone. Observations from Strodtbeck's experimental nursery school for lower class Negro children in Chicago are appropriate. Strodtbeck and his associates find that at the age of four and one-half these children are less able to maintain non-aggressive close physical contact with their age mates than are children from middle class homes. The early development of these children appears to be produced by a combination of harsh socialization practices, frequent cautions about a threatening environment, and little cognitive development or verbal skill. The latter seems attributable in some measure to an almost complete absence of stimulation from reading materials or from any type of constructive play opportunities (Strodtbeck, 1963). Data from our own personality testing program indicate that gang boys are more reactive to false signals than the non-gang control group; they are less self-assertive (in this conventional testlike situation), they are slightly more anxious, neurotic, and narcissistic, and less gregarious. As we have noted elsewhere, "the possible cumulative effect of these differences is more impressive than are the individual findings, for they add up to boys who have less self-assurance and fewer of the qualities which engender confidence and nurturant relations with others" (Short and Strodtbeck, 1965).

The social disability hypothesis is important also because it differs from "all for one, one for all" explanations of gang behavior, which rest on group solidarity and rigid conformity to group norms as the chief determinants of the behavior of gang members. The carefree image of "that old gang of mine" is hardly recognizable. Its functions and imperatives are seen quite differently.

The Sherifs (1964) offer the hypothesis that "the adolescent living in a setting where opportunities for peer contacts are available, either formally or informally, turns more and more to others caught up in similar dilemmas—to his age mates who can really understand him." But the "social disability" and "status threats" hypotheses suggest that one of the major problems of our gang youngsters is that "understanding" of their problems by fellow gang members occurs at a very superficial level—extending little beyond freedom to participate in "adult" activities, such as sexual intercourse and drinking, and support for the achievement of freedom from adult control. The gang gives scant attention to adult goals, and in some instances deters the expression of interest in and achievement of these stable goals involved, for example, in employment, family life, and civic participation; the gang may also hinder the expression of dependency needs. Gang experience is hardly conducive to stable adjustment in terms of the "virtues" of modern industrial society—punctuality, discipline, and consistency on the job, the acceptance of authority relations, dependability concerning organizational commitments and interpersonal relations. It seems unlikely that gang experience, with its constant challenge to prove oneself tough, adept with the girls, "smart," "cool," "sharp," etc., alleviates status insecurities or related social disabilities except for the few who are most successful in the gang, and even then chiefly in terms of ability to respond to gang challenges. The extent to which these skills enhance one's prospects for status or achievement outside the gang is questionable at best.

I would suggest that the gang's failure to deal satisfactorily with these very real concerns and problems of its members contributes to the instability of most gangs. It contributes also to the fact that the direct influence of gang norms on gang boys' behavior appears to be limited to situations directly involving other gang boys. That is, to paraphrase the Sherifs' recent work, "the attitudes (stands) the individual upholds and cherishes, the rules that he considers binding for regulating his behavior," are those defined by the gang only in special circumstances when other gang boys are directly involved. When in instances *not* involving other gang boys they still behave as gang boys, I suggest it is not due to gang norms, but to other features of the situation and of their abilities to cope with it. Much latitude is given individual boys even when they are with other gang boys, sometimes under circumstances most provocative of aggression and other forms of delinquent behavior. It seems a good hypothesis that the degree of such latitude for a given boy depends upon his own investment in the gang, his role in the gang and in the situation, and the importance of the situation to the gang. We can cite instances in which each of these elements seem clearly related to behavior of boys in a given situation.

Conclusion

The authors of the various chapters in this book are engaged in common cause. We have sought to describe and understand reality, and more than this, to explain it by general theoretical statements. In terms of the latter criterion, the work reported in this chapter is largely exploratory, tending to generate hypotheses rather than test them. Our *data* are drawn chiefly from Negro gangs, and the implications of the social disability hypothesis, in particular, appear to be more characteristic of the Negro gangs we have studied than of the white. Preliminary observations from a study of Negro gangs in Los Angeles suggest that social disabilities of these boys are a good deal less serious than those of our boys. The area in which these Los Angeles boys live looks very much like the community settings of our Negro *middle* class, not our lower class. The institutional setting in the Los Angeles communities is more conventional and less like the lower class varieties we have described.

If the hypothesis is to be theoretically significant, however, it must be the case that *to the extent* that a group is characterized by social disabilities such as those to which we have drawn attention, it will be characterized by attempts by its members, individually and collectively, to create symbols and situations which will allow for—perhaps even demand—the expression of dependency needs and the achievement of interpersonal gratifications. Friendships and loyalties which derive from this process are no less real, and may prove to be quite as binding and lasting as any. But if they must continue to exist in an unstable gang context, which serves as an arena for playing out the consequences of status threats, they are likely to be undermined and, therefore, shorter-lived and less binding. Certainly it cannot be denied that friendships exist among our gangs and that their gratifications are an important source of stability and continuity. Indeed, the ability of some—but not all—of our gangs to survive without support from conventional institutions, and often with considerable pressure against their continued existence, is remarkable. Derivation of the social disability and status threats hypotheses from our material should not obscure these facts. It has been our intention to draw attention to processes which might account for the specifically delinquent behavior among our gangs. We have attempted, on the one hand, to account for the delinquent content of group norms; and on the other, to discover the circumstances under which delinquent norms are invoked. Perhaps empirical differences of this nature between the groups studied by the Sherifs and those to which we have had access in Chicago may account for differences in interpretation of the two studies. If so, it should be possible to resolve our differences by further empirical inquiry and theoretical synthesis.

In his summary (1959) of problems and prospects concerning "Personality and Social Structure," Inkeles argues strongly that the translation of social structural variables into behavior must include an explicit theory of human personality. Thus, to the sociological S—R (State of Society—Rate of behavior) proposition should be added P (Personality). "The simplest formula (S) (P) = R, although probably far from adequate, would be greatly superior to the S—R formula, since it provides for the simultaneous effect of two elements influencing action" (Inkeles, 1959, p. 255). The social disability hypothesis is hardly a theory of personality, but it is a step in this direction. It represents the introduction of a personality level variable which may provide an important link between social structure, early and later socialization, and behavior. If our observations concerning institutional relations, subcultural participation, and group process are correct, the equation may be further refined and a significant variable added. Experiences in conventional institutions and in lower class, ethnic, and peer group "institutional" or subcultural patterns of association may be viewed as refinements of S (social structure), or more specifically, the state of society so far as a particular individual is concerned. Group process, on the other hand, represents yet another *level* of variable in the equation, in addition to S, P, and R. It should be clear that no simple linear relation exists between these variables. P, social disability in our terms, interacts with institutional and subcultural experience and with group process; and each of these acts in turn with the others. It seems likely that social disability is a factor both in selection for gang membership and in participation within the gang, and therefore in group process involvement. The precise nature of these relationships, and of other parameters and other variables, is not well established, either theoretically or empirically. In their specification may lie the resolution of fundamental differences in perspective among and within disciplines.

53 / The Mental Health of the Industrial Worker

Arthur Kornhauser

The aim of this study was to obtain evidence regarding the mental condition of workers in modern mass-production industry. Specifically, the study focused on Detroit automobile workers in the mid-1950's. Small samples from other occupations were studied for purposes of comparison. It was hoped that the research not only would contribute a somewhat clearer assessment than previously available of the quality of factory workers' life adjustments at different occupational levels, but also that it would provide useful indications of factors responsible for better or poorer mental health in the occupational groups. We come now to a summing up of what has been accomplished toward achieving these objectives and to a consideration of implications the findings may have in regard to industrial organization and social policy.

Summary of Results

We shall begin with a brief recapitulation of our principal results and then proceed to questions and interpretations that extend beyond the empirical findings.

1. Large numbers of the automobile workers manifest feelings, attitudes, and behavior that signify none too satisfactory life adjustments or mental health. This is illustrated by such specific facts as these: from one-fourth to one-half of the men studied say that they are "often worried and upset," are "bothered by nervousness," that "most people cannot be trusted," that they sometimes "get so blue and discouraged that [they] wonder whether anything is worthwhile," that they "often feel restless, wanting to be on the move doing something but not knowing what," that they feel either dissatisfied with life or "neither satisfied nor dissatisfied," that they are not accomplishing the things they would like to in life, and they do not feel that they can do much to make their future what they want it to be. These and many other responses reveal extensive enough feelings of inadequacy, low self-esteem, anxiety, hostility, dissatisfaction with life, and low personal morale to raise serious questions concerning the general condition of psychological and social health of industrial workers.

2. *The outstanding finding is that mental health varies consistently with the level of jobs the men hold.* When we compare the factory workers by occupational categories, the higher the occupation (in respect to skill and associated attributes of variety, responsibility, and pay), the better the average mental

health. Those in skilled jobs have highest mental-health scores, followed by the upper semiskilled, the ordinary semiskilled, and lowest of all, the men in routine, repetitive types of work. Data from comparable groups of small-town factory workers, Detroit blue-collar workers in nonfactory employment, and white-collar workers support the conclusion that mental health is least satisfactory among men in low-level production jobs.

The preceding comparisons are based on a quantitative index of mental health which utilizes responses to some 50 interview questions. Justification for the use of the index is demonstrated by its close correspondence with global estimates of mental health given by several highly qualified psychiatrists and clinical psychologists who systematically read and rated a subsample of the interview protocols. The agreement of the index with the independent judgments gives assurance that our results have to do with better and poorer mental health in fundamentally the same sense that the concept is used by professional clinicians. It is to be remembered that here and throughout the study we refer solely to degrees of *positive* mental health, not at all to mental *illness*.

3. A crucial question arises whether the occupational differences in mental health are effects of the job and its associated conditions or are due to *differential selection* of the kinds of persons who enter and remain in the several types of work. Analysis of our data strongly indicates that the observed differences of mental health are not accounted for by the amount of education or other prejob characteristics of the men in different job categories. The dependence of mental health on occupational level is genuine; the relationship cannot be explained away as due to extraneous factors. This does not mean, of course, that personal characteristics are not also important; mental health has many independent roots, but here our interest centers on the influence of occupation. And regarding this, the evidence underscores the existence of significant occupational effects apart from other determinants.

In more general terms, the results emphasize the importance of *situational factors*. Persons differently situated in the economic system tend to enjoy better mental health or to suffer poorer mental health according to their position. This finding becomes the more striking since it occurs within the limited range represented by the comparatively secure, well-paid auto workers of this study. We are not making comparisons of successful working men with submerged underprivileged, poverty-stricken groups but with other successful members of the labor force. The evidence of substantial differences of mental health by job strata within this population leads us to reject both the idea that problems of emotional adjustment are to be charged to the "human condition," equally affecting all persons in a distressingly imperfect world, and also the too commonly held view that observed variations of mental health are attributable solely to individual differences of personality makeup. In addition to differences by skill level within Detroit factories, our evidence also indicates that white-collar workers, small-town workers, and young nonfactory workers have better mental health than the Detroit factory group.

4. The relationship of mental health to job satisfaction is central to our interpretation of both the foregoing results and the subsequent more specific findings. We conceive of job feelings as constituting a link between the gratifications and deprivations of the total job situation and the mental-health effects of these

conditions. Poorer mental health occurs in lower-level jobs as a consequence of the more severe deprivations and frustrations in such jobs compared to higher-level occupations. Workers' expressions of job satisfaction or dissatisfaction are the overt manifestations of these occupational experiences. Actually, of course, the relationship is more complex; job feelings and the components of mental health are parts of a constellation of interdependent variables in which each is both cause and effect of others. For our analysis, however, attention is focused on one aspect of the interrelationships; job feelings are construed as an intervening link between the job and its impact on mental health.

The empirical evidence is congruent with this view of the relationship: (a) Large differences in the prevalence of job satisfaction do occur between higher and lower occupational groups. Dissatisfaction is notably great among workers in routine, repetitive production jobs. (b) Jobs in which workers tend to be most satisfied are likewise the ones conducive to better mental health; those in which larger proportions are dissatisfied are ones with poorer mental health. (c) In each occupational category, the better-satisfied individuals enjoy better mental health on the average than do those less satisfied. (d) When we partially eliminate the influence of job satisfaction by taking separately the men having above-average satisfaction and those below average, the mental-health differences between occupations diminish. *Satisfied* workers in low-level jobs differ little in mental health from the upper groups; the *dissatisfied* in higher occupations tend to be similar to men at lower levels. All these relationships accord with the hypothesis that gratifications and deprivations experienced at different occupational levels and manifested in expressions of job satisfaction and dissatisfaction constitute an important determinant of workers' mental health. Job satisfaction is the link between objective conditions prevailing at different occupational levels and the observed occupational variations in mental health.

5. Job satisfactions and dissatisfactions arise from the varied liked and disliked attributes of the work situation. Examination of the way these feelings and attitudes toward various job characteristics relate to mental health enables us to discover which attributes appear to be especially responsible for better mental health in more skilled and varied occupations and for poorer mental health in less-skilled routine jobs.

The analysis suggests that many interrelated characteristics of jobs contribute jointly to the comparatively high or low average mental health of occupational groups. The following specific conclusions emerge: (a) By far the most influential attribute is the opportunity the work offers—or fails to offer—for use of the worker's abilities and for associated feelings of interest, sense of accomplishment, personal growth, and self-respect. (b) Next most clearly important are feelings in regard to income and financial stress at upper and lower skill levels. (c) Feelings toward several other aspects of jobs show more limited and irregular relationship to mental health, including the pace, intensity, and repetitiveness of work operations; supervision and other human relations on the job; and opportunities for advancement and improved social status. (d) Attitudes toward wage rates (as distinguished from problems of income mentioned under b), job security, and physical conditions of work appear to have little or no explanatory value in accounting for poorer mental health at lower versus upper job levels. The relatively small part played by a number of these job attributes presents some surprising departures from traditional beliefs; their meaning is discussed later, in the section of the chapter devoted to interpretations.

6. Comparisons of industrial establishments also reveal large differences in employees' mental health, job satisfaction, and job-related attitudes. The substantial variations from company to company, even within a single industry and locality, underscore the importance of organizational and management influences which, by the nature of the case, play a small part in the preceding comparisons of *occupational groups* within identical organizational settings. The variations between companies are associated with a number of company attributes that provide suggestive clues as to some of the explanatory factors accounting for the differences. In part we see the same underlying factors at work in the company differences as in the occupational comparisons, but other explanatory variables also appear. Company ranking on mental health is clearly related to size of plant, for example. Mental health is poorer in large establishments and, in Detroit companies, men on repetitive jobs have particularly poor mental health only in the very large establishments, not in the medium-sized ones. Companies also rank lower in mental health if they have a large proportion of employees at low levels of education and skill, if the quality of personnel policies and services is below average, and if workers' attitudes are unfavorable toward use of their abilities and opportunities for promotion. When companies are compared in respect to job satisfaction, other company characteristics also become significant—for example, employees' feelings about speed and intensity of work, working conditions, wages, and supervision.

7. Although the present research is concerned primarily with the way in which *occupation* affects mental health, it is recognized that the characteristics of *individuals* are also important determinants. Under the conditions of this study, the two broad sets of factors, those associated with occupational level and those pertaining to personal and social characteristics of workers, account in roughly equal degree for observed differences of mental health *among individuals*. As previously stated, however, mental-health differences between *occupational groups* are attributable in only very slight degree to the personal variables.

Results here are based on personal factors of four kinds: samples of objective descriptive facts like age, education, and childhood economic level; prejob personality attributes; childhood goals and values; and current life goals. Mental health of individuals is most clearly associated with differences of education, childhood socioeconomic advantages, and childhood personality traits. Further analysis of these and the other personal variables brings to light complex interrelationships which, though not unequivocal, nevertheless provide useful insights regarding the varying subjective effects of occupational position.

In the main, the personal attributes and the current situational variables represented by occupation exert their influence relatively independently of one another. The effects tend to be additive so that a combination of good childhood conditions and skilled occupation yields the best mental health whereas poor background and low job placement result in fewest satisfactory mental-health scores. In other words, favorable or unfavorable prejob influences generally continue to be evidenced in later life adjustments. However, there are also more complex causal interactions that produce incongruency effects which result in especially *poor* mental health for persons of good background and correspondingly high expectations who are presently in low-level jobs. One form of this disparity is that between high aspirations and low achievement. Our results offer some support for explanations in terms of such disparities, though the observed effects are not of impressive size or consistency.

8. In Chapters 8 to 11 we no longer confined our analysis to the measure of mental health but considered a wider sampling of behavior and attitudes having to do with working men's outlook on life and their orientation to their world. The primary aim of these chapters is to bring together evidence on the basis of which readers, each according to his own standards, can better arrive at evaluative judgments of how satisfactory the attitudes and adjustments of industrial workers are, as represented by our sample from the Detroit automobile plants. Closely associated with this aim is the effort to specify problem areas and points of unsatisfactory adjustment which particularly call for remedial action and improvement. These implications for social action are discussed in the final part of the present chapter.

Analyses of workers' orientations, treated under the four broad headings of these last chapters, are very briefly summarized in the following paragraphs.

(a) In regard to work and the job, the predominant orientation is moderatively positive. Most workers are satisfied but not too well satisfied; most are neither acutely discontented with their work nor do they find it stimulating and enjoyable. There is little bitterness and likewise little enthusiasm. Relatively few would choose to go into the same work again and most do not speak well of factory employment, particularly production jobs. Especially in simple routine jobs they are keenly aware of the lacks, irritations, and debilitating grind. In more skilled and varied jobs, intrinsic rewards of the work itself supply a strong additional element of attraction along with opportunities for growth and self-actualization. Despite the absence of such satisfactions in low-level positions, most workers find substitute and compensating extrinsic rewards that enable them to accept their work life without distress and even in most cases with a kind of mild, passive, somewhat fatalistic contentment.

(b) In regard to their lives away from the job, factory workers express predominant satisfaction and positive outlook differing only a little either from one job level to another or in comparison with nonfactory groups. Although the men's volunteered comments contain many complaints concerning both their economic circumstances and a variety of personal and social problems, other important areas of life are seen in a sufficiently favorable light to more than balance the disagreeable features. For most workers the result is a definitely positive orientation. Even routine production workers have overall feelings of life satisfaction only slightly lower than other groups and not at all commensurate with their relatively great *job* discontent. In general, however, feelings toward different sectors of life tend to be in agreement; the tendency is not, as often alleged, for individuals dissatisfied with their jobs to find extra, compensatory enjoyment in their leisure, nor for those least contented away from the job to be especially satisfied at work.

Factory workers as a whole have moderately satisfactory family and social relationships, not greatly different from comparable occupational groups. The routine semiskilled men, however, compare unfavorably with other groups and with generally accepted ideas of desirable social adjustment. Spare-time activities of most workers tend to be narrow and routine, with little indication of self-development and self-expression or devotion to larger social purposes. Many appear to be groping for meaningful ways to fill their spare time but with little conception of the possibilities and with inadequate preparation or stimulation.

(c) Our inquiry into the sociopolitical orientation of working people takes two directions, one concerned with their working-class and prolabor views, the other with their attitudes toward basic tenets of democracy and their own relationships to the larger society. The former, as would be expected, shows factory workers heavily favorable to labor unionism, to government aid for the needy, public regulation of business, and other collective actions they perceive as protecting and benefiting the common man. On these matters, they do not appear to be going "middle class." In regard to broad questions of democratic values and personal identification with the society, we find enough evidence of authoritarian attitudes and alienation from social norms and democratic principles (including substantial opposition to racial equality and free speech) to present seriously disturbing problems. Though such problems are by no means confined to industrial workers, the factory men do show up worse than our comparison groups—and this is particularly true of those on low-level production jobs.

It thus appears that the same occupational and social disadvantages that tend to produce low personal morale and other features of poor mental health also lead to certain antidemocratic feelings as well as to greater motivation toward prolabor economic and political changes. The conjunction poses the challenging question whether the sociopolitical reform orientation is *necessarily* associated with the unhealthy mental conditions or, alternatively, whether the connection is fortuitous, occurring only under certain existing cultural conditions. Under other conditions, one suspects, the predominant tendency might be for workers' dissatisfaction to express itself in vigorous social protest and reform without at the same time turning into personal frustration and negative self-feelings.

(d) Finally, a further look at the men's attitudes toward themselves and their life goal discloses a picture that bears little resemblance to the idealized image of sturdy, self-confident, enterprising American working men. Fewer than one-fourth of the factory workers could be classified as exhibiting strong, healthy, purposeful orientations. Men engaged in routine production show notably weak ambition and initiative in regard to work compared to other occupational groups; among young workers this deadening of purposive striving is likewise evident in regard to the nonwork sector of life.

When the working men were questioned about what they really want most in life, their answers overwhelmingly specify financial and material goals and wishes for security, family welfare, health, and happiness. There are strikingly few expressions of interest in personal achievement, self-development, and self-expressive activities; even fewer references to altruistic aims or desires to participate in collective efforts to help others or to work for the improvement of society. In the main, the same emphasis on earthy, self-centered goals characterizes all the occupational groups, suggesting that the effects arise from common cultural influences rather than from circumstances peculiar to parts of the industrial population. There are enough exceptions, however, among factory workers as well as others, to brightly illustrate the humanly rewarding possibilities of more imaginative and idealistic life purposes.

Working people's feelings toward themselves also reveal many negative features. On a general index of self-esteem, for example, factory workers have more low scores than do comparable groups—and again the less-skilled factory groups are worst off. The attitudes include feelings of ineffectualness, inadequacy, lack of accomplishment, self-blame, and discouragement. Related evidence comes from interview items and indexes that show greater anxiety and hostility in the factory groups. Larger numbers are also rated as exhibiting over-all reactions to life that reflect either frustration and emotional defensive tendencies or resigned, weak, and passive acceptance devoid of confidence and enthusiasm.

Meaning of the Results

Our findings dictate conclusions that are neither extremely bright nor extremely somber in respect to the mental health of industrial workers. The great majority of the men studied are living simple, normal family lives, rather circumscribed and routine but moderately happy and active, without serious emotional problems or personal maladjustments. Not a few, however, manifest low self-esteem, social alienation, anxiety, and related symptoms that add up to decidedly less than satisfactory mental health. A meliorative interest naturally focuses attention primarily on this darker part of the picture in order to inquire why the psychological condition of many workers falls short of what appears possible and desirable. How are we to understand the inadequacies, their nature and their causes? Why do working people, particularly those in low-skilled production jobs, not enjoy better mental health than they do?

The general answer, we believe, is given in the psychological guidelines proposed in Chapter 1. Like any other complex social behavior, the indicators of mental health have *many* determinants, partly in the background and present make-up of the persons involved and partly in the total range of circumstances now affecting them. Our major interpretation is that poorer mental health occurs whenever conditions of work and life lead to continuing frustration by failing to offer means for perceived progress toward attainment of strongly desired goals which have become indispensable elements of the individual's self-identity as a worthwhile person. Persistent failure and frustration bring lowered self-esteem and dissatisfaction with life, often accompanied by anxieties, social alienation and withdrawal, a narrowing of goals, and curtailing of aspirations—in short, tendencies toward the varied feelings, attitudes, and behaviors we have assessed as constituting poor mental health.

What our comparisons of occupational groups signify is that conditions of work and accompanying mode of life at lower skill levels do, in fact, impose more severe deprivations, frustrations, and feelings of hopelessness, with consequences of the kind described. Workers in better positions experience a greater degree of fulfillment of their wants and enjoy correspondingly greater feelings of satisfaction, adequacy, and self-regard.

The foregoing interpretation needs to be extended in several directions. First, consideration must be given to the fact that there are significant variations of wants and expectations as well as underlying constancies. Our basic explanation emphasizes the common goals, the fact that workers at different occupational levels share fundamentally similar wants but are confronted by decidedly dissimilar opportunities for satisfying these wants. The proposition that our egalitarian American culture develops such common desires—for material well-being, success, freedom, equality, respect, to name a few—scarcely requires defense. But adequate interpretation of our mental-health findings must go beyond this general relationship to take into account, also, the development of aims that differ from one person to another, from group to group, and from situation to situation.

A most important example is seen in the tendency of men to accommodate their aspirations to their appraisal of the opportunities open to them—hence the frequently commented on "wantlessness" of the poor. Our own results present repeated illustrations; the unsatisfactory mental health of working people consists in no small measure of their dwarfed desires and deadened initiative, reduction of their goals and restriction of their efforts to a point where life is relatively empty and only half meaningful. Industrial workers, like all the rest of us, are caught on the horns of a dilemma: if they want *too much* relative to what they are prepared to strive for with some degree of success, the result is defeat and frustration; if they want *too little,* the consequence is a drab existence devoid of color, exhilaration, and self-esteem. Good mental health demands a middle course. Men in lower-level occupations, where means for want satisfaction are more limited, least often find the happy middle ground. Their poorer mental health reflects a loss of motivation and initiative as well as greater dissatisfaction and frustration in respect to the reduced aims that remain.

No blanket indictment is warranted, however, to the effect that curtailment of desires and contented acceptance of whatever life offers necessarily signifies poor mental health. It depends on how extreme the abandonment of active striving and what alternative possibilties exist for reasonably successful purposive behavior. There can be little doubt that in our culture passive contentment is deemed less psychologically healthy than a vigorous, self-reliant, problem-solving orientation aimed at satisfying persistent wants. On the other hand, when the alternative to quiescent acceptance is a continued sense of frustration and defeat, with embittered feelings toward self and others, then a realistic reduction of expectations is judged preferable by comparison. Thus reduction of striving is at one and the same time an aspect of poor mental health and a safeguard against even worse mental health.

This explanation in terms of wants that are too great or too small is clearly an oversimplification; it entirely omits vital questions concerning the *direction* of the wants. Instead of merely suppressing or abandoning goals, men may *redefine* their aims; they may develop alternative, more appropriate goals toward which they can strive with a sense of worthwhile accomplishment and genuine satisfaction. Our research reveals many instances of this process—for example, when workers in jobs devoid of intrinsic interest focus instead on extrinsic rewards like wages and security; or when they turn to self-actualizing, creative hobbies away from the job to take the place of what is unattainable at work. To some extent, that is, industrial workers maintain their mental health by adapting their wants to available opportunities for gratification.

Our results indicate, however, that most workers are not too successful in this regard; we have repeatedly had to note not only deficiencies of motivation and enjoyment in work but also the relative barrenness of leisure-time interests and the restricted character of life aims. Given the structure of wants and expectations that our culture typically instills into workers, there is little tendency for them to develop other aims that might better fit their situation and better contribute to mental health. Insofar as industrial workers set their sights on material possessions, individual success, and employment in interesting, independent, self-expressive work, most of them are headed for disappointment—often with feelings of failure, self-blame, and accompanying symptoms of unsatisfactory mental health. The basic question raised here is whether the prevailing value system of our society interferes with good mental health for large sections of the population. It sometimes seems almost as if the pervasive emphasis on money, competitive success, and pleasures of consumption had been designed to produce frustration and undermine self-esteem among the disadvantaged and less successful. One can feel sure that the consequences would be very different if societal influences operated more strongly to develop and reinforce goals of personal growth, self-expressive use of leisure, participation in collective efforts for social improvement, and other opportunities for self-actualization not dependent on the very things that are largely denied the general run of industrial workers. But perhaps the cultural values are too firmly rooted to permit of such change. We shall deal further with this difficult and challenging problem in the last part of the present chapter when we reflect on possible social policy implications of our results.

The preceding discussion refers primarily to gross findings pertaining to broad categories of people. We wish now to add that the same explanatory motivational concepts apply to our more detailed results as well. Such interpretations have been suggested at many points, in respect both to personal determinants of mental health (individual differences) and to specific job characteristics (occupational differences).

In regard to *individual variations*, we interpret mental-health effects as reflecting the degree to which each person's wants, expectations, and self-conception meet with gratifying or frustrating conditions. His mental health is less satisfactory to the extent that his world proves irreconcilable with his conception of the person he is and the person he is striving to become. Workers who want what they cannot realistically hope to achieve tend to be in poorer mental health; those who can move toward satisfying their wants tend to enjoy better mental health. Our results as a whole indicate that both the personal and the occupational aspects of want gratification possess explanatory power: the quality of workers' adjustment varies with their differing personal goals and needs but it turns quite as fully on the differing opportunities for gratification afforded by the positions they occupy, even within the limited range of occupations dealt with in this study.

The foregoing interpretation might be called a "general theory of incongruence" in contrast to "special theories" of aspiration-achievement discrepancy and status incongruence. The *general* theory is identical with the explanatory guidelines we have employed: variations in mental health reflect the degree of discrepancy between what people want and the opportunities available to them for gratifying those wants. When formulated more narrowly, however, as a *special* theory which specifies discrepancy between level of aspiration for success and level of achievement, indicated by present occupation, we find it has only limited validity within the factory population studied. The reason, we believe, is that motivations are so diverse and interact with other determinants of adjustment in so intricate a manner that this *particular* influence, though an important element of the total process, may or may not be powerful enough to show itself, depending on the entire context. Desires for status and success are parts of a complex motivational structure in which other unsatisfied wants may loom larger as sources of incongruence, disturbing frustrations, and unsatisfactory mental health.

Finally, a few further notes are needed in regard to our analysis of *occupational characteristics* that make for better or poorer mental health. In the framework of our explanatory concepts, what the results mean is that various job attributes are more important or less important as determinants of mental health depending on how they relate to the total structure of workers' wants and expectations at the time. Most significant for mental health is *whatever* the working men perceive as especially satisfying and ego enhancing or especially thwarting and frustrating. These perceptions, in turn, depend on the entire network of influences, subjective and objective, temporary and enduring, that shape men's desires, self-images, and beliefs about their situation.

In this perspective, a crucial question arises whether the influences are so varied and shifting, from time to time and situation to situation, that no stable conclusions can be drawn concerning separate factors. For example, when wages are good and steady employment seems assured, these aspects of jobs are likely to be of small concern; but let earnings deteriorate or unemployment threaten and the same characteristics take on vital importance for workers' life adjustments. So it is with many other changing conditions of working life. Moreover, not only the absolute amount of change counts but also the *relative* favorableness or unfavorableness—relative, that is, to what has been customary; relative to other groups, near and far; relative to basic living standards, to the profits of industry, and so on; and above all, perhaps, relative to what is currently believed possible, reasonable, and just. These comparative judgments obviously involve not only the objective conditions but likewise the expectations that have been created by the worker's past and present experiences, including the social and political forces operating to arouse and intensify particular demands. In the aggregate, these considerations carry an impressive warning against acceptance of specific empirical findings as supplying stable, dependable conclusions to the effect that this job characteristic is important and that one is unimportant as a determinant of mental health.

Shall we then conclude that there is no stability or generality at all to such results as we have reported concerning job attributes? We believe that this extreme position is unwarranted since, despite the forces of change, there is a considerable degree of constancy to men's deep-seated wants and likewise to the availability of means for gratifying the wants. It can be safely predicted, for example, that working people in our culture will continue to crave more of the material goods and comforts of life and that many of the less fortunate will inevitably experience strains of relative deprivation. Similarly, a vague desire to engage in more interesting, self-actualizing activities appears to be sufficiently widespread and deep-rooted, and commonly enough unrealized, to constitute an enduring source of discontent and unsatisfactory adjustment for considerable numbers of men in low-skilled occupations. Since analysis of our data accords with these expectations, it seems plausible to interpret the findings on these variables as having probable significance beyond the particular conditions of the study. On the other hand, when we find that feelings concerning job security and wage rates do not account for mental-health differences among occupational groups, we may well question whether this result possesses stability or general validity. It appears more reasonable to suppose that in respect to such variables severe differential strains are likely to occur with changing industrial situations and economic conditions. Reflections like the foregoing lead us to adopt a middle position on the issue of whether *general* conclusions can be drawn in regard to the relative contribution of separate job factors to group differences of mental health.

Reviewing the meaning of our findings in regard to occupational differences in this perspective, we arrive at the following summary statements.

(*a*) Only future research can discover how much such results change from one situation to another. Meanwhile it may be noted that the Detroit automobile plants of the 1950's cannot be dismissed as exceptional; in many ways they have become a symbol of modern manufacturing conditions.

(*b*) Under these conditions, poorer mental health in lower-level occupations was accounted for in only the slightest degree by workers' reactions to wages, job security, and working conditions, factors ordinarily given major emphasis as causes of adverse effects. We interpret our findings to mean that glaring and remedial sources of frustration and discontent have been moderately well corrected as a result of union and management efforts, thus tending to equalize workers' reactions at different job levels. Nevertheless, enough effects are evidenced, both favorable and adverse, to suggest that these job attributes *could* readily exert salient influence on mental health under changed circumstances.

(*c*) Several aspects of jobs that have been greatly stressed in the human-relations literature as key factors determining employee morale turn out to have quite limited relationship to our observed differences of mental health. These results serve, at very least, to underscore the need for skepticism and caution about assigning a dominant role to supervision, status, and other social attributes of the job.

(*d*) The largest effects we find arise from intrinsic rewards and constraints of the work itself, particularly the chance the job affords men to use their abilities, with all that this signifies. This influence and that of income differences were commented on earlier. Our interpretation is that, at higher- and lower-level jobs respectively, these factors are subject to the most satisfying gratifications or the most severe and persistent incongruence between what workers want and what the jobs provide.

(*e*) The motivation theory employed in this interpretation of job effects is to be distinguished from several other psychological views that have been prominently used for such purposes.

In the first place we have explicitly avoided the idea that the job must satisfy certain immutable needs; also the view that wants are structured in a fixed hierarchical order of potency, such that lower, more compelling motives have to be satisfied in set sequence before higher ones exert their influence. Rather, we believe, many different motives may become dominant, depending on the cultural and subcultutral influences, the changing conditions and degree of thwarting experienced, and the perceived opportunities to implement the desires.

We likewise seriously question attempts to classify wants into ego motives and nonego motives, with the latter (including economic goals, security, etc.) relegated to a position of secondary importance. We find more theoretically tenable and empirically valid a conception that recognizes some degree of ego involvement in *all* socially meaningful motives. Economic goals, for example, are of intense *personal* concern to working men and profoundly affect their adjustments to life.

Finally, and not unrelated, there is a third view that conceives of job attributes as divided into "motivators," the positive "satisfiers," versus "hygiene factors" which pertain to maintenance or security and which have importance only in a negative sense, as "dissatisfiers" when they are deficient. All through our analysis of occupational characteristics, we encountered evidence that points to an opposite conclusion. Both theory and data appear to us to make the distinction unacceptable. Workers find satisfaction and positive motivation not only in workmanship and achievement but likewise in income, job conditions, and the various other so-called hygiene factors.

Lest the core meaning of the study be lost in the consideration of these subordinate issues, we shall close this section by restating the major conclusion—that men's position in the occupational hierarchy substantially affects their mental health, that low-level jobs have especially adverse effects on the average, and that this result occurs largely by reason of the incongruity between personality needs and the nature of job characteristics, opportunities, and demands. The balance of our inquiry has sought to discover workers' characteristics, job attitudes, and orientations to life that are associated with the occupational effects on mental health.

The Problem for Industry and Society

In the remaining pages we want to consider some possible implications of the study for the guidance of social aims and policies. This means that while we shall continue to keep one eye on the relevant results, our speculations will range far beyond conclusions based on the data. Furthermore, we shall assume in this discussion that the key conclusions we have reported will be confirmed and extended by subsequent studies.

Let there be no ambiguity regarding our conception of the psychologist's role here. The questions to be dealt with involve basic value issues to be decided by the whole of society. On such matters the psychologist must not presumptuously attempt to play God; his function is not to prescribe but modestly to offer what facts he possesses and to suggest alternative directions and perspectives for consideration and debate by all concerned. There is great merit, we believe, in the mere posing of critical questions that are commonly avoided. Hopefully the questions may possess some distinctive quality by reason of the special knowledge and insights that a psychologist brings to bear. But the psychologist also has values; his own orientation is bound to influence the selection of questions he asks and the possible answers he emphasizes. With this caveat, we proceed to state our own considered judgments and queries.

The first and most important requirement is a more general recognition of the problem. Only as people become convinced that a seriously unsatisfactory condition exists, and only as the condition is defined and clarified by descriptive facts, can it be expected that remedial action will ensue. Three principal elements enter into an appreciation of the problem: (a) understanding of the meaning of "positive mental health" as a salient goal of a good society and recognition of the enormous possibilities of fuller and richer psychological development for most individuals; (b) knowledge of the large differences of mental health among population groups in higher and lower socioeconomic positions and in different organizational settings; specifically, in terms of our results, the relatively poor mental health of semiskilled workers, particularly of those employed in routine production jobs; (c) recognition that routine jobs are not about to vanish as a result of automation, that the problem is not about to be solved through the complete replacement of men by machines, but that many millions of American workers will continue to be employed in low-level semiskilled occupations and will continue to make their life adjustments as best they can. As knowledge of these matters becomes more widespread, one may anticipate intensified efforts by the lower-placed groups, their leaders, and agencies concerned with their welfare to bring about social and industrial changes aiming to ameliorate the condition.

The grand purpose of such efforts will be nothing less than the creation of a better society in which men can more fully realize their best potentialities. The goal is an industrial and social system that functions with consistent regard for the psychological well-being of people. Along lines of our earlier discussion, this must include increased attention both to the adequate gratification of "worthy" existing wants and to the development of new, more "appropriate" goals. These statements, if they do nothing else, serve to make vividly clear the difficult value questions which are unavoidable in proposals for improving mental health.

For example, how much weight should be given to considerations of individual freedom and self-development compared to such powerful contending objectives as increased productivity and the growth, military defense, and competitive strength of the nation? What proportionate resources should be devoted to upgrading the mental health of "the masses" as against the cultivation of special excellence (artistic, intellectual, administrative) among those endowed with natural talent and leadership potential? Perhaps most acutely difficult of all, what is "adequate" gratification or self-realization; what are "worthy" desires and "appropriate" goals—and who decides? These questions must be answered —but not by the psychologist or, in our view, by any other elite group. The answers, usually accepted on faith with a minimum of critical thought, need to be hammered out, we believe, through processes of endless discussion, group pressures, social experimentation, and working compromises, involving all sectors of society.

Some of the questions become less baffling once they are defined and placed in a psychological frame of reference, though in large part the answers will still depend on people's basic value positions and social philosophy. To begin with, it helps to recognize that the shorthand expressions "adequate gratification of existing wants," "self-actualization," and "realization of men's full potential" are not used in any definitive or absolute sense. One critic, for example, complains that he has "difficulty in seeing concretely the self-actualized man." This misses the whole point that what is sought for *all* men is a greater *degree* of gratification, self-development, and self-expression than that previously attained. There is no "right" amount; only "more," in keeping with rising desires and expectations of the persons under consideration.

A further, less obvious point of clarification appears necessary to deal with the troublesome problem of destructive, petty, and antisocial impulses. Is the gratification of these motives also to be encouraged? The approach to an answer lies, we think, in conceiving of good mental health as limited to the actualization of motives and abilities that have become integral parts of the person's *approved self.* In general, this positive self-conception incorporates the prevalent value norms of the culture, internalized by the individual in the course of his personal development. Hence, for most people, self-actualization consists of attitudes and behaviors that express, in higher or lower degree, the motives and human potentialities positively valued in civilized society. To the extent that individuals remain "unsocialized," that is, with self systems that have failed to internalize basic cultural values, improvement of their mental health demands not actualization of the present wants but emotional and motivational reeducation to bring them into accord with fundamental human values.

Application of this criterion of acceptable versus unacceptable self-actualization is fraught with difficulties and dangers. Contrary to our intent, it could easily be turned into a defense of conformity. Nevertheless, some such distinction appears indispensable. But it surely must not be construed in a manner that would rule out honest dissent or even rebellion as esteemed forms of self-actualization. Under certain conditions the most highly "socialized" persons may well be the most revolutionary.

We indicated earlier that social efforts to improve mental health can be divided into measures for providing better satisfaction of present personality needs, discussed in the preceding paragraphs, and, second, programs for the development of more appropriate wants. In respect to efforts of the latter type, two underlying assumptions that have been implicit throughout our discussion should be stated explicitly. The first is the proposition that men can grow; that human personality is malleable; that it is largely a product of social learning and undergoes continuing modification by changing social conditions and influences. To be sure there are limits imposed by the biological nature of man and the particular characteristics of individuals. But we believe that, in the present state of knowledge on these matters, the most defensible working conception is one which stresses the vast possibilities of new and varied goals that men at all economic levels can set for themselves. This contrasts with the contention that "human nature" is fixed; that men's current goals and predilections can be taken as unchanging; that working people are passive, dependent, intent only on immediate bread-and-butter objectives and this is the way they always will be.

The second guiding thought in regard to men's acquirement of new goals is concerned with the issue of what alteration of wants is desirable and who decides. Again our answer is that people must decide for themselves; it is not for the "experts" to prescribe what men *should* want. To a great extent, of course, the decisions are made impersonally, by social-historical forces which have shaped the traditional values of the society that are now passed on, without deliberate choice, from generation to generation. The deep-cutting query here is whether these conventional goals call for much more critical assessment and reevaluation than is accorded them. A society like ours, in a world of revolutionary change, a world increasingly aware of psychological needs and potentialities, must debate not only its "national goals" but the personal goals of the individual as well.

In the interests of good mental health for the ordinary run of working people, for example, it could be that our society might decide to reduce the tremendous emphasis on goals of personal achievement and competitive individual success and to cultivate stronger interests in cooperative group activities, altruistic social service, participation in political and economic reform movements, creative leisure-time pursuits, and other presently neglected life purposes. Such shifts might go far to enrich life, to diminish painful experience of failure, to let men move toward satisfying, attainable goals with attendant positive feelings of self-esteem. Whether deemphasis of individualistic achievement motives would retard "progress," as is often alleged, and how it might change the definition and direction of progress for good or ill, no one can say with assurance. It is precisely these basic questions that call for continuing debate and collective decision in the light of all the wisdom that can be mustered.

Obviously persons in positions of leadership, at all levels and in all kinds of organizations, bear a grave responsibility in this connection. So, too, do social scientists and intellectuals generally. Although they cannot give answers, they have an obligation to raise questions, to point out alternatives, and to indicate comparative gains and losses likely to result from given changes—and from failure to change. The present study finds its place here; it produces small bits of evidence relevant for society's evaluative judgments. More important, perhaps, it evokes questions of the kind already suggested.

With the foregoing as background, we shall now ask more pointedly what industry can and should do about mental health and then, similarly, what can be expected and hoped for in the larger society.

Industrial Management and the Mental Health of Workers[1]

Our purpose here is to indicate directions for further inquiry and debate. The following propositions and questions aim to give a realistic perspective on management's role in respect to the mental health of industrial workers and to stimulate critical examination of the part management plays.

1. The essential function of the industrial organization is effective production;

[1] A vast literature has come into being that grapples with the human problems of industry. This is obviously not the place to attempt a review of thought and research in this area. The best we can do, as an aid to readers who may wish to pursue the matters touched upon in the text is to include a sampling of references to some of the better books and articles that have appeared in recent years. These sources contain many additional references. We suggest the following: Argyris (1957, 1960, 1964); Bennis (1959, 1961a); Blum (1953); Drucker (1954), Dubin (1958); Friedmann (1955, 1961); Gellerman (1963); Haire (1959); Knowles (1958); Landsberger (1958); Levinson et al. (1962); Likert (1961); McGregor (1960); Presthus (1962); H. C. Smith (1964); Strauss (1963); Warner and Martin (1959); Whyte (1955, 1961); Wilensky (1957).

it is not industry's responsibility to improve mental health. This is true, that is, save as (*a*) such improvement is a means for the better achievement of management's ends, the building of a successful, growing, profitable organization; or (*b*) management is induced by laws, contracts, and informal pressures from inside and outside the organization to make changes in the interests of mental health. This is simply to assert that productivity, costs, and related economic criteria are paramount in management's policy decisions. The business firm is not a welfare agency. An enterprise operating in a competitive economy cannot sacrifice any part of its productive efficiency without suffering a relative disadvantage and to that extent jeopardizing its survival. It follows that any single firm can work for the fulfillment of noneconomic values, including the psychological well-being of its employees, only to the extent that such objectives are compatible with maintenance or increase of overall efficiency. Hence enlightened personnel policies that create favorable attitudes and contribute to mental health must be justified by evidence or argument showing that they pay off in long-run productivity and profits. Socially conscious industrial executives of high moral purpose will be unable, generally speaking, to implement humane feelings that cannot be *economically* justified.

Even within the restrictions imposed by adherence to efficiency principles, management's actions may contribute substantially to better or poorer mental health. It is this impact that is referred to in the preceding exception *a*. The effect is evident in the large differences that occur among companies. More fully stated, the point is that better mental health of workers comes as a by-product of the organization's self-interested, enlightened efforts in regard to personnel and labor relations. Although few companies set themselves the explicit objective of improving mental health, it has become commonplace for most companies to try to increase job satisfaction, motivation in work, and general "morale," with emphasis on favorable feeling and loyalty toward the company. The varied human-relations activities directed to these ends, if carried on with reasonable honesty and intelligence, are likely at the same time to produce better mental health. This benign side effect cannot be taken for granted, however; mental health is surely not synonymous with heightened company morale though the two tend to be associated. Demands for production and profits often negate the favorable influence of well-intentioned human relations performance.

We shall comment further on the possibilities and limitations of management efforts in their relation to mental health under section 2. Even though it is our judgment that management's human-relations activities, taken as a whole, make a significant positive contribution to mental health in industry, we must add this strong reservation: if improved mental health of workers is really a vital social objective in and of itself, then it is much too important to be left chiefly to the indirect and sometimes contradictory effects produced by the voluntary actions of management oriented toward a different set of goals.

These last statements bring us to the second significant exception *b* noted at the beginning of these remarks on management's role. Insofar as the industrial organization is oriented (properly) to its own economic ends, it seems obvious that other important human values will tend to be neglected unless they are forcefully pressed by groups concerned with these other, often conflicting, goals. This, of course, is what has happened throughout the industrial revolution, both in respect to economic interests opposed to those of the business firm and in regard to varied human values divergent from the productivity-efficiency-profit objective. It is no accident, for example, that factory laws and labor-union pressures were required to secure adequate protection of workers' physical health and safety. The patent fact is that employees have diverse needs that are not going to be met by voluntary action of managements operating within a system of single-minded devotion to economic goals. The interests of efficiency have to be balanced against other human interests; compromises have to be reached that are acceptable to employees (and their unions) and to society as a whole. After all, industrial organizations are instruments of a changing society, subject to its control.

Social controls and pressures directed toward improved mental health of workers will depend primarily on influences and agencies independent of management. It is for these reasons that we specially stress the possibilities of and need for programs concerned with positive mental health by workers' own organizations, by the community as a whole (including participation by business leaders in their role as socially minded citizens), and by agencies of government. The initiative for significant change cannot be expected from management functioning as management; it must come from elsewhere. But if substantial changes affecting industry are brought about by pressures from below and from outside, management will learn to accept them—even perhaps welcome them—insofar as the changes are imposed on competitors as well as themselves and consequently do not place them at a disadvantage compared to others. The final section of this chapter focuses on these possibilities in the society at large. But first we take a closer look at what management contributes and fails to contribute.

2. Management thinking has been undergoing extensive alteration during the past few decades. There has been a striking increase in the attention paid to "human relations." It is now recognized by almost all industrialists that the health, perhaps the very survival, of the organization depends on achieving and maintaining human conditions that are satisfying and productive. In part, the rising expectations of working people and the growth of labor unions pushed industry into action; in part, executives independently become aware of the enormous possibilities and constructive advantages of more fully developing and motivating their employees.

The core of the change is a shift from strict, hierarchical, authoritarian leadership to looser controls and leadership by persuasion. This signifies more than first meets the eye. To persuade, it is necessary to *understand* people's attitudes and feelings, to deal with the worker as a complete person rather than as a "hired hand." If the manager is to be successful, moreover, it is unlikely that he can "get away with" clever techniques and manipulative skills as a substitute for genuine respect and good will toward his subordinates. This requirement applies from top to bottom of the organization. Our choice of the phrase "management by persuasion" means something more; it expresses our deep suspicion of slogans and preachments that falsely imply more radical moves by management toward "industrial democracy" or voluntary yielding of power over the determination of significant goals and policies of the enterprise. Whether by gentle persuasion or otherwise, management still manages. But if it does so with greater appreciation and consideration for the people managed, this can scarcely fail to have favorable effects on the self-feelings and mental health of men so treated.

To fill in these sketchy statements, we shall mention a few characteristic trends of enlightened human-relations programs and then proceed to the critical question of how much these newer management developments may be expected to do for the mental health of workers. The three descriptive points of emphasis we have chosen are these: (1) The need for managerial understanding and acceptance of men's varied *noneconomic* motives and complex personality needs as well as the economic ones, and appreciation of individual *potentialities;* efforts to adjust conditions, rewards, opportunities, and appeals accordingly, including both substantive job changes (advancement and job enlargement, for example) and personnel practices, supervisory treatment, and so on, geared to workers' pride, workmanship impulses, personal insecurity, and other diverse wishes and expectations. (2) Appreciation of the vital place occupied by group processes and influences; the opportunity and need for management to foster healthy, cohesive, loyal work groups (for example, by limiting their size and keeping them intact, by best arrangement of work stations, favorable conditions for social interaction at work and during rest periods, and many other such procedures); encouragement, within the limits of feasibility and considered policy, of group decision making and shared responsibility on specified matters; supervisory relationship to the group that, above all else, is forthright, honest, and expressive of genuine sentiments (no gimmicks and charm-school artificiality). (3) Careful evaluation of the total organization, its philosophy and structure from a human-relations standpoint and adoption of modifications that can be agreed on—even drastic ones affecting top-level personnel, decentralization of authority, elimination of entire echelons from the chain of command, and so on; in general, recognition that improved human relations at lower levels depend on the reality of support received from higher levels.

It is highly probable that management changes of the kind indicated will continue and will expand. They represent a necessary corrective to the human deficiencies of the bureaucratic organization with its tight hierarchical authority system and "scientific management" principles. The newer style management will flourish because it contributes to the overall effectiveness of the enterprise. But our question here is whether it also contributes to the personal happiness and mental health of working people. The general answer, though with later qualifications, seems clearly affirmative, even with reference to workers employed in semiskilled production jobs upon whom our interest centers. More pronounced benefits probably accrue to professional, technical, and managerial employees.

Focusing on semiskilled only, and assuming that human-relations procedures are conducted with integrity and competence, we would anticipate gains such as the following: Work and employment relations are presumably made somewhat more agreeable and less frustrating as a result of increased respect and consideration by bosses and the removal of unnecessary irritations; by a generally improved climate of friendliness and support; by assurance of fair treatment (on this and many other points the credit due the union must not be overlooked); by increased pride and satisfaction through identification with a company "that cares," having a job at "a good place to work," and, where such possibilities exist, having opportunities for training and advancement, counseling services, and a wide variety of other employee services. In addition, employees *may* derive gratification from increased individual or group participation and responsibility, though managerial efforts in this direction can easily backfire if they lack real substance, appear manipulative, or arouse false expectations with subsequent disillusionment. Significant gains, little realized as yet, may also be provided by job-enlargement procedures which permit the worker to perform more challenging tasks that combine previously fragmented operations.

Without in any sense belittling constructive contributions such as those listed, it is necessary to view the other side of the coin as well, to consider what is left undone with regard to mental health even when management performs beyond reproach. Managerial activities that have positive value for workers naturally lie in areas where the needs and aims of the individual and those of the organization are compatible. But there are likewise important areas of incompatibility. Too often the tendency has been to assume complete identity, or at least basic harmony, between management's objectives and those of workers, ignoring opposed interests and conflicts inherent in the contrast between goals of *economic efficiency* and the intangible goals of peaceful unpressured living, free self-actualizing activities, and the entire gamut of nonutilitarian human purposes. With few exceptions, experts in the field of industrial human relations shy away from these problems of continuing conflict, or dismiss them with glib suggestions of how employees can be shown that they can best satisfy their own needs by working for organizational objectives.

By the nature of its functions, management is not in a position to initiate actions for better satisfying all the important intangible needs of working people. It cannot introduce changes that either run counter to the economic interests of the enterprise or that lie outside its legitimate sphere of concern. An example of such limitations is seen in unwillingness to abandon productive but distasteful methods of work. A great deal of evidence, in the present study and others, shows that workers on repetitive jobs feel deprived and stultified by the endless dull routine, that many of them poignantly wish for more interesting and challenging work in which they could use their abilities and derive a sense of worth and self-respect. But it is this brute fact of specialized, simplified tasks that is basic to efficiency in numerous mass-production processes. With the most considerate supervision imaginable and with the entire repertoire of enlightened management methods, such jobs will still be what they are; they will still produce their adverse effects on mental health.

Even if a little job enlargement is introduced and a little leeway is granted for the worker to do the job his own way, it still falls far short of really using his abilities or challenging his resources. Similarly, typical plans that permit participation in trivial decisions are at best a pleasant, appreciated gesture; at worst a deeply resented sham. It seems most doubtful, too, that administrative skills or salesmanship to make workers *want* to do what they *have* to do contributes to their self-fulfillment. Yet a highly regarded psychologist can refer to this sort of manipulative control and engineered consent as a way "to maximize the satisfactions" of the workers—implying a startling curtailment, indeed, of working people's range of satisfactions.

Other illustrations of necessary limitations on management's contributions to mental health may be briefly noted. Many workers are oppressed by feelings of futility and powerlessness; they yearn for an effective voice in the control of their own work, a genuine sharing in decisions and responsibility. But industry, even where the management is most progressive, is a long way from really meaningful dispersion of decision-making authority at low job levels. *Significant* involvement of semiskilled and unskilled workers (as in plans of "workers' management") can be expected only if pressures *outside of management* were to mount to a point that would mean fundamental changes of the enterprise system, an outcome certainly not visible in America at present. With more immediate relevance, workers' desires to exercise effective, independent influence in industry cause them to turn to organizations and leadership of their own choosing. Labor unions are in a position to satisfy important psychological needs that management cannot, precisely because the union (assuming that it is democratically run) offers opportunity for achievement in which the individual fully shares. Wage increases, job security, improved working conditions are vastly more satisfying and ego enhancing if won by the men's own organization than if graciously bestowed by management.

A final most significant limitation on management's actual and potential accomplishments in respect to mental health has to do with the need for expansion of working people's horizons and the creation of new goals. The business organization, in its own self-interests, can scarcely engage in the stimulation of heightened self-expectations among workers at low job levels when industry is unable to provide opportunities for gratifying the aroused wants. Passivity, "wantlessness," lack of purpose as aspects of unsatisfactory mental health, whether or not they are *caused* by industrial influences, certainly are not being widely *remedied* by industry. Nor is the redirecting of life aims into paths more promising of self-fulfillment in leisure an undertaking to be left primarily to industry.

None of the foregoing is intended to blame or condemn industry. It is simply not the function of the industrial organization to do nearly everything that may be socially desirable for the sake of mental health. Fortunately, much of what progressive business management has learned to do in its own interests does contribute at the same time to the psychological health of its employees. This positive role of industry will doubtless expand over the years in response to increasing pressures and demands of workers and the community. Yet much of life is lived away from the job; industry is one of many institutions. Our final comments will be concerned with these other influences on mental health in the larger society, particularly the possibilities they present for general improvement of working people's "positive mental health."

Contemporary Society and the Mental Health of Workers[2]

Let us begin this final section with the reminder that our study does not indicate especially *poor* mental health among Detroit industrial workers. We have no reason to conclude that they are worse off psychologically than other major

[2] These final pages merely nibble at the edges of enormously large and forbiddingly difficult problems. For centuries, thoughtful men and women have sought better answers to the questions raised here. Again, all we can attempt is to list a limited number of references, restricting ourselves to illustrations of modern psychological and "behavioral science" thinking. We make no mention at all of the rich body of social-historical and philosophical writing by great thinkers of the past. Among recent publications we select a number that seem related to our present discussion—and particularly ones having a bearing on humanly oriented industrial change, the use of leisure, and more active participation in organizations and social movements. Illustratively, then, we suggest the following: Arendt (1958); Bell (1960); Brown (1954); Drucker (1950); Friedmann (1955, 1961); Fromm (1955); Kerr *et al.* (1960); Lerner (1957); Lipset (1960); Mayo (1933, 1945); Merton (1957b); Mills (1956); Moore (1951); Presthus (1962); Riesman (1950); Staley (1952); Walker (1962); Weiss and Riesman (1961); Wilensky and Lebeaux (1958).

groups of comparable income and education who constitute the "working class" and "lower middle class." By ordinary standards the attitudes and life adjustments, particularly of the men in skilled and upper-level semiskilled jobs, are reasonably satisfactory. Our concentration on what can be done to *improve* mental health does not imply that it is now notably bad but expresses rather our conviction that it can be made much better. The desirability of improvement is especially clear in the case of men employed in routine, repetitive production jobs.

In line with our previous analysis, we see efforts to improve the general level of psychological well-being as requiring attack on two broad fronts. One has to do with more satisfactory gratification of existing wants that have become significant to the individuals' self-identity; the other deals with the creation and arousal of new wants and expectations that may bring about richer satisfactions and self-development.

The first is most familiar and can be dismissed with a few words. Outside of industry as well as inside, innumerable specific changes can be made to reduce frustrations and increase the joys of living. Most obvious and pervasive are increases of the material goods of life, all the things that money can buy. "War on poverty" is at the same time war for better mental health. Workers' steadily rising planes of living, including greater economic security, more leisure time, improved housing and wholesome environment for children, medical care, and and everyday comforts, although they do not in themselves assure good mental health, do furnish invaluable assistance. Beyond these, and to some extent built upon them as a foundation, loom endless possibilities of intangible gratifications suggested by a mere listing of categories such as readily available opportunities for appropriate continuing education and training; better recreational and entertainment facilities (for music, drama, art; libraries, museums, parks and playing fields in greater numbers and more conveniently located, and so on); more inviting, realistic opportunities for individual and group participation in all manner of social, political, religious, labor, and community activities. Nothing new here; but still enormously important that the linkage to positive mental health be recognized—along with the dismal fact that vast and damaging inequalities persist between socioeconomic groups in all these matters.

It is apparent, however, that progress toward superior mental health requires inner changes of *men*, not merely improved external conditions. What is most importantly called for, we would argue, is nothing less than a drastically modified system of values, a new philosophy of life. People of the kind we studied, and to a considerable extent the same is true of other groups, are living humdrum existences. Though most are moderately happy, few are enthusiastic; almost none are fully, intensely alive.

What is missing is a purposeful spirit of trying to live up to their true potentialities, to guide their activities in terms of future-oriented self-conceptions. As far as we can judge, only a tiny fraction holds any firm faith or energizing belief in worthy ends beyond the immediate and personal. The trouble is that without worthwhile goals life is empty and, beneath the surface, deeply unsatisfying. Moreover, those workers who are most purposive predominantly set their sights on personal success. It would be strange if it were otherwise in a culture so permeated with worship of this goal. For great numbers of manual workers the result is disappointment and frustration.

We have referred to these matters at previous points and have mentioned directions in which society may move toward solutions. The problem in its full dimensions amounts to that of remaking man and society, a somewhat too formidable project to be outlined here. Instead, we are content merely to add a bit of concreteness to our earlier suggestions. In essence, what we have proposed is that vigorous continuing public discussion and further extensive research be carried on to make people vividly aware of the problem and the feasibility of changes in the interests of better mental health. We would hope that as many agents of opinion formation as possible, certainly not neglecting grass-roots influencers among working people themselves, will see the importance of fostering different life goals and a new appreciation of what life can mean for people at all income levels.

The general run of men do almost no critical thinking about their aims in life or what their world would really permit them to be and do. If they can be stimulated to serious consideration of the matter, we believe that many will feel the appeal of intangible objectives and enlarged conceptions of themselves and their potential roles. We do not intend to play down the importance of personal success and economic gratifications but to keep them from preempting all of life. It is necessary that other interests also be aroused, so that a person's life include a wide choice of valued goals among which he may discover ones that win his deep and enduring commitment.

Examples of potential psychological enrichment lie both in individualized forms of self-expression and in significant group activities. Let us begin with the working man's spare time at home. Our evidence on this is unambiguous: a small minority devote themselves to absorbing hobbies, largely in home workshops, but the vast majority engage in no constructive pursuits that would yield a sense of achievement, forward movement, and personal dignity. Most of the men have formed no special interests or given thought to the limitless range of things they could do to develop themselves and enjoy the use of their talents. The striking need, trite though the idea has become, is education for interesting, constructive use of leisure. Above all, this presents a problem of *motivation*, of reaching men's latent springs of action by means of effective personal discussion and concrete example. This can hardly be an achievement beyond the powers of agencies devoted to workers' education.

If this ball once really gets rolling, workers themselves can be counted on to exert pressure on the community to provide the desired instruction and facilities. A constant refrain in our interviews is the lament that "you can't get anywhere without an education"—but scarcely anyone follows through to ask what he can still do about overcoming the lack, either in respect to vocational or avocational objectives. In this connection we would particularly urge greater effort to expand working people's enjoyment of *intellectual* pursuits, however elementary the initial exercises may need to be. We are convinced that much larger numbers of workers than is ordinarily supposed would eagerly respond to stimulating opportunities to "figure things out," to arrive at new insights and understandings on the basis of inquiry and thoughtful discussion. This need not imply, of course, any neglect of education and training directed to acquisition of facts, manual skills, music and fine arts, physical prowess, and every other human interest.

Apart from potential educational influences, another change may be in prospect which carries large implications for the use of leisure. We refer to the perennial proposals for joining manufacturing plants with farms and gardens in a symbiotic relationship that would permit workers to divide their time between factory work and agriculture—perhaps along with time for home industry, hobbies, study, and travel. This old dream *could* be in for rapid implementation, made feasible by advancing technology and made attractive by workers' broadening horizons regarding the good life.

However, it is in a different direction that we would place our principal hopes and emphasis. The outstanding "psychological deficit" of industrial workers as we see it in our interviews (equally perhaps of most other groups) is the paucity of meaningful social involvement and the lack of social goals. With rare exceptions, the men are wrapped up in their own very narrow private worlds. There is little evidence of devotion to the welfare and happiness of others, little activity that transcends strictly personal and family interests. This is revealed both in their restricted leisure activities and in their life aims. What would give new import and zest to their lives more than anything else, we suggest, is aroused motivation to join with their fellows in efforts to build a better world. Here lie explosive possibilities both for mental health and for significant social action.

Two questions are crucial: (1) Do working men possess latent motivation of the kind here assumed that can be tapped for such idealistic social purposes? Do they feel compassionate urges to make life better for others and to work for greater social justice? Are they prepared to seek a larger measure of self-fulfillment and meaning in their own lives through good works, personally rewarding activities, and commitment to social causes? (2) Are existing institutions and existing leadership prepared to supply the stimulation and guidance needed? And how powerful are the forces of opposition and resistance that prefer an *unaroused* working class? We do not have answers to the questions. We do have the conviction that all interested groups and persons should strenuously seek answers.

This is not the place to explore the role of the various groups and organizations that might play a leading part in pushing action programs of a kind implicit in the foregoing reflections. A comment is in order, however, in regard to labor unions since they stand out as obvious key organizations for the purpose. Under some circumstances, indeed, unions have gone far toward meeting the need for active and rewarding membership participation in imaginative social programs. This apparently occurs most notably during early enthusiastic stages of union advances and proves difficult to maintain. Generally speaking, American unionism concentrates its efforts on restricted economic gains for the members. The findings of our study, as well as a great deal of other evidence, show how shallowly these usual activities of the organization enter into the life patterns of workers and how very slightly they engender active involvement. The question we would press is whether bolder, more idealistic programs of social and economic change (in the local shop and community as well as on the national scene) might not have much stronger appeal. Perhaps unions are not now the most promising agencies; perhaps their functions and their leadership are so far committed to businesslike bargaining and institutionalized responsibility that workers must look elsewhere to find new vistas and crusading spirit of the kind suggested.

The principal issue confronting us, however, is not whether any particular organization is best suited to the task but why so little is being done by *all* organizations. If the interests of democratic social progress and the interests of individual mental health merge in the designated activities, it would seem that here is a place for educational and leadership resources of the entire community to exert their most intense efforts. Surely there are enough seriously disturbing problems to which the thought and energy of working men may valuably be directed. Many of the challenging problems, moreover, lie close at hand and are of a kind that the common man can get his teeth into if only he is encouraged to do so.

A common thread runs through all the foregoing questions and proposals. In brief, we have suggested that positive mental health depends on the total relationship between what a person wants, what he would truly like to be as a person, and what he perceives himself as actually being and becoming, the latter largely determined by what his world permits—or what he *thinks* it permits. Individuals at every economic level have their life-long difficulties making the necessary compromises and readjustments; keeping their sights high enough to satisfy their standards of self-worth and yet not so high as to produce persistent feelings of failure and frustration. Our study shows the special difficulty of this reconciliation for the industrial worker, particularly if he is in a routine factory job. Hence we tried, in these late pages, to point to possible changes of cultural emphasis and individual life aims that might alleviate the frustrations and, hopefully, lead both to improvement of mental health and to progress toward the "good society."

54 / On Death and Death Symbolism: The Hiroshima Disaster

Robert Jay Lifton

There are many reasons why the study of death and death symbolism has been relatively neglected in psychiatry and psychoanalysis: Not only does it arouse emotional resistances in the investigator—all too familiar, though extraordinarily persistent nonetheless—but it confronts him with an issue of a magnitude far beyond his empathic and intellectual capacities. Yet whatever the difficulties, the nuclear age provides both urgent cause and vivid stimulus for new efforts to enhance our understanding of what has always been man's most ineradicable problem. Certainly no study of an event like the Hiroshima disaster can be undertaken without some exploration of that problem.

I conducted the study over a six-month period, from April to September, 1962, mostly in Hiroshima itself. This was the last portion of a two and one-half year

From *Psychiatry*, 1964, **27**, 191–210. Copyright © 1964. Reprinted by permission of the author and The William Alanson White Psychiatric Foundation, Inc.

stay in Japan, the greater part of which was spent investigating psychological and historical patterns of Japanese youth (Lifton, 1962, 1964). The Hiroshima study consisted primarily of individual interviews with two groups of atomic bomb survivors: One group of 33 chosen at random from the list of more than 90,000 survivors (or *hibakusha*) kept at the Hiroshima University Research Institute for Nuclear Medicine and Biology; and an additional group of 42 survivors specially selected because of their prominence in dealing with atomic bomb problems or their capacity to articulate their experiences—including physicians, university professors, city officials, politicians, writers and poets, and leaders of survivor organizations and peace movements.

Hibakusha is a coined word which is by no means an exact equivalent of "survivor" (or "survivors"), but means, literally, "explosion-affected person" (or people), and conveys in feeling a little more than merely having encountered the bomb, and a little less than having experienced definite physical injury from it. According to official definition, the category of *hibakusha* includes four groups of people considered to have had possible exposure to significant amounts of radiation: Those who at the time of the bomb were within the city limits then defined for Hiroshima, an area extending from the bomb's hypocenter to a distance of 4,000, and in some places up to 5,000, meters; those who were not in the city at the time, but within 14 days entered a designated area extending to about 2,000 meters from the hypocenter; those who were engaged in some form of aid to, or disposal of, bomb victims at various stations which were set up; and those who were *in utero*, and whose mothers fit into any of the first three groups. In addition to these interviews with *hibakusha*, I tried to learn all I could, from a variety of sources and in a variety of informal ways, about the extraordinary constellation of influences felt by the city and its inhabitants in relationship to the bomb during the 17-year period that had elapsed between the disaster itself and the time of my research.[1]

Work in a foreign culture, or even in one's own, must depend heavily upon assistance from individuals and groups in the local community. In Hiroshima the sensitivities inherent in the situation of an American psychiatrist undertaking a study of reactions to the atomic bomb made such assistance particularly imperative. Meetings and interviews were arranged, whenever possible, through personal introduction. And with the randomly selected group, my first contact with the survivor was made through a visit to the home, together with a Japanese social worker from Hiroshima University, during which I would briefly explain (either to the survivor himself or to a family member) my purpose in undertaking the work, and then arrange for a later meeting at the office I maintained in the city. In retrospect I feel that the consistently cooperative responses I encountered were significantly related to my conveying to both colleagues and research subjects my own sense of personal motivation in the study—the hope that it might shed light on these difficult problems and thereby in a small way contribute to the mastery of nuclear weapons and the avoidance of their use.[2]

Interviews generally lasted two hours, and I tried to see each research subject

---

[1] A listing of relevant Japanese and American writings on the various aspects of the atomic bomb problem can be found in Lifton (1963).

[2] Familiarity with various features of Japanese culture and the ability to speak some Japanese were also important; but always crucial in obtaining cooperation were introductions by trusted and respected individuals and groups in the Hiroshima community.

twice, though I saw some three or four times, and others just once. They were conducted in Japanese, with a research assistant always present to interpret; the great majority (particularly with subjects in the randomly selected group) were tape-recorded, always with the subject's consent. While I attempted to cover a number of basic questions with all research subjects, I encouraged them to associate freely to whatever ideas and emotions were brought up.

In an earlier publication I described the general psychosocial patterns of the atomic bomb experience, and related them to the predominant theme of death.[3] Now I wish to explore more specifically the psychological elements of what I have referred to as the *permanent encounter with death* which the atomic bomb created within those exposed to it. I shall discuss, in sequence, four different stages of experience with death—that is, four aspects of this encounter. Under examination, therefore, will be shared individual responses to an atmosphere permeated by death. Then, in the latter portion of the paper, I shall attempt to suggest a few general principles in the difficult area of the psychology of death and dying, essentially derived from this investigation but by no means limited to the Hiroshima experience.

Immersion in Death

The overwhelming immersion in death directly following the bomb's fall began with the terrible array of dead and near-dead in the midst of which each survivor found himself. Important here was the extreme sense of surprise and unpreparedness. Survivors were unprepared because, following an air-raid alarm, an all-clear signal had been sounded just a few minutes before the bomb fell; because of the psychological sense of invulnerability all people tend to possess, even in the face of danger; and because of the total inability of anyone to anticipate a weapon of such unprecedented dimensions. The number of deaths, both immediate and over a period of time, will probably never be fully known. Variously estimated from 63,000 to 240,000 or more, the official figure is usually given as 78,000, but the city of Hiroshima estimates 200,000; the enormous disparity is related to the extreme confusion at the time, to differing methods of calculation, and to underlying emotional influences, quite apart from mathematical considerations, which have at times affected the estimators. But the point here is that anyone exposed relatively near the center of the city could not escape the sense of ubiquitous death around him—resulting from the blast itself, from radiant heat, and from ionizing radiation. For instance, if the survivor had been within 1,000 meters (.6 miles) from the hypocenter, and out of doors (that is, without benefit of shielding from heat or radiation), more than nine-tenths of the people around him were fatalities; and if he had been unshielded at 2,000 meters (1.2 miles), more than eight of ten people around him were killed. For those indoors mortality was lower, but even then in order to have even a 50 per cent chance of escaping both death and injury, one had to be about 2,200 meters (1.3 miles) from the

[3] Lifton (1963) describes the three basic emphases of the study: Recollection and inner meaning of the experience 17 years later; residual concerns and fears relating to delayed radiation effects; and survivors' sense of group identity. Many of the reactions mentioned in what follows were dealt with in somewhat greater descriptive detail in the earlier paper. The question of similarities to, and differences from, "ordinary disaster" was also taken up, and will not be discussed here.

hypocenter.[4] Therefore the most significant psychological feature at this point was the sense of a sudden and absolute shift from normal existence to an over-whelming encounter with death.

Recall of the experience was extremely vivid, despite the 17-year interval. For those closest to the hypocenter, first memories of the event were frequently only of a sudden flash, an intense sensation of heat, of being knocked down or thrown some distance and finding themselves pinned under debris, or of simply awakening from an indeterminate period of unconsciousness. Nonetheless, among the initial emotions experienced, many stressed (partly, undoubtedly, with retrospective reconstruction, but not without significance in any case)[5] feelings related to death and dying, such as: "My first feeling was, I think I will die"; "I was dying without seeing my parents"; and, "I felt I was going to suffocate and then die, without knowing exactly what had happened to me."

Beyond this sense of imminent individual death was the feeling of many that the whole world was dying. A science professor, covered by falling debris, found himself temporarily blinded:

> My body seemed all black, everything seemed dark, dark all over. . . . Then I thought, "The world is ending."

A Protestant minister, himself uninjured, responded to the evidence of mutilation and destruction he saw everywhere around him when walking through the city:

> The feeling I had was that everyone was dead. The whole city was destroyed. . . . I thought all of my family must be dead—it doesn't matter if I die. . . . I thought this was the end of Hiroshima—of Japan—of humankind.

And a woman writer:

> I just could not understand why our surroundings had changed so greatly in one instant. . . . I thought it might have been something which had nothing to do with the war, the collapse of the earth which it was said would take place at the end of the world, and which I had read about as a child. It was quiet around us. In fact, there was a fearful silence, which made one feel that all people and all trees and vegetation were dead (Ota, 1955, p. 63).

This "deathly silence" was consistently reported by survivors. Rather than wild panic, most described a ghastly stillness and a sense (whether or not literally true) of slow motion: Low moans from those incapacitated, the rest fleeing, but usually not rapidly, from the destruction, toward the rivers (whose many branches run throughout the city), toward were they thought their family members might be, or toward where they hoped to find authorities of some sort or

---

[4] See particularly Oughterson and Warren (1956) for detailed studies of early mortality. Other sources for overall mortality estimates are listed in Lifton (1963, p. 492). Without here attempting to enter into the complexities of mortality estimates, one may say that it is significant that Japanese estimates are consistently higher than American ones.

[5] Selectivity and distortion were inevitable in descriptions of an event that occurred 17 years before. What the survivors' recollections revealed was not so much a literal rendition of what had occurred as the symbolic significance the event held for them at the time of the interviews. Nonetheless, a study of various accounts of the event recorded closer to the time that it occurred revealed surprisingly similar descriptions of behavior and psychological tendencies, suggesting perhaps that particularly impressive kinds of human experience (whether during childhood or adulthood) can create a lasting psychic imprint, and, under conditions of reasonably good rapport, can be recalled with extraordinary vividness and considerable accuracy. See Lifton (1963, pp. 491–492).

medical personnel, or simply toward accumulations of other people, in many cases merely moving along with a growing crowd and with no clear destination. This feeling of *death in life* was described by a store clerk as follows:

> The appearance of people was . . . well, they all had skin blackened by burns. . . . They had no hair because their hair was burned, and at a glance you couldn't tell whether you were looking at them from in front or in back. . . . They held their arms bent [forward] like this [and he proceeded to demonstrate their position] . . . and their skin—not only on their hands, but on their faces and bodies too—hung down. . . . If there had been only one or two such people . . . perhaps I would not have had such a strong impression. But wherever I walked I met these people. . . . Many of them died along the road —I can still picture them in my mind—like walking ghosts. . . . They didn't look like people of this world. . . . They had a special way of walking—very slowly. . . . I myself was one of them.

Characteristic here is the other-worldly grotesqueness of the scene, the image of neither-dead-nor-alive human figures with whom the survivor closely identifies himself. Similar emotions were frequently described in the imagery of a Buddhist hell, or expressed even more literally—as one man put it, "I was not really alive."

Examining the further psychological meaning of this early immersion in death, one is struck by the importance of feelings of helplessness and abandonment in the face of threatened annihilation. The fear and anticipation of annihilation dominate this phase, though it is not always easy to say exactly what it is that the *hibakusha* fears is about to be annihilated. Here I believe that his overall organism is included insofar as he is capable of symbolically perceiving it—in other words, he fears annihilation of his own self.[6] But one also must include his sense of relationship to the world of people and objects in which he exists: He anticipates the annihilation of both the field or context of his existence and his attachment to it—of his "being-in-the-world," as the existentialists would put it (May *et al.*, 1958), and his "nonhuman environment," as described in recent psychoanalytic writings (Searles, 1960). And he fears the annihilation of that special set of feelings and beliefs which both relate him to others and allow for his sense of being a unique and particular person—in other words, his sense of inner identity (Erikson, 1956; Grotjahn, 1960). This *anticipation of annihilation*—of self, of being, of identity—was related to overwhelming stimuli from without and within, an ultimate sense of threat that has been referred to by such names as "basic fear" and "the fear of the universe."[7]

And indeed so overwhelming was this experience that many would have undoubtedly been unable to avoid psychosis were it not for an extremely widespread and effective defense mechanism which I shall refer to as "psychic

---

[6] This concept of self follows that of Robert E. Nixon, who states (1961) that ". . . *self* is the person's symbol for his organism" (p. 29). Also relevant is Susanne Langer's idea that "The conception of 'self' . . . may possibly depend on this process of symbolically epitomizing our feelings" (1953, p. 111).

[7] See, respectively, Heilbrunn (1955) and James (1952). Erikson (1958) speaks of "a shudder which comes from the sudden awareness that our nonexistence . . . is entirely possible"; and I found similar responses in many exposed to Chinese thought reform (Lifton, 1961). It seems particularly significant that this anticipation of annihilation can occur under a wide variety of circumstances in which one's sense of relationship to the world is profoundly impaired, whether or not actual death is threatened. It represents a symbolic expectation of death, which is the only kind of anticipation of death possible for humankind.

closing-off." In the face of grotesque evidences of death and near-death, people —sometimes within seconds or minutes—simply ceased to feel. They had a clear sense of what was happening around them, but their emotional reactions were unconsciously turned off.

A physicist, observing this process in himself, compared it to an overexposed photographic plate. A clerk who witnessed others dying around him at a temporary first-aid area reached a point where "I just couldn't have any reaction. . . . You might say I became insensitive to human death." And the woman writer quoted before described "a feeling of paralysis that came over my mind."

The unconscious process here is that of closing oneself off from death itself; the controlling inner idea, or fantasy, is, "If I feel nothing, then death is not taking place." Psychic closing-off is thus related to the defense mechanisms of denial and isolation, as well as to the behavioral state of apathy. But it deserves to be distinguished from these in its sudden, global quality, in its throwing out a protective symbolic screen which enables the organism to resist the impact of death—that is, to survive psychologically in the midst of death and dying. It may well represent man's most characteristic response to catastrophe: one which is at times life-enhancing, or even, psychologically speaking, life-saving; but at other times, particularly when prolonged and no longer appropriate to the threat, not without its own dangers. Certainly the investigator of nuclear disaster finds himself experiencing a measure of such closing-off, as indeed does the reader of an account such as this one.[8]

Effective as it is, psychic closing-off has its limitations even as a protective reaction. It cannot entirely succeed in neutralizing either the threatening stimuli from without or those from within—the latter taking the form of self-condemnation, guilt, and shame. For at the very beginning of the atomic bomb experience a need is initiated for justifying one's own survival in the face of others' deaths, a form of guilt which plagues the survivor from then on, and to which I shall return. Here I shall only say *that the quick experience of self-condemnation intensifies the lasting imprint of death created by this early phase of atomic bomb exposure.* Contained within this imprint is something very close to witnessing in actuality that which ordinarily takes place only in psychotic fantasy—namely, an end-of-the-world experience. Normally a projection of inner psychological "death" onto the outside world, the process is here reversed so that an overwhelming external experience of near-absolute destruction becomes internalized and merged with related tendencies of the inner life.[9]

A type of memory which symbolizes this relationship of death to guilt appears in what I have called the *ultimate horror*—a specific image of the dead or dying

[8] In my previous paper (Lifton, 1963) I referred to this defensive maneuver as "psychological closure," and mentioned some of its wider implications for survivors, its necessity for me in carrying out the investigation, and its relationship to attitudes concerning nuclear weapons in general. The term "psychic closing-off," however, more directly conveys the threefold process involved: Numbing of affect, symbolic walling-off of the organism, and abrupt disconnection in communication between inner and outer worlds.

[9] In other words, one may assume that everyone has some tendency toward this form of "psychological death"—toward withdrawal of psychic connection to the world—originating in earliest separation experiences, including that of birth itself; but that the tendency becomes most characteristically predominant in psychosis. Thus, when *hibakusha* underwent their end-of-the-world experience, they had, so to speak, a previous psychic model for it, upon which it could be grafted. For an interesting discussion of the significance of the end-of-the-world fantasy in the history of psychoanalysis, see Selesnick (1963).

with which the survivor strongly identifies himself, and which evokes in him particularly intense feelings of pity and self-condemnation. The scene may include his own family members, or anonymous people in particularly grotesque physical array; or, as was frequent, pitiful images of women and children, universal symbols of purity and vulnerability, and especially so in Japanese culture.

One particular form of ultimate horror seemed, more than any other, to epitomize the association of death and guilt. It was the recollection of requests (whether overt or implicit) by the dying which could not be carried out, most specifically their pleas for a few sips of water. Water was withheld not only because of survivors' preoccupation with saving themselves and their own families, but because authorities spread the word that water would have harmful effects upon the severely injured. The request for water by the dying, however, in addition to reflecting their physical state, has special significance in Japanese tradition, as it is related to an ancient belief that water can restore life by bringing back the spirit that has just departed from the body (Inoguchi, 1959). These pleas were therefore as much psychological expressions of this belief as they were of physical need; indeed, one might say that they were pleas for life itself. The survivor's failure to acquiesce to them, whatever his reasons, could thus come to have the psychological significance for him of refusing the request of another for the privilege of life—while he himself clung so tenaciously to that same privilege.

Invisible Contamination

The second encounter with death took the form of *invisible contamination*. After the bomb fell—sometimes within hours or even minutes, often during the first 24 hours, and sometimes during the following days and weeks—many *hibakusha* began to notice in themselves and others a strange form of illness. It consisted of nausea, vomiting, and loss of appetite; diarrhea with large amounts of blood in the stools; fever and weakness; purple spots on various parts of the body from bleeding into the skin (purpura); inflammation and ulceration of the mouth, throat, and gums (orapharyngeal lesions and gingivitis); bleeding from the mouth, gums, nose, throat, rectum, and urinary tract (hemorrhagic manifestations); loss of hair from the scalp and other parts of the body (epilation); extremely low white blood-cell counts when these were taken (leukopenia)—these symptoms in many cases taking a progressive course until death. Such manifestations of irradiation, and the fatalities associated with them, aroused a special terror in the people of Hiroshima, an image of a weapon which not only instantaneously kills and destroys on a colossal scale but also leaves behind in the bodies of those exposed to it deadly influences which may emerge at any time and strike down their victims. This image was made particularly vivid by the delayed appearance of these radiation effects—often two to four weeks after the bomb fell—in people who had previously seemed to be in perfect health, externally untouched by atomic bomb effects.[10]

[10] See particularly Oughterson and Warren (1956). They and other authors demonstrate statistically that the great majority of cases of radiation effects occurred within the 2,000-meter radius (depending partly upon degree of shielding); but this correlation with distance was not understood at the time, nor has it eliminated subsequent fears of aftereffects in survivors exposed at greater distances.

No one at first had any understanding of the cause of the symptoms, and in the few medical facilities that were still functioning, isolation procedures were instituted in the belief that they were part of some kind of infectious gastrointestinal condition.[11] Ordinary people also suspected some form of epidemic, possibly in the nature of cholera. But very quickly, partly by word-of-mouth information and misinformation about the atomic bomb, people began to relate the condition to a mysterious "poison" emanating from the weapon itself. Whatever their idea of cause, survivors were profoundly impressed not only by the fact that others were dying around them, but by the way in which they died—a gruesome form of rapid bodily deterioration which seemed unrelated to more usual and "decent" forms of death. They were struck particularly by the loss of scalp hair, the purple spots on the skin, and (whether or not always true) by the way in which victims appeared to remain conscious and alert almost to the moment of their death. As a middle-aged electrician relates,

> There was one man who asked me for help and everything he said was clear and normal. . . . But in another three hours or so when I looked at him he was already dead. . . . And even those who looked as though they would be spared were not spared. . . . People seemed to inhale something from the air which we could not see. . . . The way they died was different . . . and strange.

Some were intrigued, and even attracted, by the weirdness of the symptoms— as in the case of a doctor quoted in a later written account:

> I know it is terrible to say this, but those spots were beautiful. They were just like stars—red, green, yellow, and black . . . all over the body, and I was fascinated by them (Ota, 1955).

But the predominant feeling among survivors was that they themselves were imminently threatened by this same "poison"—as conveyed in such statements as: "Soon we were all worried about our health, about our bodies—whether we would live or die"; "I thought, sooner or later I too will die. . . . I never knew when some sign of the disease would show itself"; and, "We waited for our own deaths."

The nature of the death symbolism of this second stage was revealed in three rumors which swept Hiroshima during the period immediately following the bomb. The first rumor simply held that all those who had been exposed to the bomb in the city would be dead within three years. The psychological message here was: None can escape the poison; the epidemic is total; all shall die.

But a second rumor, even more frequently related to me, and, I believe, with greater emotion, was that trees, grass, and flowers would never again grow in Hiroshima; from that day on the city would be unable to sustain vegetation of any kind. The message here was: Nature was drying up altogether; life was being extinguished at its source—suggesting an ultimate form of desolation which not only encompassed human death but went beyond it.

The third rumor, closely related to the other two, held that for a period of 70 or 75 years Hiroshima would be uninhabitable; no one would be able to live there. Here was the sense that Hiroshima was to become totally deurbanized—

[11] For a vivid description of these reactions in one of the hospitals that remained functional, see Hachiya (1955).

literally, devitalized—that the bomb's invisible contamination had more or less permanently deprived the area of its life-sustaining capacity.

Other rumors, particularly during the first few days after the bomb fell, expressed further ramifications of these emotions: there were rumors that there would be new attacks with "poison gases" or "burning oil"; that America, having dropped such a terrible "hot bomb," would next drop a "cold bomb" or "ice bomb" which would freeze everything so that everyone would die; and there was even a rumor that America would drop rotten pigs so that, as one man put it, "Everything on the earth would decay and go bad." These additional rumors conveyed the sense that the environment had be so fundamentally disturbed, and the individual sense of security and invulnerability in relationship to life and death so threatened, that further life-annihilating assaults must be anticipated.

The psychological aspects of the second encounter with death may thus be summarized as follows: There was a fear of epidemic contamination to the point of bodily deterioration; a sense of individual powerlessness in the face of an invisible, all-enveloping, and highly mysterious poison (and in regard to this mysteriousness, there has been some evidence of psychological resistance toward finding out the exact nature of radiation effects); the sense, often largely unconscious and indirectly communicated, that this *total contamination*—seemingly limitless in time and space—must have a supernatural, or at least more-than-natural origin, must be something in the nature of a curse upon one's group for some form of wrongdoing that had offended the forces which control life and death. This latter formulation was occasionally made explicit in, for instance, survivors' Buddhistic references to misbehavior in previous incarnations; it was implicit in their repeated expressions of awe, in the elaborate mythology (only a portion of which I have mentioned) they created around the event, and in their various forms of self-condemnation relating to guilt and punishment as well as to shame and humiliation.

"A-Bomb Disease"

The third encounter with death occurred with later radiation effects, not months but years after the atomic bomb itself, and may be summed up in the scientifically inaccurate but emotionally charged term, "A-bomb disease." The medical condition which has become the model for "A-bomb disease" is leukemia, based upon the increased incidence of this always fatal malignancy of the blood-forming organs, first noted in 1948 and reaching a peak between 1950 and 1952.[12] The symptoms of leukemia, moreover, rather closely resemble those of acute radiation effects, both conditions sharing various manifestations of blood

[12] For extensive studies of delayed physical aftereffects of radiation, see the series of Technical Reports of the Atomic Bomb Casualty Commission (an affiliate of the United States National Academy of Sciences-National Research Council, functioning with the cooperation of the Japanese National Institute of Health of the Ministry of Health and Welfare), as recently summarized in "Medical Findings and Methodology of Studies by the Atomic Bomb Casualty Commission on Atomic Bomb Survivors in Hiroshima and Nagasaki," in *The Use of Vital and Health Statistics for Genetic and Radiation Studies, Proceedings of the Seminar Sponsored by the United Nations and the World Health Organization,* held in Geneva, 5–9 September 1960, A/AC.82/Seminar, United Nations, New York, 1962; pp. 77–100. Additional Japanese and American studies are cited in Lifton (1963).

abnormalities, as well as the more visible and dreaded "purple spots" and other forms of hemorrhage, progressive weakness, and fever; leukemia, however, unlike acute irradiation, inevitably results in death.

Psychologically speaking, leukemia—or the threat of leukemia—became an indefinite extension of the earlier "invisible contamination." And individual cases of leukemia in children have become the later counterpart of the "ultimate horror" of the first moments of the experience, symbolizing once more the bomb's desecration of that which is held to be most pure and vulnerable—the desecration of childhood itself. Indeed, Hiroshima's equivalent of an Anne Frank legend has developed from one such case of leukemia in a 12-year-old girl, Sadako Sasaki, which occurred in 1954; her death resulted in a national campaign for the construction of a monument (which now stands prominently in the center of Hiroshima's Peace Park) to this child and to all other children who have died as a result of the atomic bomb (B. J. Lifton, 1963; Jungk, 1961).

And just at the time that the incidence of leukemia was recognized as diminishing and approaching the normal, evidence began accumulating that the incidence of various other forms of cancer was increasing among survivors—including carcinoma of the stomach, lung, thyroid, ovary, and uterine cervix. Leukemia is a rare disease (even with its increased incidence, only 122 cases were reported in Hiroshima between 1945 and 1959) but cancer is not; and should the trend continue, as appears likely, the increase in cancer will undoubtedly give further stimulus to various elaborations of death symbolism, just as some of these were beginning to decline. Thus on a chronic level of bodily concern, there is again evoked the feeling that the bomb can do anything, and that anything it does is likely to be fatal.

I shall not dwell on the other medical conditions which, with varying amounts of evidence, have been thought to be produced by delayed radiation effects. These include impairment in the growth and development of children; a variety of anemias and of liver and blood diseases; endocrine and skin disorders; impairment of central nervous system (particularly midbrain) function; premature aging; and a vague but persistently reported borderline condition of general weakness and debilitation. The exact consequences of radiation effects remain in many areas controversial, and are still under active investigation by both American and Japanese groups. My concern here, however, is the association in the minds of survivors of any kind of ailment with atomic bomb effects—whether it be fatigue, mild anemia, fulminating leukemia, or ordinary cardiovascular disease; and whether a scientific relationship to radiation effects seems probable, or possible but inconclusive, or apparently nonexistent. Bodily concerns of survivors are also intensified by the continuous publicizing of "A-bomb disease" by the mass media and by survivor and peace organizations, often in the form of lurid reports of patients dying in the "A-bomb hospital" (a special facility set up for the exposed population) of "A-bomb disease." Even though in many cases the relationship between the actual condition and the atomic bomb effects may be questionable, the ordinary survivor tends to identify himself directly with the victim and with the process of dying. As one man stated, "When I hear about people who die from A-bomb disease . . . then I feel that I am the same kind of person as they."

The survivor thus becomes involved in a vicious circle on the psychosomatic plane of existence: He is likely to associate even the mildest everyday injury or sickness with possible radiation effects; and anything he relates to radiation effects becomes in turn associated with death. The process is accentuated, though not created, by the strong Japanese cultural focus upon bodily symptoms as expressions of anxiety and conflict. The psychosomatic dilemma can also take on complicated ramifications. For instance, some survivors develop vague borderline symptoms, inwardly fear that these might be evidence of fatal "A-bomb disease," but resist seeking medical care because they do not wish to be confronted by this diagnosis. When such a pattern occurs in relationship to physical disease, it is usually referred to as "denial of illness"; but here the "illness" being denied is itself likely to be a symbolic product of psychological currents; and the "denial" is a specific response to the death symbolism associated with these currents. Others become involved in a lifelong preoccupation with "A-bomb disease," referred to by Hiroshima physicians as "A-bomb neurosis"; they become weak and sometimes bedridden, are constantly preoccupied with their blood counts and bodily symptoms, and precariously maintain an intricate inner balance between the need for their symptoms as an expression of various psychological conflicts and the anxious association of these symptoms with death and dying. At best, survivors find themselves constantly plagued with what may be called a nagging doubt about their freedom from radiation effects, and look upon themselves as people who are particularly vulnerable, who cannot afford to take chances.

Beyond their own sense of impaired body-image, survivors carry the fear that this impairment will manifest itself in subsequent generations. The issue of genetic effects from the A-bomb is also controversial and unresolved. Fortunately, studies on comparative populations have revealed no increase in abnormalities among children of survivors. But it is widely known that such abnormalities can be caused by radiation, and there are again the problems of variation in medical opinion (some Japanese pathologists think that some evidence of increase in genetic abnormalities exists), and of lurid, sometimes irresponsible, journalistic reports. There is, moreover, one uncomfortably positive genetic finding among significantly exposed survivors, that of a disturbance of sex ratio of offspring, the significance of which is difficult to evaluate (Lifton, 1963). Still another factor in the survivors' psychological associations has been the definite damage from radiation to children exposed *in utero*, including the occurrence of microcephaly with and without mental retardation; this phenomenon is, scientifically speaking, quite unrelated to genetic effects, but ordinary people often fail to make the distinction.

Thus, at this third level of encounter with death, the sudden "curse" mentioned before becomes an *enduring taint*—a taint of death which attaches itself not only to one's entire psychobiological organism, but to one's posterity as well. Although in most cases survivors have been able to live, work, marry, and beget children in more or less normal fashion, they have the sense of being involved in an *endless chain of potentially lethal impairment* which, if it does not manifest itself in one year—or in one generation—may well make itself felt in the next. Once more elements of guilt and shame become closely involved with this taint. But the whole constellation of which they are part is perceived not as an epidemic-like experience, but as a permanent and infinitely transmissible form of impaired body substance.

Identification with the Dead

The fourth level of encounter is a life-long identification with death, with dying, and with an anonymous group of "the dead." Indeed, the continuous encounter with death, in the sequence described, has much to do with creating a sense of group identity as *hibakusha,* or survivors. But it is an unwanted, or at best ambivalent, identity, built around the inner taint I have discussed and symbolized externally by disfigurement—that is, by keloid scars which, although possessed only by a small minority of survivors, have come to represent the stigmata of atomic bomb exposure.

A central conflict of this *hibakusha* identity is the problem of what I have come to speak of as *survival priority*—the inner question of why one has survived while so many have died, the inevitable self-condemnation in the face of others' deaths. *For the survivor can never, inwardly, simply conclude that it was logical and right for him, and not others, to survive. Rather, I would hold, he is bound by an unconscious perception of organic social balance which makes him feel that his survival was made possible by others' deaths: If they had not died, he would have had to; and if he had not survived, someone else would have.* This kind of guilt, as it relates to survival priority, may well be that most fundamental to human existence. Also contributing greatly to the survivor's sense of guilt are feelings (however dimly recalled) of relief, even joy, that it was the other and not he who died. And his guilt may be accentuated by previous death wishes toward parents who had denied him nurturance he craved, or toward siblings who competed for this nurturance, whether this guilt is directly experienced in relationship to the actual death of these family members, or indirectly through unconsciously relating such wishes to the death of any "other," however anonymous.

In ordinary mourning experiences, and in most ordinary disasters, there is considerable opportunity to resolve this guilt through the classical psychological steps of the mourning process. But with the atomic bomb disaster, my impression was that such resolution has been either minimal or at best incomplete. As in other mourning experiences, survivors have identified themselves with the dead (in this case, with the latter both as specific people and as an anonymous concept), and have incorporated the dead into their own beings; indeed one might say that survivors have imbibed and incorporated the entire destruction of their city, and in fact the full atomic bomb experience. But they have found no adequate ideological interpretation—no spiritual explanation, no "reason" for the disaster—that might release them from this identification, and have instead felt permanently bound by it. They have felt compelled virtually to merge with the dead and to behave, in a great variety of ways, *as if* they too were dead. Not only do they judge all behavior by the degree of respect it demonstrates toward the dead, but they tend to condemn almost any effort which suggests strong self-assertion or vitality—that is, which suggests life.

The *hibakusha* identity, then, in a significant symbolic sense, becomes an identity of the dead—taking the following inner sequence: I almost died; I should have died; I did die, or at least am not really alive; or if I am alive it is impure for me to be so; and anything I do which affirms life is also impure and an insult to the dead, who alone are pure. Of great importance here, of course, is the Japanese cultural stress upon continuity between the living and the dead; but the identity sequence also has specific relationship to the nature of the disaster itself.[13]

Yet one must not conclude that all survivors are therefore suicidal. This is by no means the case, and I was in fact struck by the tenacity with which *hibakusha*, at all of the stages mentioned, have held on to life. Indeed, I have come to the conclusion that this identification with death—this whole constellation of inwardly experienced death symbolism—is, paradoxically enough, the survivor's means of maintaining life. In the face of the burden of guilt he carries with him, and particularly the guilt of survival priority, his obeisance before the dead is his best means of justifying and maintaining his own existence. But it remains an existence with a large shadow cast across it, a life which, in a powerful symbolic sense, the survivor does not feel to be his own.[14]

General Principles

Through the experiences of Hiroshima survivors we have been thrust into the more general realm of the interrelationship between the anticipation of death and the conduct of life. It is an interrelationship that has been recognized and commented upon by generations of philosophers, though mentioned with surpris-

[13] The various elements of *hibakusha* identity are developed in somewhat greater detail in Lifton (1963). The point of view I wish to suggest about cultural factors in this response—and in other responses to the disaster—is that they are particular emphases of universal tendencies. Here, for instance, survivors' identification with the dead reflects a strong Japanese cultural tendency related in turn to a long tradition of ancestor worship; but this cultural emphasis should be seen as giving a special kind of intensity to a universal psychological pattern. Thus, "extreme situations" such as the Hiroshima disaster, through further intensifying culturally-stressed behavior patterns, throw particularly vivid light upon universal psychological function.

[14] This "identity of the dead" strikingly resembles findings that have been reported in survivors of Nazi concentration camps. Niederland (1961) describes a "psychological imprint" in concentration camp survivors which includes elements of depressive mood, withdrawal, apathy, outbursts of anger, and self-deprecatory attitudes which, in extreme cases, lead to a "living corpse" appearance; this is in turn attributed to their owing their survival to maintaining an existence of a "walking corpse" while their fellow inmates succumbed. Without attempting a full comparison here, one may say that in Nazi concentration camps, in addition to the more prolonged physical and psychological assault upon identity and character structure, the problem of survival priority was more directly experienced: Each inmate became aware that either he or someone else would be chosen for death, and went to great lengths to maintain his own life at the expense of the known or anonymous "other" (see Bettelheim, 1960). In the atomic bomb experience, the problem of survival priority was more symbolically evoked, as I have described, though the end result may be psychologically quite similar. Moreover, two additional factors—the fear of aftereffects (of "A-bomb disease"), and the survivors' tendency to relate their experience to the present world threat of nuclear weapons—have the effect of perpetuating their death symbolism and their sense of permanent encounter with death in a manner not true for concentration camp survivors (although the latter have had their anxieties and concerns over survival priority revived and intensified by such reminders of their experience as outbreaks of anti-Semitism anywhere in the world and, more importantly, the Eichmann trial). Despite their importance, these psychological problems of death symbolism have too often been overlooked or minimized by psychiatric examiners and other investigators concerned with later behavior of concentration camp victims, and by those studying other forms of persecution and disaster as well.

ing infrequency in psychiatric work. There are many signs that this psychiatric neglect is in the process of being remedied (Eissler, 1955; Feifel, 1959; Brown, 1959; Weisman and Hackett, 1961; Shneidman, 1963), and indeed the significance of problems in this area so impresses itself upon us in our present age that matters of death and dying could well serve as a nucleus for an entire psychology of life. But I will do no more than state a few principles which I have found to be a useful beginning for comprehending the Hiroshima experience, for relating it to universal human concerns, and for examining some of the impact upon our lives of the existence of nuclear weapons. Attempting even this much is audacious enough to warrant pause and examination of some rather restraining words of Freud, which are made no less profound by the frequency with which they have been quoted in the past:

> It is indeed impossible to imagine our own death; and whenever we attempt to do so we can perceive that we are in fact still present as spectators. Hence the psychoanalytic school could venture on the assertion that at bottom no one believes in his own death, or, to put the same thing in another way, that in the unconscious every one of us is convinced of his own immortality.

These words, which were written in 1915, about six months after the outbreak of World War I,[15] have found many recent echoes. (Merleau-Ponty, the distinguished French philosopher, has said (Beberman, 1963), "Neither my birth nor my death can appear to me as *my* experiences . . . I can only grasp myself as 'already born' and 'still living'—grasping my birth and death only as pre-personal horizons.")

Profound as Freud's words are, it is possible that psychological investigations of death have been unduly retarded by them. For they represent the kind of insight which, precisely because of its importance and validity, must be questioned further and even transcended. I believe it is more correct to say that our own death—or at least our own dying—is not entirely unimaginable but can be imagined only with a considerable degree of distance, blurring, and denial; that we are not absolutely convinced of our own immortality, but rather have a need to maintain a *sense of immortality* in the face of inevitable biological

---

[15] Freud (1957, p. 289). The editor of this edition, James Strachey, states (p. 274) that the two essays contained in the paper were written "round about March and April, 1915." Eissler (1955, pp. 24–25) dates them "at the end of 1914 or at the beginning of 1915," emphasizing that they were not written after exhausting years of despair and horror but were "a rather quick response to the very evident fact . . . that there is more aggression in man than one would have thought from his behavior in peacetime and that man's attitude toward death is usually the outcome of the mechanism of denial, so long as he does not face death as a reality which may befall him or his loved ones at any moment." Jones (1955, pp. 367–368) points out that the essays were written in response to a request from the publisher (Hugo Heller) of the psychological periodical, *Imago*, though he adds that Heller probably did not suggest the theme and that Freud, in writing them, must have been "like all highly civilized people . . . not only greatly distressed, but also bewildered, by the frightful happenings at the onset of the first World War, when so many things took place of which no living person had any experience or any expectation." Jones adds that these two essays "may be regarded as an effort to clear his mind about the most useful attitude to adopt to the current events." In any case it seems clear that with this paper, more than with most of his writings, Freud was responding to the stimulus of a great and highly threatening historical event; it is also significant that while his private reactions to the war were at times impulsive and quite variable, his public statement contained only a controlled series of ideas growing directly out of his previous concepts.

death; and that this need represents not only the inability of the individual unconscious to recognize the possibility of its own demise but also a compelling universal urge to maintain an inner sense of continuous symbolic relationship, over time and space, to the various elements of life. Nor is this need to transcend individual biological life *mere* denial (though denial becomes importantly associated with it): Rather it is part of the organism's psychobiological quest for mastery, part of an innate imagery that has apparently been present in man's mind since the earliest periods of his history and prehistory. This point of view is consistent with the approach of Joseph Campbell, the distinguished student of comparative mythology, who has likened such innate imagery or "elementary ideas" to the "innate releasing mechanisms" described by contemporary ethologists. It also bears some resemblance to Otto Rank's stress upon man's longstanding need of "an assurance of eternal survival for his self," and to Rank's further assertion that "man creates culture by changing natural conditions in order to maintain his spiritual self."[16]

The sense of immortality of which I speak may be expressed through any of several modes. First, it may be expressed biologically—or, more correctly, biosocially—by means of family continuity, living on through (but in an emotional sense, *with*) one's sons and daughters and their sons and daughters, by imagining (however vaguely and at whatever level of consciousness) an endless chain of biological attachment. This has been the classical expression of the sense of individual immortality in East Asian culture, as particularly emphasized by the traditional Chinese family system, and to a somewhat lesser extent by the Japanese family system as well. But it is of enormous universal importance, perhaps the most universally significant of all modes. This mode of immortality never remains purely biological; rather it is experienced psychically and symbolically, and in varying degree extends itself into social dimensions, into the sense of surviving through one's tribe, organization, people, nation, or even species. On the whole, this movement from the biological to the social has been erratic and in various ways precarious; but some, like Julian Huxley and Pierre Teilhard de Chardin,[17] see it as taking on increasing significance during the course of human evolution. If this is so, individual man's sense of immortality may increasingly derive from his inner conviction, "I live on through mankind."

Second, a sense of immortality may be achieved through a theologically-based idea of a life after death, not only as a form of "survival" but even as a "release" from profane life burdens into a "higher" form of existence. Some such concept has been present in all of the world's great religions and throughout human mythology. The details of life after death have been vague and logically

---

[16] In developing his ideas on the "inherited image," Campbell (1959) follows Adolf Bastian and C. G. Jung. Rank (1958) develops his concepts of man's quest for immortality through the literary and psychological concept of "The Double as Immortal Self." While I do not agree with all that Rank and Campbell say on these issues (I would, in fact, take issue with certain Jungian concepts Campbell puts forward), their points of view at least serve to open up an important psychological perspective which sees the quest for immortality as inherent in human psychology and human life.

[17] Huxley and Père Teilhard, of course, go further, and visualize the development of a unifying, more or less transcendent idea-system around this tendency. Huxley (1961) refers to this as "evolutionary humanism" and Père Teilhard (1959) speaks of the "Omega point," at which a "hyperpersonal" level of advanced human consciousness may be attained.

contradictory in most theologies, since the symbolic psychological theme of transcending death takes precedence over consistency of concrete elaboration. Christianity has perhaps been most explicit in its doctrine of life after death, and most demanding of commitment to this doctrine; but intra-Christian debate over interpretation of doctrine has never ceased, with present thought tending toward a stress upon transcendent symbolism rather than literal belief.

Third, and this is partly an extension of the first two modes, a sense of immortality may be achieved through one's creative works or human influences—one's writings, art, thought, inventions, or lasting products of any kind that have an effect upon other human beings. (In this sense, lasting therapeutic influences upon patients, who in turn transmit them to their posterity, can be a mode of immortality for physicians and psychotherapists.) Certainly this form of immortality has particular importance for intellectuals conscious of participating in the general flow of human creativity, but applies in some measure to all human beings in their unconscious perceptions of the legacy they leave for others.

Fourth, a sense of immortality may be achieved through being survived by nature itself: the perception that natural elements—limitless in space and time—remain. I found this mode of immortality to be particularly vivid among the Japanese, steeped as their culture is in nature symbolism; but various expressions of Western tradition (the romantic movement, for instance) have also placed great emphasis upon it. It is probably safe to say—and comparative mythology again supports this—that there is a universal psychic imagery in which nature represents an "ultimate" aspect of existence.

These psychological modes of immortality are not merely problems one ponders when dying; they are, in fact, constantly (though often indirectly or unconsciously) perceived standards by which people evaluate their lives. They thus make possible an examination of the part played by death and death symbolism during ordinary existence, which is what I mean by the beginnings of a death-oriented psychology of life. I shall for this purpose put forth three propositions, all of them dealing with death as a standard for, or test of, some aspect of life.

(1) Death is anticipated as a *severance of the sense of connection*—or the inner sense of organic relationship to the various elements, and particularly to the people and groups of people, most necessary to our feelings of continuity and relatedness. Death is therefore a test of this sense of connection in that it threatens us with that which is most intolerable: *total severance.* Indeed, all of the modes of immortality mentioned are symbolic reflections of that part of the human psychic equipment which protects us from such severance and isolation.

Another expression of the threat to the sense of connection represented by death is the profound ambivalence of every culture toward the dead. One embraces the dead, supplicates oneself before them, and creates continuous rituals to perpetuate one's relationship to them, and (as is so vividly apparent in the case of the Hiroshima survivors) to attenuate one's guilt over survival priority. But one also pushes away the dead, considers them tainted and unclean, dangerous and threatening, precisely because they symbolize a break in the sense of connection and threaten to undermine it within the living. These patterns too were strongly present in Hiroshima survivors (and can be found in general Japanese cultural practice), although less consciously acceptable and therefore more indirectly expressed. Indeed, in virtually every culture the failure of the living to enact the rituals necessary to appease the dead is thought to so anger the latter (or their sacred representatives) as to bring about dangerous retribution for this failure to atone for the guilt of survival priority.

(2) Death is a test of the meaning of life, of the symbolic integrity—the cohesion and significance—of the life one has been living. This is a more familiar concept, closely related to ideas that have long been put forth in literature and philosophy, as well as in certain psychoanalytic writings of Freud, Rank, and Jung; and it has a variety of manifestations. One is the utilization of a *way or style of dying* (or of anticipated dying) as an epitome of life's significance. An excellent example of this is the Japanese *samurai* code, in which a heroic form of death in battle on behalf of one's lord (that is, a death embodying courage and loyalty) was the ultimate expression of the meaning of life.[18] Various cultures and subcultures have similarly set up an ideal style of dying, rarely perfectly realized, but nonetheless a powerful standard for the living. The anticipation of dying nobly, or at least appropriately—of dying for a meaningful purpose—is an expression of those modes of immortality related both to man's works (his lasting influences) and his biosocial continuity. And I believe that much of the passionate attraction man has felt toward death can be understood as reflecting the unspoken sense that only in meaningful death can one simultaneously achieve a sense of immortality and articulate the meaning of life.

Apart from dramatically perfect deaths on the *samurai* model, timing and readiness play an important part. Can one visualize, in association with death, sufficient accomplishment to justify one's life? Or has life become so burdensome and devoid of meaning that death itself (whatever the style of dying) seems more appropriate? The latter was the case with a remarkable group of people undergoing surgery recently described by Avery Weisman and Thomas P. Hackett (1961, p. 254). These "predilection patients" were neither excessively anxious nor depressed, and yet correctly predicted their own deaths. For them, "death held more appeal . . . than did life because it promised either reunion with lost love, resolution of long conflict, or respite from anguish," and one is led to conclude that this psychological state interacted with their organic pathology and their reactions to surgical procedures to influence significantly the timing of their deaths. Their surrender to death was apparently related to their sense that they could no longer justify their continuing survival.

A classical literary expression of anticipated death as a test of the integrity of one's entire life (and one which has inspired many commentaries) occurs in Tolstoy's *The Death of Ivan Ilych* (1960). Here the protagonist, in becoming aware of the incurable nature of his illness, reviews his past and is tormented by the thought that "the whole arrangement of his life and of his family, and all his social and official interests, might all have been false," and that the only authentic expressions of his life have been "those scarcely noticeable impulses which he had immediately suppressed." His lament in the face of approaching

[18] The *Hagakure*, the classical eighteenth-century compilation of principles of *Bushidō* (The Way of the Samurai), contains the famous phrase: "The essence of *Bushidō* lies in the act of dying." And another passage, originally from The *Manyōshū*, a poetic anthology of the eighth century: " 'He who dies for the sake of his Lord does not die in vain, whether he goes to the sea and his corpse is left in a watery grave, or whether he goes to the mountain and the only shroud for his lifeless body is the mountain grass.' This is the way of loyalty" (Bellah, 1957).

death is that of wasted opportunity ("I have lost all that was given me and it is impossible to rectify it") and existential guilt: The awareness of the enormous gap between what he has been and what he feels he might have been. But his torment disappears through a sudden spiritual revelation, his own capacity to feel love and pity for his wife and son. And at this point, for Ivan Ilych, "death" disappears: "Death is finished . . . it is no more!" "Death" has meant emptiness, the termination of a life without significance; death is transcended through a revelation which revivifies Ivan Ilych's sense of immortality by transporting him, even momentarily, into a realm of what he can perceive as authentic experience, and one in which he can feel in contact with eternal human values of pity and love, whether these are derived from a theologically-defined supernatural source, or from man's own creative works and influences.

Highly significant in Ivan Ilych's search for integrity is his disgust for the lying and evasiveness of those around him concerning the true nature of his illness (and concerning everything else), his yearning for an end to "this falsity around and within him [which] did more than anything else to poison his last days." But his family members are incapable of acting otherwise, because their deception is also self-deception, their own need to deny death; and because they are immersed in their own guilt over survival priority in relationship to Ivan Ilych—guilt made particularly intense by their hypocrisy, lack of love for him, and relief that death is claiming him and not them. Similar emotions are present in his colleagues and friends immediately after his death: "Each one thought or felt, 'Well, he's dead but I'm alive!'" The one voice of integrity around Ivan Ilych is that of a simple peasant servant who makes no effort to hide from him the fact that he is dying but instead helps him understand that death is, after all, the fate of everyone, that "We shall all of us die. . . ." Here the "survivor" lessens the emotional gap between himself and the dying man by stressing their shared destiny; this in turn enables the dying man to see his experience in relationship to the larger rhythms of life and death, and thereby awakens his biologically-linked mode of immortality.[19]

Very similar in theme to the death of Ivan Ilych, and probably influenced by it, is a recent Japanese film, *Ikiru* (*To Live*), made by the accomplished director, Akira Kurosawa. The film is also about a dying man who critically reviews his life—a petty official whose past actions have been characterized by bureaucratic evasion, and who overcomes his self-condemnation by an almost superhuman dedication to a final task, the building of a park for children. He thus

[19] Psychiatrists attending dying patients serve functions similar to that of the peasant servant in *The Death of Ivan Ilych*. Eissler (1955) speaks of helping the patient during the "terminal pathway" to "accomplish the maximum individualization of which he is capable." And Weisman and Hackett similarly stress psychiatric intervention "to help the dying patient preserve his identity and dignity as a unique individual, despite the disease, or, in some cases, because of it." I would hold that achieving these goals depends also upon restoring the patient's sense of immortality through the various modes which have been discussed. Weisman and Hackett describe a "middle knowledge," or partial awareness which patients have of their impending death, and find that patients' relatives (like those of Ivan Ilych) and attending physicians, because of their own conflicts over death, often have a greater need to deny this outcome than the patient himself. A situation is thus created in which the patient is reluctant to admit his "middle knowledge" to those around him for fear (and it is by no means an inappropriate fear) that they will turn away from him—so that he feels threatened with total severence (Weisman and Hackett, 1961).

achieves his sense of immortality mainly by his "works," by the final monument he leaves behind for others (even though surviving fellow-bureaucrats, who had actually tried to block the enterprise, claim complete credit for it). This form of immortality is more consistent with East Asian stress upon the contribution to the social order—and with the Japanese *deification of the human matrix*[20]— than is the Western mode of spiritual revelation or faith expressed in the Tolstoy story. Moreover, the sequence of the bureaucrat's behavior on discovering he is dying—first his withdrawal into petulant inactivity and then his extraordinary rush of productive energy—provides evidence of the East Asian tendency to deal with problems of despair over life and death by means of a polarity of purposeless withdrawal or active involvement, rather than by the more characteristically Western pattern of self-lacerating inner struggle against the forces creating despair.[21] But concerning the problems of death and the sense of immortality, the essential message of *Ikiru* is not different from that of *The Death of Ivan Ilych*.

The foregoing may suggest some of the wider meaning of the concept of the survivor. All of us who continue to live while people anywhere die are survivors, and both the word and the condition suggest a relationship which we all have to the dead. Therefore, the Hiroshima survivors' focus upon the dead as arbiters of good and evil, and invisible assigners of guilt and shame, is by no means as unique as it at first glance appears to be. For we all enter into similar commitments to the dead, whether consciously or unconsciously, whether to specific people who lived in the past or to the anonymous dead; or whether these commitments relate to theological or quasi-theological ideas about ties to the dead in another form of existence, or to more or less scientific ideas about a heritage we wish to affirm or a model we wish to follow. In fact, in any quest for perfection there is probably a significant identification with the imagined perfection of the dead hero or heroes who lived in the golden age of the past. Most of our history has been made by those now dead, and we cannot avoid calling upon them, at least in various symbolic ways, for standards that give meaning to our lives.

(3) And a last proposition: Death, in the very abruptness of its capacity to terminate life, becomes a test of life's sense of movement, of development and change—of sequence—in the continuous dialectic between fixed identity on the

[20] Lifton (1962). There are, of course, East Asian forms of spiritual revelation, particularly in Buddhism, but these are of a somewhat different nature; moreover, as Buddhism has moved eastward from its Indian origins—and particularly in its expressions in Japan—it has lost much of its original concern with spiritual revelation, and with doctrine in general, and these have become in various ways subordinated to the sectarian tendencies of the various human groups involved. See Nakamura (1960).

[21] Again the distinction should be understood as reflecting patterns emerging from varying degrees of psychological emphasis rather than absolute difference. Nonetheless, this East Asian, and perhaps particularly Japanese, pattern of despair has considerable importance for such problems as the emotional context of suicide in Japanese life, and the differences in Japanese and Western attitudes toward psychological constellations which the Westerner speaks of as tragedy. In all of these, I believe, Japanese show less of an inner struggle against the forces of nature or man creating the despair, potential suicide, or tragedy, and instead a greater tendency either to acquiesce to these forces or else to cease life-involving activity altogether. The degree of relevance of Western writings on despair for the Japanese situation can best be appreciated by keeping these distinctions in mind. See Farber (1958, 1962).

one hand and individuation on the other. To the extent that death is anticipated as absolute termination of life's movement, it calls into question the degree to which one's life contains, or has contained, any such development. Further, I would hold that a sense of movement in the various involvements of life is as fundamental a human need, as basic to the innate psychic imagery, as is the countervailing urge toward stillness, constancy, and reduction of tension which Freud (after Barbara Low) called the "Nirvana principle."[22] Freud referred to the Nirvana principle as "the dominating tendency of mental life" and related it to the "death instinct"; but I would prefer to speak instead of polarizing psychic tendencies toward continuous movement and ultimate stillness, both equally central to psychic function. Given the preoccupation with and ambivalence toward death since mankind's beginnings, Freud's concept of the death instinct may be a much more powerful one than his critics will allow. At the same time, it may yield greater understanding through being related to contemporary thought on symbolic process and innate imagery, rather than to older, more mechanistic views on the nature of instinct (see, e.g., Langer, 1953; Campbell, 1959; Boulding, 1956; Barnett, 1963; Portmann, 1964).[23]

To express this human necessity for a sense of movement, I find it often useful to speak of "self-process" rather than simply of "self." And I believe that the perpetual quest for a sense of movement has much to do with the appeal of comprehensive ideologies, particularly political and social ones, since these ideologies contain organized imagery of wider historical movement, and of individual participation in constant social flux. Yet ideologies, especially when totalist in character, also hold out an ultimate vision of Utopian perfection in which all movement ceases, because one is, so to speak, *there*. This strong embodiment of both ends of the psychic polarity—of continuous movement as well as perfect stillness—may well be a fundamental source of ideological appeal. For in this polarity, ideologies represent a significant means of transcending linear time, and, at least symbolically, of transcending death itself. In the promise of an interminable relationship to the "Movement," one can enter into both a biosocial mode of immortality and a very special version of immortality through man's works, in this case relating to man's symbolic conquest of time. Nor is it accidental that ideologies appear and gather momentum during periods of cultural breakdown and historical dislocation, when there tends to be a sense of cessation of movement and of prominent death symbolism. For central to the revitalizing mission of ideologies is their acting out, in historical (and psychological) context, the classical mythological theme of death and rebirth.[24]

[22] Freud (1955). Choisy (1963) has pointed out that Freud (and presumably Barbara Low), in employing this terminology, misunderstood the actual significance of Nirvana—to which I would add that Nirvana (whether the ideal state or the quest for that state) probably involves various kinds of indirect activity and sense of movement, and not simply ultimate stillness.

[23] What Freud refers to as the death instinct may well be an innate imagery of death which the organism contains from birth, which becomes in the course of life further elaborated into various forms of conscious knowledge, fear, and denial; and which interacts with other forms of innate imagery relating to life-enhancement (sexual function, self-preservation, and development) as well as to mastery. From this perspective, the need to transcend death involves the interrelationship of all three of these forms of imagery, with that of mastery of great importance.

[24] For a discussion of psychological and historical aspects of ideology, and particularly of ideological extremism, see Lifton (1961).

The psychic response to a threat of death, actual or symbolic, is likely to be either that of stillness and cessation of movement, or else of frenetic, compensatory activity. The former was by far the most prominent in the Hiroshima situation, though the latter was not entirely absent. The psychic closing-off which took place right after the bomb fell was, in an important sense, a cessation of psychic motion—a temporary form of symbolically "dying"—in order to defend against the threat of more lasting psychological "death" (psychosis) posed by the overwhelming evidence of actual physical death. And the same may be said of the later self-imposed restraint in living which characterizes the "identity of the dead," an identity whose very stillness becomes a means of carrying on with life in the face of one's commitment to death and the dead. But there were occasional cases of heightened activity, usually of an unfocused and confused variety, even at the time of the bomb. And later energies in rebuilding the city—the "frontier atmosphere" that predominated during much of the postwar period—may also be seen as a somewhat delayed intensification of movement, though it must be added that much of this energy and movement came from the outside.

Can something more be said about these propositions concerning death, and about the various modes of immortality, as they specifically apply to the nuclear age? I believe that from these perspectives we can see new psychological threats posed by nuclear weapons—right now, to all of us among the living.

Concerning the first proposition, that death is a test of our sense of connection, if we anticipate the possibility of nuclear weapons being used (as I believe we all do in some measure), we are faced with a prospect of being severed from virtually all of our symbolic paths to immortality. In the postnuclear world, we can imagine no biological or biosocial posterity; there is little or nothing surviving of our works or influences; and theological symbolism of an afterlife may well be insufficiently strong in its hold on the imagination to still inner fears of total severance. Certainly in my Hiroshima work I was struck by the inability of people to find adequate transcendent religious explanation—Buddhist, Shinto, or Christian—for what they and others had experienced. This was partly due to the relatively weak state of such theological symbolism in contemporary Japan, but perhaps most fundamentally due to the magnitude of the disaster itself. And whatever the mixed state of religious symbolism in the rest of the world, there is grave doubt as to whether the promise of some form of life after death can maintain symbolic power in an imagined world in which there are none (or virtually none) among the biologically living. This leaves only the mode of immortality symbolized by nature, which I found to be perhaps the most viable of all among Hiroshima survivors—as expressed in the Japanese (originally Chinese) proverb quoted to me by several of them: "The state may collapse but the mountains and rivers remain." And with all the other modes of immortality so threatened, we may raise the speculative possibility that, independent of any further use of nuclear weapons, one outcome of the nuclear age might be the development of some form of natural theology (or at least of a theology in which nature is prominent) as a means of meeting man's innate need for a sense of immortality.

Concerning the second proposition, relating to the meaning and integrity of life, we find ourselves even more directly threatened by nuclear weapons. As many have already pointed out, nuclear weapons confront us with a kind of death that can have no meaning (see, e.g., Morgenthau, 1961; Frank, 1960; Grinspoon,

1964). There is no such thing as dying heroically, for a great cause, in the service of a belief or a nation—in other words, for a palpable purpose—but rather only the prospect of dying anonymously, emptily, without gain to others. Such feelings were prominent among Hiroshima survivors both at the time of their initial immersion in death and during the months and years following it. They could not view their experience as purposeful, in the sense of teaching the world the necessity for abandoning nuclear weapons, but rather saw themselves as scapegoats for the world's evil, "guinea pigs" in a historical "experiment," or else as victims of a war made infinitely more inhuman by the new weapon. Part of their problem was the difficulty they had in knowing whom or what to hate, since, as one of my colleagues put it, "You can't hate magic." They did find in postwar Japanese pacifism an opportunity for organized rechanneling of resentment into a hatred of war itself; this was of considerable importance, but has by no means resolved the issue. The only consistent "meaning" survivors could find in all of the death and destruction around them was in the application of an everyday expression of East Asian fatalism—*shikataganai* ("It can't be helped") —which is a surface reflection of a profoundly important psychological tendency toward accepting whatever destiny one is given. But however great the psychological usefulness of this attitude, one can hardly say that it enabled survivors to achieve full mastery of their experience. And concerning the question of the "appropriateness" of anticipated death, Hiroshima survivors were the very antithesis of the "predilection patients" mentioned before: Rather than being ready for death, they found its intrusion upon life to be unacceptable, even absurd; and when seeming to embrace death, they were really clinging to life.

But considering the destructive power of present nuclear weapons (which is more than a thousandfold that of the Hiroshima bomb), and considering the impossibility of a meaningful nuclear death, is not life itself deprived of much of its meaning? Does not nuclear death threaten the deep significance of all of our lives? Indeed, the attraction some feel toward the use of nuclear weapons might be partly a function of this meaninglessness, so that in a paradoxical way they want to "end it all" (and perhaps realize their own end-of-the-world fantasies) as a means of denying the very emptiness of the nuclear death toward which they press. Here the principle of individual suicide as an attempt to deny the reality of death[25] is carried further to encompass nuclear suicide-murder as an attempt to deny the threat to meaningful human existence posed by these weapons.

And finally, in relationship to the proposition of death as a test of life's sense of movement, I think the matter is more ambiguous, though hardly encouraging. There is a sense in all of us, in greater or lesser degree, that nuclear weapons might terminate all of life's movement. Yet there is also, at least in some, a strange intensity and excitement in relationship to the confrontation with danger which nuclear weapons provide; and this, it might be claimed, contributes to a sense of movement in present-day life. But this exhilaration—or perhaps pseudo exhilaration—is less a direct function of the nuclear weapons themselves than of

[25] Eissler (1955) notes the frequently observed psychological relationship between suicide and murder, and goes on to speak of suicide as "the result of a rebellion against death," since "for most suicides the act does not mean really dying" but is rather a means of active defiance of, rather than passive submission to, death.

the universal historical dislocation accompanying a wider technological revolution. In other words, there is in our world an extraordinary combination of potential for continuously enriching movement and development of self-process, side by side with the potential for sudden and absolute termination. This latter possibility, which I have called the *potentially terminal revolution* (Lifton, 1963a), has not yet been seriously evaluated in its full psychological consequences; and whatever its apparent stimulus to a sense of movement, one may well suspect that it also contributes to a profound listlessness and inertia that lurk beneath.

I am aware that I have painted something less than an optimistic picture, both concerning the Hiroshima disaster and our present relationship to the nuclear world. Indeed it would seem that we are caught in a vicious psychological and historical circle, in which the existence of nuclear weapons impairs our relationship to death and immortality, and this impairment to our symbolic processes in turn interferes with our ability to deal with these same nuclear weapons. But one way of breaking out of such a pattern is by gaining at least a dim understanding of our own involvement in it. And in studying the Hiroshima experience and other extreme situations, I have found that man's capacity for elaborating and enclosing himself in this kind of ring of destructiveness is matched only by his equal capacity for renewal. Surely the mythological theme of death and rebirth takes on particular pertinence for us now, and every constructive effort we can make to grasp something more of our relationship to death becomes, in its own way, a small stimulus to rebirth.

REFERENCES

Adams, E. C. Problems in attitude therapy in a mental hospital. *Amer. J. Psychiat.*, 1948, **105**, 456–461.

Adams, H. B. "Mental illness" or interpersonal behavior? *Amer. Psychol.*, 1964, **19**, 191–197.

Adler, Alexandra. The individual psychology of the alcoholic patient. *J. Crim. Psychopath.*, 1941, **3**, 74–77.

Adorno, T. W., E. Frenkel-Brunswik, D. J. Levinson, and R. N. Sanford. *The authoritarian personality*. New York: Harper, 1950.

Ainsworth, Mary D. The effects of maternal deprivation: A review of findings and controversy in the context of research strategy. In John Bowlby *et al.*, *Maternal care and mental health*. New York: Schocken, 1952.

Akimoto, H., T. Simazaki, and S. Hanasiro. S. Demographische und psychiatrische Untersuchung über abgegrenzte Kleinstadtgevölkerung. *Psychiat. Neurol. Jap.*, 1942, **47**, 351–374.

Alcoholics Anonymous. *Is A.A. for you?* New York: Alcoholics Anonymous, 1956.

Alexander, F., and T. M. French. *Psychoanalytic therapy*. New York: Ronald Press, 1946.

Allinsmith, W., and G. W. Goethals. Cultural factors in mental health. *Rev. Educ. Res.*, 1956, **26**, 429–450.

Allport, F. H. A structuronomic conception of behavior: Individual and collective. I.

Structural theory and the master problem of social psychology. *J. abnorm. soc. Psychol.*, 1962, **64**, 1–30.

Allport, Gordon W. *Becoming: Basic considerations for a psychology of personality.* New Haven: Yale Univ. Press, 1955.

———. The historical background of modern social psychology. In Gardner Lindzey (Ed.), *Handbook of social psychology.* Vol. 1. Cambridge, Mass.: Addison-Wesley, 1954.

———. The open system in personality theory. *J. abnorm. soc. Psychol.*, 1960, **61**, 301–310.

———. *Pattern and growth in personality.* New York: Holt, 1961.

———. Personality: Normal and abnormal. In his *Personality and social encounter.* Boston: Beacon, 1964.

———. *Personality, a psychological interpretation.* New York: Holt, 1937.

American Psychiatric Association. *Diagnostic and statistical manual: Mental disorders.* Washington, D.C.: Amer. Psychiatric Assn., 1952.

American Psychological Association. Ad hoc planning group on the role of the APA in mental health programs and research. Mental health and the American Psychological Association. *Amer. Psychol.*, 1959, **14**, 820–825.

Anastasi, Anne. *Differential psychology.* (3rd ed.) New York: Macmillan, 1958.

Anderson, N. *The hobo.* Chicago: Univ. of Chicago Press, 1923.

Anderson, T. Mental health. *Independ. Amer.*, 1962, **8**, 4.

Angrist, S., S. Dinitz, M. Lefton, and B. Pasamanick. *Women after treatment: A study of former mental patients and their normal neighbors.* New York: Appleton, 1968.

Angyal, A. A theoretical model for personality studies. In D. Krech and G. S. Klein (Eds.), *Theoretical models and personality theory.* Durham: Duke Univ., 1952.

Arendt, H. *The human condition.* Chicago: Univ. of Chicago Press, 1958.

Argyris, C. Individual actualization in complex organizations. *Ment. Hyg.*, 1960, **44**, 226–237.

———. *Integrating the individual and the organization.* New York: Wiley, 1964.

———. *Personality and organization.* New York: Harper, 1957.

Arieti, S. *Interpretation of schizophrenia.* New York: Brunner, 1955.

Aronfreed, J. The nature, variety, and social patterning of moral responses to transgression. *J. abnorm. soc. Psychol.*, 1961, **63**, 223–240.

Asch, Solomon E. Studies of independence and conformity: I. A minority of one against a unanimous majority. *Psychol. Monogr.*, 1956, **70**, 1–70.

Ashbrook, J. Brainpicking in school: A study of psychiatric testing. *Hum. Events*, 1962, **19**, 883–886.

Astrup, Christian, and Ørnulv Ødegaard. Internal migration and disease in Norway. *Psychiat. Quart. Suppl.*, 1960, **34**, 116–130.

Atkinson, John W. Motivational determinants of risk-taking behavior. *Psychol. Rev.*, 1957, **64**, 359–372.

———. Explorations using imaginative thought to assess the strength of human motives. In M. R. Jones (Ed.), *Nebraska symposium on motivation.* Lincoln: Univ. of Nebraska Press, 1957a.

———, Jarvis R. Bastian, Robert W. Earl, and George H. Litwin. The achievement motive, goal setting, and probability preferences. *J. abnorm. soc. Psychol.*, 1960, **60**, 27–36.

Atthowe, J. M., Jr. Ward 113 program: Incentives and costs—a manual for patients. Palo Alto, Calif.: Vet. Admin. Hospital, 1964.

Auerbach, A. H., and J. H. Ewing. Some limitations of psychiatric rating scales: The clinician's viewpoint. *Comp. Psychiat.*, 1964, **5**, 93–100.

Auerback, A. The anti-mental health movement. *Amer. J. Psychiat.*, 1963, **120**, 105–111.

Auld, Frank, Jr. Influence of social class on personality test responses. *Psychol. Bull.*, 1952, **49**, 318–332.

Ausubel, David P. *Ego development and the personality disorders*. New York: Grune & Stratton, 1952.

————. Personality disorder in disease. *Amer. Psychol.*, 1961, **16**, 69–74.

————. Relationships between psychology and psychiatry: The hidden issues. *Amer. Psychol.*, 1956, **11**, 99–105.

Ayllon, T. Intensive treatment of psychotic behavior by stimulus satiation and food reinforcement. *Behavior Res. Therapy*, 1963, **1**, 53–61.

————, and N. H. Azrin. The measurement and reinforcement of behavior of psychotics. *J. exp. Anal. Behavior*, 1965, **8**, 357–384.

Ayllon, T., and E. Houghton. Control of the behavior of schizophrenic patients by food. *J. exp. Anal. Behavior*, 1962, **5**, 343–352.

Ayllon, T., and J. Michael. The psychiatric nurse as a behavioral engineer. *J. exp. Anal. Behavior*, 1959, **2**, 323–334.

Bailyn, L., and H. C. Kelman. The effects of a year's experience in America on the self-image of Scandinavians: A preliminary analysis of reactions to a new environment. *J. Social Issues*, 1962, **18**, 30–40.

Bain, Howard G. A sociological analysis of the Chicago skid-row lifeway. Unpublished M.A. thesis, Dept. of Sociology, Univ. of Chicago, Sept. 1950, esp. "The rationale of the skid-row drinking group," 141–146.

Bakke, E. Wight. *Citizens without work*. New Haven, Conn.: Yale Univ. Press, 1940.

Baldwin, A. L. *Behavior and development in childhood*. New York: Dryden, 1955.

Baldwin, James. *Giovanni's room*. New York: Dial, 1956.

Bales, R. F. *Interaction process analysis: A method for the study of small groups*. Cambridge, Mass.: Addison-Wesley, 1950.

Barker, R. G., and H. F. Wright. *Midwest and its children*. Evanston, Ill.: Row, Peterson, 1957.

Barnett, S. A. Instinct. *Daedalus*, 1963, **92**, 564–580.

Barron, F. Toward a positive definition of psychological health. Paper presented at the Annual Meeting of the American Psychological Association, San Francisco, Sept. 1955.

Barzun, J. *Darwin, Marx, Wagner: Critique of a heritage*. (2nd ed.) Garden City, N.Y.: Doubleday, 1958.

Bateman, J. B., and H. W. Dunham. The state mental hospital as a special community experience. *Amer. J. Psychiat.*, 1948, **105**, 445–448.

Bateson, G. The biosocial integration of behavior in the schizophrenic family. In N. Ackerman, *et al.* (Eds.), *Exploring the base for family therapy*. New York: Fam. Serv. Assn. Amer., 1961.

————. Cultural problems posed by a study of schizophrenic process. In A. Auerback (Ed.), *Schizophrenia: An integrated approach*. New York: Ronald Press, 1959.

————. Minimal requirements for a theory of schizophrenia. *Arch. gen. Psychiat.*, 1960, **2**, 477–491.

———, Don Jackson, Jay Haley, and John Weakland. Toward a theory of schizophrenia. *Behav. Science*, 1956, **1**, 251–264.

Bean, Lee L., Jerome K. Myers, and Max P. Pepper. Social class and schizophrenia: A ten-year follow-up. In Arthur B. Shostak and William Gomberg (Eds.), *Blue-collar world*. Englewood Cliffs, N.J.: Prentice-Hall, 1964.

Beberman, Arleen. Trans. of Phénoménologie de la Perception. In Death and my life. *Review of Metaphysics*, 1963, **17**, 18–32.

Beck, D. F. The dynamics of group psychotherapy as seen by a sociologist. Part I: The basic process. *Sociometry*, 1958, **21**, 98–128.

Becker, Howard S. Marihuana use and social control. *Soc. Problems*, 1955, **3**, 35–44.

Becker, Joseph. Achievement related characteristics of manic-depressives. *J. abnorm. soc. Psychol.*, 1960, **60**, 334–339.

Becker, W. C. The process-reactive distinction: A key to the problem of schizophrenia? *J. nerv. ment. Dis.*, 1959, **129**, 442–449.

———. The relation of severity of thinking disorder to the process-reactive concept of schizophrenia. Unpublished doctoral dissertation, Stanford Univ., 1955.

Beers, C. W. *A mind that found itself.* (5th ed.) New York: Longmans, 1921.

Beilin, H. Effect of social (occupational) role and age upon the criteria of mental health. *J. soc. Psychol.*, 1958, **48**, 247–256.

———. The prediction of adjustment over a four year interval. *J. clin. Psychol.*, 1957, **13**, 270–274.

Belknap, Ivan. *Human problems of a state mental hospital.* New York: McGraw-Hill, 1956.

———, and E. G. Jaco. The epidemiology of mental disorders in a political-type city, 1946–1952. In Milbank Memorial Fund, *Interrelations between the social environment and psychiatric disorders*. New York: Milbank Mem. Fund, 1953.

Bell, D. *The end of ideology.* New York: Free Press, 1960.

Bellah, Robert N. *Tokugawa religion.* New York: Free Press, 1957.

Bellak, Leopold (Ed.). *Schizophrenia: A review of the syndrome.* New York: Logos Press, 1958.

Bellin, S. S., and R. H. Hardt. Marital status and mental disorders among the aged. *Amer. Sociol. Rev.*, 1958, **23**, 155–162.

Benedict, Paul K. Sociocultural factors in schizophrenia. In Leopold Bellak (Ed.), *Schizophrenia: A review of the syndrome*. New York: Logos Press, 1958.

———, and Irving Jacks. Mental illness in primitive societies. *Psychiatry*, 1954, **17**, 377–389.

Bennett, E. B. The relationship of group discussion, decision, commitment, and consensus to individual action. *Disstr. Abstr.*, 1953, **13**, 444–445.

Bennis, W. G. A case study in research formulation. *Internat. J. Group Psychother.*, 1961, **11**, 272–283.

———. Leadership theory and administrative behavior: The problem of authority. *Admin. Sci. Quart.*, 1959, **4**, 259–301.

———. Revisionist theory of leadership. *Harvard Bus. Rev.*, 1961a, **39**, 26–150 passim.

Bereiter, C., *et al.* An academically-oriented preschool for culturally deprived children. Paper presented at AERA meeting, Chicago, Feb., 1965.

Berger, D. G., C. E. Rice, L. G. Sewall, and P. V. Lemkau. Factors affecting the adequacy of patient community adjustment information obtained from the community. *Ment. Hyg.*, 1963, **47**, 452–460.

————. Posthospital evaluation of psychiatric patients: The social adjustment inventory. *Psychiat. Stud. Projects,* 1964, **2** (Whole No. 15).

Bergin, A. Some implications of psychotherapy research for therapeutic practice. *J. abnorm. soc. Psychol.,* 1966, **71,** 235–246.

Berkowitz, L. Group standards, cohesiveness and productivity. *Hum. Relat.,* 1954, **7,** 509–519.

Bernstein, B. Social class, speech systems, and psychotherapy. *Brit. J. Sociol.,* 1964, **15,** 54–64.

Bettelheim, B. Individual and mass behavior in extreme situations. *J. abnorm. soc. Psychol.,* 1943, **38,** 417–452.

————. *Love is not enough.* New York: Free Press, 1950.

————. *The informed heart: Autonomy in a mass age.* New York: Free Press, 1960.

Bidwell, C. E., and S. Vreeland. College education and moral orientations: An organizational approach. *Admin. Sci. Quart.,* 1963, **8,** 166–191.

Bill, W. *A.A. tradition: How it developed.* New York: Alcoholics Anonymous, 1955.

Blake, Judith. *Family structure in Jamaica.* New York: Free Press, 1961.

Blane, Howard T., Willis F. Overton, and Morris E. Chafetz. Social factors in the diagnosis of alcoholism: I. Characteristics of the patient. *Quart. J. Stud. Alcohol,* 1963, **24,** 640–663.

Blau, Abram. The diagnosis and therapy of health. *Amer. J. Psychiat.,* 1954, **110,** 594–598.

Blau, Peter M. Social mobility and interpersonal relations. *Amer. Sociol. Rev.,* 1956, **21,** 290–295.

Bleuler, Eugen. *Dementia Praecox or the group of schizophrenias.* New York: Internat. Univ. Press, 1950. (Monograph Series on Schizophrenia, No. 1, trans. from German Edition, 1911).

Bloch, H. A., and A. Niederhoffer. *The gang.* New York: Philosophical Library, 1958.

Bluhm, H. O. How did they survive? Mechanisms of defense in nazi concentration camps. *Amer. J. Psychother.,* 1948, **2,** 3–32.

Blum, F. *Toward a democratic work process.* New York: Harper, 1953.

Blum, R. H. Case identification in psychiatric epidemiology: Methods and problems. *Milbank Mem. Fund Quart.,* 1962, **40,** 253–288.

Bockoven, J. S. Moral treatment in American psychiatry. *J. nerv. ment. Dis.,* 1956, **124,** 167–194, 292–321. (Reprinted in book form: New York: Springer, 1963.)

————. Some relationships between cultural attitudes toward individuality and care of the mentally ill: An historical study. In M. Greenblatt, D. J. Levinson, and R. H. Williams (Eds.), *The patient and the mental hospital.* New York: Free Press, 1957.

Boder, D. P. *I did not interview the dead.* Urbana, Ill.: Univ. of Illinois Press, 1949.

Boison, A. *The exploration of the inner world.* New York: Willett Clark, 1936.

Bordua, David J. Delinquent subcultures: Sociological interpretations of gang delinquency. *Ann. Amer. Acad. Pol. Soc. Sci.,* 1961, **338,** 120–136.

Boring, E. G. A note on the origin of the word psychology. *J. Hist. behav. Sci.,* 1966, **2,** 167.

Boston Medical and Surgical Journal, *Editorial.* 1852, **45,** 537.

Bott, Elizabeth. *Family and social network.* London: Tavistock, 1957.

Boulding, Kenneth. *The image: Knowledge in life and society.* Ann Arbor: Univ. of Mich. Press, 1956.

Bowen, M. Family relationships in schizophrenia. In A. Auerback (Ed.), *Schizophrenia: An integrated approach.* New York: Ronald Press, 1959.

———. A family concept of schizophrenia. In D. Jackson (Ed.), *The etiology of schizophrenia.* New York: Basic Books, 1960.

Bowlby, John. *Maternal care and mental health.* New York: Schocken, 1952.

Boyer, Ruth M. The matrifocal family among the Mescalero: Additional data. *Amer. Anthropol.,* 1964, **66,** 593–602.

Brackbill, G. A., and H. J. Fine. Schizophrenia and central nervous system pathology. *J. abnorm. soc. Psychol.,* 1956, **52,** 310–313.

Bradburn, Norman M. *Structure of psychological well-being.* Chicago: Aldine, 1969.

———, and D. Caplovitz. *Reports on happiness.* Chicago: Aldine, 1964.

Brazziel, W. F., and M. Terrell. An experiment in the development of readiness in a culturally disadvantaged group of first-grade children. *J. Negro Educ.,* 1962, **31,** 4–7.

Bremer, J. A social psychiatric investigation of a small community in northern Norway. *Acta Psychiat. Neurol. Scand.,* 1951, Suppl. **62.**

Brengel, M. H. Mental health bill—A new weapon for the Kennedy brothers? *Independ. Amer.,* 1963, **9,** 3.

Broderick, Alfred B. Social heterosexual development among urban Negroes and whites. *J. Marriage Fam.,* 1965, **27,** 200–212.

Brodey, W. Some family operations and schizophrenia. *Arch. gen. Psychiat.,* 1959, **1,** 379–402.

Bronfenbrenner, U. Socialization and social class through time and space. In E. E. Maccoby, T. M. Newcomb, and E. L. Hartley (Eds.), *Readings in social psychology.* (3rd ed.) New York: Holt, 1958.

Brotz, Howard. *The black Jews of Harlem.* New York: Free Press, 1964.

Brown, G. W. Length of hospital stay and schizophrenia: A review of statistical studies. *Acta Psychiat. Neurol. Scand.,* 1960, **35,** 414–430.

———, and J. K. Wing. A comparative clinical and social survey of three mental hospitals. In Paul Halmos (Ed.), *Sociology and medicine: Studies within the framework of the British National Health Service. The Sociological Review Monograph,* July 1962, **5.**

Brown, J. A. C. *The social psychology of industry.* Harmondsworth, England: Penguin, 1954.

Brown, Norman O. *Life against death: The psychoanalytical meaning of history.* Middletown, Conn.: Wesleyan Univ. Press, 1959.

Brugger, C. Psychiatrische Bestandaufnahme im Gebiet eines medizinisch-anthropologischen Zensus in der Nähe von Rosenheim. *Z. Ges. Neurol. Psychiat.,* 1937, **160,** 189–207.

———. Psychiatrische Ergebnisse einer medizinischen, anthropologischen, und soziologischen Bevolkerunguntersuchung. *Z. Ges. Neurol. Psychiat.,* 1933, **146,** 489–524.

———. Versuch einer Geisteskrankenzahlung in Thuringen. *Z. Ges. Neurol. Psychiat.,* 1931, **133,** 352–390.

Brunswik, E. *Systematic and representative design of psychological experiments.* Berkeley, Calif.: Univ. of Calif. Press, 1947.

Brzezinski, Z. America in the technetronic age. *Encounter,* 1968, **30,** 16–26.

Buck, Carol, with J. M. Wanklin and G. E. Hobbs. An analysis of regional differences in mental illness. *J. nerv. ment. Dis.,* 1955, **122,** 73–79.

————. Symptom analysis of rural-urban differences in first admission rates. *J. nerv. ment. Dis.*, 1955a, **122**, 80–82.

Bühler, Charlotte. The reality principle. *Amer. J. Psychother.*, 1954, **8**, 626–640.

Burt, C. *The backward child*. London: Univ. of London Press, 1937.

————. The distribution of intelligence. *Brit. J. Psychol.*, 1957, **48**, 161–175.

————. The evidence for the concept of intelligence. *Brit. J. educ. Psychol.*, 1955, **25**, 158–177.

————. The genetic determination of differences in intelligence: A study of monozygotic twins reared together and apart. *Brit. J. Psychol.*, 1966, **57**, 137–153.

————. The inheritance of mental ability. *Amer. Psychol.*, 1958, **13**, 1–15.

————. Intelligence and social mobility. *Brit. J. Psychol.*, 1961, **48**, 3–24.

————. Is intelligence distributed normally? *Brit. J. Stat. Psychol.*, 1963, **16**, 175–190.

Burton, Eleanor. Report on project fifteen. In *Highlights of the twelfth annual conference in cooperative studies in psychiatry,* Denver, Apr., 1967.

Bushard, B. L. The U.S. Army's mental hygiene consultation service. In *Symposium on preventive and social psychiatry, 15–17 April 1957.* Walter Reed Army Institute of Research. Washington, D.C.: U.S. Gov't. Ptg. Office, 1958.

Buss, A. H., H. Fischer, and A. J. Simmons. Aggression and hostility in psychiatric patients. *J. consult. Psychol.*, 1962, **26**, 84–89.

Butler, J. M., and G. V. Haigh. Changes in the relation between self concepts and ideal concepts consequent upon client centered counseling. In C. R. Rogers and R. F. Dymond (Eds.), *Psychotherapy and personality change.* Chicago: Univ. of Chicago Press, 1954.

Cade, J. F. J. The aetiology of schizophrenia. *Med. J. Australia*, 1956, **2**, 135–139.

Cameron, Norman. *The psychology of behavior disorders.* Boston: Houghton Mifflin, 1947.

————. The functional psychoses. In J. McV. Hunt (Ed.), *Personality and the behavior disorders.* Vol. 2. New York: Ronald Press, 1944.

Campbell, Joseph. *The masks of God: Primitive mythology.* New York: Viking, 1959.

Caplan, Gerald. Emotional crises. In A. Deutsch and H. Fishman (Eds.), *The encyclopedia of mental health.* Vol. 2. New York: F. Watts, 1963.

Caputo, D. The parents of the schizophrenic. *Fam. Process*, 1963, **2**, 339–356.

Carothers, J. C. A study of mental derangement in Africans, and an attempt to explain its peculiarities, more especially in relation to the African attitude to life. *Psychiatry*, 1948, **11**, 47–85.

Cartwright, Ann. The effect of obtaining information from different informants on a family morbidity inquiry. *Appl. Statist.*, 1957, **6**, 18–25.

Cartwright, D., and A. Zander. *Group dynamics.* (2nd ed.) Evanston, Ill.: Row, Peterson, 1960.

Cassel, J. Social class and mental disorders: An analysis of the limitations and potentialities of current epidemiological approaches. In K. S. Miller and C. M. Grigg (Eds.), *Mental health and the lower social classes.* Tallahassee, Fla.: Florida State Univ. Studies, 1966.

————, Ralph Patrick, and David Jenkins. Epidemiological analysis of health implications of culture change: A conceptual model. *Ann. N.Y. Acad. Sciences*, 1960, **84**, 938–949.

Caudill, William. *The psychiatric hospital as a small society.* Cambridge, Mass.: Harvard Univ. Press, 1958.

——. Sibling rank and style of life among Japanese psychiatric patients. *Proceedings of the joint meeting of the Japanese Society of Psychiatry and Neurology and the American Psychiatric Association.* Tokyo, Japan, 1963.

——, F. C. Redlich, H. R. Gilmore, and E. B. Brody. Social structure and interaction processes on a psychiatric ward. *Amer. J. Orthopsychiat.,* 1952, **22**, 314–334.

Cayton, Horace R., and St. Clair Drake. *Black metropolis.* New York: Harper, 1962.

Cederlof, Rune, Lars Friberg, Erland Jonsson, and Lennart Kaij. Studies on similarity diagnosis in twins with the aid of mailed questionnaires. *Acta Genetica* (Basel), 1961, **11**, 338–362.

Centers, Richard. Occupational mobility of urban occupational strata. *Amer. Sociol. Rev.,* 1948, **13**, 197–203.

——, and Hadley Cantril. Income satisfaction and income aspiration. *J. abnorm. soc. Psychol.,* 1946, **41**, 64–69.

Chance, June Elizabeth. Personality differences and level of aspiration. *J. consult. Psychol.,* 1960, **24**, 111–115.

Charters, W. W. Social class and intelligence tests. In W. W. Charters and N. L. Gage (Eds.), *Readings in the social psychology of education.* Boston: Allyn & Bacon, 1963.

Chatham Courier, Chatham, New York, March 24, 1960.

Chase, P. Concepts of self and concepts of others in adjusted and maladjusted hospital patients. Unpublished doctoral dissertation, Univ. of Colorado, 1956.

Cheek, Frances. The schizophrenogenic mother in word and deed. *Fam. Process,* 1964, **3**, 155–177.

——. A serendipitous finding: Sex roles and schizophrenia. *J. abnorm. soc. Psychol.,* 1964a, **69**, 392–400.

Chein, I. The awareness of self and the structure of the ego. *Psychol. Rev.,* 1944, **51**, 304–314.

——, and E. Rosenfeld. Juvenile narcotics use. *Law contemp. Probs.,* 1957, **22**, 52–68.

Childers, B. A ward program based on graduated activities and group effort. *Hosp. comm. Psychiat.,* 1967, **18**, 289–295.

Choisy, Maryse. *Sigmund Freud: A new appraisal.* New York: Philosophical Library, 1963.

Christie, R. Authoritarianism re-examined. In R. Christie and M. Jahoda, *Studies in the scope and method of "The authoritarian personality."* New York: Free Press, 1954.

——, J. Havel, and B. Seidenberg. Is the *F* Scale irreversible? *J. abnorm. soc. Psychol.,* 1958, **56**, 143–159.

Clark, J. P., and E. P. Wenninger. Socio-economic class and area as correlates of illegal behavior among juveniles. *Amer. Sociol. Rev.,* 1962, **27**, 826–834.

Clark, Kenneth B. *The dark ghetto.* New York: Harper, 1965.

Clark, Robert E. Psychoses, income, and occupational prestige. *Amer. J. Sociol.,* 1949, **54**, 433–440.

——. The relationship of occupation to various psychoses. Unpublished doctoral dissertation, Univ. of Chicago, 1947.

——. The relationship of schizophrenia to occupational income and occupational prestige. *Amer. Sociol. Rev.,* 1948, **13**, 325–330.

Clausen, J. A. The ecology of mental illness. In *Symposium on preventive and social psychiatry, 15–17 April 1957.* Walter Reed Army Institute of Research. Washington, D.C.: U.S. Gov't. Ptg. Office, 1958.

————. Mental disorders. In R. K. Merton and R. A. Nisbet (Eds.), *Contemporary social problems*. New York: Harcourt, 1961.

————. *Sociology and the field of mental health*. New York: Russell Sage Foundation, 1956.

————. The sociology of mental illness. In R. K. Merton *et al.* (Eds.), *Sociology today, problems and prospects*. New York: Basic Books, 1959.

————. Values, norms and the health called "mental." Purposes and feasibility of assessment. Paper presented at the Symposium on Definition and Measurement of Mental Health, Washington, D.C., May, 1966.

————, and M. L. Kohn. The ecological approach in social psychiatry. *Amer. J. Sociol.*, 1954, **60**, 140–151.

————. Relation of schizophrenia to the social structure of a small city. In B. Pasamanick (Ed.), *Epidemiology of mental disorder*. Washington, D.C.: American Association for the Advancement of Science, 1959.

————. Social relations and schizophrenia: A research report and a perspective. In D. D. Jackson (Ed.), *The etiology of schizophrenia*. New York: Basic Books, 1960.

Clausen, J. A., and M. R. Yarrow (Eds.). The impact of mental illness on the family. *J. Social Issues*, 1955, **11** (4).

————. Paths to the mental hospital. *J. Social Issues*, 1955a, **11**, 25–32.

Cloward, R. A., Illegitimate means, anomie, and deviant behavior. *Amer. Sociol. Rev.*, 1959, **24**, 164–176.

————, and L. E. Ohlin. *Delinquency and opportunity*. New York: Free Press, 1960.

Coch, L., and J. R. P. French, Jr. Overcoming resistance to change. *Hum. Relat.*, 1948, **1**, 512–532.

Cohen, A. K. *Delinquent boys: The culture of the gang*. New York: Free Press, 1955.

————, and H. M. Hodges. Characteristics of the lower-blue-collar-class. *Soc. Problems*, 1963, **10**, 303–334.

Cohen, A. K., and J. F. Short, Jr. Research in delinquent subcultures. *J. Social Issues*, 1958, **14**, 20–37.

Cohen, B. M., R. Fairbank, and E. Greene. Statistical contributions from the eastern health district of Baltimore. III. Personality disorder in the eastern health district in 1933. *Hum. Biol.*, 1939, **11**, 112–129.

Cohen, Elie A. *Human behavior in the concentration camp*. London: Jonathan Cape, 1954.

Cohen, J. Some statistical issues in psychological research. In B. B. Wolman *et al.* (Eds.), *Handbook of clinical psychology*. New York: McGraw-Hill, 1965.

————. The statistical power of abnormal-social psychological research: A review. *J. abnorm. soc. Psychol.*, 1962, **65**, 145–153.

————, L. Gurel, and J. C. Stumpf. Dimensions of psychiatric symptom ratings determined at thirteen timepoints from hospital admission. *J. consult. Psychol.*, 1966, **30**, 39–44.

Cohen, J., and E. L. Struening. Opinions about mental illness in the personnel of two large mental hospitals. *J. abnorm. soc. Psychol.*, 1962, **64**, 349–360.

————. Opinions about mental illness: Mental hospital occupational profiles and profile clusters. *Psychol. Rep.*, 1963, **12**, 111–124.

Cohen, Louis D. Level-of-aspiration behavior and feelings of adequacy and self-acceptance. *J. abnorm. soc. Psychol.*, 1954, **49**, 84–86.

Cohen, R. E. Patient-oriented administration in a day hospital. *Ment. Hospitals*, 1960, **11**, 22–24.

Cole, N. J., C. H. H. Branch, and M. Orla. Mental illness. *A.M.A. Arch. Neurol. Psychiat.*, 1957, **77**, 393–398.

Cole, N. J., D. L. Brewer, and C. H. H. Branch. Socio-economic adjustment of a sample of schizophrenic patients. *Amer. J. Psychiat.*, 1963, **120**, 465–471.

Coleman, J. S. Equal schools or equal students? *The Public Interest*, 1966, **4**, 70–75.

———, *et al.* Equality of educational opportunity. Washington, D.C.: U.S. Gov't. Ptg. Office, 1966.

Colman, A., and M. Greenblatt. Day hospital and meaning of bed to patients. *Proceedings of the Third World Congress of Psychiatry.* Vol. III. Montreal: Univ. of Toronto Press, McGill Univ. Press, 1961.

The Conference Committee, C. C. Bennett (Chm.). *Community psychology, a report of the Boston conference on the education of psychologists for community mental health.* Boston: Boston Univ. Press, 1966.

Conrad, Dorothy C. Toward a more productive concept of mental health. *Ment. Hyg.*, 1952, **36**, 456–473.

Cope, T. P., and F. A. Packard. *A second appeal to the people of Pennsylvania on the subject of an asylum for the insane poor of the commonwealth.* Philadelphia: Waldie, 1841.

Couch, A., and K. Kenniston. Yeasayers and naysayers: Agreeing response set as a personality variable. *J. abnorm. soc. Psychol.*, 1960, **60**, 151–174.

Counts, G. S. The social status of occupations. *School Rev.*, 1925, **33**, 16–27.

Crawford, F., G. Rollins, and R. Sutherland. Variations in the evaluation of the mentally ill. *J. Hlth. hum. Behav.*, 1960, **1**, 211–219.

———. Variations in the evaluation of the mentally ill. *J. Hlth. hum. Behav.*, 1961, **2**, 267–275.

Crawford, L., D. I. Malamud, and J. R. Dumpson. *Working with teen-age gangs.* New York: Welfare Council of N.Y.C., 1950.

Cressey, P. G. *The taxi-dance hall.* Chicago: Univ. of Chicago Press, 1932.

Cronbach, L. J., and P. E. Meehl. Construct validity in psychological tests. *Psychol. Bull.*, 1955, **52**, 281–302.

Crumpton, E., A. D. Weinstein, C. W. Acker, and A. P. Annis. How patients and normals see the mental patient. *J. clin. Psychol.*, 1967, **23**, 46–49.

Cumming, Elaine. Phase movement in the support and control of the psychiatric patient. *J. Hlth. hum. Behav.*, 1962, **3**, 235–241.

———, and John Cumming. *Closed ranks.* Cambridge, Mass.: Harvard Univ. Press, 1957.

Cumming, John, and Elaine Cumming. *Ego and milieu.* New York: Atherton, 1962.

Dahlstrom, W. G., and G. S. Welsh. *An MMPI handbook: A guide to use in clinical practice and research.* Minneapolis: Univ. of Minnesota Press, 1960.

Davé, R. H. The identification and measurement of environmental process variables that are related to educational achievement. Unpublished doctoral dissertation, Univ. of Chicago, 1963.

Davids, Anthony, and Augustus A. White. Effects of success, failure, and social facilitation on level of aspiration in emotionally disturbed and normal children. *J. Pers.*, 1958, **26**, 77–93.

Davidson, P. E., and H. D. Anderson. *Occupational mobility in an American community.* Stanford, Calif.: Stanford Univ. Press, 1937.

Davis, Allison. Socialization and adolescent personality. In Theodore M. Newcomb and Eugene L. Hartley (Eds.), *Readings in social psychology.* New York: Holt, 1947.

————. *Social-class influences upon learning.* Cambridge, Mass.: Harvard Univ. Press, 1948.

————, Burleigh B. Gardner, and Mary R. Gardner. *Deep south.* Chicago: Univ. of Chicago Press, 1941.

Davis, K. Mental hygiene and the class structure. *Psychiatry,* 1938, **1**, 55–65.

Dayton, N. A. *New facts on mental disorders.* Springfield, Ill.: Charles C. Thomas, 1940.

Deasy, Leila C., and Olive W. Quinn. The wife of the mental patient and the hospital psychiatrist. *J. Social Issues,* 1955, **11**, 49–60.

Dee, William L. J. An ecological study of mental disorders in metropolitan St. Louis. Unpublished M. A. thesis, Washington Univ., 1939.

Dembo, T., and E. Haufmann. The patient's psychological situation upon admission to a mental hospital. *Amer. J. Psychol.,* 1935, **47**, 381–408.

Demerath, N. J. Schizophrenia among primitives. In Arnold M. Rose (Ed.), *Mental health and mental disorder.* New York: Norton, 1955.

Deutsch, A. *The mentally ill in America: A history of their care and treatment from colonial times.* New York: Doubleday, 1937.

————. *The mentally ill in America.* (2nd ed.) New York: Columbia Univ. Press, 1949.

————. Minority group and class status as related to social and personality factors in scholastic achievement. *Appl. Anthrop. Monogr.,* 1960, **2**.

————, J. Fishman, L. Kogan, R. North, and M. Whitman. Guidelines for testing minority group children. *J. Social Issues,* 1964, **20**, 129–145.

Devereux, G. The social structure of a schizophrenic ward and its therapeutic fitness. *J. clin. Psychopathol.,* 1944, **6**, 231–265.

————. The social structure of the hospital as a factor in total therapy. *Amer. J. Orthopsychiat.,* 1949, **19**, 492–500.

Dexter, J. B., D. B. Hanford, R. T. Hummel, and J. E. Lubach. Brief inpatient treatment—a pilot study. *Ment. Hosp.,* 1965, **16**, 95–98.

Diamond, B. L. Review of T. S. Szasz, *Law, liberty and psychiatry: An inquiry into the social uses of mental health practices. Calif. Law Rev.,* 1964, **52**, 899–907.

Dicks, H. V. Personality traits and national socialist ideology. *Hum. Relat.,* 1950, **3**, 111–154.

Dillard, L. Personal interviews. Jan. 31, Feb. 15, 1961.

Dittes, J., and H. Kelley. Effects of different conditions of acceptance upon conformity to group norms. *J. abnorm. soc. Psychol.,* 1956, **53**, 629–636.

Dittmann, A. T. Problems of reliability in observing and coding social interactions. *J. consult. Psychol.,* 1958, **22**, 430.

Dohrenwend, Barbara S., and Bruce P. Dohrenwend. Sources of refusals in surveys. *Pub. Opin. Quart.,* 1968, **32**, 74–83.

Dohrenwend, Bruce P. The social psychology nature of stress: A framework for causal inquiry. *J. abnorm. soc. Psychol.,* 1961, **62**, 294–302.

————. Social status and psychological disorder: An issue of substance and an issue of method. *Amer. Sociol. Rev.,* 1966, **31**, 14–34.

————. Some aspects of the appraisal of abnormal behavior by leaders in an urban area. *Amer. Psychol.,* 1962, **17**, 190–198.

————. Urban leadership and the appraisal of abnormal behavior. In L. J. Duhl (Ed.), *The urban condition.* New York: Basic Books, 1963.

————, Viola Bernard, and L. C. Kolb. The orientations of leaders in an urban area towards problems of mental illness. *Amer. J. Psychiat.*, 1962, **118**, 683–691.

Dohrenwend, Bruce P., and Barbara S. Dohrenwend. Class and race as status-related sources of stress. In Sol Levine and Norman A. Scotch (Eds.), *The study of stress.* Chicago: Aldine, in press.

————. The problem of validity in field studies of psychological disorder. *J. abnorm. Psychol.*, 1965, **70**, 52–69.

Dohrenwend, Bruce P., and R. J. Smith. Toward a theory of acculturation. *Southwest. J. Anthrop.*, 1962, **18**, 30–39.

Dollard, John. *Caste and class in a southern town.* New Haven: Yale Univ. Press, 1937.

Downes, Jean, and Katherine Simon. Characteristics of psychoneurotic patients and their families as revealed in a general morbidity study. *Milbank Mem. Fund Quart.*, 1954, **32**, 42–64.

Drake, St. Clair. The social and economic status of the Negro in the United States. *Daedalus*, 1965, **94**, 771–814.

————, and H. R. Cayton. *Black metropolis: A study of Negro life in a northern city.* Vol. II. (Rev. and enl. ed.) New York: Harper, 1962.

Dreher, R. H. Origin, development and present status of insanity as a defense to criminal responsibility in the common law. *J. Hist. Behav. Sci.*, 1967, **3**, 47–57.

Dreyfuss, F., and J. W. Czaczkes. Blood cholesterol and uric acid of healthy medical students under the stress of an examination. *AMA Arch. Intern. Med.*, 1959, **103**, 708–711.

Drucker, P. F. *The new society.* New York: Harper, 1950.

————. *The practice of management.* New York: Harper, 1954.

Dubin, R. *The world of work.* Englewood Cliffs, N.J.: Prentice-Hall, 1958.

Dublin, L. I., and B. Bunzel. *To be or not to be. A study of suicide.* New York: Smith, 1933.

Dubois, Cora. *The people of Alor.* Minneapolis: Univ. of Minnesota Press, 1944.

Duhl, Leonard J. Crisis, adaptive potential and the school. *Psychol. in the Schools,* 1964, **1**, 263–266.

Duncan, O. D. A socioeconomic index for all occupations, and properties and characteristics of the socioeconomic index. In A. J. Reiss, Jr., *et al. Occupations and status.* New York: Free Press, 1961.

Duncker, Karl. On problem-solving. *Psychol. Monogr.*, 1945, **58** (Whole No. 270).

Dunham, H. Warren. *Community and schizophrenia: An epidemiological analysis.* Detroit: Wayne State Univ. Press, 1965.

————. Current status of ecological research in mental disorder. *Soc. Forces,* 1947, **25**, 321–326.

————. Epidemiology of psychiatric disorders as a contribution to medical ecology. *Arch. gen. Psychiat.*, 1966, **14**, 1–19.

————. Social class and schizophrenia. *Amer. J. Orthopsychiat.*, 1964, **34**, 634–642.

————. The social personality of the catatonic-schizophrene. *Amer. J. Sociol.*, 1944, **49**, 508–518.

————. Social psychiatry. *Amer. Sociol. Rev.*, 1948, **13**, 183–197.

————. Social structures and mental disorders: Competing hypotheses of explanation. In Milbank Memorial Fund, *Causes of mental disorders: A review of epidemiological knowledge, 1959.* New York: Milbank Mem. Fund, 1961.

———. *Sociological theory and mental disorder*. Detroit: Wayne State Univ. Press, 1959.

———. Some persistent problems in the epidemiology of mental disorders. *Amer. J. Psychiat.*, 1953, **109**, 567–575.

———, Patricia Phillips, and Barbara Srinivasan. A research note on diagnosed mental illness and social class. *Amer. Sociol. Rev.*, 1966, **31**, 223–227.

Dunham, H. Warren, and S. Kirson Weinberg. *The culture of the state mental hospital*. Detroit: Wayne State Univ. Press, 1960.

Durkheim, E. *On the division of labor in society*. New York: Macmillan, 1933.

———. *Professional ethics and civic morals*. London: Routledge, 1957.

———. *The rules of sociological method*. Chicago: Univ. of Chicago Press, 1938.

———. *Le Suicide*. Paris: F. Alcan, 1897. (English trans., New York: Free Press, 1951.)

Eaton, J. W., and R. J. Weil. *Culture and mental disorders: A comparative study of the Hutterites and other populations*. New York: The Free Press, 1955.

———. The mental health of the Hutterites. In A. M. Rose (Ed.), *Mental health and mental disorder*. New York: Norton, 1955a.

Edwards, A. L. *Experimental design in psychological research*. New York: Holt, 1960.

Eells, K. W. *et al. Intelligence and cultural differences*. Chicago: Univ. of Chicago Press, 1951.

Eissler, K. R. *The psychiatrist and the dying patient*. New York: Internat. Univ. Press, 1955.

Ekblad, Martin. A psychiatric and sociologic study of a series of Swedish naval conscripts. *Acta Psychiat. Neurol.*, 1948, Suppl. **49.**

Elinson, J., and R. Loewenstein. *Community fact book for Washington Heights, New York City, 1960–61*. New York: Columbia Univ. School. of Publ. Hlth. and Admin. Med., 1963.

Ellis, A. Should some people be labeled mentally ill? *J. consult. Psychol.*, 1967, **31,** 435–446.

Ellison, Ralph. *Shadow and act*. New York: Random House, 1964.

Ellsworth, R. B. A behavioral study of staff attitudes toward mental illness. *J. abnorm. Psychol.*, 1965, **70,** 194–200.

———. *The MACC behavioral adjustment scale*. Beverly Hills, Calif.: Western Psychological Services, 1962.

———. *Nonprofessionals in psychiatric rehabilitation*. New York: Appleton, 1968.

———. Some observations of patient government: Problems and parameters. *J. clin. Psychol.*, 1956, **12,** 353–357.

Empey, LaMar T. Social class and occupational aspiration: A comparison of absolute and relative measurement. *Amer. Sociol. Rev.*, 1956, **21,** 703–709.

———, and J. Rabow. The Provo experiment in delinquency prevention. *Amer. Sociol. Rev.*, 1961, **26,** 679–695.

Endler, N. S., J. McV. Hunt, and A. J. Rosenstein. An S-R inventory of anxiousness. *Psychol. Monogr.*, 1962, **76** (Whole No. 536).

Erikson, E. H. Growth and crises of the healthy personality. In M. J. E. Senn (Ed.), *Symposium on the healthy personality*. New York: Josiah Macy, Jr., Foundation, 1950.

———. Identity and the life cycle. *Psychol. Issues*, 1959, **1**, Monogr. 1.

———. The problem of ego identity. *J. Amer. Psychoanal. Assn.*, 1956, **4,** 56–121.

————. *Young man Luther.* New York: Norton, 1958.

Erikson, Kai T. Notes on the sociology of deviance. *Soc. Problems,* 1962, **9,** 307–314.

Erlenmeyer-Kimling, L., and L. F. Jarvik. Genetics and intelligence: A review. *Science,* 1963, **142,** 1477–1479.

Esquirol, E. *Des passions.* Paris: Didot Jeune, 1805. Cited in E. T. Carlson and N. Dain, The psychotherapy that was moral treatment. *Amer. J. Psychiat.,* 1960, **117,** 519–524.

Essen-Möller, E. U. A current field study in the mental disorders in Sweden. In Paul H. Hoch and Joseph Zubin (Eds.), *Comparative epidemiology of the mental disorders.* New York: Grune & Stratton, 1961.

————. Individual traits and morbidity in a Swedish rural population. *Acta Psychiat. Neurol. Scand.,* 1956, Suppl. **100.**

————. Psychiatrische untersuchungen an einer serie von zwillingen. *Acta Psychiat. Scand.,* 1941, Suppl. **23.**

————. Twin research and psychiatry. *Acta Psychiat. Scand.,* 1963, **39,** 65–77.

Essien-Udom, E. U. *Black nationalism: A search for an identity in America.* Chicago: Univ. of Chicago Press, 1962.

Ewalt, J. R. Personal communication, 1956.

————, G. L. Alexander, and L. L. Grinspoon. Changing practices: A plea and some predictions. *Ment. Hosp.,* 1960, **11,** 9–13.

Eysenck, H. J. *The psychology of politics.* London: Routledge, 1954.

————, and H. T. Himmelweit. An experimental study of the reactions of neurotics to experiences of success and failure. *J. gen. Psychol.,* 1946, **35,** 59–75.

Fairweather, G. W. (Ed.). *Social psychology in treating mental illness: An experimental approach.* New York: Wiley, 1964.

————, *et al.* Relative effectiveness of psychotherapeutic programs: A multicriteria comparison of four programs for three different patient groups. *Psychol. Monogr.,* 1960, **74** (Whole No. 492).

Farber, Leslie H. Despair and the life of suicide. *Rev. exist. Psychol.,* 1962, **2,** 125–139.

————. The therapeutic despair. *Psychiatry,* 1958, **21,** 7–20.

Farina, A. Patterns of role dominance and conflict in parents of schizophrenic patients. *J. abnorm. soc. Psychol.,* 1960, **61,** 31–38.

Faris, Robert E. L. Cultural isolation and the schizophrenic personality. *Amer. J. Sociol.,* 1934, **39,** 155–169.

————, and H. W. Dunham. *Mental disorders in urban areas: An ecological study of schizophrenia and other psychoses.* Chicago: Univ. of Chicago Press, 1939.

Farndale, J. *The day hospital movement in Great Britain.* New York: Pergamon, 1961.

Fearing, F. A word of caution for the intelligent consumer of motion pictures. *Quart. Film, Radio, and Television,* VI (2), n.d.

Feifel, Herman (Ed.). *The meaning of death.* New York: McGraw-Hill, 1959.

Felix, R. H., and R. V. Bowers. Mental hygiene and socio-environmental factors. *Milbank Mem. Fund Quart.,* 1948, **26,** 125–147.

Ferguson, Eva D. The effect of sibling competition and alliance on level of aspiration, expectation, and performance. *J. abnorm. soc. Psychol.,* 1958, **56,** 213–223.

Fiedler, F. The concept of an ideal therapeutic relationship. *J. consult. Psychol.,* 1950, **14,** 239–245.

————. A comparison of therapeutic relationships in psychoanalytic, non-directive and Adlerian therapy. *J. consult. Psychol.,* 1950a, **14,** 436–445.

Fiedler, Leslie. *Waiting for the end.* New York: Stein and Day, 1964.

Finestone, H. Cats, kicks and color. *Soc. Problems,* 1957, **5,** 3–13.

Finney, B. C. A scale to measure interpersonal relationships in group psychotherapy. *Group Psychother.,* 1954, **7,** 52–66.

Fiske, D. W., and S. R. Maddi. *Functions of varied experience.* Chicago: Dorsey, 1961.

Flanagan, J. C. General considerations in the selection of test items and a short method of estimating the product-moment coefficient from data at the tails of the distribution. *J. educ. Psychol.,* 1939, **30,** 674–680.

Foa, U. G. Convergences in the analysis of the structure of interpersonal behavior. *Psychol. Rev.,* 1961, **68,** 341–353.

Foote, N. N., and L. S. Cottrell, Jr. *Identity and interpersonal competence.* Chicago: Univ. of Chicago Press, 1955.

Forstenzer, H. M., and R. C. Hunt. The New York State community mental health act: Its origins and first four years of development. *Psychiat. Quart. Suppl.,* 1958, **32,** 41–67.

Fowler, W. L. A comparative analysis of pupil performance on conventional and culture-controlled mental tests. *Fourteenth Yearb. Natl. Council on Measmts. in Educ.* Princeton, N.J., 1957.

Frank, J. D. Breaking the thought barrier: Psychological challenges of the nuclear age. *Psychiatry,* 1960, **23,** 245–266.

———. The dynamics of the psychotherapeutic relationship: Determinants and effects of the therapist's influence. *Psychiatry,* 1959, **22,** 17–39.

———. *Persuasion and healing.* Baltimore: Johns Hopkins Univ. Press, 1961.

———. Some determinants, manifestations, and effects of cohesiveness in therapy groups. *Internat. J. Group Psychother.,* 1957, **7,** 53–63.

———. Some values of conflict in group psychotherapy. *Group Psychother.,* 1955, **8,** 142–151.

———, and E. Ascher. Corrective emotional experiences in group therapy. *Amer. J. Psychiat.,* 1951, **108,** 126–131.

———, *et al.* Two behavior patterns in therapeutic groups and their apparent motivations. *Hum. Relat.,* 1952, **5,** 289–317.

Frank, L. K. The promotion of mental health. *Ann. Amer. Acad. Pol. Soc. Sci.,* 1953, **286,** 167–174.

Franklin, John Hope. *From slavery to freedom.* (2nd ed.) New York: Knopf, 1952.

Frazier, E. F. *The Negro family in the United States.* Chicago: Univ. of Chicago Press, 1939.

———. *The Negro family in Chicago.* Chicago: Univ. of Chicago Press, 1932.

———. *Black bourgeoisie.* New York: Collier, 1962.

Freedman, J., and R. Rivera. Education, social class and patterns of delinquency. Paper presented at the Annual Meeting of the American Sociological Association, Washington, D.C., Sept., 1962.

Freedman, M. B., *et al.* The interpersonal dimension of personality. *J. Pers.,* 1951, **20,** 143–161.

Freeman, Howard E. Attitudes toward mental illness among relatives of former mental patients. *Amer. Sociol. Rev.,* 1961, **26,** 59–66.

———, and G. G. Kassebaum. Relationship of education and knowledge to opinions about mental illness. *Ment. Hyg.,* 1960, **44,** 43–47.

Freeman, Howard E., and D. G. Simmons. *The mental patient comes home.* New York: Wiley, 1963.

———. Feelings of stigma among relatives of former mental patients. *Soc. Problems,* 1961, **8,** 312–321.

Fremming, K. H. *The expectation of mental infirmity in a sample of the Danish population.* London: Eugenics Society, 1951.

French, T. M. An analysis of the goal concept based upon study of reactions to frustration. *Psychoanal. Rev.,* 1941, **28,** 61–71.

Freud, S. Beyond the pleasure principle. In *Complete psychological works of Sigmund Freud.* Vol. XVIII. London: Hogarth, 1955.

———. Civilization and its discontents (1930). In *Complete psychological works of Sigmund Freud.* Vol. XXI. London: Hogarth, 1962.

———. "Civilized" sexual morality and modern nervous illness (1908). In *Complete psychological works of Sigmund Freud.* Vol. IX. London: Hogarth, 1959.

———. *Collected papers.* Vol. II. London: Hogarth, 1950.

———. The future of an illusion (1927). In *Complete psychological works of Sigmund Freud.* Vol. XXI. London: Hogarth, 1962.

———. Group psychology and the analysis of the ego (1921). In *Complete psychological works of Sigmund Freud.* Vol. XVIII. London: Hogarth, 1955.

———. The neuro-psychoses of defence (1894). In *Complete psychological works of Sigmund Freud.* Vol. III. London: Hogarth, 1962.

———. A reply to criticisms of my paper on anxiety neurosis (1895). In *Complete psychological works of Sigmund Freud.* Vol. III. London: Hogarth, 1962.

———. Thoughts for the times on war and death (1915). In *Complete psychological works of Sigmund Freud.* Vol. XIV. London: Hogarth, 1957.

———. Totem and taboo (1913). In *Complete psychological works of Sigmund Freud.* Vol. XIII. London: Hogarth, 1962.

Fried, M. Effects of social change on mental health. *Amer. J. Orthopsychiat.,* 1964, **34,** 3–28.

———. Grieving for a lost home. In L. J. Duhl (Ed.), *The urban condition.* New York: Basic Books, 1963.

———. Transitional functions of working-class communities: Implications for forced relocation. In M. Kantor (Ed.), *Mobility and mental health.* Springfield, Ill.: Charles C. Thomas, 1965.

Friedman, P. Some aspects of concentration camp psychology. *Amer. J. Psychiat.,* 1949, **105,** 601–605.

Friedmann, G. *The anatomy of work.* New York: Free Press, 1961.

———. *Industrial society.* New York: Free Press, 1955.

Frochter, B. *Introduction to factor analysis.* New York: Van Nostrand, 1954.

Fromm, E. *Escape from freedom.* New York: Farrar & Rinehart, 1941.

———. *Man for himself.* New York: Farrar & Rinehart, 1947.

———. *The sane society.* New York: Farrar & Rinehart, 1955.

Fromm-Reichmann, Frieda. *Principles of intensive psychotherapy.* Chicago: Univ. of Chicago Press, 1950.

———. Problems of therapeutic management in a psychoanalytic hospital. *Psychoanal. Quart.,* 1947, **16,** 325–356.

Frumkin, Robert M. Occupation and major mental disorders. In A. M. Rose (Ed.), *Mental health and mental disorder.* New York: Norton, 1955.

———. Occupation and mental illness. *Publ. Welfare Stat.*, 1952, **7**, 4–13.

Fuller, R. C., and R. R. Myers. The natural history of social problems. *Amer. Sociol. Rev.*, 1941, **6**, 320–328.

———. Some aspects of a theory of social problems. *Amer. Sociol. Rev.*, 1941a, **6**, 24–32.

Fuson, William M. Research note: Occupations of functional psychotics. *Amer. J. Sociol.*, 1943, **48**, 612–613.

Gallagher, E. B., D. J. Levinson, and I. Erlich. Some sociopsychological characteristics of patients and their relevance for psychiatric treatment. In M. Greenblatt, D. J. Levinson, and R. H. Williams (Eds.), *The patient and the mental hospital*. New York: Free Press, 1957.

Gans, H. J. *The urban villagers*. New York: Free Press, 1962.

Gardner, Elmer A., and Haroutin M. Babigian. A longitudinal comparison of psychiatric service to selected socioeconomic areas of Monroe County, New York. *Amer. J. Orthopsychiat.*, 1966, **36**, 818–828.

Garfinkel, Harold. Conditions of successful degradation ceremonies. *Amer. J. Sociol.*, 1956, **61**, 420–424.

Gebhard, Paul H., *et al. Pregnancy, birth and abortion*. New York: Harper, 1958.

Geiger, H. Jack, and Norman Scotch. The epidemiology of essential hypertension: A review with special attention to psychological and sociocultural factors. I: Biologic mechanisms and descriptive epidemiology. *J. chron. Dis.*, 1963, **16**, 1151–1182.

Gellerman, S. W. *Motivation and productivity*. New York: Amer. Mgmt. Assn., 1963.

Gerard, Donald L., and Lester G. Houston. Family setting and the social ecology of schizophrenia. *Psychiat. Quart.*, 1953, **27**, 90–101.

Ghiselli, E. E., and C. W. Brown. *Personnel and industrial psychology*. New York: McGraw-Hill, 1955.

Gilbert, Doris C. Ideologies concerning mental illness: A sociopsychological study of mental hospital personnel. Unpublished doctoral dissertation, Radcliffe College, 1954.

Gillis, L. S., J. B. Lewis, and M. Slabert. Psychiatric disturbance and alcoholism in the coloured people of the Cape Peninsula. Cape Town: Univ. of Cape Town, Department of Psychiatry, 1965.

Ginsburg, S. W. The mental health movement and its theoretical assumptions. In Ruth Kotinsky and Helen Witmer (Eds.), *Community programs for mental health*. Cambridge, Mass.: Harvard Univ. Press, 1955.

Ginzberg, E., *et al. The lost divisions*. New York: Columbia Univ. Press, 1959.

———. *Patterns of performance*. New York: Columbia Univ. Press, 1959a.

Glane, S. Juvenile gangs in east side of Los Angeles. *Focus*, 1950, **29**, 136–141.

Glick, Paul C. *American families*. New York: Wiley, 1957.

Glidewell, J. C., *et al.* Behavior symptoms in children and degree of sickness. *Amer. J. Psychiat.*, 1957, **114**, 47–53.

Glover, E. Medico-psychological aspects of normality. *Brit. J. Psychol.*, 1932, **23**, 152–166.

Gnat, T., J. Henisz, and A. Sarapata. A psychiatric-socio-statistical study of two Polish towns. Paper read at First International Congress of Social Psychiatry, London, Aug. 1964.

Goffman, Erving. *Asylums*. Bristol, England: Aldine, 1962.

———. *Asylums. Essays on the social situation of mental patients and other inmates*. Garden City, N.Y.: Doubleday, 1961.

————. *Behavior in public places.* New York: Free Press, 1963.

————. Characteristics of total institutions. In *Symposium on preventive and social psychiatry, 15–17 April 1957.* Walter Reed Army Institute of Research. Washington, D.C.: U.S. Gov't. Ptg. Office, 1958.

————. Discrepant roles. Chapter 4 in his *The presentation of self in everyday life.* New York: Anchor, 1959.

————. Interpersonal persuasion. In Bertram Schaffner (Ed.), *Group processes: Transactions of the third conference.* New York: Josiah Macy, Jr., Foundation, 1957. (A shorter version was presented at the Annual Meeting of the American Sociological Association, Washington, D.C., Aug. 1957.)

————. *Stigma. Notes on the management of spoiled identity.* Englewood Cliffs, N.J.: Prentice-Hall, 1963a.

Gold, M. *Status forces in delinquent boys.* Ann Arbor, Mich.: Institute for Social Research, 1963.

Goldberg, E. M., and S. L. Morrison. Schizophrenia and social class. *Brit. J. Psychiat.,* 1963, **109,** 785–802.

Goldberg, S. C., and M. Katz. Discussion of Dr. Hylan Lewis' paper. In M. Greenblatt, P. E. Emery, and B. C. Glueck (Eds.), Poverty and mental health. *Psychiatric Res. Rep.,* 1967, **21,** 17–21.

Goldfarb, W. The effects of early institutional care on adolescent personality. *J. exp. Educ.,* 1943, **12,** 106–129.

Goldhamer, Herbert, and Andrew W. Marshall. *Psychosis and civilization.* New York: Free Press, 1953.

Goldhamer, Herbert, and E. A. Shils. Types of power and status. *Amer. J. Sociol.,* 1939, **45,** 171–182.

Goldman-Eisler, Frieda. Breastfeeding and character formation. In C. Kluckhohn and H. A. Murray (Eds.), *Personality in nature, society, and culture.* (2nd ed.) New York: Knopf, 1956.

Goldstein, K. *Human nature in the light of psychopathology.* Cambridge, Mass.: Harvard Univ. Press, 1940.

Goodenough, W. H. *Cooperation in change: An anthropological approach to community development.* New York: Russell Sage Foundation, 1963.

Gordon, E. W. Characteristics of socially disadvantaged children. *Rev. Educ. Res.,* 1965, **35,** 377–388.

Gordon, J. E., *et al.* An epidemiologic analysis of suicide. In Milbank Memorial Fund, *Epidemiology of mental disorder.* New York: Milbank Mem. Fund, 1950.

Gordon, R. A., and J. F. Short, Jr. Social level, social disability, and gang interaction. Unpublished manuscript, 1962.

————, D. S. Cartwright, and F. L. Strodtbeck. Values and gang delinquency: A study of street-corner groups. *Amer. J. Sociol.,* 1963, **69,** 109–128.

Gottlieb, A. L., and O. A. Parsons. A coaction compass evaluation of Rorschach determinants in brain damaged individuals. *J. consult. Psychol.,* 1960, **24,** 54–60.

Gould, Rosalind. Some sociological determinants of goal strivings. *J. soc. Psychol.,* 1941, **13,** 461–473.

Gouldner, Alvin W. Reciprocity and autonomy in functional theory. In Llewellyn Gross (Ed.), *Symposium on sociological theory.* New York: Harper, 1959.

————, and R. A. Peterson. *Notes on technology and the moral order.* Indianapolis, Ind.: Bobbs-Merrill, 1962.

Gove, W. Post hospital adjustment of northwest Washington hospital—community pilot program patients. *The Bulletin,* Division of Mental Health, Department of Institutions, State of Washington, 1965, **9,** 140–145.

Gowman, Alan G. Blindness and the role of the companion. *Soc. Problems,* 1956, **4,** 68–75.

Graham, Frances K., *et al.* Development three years after perinatal anoxia and other potentially damaging newborn experiences. *Psychol. Monogr.,* 1962, **76** (Whole No. 522).

Green, Arnold W. The cult of personality and sexual relations. *Psychiatry,* 1941, **4,** 343–344.

Green, Howard W. *Persons admitted to the Cleveland State Hospital, 1928–37.* Cleveland: Health Council, 1939.

Greenbaum, J., and L. I. Pearlin. Vertical mobility and prejudice: A social psychological analysis. In R. Bendix and S. M. Lipset (Eds.), *Class, status and power: A reader in social stratification.* New York: Free Press, 1953.

Greenblatt, M., D. J. Levinson, and G. L. Klerman (Eds.). *Mental patients in transition.* Springfield, Ill.: Charles C. Thomas, 1961.

Greenblatt, M., R. York, and E. L. Brown. *From custodial to therapeutic care in mental hospitals.* New York: Russell Sage Foundation, 1955.

Greenson, R. R. Psychology of apathy. *Psychoanal. Quart.,* 1949, **18,** 290–302.

Greenspoon, J. The reinforcing effect of two spoken sounds on the frequency of two responses. *Amer. J. Psychol.,* 1955, **68,** 409–416.

Greenwald, Harold. *The call girl.* New York: Ballantine, 1958.

Grinspoon, L. Fallout shelters and the unacceptability of disquieting facts. In G. H. Grosser, H. Wechsler, and M. Greenblatt (Eds.), *The threat of impending disaster: Contributions to the psychology of stress.* Cambridge, Mass.: M.I.T. Press, 1964.

Gromoll, H. F. The process-reactive dimension of schizophrenia in relation to cortical activation and arousal. Unpublished doctoral dissertation, Univ. of Illinois, 1961.

Grotjahn, Martin. Ego identity and the fear of death and dying. *J. Hillside Hosp.,* 1960, **9,** 147–155.

Group for the Advancement of Psychiatry (Committee on Social Issues). Psychiatric aspects of the prevention of nuclear war. *GAP Publications,* 1964, **57.**

Gruenberg, E. M. Comment. In Milbank Memorial Fund, *Interrelations between the social environment and psychiatric disorders.* New York: Milbank Mem. Fund, 1953.

———. Community conditions and psychoses of the elderly. *Amer. J. Psychiat.,* 1954, **110,** 888–896.

———. Problems of data collection and nomenclature. In C. H. H. Branch, E. G. Beier, R. H. Anderson, and C. A. Whitmer (Eds.), *The epidemiology of mental health.* Brighton, Utah: Univ. of Utah, 1955.

Gump, P., R. Schoggen, and F. Redl. The camp milieu and its immediate effects. *J. Social Issues,* 1957, **13,** 40–46.

Gurel, L. A forward-looking backward glance: An overview of past, present, and projected program evaluation staff research. In *Highlights of the twelfth annual conference in cooperative studies in psychiatry,* Denver, Colorado, April 1, 1967.

———. *Patterns of mental patient post-hospital adjustment.* Washington, D.C.: V.A. Psychiatric Evaluation Project, 1965.

———. Release and community stay criteria in evaluating psychiatric treatment. In P. Hoch and J. Zubin (Eds.), *The psychopathology of schizophrenia.* New York: Grune & Stratton, 1966.

Gurin, G., J. Veroff, and S. Feld. *Americans view their mental health.* New York: Basic Books, 1960.

Gursslin, Orville R., and Jack L. Roach. Some issues in training the employed. *Soc. Problems,* 1964, **12,** 68–77.

Haase, William. Rorschach diagnosis, socio-economic class and examiner bias. Unpublished doctoral dissertation, New York Univ., 1955.

Hachiya, Michihiko. *Hiroshima diary.* Trans. by Warner Wells. Chapel Hill: Univ. of North Carolina Press, 1955.

Hacker, F. J. The concept of normality and its practical significance. *Amer. J. Orthopsychiat.,* 1945, **15,** 53–55.

Hackett, T. P., and A. D. Weisman. Reactions to the imminence of death. In G. H. Grosser, H. Wechsler, and M. Greenblatt (Eds.), *The threat of impending disaster: Contributions to the psychology of stress.* Cambridge, Mass.: M.I.T. Press, 1964.

Hadley, E. E., *et al.* Military psychiatry: An ecological note. *Psychiatry,* 1944, **7,** 379–407.

Haggard, E. A. Social status and intelligence: An experimental study of certain cultural determinants of measured intelligence. *Genet. Psychol. Monogr.,* 1954, **49,** 141–186.

Hagnell, Olle. *A prospective study of the incidence of mental disorder.* Stockholm: Scandinavian Univ. Books, Svenska Bokforlaget Norstedts-Bonniers, 1966.

Haire, M. Psychological problems relevant to business and industry. *Psychol. Bull.,* 1959, **56,** 169–194.

Haley, J. The family of the schizophrenic: A model system. *J. nerv. ment. Dis.,* 1959, **129,** 357–374.

———. An interactional description of schizophrenia. *Psychiatry,* 1959a, **22,** 321–332.

———. Observation of the family of the schizophrenic. *Amer. J. Orthopsychiat.,* 1960, **30,** 460–467.

———. Research on family patterns: An instrumental measurement. *Fam. Process,* 1964, **3,** 41–65.

———. *Strategies of psychotherapy.* New York: Grune & Stratton, 1963.

Hall, C. S., and G. Lindzey. *Theories of personality.* New York: Wiley, 1957.

Hall, Oswald. The stages of a medical career. *Amer. J. Sociol.,* 1948, **53,** 327–336.

Halmos, P. *Solitude and privacy.* London: Routledge, 1952.

Hammond, Boone. The contest system: A survival technique. Unpublished M.A. thesis, Washington Univ., 1965.

Handel, Gerald, and Lee Rainwater. Persistence and change in working-class life style. In Arthur B. Shostak and William Gomberg (Eds.), *Blue-collar world.* Englewood Cliffs, N.J.: Prentice-Hall, 1964.

Handlin, Oscar. *Boston's immigrants: A study in acculturation.* (Rev. ed.) Cambridge, Mass.: Harvard Univ. Press, 1959.

———. *The uprooted.* Boston: Little, Brown, 1952.

Hansen, Marcus Lee. *The Atlantic migration, 1607–1860.* New York: Harper, 1961.

Hare, A. P., E. F. Borgatta, and R. F. Bales (Eds.). *Small groups—Studies in social interaction.* New York: Knopf, 1955.

Hare, E. H. Family setting and the urban distribution of schizophrenia. *J. ment. Sci.,* 1956, **102,** 753–760.

———. Mental illness and social conditions in Bristol. *J. ment. Sci.,* 1956a, **102,** 349–357.

————, and G. K. Shaw. *Mental health on a new housing estate*. New York: Oxford Univ. Press, 1965.

Harms, E. The early historians of psychiatry. *Amer. J. Psychiat.*, 1957, **113**, 749–752.

————. Historical considerations in the science of psychiatry. *Dis. Nerv. Sys.*, 1957a, **18**, 397–400.

————. Modern psychotherapy—150 years ago. *J. ment. Sci.*, 1957b, **103**, 804–809.

Hartmann, Heinz. Ego psychology and the problem of adaptation. In D. Rapaport (Ed.), *Organization and pathology of thought*. New York: Columbia Univ. Press, 1951.

————. *The ego and the problem of adaptation*. New York: International Universities Press, 1958.

————. Notes on the reality principle. *Psychoanal. Study Child*, 1956, **11**, 31–53.

————. On rational and irrational action. In G. Roheim (Ed.), *Psychoanalysis and the social sciences*. Vol. 1. New York: International Universities Press, 1947.

————. Psychoanalysis and the concept of health. *Internat. J. Psychoanal.*, 1939, **20**, 308–318.

————, and Ernest Kris. The genetic approach in psychoanalysis. *Psychoanal. Study Child*, 1945, **1**, 11–30.

Hartshorne, H., and M. A. May. *Studies in deceit*. New York: Macmillan, 1928.

Hassler, Alfred. *Diary of a self-made convict*. Chicago: Regnery, 1954.

Hastings, D. W. Psychiatry in the Eighth Air Force. *Air Surgeon's Bull.*, 1944, **1**, 4–5.

Hathaway, S. R., and E. D. Monachesi. The Minnesota Multiphasic Personality Inventory in the study of juvenile delinquents. In A. M. Rose (Ed.), *Mental health and mental disorder*. New York: Norton, 1955.

Hausmann, M. F. A test to evaluate some personality traits. *J. gen. Psychol.*, 1933, **9**, 179–189.

Havighurst, R. J. Who are the socially disadvantaged? *J. Negro Educ.*, 1964, **33**, 210–217.

Hayner, N. S. *Hotel life*. Chapel Hill: Univ. of North Carolina Press, 1936.

————, and E. Ash. The prisoner community as a social group. *Amer. Sociol Rev.*, 1939, **4**, 362–369.

Heckstall-Smith, Anthony. *Eighteen months*. London: Wingate, 1954.

Heggen, T. *Mister Roberts*. Boston: Houghton Mifflin, 1946.

Heilbrunn, Gert. The basic fear. *J. Amer. Psychoanal. Assn.*, 1955, **3**, 447–466.

Helgason, T. Epidemiology of mental disorders in Iceland. *Acta Psychiat. Scand. Suppl.*, 1964, **173**, 1-258.

Henriques, F. M. *Family and colour in Jamaica*. London: Eyre & Spottiswoode, 1953.

Henry, A. E., and J. F. Short, Jr. *Suicide and homicide*. New York: Free Press, 1954.

Henry, W. E. Psychology. In Milbank Memorial Fund, *Interrelations between the social environment and psychiatric disorders*. New York: Milbank Mem. Fund, 1953.

Herskovits, Melville J. *The myth of the Negro past*. New York: Harper, 1941.

Herzberg, F., B. Mausner, and B. Snyderman. *The motivation to work*. New York: Wiley, 1959.

Hess, R. D., and G. Handel. *Family worlds: A psychosocial approach to family life*. Chicago: Univ. of Chicago Press, 1959.

Hess, R. D., and V. Shipman. Early blocks to children's learning. *Children*, 1965, **12**, 189–194.

——. Early experience and the socialization of cognitive modes in children. *Child Develpm.*, 1965a, **36**, 869–886.

Heyns, R. W., and R. Lippitt. Systematic observational techniques. In G. Lindzey (Ed.), *Handbook of social psychology.* Vol. 1. Cambridge, Mass.: Addison-Wesley, 1954.

Higgins, C., and C. M. Sivers. A comparison of the Stanford-Binet and the Colored Raven Progressive Matrices IQ's for children with low socio-economic status. *J. consult. Psychol.*, 1958, **22**, 465–468.

Hillyer, J. *Reluctantly told.* New York: Macmillan, 1926.

Himelhoch, J. Socioeconomic status and delinquency in rural New England. Paper presented at the Annual Meeting of the American Sociological Association, Montreal, Sept. 1964.

Himmelweit, Hilda. A comparative study of the level of aspiration of normal and neurotic persons. *Brit. J. Psychol.*, 1947, **37**, 41–59.

Hinkle, Lawrence E., and Harold G. Wolff. Health and the social environment: Experimental investigations. In Alexander H. Leighton, John A. Clausen, and Robert N. Wilson (Eds.), *Explorations in social psychiatry.* New York: Basic Books, 1957.

Hoban, C. F., Jr., and E. B. van Ormer. Instructional film research, 1918–1950. *Instructional film research program.* The Penn. State Coll. Tech. Rep. SDC 269-7-19, n.d.

Hoch, Paul H., and Joseph Zubin (Eds.). *Comparative epidemiology of the mental disorders.* New York: Grune & Stratton, 1961.

Hollingshead, A. B. *Elmtown's youth: The impact of social classes on adolescents.* New York: Wiley, 1949.

——. Selected characteristics of classes in a middle western community. *Amer. Sociol. Rev.*, 1947, **12**, 385–395.

——. Some issues in the epidemiology of schizophrenia. *Amer. Sociol. Rev.*, 1961, **26**, 5–13.

——. *Two-factor index of social position.* Mimeo'd. ms., Dept. of Sociology, Yale Univ., 1957.

——, R. Ellis, and E. Kirby. Social mobility and mental illness. *Amer. Sociol. Rev.*, 1954, **19**, 577–584.

Hollingshead, A. B., and F. C. Redlich. Schizophrenia and social structure. *Amer. J. Psychiat.*, 1954, **110**, 695–701.

——. *Social class and mental illness.* New York: Wiley, 1958.

——. Social mobility and mental illness. *Amer. J. Psychiat.*, 1955, **112**, 179–185.

——. Social stratification and psychiatric disorders. *Amer. Sociol. Rev.*, 1953, **18**, 163–169.

——. Social stratification and schizophrenia. *Amer. Sociol. Rev.*, 1954a, **19**, 302–306.

Homans, G. C. *The human group.* New York: Harcourt, 1950.

Hooker, Evelyn. The adjustment of the male overt homosexual. *J. Project. Techniques Personality Assessm.*, 1957, **21**, 18–31.

——. Male homosexuality in the Rorschach. *J. Project. Techniques Personality Assessm.*, 1958, **22**, 31–54.

——. A preliminary analysis of group behavior of homosexuals. *J. Psychol.*, 1956, **42**, 217–225.

Horney, Karen. *The neurotic personality of our time.* New York: Norton, 1937.

Hovland, C. I., I. L. Janis, and H. H. Kelley. *Communication and persuasion; psychological studies of opinion change.* New Haven: Yale Univ. Press, 1953.

Howard, K. E., A. E. Hendrickson, and D. S. Cartwright. Psychological assessment of street corner youth: intelligence. Unpublished manuscript, Youth Studies Program, Univ. of Chicago, 1962.

Hughes, C. C., *et al. People of Cove and Woodlot.* New York: Basic Books, 1960.

Hughes, Everett. Dilemmas and contradictions of status. *Amer. J. Sociol.,* 1945, **50,** 353–359.

Hunt, J. McV. *Intelligence and experience.* New York: Ronald Press, 1961.

Hunter, M., C. Schooler, and H. E. Spohn. The measurement of characteristic patterns of ward behavior in chronic schizophrenics. *J. consult. Psychol.,* 1962, **26,** 69–73.

Huxley, Julian (Ed.). *The humanist frame.* New York: Harper, 1961.

Hyde, R. W., and R. M. Chisholm. The relation of mental disorders to race and nationality. *New England J. Med.,* 1944, **231,** 612–618.

Hyde, R. W., and L. V. Kingsley. Studies in medical sociology. I. The relation of mental disorders to the community socio-economic level. *New England J. Med.,* 1944, **231,** 543–548.

Hyde, R. W., and H. C. Solomon. Patient government: A new form of group therapy. *Dig. Neurol. Psychiat.,* 1950, **18,** 207–218.

Hyman, Herbert H. The value system of different classes: A social psychological contribution to the analysis of stratification. In Reinhard Bendix and Seymour M. Lipset (Eds.), *Class, status, and power.* New York: Free Press, 1953.

Inkeles, Alex. Personality and social structure. In R. K. Merton, L. Broom, and L. S. Cottrell (Eds.), *Sociology today.* New York: Basic Books, 1959.

———. Sociology and psychology. In S. Koch (Ed.), *Psychology: A study of science.* Vol. 6. New York: McGraw-Hill, 1963.

Inoguchi, Shoji. Funerals. In Oma Chitomi, *et al.* (Eds.), *Nihon Minzoku Gakutaikei.* Vol. 4. An outline of the ethnological study of Japan. Tokyo: Heibonsha, 1959.

Inouye, Eiji. Similarity and dissimilarity of schizophrenia in twins. In *Proceedings of the Third World Congress of Psychiatry.* Vol. 1. Montreal: Univ. of Toronto Press, McGill Univ. Press, 1961.

Jackson, Don D. Introduction. In D. D. Jackson (Ed.), *The etiology of schizophrenia.* New York: Basic Books, 1960.

Jackson, D. N., and S. Messick. Acquiescence and desirability as response determinants on the MMPI. *Educ. psychol. measmt.,* 1961, **21,** 771–790.

———. Response styles on the MMPI: Comparison of clinical and normal samples. *J. abnorm. soc. Psychol.,* 1962, **65,** 285–299.

Jackson, Elton F. Status consistency and symptoms of stress. *Amer. Sociol. Rev.,* 1962, **27,** 469–480.

———, and Peter J. Burke. Status and symptoms of stress: Additive and interaction effects. *Amer. Sociol. Rev.,* 1965, **30,** 556–564.

Jackson, J. D., R. D. Hess, and V. Shipman. Communication styles in teachers: An experiment. Paper presented at AERA meeting, Chicago, Feb. 1965.

Jaco, E. G. Incidence of psychoses in Texas. *Texas State J. Med.,* 1957, **53,** 1–6.

———. *The social epidemiology of mental disorders.* New York: Russell Sage Foundation, 1960.

———. The social isolation hypothesis and schizophrenia. *Amer. Sociol. Rev.,* 1954, **19,** 567–577.

———. Social stress and mental illness in the community. In Marvin B. Sussman (Ed.), *Community structure and analysis.* New York: Crowell, 1959.

Jacobson, E. Observations on the psychological effect of imprisonment on female political prisoners. In K. R. Eissler (Ed.), *Searchlights on delinquency.* New York: International Universities Press, 1949.

Jahoda, M. *Current concepts of positive mental health.* New York: Basic Books, 1958.

———. The meaning of psychological health. *Soc. Casework,* 1953, **34,** 349–354.

———. Social psychology. In Milbank Memorial Fund, *Interrelations between the social environment and psychiatric disorders.* New York: Milbank Mem. Fund, 1953a.

———. Toward a social psychology of mental health. In A. M. Rose (Ed.), *Mental health and mental disorder.* New York: Norton, 1955.

———. Toward a social psychology of mental health. In M. J. E. Senn (Ed.), *Symposium on the healthy personality.* New York: Josiah Macy, Jr., Foundation, 1950.

———. Toward a social psychology of mental health. In R. Kotinsky and H. Witmer (Eds.), *Community programs for mental health.* Cambridge, Mass.: Harvard Univ. Press, 1955a.

James, William. *The varieties of religious experience.* London: Longmans, 1952.

Janis, I. L. *Air war and emotional stress.* New York: McGraw-Hill, 1951.

Janowitz, M., and D. Marvick. Authoritarianism and political behavior. *Publ. Opin. Quart.,* 1953, **17,** 195–201.

Jansyn, L. Solidarity and delinquency in a street corner group: A study of the relationship between changes in specified aspects of group structure and variations in the frequency of delinquent activity. Unpublished M.A. thesis, Univ. of Chicago, 1960.

Jenkins, R. L., and L. Gurel. Predictive factors in early release. *Ment. Hosp.,* 1959, **10,** 11–14.

Jensen, A. R. The culturally disadvantaged: Psychological and educational aspects. *Educ. Res.,* 1967, **10,** 4–20.

———. Estimation of the limits of heritability of traits by comparison of monozygotic and dizygotic twins. *Proc. Nat. Acad. Sci.,* 1967a, **58,** 149–156.

———. Learning abilities in Mexican-American and Anglo-American children. *Calif. J. educ. Res.,* 1961, **12,** 147–159.

———. Learning abilities in retarded, average, and gifted children. *Merrill-Palmer Quart.,* 1963, **9,** 123–140. Reprinted in John P. Dececco (Ed.), *Educational technology: Readings in programmed instruction.* New York: Holt, 1964.

———. Rote learning in retarded adults and normal children. *Amer. J. Ment. Defic.,* 1965, **69,** 828–834.

———. Social class and perceptual learning. *Ment. Hyg.,* 1966, **50,** 226–239.

———. Social class and verbal learning. In M. Deutsch, A. R. Jensen, and I. Katz (Eds.), *Social class, race and psychological development.* New York: Holt, 1968.

———. Social class, race, and genetics: Implications for education. *Amer. Educ. Res. J.,* 1968a, **5,** 1–42.

———. Social class, race, genes and educational potential. Paper presented at AERA meeting, New York, Feb. 1967b.

———. Varieties of individual differences. In R. M. Gagne (Ed.), *Learning and individual differences.* Columbus, Ohio: Charles E. Merrill, 1967c.

———. Verbal mediation and educational potential. *Psychol. in the Schools,* 1966a, **3,** 99–109.

Johanson, Eva. A study of schizophrenia in the male: A psychiatric and social study based on 138 cases with follow up. *Acta Psychiat. Neurol. Scand.*, 1958, Suppl. **125**.

Johnson, W. *People in quandaries*. New York: Harper, 1946.

Johnston, R., and B. F. McNeal. Residual psychopathology in released psychiatric patients and its relation to re-admission. *J. abnorm. Psychol.*, 1965, **70**, 337–342.

Joint Commission on Mental Illness and Health. *Action for mental health*. New York: Basic Books, 1961.

Jones, E. *The life and work of Sigmund Freud*. Vol. II. New York: Basic Books, 1955.

————. *The life and work of Sigmund Freud*. Vol. III. New York: Basic Books, 1957.

Jones, E. E., *et al.* Reactions to unfavorable personal evaluations as a function of the evaluator's perceived adjustment. *J. abnorm. soc. Psychol.*, 1959, **59**, 363–370.

Jones, Kathleen. *Lunacy, law, and conscience*. London: Routledge, 1955.

Jones, Maxwell. *The therapeutic community*. New York: Basic Books, 1953.

Jost, Kenneth C. The level of aspiration of schizophrenic and normal subjects. *J. abnorm. soc. Psychol.*, 1955, **50**, 315–320.

Juel-Nielsen, N., A. Nilsen, and M. Hauge. On the diagnosis of zygosity in twins and the values of blood groups. *Acta Genetica* (Basel), 1958, **8**, 256–273.

Jungk, Robert. *Children of the ashes*. New York: Harcourt, 1961.

Kaila, M. Über die Durchschnittshäufigkeit der Geisteskrankheiten und des Schwachsinns in Finnland. *Acta Psychiat. Neurol.*, 1942, **17**, 47–67.

Kallmann, Franz J. The genetic theory of schizophrenia. An analysis of 691 schizophrenic index families. *Amer. J. Psychiat.*, 1946, **103**, 309–322.

————. The genetic theory of schizophrenia. In C. Kluckhohn and H. Murray (Eds.), *Personality in nature, society, and culture*. New York: Knopf, 1956.

————. *Heredity in health and mental disorder*. New York: Norton, 1953.

Kant, O. A comparative study of recovered and deteriorated schizophrenic patients. *J. nerv. ment. Dis.*, 1941, **93**, 616–624.

Kaplan, Bert, Robert B. Ree, and Wyman Richardson. A comparison of the incidence of hospitalized and non-hospitalized cases of psychoses in two communities. *Amer. Sociol. Rev.*, 1956, **21**, 472–479.

Kardiner, Abram, and Lionel Ovesey. *The mark of oppression: A psychosocial study of the American Negro*. New York: Norton, 1951.

Karp, J. M., and I. Sigel. Psychoeducational appraisal of disadvantaged children. *Rev. Educ. Res.*, 1965, **35**, 301–412.

Katz, D., and K. Braly. Racial stereotypes of 100 college students. *J. abnorm. soc. Psychol.*, 1933, **28**, 280–290.

Katz, M. M., and S. B. Lyerly. Methods for measuring adjustment and social behavior in the community: A rationale, description, discriminative validity and scale development. *Psychol. Rep.*, 1963, **13**, 503–535.

Keeping, E. S. The problem of birth ranks. *Biometrics*, 1952, **6**, 112–119.

Kelman, H. C. Compliance, identification and internalization: Three processes of attitude change. *J. Conflict Resolution*, 1958, **2**, 51–60.

————. Processes of opinion change. *Pub. Opin. Quart.*, 1961, **25**, 57–78.

————. Two phases of behavior change. *J. Social Issues*, 1952, **8**, 81–88.

Kennedy, W. A., V. Van De Riet, and J. C. White, Jr. A normative sample of intelligence and achievement of Negro elementary school children in the southeastern United States. *Monogr. Soc. Res. Child Develpm.*, 1963, **28**, 1–112.

Kerkhoff, J. *How thin the veil: A newspaperman's story of his own mental crack-up and recovery.* New York: Greenberg, 1952.

Kerr, C., *et al. Industrialism and industrial man.* Cambridge, Mass.: Harvard Univ. Press, 1960.

Kety, Seymour S. Recent biochemical theories of schizophrenia. In Don D. Jackson (Ed.), *The etiology of schizophrenia.* New York: Basic Books, 1960.

Kindwall, J. A., and E. F. Kinder. Postscript on a benign psychosis. *Psychiatry,* 1940, **3,** 527–534.

King, M. *The recovery of myself.* New Haven: Yale Univ. Press, 1931.

Kinsey, A. C., W. B. Pomeroy, and C. E. Martin. *Sexual behavior in the human female.* Philadelphia: Saunders, 1953.

———— *Sexual behavior in the human male.* Philadelphia: Saunders, 1948.

Klee, Gerald D., with Evelyn Spiro, Anita K. Bahn, and Kurt Gorwitz. An ecological analysis of diagnosed mental illness in Baltimore. Paper presented at the American Psychiatric Association Regional Research Conference, Baltimore, Maryland, April 21, 1966.

Klein, D. C. Some concepts concerning the mental health of the individual. *J. consult. Psychol.,* 1960, **24,** 288–293.

Klein, Edward B., and Herbert E. Spohn. Behavioral dimensions of chronic schizophrenia. *Psychol. Rep.,* 1962, **11,** 777–783.

————. Further comments on characteristics of untestable chronic schizophrenics. *J. abnorm. soc. Psychol.,* 1964, **68,** 355–358.

Kleiner, Robert J., and Seymour Parker. Goal striving and psychosomatic symptoms in a migrant and non-migrant population. In M. B. Kantor (Ed.), *Mobility and mental health.* Springfield, Ill.: Charles C. Thomas, 1965.

————. Goal-striving, social status, and mental disorder: A research review. *Amer. Sociol. Rev.,* 1963, **28,** 189–203.

————. Occupational status, goal striving behavior, and mental disorder. Paper presented at the annual meeting of the American Psychological Association, St. Louis, Sept. 1962.

————. Social mobility, anomie, and mental disorder. In R. B. Edgerton, S. Ploq, and W. Beckwith (Ed.), *Determinants of mental illness.* New York: Holt, 1969.

————, and Hayward G. Taylor. Goal striving and psychosomatic symptoms in a migrant and non-migrant population. Paper presented at the meeting of the World Federation for Mental Health, Paris, Sept. 1961.

————. Level of aspiration and mental disorder: A research proposal. *Ann. N.Y. Acad. Sciences,* 1960, **84,** 878–886.

Kleiner, Robert J., and J. Tuckman. Discrepancy between aspiration and achievement as a predictor of schizophrenia. *Behav. Science,* 1962, **7,** 443–447.

————. Multiple group membership and schizophrenia. *Behav. Science,* 1961, **6,** 292–296.

————, and Martha Lavell. Mental disorder and status based on race. *Psychiatry,* 1960, **23,** 271–274.

————. Mental disorder and status based on religious affiliation. *Hum. Relat.,* 1959, **12,** 273–276.

Klugman, Samuel F. Emotional stability and level of aspiration. *J. gen. Psychol.,* 1948, **38,** 101–118.

————. Relationship between performance on the Rotter Aspiration Board and various types of tests. *J. Psychol.,* 1947, **23,** 51–54.

Knobloch, H., and B. Pasamanick. The developmental approach to the neurologic examination in infancy. *Child Develpm.*, 1962, **33**, 181–198.

———. A developmental questionnaire for infants 40 weeks of age: An evaluation. *Monogr. Soc. Res. Child Developm.*, 1955, **20** (2).

———. Distribution of intellectual potential in an infant population. In B. Pasamanick (Ed.), *Epidemiology of mental disorder*. Washington, D.C.: Amer. Assn. Advancement of Sci., 1959.

———. Environmental factors affecting human development before and after birth. *Pediatrics*, 1960, **26**, 210–218.

———. An evaluation of the consistency and predictive value of the 40 week Gesell developmental schedule. *Psychiat. Res. Rep.* No. 13. Washington, D.C.: Amer. Psychiat Assn., 1960a.

———. Further observations on the behavioral development of Negro children. *J. gen. Psychol.*, 1953, **83**, 137–157.

———. Intellectual potential and heredity—A reply to Dr. Gordon Allen. *Science*, 1961, **133**, 379–380.

———. Prematurity and development. *J. Obstet. Gynecol.*, 1959a, **66**, 729–731.

———. Prospective studies on the epidemiology of reproductive casualty: Methods, findings, and some implications. *Merrill-Palmer Quart.*, 1966, **12**, 27–43.

———. Psychiatry. The epidemiology of mental subnormality. In D. A. Rytand and W. P. Creger (Eds.), *Annual review of medicine*. Vol. 13. Palo Alto, Calif.: Annual Review, Inc., 1962a.

———. The relationship of race and socio-economic status to development of motor behavior patterns in infancy. In B. Pasamanick (Ed.), *Social aspects of psychiatry*. Washington, D.C.: Amer. Psychiat. Assn., 1959b.

———. Some thoughts on the inheritance of intelligence. *Amer. J. Orthopsychiat.*, 1961a, **31**, 454–473.

———. Syndrome of minimal cerebral damage in infancy. *J. Amer. Med. Assn.*, 1959c, **170**, 1384–1387.

———, P. Harper, and R. Rider. The effect of prematurity on health and growth. *Amer. J. Pub. Hlth.*, 1959, **49**, 1164–1173.

Knobloch, H., R. Rider, P. Harper, and B. Pasamanick. Neuropsychiatric sequelae of prematurity: A longitudinal study. *J. Amer. Med. Assn.*, 1956, **161**, 581–585.

Knobloch, H., R. Rider, B. Pasamanick, and P. Harper. An evaluation of a questionnaire on infant development. *Amer. J. Publ. Hlth.*, 1955, **45**, 1309–1320.

Knowles, W. H. Human relations in industry: Research and concepts. *California Mgmt. Rev.*, 1958, **1**, 87–105.

Knupfer, Genevieve. Portrait of the underdog. *Pub. Opin. Quart.*, 1947, **11**, 103–114.

Kobrin, S. The conflict of values in delinquency areas. *Amer. Sociol. Rev.*, 1951, **16**, 653–661.

———. Sociological aspects of the development of a street corner group: An exploratory study. *Amer. J. Orthopsychiat.*, 1961, **31**, 685–702.

———, J. Puntil, and E. Peluso. Criteria of status among street gangs. Paper presented at the Annual Meeting of the American Sociological Association, Los Angeles, Aug. 1963.

Kohn, Melvin L. On the social epidemiology of schizophrenia. *Acta Sociol.*, 1966, **9**, 209–221.

———. Social class and parent-child relationships: An interpretation. *Amer. J. Sociol.*, 1963, **68**, 471–480.

————, and John A. Clausen. Parental authority behavior and schizophrenia. *Amer. J. Orthopsychiat.*, 1956, **26**, 297–313.

————. Social isolation and schizophrenia. *Amer. Sociol. Rev.*, 1955, **20**, 265–273.

Komarovsky, Mirra. *Blue-collar marriage.* New York: Random House, 1962.

————. *The unemployed man and his family.* New York: Dryden, 1940.

Koos, Earl L. *Families in trouble.* New York: King's Crown Press, 1946.

Kornhauser, Arthur. *The mental health of the industrial worker: An analysis and review.* New York: Wiley, 1965.

————. Rejoinder to book review of *The mental health of the industrial worker: An analysis and review,* by William H. McWhinney and Sidney R. Adelman. *Hum. Organization,* 1966, **25**, 182–184.

Kramer, B. M. The day hospital: A case study. *J. Social Issues,* 1960, **16**, 14–19.

————. *Day hospital.* New York: Grune & Stratton, 1962.

Kramer, M. Comment. In Milbank Memorial Fund, *Interrelations between the social environment and psychiatric disorders.* New York: Milbank Mem. Fund, 1953.

————. A discussion of the concepts of incidence and prevalence as related to epidemiologic studies of mental disorders. *Amer. J. Publ. Hlth.,* 1957, **47**, 826–840.

————, et al. Application of life table methodology to the study of mental hospital populations. *Psychiat. Res. Rep.,* 1956, **5**, 49–76.

Kramer, M., E. S. Pollack, and R. W. Redick. Studies of the incidence and prevalence of hospitalized mental disorders in the United States: Current status and future goals. In Paul Hoch and Joseph Zubin (Eds.), *Comparative epidemiology of the mental disorders.* New York: Grune & Stratton, 1961.

Krasner, L. Studies of the conditioning of verbal behavior. *Psychol. Bull.,* 1958, **5**,. 148–170.

————. The therapist as a social reinforcement machine. In H. H. Strupp and L. Luborsky (Eds.), *Research in psychotherapy.* Washington, D.C.: Amer. Psychol. Assn., 1962.

Kringlen, E. Discordance with respect to schizophrenia in monozygotic twins: Some genetic aspects. *J. nerv. ment. Dis.,* 1964, **138**, 26–31.

————. *Schizophrenia in male monozygotic twins.* Oslo: Universitetsforlaget, 1964. Also in *Acta Psychiat. Scand.,* 1964a, Suppl. **178**.

————. Schizophrenia in twins: An epidemiological clinical study. *Psychiatry,* 1966, **29**, 172–184.

Kris, E. The psychology of caricature. *Int. J. Psychoanal.,* 1936, **17**, 285–303.

Kubie, L. S. The fundamental nature of the distinction between normality and neurosis. *Psychoanal. Quart.,* 1954, **23**, 187–188.

Kulkarni, B. S., et al. Electrophoretic studies of serum protein patterns in newborn Indian infants. *Arch. Dis. Childh.,* 1959, **34**, 392–397.

Kunstadter, Peter. A survey of the consanguine or matrifocal family. *Amer. Anthropologist,* 1963, **65**, 56–66.

Laing, R. *The self and others: Further studies in sanity and madness.* Chicago: Quadrangle Books, 1961.

Landesco, J. Organized crime in Chicago. Part III of *Illinois crime survey,* Chicago, Ill., 1929.

————. *Organized crime in Chicago.* (2nd ed.) Chicago: Univ. of Chicago Press, 1968.

Landsberger, H. A. *Hawthorne revisited.* Ithaca, N.Y.: Cornell Univ. Press, 1958.

Landy, David, and Milton Greenblatt. *Halfway house. A sociocultural and clinical study of Rutland Corner House, a transitional aftercare residence for female psychiatric patients.* Washington, D.C.: Vocational Rehabilitation Administration, 1965.

Lane, W. C., and R. A. Ellis. Social mobility and social isolation: A test of Sorokin's dissociative hypothesis. *Amer. Sociol. Rev.*, 1967, **32**, 237–253.

Langer, Susanne K. *Philosophy in a new key.* New York: Mentor Books, 1953.

Langfeldt, G. *The schizophreniform states.* London: Oxford Univ. Press, 1939.

Langner, T. S. Environmental stress, degree of impairment, and type of disturbance. *Psychoanal. Rev.*, 1960, **47**, 3–16.

———. Psychophysiological symptoms and the status of women in two Mexican communities. In J. M. Murphy and A. H. Leighton (Eds.), *Approaches to cross-cultural psychiatry.* Ithaca, N.Y.: Cornell Univ. Press, 1965.

———. A twenty-two item screening score of psychiatric symptoms indicating impairment. *J. Hlth. hum. Behav.*, 1962, **3**, 269–276.

———, and S. T. Michael. *Life stress and mental health: The midtown Manhattan study.* Vol. II. London: Free Press, 1963.

LaPiere, R. T. *A theory of social control.* New York: McGraw-Hill, 1954.

Lapouse, Rema, Mary A. Monk, and Milton Terris. The drift hypothesis and socioeconomic differentials in schizophrenia. *Amer. J. Publ. Hlth.*, 1956, **46**, 978–986.

Last, J. M. The health of immigrants: Some observations from general practice. *Med. J. Australia*, 1960, **1**, 158–162.

Lazarus, Judith, Ben Z. Locke, and Dorothy S. Thomas. Migration differentials in mental disease. *Milbank Mem. Fund Quart.*, 1963, **41**, 25–42.

Leacock, Eleanor. Three social variables and the occurrence of mental disorder. In Alexander H. Leighton, John A. Clausen, and Robert N. Wilson (Eds.), *Explorations in social psychiatry.* New York: Basic Books, 1957.

Leary, T. *Interpersonal diagnosis of personality.* New York: Ronald Press, 1957.

———. *Multilevel measurement of interpersonal behavior.* Berkeley, Calif.: Psychological Consultation Service, 1956.

Lee, Everett S. Socio-economic and migration differentials in mental disease. *Milbank Mem. Fund Quart.*, 1963, **41**, 249–268.

Leighton, A. H. *The governing of men.* Princeton, N.J.: Princeton Univ. Press, 1944.

———. *My name is Legion.* New York: Basic Books, 1959.

———, et al. *Psychiatric disorder among the Yoruba.* Ithaca, N.Y.: Cornell Univ. Press, 1963.

———. Psychiatric disorder in West Africa. *Amer. J. Psychiat.*, 1963, **120**, 521–525.

Leighton, A. H., and J. H. Hughes. Cultures as causative of mental disorder. In Milbank Memorial Fund. *Causes of mental disorders: A review of epidemiological knowledge, 1959.* New York: Milbank Mem. Fund, 1961.

Leighton, D. C., et al. Psychiatric findings of the Stirling County study. *Amer. J. Psychiat.*, 1963, **119**, 1021–1026.

Leighton, D. C., et al. *The character of danger: Psychiatric symptoms in selected communities.* New York: Basic Books, 1963.

Lemert, E. M. An exploratory study of mental disorders in a rural problem area. *Rural Sociol.*, 1948, **13**, 18–60.

———. Legal commitment and social control. *Sociol. soc. Res.*, 1946, **30**, 370–378.

———. *Social pathology.* New York: McGraw-Hill, 1951.

Lemkau, P. V., and G. M. Crocetti. An urban population's opinion and knowledge about mental illness. *Amer. J. Psychiat.*, 1962, **118**, 692–700.

―――. Vital statistics of schizophrenia. In Leopold Bellak (Ed.), *Schizophrenia: A review of the syndrome*. New York: Logos Press, 1958.

Lemkau, P., C. Tietze, and M. Cooper. Mental-hygiene problems in an urban district. *Ment. Hyg.*, 1941, **25**, 624–646.

―――. Mental-hygiene problems in an urban district. Second paper. *Ment. Hyg.*, 1942, **26**, 100–119.

―――. A survey of statistical studies on the prevalence and incidence of mental disorder in sample populations. *Publ. Hlth. Rep.*, 1943, **58**, 1909–1927.

Lendt, Lee. A social history of Washington Heights, New York City. Department of Psychiatry, Columbia Univ., mimeographed, n.d.

Lenski, G. Status crystalization: A non-vertical dimension of social status. *Amer. Sociol. Rev.*, 1954, **19**, 405–413.

―――. Status inconsistency and the vote: A four nation test. *Amer. Sociol. Rev.*, 1967, **32**, 298–301.

Lerner, M. *America as a civilization*. New York: Simon & Schuster, 1957.

Lesser, G. S., G. Fifer, and D. H. Clark. Mental abilities of children from different social-class and cultural groups. *Monogr. Soc. Res. Child Develpm.*, 1965, **30** (4).

Levine, L. S., and R. E. Kantor. Psychological effectiveness and imposed social position: A descriptive framework. Paper presented at the symposium, Positive conceptions of mental health: Implications for research and service. American Psychological Association, Chicago, Sept. 1960.

Levinson, D. J. Role, personality, and social structure in the organizational setting. *J. abnorm. soc. Psychol.*, 1959, **58**, 170–180.

―――, and Phyllis E. Huffman. Traditional family ideology and its relations to personality. *J. Pers.*, 1955, **23**, 251–273.

Levinson, H., *et al.* *Men, management, and mental health*. Cambridge, Mass.: Harvard Univ. Press, 1962.

Levy, R. A. A crisis oriented community clinic. *Ment. Hosp.*, 1965, **16**, 336–339.

Lewin, K. Psychoanalysis and topological psychology. *Bull. Menninger Clinic*, 1937, **1**, 202–211.

―――, T. Dembo, L. Festinger, and P. Sears. Level of aspiration. In J. McV. Hunt (Ed.), *Personality and the behavior disorders*. Vol. 1. New York: Ronald Press, 1944.

Lewinsohn, P. M., and R. C. Nichols. The evaluation of changes in psychiatric patients during and after hospitalization. *J. clin. Psychol.*, 1964, **20**, 272–279.

Lewis, Aubrey. Social aspects of psychiatry. Part I. *Edinburgh Med. J.*, 1951, **58**, 214–230.

―――. Social aspects of psychiatry. Part II. *Edinburgh Med. J.*, 1951a, **58**, 231–247.

Lewis, Hylan. *Blackways of Kent*. Chapel Hill: Univ. of North Carolina Press, 1955.

―――. Child rearing practices among low income families in the District of Columbia. Paper presented at Nat. Conf. Soc. Welfare, Minneapolis, May 1961.

Lewis, Oscar. *Life in a Mexican village: Tepoztlan restudied*. Urbana: Univ. of Illinois Press, 1951.

―――. *La Vida: A Puerto Rican family in the culture of poverty—San Juan and New York*. New York: Random House, 1966.

Leyberg, J. T. A follow-up study on some schizophrenic patients. *Brit. J. Psychiat.*, 1965, **11**, 617–624.

Lidz, T. *The family and human adaptation.* New York: International Universities Press, 1963.

———, A. Cornelison, S. Fleck, and D. Terry. The intrafamilial environment of schizophrenic patient: I. The father. *Psychiatry*, 1957, **20**, 329–342.

———. The intrafamilial environment of schizophrenic patients: II. Marital schism and marital skew. *Amer. J. Psychiat.*, 1957a, **114**, 241–248.

Lidz, T., and S. Fleck. Family studies and a theory of schizophrenia. Unpublished ms., 1964.

———, Y. Alanen, and A. Cornelison. Schizophrenic patients and their siblings. *Psychiatry*, 1963, **26**, 1–18.

Lifton, Betty Jane. A thousand cranes. *The Horn Book Magazine*, April 1963.

Lifton, R. J. Individual patterns in historical change: Imagery of Japanese youth. In David McK. Rioch (Ed.), *Disorders in communication.* Vol. 42, *Proceedings of the assn. for research in nervous and mental disease.* Baltimore: Waverly, 1964.

———. Psychological effects of the atomic bomb in Hiroshima: The theme of death. *Daedalus*, 1963, **92**, 462–497.

———. *Thought reform and the psychology of totalism: A study of "brainwashing" in China.* New York: Norton, 1961.

———. *Thought reform and the psychology of totalism.* New York: Norton Library Edition, 1963a.

———. "Thought reform" of Western civilians in Chinese communist prisons. *Psychiatry*, 1956, **19**, 173–195.

———. Youth and history: Individual change in postwar Japan. *Daedalus*, 1962, **91**, 172–197.

Likert, R. *New patterns of management.* New York: McGraw-Hill, 1961.

Lilienfeld, A. M., and B. Pasamanick. Association of maternal and fetal factors with mental deficiency. *Amer. J. ment. Defic.*, 1956, **60**, 557–569.

Lin, Tsung-Yi. Mental disorders in Taiwan, fifteen years later: A preliminary report. Paper presented to the Conference on Mental Health in Asia and the Pacific, Honolulu, March 1966.

———. A study of the incidence of mental disorder in Chinese and other cultures. *Psychiatry*, 1953, **16**, 313–336.

Lindemann, E. Comment. In Milbank Memorial Fund, *Interrelations between the social environment and psychiatric disorders.* New York: Milbank Mem. Fund, 1953.

———. Psycho-social factors as stressor agents. In J. M. Tanner (Ed.), *Stress and psychiatric disorders.* Oxford: Blackwell Scientific Pubs., 1960.

———. Symptomatology and management of acute grief. *Amer. J. Psychiat.*, 1944, **101**, 141–148.

———. The use of psychoanalytic constructs in preventive psychiatry. *Psychoanal. Study Child*, 1952, **7**, 429–448.

———, et al. Minor disorders. In Milbank Memorial Fund, *Epidemiology of mental disorders.* New York: Milbank Mem. Fund, 1950.

Lindner, R. *Must you conform?* New York: Rinehart, 1956.

Linton, R. Problems of status personality. In S. S. Sargent and M. W. Smith (Eds.), *Culture and personality.* New York: Viking Fund, 1949.

———. *The study of man.* New York: Appleton, 1936.

Lippit, R. Field theory and experiment in social psychology: Autocratic and democratic group atmospheres. *Amer. J. Sociol.*, 1939, **45**, 26–49.

———, N. Polansky, F. Redl, and S. Rosen. The dynamics of power. *Hum. Relat.*, 1952, **5**, 37–64.

Lippitt, R., and R. K. White. An experimental study of leadership and group life. In T. M. Newcomb and E. L. Hartley (Eds.), *Readings in social psychology*. New York: Holt, 1947.

Lipset, S. M. *Political man: The social bases of politics*. Garden City, N.Y.: Doubleday, 1963.

———. Political sociology. In R. K. Merton, L. Broom, and L. S. Cottrell, Jr. (Eds.), *Sociology today: Problems and prospects*. New York: Basic Books, 1959.

———, and R. Bendix. *Social mobility in industrial society*. Berkeley, Calif.: Univ. of Calif. Press, 1963.

Little, Sue W., and Louis D. Cohen. Goal setting behavior of asthmatic children and of their mothers for them. *J. Pers.*, 1951, **19**, 376–389.

Litwak, E. Conflicting values and decision-making. Unpublished doctoral dissertation, Columbia Univ., 1956.

Llewellyn-Thomas, E. The prevalence of psychiatric symptoms within an island fishing village. *Canad. Med. Assoc. J.*, 1960, **83**, 197–204.

Locke, Ben Z., Morton Kramer, and Benjamin Pasamanick. Immigration and insanity. *Publ. Hlth. Rep.*, 1960, **75**, 301–306.

———, Charles E. Timberlake, and Donald Smeltzer. Problems of interpretation of patterns of first admissions to Ohio state public mental hospitals for patients with schizophrenic reactions. In Benjamin Pasamanick and Peter H. Knapp (Eds.), *Social aspects of psychiatry*. Washington, D.C.: Amer. Psychiat. Assn., Psychiatric Research Reports #10, 1958.

Locke, H. *Predicting adjustment in marriage: A comparison of a divorced and a happily married group*. New York: Holt, 1951.

Lodge, G. T., and R. L. Gibson. A coaction map of the personalities described by H. Rorschach and S. J. Beck. *J. Proj. Techn. Pers. Assessm.*, 1953, **17**, 482–488.

Lopreato, Joseph. Upward social mobility and political orientation. *Amer. Sociol. Rev.*, 1967, **32**, 586–592.

Lorge, I. Difference or bias in tests of intelligence. In Anne Anastasi (Ed.), *Testing problems in perspective*. Washington, D.C.: Amer. Council on Educ., 1966.

Low, A. A. *Mental health through will training*. Boston: Christopher Publishing House, 1950.

Low, A. A. (Mrs.) How a panel example should be constructed. Chicago: Mimeographed, 1956.

Lu, Yi-chuang. Contradictory parental expectations in schizophrenia. *Arch. gen. Psychiat.*, 1962, **6**, 219–234.

———. Mother-child role relations in schizophrenia: A comparison of schizophrenic patients with non-schizophrenic siblings. *Psychiatry*, 1961, **24**, 133–142.

Luxenburger, Hans. Die Manifestationswahrschein-lichkeit der Schizophrenie im Lichte der Zwillingsforschung. *Zeitschrift psych. Hygiene*, 1934, **7**, 174–184.

———. Untersuchungen an Schizophrenen Swillingen und ihren Geschwistern zur Prüfung der Realität von Manifestationsschwankungen. *Zeitschrift für die gesamte Neurologie und Psychiatrie*, 1936, **154**, 351–394.

———. Vorläufiger Bericht über Psychiatrischen Serienuntersuchungen an Zwillingen. *Zeitschrift für die gesamte Neurologie und Psychiatrie*, 1928, **116**, 297–326.

Lystad, Mary H. Social mobility among selected groups of schizophrenic patients. *Amer. Sociol. Rev.,* 1957, **22,** 288–292.

MacCarthur, R. S., and W. B. Elley. The reduction of socio-economic bias in intelligence testing. *Brit. J. educ. Psychol.,* 1963, **33,** 107–119.

MacGregor, G. *Warriors without weapons.* Chicago: Univ. of Chicago Press, 1946.

Mack, J. E., and A. Pandiscio. Activities program in day hospital. In American Psychiatric Association, *Proceedings of the 1958 day hospital conference.* Washington, D.C.: Amer. Psychiat. Assn., 1958.

MacMahon, B., and J. M. Sowa. Physical damage to the fetus. In Milbank Memorial Fund, *Causes of mental disorders: A review of epidemiological knowledge, 1959.* New York: Milbank Mem. Fund, 1961.

MacMahon, B., T. F. Pugh, and J. Ipsen. *Epidemiologic methods.* Boston: Little, Brown, 1960.

MacMillan, Allister M. A survey technique for estimating the prevalence of psychoneurotic and related types of disorders in communities. In Benjamin Pasamanick (Ed.), *Epidemiology of mental disorder.* Washington, D.C.: American Association for the Advancement of Science, 1959.

Maher, Brendan A. *Principles of psychopathology.* New York: McGraw-Hill, 1966.

Mahone, Charles H. Fear of failure and unrealistic vocational aspiration. *J. abnorm. soc. Psychol.,* 1960, **60,** 253–261.

Mailer, Norman. *The white Negro.* San Francisco: City Lights Books, 1957.

Maisel, A. Q. When would you consult a psychiatrist? *Collier's,* May 12, 1951, **127,** No. 19, pp. 13–75 passim.

Malinowski, B. *Magic, science, and religion.* Boston: Beacon, 1948.

Malzberg, B. *Social and biological aspects of mental disease.* Utica, N.Y.: N.Y. State Hospital Press, 1940.

————, and E. S. Lee. *Migration and mental disease, a study of first admissions to hospitals for mental disease, New York, 1939–1941.* New York: Social Science Research Council, 1956.

Manis, J. G., et al. Estimating the prevalence of mental illness. *Amer. Sociol. Rev.,* 1964, **29,** 84–89.

————. Validating a mental health scale. *Amer. Sociol. Rev.,* 1963, **28,** 108–116.

Mann, T. *The magic mountain.* New York: Knopf, 1930.

Mark, H. J., and B. Pasamanick. Asynchronism and apparent movement thresholds in brain-injured children. *J. consult. Psychol.,* 1958, **22,** 173–177.

————. Variability of light perception thresholds in brain-injured children. *J. abnorm. soc. Psychol.,* 1958a, **57,** 25–28.

————, and P. Meier. Variability of critical flicker fusion thresholds in brain-injured children. *A.M.A. Arch. Neurol. Psychiat.,* 1958, **80,** 682–688.

Marmor, J., V. Bernard, and P. Ottenberg. Psychodynamics of group opposition to health programs. *Amer. J. Orthopsychiat.,* 1960, **30,** 330–345.

Marshall, H. Slum community organization: Analysis of a concept. Unpublished M.A. thesis, Washington State Univ., 1964.

Martin, J., and F. Westie. The tolerant personality. *Amer. Sociol. Rev.,* 1959, **24,** 521–528.

Maslow, A. H. Deficiency motivation and growth motivation. In M. R. Jones (Ed.), *Nebraska symposium on motivation.* Lincoln: Univ. of Nebraska Press, 1957.

————. *Motivation and personality.* New York: Harper, 1954.

————. Self-actualizing people: A study of psychological health. *Personality*, 1950, **I** (16).

Matthews, J. B. The World Health Organization. *Amer. Opin.*, May 1958, **1**, No. 4, pp. 7–35 passim.

May, Rollo. A psychologist looks at mental health in to-day's (sic) world. *Ment. Hyg.*, 1954, **38**, 1–11.

————, Ernest Angel, and Henry F. Ellenberger (Eds.). *Existence: A new dimension in psychiatry and psychology.* New York: Basic Books, 1958.

Mayer, A. J., and P. Hauser. Class differentials in expectation of life at birth. *Rev. Inst. Int. Statist.*, 1950, **18**, 197–200.

Mayer-Gross, W. Mental health survey in a rural area. *Eugen. Rev.*, 1948, **40**, 140–148.

Mayhew, Henry. Those that will not work. In his *London labour and the London poor.* Vol. 4. London: Griffin, 1862.

Mayman, M. The diagnosis of mental health. Unpublished: Menninger Foundation, 1955.

Mayo, E. *Human problems of industrial civilization.* Cambridge, Mass.: Harvard Univ. Press, 1933.

————. *The social problems of an industrial civilization.* Boston: Grad. School of Bsns. Admin., Harvard Univ., 1945.

McClay, Ellen. *Bats in the belfry.* Los Angeles: Rosewood, 1964.

McGinnies, E. A method for matching anonymous questionnaire data with group discussion material. *J. abnorm. soc. Psychol.*, 1956, **52**, 139–140.

McGregor, D. *The human side of enterprise.* New York: McGraw-Hill, 1960.

McGurk, F. C. J. A scientist's report on race differences. *U.S. News & World Report*, 21 Sept. 1956. Reprinted in H. H. Humphrey (Ed.), *School desegregation: Documents and commentaries.* New York: Crowell, 1964.

McKay, H. D. The neighborhood and child conduct. *Ann. Amer. Acad. polit. soc. Sci.*, 1949, **261**, 32–41.

McNemar, Quinn. *Psychological statistics.* (3rd ed.) New York: Wiley, 1962.

McPartland, T. S., and R. H. Richart. Social and clinical outcomes of psychiatric treatment. *Arch. gen. Psychiat.*, 1966, **14**, 179–184.

McQuitty, L. L. Theories and methods in some objective assessments of psychological well-being. *Psychol. Monogr.*, 1954, **68** (Whole No. 385).

Mead, G. H. *Mind, self and society.* Chicago: Univ. of Chicago Press, 1934.

Mechanic, David, and Edmund H. Volkart. Stress, illness behavior, and the sick role. *Amer. Sociol. Rev.*, 1961, **16**, 51–58.

Meissner, W. W. Thinking about the family—psychiatric aspects. *Fam. Process*, 1964, **3**, 1–40.

Mendel, W. M. Effects of length of hospitalization on rate and quality of remission from acute psychotic episodes. *J. nerv. ment. Dis.*, 1966, **143**, 226–233.

Menninger, K. *Theory of psychoanalytic technique.* New York: Basic Books, 1958.

Menninger, W. C. Psychoanalytic principles applied to the treatment of hospitalized patients. *Bull. Menninger Clinic*, 1937, **1**, 35–43.

Merton, Robert K. Conformity, deviation and opportunity structures. *Amer. Sociol. Rev.*, 1959, **24**, 177–188.

————. Continuities in the theory of social structure and anomie. In his *Social theory and social structure.* London: Free Press, 1957.

————. The role set: Problems in sociological theory. *Brit. J. Sociol.*, 1957a, **8**, 106–120.

————. *Social theory and social structure.* Glencoe, Ill.: Free Press, 1949.

————. *Social theory and social structure.* (Rev. and enl. ed.) London: Free Press, 1957b.

Meyer, Jon K. Attitudes towards mental illness in a Maryland community. *Pub. Hlth. Rep.,* 1964, **79,** 769–772.

Milbank Memorial Fund. *Causes of mental disorders: A review of epidemiological knowledge, 1959.* New York: Milbank Mem. Fund, 1961.

————. *Epidemiology of mental disorder.* New York: Milbank Mem. Fund, 1950.

Miller, D. R., and G. E. Swanson. *The changing American parent.* New York: John Wiley, 1958.

————. A proposed study of the learning of techniques for resolving conflicts of impulses. In Milbank Memorial Fund, *Interrelations between the social environment and psychiatric disorders.* New York: Milbank Mem. Fund, 1953.

————. *Inner conflict and defense.* New York: Holt, 1960.

Miller, S. M. The American lower classes: A typological approach. In Arthur B. Shostak and William Gomberg (Eds.), *Blue-collar world.* Englewood Cliffs, N.J.: Prentice-Hall, 1964.

————, and Elliot G. Mishler. Social class, mental illness, and American psychiatry: An expository review. *Millbank Mem. Fund Quart.,* 1959, **37,** 174–199.

Miller, Walter B. The corner gang boys get married. *Trans-action,* 1963, **1,** 10–12.

————. Lower class culture as a generating milieu of gang delinquency. *J. Social Issues,* 1958, **14,** 5–19.

Mills, C. Wright. *The power elite.* New York: Oxford Univ. Press, 1956.

————. The professional ideologies of social pathologists. *Amer. Sociol.,* 1943, **49,** 165–180.

Milner, Esther. A study of the relationship between reading readiness in grade-one school children and patterns of parent-child interactions. *Child Develpm.,* 1951, **22,** 95–122.

Mintz, Norbett L., and David T. Schwartz. Urban ecology and psychosis: Community factors in the incidence of schizophrenia and manic-depression among Italians in greater Boston. *Internat. J. soc. Psychiat.,* 1964, **10,** 101–118.

Minuchin, S., *et al. Families of the slums.* New York: Basic Books, 1967.

Mishler, Elliot G., and Norman A. Scotch. Sociocultural factors in the epidemiology of schizophrenia. *Psychiatry,* 1963, **26,** 315–343.

Mishler, Elliot G., and Nancy E. Waxler. Family interaction processes and schizophrenia: A review of current theories. *Merrill-Palmer Quart.,* 1965, **11,** 269–315.

————. *Interaction in families: An experimental study of family processes and schizophrenia.* New York: Wiley, 1968.

————. Interaction in families of schizophrenics: An experimental study. Paper presented at the Annual Meeting of the American Sociological Association, Montreal, Sept. 1964.

Mizruchi, Ephriam. *Success and opportunity; A study of anomie.* New York: Free Press, 1954.

Money, John. Linguistic resources and psychodynamic theory. *Brit. J. Med. Psychol.,* 1955, **28,** 264–266.

Montague, D. O. Arithmetic concepts of kindergarten children in contrasting socio-economic areas. *Elem. School J.,* 1964, **64,** 393–397.

Moore, W. E. Industrial relations and the social order. (2nd ed.) New York: Macmillan, 1951.

Morgan, N. C., and N. A. Johnson. Failures in psychiatry: The chronic hospital patient. *Amer. J. Psychiat.*, 1957, **113**, 824–830.

Morganthau, Hans J. Death in the nuclear age. *Commentary*, September, 1961.

Morris, J. N. Health and social class. *The Lancet*, 1959, **1**, 303–305.

Mowrer, E. A study of personal disorganization. *Amer. Sociol. Rev.*, 1939, **4**, 475–487.

Mowrer, O. H. "Sin," the lesser of two evils. *Amer. Psychol.*, 1960, **15**, 301–304.

Moynihan, Daniel P. Education of the urban poor. *Harvard Grad. School of Educ. Assn. Bull.*, 1967, **12**, 2–13.

———. Employment, income and the ordeal of the Negro family. *Daedalus*, 1965, **94**, 745–770.

Murphy, H. B. M. Migration and the major mental disorders: A reappraisal. In M. Kantor (Ed.), *Mobility and mental health*. Princeton, N.J.: Van Nostrand, 1964.

———. Social change and mental health. In Milbank Memorial Fund, *Causes of mental disorders: A review of epidemiological knowledge, 1959*. New York: Milbank Mem. Fund, 1961.

Murray, E. J. A case study in a behavioral analysis of psychotherapy. *J. abnorm. soc. Psychol.*, 1954, **49**, 305–310.

———. A content-analysis method for studying psychotherapy. *Psychol. Monogr.*, 1956, **70** (Whole No. 420).

———, and M. Cohen. Mental illness, milieu therapy, and social organization in ward groups. *J. abnorm. soc. Psychol.*, 1959, **58**, 48–54.

Murray, Henry A. *Explorations in personality*. New York: Oxford, 1938.

Myers, Jerome K., and Bertram H. Roberts. *Family and class dynamics in mental illness*. New York: Wiley, 1959.

Myers, Jerome K., and Leslie Schaffer. Social stratification and psychiatric practice: A study of an out-patient clinic. *Amer. Sociol. Rev.*, 1954, **19**, 307–310.

Myers, R. C. Influence of age on physicians' views concerning mental health matters. *Pub. Opin. Quart.*, 1955, **19**, 252–258.

Myerson, A. Review of R. E. L. Faris and H. W. Dunham, *Mental disorders in urban areas*. *Amer. J. Psychiat.*, 1940, **96**, 995–997.

Myrdal, G. *An American dilemma*. New York: Harper, 1944.

———. *Challenge to affluence*. New York: Pantheon Books, 1963.

Nakamura, Hajime. *Ways of thinking of Eastern peoples*. Tokyo: Japanese National Commission for UNESCO, 1960.

National Assembly on Mental Health Education. *Mental health education: A critique*. Philadelphia: Pennsylvania Mental Health, Inc., 1960.

National Health Federation. Counselors and the schools. *Nat. Hlth. Fed. Bull.*, 1962, **8**.

National Opinion Research Center. Popular thinking in the field of mental health. National Opinion Research Center, Univ. of Chicago, Survey 272, 1950.

———. Confidential forecast of the results of the survey of "Popular thinking in the field of mental health." National Opinion Research Center, Univ. of Chicago, Survey 272, Sept. 1952.

Nettler, Gwynn. Test burning in Texas. *Amer. Psychol.*, 1959, **14**, 682–683.

New Jersey mental health survey of the general public. Princeton, N.J.: Audience Research, Inc., 1954.

New Jersey mental health survey of physicians. Princeton, N.J.: Audience Research, Inc., 1954a.

New York State Department of Mental Hygiene, Mental Health Research Unit. A mental health survey of older people. Part 1. *Psychiat. Quart. Suppl.,* 1959, **33,** 45–99.

Newcomb, T. M. Autistic hostility and social reality. *Hum. Relat.,* 1947, **1,** 69–86.

Niederland, William G. The problems of the survivor: Part I, Some remarks on the psychiatric evaluation of emotional disorders in survivors of nazi persecution. *J. Hillside Hosp.,* 1961, **10,** 233–247.

Nietz, J. A. The depression and the social status of occupations. *Elem. School J.,* 1935, **35,** 454–461.

Nixon, Robert E. An approach to the dynamics of growth in adolescence. *Psychiatry,* 1961, **24,** 18–31.

Noble, D. Some factors in the treatment of schizophrenia. *Psychiatry,* 1941, **4,** 25–30.

Nolan, William J. Occupation and dementia praecox. *N.Y. State Hosp. Quart.,* 1917, **3,** 127–154.

———. Occupation and manic-depressive psychosis. *N.Y. State Hosp. Quart.,* 1918, **4,** 75–102.

Norris, Vera. Mental illness in London. (Maudsley Monograph No. 6) London: Chapman and Hall, 1959.

Noyes, A. P., and L. C. Kolb. *Modern clinical psychiatry.* (5th ed.) Philadelphia: Saunders, 1958.

Nunnally, J. C., Jr. *Opinion-attitude factors in the mental health area.* Washington, D.C.: National Institute of Mental Heatlh, P.H.S., Institute of Communication, Res. Prog. Rep., 1954 (mimeographed).

———. *Popular conceptions of mental health.* New York: Holt, 1961.

———, and J. M. Kittross. Public attitudes toward mental health professions. *Amer. Psychol.,* 1958, **13,** 589–594.

Nuttall, R., and L. Solomon. Factorial structure and prognostic significance of pre-morbid adjustment in schizophrenia. *J. consult. Psychol.,* 1965, **29,** 362–372.

———. Prognosis in schizophrenia: The role of premorbid, social class and demographic factors. *Behav. Science,* 1970, **15,** 255–264.

Ødegaard, Ørnulv. Current studies of incidence and prevalence of hospitalized mental patients in Scandinavia. In P. H. Hoch and J. Zubin (Eds.), *Comparative epidemiology of the mental disorders.* New York: Grune & Stratton, 1961.

———. Emigration and insanity: A study of mental disease among the Norwegian-born population of Minnesota. *Acta Psychiat. Neurol.,* 1932, Suppl. **4,** esp. 182–184.

———. Emigration and mental health. *Ment. Hyg.,* 1936, **20,** 546–553.

———. The incidence of psychoses in various occupations. *Internat. J. soc. Psychiat.,* 1956, **2,** 85–104.

———. Occupational incidence of mental disease in single women. *Living Conditions and Health,* 1957, **1,** 169–180.

———. Psychiatric epidemiology. *Proceed. Royal Society Med.,* 1962, **55,** 831–837.

———. A statistical investigation of the incidence of mental disorder in Norway. *Psychiat. Quart.,* 1946, **20,** 381–399.

Olim, E. G., R. D. Hess, and V. Shipman. Relationship between mothers' abstract language style and abstraction styles of urban pre-school children. Paper presented at the Midwest Psychological Association Meeting, Chicago, April 1965.

Olson, Gordon W. Failure and the subsequent performance of schizophrenics. *J. abnorm. soc. Psychol.*, 1958, **57**, 310–314.

Orzack, M. H., and C. Kornetsky. Attention dysfunction in chronic schizophrenia. *Arch. gen Psychiat.*, 1966, **14**, 323–326.

Osborne, R. T. Racial differences in mental growth and school achievement: A longitudinal study. *Psychol. Rep.*, 1960, **7**, 233–239.

Osgood, C. E., G. J. Suci, and P. H. Tannenbaum. *The measurement of meaning.* Urbana, Ill.: Univ. of Illinois Press, 1957.

Ota, Yoko. *Shikabane no Machi* (Town of corpses). Tokyo: Kawade Shobō, 1955.

Oughterson, Ashley W., and Shields Warren. *Medical effects of the atomic bomb in Japan.* New York: McGraw-Hill, 1956.

Owen, Mary Bess. Alternative hypotheses for the explanation of some of Faris' and Dunham's results. *Amer. J. Sociol.*, 1941, **47**, 48–52.

Parker, S., and R. J. Kleiner. *Mental illness in the urban Negro community.* New York: Free Press, 1966.

———, and R. Eskin. Social status and psychopathology. Paper presented at the annual meeting of the society of Physical Anthropology, Philadelphia, April, 1962.

Parker, S., R. J. Kleiner, and H. G. Taylor. Level of aspiration and mental disorder: A research proposal. *Ann. N.Y. Acad. Sciences,* 1960, **84**, 878–886.

Parsons, Talcott. The mental hospital as a type of organization. In M. Greenblatt, D. J. Levinson, and R. H. Williams (Eds.), *The patient and the mental hospital.* New York: Free Press, 1957.

———. *The social system.* New York: Free Press, 1951.

———, and Robert F. Bales. *Family, socialization and interaction process.* New York: Free Press, 1955.

Pasamanick, B. Comparative psychological studies of Negroes and whites in the United States: A clarification. *Psychol. Bull.*, 1962, **59**, 243–247.

———. A comparative study of the behavioral development of Negro infants. *J. gen. Psychol.*, 1946, **69**, 3–44.

———. Determinants of intelligence. In S. M. Farber and R. H. L. Wilson (Eds.), *Conflict and creativity: Man and civilization.* New York: McGraw-Hill, 1963.

———. (Ed.). *Epidemiology of mental disorder.* Washington, D.C.: Amer. Assn. for the Advancement of Science, 1959.

———. Latent resources for fostering health personality development. *Quart. J. Child Behav.*, 1952, **4**, 117–138.

———. Patterns of research in mental hygiene. *Psychiat. Quart.*, 1952a, **26**, 577–589.

———. Research on the influence of socio-cultural variables upon organic factors in mental retardation. *Amer. J. ment. Def.*, 1959a, **64**, 316–320.

———. Thoughts on some epidemiologic studies of tomorrow. In P. H. Hoch and J. Zubin (Eds.), *The future of psychiatry.* New York: Grune & Stratton, 1962a.

———, and H. Knobloch. Early language behavior in Negro children and the testing of intelligence. *J. abnorm. soc. Psychol.*, 1955, **50**, 401–402.

———. Retrospective studies on the epidemiology of reproductive casualty: Old and new. *Merrill-Palmer Quart.*, 1966, **12**, 7–26.

Pasamanick, B., D. W. Roberts, P. W. Lemkau, and D. B. Krueger. A survey of mental disease in an urban population: Prevalence by race and income. In B. Pasamanick (Ed.), *Epidemiology of mental disorder.* Washington, D.C.: Amer. Assn. for the Advancement of Science, 1959.

Pasamanick, B., F. Scarpetti, and S. Dinitz. *Schizophrenics in the community: An experimental study in the prevention of hospitalization.* New York: Appleton, 1967.

Payne, Arlene. Early prediction of achievement. *Administrator's Notebook,* 1964, **13** (1).

Pearlin, L. I., and M. L. Kohn. Social class, occupation, and parental values: A cross-national study. *Amer. Sociol. Rev.,* 1966, **31,** 466–479.

Pearlin, L. I., and M. Rosenberg. Nurse-patient social distance and the structural context of a mental hospital. *Amer. Sociol. Rev.,* 1962, **27,** 56–65.

Peck, James. The ship that never hit port. In Holley Cantine and Dachine Rainer (Eds.), *Prison etiquette.* Bearsville, N.Y.: Retort Press, 1950.

Perceval, John. *Perceval's narrative.* Gregory Bateson (Ed.). Stanford, Calif.: Stanford Univ. Press, 1961.

Perry, Stewart E. Some theoretic problems of mental deficiency and their action implications. *Psychiatry,* 1954, **17,** 45–73.

———, and Lyman Wynne. Role conflict, role redefinition and social change in a clinical research organization. *Soc. Forces,* 1959, **38,** 62–65.

Peters, C. C., and W. R. Van Voorhis. *Statistical procedures and their mathematical bases.* New York: McGraw-Hill, 1940.

Peters, F. *The world next door.* New York: Farrar, Straus, 1949.

Peters, R. S. *The concept of motivation.* London: Routledge, 1958.

———. Private wants and public tradition. *Listener,* 1960, **14,** 46–47.

Peterson, R. A., and L. Debord. Educational supportiveness of the home and academic performance of disadvantaged boys. *IMRID Behavioral Sci. Monogr.,* George Peabody Coll., 1966, **3.**

Peterson, R. C., and L. L. Thurstone. *Motion pictures and the social attitudes of children.* New York: Macmillan, 1933.

Pettigrew, Thomas F. *A profile of the Negro American.* Princeton, N.J.: Van Nostrand, 1964.

Phillips, D. L. Rejection: A possible consequence of seeking help for mental disorders. *Amer. Sociol. Rev.,* 1963, **28,** 963–972.

———. The true prevalence of mental illness in a New England state. *Comm. ment. hlth. J.,* 1966, **2,** 35–40.

Phillips, Leslie. Case history data and prognosis in schizophrenia. *J. nerv. ment. Dis.,* 1953, **117,** 515–525.

Piaget, J. *The origins of intelligence in children.* (Trans. by Margaret Cook.) New York: International Universities Press, 1952.

Pine, F. *Conceptions of the mentally ill and the self: A study of psychiatric aides.* Unpublished doctoral dissertation, Harvard Univ., 1955.

———, and D. J. Levinson. A sociopsychological conception of patienthood. *Internat. J. soc. Psychiat.,* 1961, **7,** 106–123.

———. Two patterns of ideology, role conception, and personality among hospital aides. In M. Greenblatt, D. J. Levinson, and R. H. Williams (Eds.), *The patient and the mental hospital.* New York: Free Press, 1957.

Platt, A. M., and B. L. Diamond. The origins and development of the "wild beast" concept of mental illness and its relations to theories of criminal responsibility. *J. Hist. behav. Sci.,* 1965, **1,** 355–367.

Plunkett, Richard J., and John E. Gordon. *Epidemiology and mental illness.* (Monograph No. 6, Joint Commission on Mental Illness and Health) New York: Basic Books, 1960.

Polansky, N., R. Lippitt, and F. Redl. An investigation of behavioral contagion in groups. *Hum. Relat.*, 1950, **3**, 319–348.

Polk, K. An exploration of rural juvenile delinquency. Mimeographed paper from Lane County Youth Study Project, Sept. 1963.

Pollak, Otto. *Social adjustment in old age.* New York: Soc. Sci. Res. Council, Bull. 59, 1948.

Portmann, Adolf. *New paths in biology.* New York: Harper, 1964.

Powelson, H., and R. Bendix. Psychiatry in prison. *Psychiatry*, 1951, **14**, 73–86.

Pratt, S., *et al.* The mental hospital and the "treatment field." *J. psychol. Stud.*, 1960, **11**, 1–179.

Presthus, R. *The organizational society.* New York: Knopf, 1962.

Primrose, E. J. R. *Psychological illness: A community study.* London: Tavistock, 1962.

Proctor, W. N. Occupation and intelligence. *J. educ. Res.*, 1920, **2**, 537.

Pugh, T. F., and B. MacMahon. *Epidemiologic findings in United States mental hospital data.* Boston: Little, Brown, 1962.

Queen, Stuart A. The ecological study of mental disorders. *Amer. Sociol. Rev.*, 1940, **5**, 201–209.

Raifman, Irving. Level of aspiration in a group of peptic ulcer patients. *J. consult. Psychol.*, 1957, **21**, 229–231.

Rainwater, L. *And the poor get children.* Chicago: Quadrangle Books, 1960.

———. Crucible of identity: The Negro lower-class family. *Daedalus*, 1966, **95**, 172–216.

———. *Family design: Marital sexuality, family size, and contraception.* Chicago: Aldine, 1965.

———. Fear and the house-as-haven in the lower class. *J. Amer. inst. Planners*, Feb. 1966a.

———. Marital sexuality in four cultures of poverty. *J. Marr. Family*, 1964, **26**, 457–466.

———. Work and identity in the lower class. In S. B. Warner, Jr. (Ed.), *Planning for a nation of cities.* Cambridge, Mass.: M.I.T. Press, 1966b.

———, Richard P. Coleman, and Gerald Handel. *Workingman's wife.* New York: Oceana Publications, 1959.

Ramsey, G. V., and M. Seipp. Attitudes and opinions concerning mental illness. *Psychiat. Quart.*, 1948, **22**, 428–444.

———. Public opinions and information concerning mental health. *J. clin. Psychol.*, 1948a, **4**, 397–406.

Rank, Otto. *Beyond psychology.* New York: Dover, 1958.

Rao, S. Birth order and schizophrenia. *J. nerv. ment. Dis.*, 1964, **138**, 87–89.

Rapaport, D. The structure of psychology of psychoanalytic theory. *Psychol. Issues*, 1960, **11**, 7–144.

Raush, H. L. Interaction sequences. *J. Pers. soc. Psychol.*, 1965, **2**, 487–499.

———, A. T. Dittmann, and T. J. Taylor. Person, setting, and change in social interaction. *Hum. Relat.*, 1959, **12**, 361–378.

Raush, H. L., I. Farbman, and L. G. Llewellyn. Person, setting, and change in social interaction II: A normal control study. *Hum. Relat.*, 1960, **13**, 305–332.

Raush, H. L., with C. L. Raush. *The halfway house movement: A search for sanity.* New York: Appleton, 1968.

Reckless, W. C. *Vice in Chicago.* Chicago: Univ. of Chicago Press, 1933.

Redl, Fritz. *When we deal with children.* New York: Free Press, 1966.

———, and D. Wineman. *The aggressive child.* New York: Free Press, 1957.

Rees, T. P. Back to moral treatment and community care. *J. ment. Sci.,* 1957, **103,** 303–313.

Register-Star. Hudson, New York, March 17, 1960.

Reid, D. D. Precipitating proximal factors in the occurrence of mental disorders: Epidemiological evidence. In Milbank Memorial Fund, *Causes of mental disorders: A review of epidemiological knowledge, 1959.* New York: Milbank Mem. Fund, 1961.

Reiss, A. J., Jr., et al. *Occupations and social status.* New York: Free Press, 1961.

Reiss, A. J., Jr., and A. L. Rhodes. Delinquency and social class structure. *Amer. Sociol. Rev.,* 1961, **26,** 720–732.

Reiss, Ira L. Premarital sexual permissiveness among Negroes and whites. *Amer. Sociol. Rev.,* 1964, **29,** 688–698.

Rennie, T. A. C. The Yorkville community mental health research study. In Milbank Memorial Fund, *Interrelations between the social environment and psychiatric disorders.* New York: Milbank Mem. Fund, 1953.

———, et al. Urban life and mental health. *Amer. J. Psychiat.,* 1957, **113,** 831–836.

Rice, Robert. The Persian queens. *The New Yorker,* Oct. 19, 1963, **39,** No. 35, pp. 153–187 passim.

Riesman, D. *The lonely crowd.* New Haven: Yale Univ. Press, 1950.

Riezler, Kurt. Comment on the social psychology of shame. *Amer. J. Sociol.,* 1943, **48,** 458.

Rin, H., H. Chu, and T. Lin. Psychophysiological reactions of a rural and suburban population in Taiwan. *Acta Psychiat. Scand.,* 1966, **42,** 410–473.

Rin, H., and T. Lin. Mental illness among Formosan aborigines as compared with the Chinese in Taiwan. *J. ment. Sci.,* 1962, **108,** 134–146.

Rivera, R. Occupational goals: A comparative analysis. Unpublished M.A. thesis, Univ. of Chicago, 1964.

Roback, A. A. *History of psychology and psychiatry.* New York: Citadel Press, 1961.

Robinson, D. The far right's fight against mental health. *Look,* Jan. 26, 1965, **29,** No. 2, 30–32.

Robinson, W. S. Ecological correlations and the behavior of individuals. *Amer. Sociol. Rev.,* 1950, **15,** 351–357.

Rodman, Hyman. The lower-class value stretch. *Soc. Forces,* 1963, **42,** 205–215.

Rodnick, E. H., and N. Garmezy. An experimental approach to the study of motivation in schizophrenia. In M. R. Jones (Ed.), *Nebraska symposium on motivation.* Lincoln: Univ. of Nebraska Press, 1957.

Rogers, Carl R. *Client-centered therapy.* Boston: Houghton Mifflin, 1951.

———. The necessary and sufficient conditions of therapeutic personality change. *J. consult. Psychol.,* 1957, **21,** 95–103.

———, and Rosalind Dymond (Eds.), *Psychotherapy and personality change.* Chicago: Univ. of Chicago Press, 1954.

Rogler, Lloyd H., and August B. Hollingshead. *Trapped: Families and schizophrenia.* New York: Wiley, 1965.

Rohwer, W. D. Verbal and visual elaboration in paired-associate learning. *Project Literacy Rep.*, 1966, **7**, 18–28.

Rokeach, M. *The open and closed mind.* New York: Basic Books, 1960.

Rolph, C. H. (Ed.). *Women of the streets.* London: Secker and Warburg, 1955.

Roman, P. M., and H. M. Trice. *Schizophrenia and the poor.* Ithaca, N.Y.: Cayuga Press, 1967.

Rosanoff, A. J. Survey of mental disorders in Nassau County, New York, July–October 1916. *Psychiat. Bull.*, 1917, **2**, 109–231.

————, *et al.* The etiology of so-called schizophrenic psychoses, with special reference to their occurrence in twins. *Amer. J. Psychiat.*, 1934, **91**, 247–286.

Rose, A. M., and H. R. Stub. Summary of studies on the incidence of mental disorders. In A. M. Rose (Ed.), *Mental health and mental disorder.* New York: Norton, 1955.

Rosenberg, M. Power and desegregation. *Soc. Problems*, 1956, **3**, 215–223.

Rosenthal, David. Familial concordance by sex with respect to schizophrenia. *Psychol. Bull.*, 1962, **59**, 401–421.

————. Problems of sampling and diagnosis in the major twin studies of schizophrenia. *J. psychiat. Res.*, 1962a, **1**, 116–134.

————. Sex distribution and the severity of illness among samples of schizophrenic twins. *J. psychiat. Res.*, 1961, **1**, 26–36.

————. Some factors associated with concordance and discordance with respect to schizophrenia in monozygotic twins. *J. nerv. ment. Dis.*, 1959, **129**, 1–10.

Roth, J. A. *Timetables—Structuring the passage of time in hospital treatment and other careers.* Indianapolis: Bobbs-Merrill, 1963.

Roth, W. F., and F. H. Luton. The mental health program in Tennessee. *Amer. J. Psychiat.*, 1943, **99**, 662–675.

Roueché, Berton. Ten feet tall. In his *The incurable wound, and further narratives of medical detection.* Boston: Little, Brown, 1954.

Rowland, H. Friendship patterns in a state mental hospital. *Psychiatry*, 1939, **2**, 363–373.

————. Interaction processes in a state mental hospital. *Psychiatry*, 1938, **1**, 323–337.

Rowntree, L. G., K. H. McGill, and L. P. Hellman. Mental and personality disorders in Selective Service registrants. *J. Amer. Med. Assn.*, 1945, **128**, 1084–1087.

Ruesch, Jurgen. *Chronic disease and psychological invalidism: A psychosomatic study.* New York: American Society for Research in Psychosomatic Problems, 1946.

————. Social technique, social status, and social change in illness. In Clyde Kluckhohn, Henry A. Murray, and David M. Schneider (Eds.), *Personality in nature, society, and culture.* New York: Knopf, 1956.

————, Annemarie Jacobson, and Martin B. Loeb. Acculturation and illness. *Psychol. Monogr.*, 1948, **62** (Whole No. 292).

Ryckoff, Irving, with Juliana Day and Lyman C. Wynne. Maintenance of stereotyped roles in the families of schizophrenics. *A.M.A. Arch. Psychiat.*, 1959, **1**, 93–98.

Ryle, G. *The concept of mind.* Oxford: Hutchinson's Univ. Press, 1948.

Sainsbury, Peter. *Suicide in London: An ecological study.* London: Chapman and Hall, 1955.

St. Louis Post Dispatch, article of July 20, 1965, beginning, "A White House study group is laying the ground work for an attempt to better the structure of the Negro family."

Salisbury, H. E. *The shook-up generation.* New York: Harper, 1958.

Sampson, E. E. Birth order, need achievement, and conformity. *J. abnorm. soc. Psychol.*, 1962, **64**, 155–159.

Sampson, Harold, Sheldon L. Messinger, and Robert D. Towne. Family processes and becoming a mental patient. *Amer. J. Sociol.*, 1962, **68**, 88–96.

Sandifer, M. J., Jr. Social psychiatry 100 years ago. *Amer. J. Psychiat.*, 1962, **118**, 749–750.

Sanford, F. H. Proposal for a study of mental health in education. Joint Commission on Mental Illness and Health, First Annual Report, 1956.

Sanford, N. Personality: Its place in psychology. In S. Koch (Ed.), *Psychology: A study of a science*. Vol. 5. New York: McGraw-Hill, 1963.

Sanua, Victor D. The etiology and epidemiology of mental illness and problems of methodology: With special emphasis on schizophrenia. *Ment. Hyg.*, 1963, **47**, 607–621.

———. Sociocultural factors in families of schizophrenics: A review of the literature. *Psychiatry*, 1961, **24**, 246–265.

Sarbin, T. R. Anxiety: The reification of a metaphor. *Arch. gen. Psychiat.*, 1964, **10**, 630–638.

———. The dangerous individual: An outcome of social identity transformations. *Brit. J. Criminol.*, 1967, **7**, 285–295.

———. Notes on the transformation of social identity. In L. M. Roberts, N. S. Greenfield, and M. H. Miller (Eds.), *Comprehensive mental health: The challenge of evaluation*. Madison: Univ. of Wisconsin Press, 1968.

———. Role theoretical analysis of schizophrenia. In J. H. Mann (Ed.), *Reader in general psychology*. New York: Rand-McNally, in press.

———. Schizophrenic thinking: A role theoretical analysis. Unpublished ms., 1968a.

———, and J. B. Juhasz. The historical background of the concept of hallucination. *J. Hist. behav. Sci.*, 1967, **3**, 339–358.

Sarbin, T. R., K. E. Scheibe, and R. O. Kroger. *The transformation of social identity*. Unpublished ms., Univ. of California, Berkeley, 1965.

Sawrey, W. L., L. Keller, and J. J. Conger. An objective method of grouping profiles by distance functions and its relation to factor analysis. *Educ. psychol. Measmt.*, 1960, **20**, 651–673.

Schacter, S. *The psychology of affiliation*. Stanford, Calif.: Stanford Univ. Press, 1959.

———, N. Ellertson, D. McBride, and D. Gregory. An experimental study of cohesiveness and productivity. *Hum. Relat.*, 1951, **4**, 229–238.

Schiff, L. The campus conservative movement. Unpublished doctoral dissertation, Harvard Univ., 1964.

Schneider, David M. The social dynamics of physical disability in Army basic training. *Psychiatry*, 1947, **10**, 323–333.

Schneider, E. V. Social concepts and psychiatric research. In Milbank Memorial Fund, *Interrelations between the social environment and psychiatric disorders*. New York: Milbank Mem. Fund, 1953.

Schooler, C. Birth order and hospitalization for schizophrenia. *J. abnorm. soc. Psychol.*, 1964, **69**, 574–579.

———. Birth order and schizophrenia. *Arch. gen. Psychiat.*, 1961, **4**, 91–97.

Schooler, N. R., *et al.* One year after discharge: Community adjustment of schizophrenic patients. *Amer. J. Psychiat.*, 1967, **123**, 986–995.

Schroeder, Clarence W. Mental disorders in cities. *Amer. J. Sociol.*, 1942, **48**, 40–48.

Schwartz, Charlotte Green. Perspectives on deviance—wives' definitions of their husbands' mental illness. *Psychiatry,* 1957, **20,** 275–291.

———. The stigma of mental illness. *J. Rehabilitation,* 1956, **22,** pp. 7–29 passim.

Schwartz, David T., and Norbett L. Mintz. Ecology and psychosis among Italians in 27 Boston communities. *Soc. Problems,* 1963, **10,** 371–374.

Schwartz, Michael, and George Henderson. The culture of unemployment: Some notes on Negro children. In Arthur B. Shostak and William Gomberg (Eds.), *Blue-collar world.* Englewood Cliffs, N.J.: Prentice-Hall, 1964.

Schwartz, Morris S. The economic and spatial mobility of paranoid schizophrenics and manic depressives. Unpublished M.A. thesis, Univ. of Chicago, 1946.

———, and A. H. Stanton. A social psychological study of incontinence. *Psychiatry,* 1950, **13,** 399–416.

Scotch, Norman, and H. Jack Geiger. The epidemiology of essential hypertension: A review with special attention to psychological and sociocultural factors. II: Psychologic and sociocultural factors in etiology. *J. chron. Dis.,* 1963, **16,** 1183–1213.

———. The epidemiology of rheumatoid arthritis: A review with special attention to social factors. *J. chron. Dis.,* 1962, **15,** 1037–1067.

Sears, Pauline Snedden. Level of aspiration in relation to some variables of personality: Clinical studies. *J. soc. Psychol.,* 1941, **14,** 311–336.

Searles, Harold F. The effort to drive the other person crazy—An element in the aetiology and psychotherapy of schizophrenia. Part 1. *Brit. J. med. Psychol.,* 1959, **32,** 1–18.

———. *The nonhuman environment.* New York: International Universities Press, 1960.

———. Positive feelings in the relationship between the schizophrenic and his mother. *Internat. J. Psychoanal.,* 1958, **39,** 569–586.

Selesnick, Sheldon T. C. G. Jung's contributions to psychoanalysis. *Amer. J. Psychiat.,* 1963, **120,** 350–356.

Semler, I. J., and I. Iscoe. Comparative and developmental study of the learning abilities of Negro and white children under four conditions. *J. educ. Psychol.,* 1963, **54,** 38–44.

Sewell, William, and A. O. Haller. Factors in the relationship between social status and the personality adjustment of the child. *Amer. Sociol. Rev.,* 1959, **24,** 511–520.

Shaw, C. R. *Delinquency areas.* Chicago: Univ. of Chicago Press, 1929.

———. *The jack-roller.* Chicago: Univ. of Chicago Press, 1930.

———, and H. D. McKay. *Juvenile delinquency and urban areas.* Chicago: Univ. of Chicago Press, 1942.

———. *Social factors in juvenile delinquency, report on the causes of crime for the national commission on law observance and enforcement, Vol. II.* Washington, D.C.: U.S. Gov't. Ptg. Office, 1931.

Sheatsley, P. B., and J. Feldman. The assassination of President Kennedy: Public reactions. *Pub. Opin. Quart.,* 1964, **28,** 189–215.

Sherif, M., and C. W. Sherif. *Reference groups: Exploration into conformity and deviation of adolescents.* New York: Harper, 1964.

Shneidman, Edwin S. Orientations toward death: A vital aspect of the study of lives. In Robert W. White (Ed.), *The study of lives.* New York: Atherton, 1963.

Shoben, E. J., Jr. Toward a concept of the normal personality. *Amer. Psychol.,* 1957, **12,** 183–189.

Short, J. F., Jr. Gang delinquency and anomie. In M. B. Clinard (Ed.), *Anomie and deviant behavior*. New York: Free Press, 1964.

—————. Street corner groups and patterns of delinquency: A progress report. *Amer. Catholic Sociol. Rev.*, 1963, **24**, 13–32.

—————, H. Marshall, and R. Rivera. Significant adults and adolescent adjustment. Mimeographed; revision of paper presented at the Annual Meeting of the Pacific Sociological Association, Coronado, Calif., March 1964.

Short, J. F., Jr., R. Rivera, and H. Marshall. Adult-adolescent relations and gang delinquency. *Pacif. Sociol. Rev.*, 1964, **7**, 59–65.

Short, J. F., Jr., R. Rivera, and R. A. Tennyson. Perceived opportunities, gang membership and delinquency. *Amer. Sociol. Rev.*, 1965, **30**, 56–67.

Short, J. F., Jr., and F. L. Strodtbeck. *Group process and gang delinquency*. Chicago: Univ. of Chicago Press, 1965.

—————. The response of gang leaders to status threats: An observation on group process and delinquent behavior. *Amer. J. Sociol.*, 1963, **68**, 571–579.

—————, and D. S. Cartwright. A strategy for utilizing research dilemmas: A case from the study of parenthood in a street corner gang. *Sociol. Inquiry*, 1962, **32**, 185–202.

Short, J. F., Jr., R. A. Tennyson, and K. I. Howard. Behavior dimensions of gang delinquency. *Amer. Sociol. Rev.*, 1963, **28**, 412–428.

Siegel, N., *et al.* Social class, diagnosis, and treatment in three psychiatric hospitals. *Soc. Problems*, 1962, **10**, 191–196.

Siemens, H. W. *Die Zwillingspathologie: Ihre Bedeutung, ihre Methodik, ihre bisherigen Ergebnisse*. Berlin: Verlag Von Julius Springer, 1924.

Silone, I. Re-thinking progress (II). *Encounter*, 1968, **30**, 27–40.

Silverberg, William V. *Childhood experience and personal destiny*. New York: Springer, 1952.

Silverman, Susan B. An annotated bibliography on education and cultural deprivation. In B. S. Bloom, A. Davis, and R. Hess (Eds.), *Compensatory education for cultural deprivation*. New York: Holt, 1965.

Sims, M. Comparative study of disease incidence in admissions to base psychiatric hospital in Middle East. *J. ment. Sci.*, 1946, **92**, 118–127.

Singer, M. T., and L. C. Wynne. Thought disorder and family relations of schizophrenics: III. Methodology using projective techniques. *Arch. gen. Psychiat.*, 1965, **12**, 187–200.

Skinner, B. F. *The behavior of organisms*. New York: Appleton, 1938.

—————. *Science and human behavior*. New York: Macmillan, 1953.

Slater, Eliot. *Psychotic and neurotic illnesses in twins*. London: H. M. Stationery Office, 1953.

—————, and Moya Woodside. *Patterns of marriage*. London: Cassell, 1951.

Smart, R. G. Alcoholism, birth order, and family size. *J. abnorm. soc. Psychol.*, 1963, **66**, 17–23.

Smith, H. C. *Psychology of industrial behavior*. (2nd ed.) New York: McGraw-Hill, 1964.

Smith, Kline, & French. Is mental health a Communist plot? *S.K. & F. Psychiatric Reporter*, Sept.–Oct. 1962.

Smith, Mapheus. An empirical scale of prestige status of occupations. *Amer. Sociol. Rev.*, 1943, **8**, 185–192.

Smith, M. Brewster. "Mental health" reconsidered: A special case of the problem of values in psychology. *Amer. Psychol.*, 1961, **16**, 299–306.

———. Optima of mental health. *Psychiatry*, 1950, **13**, 503–510.

———. Research strategies toward a conception of positive mental health. *Amer. Psychol.*, 1959, **14**, 673–681.

Smith, Raymond T. Culture and social structure in the Caribbean. *Comparative Studies in Society and History*, The Hague, The Netherlands, 1963, **6**, 24–46.

———. *The Negro family in British Guiana.* London: Routledge, 1956.

Snow, C. P. *The two cultures and the scientific revolution.* New York: Cambridge Univ. Press, 1959.

Sollenberger, Richard T. Chinese-American child-rearing practices and juvenile delinquency. *J. soc. Psychol.*, 1968, **74**, 13–23.

Solomon, L., and M. Zlotowski. The relationship between the Elgin and the Phillips measures of process-reactive schizophrenia. *J. nerv. ment. Dis.*, 1964, **138**, 32–37.

Sommer, Robert. Patients who grow old in a mental hospital. *Geriatrics*, 1959, **14**, 584.

Sorokin, Pitimin. *Social mobility.* New York: Harper, 1927.

Soskin, W., and V. John. The study of spontaneous talk. In R. Barker (Ed.), *The stream of behavior.* New York: Appleton, 1963.

Spiegel, John P. The resolution of role conflict within the family. In Norman W. Bell and Ezra F. Vogel (Eds.), *A modern introduction to the family.* New York: Free Press, 1960.

———, and Norman W. Bell. The family of the psychiatric patient. In Silvano Arieti (Ed.), *American handbook of psychiatry.* Vol. 1. New York: Basic Books, 1959.

Spinley, B. M. *The deprived and the privileged.* London: Routledge, 1953.

Spohn, Herbert E. Social psychological approaches to schizophrenia. Paper presented at the American Psychological Association meeting, Washington, D.C., Sept. 1958.

Srole, L., *et al. Mental health in the metropolis: The midtown Manhattan study.* Vol. I. New York: McGraw-Hill, 1962.

Stablein, J. E., D. S. Willey, and C. W. Thomson. An evaluation of the Davis-Eells test using Spanish and Anglo-American children. *J. educ. Sociol.*, 1961, **35**, 73–79.

Staley, E. (Ed.). *Creating an industrial civilization.* New York: Harper, 1952.

Stampp, Kenneth. *The peculiar institution.* New York: Knopf, 1961.

Stanton, A. H. Problems in analysis of therapeutic implications of the institutional milieu. In *Symposium on preventive and social psychiatry, 15–17 April 1957.* Walter Reed Army Institute of Research. Washington, D.C.: U.S. Gov't Ptg. Office, 1958.

———, and M. S. Schwartz. The management of a type of institutional participation in mental illness. *Psychiatry*, 1949, **12**, 13–26.

———. Medical opinion and the social context in the mental hospital. *Psychiatry*, 1949a, **12**, 243–249.

———. *The mental hospital.* New York: Basic Books, 1954.

———. Observations on dissociation as social participation. *Psychiatry*, 1949b, **12**, 339–354.

Star, Shirley A. The national opinion research center study. In American Psychiatric Association, *Psychiatry, the press and the public.* Washington, D.C.: Amer. Psychiat. Assn., 1956.

———. The place of psychiatry in popular thinking. Paper presented at the Annual

Meeting of the American Association for Public Opinion Research, Washington, D.C., May 1957.

———. The public's ideas about mental illness. Paper presented at the Annual Meeting of the National Association for Mental Health, Indianapolis, Nov. 1955.

———. The screening of psychoneurotics: Comparison of psychiatric diagnoses and test scores at all induction stations. In S. A. Stouffer *et al.* (Eds.), *Measurement and prediction.* Princeton, N.J.: Princeton Univ. Press, 1950.

———. The screening of psychoneurotics in the army: Technical development of tests. In S. A. Stouffer *et al.* (Eds.), *Measurement and prediction.* Princeton, N.J.: Princeton Univ. Press, 1950a.

Stein, Lilli. "Social class" gradient in schizophrenia. *Brit. J. prev. soc. Med.,* 1957, **11,** 181–195.

Stenbäck, A., and K. A. Achté. Hospital first admissions and social class. *Acta Psychiat. Scand.,* 1966, **42,** 113–124.

Stern, Curt. *Principles of human genetics.* San Francisco: Freeman, 1960.

Stieglitz, E. J. The integration of clinical and social medicine. In I. Galdston (Ed.), *Social medicine—Its derivations and objectives.* New York: Commonwealth Fund, 1949.

Stodolsky, Susan S. Maternal behavior and language and concept formation in Negro pre-school children: An inquiry into process. Unpublished doctoral dissertation, Univ. of Chicago, 1965.

Stone, Gregory P. Appearance and the self. In Arnold M. Rose (Ed.), *Human behavior and social processes.* Boston: Houghton Mifflin, 1962.

Stormer, J. *None dare call it treason.* Florissant, Mo.: Liberty Bell Press, 1964.

Stouffer, S. A. *Communism, conformity and civil liberties.* New York: Doubleday, 1955.

Strauss, A., *et al. Psychiatric ideologies and institutions.* New York: Free Press, 1964.

Strauss, G. Some notes on power equalization. In H. G. Leavitt (Ed.), *The social science of organizations, four perspectives.* Englewood Cliffs, N.J.: Prentice-Hall, 1963.

Strecker, E. A. *Fundamentals of psychiatry.* Philadelphia: Lippincott, 1942.

Strodtbeck, F. L. The family as a three-person group. *Amer. Sociol. Rev.,* 1954, **19,** 23–29.

———. The reading readiness nursery: Short-term social intervention technique. Progress report to Social Security Administration (Project 124, The Social Psychology Laboratory, University of Chicago), Aug. 1963.

———, and J. F. Short, Jr. Aleatory risks versus short-run hedonism in explanation of gang action. *Soc. Problems,* 1964, **12,** 127–140.

Strömgren, E. Beitrage zur psychiatrischen Erblehre. Auf Grund von Untersuchungen an einer Inselbevolkerung. *Acta Psychiat.,* 1938, Suppl. **19.**

———. Defining the unit of study in field investigations in the mental disorders. In J. Zubin (Ed.), *Field studies in the mental disorders.* New York: Grune & Stratton, 1961.

———. Statistical and genetic population studies within psychiatry: Methods and principal results. In *Actualités Scientifiques et Industrielles, Congress International de Psychiatrie, VI, Psychiatrie Sociale.* Paris: Herman and Cie, 1950.

Strotzka, H., *et al.* Socialpsychiatrische Feldstudie über eine ländliche. *Allgemeine-praxis. Soc. Psychiat.,* 1966, **1,** 83–87.

Struening, E. L., and J. Cohen. Factorial invariance and other psychometric characteristics of the five opinions about mental illness factors. *Educ. psychol. Measmt.*, 1963, **23**, 289–298.

Stubbins, Joseph, and Leonard Solomon. Patient government . . . A case study. *Ment. Hyg.*, 1959, **43**, 539–544.

Stycos, J. Mayone. *Family and fertility in Puerto Rico.* New York: Columbia Univ. Press, 1955.

———, and Kurt W. Back. *The control of human fertility in Jamaica.* Ithaca, N.Y.: Cornell Univ. Press, 1964.

Suedfeld, P. Birth order of volunteers for sensory deprivation. *J. abnorm. soc. Psychol.*, 1964, **68**, 195–196.

Sullivan, H. S. *Clinical studies in psychiatry.* H. S. Perry, M. L. Gawel, and M. Gibbon (Eds.), New York: Norton, 1956.

———. *Conceptions of modern psychiatry.* Washington, D.C.: William Alanson White Psychiat. Foundation, 1947.

———. Socio-psychiatric research: Its implications for the schizophrenia problem and for mental hygiene. *Amer. J. Psychiat.*, 1931, **10**, 977–991.

Sumner, W. G. *Folkways.* Boston: Ginn, 1906.

Sundby, Per, and Per Nyhus. Major and minor psychiatric disorders in males in Oslo: An epidemiological study. *Acta Psychiat. Scand.*, 1963, **39**, 519–547.

Super, Donald E. The Bernreuter personality inventory: A review of research. *Psychol. Bull.*, 1942, **39**, 105–106.

Svalastoga, Kaare. *Social differentiation.* New York: McKay, 1965.

Swinscow, Douglas. Some suicide statistics. *Brit. Med. J.*, 1951, **1**, 1417–1423.

Szasz, T. S. *Law, liberty, and psychiatry: An inquiry into the social uses of mental health practices.* New York: Macmillan, 1963.

———. Malingering: "Diagnosis" or social condemnation? *A.M.A. Arch. Neurol. Psychiat.*, 1956, **76**, 432–443.

———. Moral conflict and psychiatry. *Yale Rev.*, 1960, **49**, 555–566.

———. The moral dilemma of psychiatry: Autonomy or heteronomy? *Amer. J. Psychiat.*, 1964, **121**, 521–528.

———. The myth of mental illness. *Amer. Psychol.*, 1960a, **15**, 113–118.

———. *The myth of mental illness.* New York: Hoeber, 1961.

———. On the theory of psychoanalytic treatment. *Internat. J. Psychoanal.*, 1957, **38**, 166–182.

———. *Pain and pleasure: A study of bodily feelings.* New York: Basic Books, 1957a.

———. Politics and mental health. *Amer. J. Psychiat.*, 1958, **115**, 508–511.

———. The problem of psychiatric nosology: A contribution to a situational analysis of psychiatric operations. *Amer. J. Psychiat.*, 1957b, **114**, 405–413.

———. Psychiatric expert testimony—Its covert meaning and social function. *Psychiatry*, 1957c, **20**, 313–316.

———. Psychiatry, ethics and the criminal law. *Columbia Law Rev.*, 1958a, **58**, 183–198.

———. Some observations on the relationship between psychiatry and the law. *A.M.A. Arch. Neurol. Psychiat.*, 1956a, **75**, 297–315.

———, W. F. Knoff, and M. H. Hollender. The doctor-patient relationship and its historical context. *Amer. J. Psychiat.*, 1958, **115**, 526.

Szurek, S. A. Dynamics of staff interaction in hospital psychiatric treatment of children. *Amer. J. Orthopsychiat.*, 1947, **17**, 652–664.

Taylor, L., and S. Chave. *Mental health and environment.* London: Longmans, 1964.

Tannenbaum, Frank. *Crime and the community.* New York: Columbia Univ. Press, 1951.

———. *Slave and citizen.* New York: Knopf, 1947.

Taxel, Harold. Authority structure in a mental hospital ward. Unpublished M.A. thesis, Univ. of Chicago, 1953.

Teilhard de Chardin, Pierre. *The phenomenon of man.* New York: Harper, 1959.

Terman, L. M., and P. Wallin. The validity of marriage prediction and marital adjustment tests. *Amer. Sociol. Rev.,* 1949, **14,** 497–504.

Terman, L. M., *et al. Psychological factors in marital happiness.* New York: McGraw-Hill, 1938.

Terrell, G., K. Durkin, and M. Wiesley. Social class and the nature of incentive in discrimination learning. *J. abnorm. soc. Psychol.,* 1959, **59,** 270–272.

Thomas, Dorothy. Introduction. In Benjamin Malzberg and Everett S. Lee, *Migration and mental disease, A study of first admissions to hospitals for mental disease. New York, 1939–1941.* New York: Social Science Research Council, 1956.

———, and Ben B. Locke. Marital status, education and occupational differentials in mental disease. *Milbank Mem. Fund Quart.,* 1963, **41,** 145–160.

Thorndike, E. L. On the fallacy of imputing the correlations found for groups to the individuals or smaller groups composing them. *Amer. J. Psychol.,* 1939, **52,** 122–124.

Thrasher, F. M. *The gang.* Chicago: Univ. of Chicago Press, 1927.

Tienari, Pekka. Psychiatric illnesses in identical twins. *Acta Psychiat. Scand.,* 1963, Suppl. **171.**

Tietze, C., *et. al.* A survey of statistical studies on the prevalence and incidence of mental disorders in sample populations. *Pub. Hlth. Rep.,* 1943, **58,** 1909–1927.

Tietze, C., P. Lemkau, and M. Cooper. Personality disorder and spatial mobility. *Amer. J. Sociol.,* 1942, **48,** 29–39.

———. Schizophrenia, manic-depressive psychosis, and social-economic status. *Amer. J. Sociol.,* 1941, **47,** 167–175.

Tillich, P. *The courage to be.* New Haven: Yale Univ. Press, 1952.

Timmons, W. M. Decisions and attitudes as outcomes of the discussion of a social problem. Contrib. Educ. N.Y. Teachers Coll., Columbia Univ. Bureau of Publications, 1939, No. 777.

Tobin, James. On improving the economic status of the Negro. *Daedalus,* 1965, **94,** 878–898.

Todd, G. S., and E. Wittkower. The psychological aspects of sanitarium management. *Lancet,* 1948, **254,** 49–53.

Tolstoy, Leo. *The death of Ivan Ilych and other stories.* New York: Signet, 1960.

Tompkins, W. T., and D. G. Wiehl. *Maternal and newborn nutrition studies at Philadelphia Lying-in Hospital. Maternal studies. II. Prematurity and maternal nutrition in the promotion of maternal and newborn health.* New York: Milbank Mem. Fund, 1954.

Tooth, Geoffrey. *Studies in mental illness in the Gold Coast.* London: H. M. Stationery Office, 1950.

Trussell, R. E., J. Elinson, and M. L. Levin. Comparisons of various methods of estimating the prevalence of chronic disease in a community—The Hunterdon County study. *Amer. J. pub. Hlth.,* 1956, **46,** 173–182.

Tsuwaga, T., *et al.* Über die psychiatrische Zensusuntersuchung in einem Stadtbezirk von Tokyo. *Psychiat. Neurol. Jap.*, 1942, **46**, 204–218.

Tuckman, Jacob, and Robert J. Kleiner. Discrepancy between aspiration and achievement as a predictor of schizophrenia. *Behav. Sci.*, 1962, **7**, 443–447.

Turbayne, C. M. *The myth of metaphor.* New Haven: Yale Univ. Press, 1962.

Turner, Ralph H., and Richard H. Vanderlipp. Self ideal congruence as an index of adjustment. *J. abnorm. soc. Psychol.*, 1958, **57**, 202–207.

Turner, R. J., and M. O. Wagonfeld. Occupational mobility and schizophrenia, an assessment of the social causation and social selection hypotheses. *Amer. Sociol. Rev.*, 1967, **32**, 104–113.

Tyhurst, J. S. The role of transition states—including disasters—in mental illness. In *Symposium on preventive and social psychiatry, 15–17 April 1957.* Walter Reed Army Institute of Research. Washington, D.C.: U.S. Gov't Ptg. Office, 1958.

Uchimara, Y., *et al.* Über die vergleichend Psychiatrische und Erbpathologische Untersuchung auf einer Japanischen Insel. *Psychiat. Neurol. Jap.*, 1940, **44**, 745–782.

Ullman, Leonard. *Institution and outcome.* Long Island City, N.Y.: Pergamon, 1967.

U.S. Bureau of the Census. *Patients in mental institutions.* Washington, D.C.: Department of Commerce, U.S. Bureau of the Census, 1941.

———. *U.S. census of population: 1960. Detailed characteristics, Massachusetts.* Washington, D.C.: U.S. Gov't. Ptg. Office, 1962.

U.S. Department of Labor. *Manpower report to the President.* Washington, D.C.: U.S. Gov't. Ptg. Office, 1963.

Vaillant, G. E. A historical review of the remitting schizophrenics. *J. nerv. ment. Dis.*, 1964, **138**, 48–56.

———. The prediction of recovery in schizophrenia. *J. nerv. ment. Dis.*, 1962, **135**, 534–543.

Varon, E. Recurrent phenomena in group psychotherapy. *Internat. J. group Psychother.*, 1953, **3**, 49–58.

Venables, P. H. Input dysfunction in schizophrenia. In B. A. Maher (Ed.), *Progress in experimental personality research.* New York: Academic Press, 1964.

———, and J. K. Wing. Level of arousal and the subclassification of schizophrenia. *Arch. gen. Psychiat.*, 1962, **7**, 114–119.

Vernier, Claire M., *et al.* Psychosocial study of the patient with pulmonary tuberculosis: A cooperative research approach. *Psychol. Monogr.*, 1961, **75** (Whole No. 510).

Vincent, Clark. Familia Spongia: The adaptive function. Paper presented at the Annual Meeting of the National Council on Family Relations, Toronto, 1965.

Waelder, Robert. The principle of multiple function: Observations on overdetermination. *Psychoanal. Quart.*, 1936, **5**, 45–62.

Walker, Charles R. *Modern technology and civilization.* New York: McGraw-Hill, 1962.

Wall, James H. A study of alcoholism in men. *Amer. J. Psychiat.*, 1936, **92**, 1389–1401.

Waller, Willard. Social problems and the mores. *Amer. Sociol. Rev.*, 1936, **1**, 922–933.

Warner, W. Lloyd. The society, the individual, and his mental disorders. *Amer. J. Psychiat.*, 1937, **94**, 275–284.

———, and N. H. Martin (Eds.). *Industrial man.* New York: Harper, 1959.

Washington State Department of Health. Conference on research and evaluation of community mental health programs. Seattle: Washington State Department of Health, June 1951.

Watzlawick, P. A review of the double-bind theory. *Fam. Process,* 1963, **2**, 132–153.

Wax, John. Psychiatric social work. *Amer. J. Psychiat.*, 1963, **119**, 659–661.

Webster's New Collegiate Dictionary. Springfield, Mass.: Merriam, 1949.

Webster's Seventh New Collegiate Dictionary. Springfield, Mass.: Merriam, 1965.

Wechsler, H., and T. F. Pugh. Fit of individual and community characteristics and rates of psychiatric hospitalization. *Amer. J. Sociol.*, 1967, **73**, 331–338.

Weinberg, Abraham A. Mental health aspects of voluntary migration. *Ment. Hyg.*, 1955, **39**, 450–464.

———. Problems of adjustment of new immigrants to Israel. *World Ment. Hlth.*, 1953, **5**: Part I, 57–63; Part II, 129–135.

Weinberg, S. Kirson. Aspects of the prison's social structure. *Amer. J. Sociol.*, 1942, **47**, 717–726.

———. Social psychological aspects of schizophrenia. In L. Appelby, Jordan M. Scher, and John Cumming (Eds.), *Chronic schizophrenia*. New York: Free Press, 1960.

———. A sociological analysis of a schizophrenic type. In Arnold M. Rose (Ed.), *Mental health and mental disorder*. New York: Norton, 1955.

Weinstein, Edwin, and Robert Kahn. *Denial of illness.* Springfield, Ill.: Charles C. Thomas, 1955.

Weisman, A., and T. P. Hackett. Predilection to death: Death and dying as a psychiatric problem. *Psychosom. Med.*, 1961, **23**, 232–256.

Weiss, R. S., and D. Riesman. Social problems and disorganization in the world of work. In R. K. Merton and R. A. Nisbett (Eds.), *Contemporary social problems*. New York: Harcourt, 1961.

Welsh, G. S. Factor dimensions A and R. In G. S. Welsh and W. G. Dahlstrom (Eds.), *Basic readings on the MMPI in psychology and medicine*. Minneapolis: Univ. of Minnesota Press, 1956.

White, R. W. *Lives in progress.* New York: Holt, 1952.

———. Motivation reconsidered: The concept of competence. *Psychol. Rev.*, 1959, **66**, 297–333.

Whyte, William F. *Men at work.* Homewood, Ill.: Dorsey Press, 1961.

———. *Money and motivation.* New York: Harper, 1955.

———. A slum sex code. *Amer. J. Sociol.*, 1943, **49**, 24–31.

———. *Street corner society: The social structure of an Italian slum.* (Enl. ed.) Chicago: Univ. of Chicago Press, 1955.

Wilensky, H. L. Human relations in the workplace: An appraisal of some recent research. In Industrial Relations Research Association, *Research in industrial human relations*. New York: Harper, 1957.

———, and C. N. Lebeaux. *Industrial society and social welfare.* New York: Russell Sage Foundation, 1958.

Williams, Robin M., Jr. *American society: A sociological interpretation.* New York: Knopf, 1951.

———. *Strangers next door: Ethnic relations in American communities.* Englewood Cliffs, N.J.: Prentice-Hall, 1964.

Wilson, David C., and Edna M. Lantz. The effect of culture change on the Negro race in Virginia, as indicated by a study of state hospital admissions. *Amer. J. Psychiat.*, 1957, **114**, 25–32.

Wilson, R. S. On behavior pathology. *Psychol. Bull.*, 1963, **60**, 130–146.

Wilson, Warner. Correlates of avowed happiness. *Psychol. Bull.*, 1967, **67**, 294–306.

Wiltse, Kermit T. Orthopsychiatric programs for socially deprived groups. *Amer. J. Orthopsychiat.*, 1963, **33**, 806–813.

Wing, J. K. Social treatments of mental illness. In Michael Shepherd and David L. Davies (Eds.), *Studies in psychiatry*. London: Oxford Univ. Press, 1968.

——, *et al.* Reliability of a procedure for measuring and classifying present psychiatric state. *Brit. J. Psychiat.*, 1967, **113**, 499–515.

Winston, E. Mental disease and the army. *Ment. Hyg.*, 1935, **19**, 281–288.

Wirth, L., *The ghetto*. Chicago: Univ. of Chicago Press, 1928.

Wishner, J. The concept of efficiency in psychological health and in psychopathology. *Psychol. Rev.*, 1955, **62**, 69–80.

Witaker, C. A., and T. P. Malone. *The roots of psychotherapy*. New York: Blakiston, 1953.

Wittkower, E. D., and J. Fried. Some problems of transcultural psychiatry. In Marvin K. Opler (Ed.), *Culture and mental health*. New York: Macmillan, 1959.

——, H. B. Murphy, and H. Ellenberger. Cross-cultural inquiry into the symptomatology of schizophrenia. *Ann. N.Y. Acad. Sciences*, 1960, **84**, 854–863.

Wittman, P. A scale for measuring prognosis in schizophrenic patients. *Elgin Papers*, 1941, **4**, 20–33.

Wolf, R. M. The measurement of environments. In *Proceedings of the 1964 invitational conference on testing problems*. Princeton, N.J.: Educational Testing Service, 1965.

Wolman, B. B. *et al.* (Eds.). *Handbook of clinical psychology*. New York: McGraw-Hill, 1965.

Woodward, J. L. Changing ideas on mental illness and its treatment. *Amer. Sociol. Rev.*, 1951, **16**, 443–454.

Worcester State Lunatic Hospital Annual Report. Vol. 3. Worcester, Mass.: Worcester State Lunatic Hospital, 1835; Vol. 15, 1847.

Wynne, L. C., *et al.* Pseudo-mutuality in the family relations of schizophrenics. *Psychiatry*, 1958, **21**, 205–220.

Wynne, L. C., and M. T. Singer. Thinking disorders and family transactions. Paper presented at the Annual Meeting of the American Psychiatric Association, Los Angeles, May 1964.

——. Thought disorder and the family relations of schizophrenics. Bethesda, Md.: ditto copy, 1962.

——. Thought disorder and family relations of schizophrenics: I. A research strategy. *Arch. gen. Psychiat.*, 1963, **9**, 191–198.

——. Thought disorder and family relations of schizophrenics: II. A classification of forms of thinking. *Arch. gen. Psychiat.*, 1963a, **9**, 199–206.

Yablonsky, L. *The violent gang*. New York: Macmillan, 1962.

Yancey, William L. The culture of poverty: Not so much parsimony. Unpublished ms., Social Science Institute, Washington Univ., n.d.

Yarrow, Marian Radke, *et al.* The psychological meaning of mental illness in the family. *J. Social Issues*, 1955, **11**, 12–24.

Zigler, E. Familial mental retardation: A continuing dilemma. *Science*, 1967, **155**, 292–298.

——, and J. Delabry. Concept switching in middle-class, lower-class and retarded children. *J. abnorm. soc. Psychol.*, 1962, **65**, 267–273.

Zilboorg, G. *A history of medical psychology*. New York: Norton, 1941.

Zimmerman, C., and R. A. Bauer. The effects of an audience upon what is remembered. *Pub. Opin. Quart.*, 1956, **20**, 238–248.

Zorbaugh, H. W. *The Gold Coast and the slum.* Chicago: Univ. of Chicago Press, 1929.

Zubin, Joseph (Ed.). *Field studies in the mental disorders.* New York: Grune & Stratton, 1961.

———, *et al.* A biometric approach to prognosis in schizophrenia. In P. Hoch and J. Zubin (Eds.), *Comparative epidemiology of mental disorders.* New York: Grune & Stratton, 1961.

Index

DATE DUE